LOGIC, METHODOLOGY AND PHILOSOPHY OF SCIENCE

LOGIC, METHODOLOGY AND PHILOSOPHY OF SCIENCE

Proceedings of the 1960 International Congress

Edited by

ERNEST NAGEL

PATRICK SUPPES

ALFRED TARSKI

STANFORD UNIVERSITY PRESS

Stanford, California, 1962

Stanford University Press
Stanford, California

Library of Congress Catalog Card Number: 62-9620

Printed in the United States of America

PREFACE

This volume constitutes the proceedings of the 1960 International Congress for Logic, Methodology and Philosophy of Science. The Congress was held at Stanford University, Stanford, California, from August 24 to September 2, 1960, under the auspices of the Division of Logic, Methodology and Philosophy of Science of the International Union of History and Philosophy of Science. The 63 papers are the texts of the addresses given by invitation of the Program Committee. These papers fall in one of two categories: invited addresses and contributions to symposia. Six of the papers were read in absentia. These are the papers by P. Bernays, A. Froda, J. Kotarbińska, T. Kotarbiński, W. Schwabhäuser, and R. Stone.

Short communications presented by members of the Congress are not included in the *Proceedings*, but the titles of their papers are listed in the complete scientific program of the Congress which appears in the Appendix. Abstracts of these communications were printed in a volume issued to members at the beginning of the Congress (Stanford University, 1960).

The Congress was organized by a committee consisting of P. W. Bridgman, Rudolf Carnap, Yuen Ren Chao, Alonzo Church, Theodosius Dobzhansky, C. J. Ducasse, Frederick B. Fitch, Philipp Frank, S. C. Kleene, Paul Lazarsfeld, Henry Margenau, Ernest Nagel (Chairman), Jerzy Neyman, George Pólya, Willard V. Quine, Herbert Solomon (Adjoint Secretary and Treasurer), S. S. Stevens, Marshall H. Stone, Patrick Suppes (Secretary General), Alfred Tarski (Vice Chairman), and C. Truesdell. The editors of this volume served as the Executive Committee of the Organizing Committee. Due to unforeseen circumstances, Professor Nagel was forced to resign as Chairman of the Organizing Committee just prior to the opening of the Congress, and Professor Tarski served in that capacity during its sessions.

The work of the Congress was divided into eleven sections dealing with various topics in logic, methodology and philosophy of science. The chairmen of the various sections, who together with the Executive Committee served as the Program Committee, were: Leon Henkin, Section 1 (Mathematical Logic); Raphael M. Robinson, Section 2 (Foundations of Mathematical Theories); John Myhill, Section 3 (Philosophy of Logic and Mathematics); Henryk Mehlberg, Section 4 (General Problems of Methodology and Philosophy of Science); David Blackwell, Section 5 (Foundations of Probability and Induction); Max Schiffer, Section 6 (Methodology and Philosophy of Physical Sciences); William K. Estes, Section 7 (Methodology and Philosophy of Biological and Psychological Sciences); Kenneth J.

Arrow, Section 8 (Methodology and Philosophy of Social Sciences); Francis J. Whitfield, Section 9 (Methodology and Philosophy of Linguistics); Abraham Kaplan, Section 10 (Methodology and Philosophy of Historical Sciences); Benson Mates, Section 11 (History of Logic, Methodology and Philosophy of Science).

This was the first International Congress for Logic, Methodology and Philosophy of Science since the International Union of the History of Science and the International Union of the Philosophy of Science established the International Union of the History and Philosophy of Science on June 3, 1955. The congresses of a related character held prior to the formation of IUHPS were mainly devoted to the philosophy of science. The title of the 1960 Congress reflects its broader coverage; it was in fact the first international congress to include a large number of papers on both mathematical logic and the methodology and philosophy of science. Further congresses of the same character, at four- or five-year intervals, are planned by the Division of Logic, Methodology and Philosophy of Science of IUHPS.

The Congress was jointly sponsored by IUHPS and the United States National Academy of Sciences. The U.S. National Committee of IUHPS, an organ of the U.S. Academy, initiated the organization of the Congress. Generous financial grants from the U.S. National Science Foundation and the American Council of Learned Societies made possible the attendance of a substantial number of scholars from over 25 countries throughout the world.

The editors have confined themselves to arranging the volume and handling various technical matters relating to publication, without attempting detailed editorial treatment. Some effort was made to achieve typographical uniformity, but the choice of notation and symbolism was left to the individual authors.

On behalf of the Organizing Committee the editors wish to thank the many persons, too numerous to name, who contributed their generous assistance in arranging for the Congress and in preparing the present volume for publication.

The Editors

Columbia University
Stanford University
University of California, Berkeley

January 1962

CONTENTS

IV. GENERAL PROBLEMS OF METHODOLOGY AND PHILOSOPHY OF SCIENCE

V. FOUNDATIONS OF PROBABILITY AND INDUCTION

VI. METHODOLOGY AND PHILOSOPHY OF PHYSICAL SCIENCES

VII. METHODOLOGY AND PHILOSOPHY OF BIOLOGICAL AND PSYCHOLOGICAL SCIENCES

VIII. METHODOLOGY AND PHILOSOPHY OF SOCIAL SCIENCES

Symposium on Macro- and Microeconomics

IX. METHODOLOGY AND PHILOSOPHY OF LINGUISTICS

Symposium on Models in Linguistics

X. METHODOLOGY AND PHILOSOPHY OF HISTORICAL SCIENCES

XI. HISTORY OF LOGIC, METHODOLOGY, AND PHILOSOPHY OF SCIENCE

SECTION

I

MATHEMATICAL

LOGIC

Symposium on Decision Problems

ON A DECISION METHOD IN RESTRICTED SECOND ORDER ARITHMETIC

J. RICHARD BÜCHI

University of Michigan, Ann Arbor, Michigan, U.S.A.

Let SC be the interpreted formalism which makes use of individual variables t, x, y, z, . . . ranging over natural numbers, monadic predicate variables q( ), r( ), s( ), i( ), . . . ranging over arbitrary sets of natural numbers, the individual symbol 0 standing for zero, the function symbol ′ denoting the successor function, propositional connectives, and quantifiers for both types of variables. Thus SC is a fraction of the restricted second order theory of natural numbers, or of the first order theory of real numbers. In fact, if predicates on natural numbers are interpreted as binary expansions of real numbers, it is easy to see that SC is equivalent to the first order theory of [Re, +, Pw, Nn], whereby Re, Pw, Nn are, respectively, the sets of non-negative reals, integral powers of 2, and natural numbers.

The purpose of this paper is to obtain a rather complete understanding of definability in SC, and to outline an effective method for deciding truth

This work was done under a grant from the National Science Foundation to the Logic of Computers Group, and with additional assistance through contracts with the Office of Naval Research, Office of Ordnance Research, and the Army Signal Corps.

of sentences in SC. This answers a problem of A. Tarski's, which was discussed by R. M. Robinson [10].

A *congruence of finite rank* on words is a congruence with finite partition of concatenation; a *multi-periodic set* of words is a union of congruence classes of a congruence of finite rank. These concepts are intimately related to that of a finite automaton (Kleene [5], Myhill [6], Copi, Elgot, and Wright [3]), and turn out to be the key to an investigation of SC. Our results concerning SC may therefore be viewed as an application of the theory of finite automata to logic. In turn, SC arises quite naturally as a condition-language (Church [2]) on finite automata or sequential circuits, and "*sequential calculus*" is an appropriate name for SC. The significance of the decision method for SC is that it provides a method for deciding whether or not the input ($\mathbf{i}$)-to-output ($\mathbf{u}$) transformation of a proposed circuit $A(\mathbf{i}, \mathbf{r}, \mathbf{u})$ satisfies a condition $C(\mathbf{i}, \mathbf{u})$ stated in SC.

An important role in our theory of SC is played by Lemma 1, the *Sequential Lemma*. This is a combinatorial statement about ω-sequences, which may well be of importance elsewhere. It turns out to be a simple consequence of Ramsey's Theorem A. The usefulness of the "Unendlichkeitslemma" of König (also known as the "fan-theorem" in its intuitionistic version) in related problems of automata theory was first observed by Jesse B. Wright. Because of its affinity to König's lemma the present application of Ramsey's theorem was suggested. The author wishes to thank Dr. Wright for his continued assistance in the work presented here.

1. Notations

$\mathbf{i}$ denotes an n-tuple of predicate variables. Expressions like $A[\mathbf{i}(0)]$, $B[\mathbf{i}(t), \mathbf{i}(t')]$ denote propositional formulas in the indicated constituents. Σ_n, Π_n, denote the classes of formulas of SC of the following type:

$$\begin{aligned}
\Sigma_1 &: (\exists \mathbf{r}) \cdot A[\mathbf{r}(0)] \wedge (\forall t) B[\mathbf{i}(t), \mathbf{r}(t), \mathbf{r}(t')] \wedge (\exists t)\, C[\mathbf{r}(t)],\\
\Pi_1 &: (\forall \mathbf{r}) \cdot A[\mathbf{r}(0)] \vee (\exists t)\, B[\mathbf{i}(t), \mathbf{r}(t), \mathbf{r}(t')] \vee (\forall t)\, C[\mathbf{r}(t)],\\
\Sigma_{n+1} &: (\exists \mathbf{r}) \cdot F(\mathbf{i}, \mathbf{r}), \text{ whereby } F \in \Pi_n,\\
\Pi_{n+1} &: (\forall \mathbf{r}) \cdot F(\mathbf{i}, \mathbf{r}), \text{ whereby } F \in \Sigma_n.
\end{aligned}$$

The quantifiers $(\exists t)_x^y A(t)$ for $(\exists t)\,[x \leqq t < y \wedge A(t)]$, $(\forall t)_x^y A(t)$ for $(\forall t)[x \leqq t < y \supset A(t)]$, $(\exists^\omega t)A(t)$ for $(\forall x)(\exists t)\,[x < t \wedge A(t)]$, $(\forall_\omega t)A(t)$ for $(\exists x)(\forall t)[x < t \supset A(t)]$, $(\exists j)_\omega A(j)$ for $(\exists j)\,[(\exists^\omega t)j(t) \wedge A(j)]$ can be defined in SC. The classes Σ_1^ω and Π_1^ω of formulas are defined as follows:

$$\begin{aligned}
\Sigma_1^\omega &: (\exists \mathbf{r}) \cdot A[\mathbf{r}(0)] \wedge (\forall t)\, B[\mathbf{i}(t), \mathbf{r}(t), \mathbf{r}(t')] \wedge (\exists^\omega t)\, C[\mathbf{r}(t)],\\
\Pi_1^\omega &: (\forall \mathbf{r}) \cdot A[\mathbf{r}(0)] \vee (\exists t)\, B[\mathbf{i}(t), \mathbf{r}(t), \mathbf{r}(t')] \vee (\forall_\omega t)\, C[\mathbf{r}(t)].
\end{aligned}$$

Also the following classes of formulas will play an essential role:

$$\begin{aligned}
\Sigma^0 &: (\exists \mathbf{r}) \cdot A[\mathbf{r}(x)] \wedge (\forall t)_x^y\, B[\mathbf{i}(t), \mathbf{r}(t), \mathbf{r}(t')] \wedge C[\mathbf{r}(y)],\\
\Pi^0 &: (\forall \mathbf{r}) \cdot A[\mathbf{r}(x)] \vee (\exists t)_x^y\, B[\mathbf{i}(t), \mathbf{r}(t), \mathbf{r}(t')] \vee C[\mathbf{r}(y)].
\end{aligned}$$

These may be called *regular formulas*.

Let **i** be a k-tuple of predicates. The 2^k *states of* **i** are the k-tuples of truth-values. **i** may be viewed as an infinite sequence $\mathbf{i}(0)\mathbf{i}(1)\mathbf{i}(2)\ldots$ of states. The variables *u, v, w,* ... will be used for *words* (i.e., finite sequences) of states; *uv* denotes the result of juxtaposing the words *u* and *v*. A *congruence* is an equivalence relation $u \backsim v$ on words such that $u \backsim v$ implies $uw \backsim vw$ and $wu \backsim wv$; it is of *finite rank* n in case there are n equivalence classes. A set $\mathscr{S}$ of words is *multi-periodic* if $\mathscr{S} = \mathscr{E}_1 \cup \ldots \cup \mathscr{E}_m$, whereby $\mathscr{E}_1, \ldots \mathscr{E}_m$ are some of the congruence classes of a congruence of finite rank.

Note that the value of a regular formula $R(\mathbf{i}, x, y)$ depends only on the word $\mathbf{i}(x)\,\mathbf{i}(x+1)\ldots\mathbf{i}(y-1)$. If $\mathscr{R}$ is the set of all words $\mathbf{i}(0)\,\mathbf{i}(1)\ldots\mathbf{i}(h)$ such that $R(\mathbf{i}, 0, h+1)$, then the formula $R(\mathbf{i}, x, y)$ is said to *determine* the set $\mathscr{R}$ of words. The symbol "Σ^0" will be used also to denote the class of all sets $\mathscr{R}$ of words determined by formulas R in Σ^0. Similarly, the symbol "Σ_1^ω" is used also to denote the class of all sets $\hat{\mathbf{i}}F(\mathbf{i})$ defined by formulas $F(\mathbf{i})$ in Σ_1^ω. Corresponding remarks hold for Π^0, Π_1^ω, Σ_1, Π_1.

2. The Sequential Lemma

The working of the decision-method for SC is based on induction and a rather more sophisticated property of infinity, namely Theorem A of Ramsey [9]. Essential parts of this theorem can actually be formulated in SC, in the form of a surprising assertion about the division of infinite sequences into consecutive finite parts.

LEMMA 1. *Let* **i** *be any k-tuple of predicates, and let* $\mathscr{E}_0, \ldots, \mathscr{E}_n$ *be a partition of all words on states of* **i** *into finitely many classes. Then there exists a division* $\mathbf{i}(0)\,\mathbf{i}(1)\ldots\mathbf{i}(x_1-1),\ \mathbf{i}(x_1)\,\mathbf{i}(x_1+1)\ldots\mathbf{i}(x_2-1),\ \mathbf{i}(x_2)\,\mathbf{i}(x_2+1)\ldots\mathbf{i}(x_3-1),$ ... *of* **i** *such that all words* $\mathbf{i}(x_p)\,\mathbf{i}(x_p+1)\ldots\mathbf{i}(x_q-1)$ *belong to one and the same of the classes* $\mathscr{E}_0, \ldots, \mathscr{E}_n$.

PROOF. Assume **i**, $\mathscr{E}_0, \ldots, \mathscr{E}_n$ are as supposed in Lemma 1. For $0 \leqq c \leqq n$ let P_c consist of all $\{y_1, y_2\}$ such that $y_1 < y_2$ and $\mathbf{i}(y_1)\,\mathbf{i}(y_1+1)\ldots\mathbf{i}(y_2-1) \in \mathscr{E}_c$. Then $P_0, \ldots, P_n$ clearly is a partition of all 2-element sets of natural numbers. By Ramsey's Theorem A it follows that there is an infinite sequence $x_1 < x_2 < x_3 < \ldots$ and a $0 \leqq c \leqq n$ such that $\{x_p, x_q\} \in P_c$ for all $x_p < x_q$. By definition of P_c this yields the conclusion of Lemma 1.

3. Finite Automata, Multi-periodic Sets, and Σ^0-formulas

The following methods and results are borrowed from the theory of finite automata, and play a very essential role in the study of SC. The reader is referred to Büchi [1], where some of the details are carried out in similar form, and where further references to the mathematical literature on finite automata are given. The basic result is

LEMMA 2. *The following are equivalent conditions on a set* $\mathscr{R}$ *of words:*

(a) $\mathscr{R}$ *is determined by a formula* $F(\mathbf{i}, x, y)$ *of* Σ^0.

(b) There is a "finite automata recursion" $\mathbf{r}(0) \equiv \mathbf{I}$, $\mathbf{r}(t') \equiv \mathbf{J}[\mathbf{i}(t), \mathbf{r}(t)]$, *and an "output"* $U[\mathbf{r}(t)]$ *such that a word* $\mathbf{i}(0)\,\mathbf{i}(1)\ldots\mathbf{i}(x-1)$ *belongs to* $\mathscr{R}$ *just in case the recursion yields an* $\mathbf{r}(x)$ *such that* $U[\mathbf{r}(x)]$ *holds.*

The implication a $\to$ b is shown in essence by Myhill's [6] "subset-construction"; nearly in the present form the details are in [1] Lemma 7. The implication b $\to$ a is trivial, $(\exists \mathbf{r}) \cdot \mathbf{r}(x) \equiv \mathbf{I} \wedge (\forall t)_x^y[\mathbf{r}(t') \equiv \mathbf{J}(t)] \wedge U[\mathbf{r}(y)]$ clearly determines $\mathscr{R}$.

The set $\mathscr{R}$ defined by (b) is sometimes called the *behavior* of $[\mathbf{I}, \mathbf{J}, U]$. In this terminology Lemma 2 says that Σ^0 is exactly the class of all behaviors of finite automata with outputs. It is easy to see that the class of behaviors is closed under disjunction and complementation. For example, if $\mathscr{R}$ is the behavior of $[\mathbf{I}, \mathbf{J}, U]$, then clearly $\tilde{\mathscr{R}}$ is the behavior of $[\mathbf{I}, \mathbf{J}, \tilde{U}]$. Therefore by Lemma 2,

LEMMA 3. *If the formulas* $R(\mathbf{i}, x, y)$, $S(\mathbf{i}, x, y)$ *determine* Σ^0*-sets of words, then so do the formulas* $R(\mathbf{i}, x, y) \wedge S(\mathbf{i}, x, y)$, $R(\mathbf{i}, x, y) \vee S(\mathbf{i}, x, y)$, *and* $\sim R(\mathbf{i}, x, y)$.

Suppose next that $R(\mathbf{i}, x, y)$ is the Σ^0-formula $(\exists \mathbf{r}) \cdot K(x) \wedge (\forall t)_x^y H(t) \wedge L(y)$. Then clearly $(\exists z)_x^y R(\mathbf{i}, x, y)$ is equivalent to $(\exists s\mathbf{r}) \cdot s(x) \wedge (\forall t)_x^y[(s(t') \supset s(t)) \wedge (s(t)\tilde{s}(t') \supset K(t)) \wedge (\tilde{s}(t) \supset H(t))] \wedge [\tilde{s}(y)L(y)]$, which is again in Σ^0. Therefore by Lemma 3,

LEMMA 4. *If the formula* $R(\mathbf{i}, x, y)$ *determines a* Σ^0*-set of words, then so do the formulas* $(\exists z)_x^y R(\mathbf{i}, x, y)$ *and* $(\forall z)_x^y R(\mathbf{i}, x, y)$.

Suppose again that $R(\mathbf{i}, x, y)$ is a Σ^0-formula. By Lemma 2 it follows that

$$(1) \qquad R(\mathbf{i}, 0, y) .\equiv. (\exists \mathbf{r}) \cdot \mathbf{r}(0) \equiv \mathbf{I} \wedge (\forall t)[r(t') \equiv \mathbf{J}(t)] \wedge U(y)$$

for properly chosen matrices $\mathbf{I}$, $\mathbf{J}[\mathbf{i}(t), \mathbf{r}(t)]$, and $U[\mathbf{r}(y)]$. It clearly follows that

$$(2) \qquad R(\mathbf{i}, 0, y) .\equiv. (\forall \mathbf{r}) \cdot [\mathbf{r}(0) \equiv \mathbf{I} \wedge (\forall t)[\mathbf{r}(t') \equiv \mathbf{J}(t)]] \supset U(y).$$

By (1) it follows that $(\exists y)\ R(\mathbf{i}, 0, y)$ is equivalent to a Σ_1-formula. By (2) it follows that $(\forall y)\ R(\mathbf{i}, 0, y)$ is equivalent to $(\forall \mathbf{r}).\ [\mathbf{r}(0) \equiv \mathbf{I} \wedge (\forall t)[r(t') \equiv \mathbf{J}(t)]] \supset (\forall t)\ U(t)$, and therefore to $(\exists \mathbf{r}).\ \mathbf{r}(0) \equiv \mathbf{I} \wedge (\forall t)[r(t') \equiv \mathbf{J}(t)]U(t)$ Thus,

LEMMA 5. *If* $R(\mathbf{i}, x, y)$ *determines a* Σ^0*-set of words, then* $(\exists t)\ R(\mathbf{i}, 0, t)$ *is equivalent to a* Σ_1*-formula, and* $(\forall t)\ R(\mathbf{i}, 0, t)$ *is equivalent to a* Σ_1*-formula of type* $(\exists \mathbf{r}).\ K(0) \wedge (\forall t)H(t)$.

As a consequence of Lemma 2, one thus obtains a rather clear picture of definability by Σ^0-formulas. However, a further characterization of behaviors is needed for the study of SC.

LEMMA 6. *A set* $\mathscr{R}$ *of words satisfies* (b) *of Lemma* 2 (*i.e., is the behavior of some finite automaton with output*) *if and only if it is multi-periodic.*

This fact has been observed by several authors; a proof can be found in Rabin and Scott [8]. By Lemma 2 it follows that Σ^0 consists exactly of the multi-periodic sets of words.

4. Definability by Σ_1^ω-formulas

We will now show that also the class Σ_1^ω, just like Σ^0, is closed under Boolean operations.

LEMMA 7. *If $F_1(\mathbf{i})$ and $F_2(\mathbf{i})$ are Σ_1^ω-formulas, then also $F_1(\mathbf{i}) \vee F_2(\mathbf{i})$ is equivalent to a Σ_1^ω-formula.*

PROOF. For c = 1, 2 let $F_c(\mathbf{i})$ be the formula

$$(\exists \mathbf{r}_c) \cdot K_c(0) \wedge (\forall t)H_c(t) \wedge (\exists^\omega t)L_c(t).$$

Then clearly the Σ_1^ω-formula

$$(\exists s\, \mathbf{r}_1\mathbf{r}_2) \cdot [s(0)\, K_1(0) \vee \tilde{s}(0)\, K_2(0)] \wedge (\forall t)[[s(t) \equiv s(t')] \wedge [s(t)H_1(t) \vee \tilde{s}(t)H_2(t)]] \wedge (\exists^\omega t)[s(t)L_1(t) \vee \tilde{s}(t)L_2(t)]$$

is equivalent to $F_1(\mathbf{i}) \vee F_2(\mathbf{i})$.

That Σ_1^ω also is closed under conjunction follows by

LEMMA 8. *A formula of form $(\exists \mathbf{r}) \cdot K(0) \wedge (\forall t)H(t) \wedge (\exists^\omega t)L_1(t) \wedge (\exists^\omega t)L_2(t)$ is equivalent to a Σ_1^ω-formula.*

PROOF. If the predicate s(t) is defined from $p_1(t)$ and $p_2(t)$ by the recursion $s(0) \equiv F$, $s(t') \equiv [\tilde{s}(t)\, p_1(t) \vee s(t)\, \tilde{p}_2(t)]$, then it is easy to see that $[(\exists^\omega t)\, p_1(t) \wedge (\exists^\omega t)\, p_2(t)] \equiv (\exists^\omega t)\, s(t)$. Using this device with p_1 and p_2 corresponding to L_1 and L_2, one obtains a Σ_1^ω-formula as required in Lemma 8.

Using all previous lemmas, one can now establish the closure of Σ_1^ω under complementation.

LEMMA 9. *To every formula $A(\mathbf{i})$ in Σ_1^ω one can obtain a formula $B(\mathbf{i})$ in Σ_1^ω equivalent to $\sim A(\mathbf{i})$.*

PROOF. Suppose $A(\mathbf{i})$ is in Σ_1^ω, say

(1) $A(\mathbf{i}) : (\exists \mathbf{r}) \cdot K[\mathbf{r}(0)] \wedge (\forall t)\, H[\mathbf{i}(t), \mathbf{r}(t), \mathbf{r}(t')] \wedge (\exists^\omega t)\, L[\mathbf{r}(t)]$.

If V, W are states of $\mathbf{r}$ and if $x = X_0X_1 \dots X_h$ is a word of states of $\mathbf{i}$, then define

$$[V,x,W]_1 : \bigvee_{U_1\dots U_h} \cdot H[X_0,V,U_1] \wedge H[X_1,U_1,U_2] \wedge H[X_2,U_2,U_3] \wedge \dots \wedge H[X_h,U_h,W],$$

$$[V,x,W]_2 : \bigvee_{U_1\dots U_h} \cdot H[X_0,V,U] \wedge \dots \wedge H[X_h,U_h,W] \wedge [L[U_1] \vee \dots \vee L[U_h]].$$

(Read $[\ ]_1$ as "there is an H-transition from V by x to W", and $[\ ]_2$ as "there is an H-transition through L from V by x to W".) Next define the binary relation $\backsim$ on words of states of $\mathbf{i}$:

$$x \backsim y : \bigwedge_{VW} ([V,x,W]_1 \equiv [V,y,W]_1) \wedge \bigwedge_{VW} ([V,x,W]_2 \equiv [V,y,W]_2).$$

If m is the number of states of $\mathbf{r}$, then clearly $\backsim$ is the intersection of m^2+m^2 dichotomies. Therefore, $\backsim$ is an equivalence relation of finite rank $a \leqq 2^{2m^2}$. Furthermore, using the definitions of $[\ ]_1$ and $[\ ]_2$, one obtains, $\backsim$ is a congruence relation on words. By Lemmas 2 and 6 it therefore follows that one can find formulas $E_1(\mathbf{i}, x, y), \ldots, E_a(\mathbf{i}, x, y)$ such that (2) $E_1, \ldots, E_a$ are Σ^0-formulas, and (3) $E_1, \ldots E_a$ determine the congruence classes of $\backsim$.

Next one applies Lemma 1 to the partition $E_1, \ldots, E_a$. It follows that for any $\mathbf{i}$

$$(4)\quad (\exists s)_\omega (\forall y)(\forall x)_0^y [s(x)s(y) \supset E_1(\mathbf{i}, x, y)] \vee \ldots \vee (\exists s)_\omega (\forall y)(\forall x)_0^y [s(x)s(y) \supset E_a(\mathbf{i}, x, y)].$$

If one defines for $1 \leqq c, d \leqq a$,

$$F_{c,d}(\mathbf{i}) : (\exists s)_\omega \cdot (\exists x)[s(x) \wedge E_c(\mathbf{i}, 0, x)] \wedge (\forall y)(\forall x)_0^y [s(x)s(y) \supset E_d(\mathbf{i}, x, y)],$$

then clearly each disjunct of (4) is equivalent to a disjunction of $F_{c,d}$'s. Therefore,

$$(5)\qquad \bigvee_{1 \leqq c,d \leqq a} F_{c,d}(\mathbf{i})$$

holds for all $\mathbf{i}$.

Suppose now that $F_{c,d}(\mathbf{i}) \wedge F_{c,d}(\mathbf{j})$. Then, by definition of $F_{c,d}$ and by (3) there are $x_1 < x_2 < x_3 < \ldots$ and $y_1 < y_2 < y_3 \ldots$ such that

$$\mathbf{i}(0) \ldots \mathbf{i}(x_1 - 1) \backsim \mathbf{j}(0) \ldots \mathbf{j}(y_1 - 1),$$
$$\mathbf{i}(x_p) \ldots \mathbf{i}(x_{p+1} - 1) \backsim \mathbf{j}(y_p) \ldots \mathbf{j}(y_{p+1} - 1), \qquad p = 1, 2, 3 \ldots.$$

By definition of $\backsim$ and (1) it therefore follows that $A(\mathbf{i}) \equiv A(\mathbf{j})$. Thus if $F_{c,d}(\mathbf{i}) \wedge F_{c,d}(\mathbf{j})$, then $A(\mathbf{i}) \equiv A(\mathbf{j})$. Or restating this result,

$$(6)\quad (\forall \mathbf{i})[F_{c,d}(\mathbf{i}) \supset A(\mathbf{i})] \vee (\forall \mathbf{i})[F_{c,d}(\mathbf{i}) \supset \sim A(\mathbf{i})], \qquad \text{for } 1 \leqq c,d \leqq a.$$

If now one defines the set Φ of pairs (c, d) by

$$(7)\qquad \Phi(c,d) \equiv \sim (\exists \mathbf{j})[A(\mathbf{j}) \wedge F_{c,d}(\mathbf{j})], \qquad \text{for } 1 \leqq c,d \leqq a,$$

then it follows by (5) and (6) that,

$$(8)\qquad \sim A(\mathbf{i}) \equiv \bigvee_{\Phi(c,d)} F_{c,d}(\mathbf{i}).$$

By (2), definition of $F_{c,d}$, and Lemmas 3, 4, 5 it follows that $F_{c,d}$ is of form

$$F_{c,d}(\mathbf{i}) \equiv (\exists \mathbf{spq}) \cdot I(0) \wedge (\forall t)\, J(t) \wedge (\exists t)\, M(t) \wedge (\exists^\omega t)\, s(t)$$

for some matrices $I[\mathbf{p}(0), \mathbf{q}(0)]$, $J[\mathbf{i}(t), s(t), \mathbf{q}(t), \mathbf{p}(t), \mathbf{q}(t'), \mathbf{p}(t')]$, $M[\mathbf{q}(t)]$. Note that $(\exists t)\, M(t) \wedge (\exists^\omega t)\, s(t)$ may be replaced by $(\exists^\omega t)[(\exists x)_0^t M(x) \wedge s(t)]$. Furthermore, $(\exists x)_0^t M(x)$ may be replaced by $r(t)$, if $r(0) \equiv F$, $r(t') \equiv [r(t) \vee M(t)]$ are conjoined to $I(0)$ and $J(t)$, respectively, and $(\exists r)$ is added to the prefix. Therefore, each $F_{c,d}(\mathbf{i})$ is equivalent to a Σ_1^ω-formula. By (8) and Lemma 7 it follows that $\sim A(\mathbf{i})$ is equivalent to a Σ_1^ω-formula, which concludes the proof of Lemma 9.

Note that by definition $F_{c,d} = E_c E_d E_d E_d \ldots$, and by (5) and (6) the set A is the finite union of all $F_{c,d}$ such that $\sim \Phi(c, d)$. Furthermore, the sets of words E_c are all multi-periodic. Thus our proof also yields

LEMMA 10. *Let $\mathscr{A}$ be a set of ω-sequences of states definable by a Σ_1^ω-formula. Then $\mathscr{A} = \mathscr{S}_1 \cup \ldots \cup \mathscr{S}_m$, whereby each $\mathscr{S}_k$ is of form $\mathscr{C}\mathscr{D}\mathscr{D}\mathscr{D}\ldots$, for multi-periodic sets $\mathscr{C}$, $\mathscr{D}$ of words.*

This provides a rather clear understanding of Σ_1^ω-definability, because multi-periodic sets of words have been investigated in automata theory.

5. Definability in SC

The following lemma may be proved by methods similar to those in [1] Lemma 1.

LEMMA 11. *To every formula $A(\mathbf{i})$ in* SC *one can obtain an equivalent formula $B(\mathbf{i})$ belonging to some Σ_n.*

Furthermore a Σ_1-formula can be transformed to an equivalent Σ_1^ω-formula (see end of proof of Lemma 9). Repeated application of Lemma 9 now clearly yields an equivalent Σ_1^ω-formula to every Σ_n-formula. Thus we obtain

THEOREM 1. *To every formula $A(\mathbf{i})$ of* SC *there is an equivalent formula $B(\mathbf{i})$ in Σ_1^ω.*

We add the following remarks:

1. Because of Lemma 10 this theorem provides a clear understanding of which relations $A(i_1, \ldots, i_n)$ on predicates are definable in SC.

2. It is easy to see that Σ_1^ω- and Σ_2-formulas define the same relations. Therefore, the hierarchy Σ_n, Π_n collapses at $n = 2$. This result cannot be improved much; the set $\mathfrak{U}$ consisting of all infinite i's is definable by a Σ_2-(a Σ_1^ω)formula, but not by a Π_2-formula.

3. Using Theorem 1, one easily shows that also formulas $A(\mathbf{i}, x_1, \ldots, x_m)$ of SC, containing free individual variables, have a normal form, namely,

$$(\exists \mathbf{r})\cdot K[\mathbf{r}(0)] \wedge (\forall t)H[\mathbf{i}(t), \mathbf{r}(t), \mathbf{r}(t')] \wedge (\exists^\omega t)L[\mathbf{r}(t)] \wedge U_1[\mathbf{r}(x_1)] \wedge \ldots \wedge U[\mathbf{r}(x_m)].$$

This yields rather complete information on definability in SC. For example,

4. A conjecture of Robinson [10]: A relation $\mathscr{R}(x_1, \ldots, x_m)$ on natural numbers is definable in SC if and only if it is definable in SC_{fin}, which is like SC except that the variables i, j, r, ... range over finite sets of natural numbers. This follows by remark 3 and methods similar to those in the proof of Lemma 12, Section 6. Similarly, one shows a relation $\mathscr{R}(i_1, \ldots, i_m)$ on finite sets of natural numbers is definable in SC if and only if it is definable in SC_{fin}. For a complete discussion of definability in SC_{fin} see Büchi [1].

5. Theorem 1 holds in a stronger version: there is an algorithm which to any formula $A(\mathbf{i})$ in SC yields an equivalent formula $B(\mathbf{i})$ in Σ_1^ω. See next section.

6. A Decision Method for SC

To obtain a method for deciding truth of sentences in SC we need a further lemma, whose proof again is typical for automata theory:

LEMMA 12. *There is an effective method for deciding truth of sentences A in* Σ_1^{ω}.

PROOF. Let $C(\mathbf{r})$ be a formula of form $K[\mathbf{r}(0)] \wedge (\forall t)H[\mathbf{r}(t), \mathbf{r}(t')] \wedge (\exists^{\omega} t)\ L[\mathbf{r}(t)]$. Suppose $\mathbf{r}$ is a k-tuple of predicates such that $C(\mathbf{r})$ holds. Then there are $x_1 < x_2 < \ldots$ such that $L[\mathbf{r}(x_1)], L[\mathbf{r}(x_2)], \ldots$. Because $\mathbf{r}$ has but a finite number of states, there must be a repetition $\mathbf{r}(x_p) = \mathbf{r}(x_q)$ of some state U. Therefore, $(\exists \mathbf{r})\ C(\mathbf{r})$ implies the assertion

(1) There are words $x = X_0X_1 \ldots X_a$ and $y = Y_1Y_2 \ldots Y_b$ of states and a state U such that L[U], and $K[X_0] \wedge H[X_0, X_1] \wedge \ldots \wedge H[X_{a-1}, X_a] \wedge H[X_a, U]$, and $H[U, Y_1] \wedge H[Y_1, Y_2] \wedge \ldots \wedge H[Y_{b-1}, Y_b] \wedge H[Y_b, U]$.

Conversely (1) implies $(\exists \mathbf{r})\ C(\mathbf{r})$, because one has but to let $\mathbf{r} = xUyUyUy\ldots$. Thus, a method (I) which decides, for given propositional formulas K, H, L and given state U, whether or not (1) holds will also be a method for deciding truth of Σ_1^{ω}-sentences $(\exists \mathbf{r})\ C(\mathbf{r})$. Clearly such a method (I) can be composed from a method (II) which, for given propositional formula H[X, Y] and given states V and W, decides whether or not

(2) There is a word $x = X_1X_2 \ldots X_a$ such that $H[V, X_1] \wedge H[X_1, X_2] \wedge \ldots \wedge H[X_{a-1}, X_a] \wedge H[X_a, W]$.

Let $n = 2^k$ be the number of states, and note that in a word $x = X_1X_2 \ldots X_a$ of length $a > n$ there must occur a repetition $X_p = X_q$, $p < q \leqq a$. Clearly if x satisfies (2), then so does the shorter word $y = X_1X_2 \ldots X_pX_{q+1}X_{q+2} \ldots X_a$. Therefore, to establish whether or not (2) holds, it suffices to check among the finitely many words x of length $\leqq n$. This remark clearly yields a method (II) for (2), whereby Lemma 12 is established.

Lemma 2 is proved in automata theory in a strong effective version. Also the proof of Lemma 6 actually yields the following result:

(a) Let $\backsim$ be a congruence of finite rank on words. Given a method for deciding $x \backsim y$ and a set of representatives $x_1, \ldots, x_a$ of the congruence classes of $\backsim$, one can construct a finite automaton $[\mathbf{I}, \mathbf{J}]$ and outputs $U_1, \ldots, U_a$ such that the congruence class of x_c is equal to the behavior of $[\mathbf{I}, \mathbf{J}, U_c)$. Clearly also Lemmas 3, 4, 5, 7, 8, 11 hold effectively. This leaves only the following two critical steps in the proof of the crucial Lemma 9:

(b) The Σ^0-formulas $E_c(\mathbf{i}, x, y)$, $c = 1, \ldots, a$ can be effectively constructed from $A(\mathbf{i})$.

(c) The relation $\Phi(c, d)$ on the finite set $\{1, \ldots, a\}$ can be effectively constructed from $A(\mathbf{i})$ (so that the disjunction (8) can be effectively obtained).

To prove (b) note that given A the definition of $\backsim$ in the proof of lemma 9 provides us with a method for deciding $x \backsim y$. Because we also have a bound 2^{2m^2} on the rank a of $\backsim$, it is possible to obtain a set of representatives $x_1, \ldots, x_a$ for the congruence classes. By (a) and Lemma 2 the assertion (b) follows.

To prove (c) we refer to the definition (7) of Φ in the proof of Lemma 9. By Lemma 8 one can actually construct a Σ_1^ω-formula equivalent to $A(\mathrm{j}) \wedge F_{\mathrm{c,d}}(\mathrm{j})$. Lemma 12 therefore provides a method for deciding whether or not $\Phi(\mathrm{c, d})$ holds. This takes care of (c). Thus also Lemma 9 holds effectively.

It now follows that Theorem 1 holds effectively; in particular, to every sentence A in SC one can construct an equivalent sentence in Σ_1^ω. Applying Lemma 12 again, we have

THEOREM 2. *There is an effective method for deciding truth of sentences in* SC.

The strength of this result is best seen by noting some very special cases which occur in the literature and have been obtained by rather divergent methods:

1. The decidability of Σ_2-sentences of SC contains the result of Friedman [4], and implies the existence of various other algorithms of finite automata theory as programmed by Church [2]. It also implies some of the results of Wang [11].
2. In SC one can define $\mathrm{x} = \mathrm{y}$, $\mathrm{x} < \mathrm{y}$, $\mathrm{x} \equiv \mathrm{y} \pmod{\mathrm{k}}$ (for $\mathrm{k} = 1, 2, \ldots$). The decidability of SC therefore considerably improves a result of Putnam [7].
3. In SC one can define "i is finite". Theorem 2 therefore implies the decidability of $\mathrm{SC_{fin}}$, which was also proved in Büchi [1], and according to Robinson [10] is due to A. Ehrenfeucht.
4. The decidability of the first order theory of [Nn, +, Pw] follows from Theorem 2 and improves the classical result of Presburger.
5. Theorem 2 is closely related to another classical result, namely, the decidability of the monadic predicate calculus of second order, proved first by Th. Skolem and later by H. Behmann. A modified form of Lemma 11 yields a rather simple solution to this problem.

7. Concluding Remarks: Unsolved Problems

A careful analysis of the decision method for SC would yield a complete axiom system for SC. The most interesting candidate for an axiom schema is that part of Lemma 1 which is used in the proof of Lemma 9, namely,

$$\text{(Ax)} \qquad (\forall \mathbf{i})(\exists \mathrm{s})_\omega \cdot (\forall \mathrm{y})(\forall \mathrm{x})_0^{\mathrm{y}}[\mathrm{s(x)s(y)} \supset E(\mathbf{i}, \mathrm{x, y})] \vee (\forall \mathrm{y})(\forall \mathrm{x})_0^{\mathrm{y}}[\mathrm{s(x)s(y)} \supset \sim E(\mathbf{i}, \mathrm{x, y})]$$

for any formula $E(\mathbf{i}, \mathrm{x, y})$ in Σ^0.

Such an analysis also shows that the same method yields a decision about whether or not a sentence is true in $\mathrm{SC_{per}}$, which is like SC except that the variables i, j, r, . . . range over ultimately periodic sets of natural numbers. In particular it can be seen that (Ax) also holds in $\mathrm{SC_{per}}$. However this is not shown by using Ramsey's theorem; rather one uses the fact that every element c of a finite semi-group has a power $\mathrm{c^n}$ which is idempotent. These remarks outline a proof of

THEOREM 3. *A sentence A is true in* $\mathrm{SC_{per}}$ *if and only if it is true in* SC.

Using predicates i as binary expansions of real numbers, one obtains as a corollary to Theorems 2 and 3

THEOREM 4. *The first order theories of* [Re, +, Pw, Nn] *and* [Ra, +, Pw, Nn] *are arithmetically equivalent, and decidable.*

Here Re, Ra, Nn, Pw stand for the sets of non-negative reals, rationals, integers, integral powers of 2, respectively.

It is interesting to note that SC becomes undecidable if the function 2x is added (Robinson [10]). Also in case monadic predicate quantification is replaced in SC by quantification over monadic functions, all recursive relations become definable (Gödel).

Problem 1. Let SC^2 be like SC, except that the functions 2x+1 and 2x+2 are taken as primitives in place of x+1. Is SC^2 decidable?

This is of some interest, because the functions 2x+1 and 2x+2 can be interpreted as the right-successor functions x1 and x2 on the set of all words on two generators 1 and 2.

Problem 2. Let SC(α) be like SC, except that the domain of individuals is the ordinal α, and the well ordering on α is added as a primitive. Is SC(ω^2) decidable?

As outlined in the introduction, Theorem 2 may be interpreted as a method for deciding whether or not a given finite automaton satisfies a given condition in SC.

Problem 3. Is there a solvability algorithm for SC, i.e., is there a method which applies to any formula $C(\mathbf{i}, \mathbf{u})$ of SC and decides whether or not there is a finite automata recursion $A(\mathbf{i}, \mathbf{r}, \mathbf{u})$ which satisfies the condition C (i.e., $A(\mathbf{i}, \mathbf{r}, \mathbf{u}) \supset C(\mathbf{i}, \mathbf{u})$)?

REFERENCES

[1] BÜCHI, J. R. "Weak Second Order Arithmetic and Finite Automata", *Zeitschrift für Math. Log. und Grundl. der Math.*, 6 (1960), pp. 66–92.

[2] CHURCH, ALONZO. "Application of Recursive Arithmetic to the Problem of Circuit Synthesis", *Notes of the Summer Institute of Symbolic Logic*, Cornell, 1957, pp. 3–50, and "Application of Recursive Arithmetic in the Theory of Computing and Automata", Notes: *Advanced Theory of the Logical Design of Digital Computers*, U. of Michigan Summer Session, 1959.

[3] COPI, I. M., C. ELGOT, and J. B. WRIGHT. "Realization of Events by Logical Nets", *Journal of the Association for Computing Machinery*, Vol. 5, No. 2, April, 1958.

[4] FRIEDMAN, JOYCE. "Some Results in Church's Restricted Recursive Arithmetic", *Journal of Symbolic Logic*, 22, pp. 337–342 (1957).

[5] KLEENE, S. C. "Representation of Events in Nerve Nets and Finite Automata", *Automata Studies*, Princeton University Press, 1956, pp. 3–41.

[6] MYHILL, JOHN. "Finite Automata and Representation of Events", WADC Report TR 57–624, *Fundamental Concepts in the Theory of Systems*, October 1957, pp. 112–137.

[7] Putnam, Hillary. "Decidability and Essential Undecidability", *Journal of Symbolic Logic*, 22 (1957), pp. 39–54.

[8] Rabin, M., and D. Scott. "Finite Automata and their Decision Problems", *IBM Journal*, April 1959, pp. 114–125.

[9] Ramsey, F. P. ."On a Problem of Formal Logic", *Proc. London Math. Soc.*, (2) 30 (1929), pp. 264–286.

[10] Robinson, R. M. "Restricted Set-theoretical Definitions in Arithmetic", *Proc. Am. Math. Soc.*, 9 (1958), pp. 238–242.

[11] Wang, Hao. "Circuit Synthesis by Solving Sequential Boolean Equations", *Zeitschrift für Math. Log. und Grundl. der Math.*, 5 (1959), pp. 291–322.

THE UNDECIDABILITY OF EXPONENTIAL DIOPHANTINE EQUATIONS

JULIA ROBINSON

University of California, Berkeley, California, U.S.A.

Hilbert's tenth problem asks for an algorithm to determine whether or not an arbitrary Diophantine equation has a solution in integers. The corresponding problem for exponential Diophantine equations (i.e., equations in which exponentiation as well as addition and multiplication is permitted) can now be answered negatively: *There is no algorithm to determine whether or not an arbitrary exponential Diophantine equation is solvable in positive integers.* This result is an immediate consequence of the following theorem:[1]

Every recursively enumerable set (or relation) is exponential Diophantine.

That is, to every recursively enumerable set S of positive integers, there is an exponential Diophantine equation $E(s, u_1, \ldots, u_m)$ such that $s \in S$ if and only if $E(s, u_1, \ldots, u_m)$ is solvable in positive integers.

The proof of this result is constructive. Given a recursive enumeration of S in any of the standard forms, a corresponding exponential Diophantine equation $E(s, u_1, \ldots, u_m)$ can be constructed. Hence we can use the argument of Post [2] to obtain two corollaries:

There is a mechanical procedure which, given any axiomatization of number theory, will yield a particular exponential Diophantine equation which has no solution but which cannot be proved to be unsolvable from the given axioms.

There is a mechanical procedure which, given any proposed algorithm for testing exponential Diophantine equations for solvability, will yield a particular exponential Diophantine equation for which the algorithm gives the wrong answer.

It is not known whether exponential Diophantine sets are necessarily Diophantine. However it was shown in [3] that every exponential Diophantine equation could be transformed mechanically into an equivalent ordinary Diophantine equation in more unknowns provided that there is a Diophantine equation $D(x, y, u_1, \ldots, u_m)$ such that (1) all solutions of D satisfy $y < x^x$ and (2) for every n, there is some solution with $y > x^n$.

Hence if such a Diophantine equation exists, then every recursively enumerable set would be Diophantine and Hilbert's tenth problem would be unsolvable. On the other hand, if some particular recursively enumerable set is not Diophantine, we would obtain surprising bounds on solutions of Diophantine equations. In fact, a sharpening of the above result yields:

[1] Martin Davis and Hilary Putnam [1] obtained this theorem under the assumption that there exist arbitrarily long arithmetic progressions containing only prime numbers. In [4], I later extended and modified their argument to obtain the theorem without using the hypothesis. The proofs of the results in this summary will appear in a joint paper by Davis, Putnam, and myself in the *Annals of Mathematics*.

If there is any recursively enumerable set which is not Diophantine, then each Diophantine equation $F(x, y, u_1, \ldots, u_m)$ *either has a solution with* y *greater than the nth super power of* x *for every* n *or there is an* n *such that every solution satisfies* $y < x^n$.

References

[1] Davis, M., and H. Putnam. On Hilbert's tenth problem. *Notices of the American Mathematical Society*, Vol. 6 (1959), p. 544.

[2] Post, E. L. Recursively enumerable sets of positive integers and their decision problems. *Bulletin of the American Mathematical Society*, Vol. 50 (1944), pp. 284–316.

[3] Robinson, Julia. Existential definability in arithmetic. *Transactions of the American Mathematical Society*, Vol. 72 (1952), pp. 437–449.

[4] Robinson, Julia. The undecidability of exponential Diophantine equations. *Notices of the American Mathematical Society*, Vol. 7 (1960), p. 75.

ON A THEOREM OF COBHAM CONCERNING UNDECIDABLE THEORIES

ROBERT L. VAUGHT

University of California, Berkeley, California, U.S.A.

1. Introduction

A general method for establishing the undecidability of theories was developed in [13]. Its basic tools are the following two facts (unexplained terminology throughout is that of [13] [1]):

1.1. *There is a finitely axiomatizable and essentially undecidable theory Q which is a fragment of the arithmetic of natural numbers.*

1.2. *If a theory T is compatible with a finitely axiomatizable and essentially undecidable theory Σ, then T is undecidable.*

A still weaker fragment of number theory, the theory R, was also introduced in [13]. R is not finitely axiomatizable. Moreover,

1.3. *R is essentially undecidable,*

and

1.4. *Any member of R has a finite model.*

The simple argument which establishes 1.2 depends on the finite axiomatizability of Σ. It has, in fact, been proved (cf. [2], [8]) that 1.2 does not always hold if Σ is only assumed to be axiomatizable (i.e., to have a recursive axiom set).

A. Cobham established the important result that, nevertheless, 1.2 does hold for R and, indeed, for a somewhat weaker theory R_0 (to be described in § 3):

1.5. COBHAM'S THEOREM.[2] *If a theory T is compatible with* R_0, *then T is undecidable.*

Cobham has employed 1.5 in proving that the theory G of finite groups is hereditarily undecidable (and, hence, not axiomatizable).[3] Since the hypoth-

---

This work was supported by the National Science Foundation under grant G–8934.

[1]However, we shall identify a theory with its set of valid sentences. Moreover, a theory T_1 will only be said to be an extension of, or compatible with, a theory T_2 when T_1 and T_2 have the same constants.

[2]This result, as yet unpublished, was communicated orally by Cobham to the author and others in 1957. The full proof and various consequences were described by Cobham in correspondence with A. Tarski and the author in 1958.

[3]This solution of a problem posed in [13, p. 85], also not yet published, was stated and proved in a letter to Tarski in 1958. As Cobham has noted, for such applications it is better to replace 1.5 by the following statement, easily inferred from it: If R_0 is relatively weakly interpretable in a theory T, then T is hereditarily undecidable. (Cf. the discussion in [13, pp. 20–30] of analogous modifications of 1.2.)

esis of 1.2 obviously fails for G, this result could not be obtained by applying 1.2. Thus, it affords an excellent illustration of the additional power possessed by 1.5 as compared with 1.1 and 1.2.

We shall present here a new proof of Cobham's Theorem. Indeed, we shall show that, by a method which may be called existential interpretation, Cobham's Theorem can be derived from a theorem of Trahténbrot. Before stating the latter in 1.6, below, we need the following terminology:

L is the set of logically valid sentences. F is the set of finitely satisfiable sentences. For any set K, NgK is the set of sentences whose negations belong to K. A set Z is said to *separate* a set X from a set Y if Z includes X and is disjoint from Y. Two sets are *recursively inseparable* if no recursive set separates them and they are disjoint.

1.6. TRAHTÉNBROT'S THEOREM.[4] *L and NgF are recursively inseparable.*

In [18], the author showed that:

1.7. *If A is any axiomatizable theory separating L from NgF, then A is compatible with some finitely axiomatizable and essentially undecidable theory.*

In other words, any *axiomatizable* theory whose undecidability follows from Trahténbrot's Theorem also fulfills the hypothesis of Tarski's condition 1.2. We will show (in 5.3) that a similar conclusion applies to axiomatizable theories whose undecidability follows from Cobham's Theorem.

We shall also discuss several other ways in which Cobham's Theorem can be improved or generalized. In the final section, we mention some related problems.

2. Existential Interpretability

We deviate from [13] by considering theories in which the identity symbol may not be present; all notions and results of [13] extend to such theories in an obvious way. On the other hand, in order to avoid bothersome details, we assume that the non-logical constants of any theory are relation symbols, finite in number. (Hence, in further references to the theory R, we shall mean the equivalent theory in our sense.)

A number of principles are known which have, roughly speaking, this form: If a theory T_2 can be 'interpreted' in a theory T_1 in this or that sense, then a certain property (e.g., undecidability, recursive inseparability of T_2 and NgT_2, etc.) is preserved in passing from T_2 to T_1. (Cf. [13, 4, and 12].) In 2.1 below, we shall state some principles of the same sort concerning various properties related to Cobham's Theorem and concerning a new notion called existential interpretability. The latter turns out to be useful not only when applied to theories, but also when applied to other sets of sentences.

---

[4]Cf. [15]. 1.6 was an improvement of Trahténbrot's earlier result [14] that the set of finitely valid sentences is not recursive.

If K is any set of sentences, we denote by ExK the set of all expressions involving sentential connectives, quantifiers, variables, and only those relation symbols which occur in members of K. We denote by $L(K)$ or $F(K)$ the set of sentences $\sigma \in ExK$ such that σ is logically valid or finitely satisfiable, respectively. K will be called a *pseudo-theory* if K is a non-empty set of consistent sentences, only finitely many relation symbols occur in members of K, and any sentence $\sigma \in ExK$ logically equivalent to a member of K belongs to K.[5]

Suppose now that K_1 and K_2 are pseudo-theories. To simplify the notation, we confine ourselves, in the following definition of existential interpretation and in the proof of 2.1, below, to the case when only one relation symbol, P, having two places, occurs in members of K_2. (From this case the situation for an arbitrary K_2 will be obvious.) Suppose that natural numbers p, q, r and formulas $\epsilon(v_0, \cdots, v_{r+p})$ and $\rho(v_0, \cdots, v_{2r+1+q})$, belonging to ExK_1, are specified, the formulas having exactly the free variables indicated. Let u_n^m, y_j, z_k $(m, n = 0, 1, \cdots; j < p; k < q)$ be distinct variables. For each sentence $\sigma \in ExK_2$, let σ^* be obtained from σ by replacing each atomic formula $Pv_m v_n$ by

$$\rho(u_o^m, \cdots, u_r^m, u_o^n, \cdots, u_r^n, z_0, \cdots, z_{q-1})$$

and then replacing all subformulas $\bigwedge v_k \gamma$ or $\bigvee v_k \gamma$ by $\bigwedge u_o^k \cdots \bigwedge u_r^k [\epsilon(u_o^k, \cdots, u_r^k, y_0, \cdots, y_{p-1}) \rightarrow \gamma]$ or $\bigvee u_o^k \cdots \bigvee u_r^k [\epsilon(u_o^k, \cdots, u_r^k, y_0, \cdots, y_{p-1}) \wedge \gamma]$, respectively $(k, m, n = 0, 1, \cdots)$.[6] We say that an *existential interpretation* of K_2 in K_1 has been specified if for each σ belonging to K_2, the sentence $\bigvee y_0 \cdots \bigvee y_{p-1} \bigvee z_0 \cdots \bigvee z_{q-1} \sigma^*$ belongs to K_1.[7]

Henceforth, we shall say that an (ordinary) *interpretation* of K_2 in K_1 is specified when, in the above, $p = q = 0$. It should be noted that we are thus understanding the notion 'interpretable' somewhat more broadly than even the notion 'relatively interpretable' of [13]. Roughly speaking, the latter has been extended by allowing the identity symbol to be interpreted like any other relation symbol, and by allowing the elements of models of K_2 to be interpreted by r-tuples of elements of models of K_1.[8] This fact plays a serious role only in 6.4 and 8.3; most of the time, what matters is only the difference between existential and ordinary interpretability.

2.1. *Suppose that K_1 and K_2 are pseudo-theories and that K_2 is existentially interpretable in K_1. Then:*

---

[5]With some slight changes, the last condition could have been omitted in most of what follows.

[6]If ψ is a formula and $w_0, \ldots, w_{n-1}$ are variables, then $\psi(w_0, \ldots, w_{n-1})$ is the formula obtained by simultaneous substitution of $w_0, \ldots, w_{n-1}$ for the free occurrences of $v_0, \ldots, v_{n-1}$ in ψ, bound variables being changed (in some fixed, effective way) when necessary to avoid collisions.

[7]If the identity symbol occurs in K_2, it is to be 'interpreted' in the same way as any other relation symbol.

[8]Cf. [10], and [13, footnote 17, p. 22].

(a) *If no recursive theory separates $L(K_2)$ from NgK_2, then the same holds for K_1.*[9]

(b) *If $L(K_2)$ and NgK_2 are recursively inseparable, then so are $L(K_1)$ and NgK_1.*

(c) *If $L(K_2)$ and NgK_2 are effectively recursively inseparable,*[10] *then so are $L(K_1)$ and NgK_1.*

(d) *If every axiomatizable theory $L(K_2)$ from NgK_2 is compatible with some finitely axiomatizable, essentially undecidable theory, the the same holds for K_1.*

PROOF. For each sentence $\sigma \varepsilon Ex K_3$, let $f(\sigma)$ be the sentence

$$\Lambda y_0 \cdots \Lambda y_{p-1} \Lambda z_0 \cdots \Lambda z_{q-1} \{ \mathsf{V} u_0^0 \cdots \mathsf{V} u_r^0 \in (u_0^0, \cdots u_r^0, y_0, \cdots, y_{p-1}) \to \sigma^* \}.$$

Then, obviously:

$$(1) \qquad \begin{cases} \textit{if } \sigma \in L(K_2) \textit{ then } f(\sigma) \in L(K_1); \\ \textit{if } \sigma \in NgK_2 \textit{ then } f(\sigma) \in NgK_1. \end{cases}$$

(Indeed, the first holds by the substitution theorem of predicate logic, and the second is just what the existential interpretation has insured.) Note also that, for any sentences $\sigma_1, \sigma_2 \in ExK_2$,

$$(2) \qquad f(\sigma_1 \to \sigma_2) \to [f(\sigma_1) \to f(\sigma_2)]$$

is logically valid.

Since the function f is recursive, we have by (1) what may be called a *reduction* of the pair $L(K_2)$, NgK_2 to the pair $L(K_1)$, NgK_1. It is well known and easily proved that such a reduction allows us to infer the implications (b) and (c). The implication (a) can be inferred similarly in view of the additional condition (2). To make the ideas clear, we shall outline the details of the proof or (d).

Assume the hypothesis of (d), and suppose A_1 is an axiomatizable theory separating $L(K_1)$ from NgK_1. Let $A_2 = \{\sigma / f(\sigma) \in A_1\}$. By (1), A_2 separates $L(K_2)$ from NgK_2. By (2) and the recursiveness of f, A_2 is, moreover, an axiomatizable theory. Hence there is a sentence δ consistent with A_2 such that $Th(\delta)$[11] is essentially undecidable. Hence $\sim \delta \notin A_2$, so $f(\sim \delta) \notin A_1$ and $\sim f(\sim \delta)$ is consistent with A_1. $Th(\sim f(\sim \delta))$ is obviously essentially undecidable (indeed, this is a special case of (a).[12]

[9]If K_2 is a theory, the hypothesis of (a) obviously is equivalent to the statement that any theory compatible with K_2 is undecidable.

[10]For the definition of this notion, see [12] or [17].

[11]$Th(\delta)$ is the theory whose only axiom is δ.

[12]Just this special case of (a) is stated in [13, Part I, Theorem 8]. It may be mentioned that the notion in [13] of inessential extension obviously has the following relation to existential interpretability: T_2 is weakly existentially interpretable in T_1 if and only if T_2 is weakly interpretable in an inessential extension of T_1.

The relation of existential interpretability among pseudo-theories is easily seen to be transitive.

It can be shown by means of an example that an essentially undecidable theory is sometimes existentially interpretable in a consistent, decidable theory.

3. The Theory R_0

The relation symbols of R_0 are Δ_0, Sc, Sm, Pr, and $\leqq$, of 1, 2, 3, 3, and 2 places, respectively. Let the formulas $\Delta_{n+1}(x)$ be defined inductively by requiring that Δ_{n+1} is $\bigvee y[\Delta_n(y) \wedge Sc(y, x)]$.[13] The axioms of R_0 are:

(I) (a) $\bigvee x \Delta_m(x)$ (b) $\Delta_m(x) \rightarrow \sim \Delta_n(x)$ *(for* $m \neq n$*)*
(II) $\Delta_m(x) \wedge \Delta_n(y) \rightarrow [Sm(x, y, z) \rightarrow \Delta_{m+n}(z)]$
(III) $\Delta_m(x) \wedge \Delta_n(y) \rightarrow [Pr(x, y, z) \rightarrow \Delta_{m \cdot n}(z)]$
(IV) $\Delta_n(y) \rightarrow [x \leqq y \leftrightarrow \Delta_0(x) \vee \cdots \vee \Delta_n(x)]$.

Unlike R_0, R has the identity symbol, and has constant terms for the Δ_n. Moreover, R has an axiom schema $(V)\,(x \leqq \Delta_n \vee \Delta_n \leqq x)$ having no analogue in R_0. Schema (V) can, in fact, be removed in R itself without changing any of the essential properties of R.

R_0 shares with R the properties 1.3 and 1.4 and the property:

3.1. *Every recursive function or relation is definable in* R_0.

In 3.1 we are now to regard an $(n+1)$-ary numerical relation W (or function f) as *definable in* R_0 if, for some formula $\phi(v_0, \cdots, v_n)$ (resp., $\psi(v_0, \cdots, v_{n+1})$, with free variables as indicated,

$\Delta_{k_0}(v_0) \wedge \cdots \wedge \Delta_{k_n}(v_n) \rightarrow \phi$ is valid in R_0, whenever $Wk_0 \cdots k_n$, and

$\Delta_{k_0}(v_0) \wedge \cdots \wedge \Delta_{k_n}(v_n) \rightarrow \phi$ is valid in R_0, otherwise.

(resp., $\Delta_{k_0}(v_0) \wedge \cdots \wedge \Delta_{k_n}(v_n) \rightarrow [\psi \leftrightarrow \Delta_{f(k_0, \ldots k_n)}, (v_{n+1})]$ is valid in R_0).

That 1.4 holds for R_0 is obvious. Theorem 3.1 may be proved in essentially the usual way (cf. [13, Part II, Theorem 6] or [7, §49 and §59]) except that a device is needed where axiom schema (V) was formerly used. Roughly speaking, this device consists in relativizing some quantifiers to the formula $N(x)$:

$$\bigvee y[\Delta_0(y) \wedge y \leqq x] \wedge \bigwedge y \bigwedge z[y \leqq x \wedge S(y, z) \rightarrow x \leqq z \vee z \leqq x].$$

With these indications we shall leave the details of the proof of 3.1 to the reader. Finally, 1.3 for R_0 follows from 3.1 by an obvious modification of the old argument (cf. [13, Part II, Theorem 1]).

The possibility of modifying R and the definition of 'definable' in these ways and still establishing 3.1, and inferring from it 1.3, was observed independently by Cobham and (later) the author, about three years ago.

---

[13]For readability, we agree henceforth that x, y, z are v_0, v_1, v_2, respectively, and that x, y, z, u, w, x_0, . . ., x', etc., are distinct variables.

It may be mentioned that Cobham's proof of 1.5 involves an ingenious modification, of a much more fundamental nature than those mentioned above, in the statements and proofs of Theorems 1 and 6 of [13, Part II].

4. Trahténbrot's Theorem

The sets L and F (and hence the meanings of 1.6 and 1.7) are not determined until we specify just what relation symbols are to occur in the sentences of L and F. Trahténbrot [15] showed that for a certain, finite list of relation symbols, 1.6 is true; we shall use the notations L' and F' for this case. The notations L and F will be used for the case when only one binary relation symbol P is allowed. In [18], it was remarked that (by considering one or another of the known ways for reducing the decision problem for L' to that for L) one can infer 1.6 for L and F from 1.6 for L' and F', and the same applies to 1.7. In fact, in the light of § 2, we can say that what was remarked in [18] was, in essence, the fact that

4.1. *F' is existentially interpretable in F,*

plus the appropriate instances of 2.1, (b) and (d).[14] (Note that F and F' are obviously pseudo-theories.)

Trahténbrot's proof of 1.6 (for L' and F') showed that in fact L' and NgF' are effectively recursively inseparable. (One way to see this is to note that Trahténbrot showed there is a reduction of Kleene's pair of recursively enumerable, recursively inseparable sets to the pair L', NgF'. Since the former two sets are effectively recursively inseparable (cf., e.g., [7, § 61]), it follows that so are L' and NgF'.) Hence, by 4.1 and 2.1(c):

4.2. *L and NgF are effectively recursively inseparable.*

5. Cobham's Theorem

5.1. *F is existentially interpretable in R_0.*

PROOF. It is well known that there is a recursive ternary relation W such that for any k and any binary relation Q among the elements of $\{0, \cdots, k\}$, there is a natural number j such that for any m, n, $Wmnj$ if and only if Qmn.

Now we specify p, q, r, ϵ, and ρ so as to obtain the desired existential interpretation (cf. § 2). By 3.1, we may take for $\rho(v_0, v_1, v_2)$ a formula such that

(3) $$\rho(v_0, v_1, v_3) \textit{ defines } W \textit{ in } R_0.$$

Put $p = q = r = 1$, and for $\varepsilon(v_0, v_1)$ take the formula $v_0 \leqq v_1$.

Suppose that $\sigma \in F$ and that σ^* is obtained from σ as in § 2. Then, from (3) and axiom schema IV, one easily infers that, as desired, the formula

---

[14]Cf. § 4 and [18, footnotes 4 and 20]. (In the italicized statement in footnote 20, 'σ' and '$\hat{\sigma}$' should be interchanged.)

(4) $$\bigvee y_0 \bigvee z_0 \sigma^*$$

is valid in R_0.

Theorems 2.1 (c), 4.2, and 5.1, together, provide a new proof of Cobham's Theorem 1.5 and, indeed, of the stronger statement:

5.2. *$L(R_0)$ and NgR_0 are effectively recursively inseparable.*[15]

Similarly, from 2.1(d), 1.7, and 5.1, we infer at once a second result (also implying 1.5).

5.3. *If A is any axiomatizable theory compatible with R_0, then A is compatible with some finitely axiomatizable and essentially undecidable theory.*

Of course, in practice, one must use a fixed theory, such as Q, for Σ in applying 1.2. Thus 5.3 means only that, in theory, 1.5 yields no axiomatizable and undecidable theories not already obtainable from 1.2. Moreover, even in theory, 5.3 does not apply to non-axiomatizable theories, such as G.

6. Set Theories

One can form various set theories, concatenation theories, etc., which resemble the theories R and R_0.

One such theory, a very weak Zermelo-type set theory, is the following theory, Z_0. Z_0 has the identity symbol and the binary relation symbol ε. For any set X, let $P(X)$ be the power set of X; and let $M = 0 \cup P(0) \cup PP(0) \cup \cdots$. For $r = \{s_0, \cdots, s_{n-1}\} \in M$, the formula $D_r(x)$ is defined (inductively) to be:

$$\bigvee y_0 \cdots \bigvee y_{n-1}\Big[\mathop{\Pi}_{i<n}(D_{s_i}(y_i) \wedge y_i \in x) \wedge \bigwedge z(z \in x \rightarrow \sum_{i<n} z = y_i)\Big].$$

The axioms of Z_0 are all sentences

$$\mathop{\Pi}_{i<n} D_{s_i}(x_i) \rightarrow \bigvee y \bigwedge z(z \in y \leftrightarrow \sum_{i<n} z = x_i) \quad (\textit{for } s_0, \cdots, s_{n-1} \in M).$$

Take $\rho(x, y, z)$ to be the (Kuratowski ordered-pair) formula:

$$\bigvee w \bigvee w' \bigwedge u[(u \in z \leftrightarrow u = w \vee u = w') \wedge (u \in w \leftrightarrow u = x) \wedge (u \in w' \leftrightarrow u = x \vee u = y)].$$

One easily verifies that (4) is valid in Z_0 whenever $\sigma \in F$. Hence,

6.1. *F is existentially interpretable in Z_0.*

---

[15]It was noted in [6, Theorem 2.5B] that condition 3.1 (for R) implies the statement (A): R and NgR are recursively inseparable. In [4], Feferman showed that (B): every axiomatizable consistent extension of R is creative. Smullyan [12] established a result implying both (A) and (B), namely, (C): R and NgR are effectively recursively inseparable. Theorem 5.2, in turn, implies both (C) and 1.5. Cobham's proof of 1.5 may easily be modified by imitating the changes in the proof of 1.3 needed to prove (A), (B), and (C) so as to yield a proof of 5.2.

A theory Z_{00} still weaker than Z_0 might be formed having only the axioms $\bigvee x D_r(x)\,(r \in M)$. I have been unable to determine whether or not Z_{00} is essentially undecidable.

Next we consider a second-order set theory, T_0. T_0 was described in [18] and differs only slightly from a theory involved in [15]; it will be discussed further in § 7. T_0 has the relation symbols I, ε, and ρ of 1, 2, and 3 places, respectively. (Ix is read 'x is an individual'.) Its axioms are the sentence α:

$$\bigwedge x \bigwedge y \bigwedge u[x \in u \vee \rho(x, y, u) \vee \rho(y, x, u) \rightarrow Ix]$$
$$\wedge \bigvee u \bigwedge x x \notin u \wedge \bigvee u \bigwedge x \bigwedge y \sim \rho(x, y, u)$$
$$\wedge \bigwedge u \bigwedge y \bigwedge y'\{Iy \wedge Iy' \rightarrow \bigvee u' \bigvee u'' \bigwedge x \bigwedge x'[[x \in u' \leftrightarrow x \in u \vee x = y]$$
$$\wedge [\rho(x, x', u'') \leftrightarrow \rho(x, x', u) \vee (x = y \wedge x' = y')]]\},$$

and all the sentences

$$\bigvee x_0 \cdots \bigvee x_{n-1}\Big(\mathop{\Pi}_{i>n} Ix_i \wedge \mathop{\Pi}_{i>j<n} x_i \neq x_j\Big).$$

Again the sentence (4) is obviously valid in T_0 whenever $\sigma \in F$. Hence,

6.2. *F is existentially interpretable in* T_0.

(T_0 can be considerably weakened without losing this property.)

Finally, we consider a theory, S, which is closely related to the pseudo-theory F. S has no identity symbol, and has the relation symbols ε and ρ. Its axioms are simply all sentences (4) such that $\sigma \in F$. Obviously,

6.3. *F is existentially interpretable in S.*

Indeed, as one readily shows, S has the peculiar property:

6.4. *For any pseudo-theory K, F is existentially interpretable in K if and only if S is interpretable in K.*

By 6.1, 6.2, 6.3, 2.1, 4.1, and 4.2, we see that 5.2 and 5.3 hold for each of Z_0, T_0, and S_0, in place of R_0.

From the essential undecidability of Z_0 it follows that the stronger theory Z_1, whose only axioms are $\bigvee u \bigwedge z(z \notin u)$ and $\bigwedge x \bigwedge y \bigvee u \bigwedge z(z \in u \leftrightarrow z \in x \vee z{=}y)$, is also essentially undecidable.[16] This answers a question raised by Szmielew and Tarski, who established (cf. [13, p. 34]) the essential undecidability of the theory having, in addition to these two, the axiom of extensionality.

Cobham observed that Trahténbrot's Theorem 1.6, for the sets $L(G)$ and $F(G)$ (or the sets $L(R_0)$ and $F(R_0)$), is a consequence of his results concerning G (or R_0), because $G \subseteq F(G)\,(R_0 \subseteq F(R_0)$, by 1.4). By noting that 4.1 was shown to be valid without any specific assumptions about what relation symbols occur in members of F', we may, in fact, conclude from 4.1 that

[16]The same result can also be obtained by interpreting in Z_1 the theory T_0. Regarding the essential undecidability of the latter, cf. [18, pp. 12–13], where reference is made to a related result in [16].

6.5. *Any pseudo-theory* K, *such that* $K \subseteq F(K)$, *is existentially interpretable in* F.

Now, it is obvious that $Z_0 \subseteq F(Z_0)$, $T_0 \subseteq F(T_0)$, and $S \subseteq F(S)$. As a result, we infer from 6.5, 6.1, 6.2, 6.3, and 5.1 that in a certain sense all of the pseudo-theories F, Z_0, T_0, S, R_0, and R have the same strength. Indeed:

6.6. *Each of* F, Z_0, T_0, S, R_0, *and* R *is existentially interpretable in each of the others.*

Among the theories S, Z_0, T_0, R_0, and R one may ask: which have (ordinary) interpretations in which of the others? It is not difficult to see that Z_0 is interpretable in R_0 and that R_0 (and, hence, Z_0) is interpretable in R and also in T_0. Among Z_0, T_0, R_0, and R these may well be the only cases where the answer is positive, but we have no proof of any of these negative assertions. In general, to establish non-interpretability seems to be a rather awkward matter.

We have succeeded in showing that:

6.7. *None of* Z_0, T_0, R_0, *and* R *is interpretable in* S.

The (rather tedious) proof makes use of results of [5] concerning the elementary theory of a relational system which is the cardinal sum of other systems (cf. [5, Theorem 3.2, § 4.7, and Theorem 6.1.2]).

7. An Improvement of 5.3

J. C. Shepherdson raised the question whether one could strengthen 5.3 as follows:

7.1. *If* A *is an axiomatizable theory compatible with* R, *then* A *is compatible with some finitely axiomatizable extension of* R.

I have proved 7.1, and the corresponding statement for R_0. The proofs are obtained by making a slight change at the end of Cobham's proof of 1.5. It appears to be essential to employ in the proof of 7.1 (for R or R_0) the ideas involved in Cobham's proof of 1.5. One may also ask whether 7.1 holds for Z_0, T_0, or S in place of R. It turns out that the answer is affirmative for Z_0 and T_0, but negative for S. Most of the properties we have considered have been shown rather easily to pass from any one of R_0, Z_0, T_0, or S to the others. But in the case of 7.1 one apparently must make a detailed argument for each theory in question.

We shall not prove 7.1 here, but we shall establish the analogous result for T_0 (which we call 7.2). Indeed, the theory T_0 was formed (essentially, by Trahténbrot) in just such a way as to make possible short proofs (in [15] and [18]) of 1.6 and 1.7. Hence, the argument for 7.2, which differs only slightly from those proofs, is also short.

Proof of 7.2. Let A be an axiomatizable theory compatible with T_0. For each sentence $\sigma \in ExF$, construct the formula $\sigma^* \in Ex(T_0)$ as in § 2 (with $p = q = r = 1$). Then the sentence $\bar{\sigma}$

$$\alpha \wedge \mathsf{V} y_0 \mathsf{V} z_0 [\mathsf{V} w(w \in y_0) \wedge \sigma^*]$$

is obviously consistent with A when $\sigma \in F$ (since then $\bar{\sigma} \in T_0$). Now, if $\bar{\sigma}$ were consistent with A *only* when $\sigma \in F$, we could infer that $\sim \bar{\sigma} \in A$ if and only if $\sigma \in F$; and, hence, that F has a recursively enumerable complement. This would contradict Trahténbrot's result of 1950 [14]. Thus A is consistent with some $\bar{\sigma}$ such that σ has no finite model. By looking at the axioms of T_0 one now easily verifies that $Th(\bar{\sigma})$ is an extension of T_0, completing the proof.

Since 7.2 implies that the hypothesis of 2.1(d) holds for T_0, one obtains (noting 6.6) a proof of 1.7.

As regards Z_0, the situation is similar to that for R. To show that 7.1 holds for Z_0, one must first develop certain detailed facts about Z_0.

It can be shown that 7.1 fails for S; that, in fact:

7.3. *There is a consistent, finite extension of S having no consistent, finitely axiomatizable extension which is an extension of S.*

7.3 may be established rather easily by relying on a result of [5, Theorem 6.10—6.7.1] concerning cardinal sums.

Ehrenfeucht and Feferman [3] have shown that in any axiomatizable theory which is a consistent extension of R, every recursively enumerable set is representable.[17] Shepherdson obtained a more direct proof of the same theorem, and then, by employing the results involved in Cobham's proof of 1.5, was able to establish the stronger theorem:

7.4. (SHEPHERDSON) *In any axiomatizable theory A compatible with R, every recursively enumerable set is representable.*

Shepherdson was then motivated to propose 7.1 by observing that by means of 7.1 one could obtain 7.4 at once from the theorem of Ehrenfeucht and Feferman. (Indeed, let A be compatible with $Th(\sigma)$, which extends R; and let $\theta(x)$ represent a set Y in $Th(A \cup \{\sigma\})$. Then $\sigma \to \theta(x)$ represents Y in A.)

Putnam and Smullyan [9] have improved the Theorem of Ehrenfeucht and Feferman in another direction by showing that: in any axiomatizable theory which is a consistent extension of R, every disjoint pair of recursively enumerable sets can be 'exactly separated' (in a sense described in [9]). By the same argument of Shepherdson, one can again replace 'consistent extension of' by 'compatible with', in view of 7.1.

8. Some Problems

8.1. *Is there a theory which is finitely axiomatizable and undecidable but is not compatible with any finitely axiomatizable, essentially undecidable theory?*[18]

---

[17]For the meaning here of 'representable', see [6]. In considering representability, we shall discuss R, rather than R_0, in order to avoid considering the various alternatives that appear when one tries to define this notion for R_0.

[18]This problem, which seems to have originated with Tarski, has been discussed in [1, p. 393] and [18, p. 13].

Ehrenfeucht [3] and Putnam [8] showed that 8.1 can be answered affirmatively if the word 'finitely' is deleted. As was remarked by Cobham, a variant of 8.1, whose answer seems not to be known, is obtained by replacing 'finitely axiomatizable and undecidable' by 'axiomatizable and hereditarily undecidable'. (The same applies to 8.2 and 8.3, below.) Cobham's Theorem, 1.5, might seem at first glance to offer a possible method for finding a theory as demanded in 8.1, but 5.3 shows that in fact it does not.

The second problem was stated by Feferman [4]:

8.2. *Is there a theory which is finitely axiomatizable and undecidable but not of the highest degree of undecidability for recursively enumerable sets?*

Feferman [4] obtained an affirmative answer if 'finitely' is deleted; Shoenfield [11] showed that this remains correct if, in addition, 'undecidable' is changed to 'essentially undecidable'. Feferman [4] showed that no theory in which R is interpretable or Q is weakly interpretable can provide an example for Problem 2. By 5.2, the same applies to any theory in which R is weakly existentially interpretable.

The difficulty of Problems 8.1 and 8.2 seems to be related to another, imprecise question: Is there any way of showing that a finitely axiomatizable theory is undecidable except what is in essence the original method of Gödel and Church? In 8.3 we attempt to present a precise version of this question.

8.3. *Is there a theory which is finitely axiomatizable and undecidable but in which S is not weakly interpretable?*

By 6.4, 6.5, and 6.6, one sees that a number of possible alternatives to Problem 3 are all equivalent.

Added in proof: If ExK_2 contains $=$ (and, say, P), then the first of the assertions (1) in the proof of 2.1 need not be correct. However, 2.1 remains valid because the assertion in question *is* valid for *some* existential interpretation. Indeed it is easy to verify that such an existential interpretation is obtained from any given one by changing it only as follows: In forming the new σ^*, $x = y$ should be replaced by the old ϕ^*, where ϕ is the "built-in equality" formula:

$$\wedge z[(z = x \rightarrow z = y) \wedge (x = z \rightarrow y = z) \wedge (Pxz \rightarrow Pyz) \wedge (Pzx \rightarrow Pzy)].$$

(For this argument it is essential that there are only finitely many relation symbols in ExK_2.)

References

[1] Cobham, A. Effectively decidable theories. *Summaries of talks presented at the Summer Institute for Symbolic Logic, Cornell University*, 1957, second edition, Institute for Defense Analyses, 1960, pp. 391–395.

[2] Ehrenfeucht, A. Two theories with axioms built by means of pleonasms. *Journal of Symbolic Logic*, Vol. 22 (1957), pp. 36–38.

[3] EHRENFEUCHT, A., and S. FEFERMAN. Representability of recursively enumerable sets in formal theories. To appear in *Archiv für Math. Logik u. Grundlagenforschung.*

[4] FEFERMAN, S. Degrees of unsolvability associated with classes of formalized theories. *Journal of Symbolic Logic,* Vol. 22 (1957), pp. 161–175.

[5] FEFERMAN, S., and R. VAUGHT. The first order properties of products of algebraic systems. *Fundamenta Mathematicae,* Vol. 47 (1959), pp. 57–103.

[6] GRZYGORCZYK, A., A. MOSTOWSKI, and C. RYLL-NARDZEWSKI. The classical and the ω-complete arithmetic. *Journal of Symbolic Logic,* Vol. 23 (1958), pp. 188–206.

[7] KLEENE, S. C. *Introduction to Metamathematics.* Amsterdam, North Holland, 1952, x + 550 pp.

[8] PUTNAM, H. Decidability and essential undecidability. *Journal of Symbolic Logic,* Vol. 22 (1957), pp. 39–49.

[9] PUTNAM, H., and R. M. SMULLYAN. Exact separation of recursively enumerable sets within theories. To appear in *Proceedings of the American Mathematical Society.* (Abstract presented at this Congress.)

[10] ROBINSON, A., and A. H. LIGHTSTONE. Syntactical transforms. *Transactions of the American Mathematical Society,* Vol. 86 (1957), pp. 220–245.

[11] SHOENFIELD, J. Degrees of formal systems. *Journal of Symbolic Logic,* Vol. 23 (1958), pp. 389–392.

[12] SMULLYAN, R. M. Theories with effectively inseparable nuclei. *Journal of Symbolic Logic,* Vol. 23 (1958), p. 458.

[13] TARSKI, A., with A. MOSTOWSKI and R. M. ROBINSON. *Undecidable Theories.* Amsterdam, North-Holland, 1953, xi + 98 pp.

[14] TRAHTÉNBROT, B. A. Impossibility of an algorithm for the decision problem in finite classes *Doklady Akadémii Nauk SSSR,* Vol. 70 (1950), pp. 569–572.

[15] TRAHTÉNBROT, B. A. On recursive separability. *Ibid.,* Vol. 88 (1953), pp. 953–956.

[16] TRAHTÉNBROT, B. A. Definition of finite sets and deductive incompleteness of the theory of sets. *Izvestiya Akadémii Nauk SSSR,* ser. mat., Vol. 20 (1956), pp. 569–582.

[17] USPÉNSKI, J. Theorem of Gödel and theory of algorithms. *Doklady Akadémii Nauk SSSR,* Vol. 91 (1953), pp. 737–740.

[18] VAUGHT, R. Sentences true in all constructive models. *Journal of Symbolic Logic,* Vol. 24 (1959), pp. 1–15.

Symposium on the Notion of Recursiveness

THE THEORY OF HIERARCHIES

J. W. ADDISON

University of Michigan, Ann Arbor, Michigan, U.S.A.
University of California, Berkeley, California, U.S.A.

Surely one of the most frustrating experiences of a congress such as this is to have the expected enjoyment of listening to a talk in a field not quite one's own but just "next door" spoiled by the sober realities of the expanding babel of modern mathematics and logic.

Such frustrations call to mind the question Hilbert posed to another international congress exactly 60 years ago this month [15, p. 478]:

> "... the question is urged upon us whether mathematics is doomed to the fate of those other sciences that have split up into separate branches, whose representatives scarcely understand one another and whose connection becomes ever more loose."

It is heartening and refreshing to hear his own reply:

> "I do not believe this nor wish it. Mathematical science is in my opinion an indivisible whole, an organism whose vitality is conditioned upon the connection of its parts. For with all the variety of mathematical knowledge, we are still clearly conscious of the similarity of the logical devices, the *relationship* of the *ideas* in mathematics as a whole and the numerous analogies in its different departments. We also notice that, the farther a mathematical theory is developed, the more harmoniously and uniformly does its construction proceed, and unsuspected relations are disclosed between hitherto separate branches of the science. So it happens that, with the extension of mathematics, its organic character is not lost but only manifests itself the more clearly."

The theory of hierarchies happily bears out Hilbert's prediction, and I am glad to be able to offer to you today some bits of evidence to support his conviction.

1. The Theories of Hierarchies

What is the theory of hierarchies? Before offering a characterization of it, let us describe briefly the existing theories of hierarchies.

We have in mind here the theories of particular hierarchies that have arisen, more or less independently, in three areas of mathematics and logic, namely (1) analysis, (2) recursive function theory, and (3) pure logic.

The theory of hierarchies in analysis long ago assumed an identity and name of its own and is now usually referred to as *descriptive*[1] *set theory*. With the origins of the first of these "branches of the theory of hierarchies" we especially associate Borel, Baire, Lebesgue, Suslin, and Luzin, with the second Kleene and Mostowski (and more recently Kondô), and with the third Herbrand and Tarski and his school. In the three areas combined, results have been published by well over 100 workers.

There has been an interesting interplay between the mathematical and metamathematical approaches in these branches of the theory of hierarchies. In analysis the mathematical approach has long dominated, and only recently has the metamathematical approach made an impact. But in recursive function theory and pure logic the first approaches were metamathematical, although the mathematical point of view has now led to important contributions to both of them, especially the latter. From the pioneering work of Kuratowski and Tarski [18], we know that the kind of outlook, at least in the basic theory, is important only for psychological, heuristic reasons. And as the theory of languages with infinitely long expressions is further developed, it looks reasonably clear that this assertion can be extended to all aspects of the full-blown theories.

The theories arising in analysis and recursive function theory already have been consolidated to a large extent (cf. [1, Part II], [2], and [5]). It is our intention here to point the way to their further consolidation with the theory arising in pure logic.

2. The Theory of Hierarchies

The proper framework for our study appears to be the language of the pure and simple theory of types, i.e., of the pure predicate calculus[2] of order ω. For this language we consider various assignments of fixed interpretations to various assortments of the variables — or, to say essentially the same thing in a different way, we consider the languages of various *applied* predicate calculi of order ω.

Among the various formulations of these languages it is largely immaterial which one we choose. Whether we have equality as a primitive symbol and whether we have function variables in place of, or in addition to, predicate variables is not crucial for our purposes here. Although such

---

[1]Cf., e.g., [19, p. xiii].

[2]By a *grammar* we mean a set of primitive symbols and rules of formation, without a proof-theoretic or model-theoretic structure associated with it. By a *language* we mean a grammar together with an interpretation (i.e., with a model-theoretic structure) for it. By a *calculus* we mean a grammar with both model-theoretic and proof-theoretic structures associated with it.

variations produce some changes in details of the theory, particularly in low level results of inferior type, the theories are for the most part easily intertranslatable. Here, to fix on something, we will usually assume that equality and function variables are not present. On the other hand it is desirable that large infinities of constants be allowed, and probably also large infinities of variables, although we will not make use of the latter here.

It is well known that for each formula of one of these languages there is a logically equivalent formula in prenex normal form — that is, in which all quantifiers are at the front. The sequence of quantifiers in such a formula is called the *prefix* and the rest of the formula, the scope of the rightmost quantifier, is called the *matrix*. It is easily shown further that each formula is logically equivalent to a formula in *full prenex normal form*, i.e., in prenex normal form with no quantifier in it having a quantifier of higher type to its right.

We might now roughly characterize the theory of hierarchies as dealing with a certain class of syntactic properties of formulas in full prenex normal form, namely their kinds of prefixes.

Many such syntactic properties of formulas have been studied — the adjectives "monadic", "positive", and "Horn" come at once to mind, but perhaps none have played a more important role in logic than these kinds of prefixes, nor have many been studied longer. Already before Hilbert's talk mentioned above, this theory was being discussed in two quite far removed areas: Peirce's work on prenex normal form and Borel's treatment of the sets which now bear his name.

What are the syntactic features of prefixes that distinguish among them? The four main properties of the prefix of a formula in full prenex normal form are:

(1) the highest *type* of variable in it,

(2) the *kind* of leading (i.e., leftmost) quantifier, i.e., whether it is existential or universal,

(3) the number of "blocks" of homogeneous quantifiers (i.e., quantifiers of like *kind*) of highest type — this is 1+ the number of *alternations* among the quantifiers of highest type,

(4) the number and ranks of the quantifiers in each block.

The last feature usually appears to be the least important, although occasionally it is crucial (cf., e.g., the classic instance of the difference between the prefixes $\bigvee a_1 \bigvee a_2 \bigwedge b$ and $\bigvee a_1 \bigvee a_2 \bigvee a_3 \bigwedge b$ in the decision problem for the first-order predicate calculus). The first and third features are especially important as a measure of the complexity of formulas, and of the concepts which they define, as teachers of undergraduate mathematics often note.

We shall use, as above, lower case Roman letters for individual variables (i.e., variables of type 0) and capital Roman letters with superscripts t for variables of type t $(0 < t < \omega)$.

By a model of a formula relative to a given interpretation of the constants of the formula we mean, as usual, an ordered $(n+1)$-tuple $(n \geqq 0)$, the coordinates of which are a domain and interpretations for the n free variables of the formula which satisfy the formula relative to the given interpretation of the constants. We associate with each formula of a language the class of all its models. If $\mathfrak{P}$ is an applied predicate language of order ω (including an interpretation for the constants, and possibly also a domain), then we shall denote by $\mathbf{V}_k^t(\mathfrak{P})$ (read: "exists-t-k-of-$\mathfrak{P}$") $\{\mathbf{\Lambda}_k^t(\mathfrak{P})$ (read: "all-t-k-of-$\mathfrak{P}$")$\}$ the class of formulas of $\mathfrak{P}$ in full prenex normal form with leading quantifier existential {universal} and of type t and with k blocks of homogeneous quantifiers of type t. We shall use the same notation to denote the corresponding family of associated classes of models relative to the interpretation of the constants given in $\mathfrak{P}$.[3]

Occasionally it is desirable to section these classes further according to the type of the free variables appearing. Following a suggestion of Tugué [24, p. 99] we may then use the notation $\mathbf{V}_k^{t,t'}(\mathfrak{P})$, $\mathbf{\Lambda}_k^{t,t'}(\mathfrak{P})$, where t' is the least integer $\geqq -1$ such that there is no free variable of greater type occurring in the formula. In §§ 3—5 of this paper we want to concentrate for simplicity on the cases where $t' = -1$, 0, or 1 (even though some of the remarks generalize to higher t'), so there we will understand that the omitted t' is to be thought of as *restricted to these cases.*

For each type t, type t', and language $\mathfrak{P}$ we denote by $\mathscr{H}(t, t', \mathfrak{P})$ the hierarchy $\lambda k \langle \mathbf{V}_k^{t,t'}(\mathfrak{P}), \mathbf{\Lambda}_k^{t,t'}(\mathfrak{P})\rangle$. These "$\mathscr{H}$-hierarchies" form a very general class — many of the hierarchies of analysis, recursive function theory, and logic are such that their first ω levels are among these hierarchies.

In the general theory of hierarchies one seeks general principles that apply to large collections of these $\mathscr{H}$-hierarchies, and investigates how properties of these hierarchies vary as t varies, as t' varies, and as $\mathfrak{P}$ varies in each of several distinguishable directions.

To prevent the notation from being cumbersome, some abbreviations and special notations are in order. If $\mathfrak{P}$ is the pure language we omit "$(\mathfrak{P})$", as an abbreviation. If $\mathfrak{P}_{\mathscr{C}}$ is a language with constants for the natural numbers and for the predicates in the subset $\mathscr{C}$ of the set of all predicates on the set N of natural numbers, "$\mathbf{V}_k^t(\mathfrak{P}_{\mathscr{C}})$", "$\mathbf{\Lambda}_k^t(\mathfrak{P}_{\mathscr{C}})$" are abbreviated to "$\Sigma_k^t(\mathscr{C})$", "$\Pi_k^t(\mathscr{C})$", and if $\mathscr{C}$ is the class of recursive predicates, "$(\mathscr{C})$" may be further omitted as an abbreviation. Our general notation can thus be viewed as a generalization essentially consistent with the notation of [5].[4]

To illustrate the notation and the consolidation which it represents,

---

[3]Three restrictions to the *finite* implicit in our definitions — to *finite* types, to formulas of *finite* length, and to models of *finite* sets of formulas — can all be fruitfully relaxed, but these generalizations are not in the direction of the main attack of this paper.

[4]Our "$\Sigma_k^t(\mathscr{C})$", for example, is thus slightly different from our "$\Sigma_k^t[\mathscr{C}]$" of [5], so we have used (round) parentheses instead of (square) brackets to prevent confusion. But the abbreviations are so chosen that "Σ_k^t" keeps its same meaning.

we list some sample notations from each of the three branches of hierarchy theory next to their notation here.

(1) analysis	
$F_{\sigma\delta}$	$\Pi_3^{0,1}(2^N)$
analytic	$\Sigma_1^{1,1}(2^N)$
PCA	$\Sigma_2^{1,1}(2^N)$
projective	$\bigcup \Pi_k^{1,1}(2^N)$
(2) recursive function theory	
recursively enumerable	$\Sigma_1^{0,0}$
arithmetical	$\bigcup \Pi_k^0$
analytical	$\bigcup \Pi_k^1$
(3) pure logic	
UC	$\bigwedge_1^0$
EC (formerly AC)	$\bigcup \bigwedge_k^0$
AE	$\bigwedge_2^0$
PC	$\bigvee_1^1$

3. The Analogies

To illustrate that the proposed consolidation lies deeper than superficial definitions, several examples are open to us. Here it seems especially appropriate to discuss the analogies which led to the proposal.

For this purpose it is desirable first to review two important properties of classes of sets — the first separation property (first formulated by Luzin) and the reduction property (first formulated by Kuratowski). Denoting these two properties by $\mathrm{Sep}_{\mathrm{I}}$ and Red, respectively, as in [5], we have by definition that for any class $\mathcal{Q}$ of subsets of a set S:

$$\mathrm{Sep}_{\mathrm{I}}(\mathcal{Q}) \leftrightarrow \forall X \forall Y[X, Y \in \mathcal{Q} \;\&\; X \cap Y = \emptyset \rightarrow \exists X_1[X_1 \in \mathcal{Q}, \mathrm{c}\,\mathcal{Q} \;\&\; X_1 \supseteq X \;\&\; X_1 \cap Y = \emptyset]],$$

$$\mathrm{Red}(\mathcal{Q}) \leftrightarrow \forall X \forall Y[X, Y \in \mathcal{Q} \rightarrow \exists X_1 \exists Y_1[X_1, Y_1 \in \mathcal{Q} \;\&\; X_1 \subseteq X \;\&\; Y_1 \subseteq Y \;\&\; X_1 \cup Y_1 = X \cup Y \;\&\; X_1 \cap Y_1 = \emptyset]],$$

where $\mathrm{c}\,\mathcal{Q}$ denotes the class of complements (relative to S) of sets in $\mathcal{Q}$. It will be important to recall that $\mathrm{Red}(\mathcal{Q}) \rightarrow \mathrm{Sep}_{\mathrm{I}}(\mathrm{c}\,\mathcal{Q})$.

A number of years ago Richard Büchi suggested to me that a comparative study of the hierarchies of recursive function theory and pure logic might prove fruitful. But at that time not enough was known either to promise much success or to indicate firmly how the two should be fruitfully paired off. The real clue emerged ironically from a remark of Craig, which was profitably analyzed in terms of what might be called a "metaanalogy". The consolidations of the theories of hierarchies of analysis and recursive function theory had grown out of Mostowski's observation that the analogy between recursively enumerable and analytic sets broke down on the question of $\mathrm{Sep}_{\mathrm{I}}$, which was a property of the second but not of the first. This had led to a reformulation of the analogy which placed the recursively enumerable sets against the open sets of a suitable space, and the Σ_1^1 sets against the analytic sets. For this pairing $\mathrm{Sep_I}$ fits perfectly. This reformulation pointed the way to a consolidation of the two theories.

Now in connection with the theory of hierarchies of recursive function theory and that of pure logic, Craig made [12, p. 281] the observation that the analogy between recursively enumerable and PC sets broke down on the question of $\mathrm{Sep_I}$, which was a property of the second but not of the first. This now leads to a reformulation of the analogy which places the recursively enumerable sets against the existential classes of models, and the Σ^1_1 sets against the PC classes. Again for this pairing $\mathrm{Sep_I}$ fits perfectly. And again this reformulation points the way to a consolidation of the two (and hence of all three) theories.

The question of $\mathrm{Sep_I}$ is profitably viewed as part of a somewhat larger complex of analogies.

pure logic

the Craig separation theorem

$\swarrow_1 \qquad \uparrow_3 \qquad \searrow^2$

$\mathrm{PC} \cap \mathrm{cPC} = \mathrm{EC}$ $\qquad$ & $\qquad$ $\mathrm{Sep_I(PC)}$

$* \downarrow 4$

Beth's theorem

analysis and recursive function theory

the generalized Luzin separation theorem

$\swarrow_1 \qquad \uparrow_3 \qquad \searrow^2$

the Suslin-Kleene theorem $\qquad$ & $\qquad$ $\mathrm{Sep_I}(\Sigma^1_1(\mathscr{C}))$

$* \downarrow 4$

the arithmetical operator theorem

The *Craig separation theorem* [12, p. 281] asserts that any two disjoint classes in PC can be separated by a class in EC. It is immediately equivalent to the *Craig interpolation theorem* [11, Theorem 5]—it is simply a reformulation of the latter with some of the metamathematical concepts replaced with mathematical ones and with the resulting set-theoretic concept of interpolation replaced by that of separation.

The Craig interpolation theorem is in turn almost immediately equivalent to the *Robinson consistency theorem* [21, 2.9] — the latter follows from the former immediately and the former follows from the latter in about ten lines, including two applications of the compactness theorem. I have also learned at this congress that the Craig interpolation theorem is closely related to the *Specker (relative) interpretability theorem.* Because of its power, its growing interconnections with other results in logic, and the many applications of it, its generalizations, and its refinements, the Craig interpolation theorem begins to emerge as the most central and important result in pure logic since 1936.

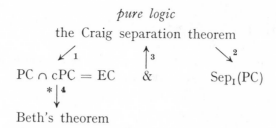

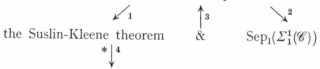

Beth's theorem asserts, roughly speaking, that at the first-order level implicit definability implies explicit definability, or, alternatively, that Padoa's method is a general method in proofs of noneliminability. More precisely it asserts

$$\Delta(\mathrm{F}, \mathrm{G}) \wedge \Delta(\mathrm{F}, \mathrm{H}) \Vdash \mathrm{G} = \mathrm{H} \rightarrow \exists \Delta'[\Delta(\mathrm{F}, \mathrm{G}) \Vdash \mathrm{G} = \lambda \mathrm{a}\Delta'(\mathrm{F}, \mathrm{a})],$$

where Δ, Δ' are variables for formulas of the pure first-order predicate calculus with exactly the free variables indicated, and where for conciseness we have represented the possibly several free variables as one and the possibly several G's as one of rank one.

Beth's theorem, which first appeared in [8], is just a special case of the corollary relativized by 1 of the Craig interpolation theorem. Yet, although it was discovered well after the interpolation theorem (which lay buried in somewhat more general form in Craig's thesis [10]), it was responsible in large part for the real "discovery" of the interpolation theorem. Indeed, Beth's paper [8], although written in such a form that only a few seem to have read it carefully, has nevertheless certainly been one of the most stimulating contributions to logic of the last decade. As testimony to this we find a dozen or more workers (including, for example, Craig, Daigneault, Keisler, Kochen, Lyndon, A. Robinson, Specker, Svenonius, and Vaught) who have extended, refined, or reproved Beth's result, a number of them reporting to this congress on these results.

The *generalized Luzin separation theorem* asserts that for a wide class of $\mathscr{C}$ any two disjoint $\Sigma_1^1(\mathscr{C})$ sets can be separated by a set superarithmetical[5] in predicates in $\mathscr{C}$. This generalizes the Luzin separation theorem [19, p. 156] (which is the special case when $t' = 1$ and $\mathscr{C} = 2^N$).

The *Suslin-Kleene theorem* asserts that for a wide class of $\mathscr{C}$ $\Sigma_1^1(\mathscr{C}) \cap \Pi_1^1(\mathscr{C})$ is exactly the class of sets (of same type) superarithmetical in predicates in $\mathscr{C}$. This generalizes both Suslin's theorem (which is the special case when $t' = 1$ and $\mathscr{C} = 2^N$) and Kleene's theorem (XXI*, XXIV*) of [16, pp. 202, 204, and 210] (which is the special case when $t' = 0$ and $\mathscr{C}$ is a singleton).

The *arithmetical operator theorem* asserts that for a wide class of $\mathscr{C}$ the values of an operator arithmetical in predicates in $\mathscr{C}$ are, roughly speaking, "uniformly" superarithmetical in predicates in $\mathscr{C}$ and their respective arguments. It appears to be closely related to the work of Luzin on implicit definitions [19, Chapter IV] and generalizes a remark made, among many places, in [4] and [13, p. 199].

The corresponding arrows in the complexes of analogies can all be argued

---

[5]Of the several definitions of superarithmetical, the most intuitive says, roughly speaking, that a set is *superarithmetical in predicates in* $\mathscr{C}$ if and only if it is in the least class of sets containing the $\Sigma_1^0(\mathscr{C}) \cap \Pi_1^0(\mathscr{C})$ sets (of same type) and closed under unions and intersections of $\Sigma_1^0(\mathscr{C}) \cap \Pi_1^0(\mathscr{C})$ sequences. For $t' = 0$ superarithmetical in predicates in $\mathscr{C}$ = hyperarithmetical in predicates in $\mathscr{C}$, but for $t' = 1$ this ceases to be the case.

by rather immediate and essentially "isomorphic" proofs. Implication 1 holds by simply taking in the hypothesis the two disjoint sets in PC {in $\Sigma_1^1(\mathscr{C})$} to be complementary, and then independently using the rather immediate fact that PC $\cap$ cPC $\supseteq$ EC {$\Sigma_1^1(\mathscr{C}) \cap \Pi_1^1(\mathscr{C}) \supseteq$ the class of sets superarithmetical in predicates in $\mathscr{C}$}. Implication 2 holds by using with the hypothesis the fact just mentioned. Implication 3 holds immediately. Implication 4 holds by using the hypothesis with an application of the standard device for converting *implicit* definitions to explicit definitions. This device amounts, incidentally, to a combination with its dual the Frege-Dedekind device for converting *inductive* definitions to explicit definitions. The asterisks next to Implication 4 signal the fact that, strictly speaking, it gives only absolutized versions of Beth's theorem and the arithmetical operator theorem — to get the full theorems one uses in the way indicated the natural set-theoretic relativizations of the separation theorems and their corollaries by Implication 1. These relativized separation theorems are immediate corollaries of the separation theorems themselves.

But although the propositions and the rather immediate implications are all in close correspondence, all known proofs of the corresponding propositions are intriguingly different. There remains a clear need, for example, for a unified proof of $\mathrm{Sep}_{\mathrm{I}}(\mathbf{V}_1^{1,1}(\mathfrak{P}))$ for as large a collection of $\mathfrak{P}$ as possible. And for the other matching pairs, even before a unified proof of a principle embracing both members, there needs to be given a simple as possible statement of such a principle.

4. Fruits of the Analogies

The present formulation of the analogy is sufficiently good that it has suggested results, suggested proofs, and even given proofs. We want to give some examples of this sort of thing, but because of limitations of space we will give only sketches or hints of proofs, reserving a fuller treatment of these topics for elsewhere.

(I) A first important observation is that for any $\mathfrak{P}$

$$\mathrm{Red}\,(\mathbf{V}_k^t) \to \mathrm{Red}\,(\mathbf{V}_k^t(\mathfrak{P})),$$

$$\mathrm{Red}\,(\mathbf{\Lambda}_k^t) \to \mathrm{Red}\,(\mathbf{\Lambda}_k^t(\mathfrak{P})).$$

Thus, in particular, if a reduction principle holds in pure logic it holds in recursive function theory. We can thus conclude at once that reduction principles in pure logic are going to be reasonably hard to prove if provable at all.

(II) Applying the contrapositives of (I), known results in recursive function theory give at once

$$\overline{\mathrm{Red}}\,(\mathbf{\Lambda}_k^t) \text{ for } t = 0 \text{ or } (t = 1 \text{ and } k = 2),$$

$$\overline{\mathrm{Red}}\,(\mathbf{V}_1^1);$$

and assuming the axiom of constructibility we can add to this

$$\overline{\mathrm{Red}}\,(\mathbf{\Lambda}_k^1) \text{ for } k \geqq 2.$$

(III) Unlike the situation with the reduction principle, there is no obvious relationship between the first separation principles of pure logic and of recursive function theory. But the knowledge of how the separation properties behave in recursive function theory can at least suggest how they might behave in pure logic. Illustrative of this is the case of $\mathrm{Sep}_{\mathrm{I}}(\bigwedge_1^1)$. Since $\mathrm{Sep}_{\mathrm{I}}(\Pi_1^1)$ is known to be false, it is suggested that $\mathrm{Sep}_{\mathrm{I}}(\bigwedge_1^1)$ should also be false. A study of this question leads to confirmation in two different ways.

(A) A simple counterexample can be constructed, viz., two inconsistent $\bigwedge_1^1$ formulas with one free variable, a singulary one, can be found such that on a countable domain the first one is satisfied exactly by finite sets, the second exactly by cofinite sets. A simple application of the compactness theorem shows they cannot be separated.

(B) Because the conjunction of Peano's axioms is Π_1^1, it can be argued that if $\mathrm{Sep}_{\mathrm{I}}(\bigwedge_1^1)$ were true, then $\mathrm{Sep}_{\mathrm{I}}(\Pi_1^1)$ would also be true.

(IV) The result mentioned in (III) gives, of course, another proof that Red $(\bigvee_1^1)$ is false, since for any $\mathscr{Q}$ Red $(\mathscr{Q}) \rightarrow \mathrm{Sep}_{\mathrm{I}}$ $(\mathrm{c}\mathscr{Q})$.

(V) One of the most interesting propositions suggested by the analogies is Red $(\bigwedge_1^1)$. If this were true it would apparently be quite a general and powerful theorem. It would have as a corollary both $\mathrm{Sep}_{\mathrm{I}}(\bigvee_1^1)$, which can at present only be proved by one of the arguments yielding the interpolation theorem (e.g., Herbrand-Gentzen-type arguments or model-theoretic arguments involving ultraproducts), and Red $(\Sigma_1^1(\mathscr{C}))$, which can at present only be proved by an argument essentially involving the Luzin-Sierpiński normal form.

Certain special cases of Red $(\bigwedge_1^1)$ can be verified. This applies for example if the $\bigwedge_1^1$ class is characterized by a formula $\bigwedge \mathrm{F} \bigvee \mathrm{a}_{\mathrm{Fa}} \bigwedge \mathrm{b}_{\mathrm{Fb}} \Delta$, where Δ is quantifier-free and contains no occurrence of F.

Various likely counterexamples to Red $(\bigwedge_1^1)$ can be disposed of, some of them not too trivially. And a counterexample to Red $(\bigwedge_1^{1,-1})$, the simplest, "parameter-free" case, where the models are simply domains, would be a counterexample to the reduction principle for cospectra (i.e., complements of spectra), and hence would disprove the proposition [7, Problem **3**, p. **263**] considered by Asser that "spectrum = cospectrum". And this proposition, although unlikely to be true, has apparently resisted for five years efforts to disprove it.

(VI) Using again the fact that the conjunction of the Peano axioms is Π_1^1, one can prove the special case of Red $(\bigvee_2^1)$ (and hence also the special case of $\mathrm{Sep}_{\mathrm{I}}(\bigwedge_2^1)$) where the domain is restricted to be countable. Although details have not been carried out, it appears likely that under the assumption of the axiom of constructibility this argument can be extended to domains with many other cardinal numbers.

(VII) All arguments mentioned in (VI) can be extended to $\mathrm{Red}(\bigvee_k^1)$ for $k > 2$, except that here the axiom of constructibility must be assumed, even in the case of countable domains.

(VIII) The remark of (VII) would also apply to $\mathrm{Red}(\mathbf{V}_k^t)$ for $t > 2$ and all k, and the remark of (II) to $\overline{\mathrm{Red}}(\mathbf{\Lambda}_k^t)$ for $t > 2$ and all k, if the conjectures of [3, p. 362], further discussed on p. 352 of [6], were fully verified. They follow from (C^t) for $t > 1$, the appropriate generalizations of the (C^1) of [6, p. 340], by the argument of [6, 5.1]. At the time [3] was written we had outlines of the proofs of (C^t) for $t > 1$, which follow closely that of (C^1). But the details have never been carried through. However, special cases of the conjectures sufficient for our present application are announced by Tugué [24, p. 112].

(IX) Since Red (Σ_1^0) and $\mathrm{Sep}_{\mathrm{I}}(\Pi_1^0)$ are true, while $\mathrm{Red}(\Pi_1^0)$ and $\mathrm{Sep}_{\mathrm{I}}(\Sigma_1^0)$ are false, one might expect corresponding statements about $\mathbf{V}_1^0$ and $\mathbf{\Lambda}_1^0$ to hold. And as far as $\mathrm{Red}(\mathbf{\Lambda}_1^0)$ is concerned our expectation must hold, and $\mathrm{Red}(\mathbf{\Lambda}_1^0)$ must be false, as we observed in (II). But as for the other three, $\mathrm{Red}(\mathbf{V}_1^0)$, $\mathrm{Sep}_{\mathrm{I}}(\mathbf{\Lambda}_1^0)$, and $\mathrm{Sep}_{\mathrm{I}}(\mathbf{V}_1^0)$, each goes the opposite of what we might expect. And even in this very simple case we gain a lot of insight into what is going on at other levels.

$\mathrm{Sep}_{\mathrm{I}}(\mathbf{V}_1^0)$ is true, and a proof of it can be given with striking similarity to the proof of $\mathrm{Sep}_{\mathrm{I}}(\mathbf{V}_1^1)$. Using, say **320 of [9, p. 181], and using an argument similar to that of [11, p. 268], one obtains that two disjoint $\mathbf{V}_1^0$ sets are separable by a quantifier-free class of models. Then repeating Implication 2 we have $\mathrm{Sep}_{\mathrm{I}}(\mathbf{V}_1^0)$. Note that Implication 1 gives here that $\mathbf{V}_1^0 \cap \mathbf{\Lambda}_1^0 =$ the set of quantifier-free classes of models. Using this last result we easily see that the formulas $\mathbf{\Lambda}$aFa and $\neg\mathbf{V}$aFa provide a counterexample to $\mathrm{Sep}_{\mathrm{I}}(\mathbf{\Lambda}_1^0)$.

Notice that here, for the first non-artificial time in the theory of hierarchies, the reduction principle fails while the first separation principle holds on the other side. There are just not enough constants around to allow the fine distinctions required for the strong reduction principle. This makes it look doubtful that the reduction principle will hold anywhere in the first-order hierarchy of pure logic,[6] and even casts some doubt on $\mathrm{Red}(\mathbf{\Lambda}_1^1)$ — but of course the higher one goes in level and type the more expressive power one captures to take the place of absent constants, and indeed by the time we are at type 2, level 2, we know (cf. (VI)) there is enough power to permit the reduction principle to hold in at least one important case.

Notice also that the switch-over of $\mathrm{Sep}_{\mathrm{I}}$ here at level 1 of type 1 mirrors the much discussed switch-over of $\mathrm{Sep}_{\mathrm{I}}$ at level 1 of type 2 — a switch-over that reverses right back at level 2 (and remains that way for higher levels, assuming the axiom of constructibility).

(X) The last comment under (IX) suggests that perhaps $\mathrm{Sep}_{\mathrm{I}}(\mathbf{V}_2^0)$ is false and $\mathrm{Sep}_{\mathrm{I}}(\mathbf{\Lambda}_2^0)$ is true. The counterexample for $\mathrm{Sep}(\mathbf{\Lambda}_1^0)$ was motivated

[6]Since this talk Shoenfield has verified by counterexample that Red $(\mathbf{V}_2^0)$ is indeed false and has shown using ultraproducts that for $k \geqq 2$ the proposition that every pair of disjoint $\mathbf{\Lambda}_k^0$ sets can be separated by a set in the Boolean set algebra generated by $\mathbf{\Lambda}_{k-1}^0$ is indeed true.

by the fundamental validity $\bigwedge$aFa $\supset$ $\bigvee$aFa. At level 2 we have the fundamental validity $\bigvee$a$\bigwedge$bFab $\supset$ $\bigwedge$b$\bigvee$aFab, which suggests that the formulas $\bigvee$a$\bigwedge$bFab and $\neg\bigwedge$b$\bigvee$aFab might provide a counterexample to $\mathrm{Sep_I}(\mathbf{V}_2^0)$. That they do can be proved by an elementary model-theoretic argument.

This counterexample and the vertical (i.e., parallel to the $\langle t, k\rangle$- rather than to the $\mathfrak{P}$-axis) analogy mentioned in (IX) now suggest the conjecture that $\overline{\mathrm{Sep_I}}(\mathbf{V}_k^0)$ for $k \geqq 2$. They further suggest, particularly in light of the vertical analogy with the Craig separation theorem, that for $k \geqq 2$ every pair of disjoint $\mathbf{\Lambda}_k^0$ sets can be separated by a set in the Boolean algebra generated by $\mathbf{\Lambda}_{k-1}^0$. Implication 2 would then yield $\mathrm{Sep_I}(\mathbf{\Lambda}_k^0)$ for $k \geqq 2$. And Implication 1, combined with the result of (IX), would yield that for all k $(k \geqq 1)\mathbf{V}_k^0 \cap \mathbf{\Lambda}_k^0 =$ the Boolean algebra generated by $\mathbf{\Lambda}_{k-1}^0$ (the definition of $\mathbf{\Lambda}_0^0$ should be obvious). The horizontal analogy with Post's theorem [17, Theorem XI, p. 293] is fully as striking. We have indeed the equation

$$\frac{\text{Kleene}}{\text{Craig}} = \frac{\text{Post}}{x},$$

which was solved for $k = 2$ during this congress by Rogers and Shoenfield. The solution is Kreisel.[7]

5. Future Development

How will the future course of these developments proceed? We want to make four remarks and suggestions here.

(a) Possible relationships between the first separation principle at higher types and the fundamental conjecture of Takeuti's GLC [23, p. 39] seem worthy of further investigation.

(b) The rapidly developing logic of infinitely long expressions may find a natural application in treating the transfinite portions of the hyperarithmetical and superarithmetical hierarchies from a point of view in which their gradual fade-out, as constants are thrown away, appears especially natural.

(c) Our proofs of special cases of $\mathrm{Red}(\mathbf{\Lambda}_1^1)$, as well as other developments, seem to hold out promise of generalizations of the Luzin-Sierpiński normal form that will embrace pure logic.

(d) The analogy between the Schütte-Henkin-Orey-(Ryll-Nardzewski) completeness theorem (Every Π_1^1 formula true in N is provable using the ω-rule) [8] and the Gödel completeness theorem (Every $\mathbf{\Lambda}_1^1$ formula true in N is provable) is very suggestive of ways for consolidating propositions and proofs in recursive function theory and pure logic.

References

[1] Addison, J. W. *On Some Points of the Theory of Recursive Functions.* Doctoral Dissertation, University of Wisconsin, 1954.

---

[7] Since this talk, as noted above, the solution for $k > 2$ has been found by, and is, Shoenfield.

[8] Cf. [22, p. 66] or [14, p. 3] or [20, Theorem 3] or [13, 3.1A].

[2] ADDISON, J. W. Analogies in the Borel, Luzin, and Kleene hierarchies, I and II. Abstracts, *Bulletin of the American Mathematical Society*, Vol. 61 (1955), p. 75 and pp. 171–172.

[3] ADDISON, J. W. Hierarchies and the axiom of constructibility. Pp. 355–362 in *Summaries of Talks Presented at the Summer Institute of Symbolic Logic in 1957 at Cornell University*. Second edition, Communications Research Division, Institute for Defense Analyses, 1960, xvi + 427 pp.

[4] ADDISON, J. W. Review of Isslédovanie častično-rékursivnyh opératorov srédstvami téorii berovskogo prostranstva by A. V. Kuznécov and B. A. Trahténbrot. *Journal of Symbolic Logic*, Vol. 22 (1957), pp. 301–302.

[5] ADDISON, J. W. Separation principles in the hierarchies of classical and effective descriptive set theory. *Fundamenta Mathematicae*, Vol. 46 (1959), pp. 123–135.

[6] ADDISON, J. W. Some consequences of the axiom of constructibility. *Fundamenta Mathematicae*, Vol. 46 (1959), pp. 337–357.

[7] ASSER, G. Das Repräsentantenproblem im Prädikatenkalkül der ersten Stufe mit Identität. *Zeitschrift für mathematische Logik und Grundlagen der Mathematik*, Vol. 1 (1955), pp. 252–263.

[8] BETH, E. W. On Padoa's method in the theory of definition. *Indagationes Mathematicae*, Vol. 15 (1953), pp. 330–339.

[9] CHURCH, A. *Introduction to Mathematical Logic*. Vol. 1, Princeton, Princeton University Press, 1956, x + 376 pp.

[10] CRAIG, W. *A Theorem about First Order Functional Calculus with Identity, and Two Applications*. Ph.D. thesis, Harvard University, 1951.

[11] CRAIG, W. Linear reasoning. A new form of the Herbrand-Gentzen theorem. *Journal of Symbolic Logic*, Vol. 22 (1957), pp. 250–268.

[12] CRAIG, W. Three uses of the Herbrand-Gentzen theorem in relating model theory and proof theory. *Journal of Symbolic Logic*, Vol. 22 (1957), pp. 269–285.

[13] GRZEGORCZYK, A., A. MOSTOWSKI, and C. RYLL-NARDZEWSKI. The classical and the ω-complete arithmetic. *Journal of Symbolic Logic*, Vol. 23 (1958), pp. 188–206.

[14] HENKIN, L. A generalization of the concept of ω-completeness. *Journal of Symbolic Logic*, Vol. 22 (1957), pp. 1–14.

[15] HILBERT, D. Mathematical problems. Translated by M. W. Newson. *Bulletin of the American Mathematical Society*, Vol. 8 (1901–02), pp. 437–479.

[16] KLEENE, S. C. Hierarchies of number-theoretic predicates. *Bulletin of the American Mathematical Society*, Vol. 63 (1955), pp. 193–213.

[17] KLEENE, S. C. *Introduction to Metamathematics*. New York, Van Nostrand; Amsterdam, North-Holland, and Groningen, Noordhoff, 1952, x + 550 pp.

[18] KURATOWSKI, K., and A. TARSKI. Les opérations logiques et les ensembles projectifs. *Fundamenta Mathematicae*, Vol. 17 (1931), pp. 240–272.

[19] LUZIN, N. *Leçons sur les Ensembles Analytiques et Leurs Applications*. Paris, Gauthier-Villars, 1930, xvi + 328 pp.

[20] OREY, S. On ω-consistency and related properties. *Journal of Symbolic Logic*, Vol. 21 (1956), pp. 246–252.

[21] ROBINSON, A. A result on consistency and its application to the theory of definition. *Indagationes Mathematicae*, Vol. 18 (1956), pp. 47–58.

[22] SCHÜTTE, K. Ein System des verknüpfenden Schliessens. *Archiv für mathematischen Logik und Grundlagenforschung*, Vol. 2 (1956), pp. 55–67.

[23] TAKEUTI, G. On a generalized logic calculus. *Japanese Journal of Mathematics*, Vol. 23 (1953), pp. 39–96. Errata, *Ibid.*, Vol. 24 (1954), pp. 149–156.

[24] TUGUÉ, T. Predicates recursive in a type-2 object and Kleene hierarchies. *Commentarii Mathematici Universitatis Sancti Pauli*, Vol. 8 (1959), pp. 97–117.

TURING-MACHINE COMPUTABLE FUNCTIONALS OF FINITE TYPES I

S. C. KLEENE

University of Wisconsin, Madison, Wisconsin, U.S.A.

Natural numbers 0, 1, 2, . . . are objects of *type* 0; arbitrary one-place (total) functions α^{j+1} from objects β^j of *type* j to natural numbers are objects of *type* $j+1$.

In RF Part I we extended the notions of general and partial recursiveness, previously published only for functions of variables of types 0 and 1, to functions with variables of higher finite types. In doing so, we gave a new formulation (equivalent to the familiar one at types 0, 1) rather than a direct extension of the original formulation or of one of its previously known equivalents.

In this new formulation, the general (partial) recursive functions are the total (partial) functions definable by repeated use of nine schemata of definition. These schemata comprise six which could be used for introducing the primitive recursive functions of natural-number variables (now admitting parameters of higher types), the schema

S7 $$\varphi(\alpha^1, a, \mathfrak{b}) \simeq \alpha^1(a)$$

for introducing a function variable α^1 of type 1, and two further schemata.

The first of these,

S8 $$\varphi(\alpha^j, \mathfrak{b}) \simeq \alpha^j(\lambda\sigma^{j-2}\,\chi(\alpha^j, \sigma^{j-2}, \mathfrak{b})),$$

where χ is a previously defined function, enables us to use a functional variable α^j of type $j \geqq 2$.

We aim in extending the notions of general and partial recursiveness to preserve Church's thesis ([1], IM p. 300 and § 62) with its previous extensions (IM pp. 314, 316, 332), according to which every "constructive" or "effectively calculable" or, intuitively speaking, "computable" total (partial) function of variables of types 0 and 1 is general (partial) recursive, and its converse. For those who do not choose to adopt Church's thesis, we wish to preserve the closure properties which constitute the reason for its adoption by those who do. With variables α^j of type $j \geqq 1$, the "computation" must use, besides (absolutely) effective operations, the operations of passing from an argument β^{j-1} for α^j to the value $\alpha^j(\beta^{j-1})$. Turing [11] expressed this (for $j = 1$ and a fixed α^j) by saying that an "oracle" is employed which, queried with β^{j-1}, replies with $\alpha^j(\beta^{j-1})$. In S8, the β^{j-1} is $\lambda\sigma^{j-2}\,\chi(\alpha^j, \sigma^{j-2}, \mathfrak{b})$; the α^j ranges over arbitrary functionals of type j.

If we confine ourselves to functionals α^j of some special kind, we may

---

The work reported herein was mainly done under a grant from the National Science Foundation during 1958–59, although we first considered the definition in the fall of 1952. We cite [2] as "IM", and [3] and [6] as "RF".

use instead of S8 a schema in which an "oracle" is queried with some number or function associated with the special way in which α^j operates on its arguments β^{j-1} (cf. RF end 3.1 and footnote 9, and [4]). Such an oracle may be more potent (cf. Tait [9]).

We are interested for different purposes both in the case of variables over arbitrary functionals (using S8), and in alternatives as just mentioned. In this paper we confine our attention to the first case.

The other schema

S9 $$\varphi(a, \mathfrak{b}, \mathfrak{c}) \simeq \{a\}(\mathfrak{b})$$

involves an "indexing", the details of which we do not repeat here (cf. RF 3.5–3.8). The idea is as follows. Each schema specifies the first step in the computation of a function φ for given arguments $\mathfrak{a}$; this step consists in passing from the expression "$\varphi(\mathfrak{a})$" on the left of the schema to that on the right. But instead of "$\varphi(\mathfrak{a})$" we can write "$\{z\}(\mathfrak{a})$", where z is a number, called an "index of φ", which via a code gives the schema in question, and also the schemata introducing the previously defined functions for that schema, etc. In effect, z constitutes an instruction for the computation step to be performed by that schema upon the arguments $\mathfrak{a}$. The role of S9 is to raise the argument a into the role of the instruction for the computation to be performed next upon the arguments $\mathfrak{b}$. Since a may have come to the position of first argument on the left of S9 through previous computation, the schema S9 permits the instructions in a part of a computation to be computed by an earlier part of the whole computation.

We have just argued that S8 is allowable in "effective calculation" with arbitrary functional arguments; and S9 is what we add to S1–S8 with the intent to get all possible effectively calculable functions, i.e., to satisfy Church's thesis.

In RF Part I, after setting up our formulation of general and partial recursiveness at all finite types, we began the investigation of its properties and applications, which we continue in RF Part II.

But also Church's thesis for our extension should be further supported by evidence that not more "effectively calculable" functions can be obtained by any natural extension of any of the previously existing equivalent notions for functions of variables of types 0 and 1 (cf. RF 3.2). While one may interest oneself in our class of functionals independently of Church's thesis, it seems to us that its significance and the value of the applications are connected with the thesis. This latter investigation tends to show that the class is a fundamental one, independent of the details of the particular formulation.

Also it seems of interest to know which of those extensions give as many functions.

To discuss exhaustively all extensions that may come to mind of all the existing equivalent notions in all their variants (IM pp. 320–321, to which must now be added Markov's algorithms [7]) would be a large undertaking.

However, the discussion of some representative notions should go much of the way toward accomplishing our aims. In RF § 8 we saw that μ-recursiveness and the formulation via recursive enumerability of a set and its complement give fewer functions. In the present paper we continue the investigation by discussing an extension of the Turing [10] and Post [8] notion of computability by machines.

1. Turing-Machine Computability: Definition

1.1. The extension of Turing-Post computability from functions of number variables only to functions with type-1 variables was obtained by relativizing the computability to (one-place) number-theoretic functions (as in Turing [11]) and requiring uniformity in those as they vary (as in IM). Three specific methods for utilizing the type-1 arguments were given in IM pp. 362—363, and a fourth is in Kleene [5, p. 148]. The first of these methods lends itself readily to generalization. In this method, a non-atomic act is performed, from a state q_c corresponding to a type-1 argument α^1, which consists in passing all at once from an argument y to the value $\alpha^1(y)$. For a higher-type object α^j $(j > 1)$, we wish the machine similarly to pass, by a non-atomic act, to the value $\alpha^j(\beta^{j-1})$, under circumstances when "previous computation" has "given" the argument β^{j-1}. This argument cannot be "given" directly as was the argument y for an α^1; but it can be "given" by giving how $\beta^{j-1}(\sigma^{j-2})$ is to be computed (from the type-1 and higher-type arguments of the function the machine is computing) for any σ^{j-2}. To "give" how something is to be computed can mean to "give" a Turing machine that will do the computation, and this can be done by giving the table of that machine. Such a table is a finite object, constructible according to prescribed rules, and can be given on the machine tape in some preassigned notation. It will be convenient to take as this notation a system of numbering, so that the machine tables will be represented by numbers called "(Turing-machine) indices".

1.2. We proceed to details, taking over IM § 67 except as we now amend and augment. It seems a bit simpler now to represent the empty tuple, i.e., the 0-tuple, of natural numbers on the tape by the 1-tuple 0 than to follow the plan of IM p. 363 Remark 1.

A machine for computing a function of number variables and the function variables $\alpha_1^1, \ldots, \alpha_{n_1}^1, \ldots, \alpha_1^r, \ldots, \alpha_{n_r}^r$ may have, besides active configurations (s_a, q_c) $(c > 0)$ from which atomic acts described by table entries of the forms $s_b L q_d$, $s_b C q_d$, $s_b R q_d$ are performed, also ones (s_1, q_c) $(c > 0)$ from each of which the machine may perform a non-atomic act described by a table entry of the form $b(j)q_d$ $(1 \leqq j \leqq r; 1 \leqq b \leqq n_j)$. (We depart from IM p. 362 in the form of this table entry for $j = 1$, and by requiring that (s_a, q_c) for $a \neq 1$ have a table entry of the form $s_b L q_d$, $s_b C q_d$, or $s_b R q_d$.) The non-atomic acts for $j > 1$ will depend on the indexing, which we describe next.

Say the machine has symbols $s_1, \ldots, s_\iota$, or square conditions $s_0, \ldots, s_\iota$

(s_0= blank), and states $q_0, \ldots, q_k$, with $l, k > 0$ (IM p. 357). The possible table entries will then have the four aforesaid forms, where $b = 0, \ldots, l$ in the first three, and $d = 0, \ldots, k$. These four kinds of table entries shall be represented by numbers $\langle b, 0, d\rangle$, $\langle b, 1, d\rangle$, $\langle b, 2, d\rangle$, $\langle b, j+2, d\rangle$, respectively (cf. RF 2.1). Then a row of a table for a given active state q_c ($c > 0$) shall be represented by $\langle e_{0c}, \ldots, e_{lc}\rangle$, where e_{ac} represents the entry for the configuration (s_a, q_c). Finally, the entire table shall be represented by the *index* $\langle\langle l, k\rangle, r_1, \ldots, r_k\rangle$, where r_c represents the row for the active state q_c.

We define the behavior of the machine (when non-atomic acts are involved) only when it is being used to compute for assigned values $\alpha_1^1, \ldots, \alpha_{n_1}^1, \ldots, \alpha_1^r, \ldots, \alpha_{n_r}^r$ of the function variables.

Suppose at a given moment t the configuration (s_1, q_c) is one for which the table entry is of the form $b(j)q_d$. Suppose (I) for $j = 1$ a natural number y {for $j > 1$ an index y of a machine $\mathfrak{M}_y$ for computing a function of $\alpha_1^1, \ldots, \alpha_{n_1}^1, \ldots, \alpha_1^r, \ldots, \alpha_{n_r}^r, \sigma^{j-2}$} is represented on the tape in standard position, i.e., $y+1$-tallies s_1 appear preceded and followed by a blank s_0, with the machine scanning the rightmost of these tallies (in state q_c). Furthermore for $j > 1$, suppose (II) $\mathfrak{M}_y$, for each σ^{j-2} and the given $\alpha_1^1, \ldots, \alpha_{n_1}^1, \ldots, \alpha_1^r, \ldots, \alpha_{n_r}^r$, computes a value $\beta^{j-1}(\sigma^{j-2})$; i.e., $\mathfrak{M}_y$, applied with σ^{j-2} if $j = 2$ (with 0 if $j > 2$) scanned in standard position in state q_1, with the tape otherwise blank, eventually comes to rest with σ^{j-2}, $\beta^{j-1}(\sigma^{j-2})$ (with 0, $\beta^{j-1}(\sigma^{j-2})$) scanned in standard position. Then between moments t and $t+1$ the machine supplies, next to the right of the representation of y, $\alpha_b^j(y)+1$ {$\alpha_b^j(\beta^{j-1})+1$} tallies and a blank, at the same time displacing by $\alpha_b^j(y)+2$ {$\alpha_b^j(\beta^{j-1})+2$} squares to the right all printing which at moment t existed to the right of the scanned square, and assumes at moment $t+1$ state q_d with the resulting pair y, $\alpha_b^j(y)$ {y, $\alpha_b^j(\beta^{j-1})$} scanned in standard position.

When Supposition (I) fails to be met, we let the machine perform the identical act. When Supposition (I) is met but not (II), we do not define the situation at moment $t+1$. (The machine does not then "stop"; that happens, IM p. 358, only when the situation is defined and passive.)

1.3. Thus, when arguments of type $j > 1$ enter into the computation via configurations (s_1, q_c) with table entry $b(j)q_d$ arising with Supposition (I) met, the behavior of the machine depends on that of other machines $\mathfrak{M}_y$ put to work to compute functions with additional arguments σ^{j-2}. The definition of 'a given machine with a given assignment of arguments from a given situation computes a value z' can be considered as a transfinite inductive definition, similar to that of $\{z\}(\mathfrak{a}) \simeq w$ in RF 3.8.

Equivalently, we can arrange the tape vs. machine situations with the machine tables (or indices) and assignments of the arguments, as they arise in a computation, on a *Turing-machine computation tree* (cf. RF 9.1). A given position in the tree will be followed by no next position, if the q_c there is the passive state ($c = 0$); by a single next position, if the q_c is active ($c > 0$), unless the configuration is one for which the table entry is of the form $b(j)\mathrm{q}_d$ with $j > 1$ and the situation meets Supposition (I). In this last case, the position constitutes a node with infinitely many lower next positions, one for each σ^{j-2} (like the nodes at applications of S4′ in RF end 9.8). The construction of the subtrees beginning at these lower next positions must each be completed with the determination of a value before the upper next position can be filled.

The proof of Theorem 1 will serve in lieu of elaboration of this. The converse of Theorem 1 will appear as Theorem 2 in the second part of the paper.

2. Recursiveness of Computable Functions

2.1. THEOREM 1. *Each computable partial (total) function* $\varphi(x_1, \ldots, x_{n_0}, \alpha_1^1, \ldots, \alpha_{n_1}^1, \ldots, \alpha_1^r, \ldots, \alpha_{n_r}^r)$ *is partial (general) recursive.*

2.2. Let $\mathrm{TIx}(i, n) \equiv n > 0$ & {i is the index of a Turing machine $\mathfrak{M}_i$ to compute a function of number variables and not more function variables than $n_1, \ldots, n_r$ of types $1, \ldots, r$, respectively, where $n = \langle n_0, n_1, \ldots, n_r\rangle$}. $\mathrm{TIx}(i, n)$ is independent of n_0, and $\mathrm{TIx}(i, n)$ & $m > 0 \rightarrow \mathrm{TIx}(i, mn)$.

TIx is primitive recursive, since, writing $l = (i)_{0,0}$, $k = (i)_{0,1}$,

$$\mathrm{TIx}(i, n) \equiv n > 0 \;\&\; l > 0 \;\&\; k > 0 \;\&\; \mathrm{lh}(i) = k+1 \;\&\; \mathrm{lh}((i)_0) = 2 \;\&\; (c)_{0<c\leqq k}[\mathrm{lh}((i)_c) = l+1 \;\&\; (a)_{a\leqq l}[(i)_{c,a} = \Pi_{u<3}\, p_u \exp (i)_{c,a,u} \;\&\; (i)_{c,a,2} \leqq k \;\&\; \{\{(i)_{c,a,1} \leqq 2 \;\&\; (i)_{c,a,0} \leqq l\} \vee \{a = 1 \;\&\; 2 < (i)_{c,a,1} \;\&\; 1 \leqq (i)_{c,a,0} \leqq (n)_{(i)_{c,a,1} \dot{-} 2}\}\}]].$$

2.3. We take over IM the lower half of p. 374 through the top paragraph of p. 375, also the last paragraph on p. 375 through the first full paragraph on p. 376.

We also use the second paragraph on p. 375, changing the notation to write $\rho_0(b, d, u, v)$ for the $\rho_{a,c}(u, v)$ when the table entry is $\mathrm{s}_b L\mathrm{q}_d$; $\rho_1(b, d, u, v)$ when $\mathrm{s}_b C\mathrm{q}_d$; $\rho_2(b, d, u, v)$ when $\mathrm{s}_b R\mathrm{q}_d$.

Consider the case the table entry is $b(j)\mathrm{q}_d$, and the Gödel number of the situation is w. For $j = 1$, Supposition (I) is expressed by $Q(w)$ as we now call the $Q_c(w)$ low on p. 376 ($c = (w)_2$), and the Gödel number of the next situation is $\tau_2(Y, \alpha_b^1(Y), d, U, V)$ for Y, U, V the functions of w on p. 376. For $j > 1$, Supposition (I) is expressed by $Q(w)$ & $\mathrm{TIx}(Y, p_{j-2}n)$ for $n = \langle n_0, n_1, \ldots, n_r\rangle$. If also Supposition (II) is met with a given β^{j-1}, the Gödel number of the next situation is $\tau_2(Y, \alpha_b^j(\beta^{j-1}), d, U, V)$.

Let

$$\tau(0, x, c, u, v) = \tau_1(0, c, u, v),$$
$$\tau(1, x, c, u, v) = \tau_1((x)_0, c, u, v),$$
$$\tau(n+2, x, c, u, v) = \tau_1((x)_{n+1}, c, (\tau(n+1, p_n x, c, u, v))_0, v).$$

Then τ is primitive recursive (cf. IM p. 271). For $n > 0$,

(1) $$\tau(n, x, c, u, v) = \tau_n((x)_0, \ldots, (x)_{n-1}, c, u, v).$$

2.4. Next we shall give, for each r, a recursion (2) such that the function val_r computed by it as in RF 10.2 will have the following property. (Here we do not bother first to state the recursion with a function variable ζ.) *Suppose* $\mathrm{TIx}(i, n)$, $n = \langle n_0, \ldots, n_r\rangle$ *with* $n_0 > 0$, w *is the Gödel number of a tape vs. machine situation for the machine* $\mathfrak{M}_i$ *of index* i, $x = \langle x_1, \ldots, x_{n_0}\rangle$, *and* $\alpha^j = \langle \alpha^j_1, \ldots, \alpha^j_{n_j}\rangle$ $(j = 1, \ldots, r)$. *Then* $\mathrm{val}_r(i, n, w, x, \alpha^1, \ldots, \alpha^r)$ *is defined if and only if* $\mathfrak{M}_i$ *from that situation with* $x_1, \ldots, x_{n_0}, \alpha^1_1, \ldots, \alpha^1_{n_1}, \ldots, \alpha^r_1, \ldots, \alpha^r_{n_r}$ *as the arguments will compute a value* z, *i.e., will continue to a terminal situation with* $x_1, \ldots, x_{n_0}, z$ *scanned in standard position, in which case* $\mathrm{val}_r(i, n, w, x, \alpha^1, \ldots, \alpha^r) = z$.

The recursion for val_r is as follows, where we write $u = (w)_0$, $a = (w)_1$, $c = (w)_2$, $v = (w)_3$, $b = (i)_{c,a,0}$, $d = (i)_{c,a,2}$, and Y, U, V are as on IM p. 376. In each case, except Case $r+3$, val_r is applied to the Gödel number of the next situation in place of w (when a next situation exists).

(2) $\qquad \mathrm{val}_r(i, n, w, x, \alpha^1, \ldots, \alpha^r)$

$\simeq \mathrm{val}_r(i, n, \rho_s(b, d, u, v), x, \alpha^1, \ldots, \alpha^r)$ if $c \neq 0$ & $(i)_{c,a,1} = s$ (CASE s; $s = 0, 1, 2$),

$\simeq \mathrm{val}_r(i, n, \tau_2(Y, (\alpha^1(Y))_{b\dot{-}1}, d, U, V), x, \alpha^1, \ldots, \alpha^r)$ if $c \neq 0$ & $(i)_{c,a,1} = 3$ & $Q(w)$ (CASE 3),

$\simeq \mathrm{val}_r(i, n, \tau_2(Y, (\alpha^2(\lambda\sigma^0\, \mathrm{val}_r(Y, 2\,\Pi_{s<n}\, (p_{s+1} \exp\, (n)_{s+1}), \tau_1(\sigma^0, 1, 1, 1), \langle\sigma^0\rangle, \alpha^1, \ldots, \alpha^r)))_{b\dot{-}1}, d, U, V), x, \alpha^1, \ldots, \alpha^r)$ if $c \neq 0$ & $(i)_{c,a,1} = 4$ & $Q(w)$ & $\mathrm{TIx}(Y, 2n)$ (CASE 4),

$\simeq \mathrm{val}_r(i, n, \tau_2(Y, (\alpha^j(\lambda\sigma^{j-2}\, \mathrm{val}_r(Y, 2p_{j-2}\, \Pi_{s<n}\, (p_{s+1} \exp\, (n)_{s+1}), \tau_1(0, 1, 1, 1), \langle 0\rangle, \alpha^1, \ldots, \alpha^{j-3}, \lambda\tau^{j-3}\, \alpha^{j-2}(\tau^{j-3})(p_{(n)_{j-2}} \exp\, \sigma^{j-2}(\tau^{j-3})), \alpha^{j-1}, \ldots, \alpha^r)))_{b\dot{-}1}, d, U, V), x, \alpha^1, \ldots, \alpha^r)$ if $c \neq 0$ & $(i)_{c,a,1} = j+2$ & $Q(w)$ & $\mathrm{TIx}(Y, p_{j-2}n)$ (CASE $j+2$; $j = 3, \ldots, r$),

$\simeq (\mu t_{t<5^{3w}}[w = \tau_1((t)_0, 0, (t)_1, (t)_2)])_0$ if $c = 0$ & $(Et)_{t<5^{3w}}[w = \tau((n)_0+1, x(p_{(n)_0} \exp\, (t)_0), 0, (t)_1, (t)_2)]$ (CASE $r+3$),

$\simeq \mathrm{val}_r(i, n, w, x, \alpha^1, \ldots, \alpha^r)$ otherwise (CASE $r+4$).

To establish the stated property of val_r, we first show by induction in the form corresponding to the inductive definition of 'a given machine with a given assignment of arguments from a given situation computes a value z' that: *If, for* i, n, w, *etc., as supposed,* $\mathfrak{M}_i$ *will continue to a terminal situation, etc.,* $\mathrm{val}_r(i, n, w, x, \alpha^1, \ldots, \alpha^r)$ *is defined and* $= z$. Thus, if $\mathfrak{M}_i$ is already in such a terminal situation, Case $r+3$ of the definition of val_r applies and gives $\mathrm{val}_r(i, n, w, x, \alpha^1, \ldots, \alpha^r) = z$ outright. If it is not already in such a terminal situation but will be eventually, then either Case 0, 1, 2, or 3, or one of Cases 4, . . ., $r+2$ with Supposition (II) met, applies. Consider, e.g., one of Cases 4, . . ., $r+2$. By Supposition (II), and the hyp. ind. applied for each σ^{j-2}, the function $\lambda\sigma^{j-2}\, \mathrm{val}_r(\ldots)$ within the expression for val_r in that case is completely defined and is the β^{j-1} for the act performed (cf. 1.2); and then $\tau_2(Y, (\alpha^j(\beta^{j-1}))_{b\dot{-}1}, d, U, V)$ is the Gödel number of the next situation, so by the hyp. ind. the whole case expression is defined and $= z$.

Second, we show by induction over the computation of $\text{val}_r(i, n, w, x, \alpha^1, \ldots, \alpha^r)$ by the recursion (2) (cf. RF end 10.2) that: *If, for i, n, w, etc., as supposed,* $\text{val}_r(i, n, w, x, \alpha^1, \ldots, \alpha^r)$ *is defined, then* $\mathfrak{M}_i$ *will continue to a terminal situation, etc.* Here either Case $r+3$ applies, and the conclusion is immediate; or Case 0, 1, 2, or 3, or one of Cases 4, . . ., $r+2$ with the function $\lambda\sigma^{j-2}\,\text{val}_r(\ldots)$ completely defined, applies. Consider, e.g., one of Cases 4, . . ., $r+2$ with $\lambda\sigma^{j-2}\,\text{val}_r(\ldots)$ completely defined. By the hyp. ind. applied for each σ^{j-2}, Supposition (II) is met; and hence, by the result of the first induction, $\tau_2(Y, (\alpha^j(\beta^{j-1}))_{b\dot{-}1}, d, U, V)$ for $\beta^{j-1} = \lambda\sigma^{j-2}\,\text{val}_r(\ldots)$ is the Gödel number of the next situation; and hence, by the hyp. ind. applied to the whole expression in the case, $\mathfrak{M}_i$ will continue to a terminal situation, etc.

2.5. The function $\lambda\tau^{j-3}\ldots$ substituted in Case $j+2$ $(j = 3, \ldots, r)$ of (2) is of the form $\lambda\tau^{j-3}\ldots$ for S4′·$(j-2)$ $(j-2 = 1, \ldots, r-2)$ in RF 9.8, and the substitutions of $\lambda\sigma^{j-2}\ldots$ in this case, and of $\lambda\sigma^0\ldots$ in Case 4, are directly as arguments of function variables and so come under S8. The other operations in building the expressions in the cases can be effected by using only S1–S7, after introductions of the function val_r by S0′ in RF 10.1. The case definition can be handled by S5′ in RF 10.1 with S1 – S6. Thus the right-hand side of (2) is $\mathsf{F}(\text{val}_r;\ i, n, w, x, \alpha^1, \ldots, \alpha^r)$ for a normal recursive functional F RF 10.1. So by the first recursion theorem RF LXIV, val_r is partial recursive.

Suppose $\varphi(x_1, \ldots, x_{n_0}, \alpha^1_1, \ldots, \alpha^1_{n_1}, \ldots, \alpha^r_1, \ldots \alpha^r_{n_r})$ with $n_r > 0$ if $r > 0$ is computable. Then there is a machine $\mathfrak{M}_i$ of index i which computes it. By 2.4,

$$(3)\qquad \begin{aligned} &\varphi(x_1, \ldots, x_{n_0}, \alpha^1_1, \ldots, \alpha^1_{n_1}, \ldots, \alpha^r_1, \ldots, \alpha^r_{n_r}) \\ &\simeq \text{val}_r(i, \langle n_0, \ldots, n_r\rangle, \tau_{n_0}(x_1, \ldots, x_{n_0}, 1, 1, 1), \\ &\qquad \langle x_1, \ldots, x_{n_0}\rangle, \langle \alpha^1_1, \ldots, \alpha^1_{n_1}\rangle, \ldots, \langle \alpha^r_1, \ldots, \alpha^r_{n_r}\rangle) \qquad (n_0 > 0), \end{aligned}$$

and similarly, replacing on the right n_0 by 1 and $x_1, \ldots, x_{n_0}$ by 0, if $n_0 = 0$. The functions $\langle \alpha^j_1, \ldots, \alpha^j_{n_j}\rangle$ $(j = 1, \ldots, r)$ on the right are of the form $\lambda\tau^{j-1}\ldots$ for RF LXI, provided $n_2, \ldots, n_{r-1} > 0$, and val_r is partial recursive, so then φ is partial recursive.

To handle computable functions with $n_2, \ldots, n_{r-1}$ not all > 0, we can proceed as in (iii) of the proof of RF LXVIII. We introduce successively sets of functions similar to $\text{val}_r(i, n, w, x, \alpha^1, \ldots, \alpha^r)$ but lacking 1, 2, . . ., $r-2$ of the variables $\alpha^2, \ldots, \alpha^{r-1}$. The successive recursions come under (a*) of RF 10.4, so by RF LXVIII (i) these functions are partial recursive.

References

[1] Church, A. An unsolvable problem of elementary number theory. *American Journal of Mathematics*, Vol. 58 (1936), pp. 345–363.

[2] Kleene, S. C. *Introduction to Metamathematics*, Amsterdam (North-Holland), Groningen (Noordhoff), New York and Toronto (Van Nostrand), 1952, X + 550 pp.

[3] KLEENE, S. C. Recursive functionals and quantifiers of finite types I. *Transactions of the American Mathematical Society*, Vol. **91** (1959), pp. 1–52.

[4] KLEENE, S. C. Countable functionals. *Constructivity in Mathematics*, Amsterdam (North-Holland), 1959, pp. 81–100.

[5] KLEENE, S. C. Mathematical logic: constructive and non-constructive operations. *Proceedings of the International Congress of Mathematicians, Edinburgh, 14–21 August, 1958*, Cambridge (Cambridge University Press), 1960, pp. 137–153.

[6] KLEENE, S. C. Recursive functionals and quantifiers of finite types II. To appear.

[7] MARKOV, A. A. *Téoriya algorifmov* (Theory of algorithms). Trudy Matematičeskogo Instituta imeni V. A. Steklova, Vol. **42**. Izdatel'stvo Akademii Nauk SSSR, Moscow-Leningrad, 1954, 375 pp.

[8] POST, E. L. Finite combinatory processes – formulation I. *Journal of Symbolic Logic*, Vol. **1** (1936), pp. 103–105.

[9] TAIT, W. W. Continuity properties of partial recursive functionals of finite type. *International Congress for Logic, Methodology and Philosophy of Science, Abstracts of Contributed Papers, Stanford University, Stanford, Calif., August 24 to September 2, 1960* (mimeographed), pp. 19–20.

[10] TURING, A. M. On computable numbers, with an application to the Entscheidungsproblem. *Proceedings of the London Mathematical Society*, Ser. 2, Vol. **42** (1936–7), pp. 230–265. A correction. *Ibid.*, Vol. **43** (1937), pp. 544–546.

[11] TURING, A. M. Systems of logic based on ordinals. *Ibid.*, Vol. **45** (1939), pp. 161–228.

RECURSIVE EQUIVALENCE TYPES AND COMBINATORIAL FUNCTIONS

JOHN MYHILL

Stanford University, Stanford, California, U.S.A.

1. Recursive Isomorphism, Recursive Equivalence

Recursion theory originated as an ancillary of Hilbertian proof-theory; but during the last decade especially it has developed into an independent branch of mathematics with no philosophical presuppositions. According to the conception of Dekker, Nerode, Rogers, and myself it is *the theory of those properties of sets of natural numbers which are preserved under recursive permutations*, where a recursive permutation is a one-one recursive function mapping the set of all natural numbers onto itself. This conception of recursion theory lies on the surface of Post's great 1944 paper and to judge by a remark of Medvedev has been entertained by Kolmogorov; but neither of these authors has developed a systematic treatment of recursive invariants.

My co-workers and I have regarded it as desirable to develop a quasi-algorithmic or at least algebraic approach to recursive isomorphism types. However, this has appeared impossible to achieve directly. Dekker introduced the conception of *recursive equivalence type*, defined as follows.

Two sets α and β (of natural numbers) are called *recursively equivalent* ($\alpha \simeq \beta$) if there is a one-one partial recursive function defined at least on α, and mapping it onto β. The class of all sets recursively equivalent to a given set α is called the *recursive equivalence type* (R.E.T.) of α, and is denoted by $\mathrm{Req}(\alpha)$. The collection of all R.E.T.'s is denoted by Ω.

The relation between recursive equivalence and recursive isomorphism is given by the following theorem, which was discovered independently by Carol Karp and myself.

THEOREM 1. (KARP-MYHILL) *α is recursively isomorphic to β (i.e., $p(\alpha)=\beta$ for some recursive permutation p) if and only if $\alpha \simeq \beta$ and $\alpha' \simeq \beta'$. (Here α' denotes the complement of the set α relative to the set of all natural numbers.)*

The significance of this theorem is that it completely reduces the study of recursive isomorphism types to the study of recursive equivalence types. This is desirable because there is beginning to exist a highly developed algebraic theory of recursive equivalence types. It is to one chapter of this theory, namely, the *theory of combinatorial functions*, that the present paper is devoted.

2. The Algebra of Recursive Equivalence Types

We define the sum and product of two recursive equivalence types by

$$\mathrm{Req}(\alpha)+\mathrm{Req}(\beta) = \mathrm{Req}(\{2n|n \in \alpha\}+\{2n+1|n \in \beta\})$$
$$\mathrm{Req}(\alpha) \cdot \mathrm{Req}(\beta) = \mathrm{Req}\{2^m \cdot 3^n|m \in \alpha \;\&\; n \in \beta\}$$

by analogy with the corresponding definitions for cardinal numbers. Uniqueness is easily proved; however, observe that in order to secure this we have to restrict the representatives of Req(α) and Req(β) in the definition of addition to be not merely disjoint but also *separated* by the sets of even and odd numbers, respectively. Without this restriction it is easy to see that uniqueness fails.

With these definitions we prove easily

THEOREM 2. (DEKKER)

$$A+B = B+A$$
$$A+(B+C) = (A+B)+C$$
$$A+0 = A$$
$$A+B = 0 \leftrightarrow A = B = 0$$
$$AB = BA$$
$$A(BC) = (AB)C$$
$$A \cdot 0 = 0, A \cdot 1 = A$$
$$AB = 0 \leftrightarrow A = 0 \vee B = 0$$
$$A(B+C) = AB+AC.$$

Much more difficult is the analog of the Cantor-Bernstein theorem

THEOREM 3. (MYHILL) $A \leqq B,\ B \leqq A \rightarrow A = B$, *where we define* $A \leqq B$ *if* $(\exists C)(A+C = B)$.

3. Isols

Let R be the R.E.T. of the set of all natural numbers. Then we have

THEOREM 4. (MYHILL) $A+B = A \leftrightarrow A \geqq RB$

the *absorption law*. It is consequently a frequent phenomenon for R.E,T.'s to (additively) absorb smaller ones (or even in the case of R.E.T.'s of the form RA, the idemmultiples, to absorb themselves). The arithmetic of Ω is therefore much closer to the arithmetic of infinite cardinals than to the arithmetic of natural numbers.

However, there is a subsystem of Ω having much closer affinities to the natural numbers than to the usual infinite cardinals; these are the *isols* (the collection of all isols is denoted by Λ), which may be characterized in any of the following ways.

(1) As those R.E.T.'s X satisfying $X \neq X+1$.

(2) As those R.E.T.'s which are not $\geqq R$.

(3) As the R.E.T.'s of those sets (the isolated sets) which contain no infinite recursively enumerable subset.

These are the recursive analogs of cardinals which are finite in the sense of Dedekind. These latter may be characterized analogously in the following ways.

(1) As those cardinals $\mathfrak{m}$ satisfying $\mathfrak{m} \neq \mathfrak{m}+1$.

(2) As those cardinals which are not $\geqq \aleph_0$.

(3) As the cardinals of those sets which contain no countably infinite subset.

Let us identify the natural number n with the R.E.T. of an n-element set; then we have

THEOREM 5. (DEKKER) (a) *Every natural number is an isol, but there are c isols which are not natural numbers.*

(b) *Every isol is a* R.E.T., *but there are c* R.E.T.'s *which are not isols.*

(c) *For* $X, Y, Z \in \Lambda : X+Y = X+Z \to Y = Z$.

(d) *For* $X, Y, Z \in \Lambda, X \neq 0 : XY = XZ \to Y = Z$.

The cancellation laws (c) and (d) do not hold without the restriction to Λ; for example, $R+0 = R+1 = R$ but $0 \neq 1$, and $R \cdot 1 = R \cdot 2 = R$, but $1 \neq 2$. These are examples of the way in which the arithmetic of Λ is closer to that of the natural numbers than is that of R.E.T.'s generally.

In view of Theorem 2 and Theorem 5(c) the isols can be extended to a ring Λ^* in exactly the same way in which the natural numbers can be extended to the integers. The properties of this ring will be explored below. Theorem 5(d) suggests the possibility that this ring is without zero-divisors; however, this has turned out to be false. Stated with variables ranging over Λ rather than Λ^*, the existence of zero-divisors in the latter asserts that

$$(*) \qquad XW+YZ = YW+XZ \to XZ \to X = Y \vee Z = W$$

is false in Λ. One is inclined to ask 'why' the cancellation laws 5(c) and 5(d) hold in Λ while (*) fails. The theory of combinatorial functions is in part designed to answer this question. More important, it affords us a general method of proving theorems about Λ (and occasionally about Ω generally) which would be very tedious to prove directly.

4. Combinatorial Functions

Here and until further notice, we shall be concerned with isols rather than arbitrary R.E.T.'s; we shall use upper-case letters from the end of the alphabet as variables ranging over Λ.

The central problem of combinatorial function theory is: what formulas 'go over' from the set of natural numbers to the collection of isols? E.g.,

$$x \neq 0, \quad xy + xz \to y = z$$

holds for natural numbers and

$$X \neq 0, \quad XY = XZ \to Y = Z$$

holds in Λ; however,

$$xw+yz = yw+xz \to x = y \vee z = w$$

holds for natural numbers while

$$XW+YZ = YW+XZ \to X = Y \vee Z = W$$

does *not* hold in Λ.

The first step in combinatorial function theory is to associate with as many number-theoretic functions as possible a *canonical extension* to Λ. We want the canonical extension of $+$ and $\cdot$ to be the $+$ and $\cdot$ defined on Λ as above. Combinatorial functions were the first class of functions to be so extended: they are constructed as follows.

Every number-theoretic function $f(n)$ can be written in the form

$$f(n) = \sum_i c_i \binom{n}{i}$$

for certain (positive, negative, or zero) integer coefficients c_i. The c_i are called the *Stirling coefficients* of f. We call $f(n)$ a combinatorial function if its Stirling coefficients are all non-negative. An analogous definition holds for functions of more than one argument; here we use the representation

$$f(n_1, \cdots, n_k) = \sum_{a_1 \cdots a_k} \left[c_{a_1 \cdots a_k} \prod_{i=1}^{k} \binom{k_i}{a_i} \right],$$

and require that all $c_{a_1 \cdots a_k}$ be non-negative. The combinatorial functions form a very extensive family; they include $x+y$, xy, x^{y+1}, (x/k) for each k, $x!$ and all constants, and are closed under composition, permutation, identification and fixing of arguments and the operators Σ and Π. In particular, they include all polynomials with non-negative integer coefficients, and a great many with some negative or rational non-integer coefficients.

For each such function

$$f(n) = \sum_i c_i \binom{n}{i}$$

we define the *canonical extension* F to Λ (and even to Ω) by

$$F(\text{Req } \alpha) = \text{Req} \bigcup_i \left[\binom{\alpha}{i} \times \{0, \cdots, c_i - 1\} \right]$$

and analogously for functions of more than one argument. Here $\binom{\alpha}{i}$ is the set of all indices of i-element subsets of α in some canonical recursive enumeration of all finite sets, and $\tau_1 \times \tau_2$ is short for

$$\{2^m \cdot 3^n | m \in \tau_1 \ \&\ n \in \tau_2\}.$$

There are various techniques whereby non-combinatorial functions (and even relations) can be extended to Λ or Ω; they are probably equivalent where more than one is applicable. (We need a metatheorem on the uniqueness of extension theories here, analogous to the classical metatheorem on the uniqueness of homology theories.) In particular, we can (by separating the positive and negative coefficients) express every number-theoretic function canonically as the difference of two combinatorial functions. Let, for example,

$$f(x) = \sum_i c_i \binom{x}{i}$$

and define

$$f^+(x) = \sum_{c_i>0} c_i \binom{x}{i}$$

$$f^-(x) = \sum_{c_i<0} -c_i \binom{x}{i}.$$

Then f^+ and f^- are combinatorial, and if F^+, F^- are their canonical extensions, we can define the canonical extension F of f by

$$F(X) = F^+(X) - F^-(X) \qquad (X \in \Lambda).$$

Note that for $A \in \Omega - \Lambda$, the expression $F^+(A) - F^-(A)$ has no defined meaning, and that for $X \in \Lambda$, $F^+(X) - F^-(X)$ may be not in Λ but in $\Lambda^* - \Lambda$. However, we have

THEOREM 6. (NERODE) *Let f be a recursive function, f^+ and f^- its positive and negative parts and $F(X) = F^+(X) - F^-(X)$, where F^+, F^- are the canonical extensions of f^+, f^-, respectively. Then F maps Λ into Λ if and only if for some number k, $f(x+k)$ is combinatorial.*

For example, the characteristic function c_α of any infinite set α does not satisfy the condition that for some k, $c_\alpha(x+k)$ is combinatorial; consequently the extension of c_α to Λ maps some isols into isolic integers which are not isols. However, it can be proved in case α is recursive that if C_α is the extension of c_α to Λ^* given in Theorem 6, then $C_\alpha(X) \in \Lambda \rightarrow C_\alpha(X) = 0$ or $C_\alpha(X) = 1$. For $C_\alpha(X) \notin \Lambda$, $C_\alpha(X)$ is a non-trivial idempotent in Λ^*; this is one way of proving that Λ^* contains zero-divisors.

A recursive function f of one argument satisfying the condition that for some k, $f(x+k)$ is combinatorial, is called *almost recursive combinatorial*; the definition for functions of more than one argument is more complicated, and I refer you to Nerode's forthcoming paper in *Annals of Mathematics*. To complete the definition of the extension of an almost recursive combinatorial function to all of Ω, we stipulate that if f is recursive and $f(x+k)$ combinatorial, then $F(A) = F_0(A)$ for $A \notin \Lambda$, where F_0 is the canonical extension of $f(x+k)$.

5. The One-Quantifier Case: Positive Results

Combinatorial functions were invented as a result of the following circumstance. Numerous cancellation laws in Λ were discovered by Dekker; in particular, $XY = XZ \rightarrow Y = Z$ $(X \neq 0)$, $X^Z = Y^Z \rightarrow X = Y$ $(Z \neq 0)$, $X^Y = X^Z \rightarrow Y = Z$ $(X \neq 0,1)$, $X^X = Y^Y \rightarrow X = Y$ $(X, Y \neq 0,1)$, $X! = Y! \rightarrow X = Y$ $(X, Y \neq 0,1)$. The pattern of proof in each of these cases was the same; and I was concerned to find for just what class of functions such cancellation laws could be proved. Nerode and I succeeded in proving far more than we had ever hoped, namely, *not only every cancellation law, but every implication whose antecedent and consequent are each equations between almost recursive combinatorial functions holds in Λ if it holds in the* *natural numbers*, the variables for natural number being replaced by variables ranging over Λ, and the function-symbols being replaced by symbols for their canonical extension. This in turn generalizes further to

THEOREM 7. (MYHILL-NERODE) *Let $\Phi(x_1, \ldots, x_n)$ be a universal Horn-sentence built up from equations between almost recursive combinatorial functions of $x_1, \cdots, x_n$, and true of all natural numbers $x_1, \cdots, x_n$, or even of all natural numbers $x_1, \cdots, x_n > k$ for some natural number k. Let $\Phi(X_1, \cdots, X_n)$ be obtained from $\Phi(x_1, \cdots, x_n)$ by replacing the numerical variables $x_1, \cdots, x_n$ by isolic variables $X_1, \cdots, X_n$, and by replacing symbols for almost recursive combinatorial functions by symbols for their canonical extensions. Then $\Phi(X_1, \cdots, X_n)$ is true for all infinite isols $X_1, \cdots, X_n$.*

Here a Horn-sentence is a truth-function of equations in each conjunct of whose conjunctive normal form at most one disjunct appears unnegated. Thus Horn-sentences comprise

(i) Equations: $f(x_1, \cdots, x_n) = g(x_1, \cdots, x_n)$.

(ii) Inequations: $f \neq g$.

(iii) Implications whose antecedents are equations or conjunctions of equations, and whose consequents are equations: $f_1 = g_1 \,\&\, \cdots \,\&\, f_k = g_k \rightarrow f^* = g^*$.

(iv) Incompatibilities between equations: $\sim(f_1 = g_1 \,\&\, \cdots \,\&\, f_k = g_k)$.

(v) Conjunctions each of whose conjuncts has one of the forms (i)—(iv).

Amongst Horn-sentences of the form (iii) are all the cancellation laws which have been mentioned; however, the sentence (*) asserting the non-existence of zero-divisors is not a Horn-sentence. Again among Horn-sentences of the form (iv) is the statement

$$\sim(X = 2Y \,\&\, X = 2Z+1)$$

that no isol is both even and odd; however, the statement that every isol is either even or odd, which can, after a little juggling, be expressed as a truth-function of equations between recursive combinatorial functions, turns out to be a disjunction of two such equations and hence does not fall under Theorem 7. It turns out to be false in Λ.

Thus combinatorial functions enable us to deal with Horn-sentences prefixed by universal quantifiers. We can also use these functions to deal with Horn-sentences prefixed by (unmixed) existential quantifiers. As a sample theorem we get

THEOREM 8. (DEKKER-MYHILL-NERODE) *Let $\Phi(x_1, \ldots, x_n)$ be a conjunction of equations between almost recursive combinatorial functions, and let $\Phi(X_1, \cdots, X_n)$ be obtained from it as in Theorem 7.*

(a) *If $\Phi(x_1, \cdots, x_n)$ holds for only finitely many n-tuples $x_1, \cdots, x_n$, it holds for no n-tuple $X_1, \cdots, X_n$ of infinite isols.*

(b) *If for every n-tuple $x_1^*, \cdots, x_n^*$, there exist $x_1 > x_1^*, \cdots, x_n > x_n^*$ satisfying $\Phi(x_1, \cdots, x_n)$, there are infinite isols $X_1, \cdots, X_n$ for which $\Phi(X_1, \cdots, X_n)$.*

6. The One-Quantifier Case: Negative Results

The sentence (*), expressing the non-existence of zero-divisors, does *not* go over to isols; and it is not a Horn-sentence. With a trivial exception, which we shall explain immediately, *no* non-Horn-sentence (in particular, no disjunction of equations and no implication whose antecedent is an equation and whose consequent is a disjunction of equations) goes over to isols.

The nature of the trivial exception is illustrated by the sentence

$$xy = 0 \to x = 0 \vee y = 0,$$

which is not a Horn-sentence and yet goes over to Λ. The reason is that it is equivalent to

$$(\forall xy \geqq 1)(xy \neq 0),$$

which holds in Λ by Theorem 9. The exact statement of the theorem on counter-examples for non-Horn-sentences is notationally tricky; we content ourselves with the one-variable case.

THEOREM 9. (MYHILL-NERODE) *Let* $f_1, \ldots, f_k, g_1, \ldots, g_k$ *be almost recursive combinatorial,* $F_1, \cdots, G_k$ *their canonical extensions* $(k \geqq 2)$. *Suppose that*

$$f_1(x) = g_1(c) \vee \cdots \vee f_k(x) = g_k(x)$$

holds for all natural numbers x. Then

$$F_1(X) = G_1(X) \vee \cdots \vee F_k(X) = G_k(X)$$

does not hold in Λ *except in the trivial case, where for some* $i \leqq k$

$$f_i(x) = g_i(x)$$

holds for all, or all but finitely many, x (and in that case by Theorem 7 $F_i(X) = G_i(X)$ *holds for all infinite X).*

A similar theorem holds for implications

$$f_0(x) = g_0(x) \to f_1(x) = g_1(x) \vee \cdots \vee f_k(x) = g_k(x),$$

and this, or rather its extension to functions of several variables, yields another proof of the existence of zero-divisors in Λ*

7. The Two-Quantifier Case

Not every Horn-sentence with one or more alternations of quantifiers holds in Λ when it holds for the integers. A simple example is

$$x \neq 0 \,\&\, xy \leqq xz \to y \leqq z,$$

i.e., in prenex normal form

$$(\forall xyzw)(\exists u)((x+1)y+w = (x+1)z \to y+u = z),$$

to which I here found counter-examples in Λ. On the other hand, if every

Skolem function of an arithmetical formula can be chosen to be almost recursive combinatorial, then, e.g.,

$$(\forall xy)(\exists z)\mathfrak{H}(x, y, z),$$

where $\mathfrak{H}$ is Horn, can be written as

$$\mathfrak{H}(x, y, f(x, y))$$

for some almost recursive combinatorial f. Consequently, by Theorem 7, $\mathfrak{H}(X, Y, F(X, Y))$, and *a fortiori*

$$(\forall XY)(\exists Z)\mathfrak{H}(X, Y, Z)$$

holds in Λ.

Actually it is possible, as Nerode has shown, to reduce the decision problem for two-quantifier formulas in Λ to the decision problem for the arithmetic of natural numbers: the procedure is too complex to be described here. For three and more quantifiers only fragmentary results are known.

8. The Ring of Isolic Integers

To a large extent the addition of quantifiers does not make for so much further complication in Λ^* as it does in Λ; this, together with the applicability of standard algebraic methods (ring theory), makes it likely that Λ is best studied via Λ^*. In order to state some of the chief results in this area, we need the notion of the canonical extension of a recursive (not necessarily combinatorial) function from ε^* (the ring of integers) to Λ^*. For functions of one argument this goes as follows: Let $f: \varepsilon^* \to \varepsilon^*$ be recursive, and for any two non-negative integers a, b let $f^*(a, b) = f(a-b)$. f^* has a canonical decomposition $f^+ - f^-$, where f^+, f^- are recursive combinatorial. Now define the canonical extension F of f to Λ^* by

$$F(X-Y) = F^+(X, Y) - F^-(X, Y) \, (X, Y \in \Lambda).$$

(Of course, uniqueness has to be proved and is not quite trivial.) With this definition we have the following theorem, which is much more powerful than any known corresponding theorem for Λ.

THEOREM 10. (NERODE) (a) *Let Φ be a Horn-sentence with arbitrary quantifiers (in prenex normal form) in which the variables range over ε^* and the function-symbols denote recursive (not necessarily combinatorial) functions. Let Φ^* be obtained from Φ by replacing the integer variables by isolic integer variables, and the symbols for recursive functions by symbols for their canonical extensions to Λ^*. Then if Φ is true and if the Skolem functions of Φ can be chosen recursive, Φ^* is also true.*

(b) *Let $\Phi(x_1, \cdots, x_n)$ be a universal non-Horn-sentence in which the variables range over ε^* and the function symbols denote recursive functions. Let $\Phi(X_1, \cdots, X_n)$ be obtained from Φ by replacing the integer variables by isolic integer variables and the symbols for recursive functions by symbols for their* *canonical extensions to* Λ^*. *Then even if* $\Phi(x_1, \cdots, x_n)$ *is true,* $\Phi(X_1, \cdots, X_n)$ *is not true unless it is possible to write* $\Phi(x_1, \cdots, x_n)$ *as a conjunction of disjunctions such that from each disjunction all but at most one unnegated disjunct can be removed in such a way that the result is still true of the integers.*

There are corresponding results for non-universal non-Horn-sentences.

9. R.E.T.'s Which Are Not Isols

Now we turn our attention to $\Omega - \Lambda$. Combinatorial functions tend to degenerate rather badly here, on account of the ubiquity of additive absorption, and the prevalence of even multiplicative absorption. Indeed, it can be shown by straightforward computation that every recursive combinatorial function becomes outside of Λ either (a) a constant, (b) a function of the form $mA^n/n!$ $(m, n \geqq 1)$, or (c) the function 2^A. (We use letters from the beginning of the alphabet here and henceforth to denote arbitrary R.E.T.'s, and continue to use letters from the end of the alphabet to denote isols. The quotient $A^n/n!$ is uniquely determined and always exists for $A \notin \Lambda$.)

Every *identity* between almost recursive combinatorial functions goes over from the natural numbers to Ω. But the same does not hold for more complicated formulas, not even for negations of identities (cf., e.g., $n \neq n+1$). There is, however, one important implication which goes over, namely,

THEOREM 11. (FRIEDBERG) $nA = nB \rightarrow A = B$ $(n \neq 0)$.

This led to the conjectures that $XA = XB \rightarrow A = B$ for every non-zero isol X, and that $F(A) = F(B) \rightarrow A = B$ for every non-constant recursive combinatorial function F. Both these conjectures have been disproved by my student Erik Ellentuck, who proved

THEOREM 12. (ELLENTUCK) *There are distinct* $A, B \in \Omega - \Lambda$ *such that for every non-linear recursive combinatorial function* F, $F(A) = F(B)$.

Thus the study of implications and more generally Horn-sentences in $\Omega - \Lambda$ is likely to become rather trivial, at least in the one-argument case.

Theorem 11 has as a corollary that *the finite multiples of any* R.E.T. *are either all equal or all distinct. This is not true for its finite powers*: Ellentuck has an R.E.T. A for which

$$A < A^2 = A^3 = A^4 = \cdots$$

In general either all powers are distinct, or all from a certain point on are equal (in which case they also equal 2^A). Further, if any power A^k is idemmultiple (i.e., satisfies $A^k = 2A^k$), so are all greater powers. Consequently, *the system of combinatorial functions of one argument* A *is completely determined by two numerical invariants* (possibly $= \infty$); the *number of distinct powers* and the *number of idemmultiple powers of* A. From this beginning it should be easy to finish off $\Omega - \Lambda$; in fact, the theory of it may well be in a suitable sense decidable.

10. Dedekind Finite Cardinals

Until recently, it was believed that an exact correspondence probably existed between the arithmetic of isols and the arithmetic of Dedekind finite cardinals without the axiom of choice. However, a counter-example was recently discovered; the formula

$$(\forall X)(\exists Y)(X^2+X = 2Y)$$

is true in Λ but false in some variants of the Frankel-Mostowski model. It now seems more likely that isolic arithmetic corresponds to the arithmetic of Dedekind finite cardinals with the axiom of choice replaced by the axiom of simple ordering. In fact, all the *positive* results about combinatorial functions of isols almost certainly go over without change to Dedekind finite cardinals with simple ordering. Also there is a possibility that a more restricted class of functions may yield a theory applicable to Dedekind finite cardinals without the axiom of choice or any weaker substitute. In any case, I believe that the most fruitful application of the methods of Dekker, Nerode, and myself are yet to come, and that they lie within set-theory rather than recursion theory.

Bibliographical Remark

On account of the speed with which the field of recursive equivalence types has been developed, most published results in this area exist largely in the form of abstracts in the *Journal of Symbolic Logic* and the *Bulletin* and *Notices of the American Mathematical Society,* beginning in 1955. The only extensive treatment is in *Recursive Equivalence Types* (monograph by Dekker and Myhill, University of California Publications in Mathematics, N.S., Vol. 3, No. 3, pp. 67–214, 1960); however, developments since 1958 are not dealt with in this book, and much of the treatment already looks somewhat antiquated. A long detailed article by A. Nerode on combinatorial functions, containing full proofs of many theorems stated without proof in the present paper, is scheduled for publication in *Annals of Mathematics* sometime in 1961.

Added in proof (September 1961). Nerode's paper is now published (*Ann. of Math.,* Vol. 73 (1961), pp. 362–403). The anticipations of § 10 have been beautifully fulfilled in Ellentuck's thesis (University of California at Berkeley).

SOME APPLICATIONS OF DEGREES

J. R. SHOENFIELD

Duke University, Durham, North Carolina, U.S.A.

Although the theory of degrees of undecidability has progressed considerably in recent years, applications of the theory have been rather rare. Some applications can be found in recent work of Kleene; but these are mostly 'inessential' applications, for, at the expense of slightly more complicated wording, the use of degrees could be replaced by a use of the hyperarithmetical hierarchy.

Now as Kleene has emphasized, the structure of degrees is essentially a refinement of the structure of the hyperarithmetical hierarchy. Hence 'true' applications of degrees can come only when this finer structure is actually needed. It seems likely that the theory of recursive functions has now advanced to the point at which this is the case. We shall discuss two problems which use this finer structure, although the concept of degree does not appear in either problem. While not of great importance in themselves, they serve to illustrate the type of applications of degrees we may expect in the future.

The first problem is suggested by a series of theorems of Tarski [8] on undecidable theories. Suppose a theory has been proved undecidable by one of these theorems; can we conclude that it is, in some sense, effectively undecidable? For axiomatizable theories, 'effectively undecidable' can be interpreted as 'creative' (see [2] for definitions). Moreover, Tarski's theorems all depend on the fundamental theorem (essentially due to Church): if every recursive function is definable in a consistent theory T, then T is undecidable. Hence the basic question is: if every recursive function is definable in an axiomatizable consistent theory T, must T be creative?

Feferman [2] and the author [5] have shown that the answer is yes if certain further assumptions are made on T. Ehrenfeucht and Feferman [1] showed that under these additional assumptions, more is true about T; namely, every recursively enumerable set is weakly representable in T. Nevertheless, the answer to the basic question is no; there is an axiomatizable, consistent, non-creative theory T in which every recursive function is definable, and in which no non-recursive set is weakly representable.

The construction of T is given elsewhere [6]; here we merely indicate how degrees enter. Myhill [3] has shown that every creative set has degree $\mathbf{0}'$ (the highest degree of recursively enumerable sets). Hence to show T is non-creative, it is sufficient to show that (the set of Gödel numbers of theorems of) T has degree $< \mathbf{0}'$.

Suppose we have a partial recursive function $F(e, n)$ with the following property: For every recursive function $f(n)$, there is a number e such that $F(e, n)$ is defined and equal to $f(n)$ for all n. We then obtain an axiomatizable theory T in which every recursive function is definable as follows: Introduce constants 0, 1, 2, . . . and one-place function symbols $\Phi_0, \Phi_1, \Phi_2, \ldots$, and introduce $\Phi_e(n) = m$ as an axiom whenever $F(e, n)$ is defined and equal to m.

One such F may be obtained as follows: let $F(e, n) = m$ if the eth partial recursive function is defined for all arguments $\leq n$ and is equal to m for the argument n. The domain of definition of this F is a creative set. However, it can be shown that by omitting, for each e, a finite number of pairs (e, n), we may make the domain into a recursively enumerable set of degree $< \mathbf{0}'$. The new function F fails to have the above property 'by a small amount'; but it is easy to restore this property without affecting the degree.

We now have a set of axioms of degree $< \mathbf{0}'$. By introducing a further recursive set of axioms, it is possible to eliminate quantifiers effectively. It is then possible to reduce the decision problem for T to that for the domain of F; so T becomes a theory of degree $< \mathbf{0}'$.

The second problem concerns categoricity. As is well known, Peano arithmetic is not categorical in the power $\aleph_0$ (that is, there are non-standard countable models). Suppose we choose a set A of natural numbers; add a symbol 'A' for this set to Peano arithmetic; and introduce $A(n)$ as an axiom for each n in A and $\neg A(n)$ as an axiom for each n not in A. (Of course the induction axiom is to be extended to cover the new symbol.) If we do this for one set, or even for a countable number of sets A, the proof of non-categoricity remains valid. However, if we do this for all sets A, the situation changes; Rabin [4] has shown that the theory obtained is categorical in the power $\aleph_0$. More recently, Scott and Tennenbaum have shown that this is true even if we only introduce new symbols and axioms for uncountably many sets A.

The question now arises: is the Scott-Tennenbaum result really more general than the Rabin result? It is *a priori* possible that whenever we introduce symbols and axioms for an uncountable number of sets, every set of natural numbers is weakly representable in the resulting theory. To show this is not the case, it would be sufficient to find an uncountable class $\mathscr{A}$ of sets of natural numbers which is arithmetically independent, i.e., such that no member of $\mathscr{A}$ is arithmetical in the remaining members of $\mathscr{A}$. Using the measure-theoretic techniques of Spector [7], we prove a somewhat stronger result.

THEOREM. *There is an uncountable class $\mathscr{A}$ of sets of natural numbers which is hyperarithmetically independent.*

PROOF. We identify a set of natural numbers with its characteristic function. The space $\mathscr{C}$ of characteristic functions is a countable product space $\{0, 1\}^\infty$. If we give $\{0,1\}$ the measure in which each point has measure $\frac{1}{2}$, then $\mathscr{C}$ has a product measure. Hence $\mathscr{C}^2$ has a product measure. We define a function F from $\mathscr{C}^2$ to $\mathscr{C}$ as follows: $F(\alpha, \beta) = \gamma$, where γ is defined by

$$\gamma(2n) = \alpha(n),$$
$$\gamma(2n+1) = \beta(n).$$

If $\mathscr{C}$ is regarded as a product space, F is simply a permutation of factors. Hence F is an isomorphism of the measure spaces $\mathscr{C}^2$ and $\mathscr{C}$.

Let $H_n(\alpha, \beta_1, \ldots, \beta_n)$ be 1 if α is hyperarithmetical in $\beta_1, \ldots, \beta_n$, and 0 otherwise. As in [7], H_n is measurable; and, since only countably many α are hyperarithmetical in a fixed $\beta_1, \ldots, \beta_n$,

$$\int H_n(\alpha, \beta_1, \ldots, \beta_n) d\alpha = 0. \tag{1}$$

LEMMA. *If $\mathscr{A}$ is finite and $\mathscr{A} \cup \{\beta\}$ is hyperarithmetically independent for almost all β, then $\mathscr{A} \cup \{\beta, \gamma\}$ is hyperarithmetically independent for almost all pairs (β, γ).*

PROOF. Suppose $\mathscr{A} = \{\alpha_1, \ldots, \alpha_n\}$. If $\mathscr{A} \cup \{\beta, \gamma\}$ is not independent, then

$$H_{n+1}(\beta, \gamma, \alpha_1, \ldots, \alpha_n) = 1 \tag{2}$$

or

$$H_{n+1}(\gamma, \beta, \alpha_1, \ldots, \alpha_n) = 1 \tag{3}$$

or some α_i is hyperarithmetical in the remaining α_j, β, and γ, in which case

$$\mathscr{A} \cup \{F(\beta, \gamma)\} \text{ is not independent.} \tag{4}$$

The set of pairs (β, γ) satisfying (2) has measure zero. This follows from integrating $H_{n+1}(\beta, \gamma, \alpha_1, \ldots, \alpha_n)$ with respect to (β, γ), using Fubini's theorem to transform the integral to

$$\int\int H_{n+1}(\beta, \gamma, \alpha_1, \ldots, \alpha_n) d\beta\, d\gamma,$$

and using (1). Similarly, the sets of pairs (β, γ) satisfying (3) has measure zero. By hypothesis on $\mathscr{A}$ and the fact that F is an isomorphism, the set of pairs (β, γ) satisfying (4) has measure zero. The lemma follows.

Now consider all subclasses $\mathscr{B}$ of $\mathscr{C}$ satisfying the condition:

(I) For every finite subset $\mathscr{A}$ of $\mathscr{B}$, $\mathscr{A} \cup \{\beta\}$ is independent for almost all β.

Any such $\mathscr{B}$ is clearly independent.[1] By Zorn's lemma, there is a maximal class $\mathscr{B}$ satisfying (I); we need only show such a $\mathscr{B}$ cannot be countable. Suppose $\mathscr{B}$ is countable, and hence has only countably many finite subsets. Applying the lemma to these subsets, we see $\mathscr{B} \cup \{\beta, \gamma\}$ is independent for almost all pairs (β, γ). By Fubini's theorem, it follows that $\mathscr{B} \cup \{\beta\}$ has property (I) for almost all β; so almost all β are in $\mathscr{B}$. This is impossible; for $\mathscr{B}$ is countable, and hence of measure zero.

---

[1]Recall that a function is hyperarithmetical in a class $\mathscr{B}$ only if it is hyperarithmetical in a finite subclass of $\mathscr{B}$.

References

[1] Ehrenfeucht, A., and S. Feferman. Representability of recursively enumerable sets in formal theories, *Archiv für Mathematische Logik und Grundlagenforschung*, Vol. 5 (1959), pp. 37–41.

[2] Feferman, S. Degrees of unsolvability associated with classes of formalized theories, *Journal of Symbolic Logic*, Vol. 22 (1957), pp. 161–175.

[3] Myhill, J. Creative sets, *Zeitschrift für Mathematik Logik und Grundlagen der Math.*, Vol. 1 (1955), pp. 97–108.

[4] Rabin, M. O. Arithmetical extensions with prescribed cardinality, *Koninklijke Nederlandse Akademie van Wetenschappen*, Ser. A, Vol. 62 (1959), pp. 439–446.

[5] Shoenfield, J. R. Degrees of formal systems, *Journal of Symbolic Logic*, Vol. 23 (1958), pp. 389–392.

[6] Shoenfield, J. R. Undecidable and creative theories, *Fundamenta Mathematicae*, Vol. 49 (1961), pp. 171–179.

[7] Spector, C. Measure-theoretic construction of incomparable hyperdegrees, *Journal of Symbolic Logic*, Vol. 23 (1958), pp. 280–288.

[8] Tarski, A., A. Mostowski, and R. M. Robinson, *Undecidable Theories*, North-Holland Publishing Co., 1953.

SECTION

II

FOUNDATIONS OF MATHEMATICAL THEORIES

RECENT DEVELOPMENTS IN MODEL THEORY

ABRAHAM ROBINSON

Princeton University, Princeton, New Jersey, U.S.A.

1. Introduction

Model theory deals with the properties of mathematical structures, or systems of mathematical structures, which are given by sets of axioms formulated frequently — but not necessarily — in the lower predicate calculus. From its inception it has been associated closely with Algebra, both by virtue of the algebraic character of its methods, and because Algebra constitutes its most natural field of application. However, inasmuch as Set theory has in recent years been investigated most frequently from a purely axiomatic point of view, it also has come within the scope of Model theory. In the present lecture I shall not try to give a comprehensive description of the subject. Instead, I shall show how some of the pioneer results obtained in it take on a new complexion when viewed in the light of more recent developments and I shall emphasize some trends and methods which appear to be destined to play an important part in the near future. Some new results will be presented. I am indebted to M. Perlis for stimulating comments on the subject considered in the first part of this lecture.

As it happens quite frequently in Mathematics, the germs of some of the fundamental ideas of Model theory go back beyond the beginnings of the subject. Thus, some of the methods used in order to prove the extended completeness theorem of the lower predicate calculus, or the compactness theorem for arithmetical classes (varieties) or the principle of localization — all essentially equivalent as far as the applications are concerned, though formulated within different frameworks — appear already in Gödel's paper on the completeness of the Lower predicate calculus, at least in a special case, and even earlier in the work of Löwenheim. Similarly, the notion of a choice function, which is of great help in our subject, was used by Skolem, Hilbert, and Herbrand already in the twenties. Finally, Skolem's construction of a non-standard model for arithmetic is the legitimate forerunner of the method of ultraproducts which will be discussed later in this lecture.

As mentioned earlier, Algebra may serve, and has served, as an effective field of application of Model theory. We know now that some of the earliest work in this field was done by A. I. Malcev who — in a fundamental paper [13] which by reason of the unfortunate place and time in which it was published remained unknown in the Western world for more than a dozen years — applied his *principle of localization* to a number of problems in group theory. I shall now sketch Malcev's method and give a concrete example of its application. This will be followed by a more searching analysis of its range.

2. Malcev's Method

Consider the elementary theory of general (non-commutative) groups. A property P pertaining to groups is called quasi-elementary (or, by Malcev, elementary) if it is satisfied by a group G whenever all sentences of a given finite or infinite set K_P of the Lower predicate calculus hold in G. Moreover, the property P is supposed to persist under passage to subgroups. That is to say, if P is satisfied by a group G, then it is satisfied also by all subgroups of G. For example, the property of a group to be commutative is quasi-elementary. The precise formulation of the group axioms is irrelevant to the present definition but we shall suppose once and for all that they are formulated in terms of the single relation of equality $E(x, y)$ (read x equals y, $x = y$ in ordinary notation) and of the functions $g(x, y)$ and $r(x)$ (i.e., xy and x^{-1}) and the individual constant e, which is to stand for the neutral element of the group. Let K_0 be a set of axioms of this description for the concept of a group.

Let $[P_1, \cdots, P_k]$ be a set of quasi-elementary properties, $k \geqq 1$. Then we say that the group G is of type $[P_1, \cdots, P_k]$ if there exists a normal chain

$$G = G_0 \supseteqq G_1 \supseteqq G_2 \supseteqq \cdots \supseteqq G_k = (e)$$

such that the factor groups G_i/G_{i+1}, $i = 0, 1, \cdots, k-1$, have the properties $P_1, \cdots, P_k$, respectively. Malcev's main result now is that if every finitely generated subgroup of G is of type $[P_1, \cdots, P_k]$, then G also is of type $[P_1, \cdots, P_k]$. A simple application of this result is obtained if we take for $P_1 = P_2 = \cdots = P_k$, k fixed, the property of commutativity, P. Then a group of type $[P_1, \cdots, P_k]$ is a solvable group of *rank* k and Malcev's result yields the conclusion that if every finitely generated subgroup of G is solvable of rank k, then G is itself solvable of rank k.

The proof of the main theorem is based on the principle of localization which states that a set of sentences K of the Lower predicate calculus possesses a model if (and only if) every finite subset of K possesses a model.

A priori, the property of a group G to be of type $[P_1, \cdots, P_k]$ is not formulated within the Lower predicate calculus. Accordingly, we introduce new one-place relations, $H_1(x), \cdots, H_k(x)$, which are supposed to hold for any $x \in G$ precisely when $x \in G_i$, $i = 1, \cdots, k$, respectively. Using these relations it is now not difficult to express the fact that a group G is of type $[P_1, \cdots, P_k]$ by a finite or infinite set of sentences in the Lower predicate calculus. A suitable set of this kind will be denoted by K^*.

Let $\{b_\nu\}$ be the set of individual constants of G, then we may in a certain sense "embed" G in the Lower predicate calculus, by constructing its diagram D. D is the set of all atomic sentences $E(b_\mu, b_\nu)$ which hold in G, together with the sentences $E(b_\mu, b_\nu)$ if $E(b_\mu, b_\nu)$ does not hold in G (i.e., if $b_\mu \neq b_\nu$ in G), where b_μ and b_ν are arbitrary terms, i.e., expressions obtained by applying the function symbols $g(x, y)$ and $r(x)$ repeatedly to the elements of G. (For the purposes of our present discussion we may gloss over the distinction between the symbols 'b', 'g', 'r', and the entities denoted by them.) Then any group is a model of D if and only if it is an extension of G. Any relational system (or *structure*) is a group of type $[P_1, \cdots, P_k]$ if it is a model of $K_0 \cup K^*$.

Now consider the set of sentences $J = K_0 \cup K^* \cup D$. J possesses a model provided every finite subset of J possesses a model, by the principle of localization. But every finite subset of D is realized already in a finitely generated subgroup of G. Thus, if the assumption of the main theorem is satisfied, every finite subset of J possesses a model. It follows that J possesses a model, say G^*.

G^* is a group of type $[P_1, \cdots, P_k]$ and an extension of G. Let $H_1^*, \cdots, H_k^*$ be the subgroups of G^* consisting of the elements which satisfy $H_1(x), \cdots, H_k(x)$, respectively, and let $G_1, \cdots, G_k$ be the corresponding subgroups of G. Put $H_0^* = G^*$ and $G_0 = G$. Then $G_i^* = G \cap H_i^*, i = 0, \cdots, k$.

The factor group H_i^*/H_{i+1}^* possesses the property P_{i+1} by construction, $i = 0, \cdots, k-1$. The factor group $G_i/G_{i+1} = G_i/G_i \cap H_{i+1}^*$ is isomorphic to a subgroup of H_i^*/H_{i+1}^*, and hence, by one of our assumptions on P_i, possesses the property P_{i+1}. Hence G also is a group of type $[P_1, \cdots, P_k]$. This completes the proof of Malcev's main theorem.

3. Analysis of Quasi-elementary Properties

Since Malcev published his paper, a considerable amount of work has been done on the problem of correlating the model-theoretic properties of a sentence, or set of sentences, with its formal, or syntactical properties. Accordingly we now enquire into the syntactical significance of the conditions imposed in Section 2 above on the quasi-elementary properties P. Thus, we ask under what conditions a property P, which is formulated in terms of a finite or infinite set of sentences in the Lower predicate calculus, is such that whenever P is satisfied by a model M of a set of axioms K (in the above case the group axioms) it is satisfied also by every partial structure of M which is a model of K. If P is finite then it is known ([9] and [18], generalizing a result of [24]) that P may be replaced by a universal sentence, i.e., a sentence in prenex normal form with universal quantifiers only. We observe that this does not imply the corresponding result for infinite P directly. Accordingly, we shall now consider this case in more detail.

We first introduce a convenient notation. It is usual to write $K \vdash X$ if the sentence X is a deductive consequence of K or, which is the same for the Lower predicate calculus, if X holds in all models of K in which it is defined. Similarly, one writes $K \vdash K'$ if $K \vdash X$ for all elements X of the set of sentences K'. We shall use the notation $K \mathrel{\uparrow\!\vdash} X$ in order to indicate that X holds in all structures in which it is defined and which are *extensions* of models of K, and $K \mathrel{\downarrow\!\vdash} X$ if X holds in all structures in which it is defined and which are included in models of K. As before we introduce the corresponding generalizations $K \mathrel{\uparrow\!\vdash} K'$ and $K \mathrel{\downarrow\!\vdash} K'$.

THEOREM 3.1. *$K \mathrel{\uparrow\!\vdash} X$ for given K and X, if and only if there exists a finite subset K' of K such that $K' \mathrel{\uparrow\!\vdash} X$.*

In current parlance, the theorem expresses a property of localization of the relation $\mathrel{\uparrow\!\vdash}$. It is plain that the condition is sufficient. To prove that the condition is also necessary we *relativize* the set K with respect to a one-place relation $R(x)$ which does not occur in either K or X. That is to say, we transform the sentences of K according to the following inductive procedure:

$$\rho(Z) = Z \quad \text{for atomic sentences of predicates } Z$$
$$\rho(\sim Z) = \sim \rho(Z)$$
$$\rho(Z \vee W) = \rho(Z) \vee \rho(W)$$

for all well-formed Z and W, with similar definitions for the remaining connectives, if any. Finally,

$$\rho((\exists x)Q(x)) = (\exists x)[R(x) \wedge Q(x)]$$

and

$$\rho((x)Q(x)) = (x)[R(x) \supset Q(x)]$$

Thus, if M is a structure which includes the relation $R(x)$, such that $R(a)$ holds in M for at least one $a \in M$ and if Z is a sentence which is defined in M but which does not involve R, then $\rho(Z)$ holds in M if and only if Z holds in the partial structure of M which consists of the elements that satisfy R, M_R say.

We now define $\rho(K)$ as the set of transforms $\rho(Z)$ for $Z \in K$, together with the sentences $R(a)$ for all the individual constants a which occur in K. However, if no individual constants occur in K, then we add instead the sentence $(\exists x)R(x)$. Again M is a model of $\rho(K)$ if and only if M_R, as defined above, is a model of K.

Now in order to prove that the condition of 3.1 is necessary, we note that $K \mathrel{\uparrow\!\vdash} X$ is equivalent to $\rho(K) \vdash X$. But this implies, by the ordinary principle of localization that $H \vdash X$ for some finite subset H of $\rho(K)$. Let H' be the set of sentences of K whose transforms are included in H. Also, for any individual constant a such that $R(a)$ belongs to H add to H' a sentence of K which involves a. Let the resulting set be K'. Then $\rho(K') \supseteq H$ and so $\rho(K') \vdash X$. This entails $K' \mathrel{\uparrow\!\vdash} X$ and proves 3.1. Similarly we prove

THEOREM 3.2. *$K \downarrow X$ for given K and X if and only if there exists a finite subset K' of K such that $K' \downarrow X$.*

Sufficiency is obvious. Now suppose that $K \downarrow X$, and let M be any model of K, and M' any partial structure of M such that X holds in M'. By defining that $R(x)$ hold for all elements of M' and $\sim R(x)$ for the remaining elements of M, we turn M into a structure M_R such that $\rho(X)$ holds in M_R. Also, the sentences $R(a)$ hold in M_R for all a which occur in X and so does the sentence $(\exists x)R(x)$. Let K_R be the set of such $R(a)$ together with $(\exists x)R(x)$, so that K_R is not empty. Then $\rho(X)$ is deducible from $K \cup K_R$. It follows that $\rho(X)$ is deducible from $K' \cup K_R$ for some finite subset K' of K, and hence $K' \downarrow X$. This proves the theorem.

If K contains only a single sentence Y, then we write $Y \uparrow X$, $Y \downarrow X$ in place of $\{Y\} \uparrow X$, $\{Y\} \downarrow X$, respectively. In this way we obtain a new kind of propositional connective.

Suppose that for two given sentences X and Y there exists a *universal* sentence Z within the vocabulary of X and Y, i.e., whose relations and individual constants occur in either X or Y, and such that $Y \vdash Z$ and $Z \vdash X$ (i.e., such that $Y \supset Z$ and $Z \supset X$ are theorems of the predicate calculus). Let M and M' be any two structures such that Y and X are defined in M and M', respectively, and such that M' is a partial structure of M. Then Z holds in M since $Y \vdash Z$ and, furthermore, Z holds in M' since Z is universal. It then follows that X holds in M', $Y \downarrow X$. Conversely, we are now going to prove

THEOREM 3.3. *Suppose that $Y \downarrow X$. Then there exists a universal sentence Z within the vocabulary of Y and X such that $Y \vdash Z$ and $Z \vdash X$.*

PROOF. Let K be the set of universal sentences W within the vocabulary of X and Y such that $Y \vdash W$. Then K is disjunctive and conjunctive, i.e., for any $W_1, W_2 \in K$ there exist W_3, W_4 in K such that $W_1 \vee W_2 \equiv W_3$ and $W \wedge W_2 \equiv W_4$ are theorems (of the predicate calculus). Suppose now that no $W \in K$ is such that $W \vdash X$, i.e., such that $W \supset X$ is a theorem. Then it is not difficult to show that $K \cup \{\sim X\}$ is consistent, and hence possesses a model M. Y cannot hold in any extension of M, since $Y \downarrow X$. The method of diagrams then shows that for some existential sentence V, which holds in M and which is within the vocabulary of X and Y, $V \vdash \sim Y$. Hence replacing $\sim V$ by an equivalent universal sentence V', we have $Y \vdash V'$. It follows that V' belongs to K, and hence holds in M. This contradicts the fact that V holds in M, and shows that for some $Z \in K$, $Z \vdash X$, proving the theorem.

It is not difficult to "relativize" the above results, i.e., to consider the entire situation relative to a set of axioms K_0 given in advance, and to take into account only models of K_0 both in the formulation of the theorems and in the proofs. For example, $Y \downarrow X$ *relative to* K_0 signifies that for all models M and M' of K_0 such that M includes M' and such that X and Y are defined in M and M', respectively, Y holds in M only if X holds in M'.

It is also not difficult to prove a result corresponding to 3.3 for the relation $\nvdash$. The result then asserts the existence of a certain *existential* sentence Z.

We are now in a position to prove

THEOREM 3.4. *Let K be a set of sentences such that whenever K holds in a model M of a given set K_0, K holds also in all partial structures of M which are models of K_0. Then there exists a set of universal sentences K' such that K and K' are equivalent with respect to K, $K_0 \cup K \vdash K'$ and $K_0 \cup K' \vdash K$, and such that the sentences of K' are within the vocabulary of K_0 and K.*

To prove this theorem, let K' be the set of all universal sentences deducible from $K_0 \cup K$ and within the vocabulary of that set, and let $X \in K'$. Then we have to show that X is deducible from $K' \cup K_0$. Since X is in K, it holds in all partial structures of models of $K \cup K_0$, which are themselves models of K_0. Hence, by the relativized version of 3.2, there exist sentences $X_1, \cdots, X_l$ in K such that $X_1 \wedge \cdots \wedge X_l \nvdash X$ with respect to K_0. Hence, by the relativized version of 3.3 there exists an element Z of K' such that $X_1 \wedge \cdots \wedge X_l \supset Z$ and $Z \supset X$ are deducible from K_0. This proves the theorem.

There is a corresponding result if K is known to persist under extensions of models of K_0. The set K' then is a set of existential sentences.

4. Syntactical Properties of Sentences and Set-theoretic Properties of Their Models

The results of the preceding section provide us with a number of typical results from a field of research that has received a good deal of attention in recent years. This deals with the interconnection between the syntactical properties of sentences or sets of sentences on one hand (such as the property of being a universal sentence, see above), and the set-theoretic or algebraic properties of the models of these sentences. There is a good review of the subject by R. C. Lyndon [11] who also obtained one of the most penetrating results in this field [12]. Other contributors to the subject, in addition to those mentioned in the preceding section, have been G. Birkhoff, K. Bing, C. C. Chang, H. J. Keisler, A. Horn, and R. L. Vaught. Lyndon's review may be consulted for additional information. Although there still exist a few unsolved problems in this field our general understanding of the situation is by now quite satisfactory. Lyndon's main result is as follows.

THEOREM 4.1. *A sentence of the Lower predicate calculus is preserved under passage to homomorphic images if and only if it is equivalent to a positive sentence.*

A sentence is positive if it does not contain the sign of negation but is constructed from its atomic formulae by the use of conjunction, disjunction, and individual quantification alone. The difficult part of the proof is concerned with the necessity of the condition.

Lyndon proves also the following stronger result:

THEOREM 4.2. *Let X and Y be any sentences such that Y is defined in all models of X (i.e., Y is within the vocabulary of X). Suppose that whenever X*

holds in a structure M, Y holds in all homomorphic images of M. Then there exists a sentence Z within the vocabulary of X such that $X \vdash Z$ and $Z \vdash Y$.

The converse is again evident.

A related theorem, which can be proved rather more easily and which supplements the list provided in Lyndon's review, is as follows:

THEOREM 4.3. *Let X and Y be any sentences such that Y is within the vocabulary of X. Suppose that whenever X holds in a structure of M, Y holds in all homomorphic images of extensions of M. Then there exists a sentence Z in prenex normal form which is both existential and positive such that $X \vdash Z$ and $Z \vdash Y$. Moreover, Z is within the the vocabulary of X.*

Again the converse of the theorem is obvious. The special case $X = Y$ is of particular interest.

To prove 4.3, let K be the set of existential and positive sentences W within the vocabulary of X such that $W \vdash Y$. Then K is conjunctive and disjunctive. If the conclusion of 4.3 does not hold, then $X \vdash W$ is not true for any $W \in K$. Then $\{X\} \cup \{\sim W_\nu\} = H$ is consistent, where W_ν varies over the elements of K. Let M be a model of H and let D be the *positive* diagram of M, i.e., the set of all atomic sentences which hold in H. Then Y holds in all models of D, and so $X_1 \wedge \cdots \wedge X_l \supset Y$ for some $X_1, \cdots, X_l$ in D. Eliminating the constants of $X_1 \wedge \cdots \wedge X_l$ which do not occur in X by existential quantification, we obtain an existential V such that $V \vdash Y$. Thus $V \in K$ and at the same time V holds in M. This involves a contradiction and proves the theorem.

Theorems of the type of 4.2 and 4.3 have been called *interpolation theorems* by Lyndon. Another example of an interpolation theorem was given in the preceding section (Theorem 3.3). The term *interpolation* refers to the introduction of a sentence Z between X and Y. An earlier example of such a theorem is due to W. Craig [2], generalizing some work by the present author in connection with Beth's theorem on definability [1], a subject into which I shall not enter here.

It is again natural to ask whether the consequence relation which occurs in the hypothesis of 4.2 ("if X holds in M then Y holds in all homomorphic images of M") can be expressed in some way within the framework of the Lower predicate calculus. To do this, replace all relations $R(x_1, \cdots, x_n)$ in Y by distinct relations $R'(x_1, \cdots, x_n)$ which did not occur previously in X or Y. Let the result be Y' and let K' be the set of sentences

$$(x_1) \cdots (x_n)[R(x_1, \cdots, x_n) \supset R'(x_1, \cdots, x_n)].$$

Then we claim that $K' \vdash X \supset Y'$ or, which is the same, that Y' is deducible from $\{X\} \cup K'$.

Indeed, let M be a model of $\{X\} \cup K'$. Ignoring the unprimed relations in M, we obtain a structure M' which is a homomorphic image of M. Since Y is supposed to hold in all homomorphic images of models of M, it follows that Y' holds in M' and Y holds in M, and so Y is deducible from $\{X\} \cup K'$.

Conversely, if $K' \vdash X \supset Y'$. Then whenever X holds in a structure M, Y holds in every homomorphic image of M.

Similarly, we may consider a set of sentences K and a single sentence Y within the vocabulary of K such that Y holds in all homomorphic images of models of K. Introducing the primed relations and defining Y' and K' as before, we may then show that this situation is described correctly by $K \cup K' \vdash Y'$. It follows that if K is infinite, then there exists a finite subset K^* of K such that $K^* \cup K' \vdash Y'$, i.e., such that Y holds in any homomorphic image of any model of K^*. This enables us to extend Lyndon's result 4.1 (above) to infinite sets, as follows:

THEOREM 4.4. *Let K be any set of sentences such that if M is any model of K, then K holds also in all homomorphic images of M. Then there exists a set of positive sentences K' which is equivalent to K,* i.e., *$K \vdash K'$ and $K' \vdash K$.*

PROOF. Let K' be the set of all positive sentences X' which are within the vocabulary of K and such that $K \vdash X'$. In order to prove the theorem, we have to show only that $K' \vdash X$ for any $X \in K$. Now as shown above, there exists a finite subset K^* of K such that X holds in all homomorphic images of models of K^*. Let $K^* = \{X_1, \cdots, X_l\}$; then X holds in all homomorphic images of models of $X_1 \wedge \cdots \wedge X_l$. Hence, by 4.2 above, there exists a positive sentence Y within the vocabulary of K such that $X_1 \wedge \cdots \wedge X_l \vdash Y$ and $Y \vdash X$. Thus Y belongs to K' and $K' \vdash X$, as required.

Combining the above procedure with the operation of relativization considered earlier, we may prove also (compare 4.3)

THEOREM 4.5. *If all the homomorphic images of extensions of models of a set K are themselves models of K, then K is equivalent to a set of sentences which are existential and positive.*

5. Analysis of Malcev's Method — Concluded

Theorem 3.4 shows that a quasi-elementary property in the sense of Malcev's result can always be formulated in terms of a finite or infinite set of universal sentences within the vocabulary introduced in section 2 in connection with the group concept, i.e., in terms of the constant e, the functors $g(x, y)$ and $r(x)$ and the relation $E(x, y)$. Moreover, the group axioms can themselves be formulated as universal sentences within this vocabulary. Similarly, we may express by a set of universal sentences the property of G that the sets defined by $H_i(x)$ and $H_{i+1}(x)$ yield a factor group which possesses the quasi-elementary property P_{i+1}. Hence, the property of a group to be of type $[P_1, \cdots, P_k]$ may be expressed by a set K of *universal* sentences formulated in terms of $g(x, y)$, $r(x)$, e, $E(r, y)$, $H_1(x) \cdots H_k(x)$. For example the property that the factor group G_i/G_{i+1} is commutative may be expressed by

5.1. $$(x)(y)[H_i(x) \wedge H_i(y) \supset H_{i+1}(g(g(g(x, y), r(x)), r(y)))].$$

Suppose now that K holds in some subgroup G' of G. If we replace the sentences of K by all their particular instances obtained by omitting the universal quantifiers and by replacing the variables in all possible way by elements a_ν of G', then we obtain a set of sentences K' which hold in G'.

Conversely, suppose that the predicates $H_i(x)$ are not defined in G *a priori* but that we wish to introduce them in such a way that the sentences of K are all satisfied. Equivalently, we may take *all* the instances of the sentences of K obtained as above with any set of individual constants of G, e.g.,

5.2. $$[H_i(a) \wedge H_i(b) \supset H_{i+1}(g(g(g(a, b), r(a)), r(b)))]$$

and we may try to define the $H_i(x)$ in such a way that all sentences such as 5.2 are satisfied. Let the set of these sentences be K^* and note that the elements of K^* are now free of quantifiers altogether. More precisely, we have to define the $H_i(x)$ as required, knowing that such definitions are possible in all finitely generated subgroups of G. To define the $H_i(x)$ conveniently here means simply to assign truth values to the atomic sentences $H_i(a)$ for all $a \in G$ in such a way that the sentences of K^* are all satisfied. In other words we are dealing with a problem in *truth valuation*. In the original method, which was sketched in Section 2 above, this element of the proof is absorbed in the application of the principle of localization, which in turn depends on a valuation. Indeed, truth valuations constitute one of the most essential elements of Model theory, as will be explained in more detail in the next section. For the present, we shall formulate a basic lemma which will be found useful later and we shall apply a special case of it to the problem in hand.

Let A be an abstract set (which in the cases in which we are interested will be realized by a set of atomic formulae). A *partial valuation* of A is a mapping ϕ of a subset A' of A into the set $\{0, 1\}$—0 for "true" or "holds" and 1 for "false" or "does not hold". Thus A' is the domain of ϕ and we write $A' = D\phi$. ϕ is *total* if $D\phi = A$. We write $\phi|B$ for the restriction of ϕ to $B \cap D\phi$, where B is any subset of A.

A non-empty set J of non-empty subsets of a set N is called a *net* on N if for any $J_1 \in J$ and $J_2 \in J$ there exists a $J_3 \in J$ such that $J_1 \cap J_2 \supseteqq J_3$. The unit set of N, $\{N\}$ is a net on N.

Valuation Lemma 5.3. *Let $N = \{\nu\}$ be an index set for a set $\Phi = \{\phi_\nu\}$ of partial valuations of a set A. Let J be a net on N such that for every finite subset B of A and for every element J' of J there exists a $\nu \in J'$ for which $B \subseteqq D\phi_\nu$.*

Then there exists a total valuation ψ of A such that for every finite subset B of A and for every $J' \in J$ there exists a $\nu \in J'$ such that $B \subseteqq D\phi_\nu$ and $\psi|B = \phi_\nu|B$.

The proof of 5.3 will not be given here (see [21]). An important special case is obtained for $J = \{N\}$. The lemma may then be reformulated as follows:

SPECIAL VALUATION LEMMA 5.4. *Let* $\Phi = \{\phi_\nu\}$ *be a set of partial valuations of a set A such that for every finite subset B of A there exists a* $\phi_\nu \in \Phi$ *such that* $B \subseteqq D\phi_\nu$. *Then there exists a total valuation* ψ *of A such that for every* $B \subseteqq A$ *there exists a* $\phi_\nu \in \Phi$ *for which* $B \subseteqq D\phi_\nu$ *and* $\psi|B = \phi_\nu|B$.

It has been pointed out to me by Dr. R. Büchi that 5.4 coincides with a special case of a result of R. Rado [16].

Returning to our analysis of Malcev's method, we define A as the set of all atomic sentences $H_i(a_\mu)$, $i = 1, \cdots, k$, $a_\mu \in G$. We have to assign truth values ("holds", "does not hold" in G) to the elements of A in such a way that all sentences of K^* become true. The truth values of the sentences of K^* of course depend also on the truth values of the atomic sentences involving the relation of equality E which may occur in the sentence. However, these are given with G.

Now let $\Gamma = \{G'_\nu\}$ be the set of all finitely generated subgroups of G. By the assumption of Malcev's theorem the H_i can be defined in any group G'_ν in such a way that the sentences of K^* which contain only elements of G'_ν become true. This definition of the H_i is a partial valuation of A whose domain consists precisely of the elements $H_i(a_\mu)$ of A such that $a_\mu \in G_\nu$. We select one such partial valuation ϕ_ν, say, for each $G'_\nu \in \Gamma$. Let $\Phi = \{\phi_\nu\}$; then it is evident that every finite subset of A is the domain of some ϕ_ν. Thus, the conditions of 5.4 are realized. Accordingly, there exists a total valuation ψ of A which satisfies the conclusion of 5.4. Let $X \in K^*$; then all the atomic sentences $H_i(a_\mu)$ which occur in X are assigned, by ψ, the same truth values as in some G'_ν. Hence X becomes "true" for this assignment, and all sentences of K^* are satisfied. This establishes Malcev's main theorem. However, the construction of the valuation ψ shows that we have actually established a somewhat more precise result which may be expressed as follows:

THEOREM 5.5. *If for a given positive integer of every finitely generated subgroup* G' *of a group* G *possesses a normal chain* $G' = G'_0 \supseteqq \cdots \supseteqq G'_k = (e)$ *such that the factor groups* G'_i/G'_{i+1} *possess certain preassigned quasi-elementary properties* P_{i+1}, $i = 0, \cdots, k-1$, *then there exists a normal chain* $G = G_0 \supseteqq G_1 \cdots \supseteqq G_k = (e)$ *such that the factor groups* G_i/G_{i+1} *possess the quasi-elementary properties* P_{i+1}, $i = 0, \cdots, k-1$, *and such that for every finite subset B of G there exists a finitely generated subgroup* G' *of G for which* $G'_i \cap B = G_i \cap B$, $i = 0, 1, \cdots, k-1$.

We may add that for countable groups this conclusion can be obtained also by the examination of a familiar proof of the extended completeness theorem.

Our analysis of Malcev's method has shown us that wherever it applies, there is no need to introduce quantification. Thus, our task consisted ultimately in showing that we are able to supplement a given structure by the introduction of additional relations in such a way that certain conditions which can be expressed in the Lower predicate calculus without quantifiers are satisfied in the resulting structure. Similar problems arise in many other connections, e.g., if we wish to show that if all finite subsets of a given group can be ordered (totally), then the group itself can be ordered. Indeed, general principles to cover such problems have been considered also independently of the Calculus of predicates (compare [14]). However this does not detract in any way from the great merit of Malcev's pioneer work in this field.

6. The Construction of Models

I now turn to a topic which is basic to Model theory — the construction of structures (relational systems) subject to given conditions, either in terms of axioms (sentences of the Lower predicate calculus), or in connection with other structures introduced previously. Indeed the mere existence of a model for any consistent set of axioms is sufficient in order to produce a host of interesting results, but a closer inspection of the way in which such structures are produced is not only of interest in itself but may also be relevant to other problems. The construction which has become best known in this connection is that of the reduced direct product, or ultraproduct. The first example of what might be called a reduced subdirect product was given by T. Skolem [23] in order to establish the existence of non-standard models of arithmetic. The general definition of the concept was given by J. Los in 1954 [10]. More recently there has been an upsurge of interest in the subject beginning with an abstract by Frayne, Scott, and Tarski [3] and including abstracts or papers by C. C. Chang, H. J. Keisler, S. B. Kochen, and M. O. Rabin (e.g., [7, 8, 15]). The theory has found various applications. In particular it has been shown by the authors just mentioned that many of the results of Model theory which were obtained previously by the use of the extended completeness theorem or its equivalents can also be established by means of the theory of reduced direct products.

It is interesting to note that in certain important special cases the reduced direct product construction coincides with a procedure which is of great importance in the theory of rings of continous functions (see the book by Gillman and Jerison [4] or the paper of E. Hewitt [6]). However, so far as I know, the investigators in the respective fields worked independently of one another originally.

The reduced direct product construction is as follows. Let N-$\{\nu\}$ be a non-empty index set, and let J be an ultrafilter on N (a maximal dual ideal within the Boolean algebra of subsets of N). That is to say, J is a non-empty set of subsets of N which satisfies the following conditions.

6.1. J does not contain the empty set; the intersection of any two elements of J is included in J; for any subset J' of N either J' or $N-J'$ is included in J. It follows from these conditions that if $J' \subseteq J'' \subseteq N$ and $J' \in J$ then $J'' \in J$.

Now let $\{M_\nu\}$ be a set of structures with index set N such that the same relations are defined in all M_ν. Then the reduced direct product M of $\{M_\nu\}$ with respect to J is defined in the following way.

The individual elements of M are the functions $f = f(\nu)$, which are defined on N such that $f(\nu) \in M_\nu$ for all $\nu \in N$. Alternatively, distinct individual constants c_f corresponding to the different $f(\nu)$ may be taken as the elements of M.

For any relation $R(x_1, \cdots, x_n)$ which occurs in the M_ν define that $R(f_1, \cdots, f_n)$— or $R(c_{f_1}, \cdots, c_{f_n})$ — holds in M if the set

$$J' = \{\nu | R(f_1(\nu), \cdots, f_n(\nu)) \text{ holds in } M_\nu\}$$

(i.e., the set of ν such that $R(f_1(\nu), \cdots, f_n(\nu))$ holds in M_ν) is an element of J. If $J' \notin J$ so that $N - J' \in J$, define that $R(f_1, \cdots, f_n)$ does not hold in M. This determines the structure M. In particular, if all the M_ν coincide, $M_\nu = M_0$ for all ν, then M is called an ultrapower of M_0, and is denoted by $M = M_0^N/J$.

Let a be an individual constant which appears in all M_ν; then a is identified in M with the constant function $f(\nu) = a$.

The basic property of reduced direct products is given by the following

THEOREM 6.2. *Let X be a sentence which is defined and holds in all M_ν. Then X holds also in M. In particular if M is an ultrapower of M_0, then M is an arithmetical* (*or elementary*) *extension of M_0.*

We shall now present the theory of reduced direct products within a general setting which relates it more closely to the completeness and localization principles discussed in the preceding sections. It will be convenient to suppose that the vocabulary of the calculus includes as "extra-logical constants" only relations of an arbitrary number of places, but neither functors nor individual constants (which are functors of order zero). At the same time we shall suppose that a relation of equality $E(x, y)$ has been introduced once and for all, with the usual properties of an equivalence and of substitutivity. It is then possible to regard the relations $F(x_1, \cdots, x_n, y)$ in which y is defined uniquely by $x_1, \cdots, x_n$, i.e., which satisfy the conditions

$$(x_1) \cdots (x_n)(\exists y)(z)[F(x_1, \cdots, x_n, y) \wedge [F(x_1, \cdots, x_n, z) \supset E(y, z)]],$$

by virtue of axioms laid down explicitly for the purpose — as substitutes for functors. In particular, in place of the individual constants we may introduce one-place relations $F(y)$ which satisfy

$$(\exists y)(z)[F(y) \wedge [F(z) \supset E(y, z)]].$$

In this way we see that the special assumptions made above do not represent any essential limitation of our theory. It will also be sufficient to consider sentences in prenex normal form only. We shall take such sentences to be exemplified by

6.3. $$X = (\exists u)(w)(\exists x)(y)(\exists z)Q(u, w, x, y, z),$$

where $Q(u, w, x, y, z)$ does not contain any further quantifiers. Let M be a structure in which X is defined, i.e., such that the relations which occur in Q

are defined in M. Then X holds in M if and only if there exist functions χ, $\psi(w)$, $\zeta(w, y)$ which are defined on the entire domain of individuals of M (χ is a function of zero variables, i.e., a constant) such that

6.4 $$X' = Q(\chi, w, \psi(w), y, \zeta(w, y))$$

hold in M for all values of the variables w, y in M. Note that X', as it stands, cannot be part of our calculus, in view of the explicit exclusion of all functors. Each particular instance of X' represents a quantifier-free formula, which is still not part of our calculus although we may interpret it and assign it truth values in the usual way.

The functors ϕ, ψ, ζ are the so-called Herbrand or Skolem functors which belong to X, and X' is the Herbrand (or Skolem) form of X. Much of our knowledge of Model theory can be derived from an analysis of the properties of Herbrand functors and of the properties of the truth valuations which are assigned to the instances of X' and to their constituent atomic formulae. In the present section we shall be concerned chiefly with the properties of the latter. On the basis of the Valuation Lemma 5.3, we shall introduce a construction which may be regarded as a generalization of the reduced direct product formation. (We remark that one mode of construction is not necessarily either better or worse than another for being more general. In the present instance it appears that the reduced direct product formation and the mode of construction to be introduced are both of interest by providing an insight into different aspects of Model theory.)

Referring back to the Valuation Lemma 5.3, suppose that the set J on N is, more particularly, an ultrafilter in the Boolean algebra of subsets of N (see 6.1). Let ψ be a total valuation of A such as exists according to the conclusion of the lemma. For any given element $a \in A$ let $N_T(a)$ be the set of elements ν of N such that $a \in D\phi_\nu$, and $\phi_\nu(a) = 0$; let $N_F(a)$ be the set of $\nu \in N$ such that $a \in D\phi_\nu$, and $\phi_\nu(a) = 1$; and let $N_0(a)$ be the set of $\nu \in N$ such that $a \notin D\phi_\nu$. Then the sets $N_T(a)$, $N_F(a)$, and $N_0(a)$ are mutually disjoint, and together they exhaust N. It follows that precisely one of the three sets belongs to J. Now if $N_T(a) \in J$, then for some $\nu \in N_T(a)$, $\psi(a) = \phi_\nu(a) = 0$, and so in that case $\psi(a)$ obtains the value 1. Similarly, if $N_F(a) \in J$, then $\psi(a) = 1$. It follows that the values of ψ are defined uniquely by the given J and Φ on the set of elements $a \in A$ such that either $N_T(a)$ or $N_F(a)$ is in J.

In particular, if all the valuations $\phi_\nu(a)$ are total, then the set $N_0(a)$ is empty for all a and so $N_0(a)$ cannot belong to J, and ψ is defined uniquely by J and Φ on the entire set A. Again, suppose that N is infinite, and that every $a \in A$ is in the domain of all but a finite number on the ϕ_ν. Suppose on the other hand that J includes the set of complements of finite subsets of N (the *Fréchet filter*). Then $N_0(a) \notin J$ for all a, and so ψ is defined uniquely by J and Φ in this case also. More generally, this will be true whenever $N_0(a) \notin J$ for all $a \in A$.

Now let M be any structure (relational system, as before), and let K be a set of sentences which are defined and hold in M. Let X be a typical element of K, e.g., 6.3, and let $H(X)$ be a set of Herbrand functors associated with X(e.g., χ, ψ, ζ, for 6.3). We associate distinct functors with the distinct elements of K and we write $H(K)$ for the set of all these functors. We write $M(D)$ for the structure M considered in conjunction with a particular determination D of functions on M corresponding to the functors of $H(K)$.

Let $\{M_\nu\}$ be a non-empty set of structures with index set $N = \{\nu\}$. Let K^* be a set of sentences such that every finite subset K' of K^* is defined and holds in some M_ν. Let K_ν be the set of all sentences of K^* which are defined and hold in M_ν, and let R_ν be the set of relations which occur in M_ν, and $R^* = \bigcup_\nu R_\nu$.

Introduce a set of distinct Herbrand functors $H(K^*)$ for the elements of K^* and consider specific determinations D_ν in M_ν for the functions corresponding to functors of $H(K_\nu) \subseteqq H(K^*)$. It is quite possible that the same structure appears for different ν and with different D_ν.

Now let C be a non-empty abstract set of the arbitrary cardinal number, $C = \{a_\mu\}$. Consider the set C^* of all formal expressions which are obtained by applying the functors of $H(K)$ repeatedly to the elements of C, e.g., $\psi(a_\mu)$, $\zeta(a_\mu, a_\nu)$, χ, $\zeta(\chi, \psi(a_\mu))$, etc. We proceed to define a structure M^* whose set of individual constants is C^* and whose set of relations is R^*.

Let h_ν be a mapping of C into the domain of individuals of M_ν, briefly, $h_\nu : C \to M_\nu$. Let C_ν be the set of elements of C^* which are obtained by applying to the elements of C only the functors which pertain to the sentences of K_ν. Then the mapping h_ν can be extended in a natural way to the domain C_ν. Thus, if $c_1, c_2 \in C_\nu$ have been mapped already and if the functor $\zeta(w, y)$ corresponds to a function ζ' in M_ν, then we define

$$h_\nu^*(\zeta(c_1, c_2)) = \zeta'(h_\nu^*(c_1), h_\nu^*(c_2)),$$

and this example will be sufficient to indicate the general procedure. The extended map h_ν^* is then defined on all of C_ν, $h_\nu^* : C_\nu \to M_\nu$.

Let A be the set of atomic sentences $a = R(c_1, \cdots, c_n)$, where $R \in R^*$ and $c_1, \cdots, c_n \in C^*$. Denote by A_ν the set of elements of A such that $R \in R_\nu$ and $c_1, \cdots, c_n \in C_\nu$. Then h_ν^* maps $c_1, \cdots, c_n$ on elements $c_1', \cdots, c_n'$ of M_ν. For any $a \in A_\nu$, put $\phi_\nu(a) = 0$ or $\phi_\nu(a) = 1$ according as $R(c_1', \cdots, c_n')$ does or does not hold in M_ν.

For any $X \in K_\nu$ (e.g., 6.3) consider the corresponding Herbrand form X' (e.g., 6.4). Let $K_\nu(C_\nu)$ be the set of all instances of such X' obtained by replacing the variables of X' by elements of C_ν, and let $K_\nu(C^*)$ be the set obtained similarly by substituting arbitrary elements of C^* for the variables of any X', with $X \in K_\nu$. Put $K(C^*) = \bigcup_\nu K_\nu(C^*)$.

For given ν, let A_ν' be any finite subset of A_ν. If we ignore the difference between formulae which are equivalent within the rules of the propositional calculus, then there exists only a finite number of elements of $K(C^*)$ which are built up entirely by means of atomic formulae from A_ν'. Denote the set of these formulae by K_ν'. If for every element X^* of K_ν' there exists an element of $K_\nu(C_\nu)$ which is propositionally equivalent to X^*, then we say that A_ν' is an *interior subset* of A_ν. We cannot exclude the possibility of finite subsets which are not interior. However, if B is any finite subset of A, then there exists a $\nu \in N$ such that B is an interior subset of A_ν. Indeed let K_0 be the subset of $K(C^*)$ whose elements are built up entirely by means of atomic formulae that belong to B. We select a finite subset K_0' of K_0 such that every element of K_0 is propositionally equivalent to some element of K_0'. Since K_0' is finite, there exists a finite subset K' of K^* such that all relations of K_0' appear in K' and all functors of K_0' pertain to sentences of K', and moreover such that every element X_0 of K_0' is an instance of an element of K'. More precisely, if C' is the subset of C^* whose elements are obtained by means of functors pertaining to K', then there exists an $X \in K'$ with Herbrand from X' such that X_0 is obtained by substituting elements of C' for the variables of X'. Also, by assumption, there exists an M_ν such that the sentences of K' are defined and hold in M_ν. Then $K' \subseteqq K_\nu$ and $B \subseteqq A_\nu$, and moreover $K_0' \subseteqq K_\nu(C_\nu)$. It follows that B is an interior subset of A_ν.

As mentioned above, R^* and C^* are to be the set of relations and the set of individual elements of the structure M^*, respectively. Thus, in order to define M^* we only have to assign truth values to the atomic sentences which are elements of A. We take the index set N^* as the set of ordered pairs $\{\nu\mu\}$, where $\nu \in N$ and the μ are supposed to enumerate the interior finite subsets $A_{\nu\mu}$ of A_ν.

For any $\nu\mu \in N^*$ we now define the partial valuation $\phi_{\nu\mu}$ of A with domain $A_{\nu\mu}$ by $\phi_{\nu\mu}(a) = \phi(a)$ for all $a \in A_{\nu\mu}$, where ϕ_ν was defined earlier on A_ν. Since every interior finite subset of A is identical with some $A_{\nu\mu}$ the conditions of Lemma 5.4 are satisfied. We conclude that there exists a total valuation ψ of A which coincides with some $\phi_{\nu\mu}$ on any given finite subset of A. We define that the atomic formula $a = R(c_1, \cdots, c_n)$ does or does not hold in M^* according as $\psi(a) = 0$ or $\psi(a) = 1$. This completes the construction of M^*. It depends on $\{M_\nu\}$, $\{D_\nu\}$, and on the choice of ψ.

Now let X be any element of K^*, X' its Herbrand form, and X_0 an instance of X' (obtained by substituting elements of C^* for the variables of X'). If we can show that, for given X, any X_0 so obtained holds in M, then X also must hold in M^*. Let B be the set of atomic formulae which occur in X_0.

By construction, $\psi|B = \phi_{\nu\mu}|B$ for some $\nu \in N$, $\nu\mu \in N^*$ so that $B = A_{\nu\mu} = D\phi_{\nu\mu}$. $A_{\nu\mu}$ is interior to A_ν, and so there exists an $X_0' \in K_\nu(C_\nu)$ which is propositionally equivalent to X_0 (i.e., whose equivalence to X_0 is a tautology of the propositional calculus) which becomes *true* under the valuation $\phi_{\nu\mu}|B = \phi_\nu|B$. Hence $\psi|B = \phi_{\nu\mu}|B$ also yields *true* for X_0. We conclude that X holds in M^*, and so M^* is a model of K^*. *This proves the principle of localization.*

Let $A_\nu^* = \bigcup_\nu A_{\nu\mu}$ for any $\nu \in N$. If we define $\phi^*|A_\nu^* = \phi_\nu|A_\nu^*$, we then have $\phi_\nu^*|A_{\nu\mu} = \phi_{\nu\mu}|A_\mu$. Nevertheless, it appears that we may not take $\{\phi_\nu^*\}$ as the set of partial valuations in the application of 5.4.

Generalizing the above construction, we now suppose that we are given $\{M_\nu\}$ with index set N and a set J on N such that for every finite subset K'

of a given set of sentences K^* and for every $J' \in J$ there exists a $\nu \in J'$ such that all sentences of K' are defined and held in M_ν. Define K_ν, R_ν, R^*, $H(K^*)$, $H(K_\nu)$, D_ν, C, C^*, h_ν, h_ν^*, A, A_ν, ϕ_ν, $K_\nu(C_\nu)$, $K_\nu(C^*)$, $K(C^*)$, and the notion of an interior subset of A_ν exactly as before. It can then be shown that if B is an arbitrary finite subset of A and $J' \in J$, then there exists a $\nu \in J$ such that B is an interior subset of A_ν. Define the elements J'' of a net J^* on N^* by $J'' = \{\nu\mu | \nu \in J'\}$ for all $J' \in J$. (It is not difficult to see that J^* is indeed a set.) Applying Valuation Lemma 5.3 with respect to J^*, we may conclude that there exists a total valuation ψ of A such that for every $J'' \in J^*$ and for every finite subset B of A there exists a $\phi_{\nu\mu}$ with $\nu\mu \in J''$ such that ψ coincides with $\phi_{\nu\mu}$ on $B = A_{\nu\mu}$. ψ defines a structure M^* as before and M^* is a model of K^*. The case treated earlier corresponds to $J = \{N\}$, $J^* = \{N^*\}$.

Suppose in particular that J is an ultrafilter on N and that the sentences of K^* are defined and hold in all M_ν. Let $N_T(a)$ be the set of all $\nu \in N$ such that $\phi_\nu(a) = 0$. Then $\psi(a) = 0$ or $\psi(a) = 1$ according as $N_T(a)$ does or does not belong to J. Indeed, for some $\nu \in N$, $\psi(a) = \phi_{\nu\mu}(a) = \phi_\nu(a)$, where $\nu \in J'$, $J' \in J$ having been specified in advance. In particular, if $J' = N_T(a)$ belongs to J, then we must have $\psi(a) = \phi_\nu(a) = 0$, while if $J' = N_F(a) = N - N_T(a)$ belongs to J, then $\psi(a) = 1$. Thus, in the case under consideration the construction of M^* does not require the introduction of N^* and does not involve any arbitrary choice in the determination of ψ.

Again, suppose that J is an ultrafilter but that the sentences of K are not necessarily defined in all M_ν. We then add to the sets $N_T(a)$ and $N_F(a)$ the set $N_0(a)$ which consists of all $\nu \in N$ such that a does not belong to A_ν, and hence such that $\phi_\nu(a)$ is not defined. If then $N_0(a) \notin J$ for all a, ψ is still defined uniquely as before. This will be the case, for example, if every sentence of K is defined and holds in M_ν for all but a finite number of ν, while J includes the complements of the finite subsets of N. (Note that in that case $\phi_\nu(a)$ also is defined for all but a finite number of ν.)

We recall that our calculus was supposed to contain a relation of equality $E(x, y)$ with the usual properties postulated implicitly. Let K_E be a set of sentences which states that E is a relation of equivalence with substitutivity for all relations which occur in the M_ν. Since all these sentences may be formulated without existential quantifiers, we may suppose that K_E is so formulated. If K_E is not included in K^* from the outset, we may then add it to K^* without enlarging C^* or R^*. It follows that M satisfies the sentences of K_E.

We have defined the individual elements a of M^* formally by the iteration of functors on an abstract set. However, it will now be shown that we may replace these c by functions $f(x)$, defined on subsets Df of N such that $f(\nu) \in M_\nu$. Let F be the set of all such functions, let $c \in C^*$ and let $D(c)$ be the set of $\nu \in N$ such that $c \in C_\nu$. $D(c)$ is not empty and h_ν^* is defined for c if $\nu \in D(c)$. Now map c on the function $f \in F$ whose domain is $Df = D(c)$ and whose value for $\nu \in Df$ is $f(\nu) = h_\nu^*(c)$. The mapping is thus defined for all $c \in C^*$. Let F^* be the image of C^*.

If the sentences of K are defined in all M_ν, then $Df = N$ for all $f \in F^*$. We may then ensure $F^* = F$ simply by taking $C = F$ and by defining $h_\nu(c) = f(\nu)$ for $c = f(\nu)$ (i.e., h_ν is the natural mapping of f into its value at ν). It is now not difficult to verify that if J is an ultrafilter, then M^* coincides with the direct product of the M_ν reduced with respect to J. In this way we prove 6.2.

To sum up, we have shown that the reduced direct product construction may be regarded as a special case of a procedure (which might be called a *limit construction*) which leads to a proof of the principle of localization at the same time. Our procedure emphasizes the role played by valuations in all these constructions.

We shall not enter into a discusssion of the important results of T. Frayne, H. J. Keisler, and S. B. Kochen relating elementary equivalence to ultrapowers. Generally speaking we may say that just as in other branches of Mathematics (e.g., Group theory, Normed algebras) representations are of great importance, so in our present subject the detailed study of the various constructions which lead to models of a given consistent set of sentences may be expected to achieve increasing prominence.

7. Some Notions and Results of Meta-algebra

At the beginning of this lecture, I mentioned the natural link that exists between Model theory and Algebra. I then discussed Malcev's work, which depends on a direct application of (what is now called) Model theory to a concrete algebraic situation. Numerous applications of this kind have been made since. However, there are a number of questions concerning Algebra which by their very nature go beyond the classical frame and must be accommodated within a meta-theory. Of this type is the problem of bringing the different notions which lead to the formation of quotient structures (normal subgroups, ideals) under one heading, and this question can in fact be tackled via Model theory (see [17]). Another problem of this kind is how to bring the notions of algebraically closed fields and of real closed fields, which are intuitively analogous, under a common heading. We now turn to the consideration of this question.

The algebraically closed fields occupy a special position in commutative field theory. Thus, in order to solve an algebraic problem whose parameters belong to a field M, there is no need to go beyond the algebraic closure of M. Similarly, given an ordered field M, there is, for many purposes, no need to go beyond the real closure of the field. Moreover, instead of considering the algebraic, or real, closure of M, we may equally well consider any other algebraically (or real-) closed extension of M.

In order to bring these two notions under a single heading, let K be a set of axioms for the concept of a commutative field of specified characteristic (formulated in terms of the relations of equality, addition, and multiplication, and of the individual constants 0 and 1) on the one hand, or a set of axioms for the concept of an ordered field (with the inclusion of a relation of order) on the other. Let K' be a set of axioms for the concept of an algebraically closed field in the former case, or for the concept of a real-closed field if the latter case is under consideration. It is then natural (and not difficult) to ensure that the following conditions are satisfied.

7.1. The axioms of K are in prenex normal form and of class AE (i.e., they do not contain any existential quantifiers followed by universal quantifiers).

7.2. $K' \supseteqq K$ and K' does not contain any extralogical constants (i.e., relations or individual constants) which are not already contained in K — that is to say, in the terminology introduced at the beginning of this lecture K' is *within the* vocabulary of K; K' is *model-consistent* relative to K, that is to say, every model of K can be embedded in a model of K'; and K' is model-complete relative to K. That is to say, if M is a model of K, and M_1 and M_2 are models of K' which are extensions of M, while X is any sentence which is defined in M, then either X holds in both M_1 and M_2 or $\sim X$ holds in both M_1 and M_2.

It can be shown (compare [19, Theorem 2.8]) that if two sets of sentences $K' = K'_1$ and $K' = K'_2$ satisfy 7.2 relative to a given K, then they determine the same variety (arithmetical class) of models. On the other hand it is also known that there exist sets of sentences K which possess no extensions at all that satisfy 7.2. This is the case, for instance, if K is the set of all sentences formulated (in the Lower predicate calculus, as before) in terms of quality, addition, and multiplication, and which hold in the field of rational numbers. Accordingly, it is natural to try and find a test for a given K to possess an extension K' that satisfies 7.2. Such a test is indeed available [20] if K satisfies 7.1. To formulate it, we require the two following definitions.

A *primitive predicate* $Q(z_1, \cdots, z_k)$ is an existential predicate (a predicate in prenex normal form with existential quantifiers only, if any) whose matrix consists of a conjunction of atomic sentences and (or) of negations of atomic sentences.

Let K be a set of sentences and let $Q(z_1, \cdots, z_k)$ be a predicate within the vocabulary of K. We say that the predicate $Q'(z_1, \cdots, z_k)$ is *a test for* Q if Q' is an existential predicate within the vocabulary of K such that for every model M of K, and elements $a_1, \cdots, a_k$ of M, $Q'(a_1, \cdots, a_k)$ holds in M if and only if $Q(a_1, \cdots, a_k)$ holds in some model M' of K which is an extension of M.

With these definitions, we have

THEOREM 7.3. *Let K be a non-empty and consistent set of sentences of class AE. In order that there exists an extension K' of K which contains no additional relations or individual constants, such that K' is model-consistent and model-complete relative to K, it is necessary and sufficient that every primitive predicate $Q(z_1, \cdots, z_k)$ within the vocabulary of K possess a test $Q'(z_1, \cdots, z_k)$.*

It has been proved by various methods that if K is a set of axioms for the concept of a field of given characteristic, or of an ordered field, then Theorem

7.3 applies. K' then is precisely a set of axioms for the concept of an algebraically closed field of the given characteristic, or of a real-closed field. In the former case, a primitive predicate asserts the satisfiability of a particular system of equations and "inequations" (i.e., inequalities in the sense of negations of equations). Such a system can be replaced easily by an equivalent set involving equations only and the existence of *a test* is then implied by the existence of a system of resultants. However, the examples given so far are not the only ones which satisfy the assumptions and conclusions of the theorem. Using A. Seidenberg's elimination theory for Differential Algebra [22] it can in fact be shown [20] that if K is a set of axioms for the concept of a differential field of characteristic 0, then it satisfies the conditions of the theorem, and hence possesses an extension K' as indicated. On the other hand it does not appear to be possible, in the general circumstances envisaged here, to assign to every model M of K a model M' of K' which is an extension of M and which occupies a distinguished position comparable to that of the algebraic closure (or of *the* smallest real-closed extension) in the examples considered earlier.

This brings me to the end of my lecture. I have discussed some, but not all, important aspects of contemporary Model theory. Thus, I have not mentioned the subject of non-standard models, especially of arithmetic. Some relevant results have been obtained already in this field but there is no doubt that it will continue to grow vigorously. Nor was I able to enter into a discussion of infinite languages, a topic which has been developed in recent years by A. Tarski and his co-workers and in which a spectacular success was scored not long ago. Fortunately, Professor Tarski is here to tell you about it himself.

References

[1] Beth, E. W. On Padoa's method in the theory of definition, *Proceedings of the Royal Academy of Science of the Netherlands*, ser. A, Vol. 56 (1953), pp. 330–339.

[2] Craig, W. Three uses of the Herbrand-Gentzen theorem in relating Model theory and Proof theory, *Journal of Symbolic Logic*, Vol. 22 (1957), pp. 269–285.

[3] Frayne, T. E., D. S. Scott, and A. Tarski. Reduced products, *Notices of the American Mathematical Society*, Vol. 5 (1958), pp. 673–674.

[4] Gillman, L. and M. Jerison. *Rings of Continuous Functions*, Princeton, Van Nostrand, 1960, ix+300 pp.

[5] Henkin, L. Some interconnections between Modern algebra and Mathematical logic, *Transactions of the American Mathematical Society*, Vol. 74 (1953), pp. 410–427.

[6] Hewitt, E. Rings of real-valued continuous functions, I, *Transactions of the American Mathematical Society*, Vol. 64 (1948), pp. 54–99.

[7] Keisler, H. J. Isomorphism of ultraproducts, *Notices of the American Mathematical Society*, Vol. 7 (1960), pp. 70–71.

[8] Kochen, S. B. Ultraproducts in the theory of models, to be published in the *Annals of Mathematics*.

[9] Łoś, J. On the extending of models, I, *Fundamenta Mathematicae*, Vol. 42 (1955), pp. 38–54.

[10] Łoś, J. Quelques remarques, théorèmes et problèmes sur les classes définissables d'algèbres, *Symposium on the mathematical interpretation of formal systems*, Amsterdam (1954, published 1955), pp. 98–113.

[11] Lyndon, R. C. Properties preserved under algebraic constructions, *Bulletin of the American Mathematical Society*, Vol. 65 (1959), pp. 143–299.

[12] Lyndon, R. C. Properties preserved under homomorphism, *Pacific Journal of Mathematics*, Vol. 9 (1959), pp. 153–154.

[13] Malcev, A. I. On a general method for obtaining local theorems in group theory (in Russian), *Reports of the Institute of Education of Ivanovo, Mathematical-Physical Faculty*, Vol. 1 (1941), pp. 3–9.

[14] Neumann, B. H. An embedding theorem for algebraic systems, *Proceedings of the London Mathematical Society*, ser. 3, Vol. 4 (1954), pp. 138–153.

[15] Rabin, M. O. Arithmetical extensions with prescribed cardinality, *Proceedings of the Royal Academy of the Netherlands*, ser. A, Vol. 62 (1959), 439–446.

[16] Rado, R. Axiomatic treatment of rank in infinite sets, *Canadian Journal of Mathematics*, Vol. 1 (1949), pp. 337–343.

[17] Robinson, A. Théorie métamathématique des idéaux, Paris, Gauthier Villars, 1955.

[18] Robinson, A. Note on a problem of Henkin, *Journal of Symbolic Logic*, Vol. 21 (1956), pp. 33–35.

[19] Robinson, A. Some problems of definability in the lower predicate calculus, *Fundamenta Mathematicae*, Vol. 44 (1957), pp. 309–329.

[20] Robinson, A. On the concept of a differentially closed field, *Bulletin of the Research Council of Israel, Section F*, Vol. 8 (1959), pp. 113–128.

[21] Robinson, A. On the construction of models, to be published in the *A. Fraenkel anniversary volume*.

[22] Seidenberg, A. An elimination theory for differential algebra, *University of California Publication in Mathematics*, new series, Vol. 3 (1956), pp. 31–66.

[23] Skolem, T. Über die Nicht-charakterisierbarkeit der Zahlenreihe mittels endlicher oder abzählbar unendlich vieler Aussagen mit ausschliesslich Zahlenvariablen, *Fundamenta Mathematicae*, Vol. 23 (1943), pp. 150–161.

[24] Tarski, A. Contributions to the theory of model, I, II, *Proceedings of the Royal Academy of Science of the Netherlands*, ser. A., Vol. 57 (1954), pp. 572–581, 582–588.

Symposium on Foundations of Set Theory

SOME APPLICATIONS OF THE THEORY OF MODELS TO SET THEORY

H. JEROME KEISLER
University of California, Berkeley, California, U.S.A.

Introduction

In Chapter 14 [4], Tarski discusses certain classes of cardinal numbers, such as the class of *strongly incompact cardinals* and the class of cardinals α satisfying the following property P_0: *every α-complete prime ideal in the set algebra of all subsets of α is a principal ideal.* The class of strongly incompact cardinals is defined in [4] in a metamathematical way involving the infinite logics $\boldsymbol{L}_\alpha$, although when α is inaccessible an equivalent condition involving Boolean algebras is known (cf. the remarks in [4] following Theorem 4). It is stated in [4] that the class of cardinals satisfying P_0 includes the class of strongly incompact cardinals. It has been known for some time that the cardinal ω does not satisfy P_0, and that every accessible cardinal does satisfy P_0. Moreover, Hanf (cf. [2]) has recently proved (as a solution of a problem proposed by Tarski) that many inaccessible cardinals are strongly incompact, and Tarski [4] applies this metamathematical result of Hanf to obtain several mathematical conclusions, such as the unexpected result that many inaccessible cardinals satisfy P_0.

In the first section of this article we shall present a relatively simple "elementary" proof of the fact, stated in [4], that every inaccessible cardinal Θ_ξ such that $0 < \xi < \Theta_\xi$ satisfies P_0. This proof is based on the mathematical construction of *ultrapower,* as defined by Frayne, Scott, and Tarski in [1]. Similar arguments can be carried out to show that many other cardinals satisfy P_0.

Although our proof is formally mathematical, we shall see in Section 2 that, as is often the case with arguments involving ultrapowers, it is motivated by some general metamathematical considerations. These considerations lead to a model-theoretic necessary and sufficient condition for a cardinal α to satisfy P_0 (Theorem 2). Roughly speaking, the condition is that there is a relational system whose set of elements is α and which can be characterized up to isomorphism by a set of sentences of $\boldsymbol{L}_\alpha$. This is a useful condition because it has proved to be easy to verify in special cases where P_0 has been very difficult to verify directly. The sufficiency half of the proof again uses the ultrapower construction, and in fact the argument is a generalization of our proof that Θ_ξ satisfies P_0 whenever $0 < \xi < \Theta_\xi$.

For purposes of comparison we shall state a stronger condition along the same lines which is necessary and sufficient for an inaccessible cardinal α to be strongly incompact (Theorem 3).

The proofs of the results stated in Section 2 are reserved for a future publication.

We refer the reader to [4] for all conventions of notation and terminology.

1. Special Results

We shall begin by recalling the definition of the notion of ultrapower.

Let $\mathfrak{A} = \langle A, R \rangle$ be any relational system composed of a set A and a binary relation R on A. Let X be any set. We shall use the notation $\mathfrak{S}(X)$ to denote the set algebra composed of all subsets of X. Let P be a prime ideal in $\mathfrak{S}(X)$.

If f, g are two functions on X into A, i.e., $f, g \in A^X$, we say $f \equiv_P g$ if and only if $\{x \in X | f(x) = g(x)\} \notin P$.

If, in analogy with measure theory, we think of the elements of P as "small" sets, then $f \equiv_P g$ may be thought of as saying that "$f = g$ almost everywhere". The relation $\equiv_P$ is easily seen to be an equivalence relation on A^X, and the equivalence class of a function f is denoted by $f/P = \{g \in A^X | f \equiv_P g\}$. The set of all these equivalence classes is denoted by $A^X/P = \{f/P | f \in A^X\}$. Finally, we define the relation R_P on A^X/P by writing $R_P(f/P, g/P)$ if and only if $\{x \in X | R(f(x), g(x))\} \notin P$. We now define the ultrapower $\mathfrak{A}^X/P$ as the relational system $\langle A^X/P, R_P \rangle$.

THEOREM 1. *If* $0 < \xi < \Theta_\xi$, *then* Θ_ξ *satisfies* P_0.

The original proof of this result consisted of two parts: in the first part it was shown that Θ_ξ is strongly incompact for $0 < \xi < \Theta_\xi$, and in the second part it was shown that strong incompactness implies P_0. The second part had been known to Tarski for a few years. As was mentioned in the Introduction, the first part was recently obtained by Hanf. The proof of Hanf is outlined in [4]. As indicated in [4], one of several ways to prove the second part involves forming an ultraproduct [1] of a collection of α different set-theoretic models.

We shall now give a direct proof of Theorem 1. This proof not only by-

[1]The *ultraproduct* construction, which is introduced in [1], is defined in a similar way as the ultrapower except that it is applied to a family of possibly different relational systems indexed by the set X.

passes any consideration of strong incompactness, but also provides two further simplifications. First, instead of having to deal with transitive models and natural models of set theory, we employ much simpler objects, namely, well-ordered sets. Second, instead of having to form an ultraproduct of α different set-theoretic models, we need only form an ultrapower of a single well-ordered set.

PROOF OF THEOREM 1. Suppose $0 < \xi < \Phi_\xi$ but Φ_ξ does not satisfy P_0. Then there is a Θ_ξ-complete non-principal prime ideal P in $\mathfrak{S}(\Theta_\xi)$. Let $\mathfrak{A}$ be the relational system $\langle \Theta_\xi, < \rangle$, where $<$ is the usual well-ordering of the ordinals less than Θ_ξ. Form the ultrapower $\mathfrak{A}^{\Theta_\xi}/P = \langle \Theta_\xi{}^{\Theta_\xi}/P, <_P \rangle$.

We shall first show that $<_P$ well-orders $\Theta_\xi{}^{\Theta_\xi}/P$. It is at this point that we need the fact that $0 < \xi$, and thus $\omega < \Theta_\xi$. First, $<_P$ is transitive, for if $(f/P) <_P (g/P) <_P (h/P)$, then $\{x \in X \mid f(x) < h(x)\} \notin P$, and hence $(f/P) <_P (h/P)$. Second, $<_P$ is a simple ordering, for exactly one of the sets $\{x \in X \mid f(x) < g(x)\}$, $\{x \in X \mid f(x) = g(x)\}$, $\{x \in X \mid f(x) > g(x)\}$ is not in the prime ideal P. Finally, there can be no infinite descending sequence $\cdots <_P (f_2/P) <_P (f_1/P) <_P (f_0/P)$, for if we had such a sequence, then $\{x \in X \mid f_{n+1}(x) < f_n(x)\} \notin P$ for each $n < \omega$, and since P is Θ_ξ-complete and *a fortiori* ω_1-complete, $\bigcap_{n<\omega} \{x \in X \mid f_{n+1}(x) < f_n(x)\}$ would not be in P and would be non-empty, which would mean that $\langle \Theta_\xi, < \rangle$ had an infinite descending sequence. This verifies that we have a well-ordering.

Since $\mathfrak{A}^{\Theta_\xi}/P$ is a well-ordered set, there is a unique ordinal μ for which $\mathfrak{A}^{\Theta_\xi}/P$ is isomorphic to $\langle \mu, < \rangle$. Let ϕ be the unique isomorphism of $\mathfrak{A}^{\Theta_\xi}/P$ onto $\langle \mu, < \rangle$.

We now show that $\Theta_\xi < \mu$. For any two constant functions $f, g \in \Theta_\xi{}^{\Theta_\xi}$, we have $f/P \neq g/P$, because $f(x) \neq g(x)$ for all $x \in X$. On the other hand, the identity function $i \in \Theta_\xi{}^{\Theta_\xi}$ exceeds any constant function f except on a set of fewer than Θ_ξ elements of Θ_ξ. Since P is non-principal and prime, it contains all one-element sets, and by Θ_ξ-completeness of P, every set of fewer than Θ_ξ elements of Θ_ξ belongs to P. Therefore $(f/P) <_P (i/P)$ for every constant f. This means that the ordinal $\phi(i/P)$ has at least Θ_ξ distinct elements less than it. No element of Θ_ξ can have Θ_ξ elements less than it, so $\Theta_\xi < \mu$. Thus $\phi(t/P) = \Theta_\xi$ for some $t \in \Theta_\xi{}^{\Theta_\xi}$.

We shall complete our proof by arriving at a contradiction. The following sets

$$X_0 = \{x \in \Theta_\xi \mid t(x) = 0\},$$
$$X_1 = \{x \in \Theta_\xi \mid t(x) \text{ is not a cardinal}\},$$
$$X_2 = \{x \in \Theta_\xi \mid t(x) \text{ is a singular cardinal}\},$$
$$X_3 = \{x \in \Theta_\xi \mid t(x) \text{ is a regular accessible cardinal}\},$$
$$Y_\zeta = \{x \in \Theta_\xi \mid t(x) = \Theta_\zeta\} \text{ for each } \zeta < \xi,$$

form a partition of Θ_ξ into fewer than Θ_ξ classes. Therefore exactly one of these partition classes is not a member of P.

The proof now breaks down into cases. If $X_0 \notin P$, then $\phi(t/P)$ is the smallest ordinal, which gives us the false conclusion that $\Theta_\xi = 0$. Similarly if $Y_\zeta \notin P$ for some $\zeta < \xi$, then there would only be Θ_ζ ordinals $< \Theta_\xi$, so Θ_ξ would equal Θ_ζ.

Now suppose $X_1 \cup X_2 \notin P$. For each ordinal $\gamma < \Theta_\xi$ which either is not a cardinal or is a singular cardinal, we can choose $\nu_\gamma < \gamma$ and a function F_γ on ν_γ into γ such that for every $\alpha < \gamma$ there exists $\beta < \nu_\gamma$ with $\alpha \leqq F_\gamma(\beta)$. Let $\nu = \phi(n/P)$, where n is a function such that $n(x) = \nu_{t(x)}$ for all $x \in X_1 \cup X_2$; since $X_1 \cup X_2 \notin P$, we have $\nu < \Theta_\xi$. Let F be the function of ν into Θ_ξ such that whenever $\phi(f/P) < \nu$, $F(\phi(f/P)) = \phi(g/P)$, where g is a function such that $g(x) = F_{t(x)}(f(x))$ for every $x \in X_1 \cup X_2$ such that $f(x) < \nu_{t(x)}$. If $\alpha < \Theta_\xi$, there exists $\beta < \nu$ such that $\alpha \leqq F(\beta)$; namely, if $\alpha = \phi(a/P)$, then $\beta = \phi(b/P)$, where b is a function such that $b(x) < \nu_{t(x)}$ and $a(x) \leqq F_{t(x)}$ $(b(x))$ whenever $x \in X_1 \cup X_2$ and $a(x) < t(x)$. But the existence of such a function F means that either Θ_ξ is not a cardinal or Θ_ξ is a singular cardinal, which is impossible.

The only remaining case is $X_3 \notin P$. For each regular accessible cardinal $\gamma < \Theta_\xi$, we can choose $\psi_\gamma < \gamma$ such that $\gamma \leqq 2^{\psi_\gamma}$. Hence for each $\alpha < \gamma$ we can associate a subset $G_\gamma(\alpha) \subseteqq \psi_\gamma$ such that if α, $\beta < \gamma$ and $\alpha \neq \beta$, $G_\gamma(\alpha) \neq G_\gamma(\beta)$. Let $\psi = \phi(p/P)$, where p is a function such that $p(x) = \psi_{t(x)}$ for all $x \in X_3$; since $X_3 \notin P$, $\psi < \Theta_\xi$. For each $\phi(f/P) < \Theta_\xi$ let $G(\phi(f/P))$ be the set of all $\phi(g/P) < \mu$ such that $g(x) \in G_{t(x)}(f(x))$ whenever $f(x) < t(x)$ and $x \in X_3$; since $X_3 \cap \{x \in \Theta_\xi | f(x) < t(x)\} \notin P$, it follows that $G(\phi(f/P)) \subseteqq \psi$. If α, $\beta < \Theta_\xi$ and $\alpha \neq \beta$, then $G(\alpha) \neq G(\beta)$; namely, if $\alpha = \phi(a/P)$ and $\beta = \phi(b/P)$, and f is a function such that $f(x)$ lies in the symmetric difference of $G_{t(x)}(a(x))$ and $G_{t(x)}(b(x))$ whenever $x \in X_3$, $a(x) < t(x)$, $b(x) < t(x)$, and $a(x) \neq b(x)$, then $\phi(f/P)$ is in the symmetric difference of $G(\alpha)$ and $G(\beta)$. But the existence of such a function G shows that $\Theta_\xi \leqq 2^\psi$, which contradicts the inaccessibility of Θ_ξ.

We have arrived at a contradiction in every case, and thus have completed the proof of Theorem 1.

An argument similar to the one we have just carried out will also work for many other cardinals. For example, all the cardinals which have been stated in [4] to satisfy P_0 can also be shown by our methods to satisfy P_0. Sometimes it is necessary to employ relational systems which have relations other than the order relation specified.

2. Metamathematical Results

Let us now analyze the proof just given from a general standpoint. Our method of proving that a cardinal α satisfies P_0 may be broken down into four steps in the following way.

I. Assume that $\mathfrak{S}(\alpha)$ has a non-principal α-complete prime ideal P.

II. Show that the ultrapower $\mathfrak{A}^\alpha/P$ of a certain relational system $\mathfrak{A}$ is not isomorphic to $\mathfrak{A}$.

III. Show that certain properties possessed by $\mathfrak{A}$ carry over to $\mathfrak{A}^\alpha/P$.

IV. Show that, contrary to II, these properties force $\mathfrak{A}^\alpha/P$ to be isomorphic to $\mathfrak{A}$.

Step I simply assumes that α does not satisfy P_0. Step II can be carried out for any α, provided that the relational system $\mathfrak{A}$ has at least α elements, and that the relations of $\mathfrak{A}$ are sufficient to insure that any isomorphism on $\mathfrak{A}$ to $\mathfrak{A}^\alpha/P$ must map each element $a \in A$ into the equivalence class of the constant function at a. This is the only step which depends on the fact that P is non-principal.

In connection with step III, we wish to have a general criterion for a property of $\mathfrak{A}$ to be preserved under passing to the ultrapower $\mathfrak{A}^\alpha/P$. Such a criterion can best be described with the aid of metamathematical notions.

Let α be a fixed regular cardinal. A relational system $\mathfrak{A} = \langle A, R_\beta\rangle_{\beta<\beta_0}$ consists of a set A and a sequence of relations R_β on A, indexed by the ordinal β_0, and each with fewer than α argument places. A relational system $\mathfrak{B} = \langle B, S_\gamma\rangle_{\gamma<\gamma_0}$ is *similar* to $\mathfrak{A}$ if $\beta_0 = \gamma_0$ and for each $\beta < \beta_0$, R_β and S_β have the same number of argument places. By the logic $\boldsymbol{L}_\alpha{}^{(\mathfrak{A})}$ corresponding to $\mathfrak{A}$ we mean a logical system of the form $\boldsymbol{L}_\alpha$ described in [4], which has as non-logical constants relation symbols corresponding to, and having the same number of argument places as, each relation R_β of $\mathfrak{A}$. A relational system $\mathfrak{B}$ is said to be *$\boldsymbol{L}_\alpha$-equivalent* to $\mathfrak{A}$ if $\mathfrak{B}$ is similar to $\mathfrak{A}$ and if every sentence of $\boldsymbol{L}_\alpha{}^{(\mathfrak{A})}$ which holds in $\mathfrak{A}$ also holds in $\mathfrak{B}$.

A criterion for properties preserved by ultrapowers is suggested by the following theorem essentially due to Loś (cf. [3]): *if P is a prime ideal in $\mathfrak{S}(\omega)$, then $\mathfrak{A}^\omega/P$ is $\boldsymbol{L}_\omega$-equivalent to $\mathfrak{A}$.* This theorem can be generalized without difficulty to obtain the following: *if P is an α-complete prime ideal in $\mathfrak{S}(\alpha)$, then $\mathfrak{A}^\alpha/P$ is $\boldsymbol{L}_\alpha$-equivalent to $\mathfrak{A}$.* In other words, any property expressible as a sentence in $\boldsymbol{L}_\alpha{}^{(\mathfrak{A})}$ is preserved by passing from $\mathfrak{A}$ to $\mathfrak{A}^\alpha/P$. It follows that steps III and IV can be carried out whenever we can find a relational system $\mathfrak{A}$ such that any relational system which is $\boldsymbol{L}_\alpha$-equivalent to $\mathfrak{A}$ must be isomorphic to $\mathfrak{A}$.

It is instructive at this point to take a look at our proof for the special case $\alpha = \Theta_\xi$ in the light of our present discussion. In that proof we showed that the following two properties are preserved by the ultraproduct construction: "$<$ is a well-ordering relation", and "every element is either $= 0$, $= \Theta_\zeta$ for some $\zeta < \xi$, not a cardinal, a singular cardinal, or an accessible cardinal". The well-ordering property can easily be expressed in $\boldsymbol{L}_{\Theta_\xi}$ in terms of the relation $<$. However, in order to express the second property, two additional ternary relations are needed. Let $\phi(x, y)$ be the following formula of $\boldsymbol{L}_{\Theta_\xi}$:

$$\forall w \exists z \forall t[(F(x, w, t) \leftrightarrow t = z \wedge w < y) \wedge z < x].$$

Thus $\phi(x, y)$ states that $F(x)$ is a function mapping y into x. As indicated in [4], for each $\alpha < \Theta_\xi$ we can find a formula $\phi_\beta(x)$ in $\boldsymbol{L}_{\Theta_\xi}$ in terms of $<$ which is true exactly when $x = \beta$. The second property may now be expressed by saying *there exist relations* F, R *such that*:

$$\forall x[\phi_0(x) \vee (\bigvee_{\zeta<\xi}\phi_{\theta_\zeta}(x)) \vee \exists y[y < x \wedge \phi(x, y)] \wedge$$
$$\forall t \exists w, z[t < x \to (t < z \vee t = z) \wedge F(x, w, z)]] \vee$$
$$\exists y[y < x \wedge \forall z, w \exists u[w < z \wedge z < x \to u < \dot{y} \wedge \neg (R(x, z, u) \leftrightarrow R(x, w, u))]].$$

In order to relate our proof of Section 1 to the present context, we should think of our proof as dealing not with the relational system $\langle \Theta_\xi, < \rangle$ but with the relational system $\mathfrak{A} = \langle \Theta_\xi, <, F, R \rangle$. The relations F, R were actually introduced informally in the process of our proof, and were extended to the ultrapower in the natural way. With this choice of $\mathfrak{A}$, the two properties in question are expressible as sentences of $\boldsymbol{L}_{\theta_\xi}{}^{(\mathfrak{A})}$. Moreover, these two sentences, together with the "diagrams" of the relations F and R, are sufficient to ensure that the ultrapower be isomorphic to $\mathfrak{A}$, and thus step IV can be carried out.

As the above discussion suggests, it is generally easier to carry out steps III and IV when $\mathfrak{A}$ has more relations. We are thus motivated to consider the particular relational system $\mathfrak{A}_\alpha$ composed of the set α and *every* relation on α with fewer than α argument places. We can show by our argument that a sufficient condition for α to satisfy P_0 is that $\boldsymbol{L}_\alpha$-equivalence with $\mathfrak{A}_\alpha$ implies isomorphism with $\mathfrak{A}_\alpha$.

In fact, we can say even more. Let $\mathfrak{A}'_\alpha$ be the relational system composed of the set α and every unary relation (i.e., subset) of α. We then actually have the following theorem.

THEOREM 2. *The following three conditions on the regular cardinal* α *are equivalent.*

(i) α *satisfies* P_0.

(ii) *Every relational system which is* $\boldsymbol{L}_\alpha$*-equivalent to* $\mathfrak{A}_\alpha$ *must be isomorphic to* $\mathfrak{A}_\alpha$.

(iii) *Every relational system which is* $\boldsymbol{L}_\alpha$*-equivalent to* $\mathfrak{A}'_\alpha$ *must be isomorphic to* $\mathfrak{A}'_\alpha$.

We have already indicated the proof of the implication from (ii) to (i), and the implication from (iii) to (ii) is easily verified. The proof of the implication from (i) to (iii) was found jointly by Azriel Levy and the author.

Theorem 2 gives us a model-theoretic characterization which adds to our insight as to the nature of the property P_0. The condition of strong incompactness given in [4] is a sufficient condition for P_0 which has proved to be easily verified in special cases. However, condition (ii) of Theorem 2 is an equally easily verified sufficient condition for P_0 which is a necessary condition as well, and is therefore of particular interest.

The equivalence of (ii) and (iii) of Theorem 2 is a model-theoretic result which we have proved indirectly by way of the condition P_0. For the special case $\alpha = \Theta_\xi$, where $0 < \xi < \Theta_\xi$, our discussion has shown that we can easily give a set of sentences of $\boldsymbol{L}_\alpha^{(\mathfrak{A}_\alpha)}$ which characterizes $\mathfrak{A}_\alpha$ up to isomorphism. By Theorem 2 it follows that we can also do the same thing for $\mathfrak{A}'_\alpha$.

We shall now state two characterizations of strongly incompact inaccessible cardinals which are closely related to the conditions (ii) and (iii) of Theorem 2. An element $a \in A$ is said to be *α-definable* in the relational system $\mathfrak{A}$ if there is a formula $\phi(v_0)$ of $L_\alpha^{(\mathfrak{A})}$ whose only free variable is v_0 and which is satisfied in $\mathfrak{A}$ by the element $x \in A$ if and only if $x = a$. It is obvious that in each of the special relational systems $\mathfrak{A}_\alpha$ and $\mathfrak{A}'_\alpha$, every element of α is α-definable.

THEOREM 3. *The following three conditions on the inaccessible cardinal* α *are equivalent.*

(*i**) α *is strongly incompact.*

(ii*) *There exists a relational system* $\mathfrak{A}$ *composed of the set* α *and an* α*-termed sequence of relations on* α *such that every relational system* $\boldsymbol{L}_\alpha$*-equivalent to* $\mathfrak{A}$ *is isomorphic to* $\mathfrak{A}$ *and every element of* α *is* α*-definable in* $\mathfrak{A}$.

(iii*) *There exists a relational system* $\mathfrak{A}'$ *composed of the set* α *and an* α*-termed sequence of unary relations on* α *such that every relational system* $\boldsymbol{L}_\alpha$*-equivalent to* $\mathfrak{A}'$ *is isomorphic to* $\mathfrak{A}'$ *and every element of* α *is* α*-definable in* $\mathfrak{A}'$.

The implications from (iii*) to (ii*) and from (ii*) to (i*) are easily verified. The proof that (i*) implies (iii*) is also in part jointly due to Azriel Lévy and the author.

In case α is a regular accessible cardinal, we can prove that conditions (ii*) and (iii*) are always satisfied, but it is not known whether α is strongly incompact unless some additional hypothesis, such as the generalized continuum hypothesis, is made.

Theorems 2 and 3 provide us with closely parallel model-theoretic characterizations of the property P_0 and of strong incompactness, and should help us to understand the relationship between these two properties of cardinal numbers.

REFERENCES

[1] FRAYNE, T., D. SCOTT, and A. TARSKI, Reduced Products. *American Mathematical Society Notices*, Vol. 5 (1958), pp. 673–74, abstract 550–7.

[2] HANF, W. P. Models of languages with infinitely long expressions. *International Congress for Logic, Methodology and Philosophy of Science, Abstracts of Contributed Papers*. Stanford University, 1960 (mimeographed), p. 24.

[3] Łoś, J. Quelques remarques, théorèmes et problèmes sur les classes définissables d'algèbres. In Skolem, *et al.*, *Mathematical Interpretations of Formal Systems*, p. 98. Amsterdam, North-Holland Publishing Co., 1955, viii+113 pp.

[4] TARSKI, A. Some problems and results relevant to the foundations of set theory. This volume, pp. 126–36.

ON THE PRINCIPLES OF REFLECTION IN AXIOMATIC SET THEORY

AZRIEL LÉVY

University of California, Berkeley, California, U.S.A.

The aim of the present paper is to discuss the principles of reflection of axiomatic set theory which were introduced in [2] and studied further in [3]. Only those aspects of the subject which are not mentioned in [2] and [3] will be carried out in detail.

We deal with set theory formalized in the first-order predicate calculus with equality and with the binary predicate symbol ε as its only non-logical constant. Let **S** be the set theory consisting of the axioms of extensionality, pairing, union-set, power-set and the axiom schemata of subsets and foundation. Let **ZF** be the set theory obtained from **S** by addition of the axiom of infinity and the axiom schema of replacement. All the theorems in this paper are theorems in respective axiomatic set theories. The theory in which the theorem is proved will be explicitly indicated for each numbered theorem. For theorems mentioned in the discussion without being numbered the corresponding theory will not be mentioned if it is clear which one it should be.

Let $L(\alpha)$ be a formula asserting that α is a limit number. Let $R(\alpha)$ be a term defined recursively by $R(\alpha) = \cup_{\beta<\alpha} P(R(\beta))$, where $P(x)$ denotes the power set of x. Here we use the theorem schema of **S** on definitions by recursion, which asserts that a term $F(\alpha)$ can be defined by recursion so that $F(\alpha)$ satisfies the recursive condition if α is such that there is a set containing all ordered pairs $\langle\beta, F(\beta)\rangle$ for $\beta < \alpha$, and $F(\alpha)$ is 0 otherwise. Let $T(\alpha)$ stand for $R(\alpha) \neq 0$. Let $Rel(x, \phi)$, where ϕ is any formula, stand for the relativization of ϕ to the variable or term x, i.e., for the formula obtained from ϕ by replacing all quantifiers $(\forall y)$ or $(\exists y)$ by $(\forall y)(y \in x \rightarrow \cdots$ or $(\exists y)(y \in x \wedge \cdots$, respectively, after changing bound variables to avoid collisions. We shall say that the set x is an ε-model for the theory **Q** if $\langle x, \varepsilon_x\rangle$ is a model of **Q**, where $\varepsilon_x = \{\langle yz\rangle | y, z \in x \wedge y \in z\}$. We shall use freely the formalized notions of satisfaction and truth of formulas in ε-models. We shall say, e.g., that ϕ is true in x if ϕ is true in $\langle x, \varepsilon_x\rangle$, etc. An ε-model x is called a natural model if $x = R(\alpha) \neq 0$ for some limit number α. The natural models are well-ordered by inclusion, and hence it makes sense to speak about the "first natural model of **Q**", etc. A theorem of **S** which will be used tacitly in the present paper but will not be proved here is that if $\beta < \delta$ and $x \in R(\beta)$, then x and β satisfy $Rel(R(\beta), \phi(x))$ in $R(\delta)$ if and only if x satisfies $\phi(x)$ in $R(\beta)$. The proof is straightforward once the formal notion of satisfaction is developed.

The following schemata are called principles of reflection over **S**.

This work was partially supported by a National Science Foundation Grant.

$\mathsf{R}_1^{\mathsf{S}}$ $\phi \to (\exists\alpha)(L(\alpha) \wedge T(\alpha) \wedge Rel(R(\alpha), \phi))$, where ϕ is any sentence.
$\mathsf{R}_2^{\mathsf{S}}$ $\phi \to (\forall\beta)(\exists\alpha)(\alpha > \beta \wedge L(\alpha) \wedge T(\alpha) \wedge Rel(R(\alpha), \phi))$, where ϕ is any sentence.
$\mathsf{R}_3^{\mathsf{S}}$ $\phi(x_1, \cdots, x_n) \to (\exists\alpha)(L(\alpha) \wedge T(\alpha) \wedge x_1, \cdots, x_n \in R(\alpha) \wedge \mathrm{Rel}(R(\alpha), \phi))$, where ϕ is any formula with no free variables except $x_1, \cdots, x_n$.

Let $\mathsf{S}^* = \mathsf{S} + \mathsf{R}_1^{\mathsf{S}}$, $\mathsf{S}^{**} = \mathsf{S} + \mathsf{R}_2^{\mathsf{S}}$, $\mathsf{S}^{***} = \mathsf{S} + \mathsf{R}_3^{\mathsf{S}}$.

By analogy to what was done in [2], one can easily show that in S^* one can prove $T(\omega \cdot n)$ for every finite non-zero numeral n but one cannot prove $T(\omega^2)$ (if S^* is consistent) and that S^* is consistent if and only if $\mathsf{S} + \{T(\omega \cdot n) | n \text{ is a finite numeral}\}$ is consistent. In S^{**} one can prove $T(\omega^n)$ for every finite numeral n but one cannot prove $T(\omega^\omega)$ (if S^{**} is consistent). S^{**} is consistent if and only if $\mathsf{S} + \{T(\omega^n) | n \text{ is a finite numeral}\}$ is consistent. However, $R(\omega^2)$ is not a natural model of S^* and $R(\omega^\omega)$ is not a natural model of S^{**}. We shall now deal with the problem of finding the ranks β_0 and β_1 of S^* and S^{**} in the sense of r_4 of Tarski [6] ($\beta_0 = r_4\mathsf{S}^*$, $\beta_1 = r_4\mathsf{S}^{**}$ in Tarski's notation), i.e., the least ordinals β such that $R(\beta)$ is a natural model of S^* and S^{**}, respectively. We shall see that $\beta_1 = \beta_0$ and that they are denumerable but still very large.

Lemma 1 (in S). *If there exists a sentence ψ and formulas $Q(x)$ and $P(x, y)$ with no free variables except x and x, y, respectively, such that*

$$(1) \qquad \begin{aligned} &\mathsf{S} \vdash (\forall\gamma)[L(\gamma) \wedge T(\gamma) \wedge (\exists\xi)(\xi < \gamma \wedge L(\xi) \wedge Rel(R(\xi), \psi)) \to (\forall x) \\ &\quad (Q(x) \leftrightarrow x \in R(\gamma) \wedge Rel(R(\gamma), Q(x))) \wedge (\forall\eta)(\forall x)(\eta < \gamma \wedge Q(x) \to \\ &\quad (P(x, \eta) \leftrightarrow Rel(R(\gamma), P(x, \eta))))] \end{aligned}$$

and δ is a limit ordinal such that $R(\delta) \neq 0$ and the sentence

$$(\exists\xi)(L(\xi) \wedge Rel(R(\xi), \psi)) \wedge (\forall x)(Q(x) \to (\exists\gamma)P(x, \gamma)) \wedge (\forall\gamma)(\exists x)$$

$(Q(x) \wedge (\forall\sigma)(P(x, \sigma) \to \sigma = \gamma))$ *is true in $R(\delta)$, then $R(\delta)$ is not a natural model of S^*.*

Proof. Let ϕ be the sentence $(\exists\xi)(L(\xi) \wedge Rel(R(\xi), \psi) \wedge (\forall x)(Q(x) \to (\exists\eta)P(x, \eta)))$. By the hypothesis of the lemma, ϕ is true in $R(\delta)$. If $R(\delta)$ is a natural model of S^*, then $\phi \to (\exists\beta)(L(\beta) \wedge T(\beta) \wedge Rel(R(\beta), \phi))$ is true in it, and hence $(\exists\beta)(L(\beta) \wedge T(\beta) \wedge Rel(R(\beta), \phi))$ is true in it. As one can see from standard absoluteness arguments (see, e.g., Shepherdson [5]) and the theorem mentioned earlier concerning satisfaction of $Rel(R(\beta), \phi)$ by β, this implies the existence of a limit ordinal $\beta < \delta$ such that ϕ is true in $R(\beta)$.

Since the sentence in (1) is a theorem of S, it is true in $R(\delta)$ (because every $R(\delta)$ with limit number δ is a natural model of S). Thus, putting β for γ in (1) and using the fact that $(\exists\xi)(Rel(R(\xi), \psi))$ is true in $R(\beta)$ (since ϕ is true in $R(\beta)$), and hence β satisfies $(\exists\xi), (\xi < \beta \wedge Rel(R(\xi), \psi))$ in $R(\delta)$, we have that the formula

$$(\forall x)(Q(x) \leftrightarrow x \in R(\beta) \wedge Rel(R(\beta), Q(x))) \wedge (\forall\eta)(\forall x)(\eta < \beta \wedge Q(x) \to$$
$$(P(x, \eta) \leftrightarrow Rel(R(\beta), P(x, \eta))))$$

is satisfied by β in $R(\delta)$, i.e., $(\forall x)(x \in R(\delta) \rightarrow (x$ satisfies $Q(x)$ in $R(\delta) \leftrightarrow x \in R(\beta) \wedge x$ satisfies $Q(x)$ in $R(\beta))) \wedge (\forall \eta)(\forall x)(x \in R(\beta) \wedge \eta < \beta \wedge x$ satisfies $Q(x)$ in $R(\delta) \rightarrow (x, \eta$ satisfy $P(x, \eta)$ in $R(\delta) \leftrightarrow x, \eta$ satisfy $P(x, \eta)$ in $R(\beta)))$.[1] Since ϕ is true in $R(\beta)$, we have $(\forall x)(x \in R(\beta) \wedge x$ satisfies $Q(x)$ in $R(\beta) \rightarrow (\exists \eta)(\eta < \beta \wedge x$ and η satisfy $P(x, \eta)$ in $R(\beta)))$, and hence $(\forall x)(x \in R(\delta) \wedge x$ satisfies $Q(x)$ in $R(\delta) \rightarrow (\exists \eta)(\eta < \beta \wedge \eta$ satisfies $P(x, \eta)$ in $R(\delta)))$; but this contradicts the assumption that $(\forall \gamma)(\exists x)(Q(x) \wedge (\forall \sigma)(P(x, \sigma) \rightarrow \sigma = \gamma))$ is true in $R(\delta)$.

COROLLARY 2 (in S). If β_0 exists (i.e., if S^* has a natural model), then $\beta_0 \geqq \omega_{(1)}$, where $\omega_{(1)}$ is the first ordinal which is not Church-Kleene constructive.

PROOF. Let β be any Church-Kleene constructive ordinal. We take $(\forall v_0)(v_0 = v_0)$ for ψ, any one of the formulas which are usually taken to assert that x is a natural number for $Q(x)$, a formula which asserts that the natural number x is the y'th member in a fixed recursive well-ordering of the natural numbers of order-type β for $P(x, y)$ and β for δ. Since a recursive well-ordering of the natural numbers can be given by a number theoretic predicate, which is, hence, absolute with respect to natural models, the assumptions of Lemma 1 follow easily. Thus $R(\beta)$ is not a natural model of S^*.

In essentially the same way we can prove that β_0 is greater than all the order types of well-orderings of the natural numbers defined by using any finite number of quantifiers on sets of natural numbers or on sets of sets of natural numbers (still without changing ψ), and so on. Thus we see that β_0 is really enormous.

THEOREM 3 (in $\mathsf{S} + (\exists \alpha)(\alpha$ *is uncountable* $\wedge T(\alpha)))$. β_0 *(exists and) is countable and* $\beta_1 = \beta_0$.

PROOF. A single instance $\phi \rightarrow (\exists \alpha)(L(\alpha) \wedge T(\alpha) \wedge Rel(R(\alpha), \phi))$ of $\mathsf{R}_1^{\mathsf{S}}$ is obviously true in every natural model $R(\lambda)$ with countable λ except, at most, one, which is the least natural model of ϕ. Since $\mathsf{R}_1^{\mathsf{S}}$ has countably many instances, $\mathsf{R}_1^{\mathsf{S}}$ is true in all natural models $R(\lambda)$ with countable λ except, at most, countably many of them. Since there are uncountably many countable limit ordinals, there is at least one countable limit number β such that $R(\beta)$ is a natural model of S^*. The least such ordinal is β_0.

In order to show that $R(\beta_0)$ is a model of S^{**} we just have to show that for every sentence ϕ which is true in $R(\beta_0)$ and for every $\gamma < \beta_0$ there is a limit number δ, $\gamma < \delta < \beta_0$, such that ϕ is true in $R(\delta)$. Without loss of generality we can assume that γ is a limit number (otherwise we replace it by the maximal limit number less than γ, or by ω if γ is finite). First we shall note that no natural model of S^* can be of the form $R(\eta + \omega)$, where $R(\eta)$ is not a model of S^*, from which $\beta_0 > \gamma + \omega$ follows readily, since $R(\beta_0)$ is the least natural model of S^*. Since $R(\eta)$ is not a natural model of S^*, there is a

[1] Notice that this sentence is being used, not mentioned.

sentence ψ such that $R(\eta)$ is the least natural model of ψ. Let σ be the sentence $(\exists\alpha)(L(\alpha) \wedge Rel(R(\alpha), \psi))$. Then obviously $R(\eta+\omega)$ is the least natural model of σ, hence $R(\gamma+\omega)$ is not a natural model of S*. Since, as we have now established, $\gamma+\omega < \beta_0$ and $R(\beta_0)$ is the least natural model of S*, $R(\gamma)$ is not a natural model of S*, hence for some sentence χ, $R(\gamma+\omega)$ is the least natural model of χ. Let τ be the sentence $\phi \wedge (\exists\alpha)(L(\alpha) \wedge Rel(R(\alpha), \chi))$. Since τ is true in $R(\beta_0)$ and $R(\beta_0)$ is a natural model of S*, it is also true in some natural model $R(\delta)$ with $\delta < \beta_0$. $\delta > \gamma+\omega$, since $(\exists\alpha)(L(\alpha) \wedge Rel(R(\alpha), \chi))$ is true in $R(\delta)$. ϕ is true in $R(\delta)$, since τ is true in it. Thus $R(\beta_0)$ is a natural model of S** and since, obviously, $\beta_1 \geqq \beta_0$, we have $\beta_1 = \beta_0$.

We have an "effective" enumeration of β_0 which is obtained via the enumeration of the limit numbers in β_0 given by

$$\lambda \rightarrow \text{the least } \phi \text{ such that } R(\lambda) \text{ is the least natural model of } \phi,$$

where the formulas of the language are identified with the natural numbers in some definite way. Thus we get an induced well-ordering of the natural numbers of the order type β_0. Using Lemma 1 we can prove that for no ordinal γ, which is constructive in that well-ordering (except β_0 itself), is $R(\gamma)$ a natural model of S*. The proof is very similar to that of Corollary 2, only that for ψ we take now the sentence $(\exists\beta)$ (β is a natural model of S*), $Q(x)$ is the same, and $P(x, y)$ is as in Corollary 2, only that now we deal with well-orderings of the natural numbers recursive in the well-ordering above. Thus the second β for which $R(\beta)$ is a natural model of S* is immensely bigger than β_0. By a similar argument we see that the third such β is immensely bigger than the second, and so on. Even though the set of the β's such that $R(\beta)$ is a natural model of S* is very rarified in the beginning of the second-number class, as we saw, it cannot stay so throughout that class because of the cardinality argument used in the proof of Theorem 3. If we assume the axiom of choice, then there exists a countable ordinal μ such that $R(\lambda)$ is a natural model of S* for every limit ordinal $\mu < \lambda < \omega_1$.

THEOREM 4 (in S$+(\exists\alpha)$ (α *is uncountable* $\wedge\, T(\alpha)$)). *For some countable limit ordinal* β, $R(\beta)$ *is a natural model of* S* *but not of* S**.

PROOF. Let $R(\beta)$ be any natural model of S*. As was shown in the proof of Theorem 3, if for some limit number γ, $\beta = \gamma+\omega$, then $R(\gamma)$ must also be a model of S* and, since there are no limit numbers between γ and β, $R(\beta)$ is not a natural model of S**. If β is not of the form $\gamma+\omega$, then β is a limit of limit numbers. If β is a limit of limit numbers γ such that $R(\gamma)$ is not a natural model of S*, then, as in the proof of Theorem 3, we can show that $R(\beta)$ is also a natural model of S**; hence if $R(\beta)$ is not a natural model of S**, then there is a limit number $\delta < \beta$ such that for every limit number γ with $\delta < \gamma < \beta$, $R(\gamma)$ is a model of S*. In the latter case β cannot be the least natural model of S*, which is not a natural model of S**, since, by what was said above, $R(\delta+\omega\cdot 2)$ is a natural model of S* but not of S** and $\delta+\omega\cdot 2 < \beta$. Therefore the least β for which $R(\beta)$ is a natural model of S* but not of S** is $\gamma+\omega$, where γ is the least ordinal for which both $R(\gamma)$ and $R(\gamma+\omega)$ are natural models of S*. Denote the least such β with β'.

Since all the natural models $R(\lambda \cdot \omega^2)$ with countable λ are models of S*, except, at most, countably many, and the same holds also for all the natural models $R(\lambda \cdot \omega^2 + \omega)$, there is a countable λ for which both $R(\lambda \cdot \omega^2)$ and $R(\lambda \cdot \omega^2+\omega)$ are natural models of S*. Thus β' is countable.

By methods similar to those of the proof of the second part of Theorem 3 and of the remarks preceding Theorem 4 it can be proved that $R(\beta')$ of the proof of Theorem 4 is greater than the λ-th natural model of S*, where λ is any Church-Kleene constructive ordinal, etc.

Since, as shown in [3], $(\exists\alpha)$ (α is uncountable $\wedge\ T(\alpha)$) is provable in S***, we have, by Theorem 3, that in S*** one can prove the existence of natural models of S* and S**. We note that the existence of natural models of S*** can be proved in ZF (see [3]), but the cardinality of the least β for which $R(\beta)$ is a natural model of S*** is very large (as can be easily seen in §2 of [3]).

Let $In(\alpha)$ be a formula asserting that α is strongly inaccessible, where the notion of strong inaccessibility is taken as in [1]. The only property of this notion which will be used here is that $\mathsf{ZF} \vdash In(\alpha) \rightarrow R(\alpha)$ is a natural model of $\mathsf{ZF} \wedge \alpha$ is regular. Consider the following schemata:

$\mathsf{R}_1^{\mathsf{ZF}}$ $\phi \rightarrow (\exists\alpha)(In(\alpha) \wedge Rel(R(\alpha), \phi))$, where ϕ is any sentence.
$\mathsf{R}_2^{\mathsf{ZF}}$ $\phi \rightarrow (\forall\beta)(\exists\alpha)(\alpha > \beta \wedge In(\alpha) \wedge Rel(R(\alpha), \phi))$, where ϕ is any sentence.
$\mathsf{R}_3^{\mathsf{ZF}}$ $\phi(x_1, \cdots, x_n) \rightarrow (\exists\alpha)(In(\alpha) \wedge x_1, \cdots, x_n \in R(\alpha) \wedge Rel(R(\alpha), \phi))$, where ϕ is any formula with no free variables except $x_1, \cdots, x_n$.

Let $\mathsf{ZF}^* = \mathsf{ZF}+\mathsf{R}_1^{\mathsf{ZF}}$, $\mathsf{ZF}^{**} = \mathsf{ZF}+\mathsf{R}_2^{\mathsf{ZF}}$, $\mathsf{ZF}^{***} = \mathsf{ZF}+\mathsf{R}_3^{\mathsf{ZF}}$.

We shall call a natural model $R(\lambda)$ a strong natural model if λ is inaccessible. By Theorem 5.3 of Montague and Vaught [4] one can prove in ZF that for every natural model $R(\lambda)$ of a theory Q which includes ZF there is a natural model $R(\sigma)$ of Q with $\sigma \leqq \lambda$, σ confinal with ω. Thus for every strong natural model of ZF* and ZF** there is a smaller natural model of ZF* and ZF**, respectively, and the least natural models of ZF* and ZF** are of the form $R(\tau)$ with τ confinal with ω.

Let $(\mu\alpha)\chi(\alpha)$ stand for the least α such that $\chi(\alpha)$, if there is such an α, and 0 otherwise. Let $P_\eta(\alpha)$ be the functions defined by

$$P_\eta(0) = (\mu\gamma)(In(\gamma) \wedge (\forall\eta')(\eta' < \eta \rightarrow (\exists\lambda)(L(\lambda) \wedge \gamma = P_{\eta'}(\lambda))))$$
$$P_\eta(\alpha+1) = (\mu\gamma)(\gamma > P_\eta(\alpha) > 0 \wedge In(\gamma) \wedge (\forall\eta')(\eta' < \eta \rightarrow (\exists\lambda)(L(\lambda) \wedge \gamma = P_{\eta'}(\lambda))))$$

and for limit number α, $P_\eta(\alpha) = \lim_{\beta<\alpha} P_\eta(\beta)$. We shall say that $P_\eta(\alpha)$ exists just in case when $P_\eta(\alpha) \neq 0$.

As shown in [2] one can prove in ZF* the existence of $P_0(n)$ for every finite numeral n, but one cannot prove in ZF* the existence of $P_0(\omega)$ (if ZF* is consistent). ZF* is consistent if and only if $\mathsf{ZF}+\{P_0(n)$ exists$|n$ is a finite numeral} is consistent. However, one can show along the lines of Lemma 1 and Corollary 2 that the least β such that $R(\beta)$ is a natural model of **ZF*** (if there exists such a β) is greater than $P(\beta_0)$ (or even $P(\beta')$, where β' is as in the proof of Theorem 4). A strong natural model of **ZF*** is of the form $R(P_0(\lambda))$ for some λ such that $P_0(\lambda)$ is inaccessible. By analogy to Theorem 3 one can prove easily that the least such λ is countable.

As shown in [2] one can prove in **ZF**** $(\forall\alpha)(P_n(\alpha) \neq 0)$ for every finite numeral n (but one cannot prove in **ZF**** the existence of $P_\omega(0)$—if **ZF**** is consistent). Since the function $P_\alpha(\beta)$ is absolute with respect to natural models then for no $\lambda < P_n(0)$, where n is a finite numeral, is $R(\lambda)$ a natural model of **ZF****. For every countable τ, $P_0(\tau) < P_1(0)$ and hence the least natural model and the least strong natural model of **ZF*** are not natural models of **ZF****. Furthermore, one can prove in **ZF**** the existence, of a strong natural model of **ZF***. Looking now for a natural model $R(\gamma)$ of **ZF****, one can prove, by analogy to Theorem 3 and Corollary 5 in [2] and Theorem 1 and Corollary 2 here, that if $R(\gamma)$ is a natural model of **ZF****, then $\gamma > P_\lambda(0)$, where λ is any Church-Kleene constructive ordinal, or even the least ordinal β such that $R(P_0(\beta))$ is a strong natural model of **ZF***, etc. It seems now natural to assume, by analogy to what we had before, that there is an ordinal $\gamma < P_{\omega_1}(0)$ such that $R(\gamma)$ is a strong natural model of **ZF****. This indeed could be proved if the following assertion were proved. The set of all inaccessible numbers less than $P_{\omega_1}(0)$ is not the union of countably many discrete sets (in the order topology of the ordinal numbers). The author does not know whether this is true.[2] However, by Theorem 6, the least strong natural model of **ZF**** is less than $R(\nu)$, where ν is the first hyper-inaccessible number of type 1 (see [1]), since $R(\nu)$ is a natural model of the theory **ZM** which includes **ZF*****. In utilizing Theorem 6 here, we use the absoluteness of the notion of a strong natural model of **ZF**** with respect to natural models, which is easily shown.

LEMMA 5 (in **ZF*****).[3]

$$(\forall y)(\exists\alpha)(In(\alpha) \wedge y \in R(\alpha) \wedge (\forall x_1, \cdots, x_n)(x_1, \cdots, x_n \in y \rightarrow (\phi \leftrightarrow Rel(R(\alpha), \phi)))),$$

where ϕ is any formula without free variables except $x_1, \cdots, x_n$.

PROOF. Let $z = \{\langle x_1, \ldots, x_n\rangle | x_1, \ldots, x_n \in y \wedge \phi\}$. Let ψ be the formula $(\forall x_1, \cdots, x_n)(x_1, \cdots, x_n \in y \rightarrow (\langle x_1, \cdots, x_n\rangle \in z \leftrightarrow \phi))$. By R_3^{ZF} we have

$$\psi \rightarrow (\exists\alpha)(In(\alpha) \wedge y, z \in R(\alpha) \wedge Rel(R(\alpha), \psi)).$$

ψ holds by definition of z. Since $y, z \in R(\alpha)$ and by the absoluteness of the

[2]The least ordinal γ for which the author knows that the set of all inaccessible numbers $< \gamma$ is not the union of countably many discrete sets in the least hyper-inaccessible number of type 1 ν (see [1]). It is easily seen that the set of all inaccessible numbers $< \nu$ is not the union of less than ν discrete sets.

[3]The theorem corresponding to Lemma 5 in the case of **S***** is originally stated. without proof, in [3].

term $\langle x_1, \cdots, x_n\rangle$, $Rel(R(\alpha), \psi)$ is equivalent to

$$(\forall x_1, \cdots, x_n)(x_1, \cdots, x_n \in y \rightarrow (\langle x_1, \cdots, x_n\rangle \in z \leftrightarrow Rel(R(\alpha), \phi))).$$

Thus we have $(\exists\alpha)(In(\alpha) \wedge y \in R(\alpha) \wedge (\forall x_1, \cdots, x_n)(x_1, \cdots, x_n \in y \rightarrow (\langle x_1, \cdots, x_n\rangle \in z \leftrightarrow Rel(R(\alpha), \phi))))$. But since $x_1, \cdots, x_n \in y$, $\langle x_1, \cdots, x_n\rangle \in z$ can be replaced by ϕ and the statement of the Lemma is obtained.

THEOREM 6 (in ZF***). *There exists an ordinal* α *such that* $R(\alpha)$ *is a strong natural model of* ZF**.

PROOF: For every sentence x let λ_x be the least ordinal λ such that for every inaccessible $\gamma > \lambda$ x is false in $R(\gamma)$ if there is such a λ and let $\lambda_x = 0$ otherwise. Let u be the set of all sentences, let $\sigma = \sup_{x \in u}\lambda_x$, let $y = u \cup \{\sigma\}$ and let ϕ be the formula $(\forall\beta)(\exists\gamma)(\gamma > \beta \wedge \text{In}(\gamma) \wedge x$ is true in $R(\gamma))$. By Lemma 5 there is an inaccessible ordinal α such that for every sentence x $(\forall\beta)(\exists\gamma)(\gamma > \beta \wedge \text{In}(\gamma) \wedge x$ is true in $R(\gamma)) \leftrightarrow (\forall\beta)(\beta < \alpha \rightarrow (\exists\gamma)(\beta < \gamma < \alpha \wedge \text{In}(\gamma) \wedge x$ is true in $R(\gamma)))$ (here we use the standard lemmas about relativization to $R(\alpha)$). Since $\sigma \in y \in R(\alpha)$ we have for every sentence x $\lambda_x < \alpha$ and therefore 'x is true in $R(\alpha)$' implies $(\forall\beta)(\exists\gamma)(\gamma > \beta \wedge \text{In}(\gamma) \wedge x$ is true in $R(\gamma))$ which implies $(\forall\beta)(\beta < \alpha \rightarrow (\exists\gamma)(\beta < \gamma < \alpha \wedge \text{In}(\gamma) \wedge x$ is true in $R(\gamma)))$. Thus $R(\alpha)$ is a strong natural model of ZF**.

REFERENCES

[1] LÉVY, A. Axiom schemata of strong infinity in axiomatic set theory, *Pacific Journal of Mathematics*, Vol. 10 (1960), pp. 223–238.

[2] LÉVY, A. Principles of reflection in axiomatic set theory, *Fundamenta Mathematicae*, Vol. 49 (1960), pp. 1–10.

[3] LÉVY, A., and R. L. VAUGHT. Principles of partial reflection in the set theories of Zermelo and Ackermann, *Pacific Journal of Mathematics*, to appear.

[4] MONTAGUE, R., and R. L. VAUGHT. Natural models of set theories, *Fundamenta Mathematicae*, Vol. 47 (1959), pp. 219–242.

[5] SHEPHERDSON, J. C. Inner models for set theory, Part I, *Journal of Symbolic Logic*, Vol. 16 (1951), pp. 161–190.

[6] TARSKI, A. Notions of proper models for set theories (abstract), *Bulletin of the American Mathematical Society*, Vol. 62 (1956), p. 601.

TWO CONTRIBUTIONS TO THE FOUNDATIONS OF SET THEORY

RICHARD MONTAGUE

University of California, Los Angeles, California, U.S.A.

A simple alternative formulation is given for an axiom recently proposed by Lévy as an addition to the axioms of Zermelo-Fraenkel set theory;[1] and the following theorem is proved, which strengthens a result in [4]: if T is a theory obtained from Zermelo set theory by adding all instances with no more than a given number of alternations of quantifiers of a schema valid in Zermelo-Fraenkel set theory, then the consistency of T is demonstrable in Zermelo-Fraenkel set theory. (Actually, a slightly stronger result is obtained.) The two subjects of investigation turn out to depend on a common lemma.

1. Preliminary Definitions

Expressions are to be identified with natural numbers. More explicitly, we distinguish an infinite set of natural numbers which are to be known as *variables*, and, for each positive integer n, an infinite set of natural numbers to be known as *n-place predicates*. We consider also several operations on natural numbers: the *application* of a predicate to a finite sequence of numbers (denoted by juxtaposition), and the operations $\sim$, $\wedge$, V, $\urcorner$, which are the respective operations of *negation, conjunction, existential quantification*, and *definite description*. Familiar assumptions concerning recursiveness and distinctness of values are imposed.

A *quasi-term* is either a variable or a number of the form $\urcorner kn$, where k, n are natural numbers. The set of *meaningful expressions* is the smallest set K such that (1) all variables are in K, (2) for any natural numbers π, n, $\zeta_0, \cdots, \zeta_n$, if π is an $(n+1)$-place predicate and $\zeta_0, \cdots, \zeta_n$ are quasi-terms in K, then $\pi\zeta_0 \cdots \zeta_n$ is in K, (3) for any variable α and any members ϕ, ψ of K which are not quasi-terms, the numbers $\sim\phi$, $\phi \wedge \psi$, $\mathsf{V}\alpha\phi$, $\urcorner\alpha\phi$ are in K. A *term* is a meaningful expression which is a quasi-term; a *formula* is a meaningful expression which is not a quasi-term.

We distinguish certain predicates. N is to be a one-place predicate; $=$, $\in$, and Sc, distinct two-place predicates; and $+$ and $\cdot$, distinct three-place predicates. We understand by $\zeta = \eta$ and $\zeta \in \eta$ (as well as $= \zeta\eta$ and $\in \zeta\eta$) the application of $=$ and $\in$, respectively, to the terms ζ and η. The variables are to be completely enumerated by the non-repeating sequence $\langle v_0, \cdots, v_n, \cdots\rangle$.

A *model* is an ordered triple $\langle A, R, z\rangle$, where A is a set containing z as a

---

The preparation of this paper was sponsored by the National Science Foundation (U.S.A.), under grants G 13226, G-6693, and G-14006. I am indebted also to Professors Alfred Tarski and R. L. Vaught for relevant discussion.

[1]The problem of finding a simple formulation of the kind given in section 2 was proposed, in conversation, by Tarski.

member, R is a function whose domain is the set of predicates and such that, for all π and n, if π is an n-place predicate, then $R(\pi)$ is a set of ordered n-tuples of elements of A, and in addition $R(=)$ is the identity relation on A. Let $M = \langle A, R, z\rangle$, let M be a model, and let x be in A^{ω} (that is, the set of functions mapping the set of natural numbers into A). Then the notions of *satisfaction* and *value* are defined by the following simultaneous recursion. (1) The value of v_i in M with respect to x is $x(i)$. (2) Let ϕ be a formula. If there is a unique object a in A such that, for some y in A^{ω}, $y(i) = a$, $y(j) = x(j)$ for all $j \neq i$, and y satisfies ϕ in M, then the value of $\neg v_i\phi$ (in M, with respect to x) is that object a; otherwise the value of $\neg v_i\phi$ is z. (3) If π is an $(n+1)$-place predicate and $\zeta_0, \cdots, \zeta_n$ are terms, then x satisfies $\pi\zeta_0 \cdots \zeta_n$ in M if and only if $\langle a_0, \cdots, a_n\rangle$ is in $R(\pi)$, where $a_0, \cdots, a_n$ are the respective values of $\zeta_0, \cdots, \zeta_n$ in M with respect to x. (4) If ϕ is a formula, then x satisfies $\sim\phi$ in M if and only if x does not satisfy ϕ in M; similarly for conjunction and existential quantification. A formula is said to be *true in M* if it is satisfied in M by every x in A^{ω}.

Familiar syntactical notions—for example, 'occurs in' and 'is a free variable of'—are to be understood in the usual way. If ϕ is a meaningful expression and $\zeta_0, \cdots, \zeta_{n-1}$ are terms, then $\phi[\zeta_0, \cdots, \zeta_{n-1}]$ is to be the *proper simultaneous substitution* in ϕ of $\zeta_0, \cdots, \zeta_{n-1}$ for (the free occurrences of) $v_0, \cdots, v_{n-1}$ respectively (whose construction may involve rewriting bound variables of ϕ if any of them are free in any of $\zeta_0, \cdots, \zeta_{n-1}$).

By a *standard formula* is understood a formula in which no terms other than variables occur, and by a *set-theoretical formula* one in which no predicates other than $=$ and $\in$ occur.

By the *depth* of a standard set-theoretical formula is understood, roughly, a number one greater than the number of alternations of quantifiers in the formula. The exact recursive definition is the following. (1) If i, j are natural numbers, then the depth of $v_i = v_j$, as well as that of $v_i \in v_j$, is 0. (2) If ϕ, ψ are standard set-theoretical formulas, then the depth of $\sim\phi$ is that of ϕ, and the depth of $\phi \wedge \psi$ is the maximum of the depths of ϕ and ψ. (3) If ϕ is a standard set-theoretical formula with depth n, and i is a natural number, then the depth of $\mathbf{V}v_i\phi$ is n or $n+1$ according as ϕ has or has not the form $\mathbf{V}v_j\psi$.

Let A be a set of formulas. A *term, formula,* or *meaningful expression of A* is, respectively, a term, formula, or meaningful expression containing no predicates beyond those occurring in members of A. A formula ϕ is said to be *derivable* from A if ϕ is true in every model in which all members of A are true; and *valid* in A, or, in symbols, $\vdash_A \phi$, if ϕ is derivable from A and is a formula of A.

Let A, B be sets of formulas. A is called an *extension* of B if every formula valid in B is also valid in A. A and B are said to be *equivalent* if each is an extension of the other, and *equivalent within* a set C of formulas if $C \cup A$ is equivalent to $C \cup B$.

If ϕ, ψ, α are numbers, then by $\phi \vee \psi$, $\phi \rightarrow \psi$, and $\mathbf{\Lambda}\,\alpha\phi$ are understood the respective numbers $\sim((\sim\phi) \wedge (\sim\psi))$, $\sim(\phi \wedge \sim\psi)$, and $\sim\mathsf{V}\alpha\sim\phi$. If ϕ is a standard set-theoretical formula and ζ a term containing no variables in common with ϕ, then the *relativization* of ϕ to ζ, or $\phi^{(\zeta)}$, is defined recursively as follows: $(v_i = v_j)^{(\zeta)}$ is $v_i = v_j$, $(v_i \in v_j)^{(\zeta)}$ is $v_i \in v_j$, $(\sim\phi)^{(\zeta)}$ is $\sim\phi^{(\zeta)}$, $(\phi \wedge \psi)^{(\zeta)}$ is $\phi^{(\zeta)} \wedge \psi^{(\zeta)}$, and $(\mathsf{V}v_i\phi)^{(\zeta)}$ is $\mathsf{V}v_i(v_i \in \zeta \wedge \phi^{(\zeta)})$.

We must extend to theories involving terms of the form $\urcorner v_i\phi$ the notion of *relative interpretability* introduced in [8]. Accordingly, let A, B be sets of formulas. If (1) g is a function mapping the predicates occurring in members of A onto formulas of B in such a way that the formula corresponding to an n-place predicate never contains any free variables beyond $v_0, \cdots, v_{n-1}$, and (if $=$ occurs in some members of A) $g(=)$ is $v_0 = v_1$, (2) χ is a formula of B whose only free variable is v_0 such that $\vdash_B \mathsf{V}v_1 \bigwedge v_0(\chi \leftrightarrow v_0 = v_1)$, and (3) ψ is a formula of B whose only free variable is v_0 such that $\vdash_B \chi \to \psi$, then the *relative interpretation induced by* g, χ, ψ is the unique function I whose domain is the set of meaningful expressions of A and which satisfies the following conditions:

(i) If α is a variable, then $I(\alpha)$ is α.

(ii) If π is an $(n+1)$-place predicate in the domain of G, and $\zeta_0, \cdots, \zeta_n$ are terms of A, then $I(\pi\zeta_0 \cdots \zeta_n)$ is $g(\pi)[\zeta_n, \cdots, \zeta_0]$.

(iii) If ϕ_1, ϕ_2 are formulas of A, then $I(\sim\phi_1)$ is $\sim I(\phi_1)$ and $I(\phi_1 \wedge \phi_2)$ is $I(\phi_1) \wedge I(\phi_2)$.

(iv) If ϕ is a formula of A and α a variable, then $I(\mathsf{V}\alpha\phi)$ is $\mathsf{V}\alpha(\psi[\alpha] \wedge I(\phi))$, and $I(\urcorner\alpha\phi)$ is

$$\urcorner\beta[\bigwedge\alpha((\psi[\alpha] \wedge I(\phi)) \leftrightarrow \alpha = \beta)$$
$$\vee \{\sim\mathsf{V}\beta \bigwedge \alpha((\psi[\alpha] \wedge I(\phi)) \leftrightarrow \alpha = \beta) \wedge \chi[\beta]\}],$$

where β is the first variable distinct from α and not occurring in ϕ.

A is said to be *relatively interpretable* in B if there are g, χ, ψ, I such that g, χ, ψ satisfy conditions (1)—(3) above, I is the relative interpretation induced by g, χ, ψ, and for all ϕ, $\alpha_0, \cdots, \alpha_{n-1}$, if $\phi \in A$ and $\alpha_0, \cdots, \alpha_{n-1}$ are the free variables of ϕ, $\vdash_B I(\bigwedge\alpha_0 \cdots \bigwedge\alpha_{n-1}\phi)$.

By SF (the principle of *set formation*) is understood the set of formulas $\mathsf{V}\beta\bigwedge\gamma[\gamma \in \beta \leftrightarrow \phi \wedge \gamma \in \alpha]$, where α, β, γ are distinct variables and ϕ is a standard set-theoretical formula in which β does not occur. (In mentioning formulas, both here and elsewhere, we shall use the Hilbert-Ackermann conventions for associating logical operations.) Z (or *Zermelo set theory*) is the union of SF and the set consisting of the formulas

$$\bigwedge x(x \in A \leftrightarrow x \in B) \to A = B,$$
$$\mathsf{V}A\bigwedge z(z \in A \leftrightarrow z = x \vee z = y),$$
$$\mathsf{V}B\bigwedge x(x \in B \leftrightarrow \mathsf{V}y[x \notin y \wedge y \in A]),$$
$$\mathsf{V}B\bigwedge x(x \in B \leftrightarrow \bigwedge y[y \in x \to y \in A]),$$
$$\mathsf{V}x\, x \in A \to \mathsf{V}x(x \in A \wedge \sim\mathsf{V}y[y \in x \wedge y \in A]),$$
$$\mathsf{V}A(\mathsf{V}x[x \in A \wedge \sim \vee y\; y \in x] \wedge \bigwedge x[x \in A \to \vee y(y \in A$$
$$\wedge \bigwedge z[z \in y \leftrightarrow z \in x \vee z = x]\})]),$$

where A, B, x, y, z are appropriate variables. (We shall often represent variables by capital and lower-case Roman letters, making natural assumptions to avoid clash of quantifiers.) ZF (or *Zermelo-Fraenkel set theory*) is the union of Z and the set of formulas

$$\bigwedge\alpha\bigwedge\beta\bigwedge\gamma(\phi[\alpha, \beta] \wedge \phi[\alpha, \gamma] \to \beta = \gamma) \to \bigvee\gamma\bigwedge\beta[\beta \in \gamma \leftrightarrow \bigvee\alpha(\alpha \in \delta \wedge \phi[\alpha, \beta])],$$

where α, β, γ, δ are distinct variables and ϕ is a standard set-theoretical formula in which α, β, γ do not occur.

It is necessary to consider some specific terms and formulas of ZF. For instance, 0 is to be the term $\neg v_0 \sim \bigvee v_1 v_1 \in v_0$; and if ζ, η are any terms of ZF, $\zeta \cup \eta$ is to be the term $\neg\alpha\bigwedge\beta(\beta \in \alpha \leftrightarrow \beta \in \zeta \vee \beta \in \eta)$, and $\zeta \subseteq \eta$ the formula $\bigwedge\alpha(\alpha \in \zeta \to \alpha \in \eta)$, where α, β are the first two variables occurring in neither ζ nor η. In the following table, the expression in the left column is understood as denoting that term or formula of ZF which expresses in the 'natural' way the operation or relation indicated in the right column. (Here ζ, η, etc., may be any terms of ZF, and α any variable.)

$\{\zeta\}$	the unit set of ζ,
$U[\zeta]$	the union of the family ζ,
$P[\zeta]$	the power set (set of all subsets) of ζ,
$\zeta(\eta)$	the value of the function ζ for the argument η,
$\mathcal{A}\zeta$	the range (set of values) of the function ζ,
ζ^{η}	the set of functions with domain η and range included in ζ,
$\zeta\begin{pmatrix}\eta_0 & \cdots & \eta_k \\ \theta_0 & & \theta_k\end{pmatrix}$	the function ζ' which agrees with the function ζ on all arguments except possibly $\eta_0, \cdots, \eta_k$, for which the values of ζ' are respectively $\theta_0, \cdots, \theta_k$,
$\zeta \approx \eta$	the set ζ is cardinally equivalent to the set η,
$\mathrm{Ord}[\zeta]$	ζ is an ordinal (construed in such a way that an ordinal is identified with the set of smaller ordinals),
$\mathrm{Lim}[\zeta]$	ζ is a (non-zero) limit ordinal,
ω	the least limit ordinal,
$\zeta+1$	the successor of the ordinal ζ,
$\underset{\alpha}{\mathrm{Min}}\,\phi$	the least ordinal α satisfying the condition ϕ,
$\rho[\zeta]$	the rank of the set ζ (characterized recursively as the least ordinal greater than the ranks of all members of ζ),
$R[\zeta]$	the family of all sets of rank less than the ordinal ζ.

In addition, each expression in the left column of the following table is to denote the same term or formula as the (longer) expression in the right column.

$\zeta \preccurlyeq \eta$	$\bigvee A(\zeta \approx A \wedge A \subseteq \eta)$,
$\zeta \prec \eta$	$\zeta \preccurlyeq \eta \wedge \sim \eta \preccurlyeq \zeta$,
$\zeta \overset{*}{\preccurlyeq} \eta$	$\zeta = 0 \vee \bigvee f(f \in \zeta^{\eta} \wedge \mathcal{A} f = \zeta)$,
$\zeta \overset{*}{\prec} \eta$	$\zeta \overset{*}{\preccurlyeq} \eta \wedge \sim \eta \overset{*}{\preccurlyeq} \zeta$,
$\bigcup_{\alpha_0, \cdots, \alpha_k} \{\zeta \mid \phi\}$	$\neg A\bigwedge x(x \in A \leftrightarrow \bigvee\alpha_0 \cdots \bigvee\alpha_k[\phi \wedge x \in \zeta])$,

$\underset{\alpha}{R}\phi$ $\quad \neg A \bigwedge x(x \in A \leftrightarrow \bigwedge \alpha[\alpha = x \rightarrow \phi] \wedge \bigwedge \alpha[\rho[\alpha] \in \rho[x] \rightarrow \sim\phi]),$

Norm_{ζ} $\quad \bigwedge x(\mathrm{Ord}[x] \rightarrow \mathrm{Ord}[\zeta[x]]) \wedge \bigwedge x \bigwedge y(\mathrm{Ord}[x] \wedge \mathrm{Ord}[y] \wedge x \in y \rightarrow \zeta[x] \in \zeta[y]) \wedge \bigwedge x(\mathrm{Lim}[x] \rightarrow \zeta[x] = \bigcup_{y}\{\zeta[y] | y \in x\}),$

$\mathrm{In}[\zeta]$ $\quad \mathrm{Ord}[\zeta] \wedge \omega \in \zeta \wedge \bigwedge X(X \subseteq R[\zeta] \wedge X \overset{*}{\not<} R[\zeta] \rightarrow X \in R[\zeta]).$

We understand $R_{\alpha}\phi$ as denoting the set of all things of least rank satisfying ϕ, Norm_{ζ} as asserting that ζ is a normal term, and $\mathrm{In}[\zeta]$ as asserting that ζ is a strongly inaccessible ordinal.

By P (or *Peano's arithmetic*) is understood the set of formulas

$$\bigvee y \bigwedge x(Nx \leftrightarrow x = y),$$
$$\bigvee y \bigwedge x(Sc[x, a] \leftrightarrow x = y),$$
$$\bigvee y \bigwedge x(+[x, a, b] \leftrightarrow x = y),$$
$$\bigvee y \bigwedge x(\cdot[x, a, b] \leftrightarrow x = y),$$
$$Sc[x, y] \wedge Sc[x, z] \rightarrow y = z,$$
$$Nx \rightarrow \sim Sc[x, y],$$
$$Ny \rightarrow +[x, x, y],$$
$$Sc[z, y] \wedge +[u, x, y] \wedge +[v, x, z] \rightarrow Sc[v, u],$$
$$Ny \rightarrow \cdot\,[y, x, y],$$
$$Sc[z, y] \wedge \cdot\,[u, x, y] \wedge \cdot\,[v, x, z] \rightarrow +[v, u, x],$$
$$\bigwedge x(Nx \rightarrow \phi[x]) \wedge \bigwedge x \bigwedge y(\phi[x] \wedge Sc[y, x] \rightarrow \phi[y]) \rightarrow \bigwedge x \phi[x],$$

where ϕ is any standard formula containing neither of the variables x and y, and no predicates beyond $=, N, Sc, +,$ and $\cdot$

Some specific terms and formulas of P will need to be considered. The nth numeral, or $\mathring{\Delta}_n$, is characterized recursively as follows: $\mathring{\Delta}_0$ is $\neg x Nx$; $\mathring{\Delta}_{n+1}$ is $\neg x Sc[x, \mathring{\Delta}_n]$. If ζ is a term of P, then $\mathring{\sim}\zeta$ is to be that term of P which denotes in the 'natural' way the negation of the number denoted by ζ. Other terms and formulas of P, mainly with syntactical significance, are given similarly by the following informal table.

$\zeta \mathring{\wedge} \eta$	the conjunction of ζ and η,
$\mathring{\bigvee}_{\zeta}\eta$	the existential quantification of η with respect to the ζth variable,
$\mathring{=} \zeta, \eta$	the application of $=$ to the ζth and ηth variables,
$\mathring{\in}_{\zeta, \eta}$	the application of $\in$ to the ζth and ηth variables,
$T\mathring{m}[\zeta, \eta]$	ζ is a term of the finite sequence of natural numbers represented by the natural number η,
$SSF\mathring{m}[\zeta]$	ζ is a standard set-theoretical formula,
$D\mathring{p}_n[\zeta]$	ζ is a standard set-theoretical formula of depth at most n,
$G\mathring{e}n[\zeta, \eta]$	ζ is a generalization of η (that is, the result of applying universal quantification 0 or more times to η),
$C\mathring{o}nj[\eta]$	the (iterated) conjunction of all numbers in the finite sequence represented by the number η,
$P\mathring{r}[\zeta]$	ζ is a logically provable standard formula.

Finally, if α is a formula of P whose only free variable is v_0, then $\mathring{Con}_\alpha$ is to be the formula

$$\sim \bigvee f \bigvee b(\bigwedge v_0[\mathring{Tm}[v_0, f] \to \alpha] \wedge \mathring{Gen}[b, Conj[f]] \wedge \mathring{Pr}[\mathring{\sim} b]),$$

which, if α characterizes a set A of standard formulas, expresses the assertion that A is consistent.

The set of *primitive recursive terms* of P is the smallest set K such that (1) all variables are in K, (2) $\mathring{\Delta}_0$ is in K, (3) the term $\neg\beta Sc[\beta, \alpha]$ is in K for any distinct variables α and β, [4] for all ζ, $\eta_0, \cdots, \eta_n$ in K, the term $\zeta[\eta_0, \cdots, \eta_n]$ is in K, (5) if η, θ are any members of K whose free variables are among $v_0, \cdots, v_{n-1}$ and $v_0, \cdots, v_{n+1}$ respectively, and ζ is any term of P whose free variables are among $v_0, \cdots, v_n$ such that the formulas

$$\zeta[v_0, \cdots, v_{n-1}, \Delta_0] = \eta[v_0, \cdots, v_{n-1}],$$
$$\zeta[v_0, \cdots, v_{n-1}, \neg v_{n+1} Sc[v_{n+1}, v_n]] = \theta[v_0, \cdots, v_n, \zeta[v_0, \cdots, v_{n-1}, v_n]]$$

are valid in P, then ζ is in K. A *primitive recursive formula* of P is a formula of the form $\zeta = \mathring{\Delta}_0$, where ζ is a primitive recursive term of P.

By I_0 is understood the relative interpretation induced by g, χ, ψ, where (1) g is the function whose domain consists of the predicates $=$, N, Sc, $+$, $\cdot$ such that $g(=)$ is $v_0 = v_1$, $g(N)$ is $v_0 = 0$, $g(Sc)$ is $v_0 = v_1 + 1$, $g(+)$ is a set-theoretical formula with the free variables v_0, v_1, v_2 expressing in the 'natural' way that v_0 is the sum of the finite ordinals v_1 and v_2, and $g(\cdot)$ is a similar formula expressing the assertion that v_0 is the product of v_1 and v_2; (2) χ is the formula $v_0 = 0$; and (3) ψ is the formula $v_0 \in \omega$.

We shall understand by $\dot{\Delta}_n$ the term $I_0(\mathring{\Delta}_n)$ of ZF. Similarly, corresponding to each of the meaningful expressions $\zeta \mathring{\wedge} \eta, \cdots, \mathring{Pr}[\zeta]$ (that is, the meaningful expressions of P which occur in the last table), we shall have meaningful expressions $\zeta \dot{\wedge} \eta, \cdots, \dot{Pr}[\zeta]$ of ZF, which are identified with $I_0(\zeta \mathring{\wedge} \eta), \cdots, I_0(\mathring{Pr}[\zeta])$, respectively.

By an *abbreviated model* M is understood an ordered pair $\langle A, S\rangle$, where A is a non-empty set and S a set of ordered pairs of elements of S. If ϕ is a standard set-theoretical formula and x is in A^ω, then x is said to *satisfy* ϕ in M if x satisfies ϕ in some model $\langle A, R, z\rangle$ such that $R(\in) = S$.

If ζ, η, θ are terms of ZF, then $\mathrm{Sat}[\zeta, \eta, \theta]$ is to be a formula of ZF expressing in the 'natural' way that ζ is a function whose domain is the set of natural numbers, η is a standard set-theoretical formula, and ζ satisfies η in the abbreviated model $\langle \theta, S\rangle$, where S is the membership relation restricted to θ.

2. A Lemma

Loosely speaking, we may understand by a *satisfaction pair* an ordered pair $\langle R, A\rangle$, where R is a binary relation (regarded as a satisfaction relation) between sequences of type ω and certain standard formulas, and A is a collection of standard set-theoretical formulas (regarded as those formulas to which the satisfaction relation properly applies); we require that any subformula of a formula in A also be in A, and, as far as formulas in A are concerned, that R fulfill the usual recursive conditions on satisfaction (given in Tarski [7]). The notion of a satisfaction pair will itself play no part in the subsequent investigations. We shall instead be interested in the set-theoretical formula which expresses the assertion that a pair is a satisfaction pair; here the relation R and the collection A are supplanted by formulas.

DEFINITION 1. *If ϕ is a formula whose only free variables are v_0 and v_1, and ψ a formula whose only free variable is v_0, then $SP_{\phi,\psi}$ is to be the formula*

$$\begin{aligned}
&\bigwedge a(\psi[a] \rightarrow SSF\dot{m}[a]) \wedge \\
&\bigwedge a(SSF\dot{m}[a] \wedge \psi[\dot{\sim} a] \rightarrow \psi[a]) \wedge \\
&\bigwedge a \bigwedge b(SSF\dot{m}[a] \wedge SSF\dot{m}[b] \wedge \psi[a \mathbin{\dot{\wedge}} b] \rightarrow \psi[a] \wedge \psi[b]) \wedge \\
&\bigwedge a \bigwedge i(SSF\dot{m}[a] \wedge i \in \omega \wedge \psi[\dot{\bigvee}_i a] \rightarrow \psi[a]) \wedge \\
&\bigwedge i \bigwedge j \bigwedge a \bigwedge b \bigwedge x\{i, j \in \omega \wedge SSF\dot{m}[a] \wedge SSF\dot{m}[b] \wedge x \in \mathcal{U}x^{\omega} \rightarrow \\
&\qquad (\psi[\dot{=}_{i,j}] \rightarrow [\phi[x, \dot{=}_{i,j}] \leftrightarrow x(i) = x(j)]) \wedge \\
&\qquad (\psi[\dot{\in}_{i,j}] \rightarrow [\phi[x, \dot{\in}_{i,j}] \leftrightarrow x(i) \in x(j)]) \wedge \\
&\qquad (\psi[\dot{\sim} a] \rightarrow [\phi[x, \dot{\sim} a] \leftrightarrow \sim\phi[x, a]]) \wedge \\
&\qquad (\psi[a \mathbin{\dot{\wedge}} b] \rightarrow [\phi[x, a \mathbin{\dot{\wedge}} b] \leftrightarrow \phi[x, a] \wedge \phi[x, b]] \wedge \\
&\qquad (\psi[\dot{\bigvee}_i a] \rightarrow [\phi[x, \dot{\bigvee}_i a] \leftrightarrow \bigvee u \phi[x(^i_u), a]])\}.
\end{aligned}$$

Given any satisfaction pair, we can find an operation ζ such that if B is any set closed under ζ, then the 'absolute' notion of satisfaction determined by the satisfaction pair reduces to satisfaction relative to the abbreviated model composed of B and membership restricted to B. That this assertion is provable in ZF is the content of the following lemma.

LEMMA 1. *If ϕ, ψ are as in the hypothesis of Definition* 1, *then there is a term ζ whose only free variable is v_0 such that*

$$\vdash_{ZF} SP_{\phi,\psi} \wedge \bigwedge X(X \subseteq B \wedge X \overset{*}{\lesssim} \omega \rightarrow \zeta[X] \subseteq B) \wedge x \in B^{\omega} \wedge \psi[a] \rightarrow (\phi[x, a] \leftrightarrow \mathrm{Sat}[x, a, B]).$$

PROOF. Let $\zeta[X]$ be the term

$$\bigcup_{a,i,x} \left\{ \underset{u}{R} \phi[x(^i_u), a] | \psi[a] \wedge i \in \omega \wedge x \in X^{\omega} \right\}.$$

Clearly the 'existence' of the union denoted by $\zeta[X]$ is provable in ZF, because $\vdash_{ZF} \psi[a] \rightarrow a \in \omega$. Let α be the formula

$$SP_{\phi,\psi} \wedge \bigwedge X(X \subseteq B \wedge X \overset{*}{\lesssim} \omega \rightarrow \zeta[X] \subseteq B),$$

and let $\beta[a]$ be the formula

$$\psi[a] \rightarrow \bigwedge x[x \in B^{\omega} \rightarrow (\phi[x, a] \leftrightarrow \mathrm{Sat}[x, a, B])].$$

In view of the first conjunct of $SP_{\phi,\psi}$, it is sufficient, in order to prove the lemma, to show that

(1) $$\vdash_{ZF} \alpha \wedge SSF\dot{m}[a] \rightarrow \beta[a].$$

By recursive conditions in the formula $SP_{\phi,\psi}$, it is easily seen that

(2) $$\vdash_{ZF} \alpha \wedge i, j \in \omega \to \beta[\dot{=}_{i,j}] \wedge \beta[\dot{\in}_{i,j}],$$

and

(3) $$\vdash_{ZF} \alpha \wedge \beta[a] \wedge \beta[b] \to \beta[\dot{\sim} a] \wedge \beta[a \mathbin{\dot{\wedge}} b].$$

Now a certain principle of induction on standard set-theoretical formulas can be justified in ZF; in fact, if χ is any formula (satisfying certain restrictions on variables), then

(4) $$\vdash_{ZF} \bigwedge i \bigwedge j (i, j \in \omega \to \chi[\dot{=}_{i,j}] \wedge \chi[\dot{\in}_{i,j}]) \wedge \bigwedge a \bigwedge b (\chi[a] \wedge \chi[b] \to \chi[\dot{\sim} a] \wedge \chi[a \mathbin{\dot{\wedge}} b]) \wedge \bigwedge a \bigwedge i (\chi[a] \wedge i \in \omega \to \chi[\dot{\bigvee}_i a]) \to \bigwedge a (SSF\dot{m}[a] \to \chi[a]).$$

Using (4) and the conditions constituting $SP_{\phi,\psi}$, we can show that

$$\vdash_{ZF} SP_{\phi,\psi} \wedge SSF\dot{m}[a] \wedge \psi[a] \to \bigvee X[X \subseteqq \omega \wedge X \overset{*}{\precsim} \omega \wedge \bigwedge x \bigwedge y[x \in \mathcal{C}x^{\omega} \wedge y \in \mathcal{C}y^{\omega} \wedge \bigwedge j (j \in X \to x(j) = y(j)) \to (\phi[x, a] \leftrightarrow \phi[y, a])]],$$

hence that

$$\vdash_{ZF} \alpha \wedge \psi[a] \wedge i \in \omega \to \bigvee X (X \subseteqq \omega \wedge X \overset{*}{\precsim} \omega \wedge \bigwedge x \bigwedge y[x \in \mathcal{C}x^{\omega} \wedge y \in \mathcal{C}y^{\omega} \wedge \bigwedge j (j \in X \to x(j) = y(j)) \to \bigwedge u (\phi[x(^i_u), a] \leftrightarrow \phi[y(^i_u), a])]),$$

and therefore that

(5) $$\vdash_{ZF} \alpha \wedge \psi[a] \wedge i \in \omega \wedge x \in \mathcal{C}x^{\omega} \to \bigvee y (y \in \mathcal{C}y^{\omega} \wedge \mathcal{C}y \subseteqq \mathcal{C}x \wedge \mathcal{C}y \overset{*}{\precsim} \omega \wedge \underset{u}{R}\, \phi[x(^i_u), a] = \underset{u}{R}\, \phi[y(^i_u), a]).$$

Now clearly,

$$\vdash_{ZF} \bigvee u \phi[x(^i_u), a] \to \bigvee u (\phi[x(^i_u), a] \wedge u \in \underset{u}{R}\, \phi[x[^i_u), a]).$$

Hence, by (5),

$$\vdash_{ZF} \alpha \wedge \psi[a] \wedge i \in \omega \wedge x \in B^{\omega} \wedge \bigvee u \phi[x(^i_u), a] \to \bigvee u \bigvee y (\phi[x(^i_u), a] \wedge u \in \underset{u}{R}\, \phi[y(^i_u), a] \wedge y \in \mathcal{C}y^{\omega} \wedge \mathcal{C}y \subseteqq B \wedge \mathcal{C}y \overset{*}{\precsim} \omega).$$

Therefore

$$\vdash_{ZF} \alpha \wedge \psi[a] \wedge i \in \omega \wedge x \in B^{\omega} \wedge \bigvee u \phi[x(^i_u), a] \to \bigvee u \bigvee X (\phi[x(^i_u), a] \wedge u \in \zeta[X] \wedge X \subseteqq B \wedge X \overset{*}{\precsim} \omega),$$

and hence

(6) $$\vdash_{ZF} \alpha \wedge \psi[a] \wedge i \in \omega \wedge x \in B^{\omega} \wedge \bigvee u \phi[x(^i_u), a] \to \bigvee u (u \in B \wedge \phi[x(^i_u), a]).$$

Using (6), we easily see that

$$\vdash_{ZF}\alpha \wedge \beta[a] \wedge i \in \omega \wedge \psi[\dot{\mathbf{V}}_i a] \wedge x \in B^{\omega} \rightarrow (\phi[x, \dot{\mathbf{V}}_i a] \leftrightarrow \mathbf{V}u\phi[x(^i_u), a]) \wedge (\mathbf{V}u\phi[x(^i_u), a] \leftrightarrow \mathbf{V}u[u \in B \wedge \phi[x(^i_u), a]]) \wedge (\mathbf{V}u[u \in B \wedge \phi[x(^i_u), a]] \leftrightarrow \mathbf{V}u[u \in B \wedge \mathrm{Sat}[x(^i_u), a, B]]) \wedge (\mathbf{V}u[u \in B \wedge \mathrm{Sat}[x(^i_u), a, B]] \leftrightarrow \mathrm{Sat}[x, \dot{\mathbf{V}}_i a, B]),$$

and hence that

(7) $$\vdash_{ZF}\alpha \wedge \beta[a] \wedge i \in \omega \rightarrow \beta[\dot{\mathbf{V}}_i a].$$

But from (2), (3), and (7), (1) follows by another application of the induction principles (4); and the proof of the lemma is complete.

COROLLARY. *If χ is a standard set-theoretical formula whose free variables are $v_0, \cdots, v_{n-1}$, then there is a term ζ whose only free variable is v_0 such that*

$$\vdash_{ZF}\mathbf{\Lambda}X(X \subseteqq B \wedge C \overset{*}{\lesssim} \omega \rightarrow \zeta[X] \subseteqq B) \wedge v_0, \cdots, v_{n-1} \in B \rightarrow [\chi \leftrightarrow \chi^{(B)}].$$

PROOF. Let $v_0, \ldots, v_k$ include all the variables occurring in χ (whether free or bound), and let $\chi_0, \cdots, \chi_m$ be all the subformulas of χ (including χ itself). Let ψ be the formula

$$v_0 = \dot{\Delta}_{\chi_0} \vee \cdots \vee v_0 = \dot{\Delta}\chi_m,$$

and let ϕ be the formula

$$(v_1 = \dot{\Delta}_{\chi_0} \wedge \chi_0[v_0(\dot{\Delta}_0), \cdots, v_0(\dot{\Delta}_k)]) \vee \cdots \vee (v_1 = \dot{\Delta}_{\chi_m} \wedge \chi_m[v_0(\dot{\Delta}_0), \cdots, v_0(\dot{\Delta}_k)]).$$

Then $\vdash_{ZF} SP_{\phi,\psi} \wedge \psi[\dot{\Delta}_\chi]$; and thus, by Lemma 1, there is a term η whose only free variable is v_0 such that

(8) $$\vdash_{ZF}\mathbf{\Lambda}X(X \subseteqq B \wedge X \overset{*}{\lesssim} \omega \rightarrow \eta[X] \subseteqq B) \wedge x \in B^{\omega} \rightarrow (\phi[x, \dot{\Delta}_\chi] \leftrightarrow \mathrm{Sat}[x, \dot{\Delta}_\chi, B]).$$

Let $\zeta[X]$ be the term

$$\eta[X] \cup \{0\},$$

and α be the formula

$$\mathbf{\Lambda}X(X \subseteqq B \wedge X \overset{*}{\lesssim} \omega \rightarrow \zeta[X] \subseteqq B).$$

Clearly,

(9) $$\vdash_{ZF}\alpha \rightarrow B \neq 0,$$

and by (8),

(10) $$\vdash_{ZF}\alpha \wedge x \in B^{\omega} \rightarrow (\chi[x(\dot{\Delta}_0), \cdots, x(\dot{\Delta}_{n-1})] \leftrightarrow \mathrm{Sat}[x, \dot{\Delta}_\chi, B]).$$

It is easily shown (by induction on χ) that

(11) $$\vdash_{ZF} x \in B^{\omega} \rightarrow (\mathrm{Sat}[x, \dot{\Delta}_\chi, B] \leftrightarrow \chi^{(B)}[x(\dot{\Delta}_0), \cdots, x(\dot{\Delta}_{n-1})]),$$

and (by induction on n) that

$$(12)\qquad \vdash_{ZF} B \neq 0 \wedge v_0, \cdots, v_{n-1} \in B \to \mathbf{V}x(x \in B^{\omega} \wedge x(\dot{\Delta}_0) = v_0 \wedge \cdots \wedge x(\dot{\Delta}_{n-1}) = v_{n-1}).$$

By (9)—(12) we conclude that

$$\vdash_{ZF} \alpha \wedge v_0, \cdots, v_{n-1} \in B \to (\chi[v_0, \cdots, v_{n-1}] \leftrightarrow \chi^{(B)}[v_0, \cdots, v_{n-1}]),$$

that is,

$$\vdash_{ZF} \alpha \wedge v_0, \cdots, v_{n-1} \in B \to [\chi \leftrightarrow \chi^{(B)}].$$

3. On Lévy's Axiom

It is easy to prove in ZF the following closure principle:

$$(1)\qquad \mathbf{V}B[A \subseteqq B \wedge \mathbf{\Lambda}x(x \in B \to \zeta[x] \subseteqq B)];$$

here ζ may be any term in which the variable B is not free, and may be regarded as representing an operation which associates with each object a set of objects. The principle (1) then expresses the fact that any set can be extended to a set B which is closed under ζ, that is, such that if x is any member of B, then all objects associated with x by ζ are also members of B.

In this formulation we consider one-place operations. To express the closure of B under many-place operations, we might speak of operations which apply to sequences of members of B, or, to adopt a somewhat simpler mode of speech, operations on subsets of B. The most general principle of this sort,

$$\mathbf{V}B[A \subseteqq B \wedge \mathbf{\Lambda}X(X \subseteqq B \to \zeta[X] \subseteqq B)],$$

leads to contradiction in several obvious ways. More special forms, however, in which bounds are imposed on the cardinality of the subsets of B to which ζ is applied, can easily be justified. For instance, the schema

$$(2)\qquad \mathbf{V}B[A \subseteqq B \wedge \mathbf{\Lambda}X(X \subseteqq B \wedge X \overset{*}{\lneq} \omega \to \zeta[X] \subseteqq B)]$$

can be proved in ZF, and the more general schema

$$(3)\qquad \mathbf{V}B[A \subseteqq B \wedge \mathbf{\Lambda}X(X \subseteqq B \wedge X \overset{*}{\lneq} C \to \zeta[X] \subseteqq B)]$$

can be derived in ZF from the axiom of choice.

In (2) and (3) the bound on cardinalities is given in advance of the construction of B. We are therefore led to consider a principle in which the bound is given in terms of B itself; in particular, we apply the operation ζ to all subsets of B which are less numerous than B:

$$(4)\qquad \mathbf{V}B[A \subseteqq B \wedge \mathbf{\Lambda}X(X \subseteqq B \wedge X \overset{*}{\lneq} B \to \zeta[X] \subseteqq B)].$$

The schema (4) is not provable in ZF (unless ZF is inconsistent). What is more interesting, (4) turns out to be equivalent to a powerful axiom recently proposed by Azriel Lévy (in [2]; closely related axioms were suggested by Mahlo in [3]).

One form of Lévy's axiom is the schema

$$\text{(5)}\qquad \mathrm{Norm}_\zeta \to \mathbf{V}v_0(\mathrm{In}[v_0] \wedge \zeta[v_0] = v_0),$$

where ζ is any term, and another is the principle

$$\text{(6)}\qquad \mathbf{V}v_n[\mathrm{In}[v_n] \wedge \mathbf{\Lambda}v_0 \cdots \mathbf{\Lambda}v_{n-1}(v_0, \cdots, v_{n-1} \in R[v_n] \to [\phi \leftrightarrow \phi^{(R[v_n])}])],$$

where ϕ is any standard formula whose free variables are $v_0, \cdots, v_{n-1}$. All of Lévy's formulations involve rather intricate concepts of either metamathematics or the theory of ordinals, and thus seem less elegant than (4) from an axiomatic point of view.

THEOREM 1. *The principles* (4), (5), *and* (6) *are equivalent within* ZF.

PROOF. Lévy has shown in [2] that (5) and (6) are equivalent within ZF. (Actually, Lévy's formulations involve a notion of inaccessible ordinal whose equivalence with ours seems demonstrable only on the assumption of the axiom of choice. His proof, however, of the equivalence of (5) and (6) remains intact upon replacing his notion by ours.) We shall prove that (4) implies (6) and (5) implies (4).

Let ϕ be as in (6). By the Corollary of Lemma 1, there is a term ζ such that

$$\text{(7)}\qquad \vdash_{ZF} \mathbf{\Lambda}X[X \subseteqq B \wedge C \overset{*}{\lessgtr} \omega \to \zeta[X] \subseteqq B] \wedge v_0, \cdots, v_{n-1} \in B \\ \to [\phi \leftrightarrow \phi^{(B)}].$$

Let $\psi[B]$ be the formula

$$R[\omega+1] \subseteqq B \wedge \mathbf{\Lambda}X[X \subseteqq B \wedge X \overset{*}{\lessgtr} B \to \zeta[X] \cup R[\rho[X]] \cup \{X\} \subseteqq B].$$

Then

$$\text{(8)}\qquad \vdash_{ZF \cup (4)} \vee B\psi[B],$$

and it is easily seen that

$$\text{(9)}\qquad \vdash_{ZF} \psi[B] \to \mathbf{V}v_n[\mathrm{In}[v_n] \wedge B = R[v_n]],$$

$$\text{(10)}\qquad \vdash_{ZF} \psi[B] \to \mathbf{\Lambda}X[X \subseteqq B \wedge X \overset{*}{\lessgtr} \omega \to \zeta[X] \subseteqq B].$$

It follows, by (7)—(10), that

$$\vdash_{ZF \cup (4)} \mathbf{V}v_n[\mathrm{In}[v_n] \wedge \mathbf{\Lambda}v_0 \cdots \mathbf{\Lambda}v_{n-1}(v_0, \cdots, v_{n-1} \in R[v_n] \to [\phi \leftrightarrow \phi^{(R[v_n])}])],$$

and the derivation of (6) from (4) is complete.

Now let ζ be a term in which the variable B is not free. By a well-known theorem on recursive definitions, there is a term η (with the free variables v_0 and A) such that

$$\text{(11)}\qquad \vdash_{ZF} \eta[0] = \rho[A],$$

$$\text{(12)}\qquad \vdash_{ZF} \mathrm{Ord}[a] \to \eta[a+1] = \underset{b}{\mathrm{Min}}[\eta[a] \in b \\ \wedge \bigcup_X \{\zeta[X] | X \in R[\eta[a]]\} \subseteqq R[b]],$$

$$\text{(13)}\qquad \vdash_{ZF} \mathrm{Lim}[a] \to \eta[a] = \bigcup_b \{\eta[b] | b \in a\}.$$

Clearly, $\vdash_{ZF} \mathrm{Norm}_\eta$, and hence

(14) $$\vdash_{ZF\cup(5)} \bigvee a[\mathrm{In}[a] \wedge \eta[a] = a).$$

By (11),

$$\vdash_{ZF} A \subseteqq R[\eta[0]],$$

and therefore

(15) $$\vdash_{ZF} \mathrm{Ord}[a] \wedge \eta[a] = a \to A \subseteqq R[a].$$

By (12),

(16) $$\vdash_{ZF} \mathrm{Ord}[a] \wedge b \in a \wedge X \in R[\eta[b]] \to \zeta[X] \subseteqq R[\eta[a]].$$

Clearly, by (13) (and the content of the formula $\mathrm{In}[a]$),

$$\vdash_{ZF} \mathrm{In}[a] \wedge \eta[a] = a \wedge X \subseteqq R[a] \wedge X \overset{*}{\precsim} R[a] \to X \in R[\bigcup_b\{\eta[b] | b \in a\}].$$

Hence, by the fact that $\vdash_{ZF} \mathrm{Ord}[a] \to R[\bigcup_b\{\eta[b] | b \in a\}] = \bigcup_b\{R[\eta[b]] | b \in a\}$,

$$\vdash_{ZF} \mathrm{In}[a] \wedge \eta[a] = a \wedge X \subseteqq R[a] \wedge X \overset{*}{\precsim} R[a] \to \bigvee b(b \in a \wedge X \in R[\eta[b]]).$$

Therefore, by (16),

$$\vdash_{ZF} \mathrm{In}[a] \wedge \eta[a] = a \wedge X \subseteqq R[a] \wedge X \overset{*}{\precsim} R[a] \to \zeta[X] \subseteqq R[a],$$

and hence, by (14) and (15),

$$\vdash_{ZF\cup(5)} \bigvee a[A \subseteqq R[a] \wedge \bigwedge X(X \subseteqq R[a] \wedge X \overset{*}{\precsim} R[a] \to \zeta[X] \subseteqq R[a])],$$

which completes the derivation of (4) from (5).

REMARK. In [6] Tarski proposed the following 'axiom of inaccessible sets':

(17) $$\bigvee B[A \in B \wedge \bigwedge X \bigwedge Y(X \in B \wedge Y \subseteqq X \to Y \in B) \wedge \bigwedge X(X \in B \to P[X] \in B) \wedge \bigwedge X(X \subseteqq B \wedge X \prec B \to X \in B)].$$

As Tarski has pointed out in correspondence, (17) can be regarded as a special case of (4) if in the latter '$\overset{*}{\precsim}$' is replaced by '$\prec$'; we need only instantiate A to $\{A, 0, \{0\}\}$ and take for $\zeta[X]$ the term $\{X\} \cup P[U[X]] \cup \{P[U[X]]\}$. (It follows, in view of [6], that the axiom of choice is derivable from the altered version of (4).) Similarly, the result of replacing '$\prec$' by '$\overset{*}{\precsim}$' in (17) can be regarded as a special case of the original principle (4).

4. On Demonstrable Consistency

We now single out, for each positive integer n, an infinite set of n-place predicates (not among those occurring in members of P or ZF), to be known as *variable predicates*. An *atomic schema* is an expression of the form $\pi v_0 \cdots v_n$, where n is a natural number and π is an $(n+1)$-place variable predicate (and $v_0, \cdots, v_n$ are as usual the first $n+1$ variables). The set of *schemata* is the smallest set K such that (1) for all natural numbers i and j, the formulas $v_i = v_j$ and $v_i \in v_j$ are in K, (2) all atomic schemata are in K, (3) if ϕ, ψ are any members of K, then $\sim\phi$ and $\phi \wedge \psi$ are in K, and (4) if ϕ is any member of K and i is any natural number, then $\bigvee v_i \phi$ is in K.

If χ is a schema, then F is said to be an *acceptable assignment* for χ if F is a function whose domain contains all atomic schemata occurring in χ and such that, if ϕ is any such schema, then $F(\phi)$ is a standard set-theoretical formula and all variables common to χ and $F(\phi)$ occur in ϕ. If χ is a schema and F an acceptable assignment for χ, the *substitution according to F in* χ, or $S_F[\chi]$, is defined recursively as follows. (1) If i, j are natural numbers, then $S_F[v_i = v_j]$ is the formula $v_i = v_j$, and $S_F[v_j \in v_j]$ is $v_i \in v_j$. (2) If ϕ is an atomic schema, then $S_F[\phi]$ is $F(\phi)$. (3) If ϕ, ψ are schemata, then $S_F[\phi \wedge \psi]$ is $S_F[\phi] \wedge S_F[\psi]$, and $S_F[\sim\phi]$ is $\sim S_F[\phi]$. (4) If ϕ is a schema and i a natural number, then $S_F[\mathbf{V} v_i \phi]$ is $\mathbf{V} v_i S_F[\phi]$. An *instance* of a schema χ is a formula ϕ such that, for some acceptable assignment F for χ, ϕ is $S_F[\chi]$.

(We might have introduced a broader set of schemata, in which variable predicates could be accompanied by *any* sequence of variables of the appropriate length, and not necessarily by an initial segment of the sequence $v_0, \cdots, v_n, \cdots$; but it is easily seen that any schema in the broader sense is logically equivalent, within the predicate calculus with identity, to a schema of the narrower variety introduced above. An instance of a schema is, roughly, a set-theoretical formula that can be obtained from the schema by the *substitution rule for variable predicates*; see [1].)

If ζ, η are terms of ZF, then

$$Acc[\zeta, \eta]$$

is to be a formula of ZF asserting in the 'natural' way that ζ is an acceptable assignment for the schema η,

$$\dot{S}[\zeta, \eta]$$

is to be a term of ZF denoting (in the 'natural' way) the substitution according to the assignment denoted by ζ in the schema denoted by η, and

$$\mathrm{Inst}[\zeta, \eta]$$

is to be the formula $\mathbf{V}f(\mathrm{Acc}[f, \eta] \wedge \zeta = \dot{S}[f, \eta])$, which asserts that ζ is an instance of η.

Lemma 2. *If ϕ is a formula whose only free variable is v_0, ψ is a formula whose only free variables are v_0 and v_1, χ is a schema whose variables are among $v_0, \cdots, v_k$, G is an acceptable assignment for χ, and, for every β and n, if β is an atomic schema in the domain of G whose variables are exactly $v_0, \cdots, v_n$, then $G(\beta)$ is the formula $\phi[x(\tfrac{\dot{\Delta}_0}{v_0} \cdots \tfrac{\dot{\Delta}_n}{v_n}), f(\dot{\Delta}_\beta)]$, then*

$$\vdash_{ZF} SP_{\phi,\psi} \wedge \mathrm{Acc}[f, \dot{\Delta}_\chi] \wedge \psi[\dot{S}[f, \dot{\Delta}_\chi]] \wedge x \in \mathfrak{a}x^\omega \\ \rightarrow (\phi[x(\tfrac{\dot{\Delta}_0}{v_0} \cdots \tfrac{\dot{\Delta}_k}{v_k}), \dot{S}[f, \dot{\Delta}_\chi]] \leftrightarrow S_G[\chi]).$$

Proof. The lemma will be proved by induction on the schema χ. Throughout the proof, let α be the formula

$$SP_{\phi,\psi} \wedge \mathrm{Acc}[f, \dot{\Delta}_\chi] \wedge \psi[\dot{S}[f, \dot{\Delta}_\chi]] \wedge x \in \mathfrak{a}x^\omega.$$

Suppose first that χ is the formula $v_i = v_j$ (for some natural numbers i, j), and assume the hypothesis of the lemma. Then

$$\vdash_{ZF} \alpha \rightarrow (\phi[x(\tfrac{\dot{\Delta}_0}{v_0} \cdots \tfrac{\dot{\Delta}_0}{v_k}), \dot{S}[f, \dot{\Delta}_\chi]] \leftrightarrow \phi[x(\tfrac{\dot{\Delta}_0}{v_0} \cdots \tfrac{\dot{\Delta}_k}{v_k}), \dot{=}\ \dot{\Delta}_i, \dot{\Delta}_j)]$$
$$\wedge\ (\phi[x(\tfrac{\dot{\Delta}_0}{v_0} \cdots \tfrac{\dot{\Delta}_k}{v_k}), \dot{=}\ \dot{\Delta}_i, \dot{\Delta}_j)] \leftrightarrow v_i = v_j),$$

and hence, since $S_G[\chi] = \chi$,

$$\vdash_{ZF} \alpha \rightarrow (\phi[x(\tfrac{\dot{\Delta}_0}{v_0} \cdots \tfrac{\dot{\Delta}_k}{v_k}), \dot{S}[f, \dot{\Delta}_\chi]] \leftrightarrow S_G[\chi]).$$

A similar argument will show that the lemma holds if χ has the form $v_i \in v_j$ (for natural numbers i and j).

Now suppose that χ is an atomic schema whose variables are $v_0, \cdots, v_n$, and again assume the hypothesis of the lemma. Then

$$\vdash_{ZF} \alpha \rightarrow (\phi[x(\tfrac{\dot{\Delta}_0}{v_0} \cdots \tfrac{\dot{\Delta}_k}{v_k}), \dot{S}[f, \dot{\Delta}_\chi]] \leftrightarrow \phi[x(\tfrac{\dot{\Delta}_0}{v_0} \cdots \tfrac{\dot{\Delta}_k}{v_k}), f(\dot{\Delta}_\chi)])$$
$$\wedge\ (\phi[x(\tfrac{\dot{\Delta}_0}{v_0} \cdots \tfrac{\dot{\Delta}_k}{v_k}), f(\dot{\Delta}_\chi)] \leftrightarrow \phi\ [x(\tfrac{\dot{\Delta}_0}{v_0} \cdots \tfrac{\dot{\Delta}_n}{v_n}), f(\dot{\Delta}_\chi)]),$$

and hence

$$\vdash_{ZF} \alpha \rightarrow (\phi[x(\tfrac{\dot{\Delta}_0}{v_0} \cdots \tfrac{\dot{\Delta}_k}{v_k}), \dot{S}[f, \dot{\Delta}_\chi]] \leftrightarrow S_G[\chi]).$$

It is easy to see that if the lemma holds for schemata χ_1 and χ_2, then it also holds for $\sim\chi_1$ and $\chi_1 \wedge \chi_2$.

Now suppose that χ has the form $\mathbf{V} v_i \chi_1$; assume the lemma for χ_1 and the hypothesis of the lemma for χ. Then

$$\vdash_{ZF} \alpha \rightarrow (\phi[x(\tfrac{\dot{\Delta}_0}{v_0} \cdots \tfrac{\dot{\Delta}_k}{v_k}), \dot{S}[f, \dot{\Delta}_\chi]] \leftrightarrow \phi[x(\tfrac{\dot{\Delta}_0}{v_0} \cdots \tfrac{\dot{\Delta}_k}{v_k}), \dot{\mathbf{V}}_{\dot{\Delta}_i} \dot{S}[f, \dot{\Delta}_{\chi_1}]])$$
$$\wedge\ (\phi[x(\tfrac{\dot{\Delta}_0}{v_0} \cdots \tfrac{\dot{\Delta}_k}{v_k}), \dot{\mathbf{V}}_{\dot{\Delta}_i} \dot{S}[f, \dot{\Delta}_{\chi_1}]] \leftrightarrow \mathbf{V} u[x(\tfrac{\dot{\Delta}_0}{v_0} \cdots \tfrac{\dot{\Delta}_k}{v_k})(\tfrac{\dot{\Delta}_i}{u}), \dot{S}[f, \dot{\Delta}_{\chi_1}]])$$
$$\wedge\ (\mathbf{V} u \phi[x(\tfrac{\dot{\Delta}_0}{v_0} \cdots \tfrac{\dot{\Delta}_k}{v_k})(\tfrac{\dot{\Delta}_i}{u}), \dot{S}[f, \dot{\Delta}_{\chi_1}]] \leftrightarrow \mathbf{V} v_i \phi[x(\tfrac{\dot{\Delta}_0}{v_0} \cdots \tfrac{\dot{\Delta}_k}{v_k}), \dot{S}[f, \dot{\Delta}_{\chi_1}]])$$
$$\wedge\ (\mathbf{V} v_i \phi[x(\tfrac{\dot{\Delta}_0}{v_0} \cdots \tfrac{\dot{\Delta}_k}{v_k}), \dot{S}[f, \dot{\Delta}_{\chi_1}]] \leftrightarrow \mathbf{V} v_i S_G[\chi_1]),$$

and hence

$$\vdash_{ZF} \alpha \rightarrow (\phi[x(\tfrac{\dot{\Delta}_0}{v_0} \cdots \tfrac{\dot{\Delta}_k}{v_k}), \dot{S}[f, \dot{\Delta}_\chi]] \leftrightarrow S_G[\chi]),$$

which completes the inductive proof of the lemma.

LEMMA 3. *Let ϕ, ψ be as in the hypothesis of Definition* 1. *If T is an extension of ZF and χ is a schema all of whose instances are derivable from T, then there is a term ζ whose only free variable is v_0 such that*

$$\vdash_T SP_{\phi,\psi} \wedge \mathbf{\Lambda} X (X \subseteq B \wedge X \overset{*}{\precsim} \omega \rightarrow \zeta[X] \subseteq B) \wedge \psi[a]$$
$$\wedge\ \mathrm{Inst}[a, \dot{\Delta}_\chi] \wedge x \in B^\omega \rightarrow \mathrm{Sat}[x, a, B].$$

PROOF. By Lemma 2,

$$\vdash_{ZF} SP_{\phi,\psi} \wedge \psi[a] \wedge \mathrm{Inst}[a, \dot{\Delta}_\chi] \wedge x \in \mathcal{O}x^\omega \rightarrow (\phi[x(\tfrac{\dot{\Delta}_0}{v_0} \cdots \tfrac{\dot{\Delta}_k}{v_k}), a] \leftrightarrow S_G[\chi]),$$

where $v_0, \cdots, v_k$ are the variables of χ, and G is as in the hypothesis of Lemma 2. Hence, since $\vdash_T S_G[\chi]$,

$$\vdash_T SP_{\phi,\psi} \wedge \psi[a] \wedge \text{Inst}[a, \dot{\Delta}_\chi] \wedge x \in \mathfrak{A}x^\omega \to \Lambda v_0 \cdots \Lambda v_k \phi[x(\tfrac{\dot{\Delta}_\circ}{v_\circ} \cdots \tfrac{\dot{\Delta}_k}{v_k}), a].$$

Therefore

$$\vdash_T SP_{\phi,\psi} \wedge \psi[a] \wedge \text{Inst}[a, \dot{\Delta}_\chi] \wedge x \in \mathfrak{A}x^\omega \to \phi[x, a].$$

But by Lemma 1 there is a term ζ whose only free variable is v_0 such that

$$\vdash_{ZF} SP_{\phi,\psi} \wedge \Lambda X(X \subseteqq B \wedge X \overset{*}{\lessapprox} \omega \to \zeta[X] \subseteqq B) \wedge \psi[a] \wedge x \in B^\omega \to (\phi[x, a] \leftrightarrow \text{Sat}[x, a, B]),$$

and it follows that ζ satisfies the conclusion of the present lemma.

LEMMA 4. *If n is a natural number and ψ is the formula $D\dot{p}_n[v_0]$, then there is a formula ϕ whose free variables are v_0 and v_1, and such that*

$$\vdash_{ZF} SP_{\phi,\psi}.$$

PROOF. An indication of how to construct ϕ can be obtained from the construction of the formula

$$v_0 \,\text{sat}_n v_1$$

in Definition 6 of [5].

DEFINITION 2. *A formula α is said to* define *a set A of natural numbers (in P) if the only free variable of α is v_0 and, for every natural number n, $\vdash_P \alpha[\mathring{\Delta}_n]$ if $n \in A$, and $\vdash_P \sim\alpha[\mathring{\Delta}_n]$ if $n \notin A$. If A is a set of standard formulas and B any set of formulas, then the consistency of A is said to be* demonstrable in B *if there is a primitive recursive formula α such that α defines A in P and $P \cup \{\mathring{Con}_\alpha\}$ is relatively interpretable in B.*

THEOREM 2. *If T is an extension of ZF, χ is a schema all of whose instances are derivable from T, n is a natural number, and A is the set of instances of χ whose depth is at most n, then the consistency of $SF \cup A$ is demonstrable in T.*

PROOF. Let π be a one-place variable predicate, let χ' be the schema

$$\mathsf{V} v_1 \Lambda v_0 (v_0 \in v_1 \leftrightarrow \pi v_0 \wedge v_0 \in v_2),$$

let ψ be the formula $D\mathring{p}_n[v_0]$, and let ϕ be a formula (whose existence is insured by Lemma 4) with free variables v_0, v_1 such that

$$\vdash_{ZF} SP_{\phi,\psi}.$$

By Lemma 3, there is a term ζ whose only free variable is v_0 such that

(1) $\vdash_T \Lambda X(X \subseteqq B \wedge X \overset{*}{\lessapprox} \omega \to \zeta[X] \subseteqq B] \wedge \psi[a] \wedge \text{Inst}[a, \dot{\Delta}_\chi] \wedge x \in B^\omega \to \text{Sat}[x, a, B]$,

and clearly,

(2) $\vdash_{ZF} \Lambda X(X \subseteqq B \wedge X \overset{*}{\lessapprox} \omega \to \bigcup_v \{P[v] | v \in X\} \subseteqq B) \wedge \text{Inst}[a, \dot{\Delta}_{\chi'}] \wedge x \in B^\omega \to \text{Sat}[x, a, B]$.

Also

(3) $\vdash_{ZF} \bigvee B[B \neq 0 \wedge \bigwedge X(X \subseteqq B \wedge X \overset{*}{\lesssim} \omega \rightarrow \zeta[X] \cup \bigcup_{v} \{P[v] | v \in X\} \subseteqq B)]$.

Let α be the formula

$$\mathrm{Inst}[v_0, \dot{\Delta}_{\chi'}] \vee (\psi[v_0] \wedge \mathrm{Inst}[v_0, \dot{\Delta}_{\chi}]).$$

Then, by (1)—(3),

$$\vdash_T \bigvee B[B \neq 0 \wedge \bigwedge a \bigwedge x(\alpha[a] \wedge x \in B^{\omega} \rightarrow \mathrm{Sat}[x, a, B])],$$

and hence, by imitating within T a familiar metamathematical argument, we see that

(4) $\vdash_T \sim \bigvee f \bigvee b[f, b \in \omega \wedge \bigwedge v_0(v_0 \in \omega \wedge T\dot{m}[v_0, f] \rightarrow \alpha)$
$\wedge \, \mathrm{G\dot{e}n}[b, \mathrm{C\dot{o}nj}[f]] \wedge \mathrm{P\dot{r}}[\dot{\sim} b]]$.

Using well-known methods, we can construct a primitive recursive formula β of P such that

(5) β defines $SF \cup A$ (in P)

and

(6) $\vdash_{ZF} \alpha \leftrightarrow I_0(\beta)$.

By (4) and (6),

$\vdash_T \sim \bigvee f \bigvee b[f, b \in \omega \wedge \bigwedge v_0(v_0 \in \omega \wedge T\dot{m}[v_0, f] \rightarrow I_0(\beta))$
$\wedge \, \mathrm{G\dot{e}n}[b, \mathrm{C\dot{o}nj}[f]] \wedge \mathrm{P\dot{r}}[\dot{\sim} b]]$,

that is,

$$\vdash_T I_0(\mathring{Con}\ \beta).$$

Combining this with the obvious fact that, for all $\gamma, \alpha_0, \cdots, \alpha_{n-1}$, if $\gamma \in P$ and $\alpha_0, \cdots, \alpha_{n-1}$ are the free variables of γ then $\vdash_{ZF} I_0(\bigwedge \alpha_0 \cdots \bigwedge \alpha_{n-1} \gamma)$, we conclude that $P \cup \{\mathring{Con}_{\beta}\}$ is relatively interpretable in T, and hence, by (5), that the consistency of $SF \cup A$ is demonstrable in T.

Corollary. *Under the hypothesis of Theorem 2, the consistency of $Z \cup A$ is demonstrable in T.*

Proof. By Theorem 2.

Using the last Corollary, together with the Gödel-Feferman theorem, one obtains immediately the following extension of the main result in [4]: if T is a consistent extension of ZF with the same constants as ZF, then there is no schema χ all of whose instances are derivable from T and such that T is equivalent to the result to adding to Z a set of instances of χ all of which have no more than a given depth. Lévy has recently obtained a stronger result, partly employing some of the methods of this paper: under the same assumption, there will be no set A of formulas all of which have no more than a given depth and such that T is equivalent to $Z \cup A$.

REFERENCES

[1] HILBERT, D., and W. ACKERMANN. *Principles of Mathematical Logic*. Translation of the second German edition. New York, Chelsea, 1950, xii+172 pp.

[2] LÉVY, A. Axiom schemata of strong infinity in axiomatic set theory. *Pacific Journal of Mathematics*, Vol. 10 (1960), pp. 223–238.

[3] MAHLO, P. Zur Theorie und Anwendung der ρ_0-Zahlen II. *Berichte über die Verhandlungen der Königlich Sächsischen Gesellschaft der Wissenschaften zu Leipzig, Mathematisch-Physische Klasse*, Vol. 65 (1913), pp. 268–282.

[4] MONTAGUE, R. Fraenkel's addition to the axioms of Zermelo. To appear in a collection published in Israel.

[5] MONTAGUE, R. Semantical closure and non-finite axiomatizability I. *Infinitistic Methods, Proceedings of the Symposium on Foundations of Mathematics*. Warsaw, Państwowe Wydawnictwo Naukowe, 1961, 362 pp.

[6] TARSKI, A. Über unerreichbare Kardinalzahlen. *Fundamenta Mathematicae*, Vol. 30 (1938), pp. 68–89.

[7] TARSKI, A. Der Wahrheitsbegriff in den formalisierten Sprachen. *Studia Philosophica*, Vol. 1 (1936), pp. 261–405.

[8] TARSKI, A., A. MOSTOWSKI, and R. M. ROBINSON. *Undecidable Theories*. Amsterdam, North-Holland, 1953, ix+98 pp.

QUINE'S INDIVIDUALS

DANA SCOTT
University of California, Berkeley, California, U.S.A.

Professor Quine has suggested that with regard to theories of membership it would be possible to allow for the existence of *non-classes* or *individuals* by interpreting the formula '$x \in y$' as synonymous with '$x = y$' in the case that y is an individual. This suggestion is by no means a commitment, for as he stresses in [7, p. 123] the situation never arises in the formal development where it is known that any object is actually an individual in this sense. The fact that the situation did not arise in the course of one particular development is not a conclusive argument, however. By some bizarre chain of deductions, might we not prove from Quine's axioms for class membership that individuals do in fact exist? It seems clear from his remarks that Professor Quine does not imagine such a deduction is possible, nor would anyone else believe this who understands the suggestion and feels confident that the axioms are consistent. Nothing supports belief like proof, and it will be the purpose of this note to demonstrate that if Quine's axioms are consistent, then they remain so upon the adjunction either of the sentence

(*) $$\text{`}\exists y \forall x[x \in y \leftrightarrow x = y]\text{'}$$

or of its negation. Take your choice.

For the sake of simplicity, we shall not discuss the system of [7] but rather the system of [6], usually called *New Foundations*, or NF for short. As Wang in [8] has shown, every model for NF can be extended to a model of ML, the system of [7]; hence, a consistency and independence proof for (*) relative to NF easily yields one for ML. Of course, Wang's proof is not a finitary argument, because it makes use of the semantical notion of *definability* within a model. The proof given here for NF is strictly finitary, and no doubt a similar argument can be applied to ML.

For our purposes, we shall imagine NF formulated in first-order logic with *identity* and with the *descriptive operator*. The only non-logical constant is the binary predicate symbol '$\in$'. The logical constants are those in the following list

$$\wedge, \vee, \neg, \rightarrow, \leftrightarrow, =, \forall, \exists, \mathbf{T},$$

where the last symbol denotes the descriptive operator. The variables are those in the list

$$x, y, z, w, x', y', z', w', x'', \cdots, \text{etc.}$$

The note published here is not the paper read by the author at the Congress. After the presentation of the original paper, Professor E. Specker pointed out that he had published similar and overlapping material from his *Habilitationsschrift* of 1951. There was very little new to recommend the author's remarks, and so he decided to substitute another article.

Brackets '[' and ']' are used (and misused) with the (binary) propositional connectives in the usual way, but neither they nor any other additional punctuation is required in such contexts as $\ulcorner\neg\Phi\urcorner$, '$x \in y$', '$x = y$', $\ulcorner\exists x\Phi\urcorner$, $\ulcorner Tx\Phi\urcorner$, where Φ is a formula. It is assumed as clear what is meant by the statements 'Φ is a formula', 'ϕ is a term', ''x' is free in the formula Φ', and so on. As indicated, capital Greek letters (except 'Λ') will range over formulas, while the lower case Greek letters range over terms. If ϕ is a term and Φ a formula, then $\Phi(\phi)$ is the result of substituting ϕ for all free occurrences of 'x' in Φ', where Φ' is the first alphabetic variant of Φ (in some suitable ordering of all formulas) which has no bound variables identical with any free variables of ϕ. Similarly for $\phi(\psi)$. We shall write '$\Phi(y)$' rather than the more correct 'Φ('y')' to indicate substitution of particular variables for 'x'.

The theory of the descriptive operator as developed in [3] is to be applied here. From this point of view the term '$\mathbf{T}x\, x = x$' denotes an object identical with the denotations of all improper descriptive phrases. That neither the axioms of logic nor the axioms of NF indicate more definitely the nature of this privileged object is totally irrelevant. However, we must discuss how the notion of a *stratified* formula as defined in [7, pp. 157 f.] is to be carried over to this extended theory. In the first place, to avoid tiresome circumlocution, we assume that the notion is so defined that if a formula is stratified, then so are all of its alphabetic variants. Thus to check a given formula for stratification, rewrite all its bound variables so that no letter occurs twice with the operators '$\forall$', '$\exists$', '$\mathbf{T}$'. Then in assigning numerals to terms, be sure to assign $\ulcorner\mathbf{T}x\Phi\urcorner$ the same numeral as assigned to 'x', and make certain that both sides of an equation receive the same numeral. Otherwise proceed exactly as described by Quine. For example, '$x = y \wedge x \in y$' is not stratified, while the strange formula '$\mathbf{T}x\, x = x \in \mathbf{T}y\, y = y$' is stratified.

We may take as the axioms of NF the following:

(I) '$\forall x \forall y[\forall z[z \in x \leftrightarrow z \in y] \rightarrow x = y]$';

(II) $\ulcorner\exists y \forall x[x \in y \leftrightarrow \Phi]\urcorner$,

where Φ is a stratified formula in which 'y' is not free. (I) is the *axiom of extensionality*, while (the closures of) the formulas mentioned in (II) are the *axioms of class existence.*

A term τ will be called *level* if its only free variable is 'x' and if the formula $\ulcorner x = \tau(x)\urcorner$ is stratified. If we imagine for a moment that τ defines a "function" which maps the object x to the object denoted by τ, then the condition of being *level* means that the function values are of the same "level" or "type" as the arguments. In any case, whatever we have in the back of our minds, it turns out that level terms are very useful for giving reinterpretations of the membership relation. To be specific, for each formula Φ, let Φ^τ denote the result of simultaneously replacing [1] all portions of Φ of the form

[1]This replacement might better be described as a substitution of the formula $\ulcorner x \in \tau(y)\urcorner$ for the atomic formula '$x \in y$' in the sense of the $\check{S}$ substitution of Church [2, pp. 192 f.].

$\ulcorner \phi \in \psi \urcorner$, where ϕ, ψ are terms, by the formula $\ulcorner \phi \in \tau(\psi) \urcorner$. If τ is a level term and Φ is stratified, then it is very easy to see that Φ^τ is also stratified. The importance of this process is indicated by the following result.

METATHEOREM.[2] *Suppose τ is a level term for which there is a proof in NF of the sentence*

$$\ulcorner \forall y \exists z \forall x [y = \tau(x) \leftrightarrow x = z] \urcorner.$$

Then if Ψ is provable in NF, so is Ψ^τ.

PROOF. It is obvious that we have only to check the cases where Ψ is an axiom of NF. Take the case where Ψ is axiom (I). The sentence to be shown provable is

$$\ulcorner \forall x \forall y [\forall z [z \in \tau(x) \leftrightarrow z \in \tau(y)] \rightarrow x = y] \urcorner.$$

In view of axiom (I) this is equivalent to the sentence

$$\ulcorner \forall x \forall y [\tau(x) = \tau(y) \rightarrow x = y] \urcorner,$$

which is a direct consequence of the assumption on τ.

Next consider the case where Ψ is one of the axioms of (II). Here the formula to be shown provable is (the closure of) a formula of the form

$$\ulcorner \exists y \forall x [x \in \tau(y) \leftrightarrow \Phi^\tau] \urcorner,$$

where 'y' is not free in the formulas Φ and Φ^τ. From the assumption on τ it follows that the sentence

$$\ulcorner \forall z \exists y \; z = \tau(y) \urcorner$$

is provable. Hence, it is sufficient to verify that

$$\ulcorner \exists y \forall x [x \in y \leftrightarrow \Phi^\tau] \urcorner$$

is provable. But since Φ^τ is stratified, (the closure of) this formula is an axiom of (II), and hence is indeed provable.

Let us call a level term τ which satisfied the hypothesis of the Metatheorem a *permutation*. An immediate corollary of the above result is that if τ is a permutation such that Ψ^τ is provable in NF, and if NF is consistent, then the *sentence Ψ is consistent with the axioms of* NF. Clearly the exhibition of τ together with a proof of Ψ^τ yields a finitary consistency proof of Ψ relative to the axioms of NF. This is the method that will be applied to the sentence (*) and to its negation.

For the moment let Ψ be the formula (*) and let τ be a permutation. Notice that Ψ^τ is provably equivalent to the sentence

---

[2]That a similar result holds for other theories of class membership was first brought to the author's attention by the paper [4] of Reiger and reported on in the review [5]. Subsequently Specker pointed out that the idea is really contained in Bernays' article [1, see pp. 83 f.], but there it is applied only to models of the axioms, and the finitary character of the method is not stressed. Still, it seems proper to credit the idea to Bernays; hence, the remarks in the review [5] are unfair or at least misleading. The application to NF does not seem to have been suggested before, however.

(**) $$\ulcorner \exists y\, \tau(y) = \iota(y) \urcorner,$$

where $\iota(y)$ is the term denoting the *unit set* of y, or in other words ι is the term '$\mathbf{T}z\forall w[w \in z \leftrightarrow w = x]$'. Our first question, then, is whether we can find a permutation for which (**) is provable. The answer is yes, for take τ to be the term

$$\begin{aligned}&\ulcorner \mathbf{T}z[[x = \Lambda \wedge z = \iota(\Lambda)] \vee \\ &[x = \iota(\Lambda) \wedge z = \Lambda] \vee \\ &[\neg x = \Lambda \wedge \neg x = \iota(\Lambda) \wedge z = x]]\urcorner,\end{aligned}$$

where Λ is the term denoting the *empty set*, i.e. the term '$\mathbf{T}z\forall w \neg w \in z$'. In less formal terms, τ is the permutation that "interchanges" the sets Λ and $\iota(\Lambda)$.[3] That τ is level and satisfies all the conditions is obvious.

The second question is whether there exists a different term τ for which the negation of (**) is provable. This construction requires somewhat more thought, since care is always necessary to produce a level term.

To facilitate the definition of the new τ, two auxiliary terms ρ and σ are useful; they are respectively the following:

$$\begin{aligned}&\ulcorner \mathbf{T}z[[x = \Lambda \wedge z = \iota(\Lambda)] \vee \\ &[\neg x = \Lambda \wedge \neg \Lambda \in x \wedge z = \Lambda] \vee \\ &[\Lambda \in x \wedge \neg \iota(\iota(\Lambda)) \in x \wedge z = \iota(\iota(\Lambda))] \vee \\ &[\Lambda \in x \wedge \iota(\iota(\Lambda)) \in x \wedge z = \iota(\Lambda)]]\urcorner, \\ &\ulcorner \mathbf{T}z\exists w[x = \iota(w) \wedge \forall z'[z' \in z \leftrightarrow [z' = w \vee z' = \rho(w)]]]\urcorner\end{aligned}$$

Notice first that both ρ and σ are level terms, but of course neither is a permutation. The term σ will only be applied to unit sets, and the fact that the descriptive phrase is sometimes improper will have no influence on the argument. The provability of these sentences involving ρ and σ is required next:

(i) $\ulcorner \forall w\, \neg w = \rho(w)\urcorner$;

(ii) $\ulcorner \forall w \forall z'[z' \in \sigma(\iota(w)) \leftrightarrow [z' = w \vee z' = \rho(w)]]\urcorner$;

(iii) $\ulcorner \forall w \forall w'\, \neg\sigma(\iota(w)) = \iota(w')\urcorner$;

(iv) $\ulcorner \forall w\, \neg\sigma(\iota(w)) = w\urcorner$;

(v) $\ulcorner \forall w \forall w'[\sigma(\iota(w)) = \sigma(\iota(w')) \rightarrow w = w']\urcorner$.

The proof of (i) is clear by inspection of the definition of ρ. Sentence (ii) follows easily from the definition of σ by taking into account the fact that ρ is level and by applying a suitable instance of the axiom schema (II). Sentence (iii) is now a direct consequence of (i) and (ii) and the characteristic property of unit sets. To prove (iv), speaking informally, assume that $\sigma(\iota(w)) = w$. By (ii) we have $\forall z'[z' \in w \leftrightarrow [z' = w \vee z' = \rho(w)]]$; hence, $\neg w = \Lambda$. If $\neg \Lambda \in w$, then $\rho(w) = \Lambda$, and so $\Lambda \in w$; therefore, $\Lambda \in w$ and $\rho(w) = \Lambda$. On the other hand it is clear from the definition of ρ that

---

[3]For the case of the system of [1], this permutation was suggested by Bernays [1, p. 83] for an analogous purpose. Reiger also uses this permutation in [4].

$[\rho(w) = \Lambda \rightarrow \neg\Lambda \in w]$; thus a contradiction is reached. Finally to establish (v), assume that $\sigma(\iota(w)) = \sigma(\iota(w'))$ and $\neg w = w'$.From (ii) it follows at once that $w = \rho(w')$ and $w' = \rho(w)$. From the definition of ρ we see that there are only three possibilities for w, namely: Λ, $\iota(\Lambda)$, and $\iota(\iota(\Lambda))$. The corresponding values of $\rho(w)$, that is to say w', are by definition $\iota(\Lambda)$, $\iota(\iota(\Lambda))$, and Λ. In none of these three cases is the equality $w = \rho(w')$ correct. The desired conclusion now follows.

The intuitive content of the sentences (iii) and (v) above is that the class of objects of the form $\iota(w)$ and the class of objects of the form $\sigma(\iota(w))$ are two disjoint classes that are in a one-one correspondence by means of the mapping determined by σ. Whenever such a situation exists, the correspondence can always be extended to a permutation of all objects (which is actually an "involution", as we shall see). This remark brings us to the formal definition of the term τ:

$$\ulcorner \mathbf{T}z[\exists w[x = \iota(w) \wedge z = \sigma(\iota(w))] \vee$$
$$\exists w[x = \sigma(\iota(w)) \wedge z = \iota(w)] \vee$$
$$[\neg\exists w[x = \iota(w) \vee x = \sigma(\iota(w))] \wedge z = x]]\urcorner.$$

It is worthwhile to note that not only is τ a level term, but also the descriptive phrase is always used properly in this particular context.

From the foregoing provable sentences about σ, it is easy to deduce these two sentences:

$$\ulcorner \forall x\, \tau(\tau(x)) = x\urcorner;$$
$$\ulcorner \forall w\, \tau(\iota(w)) = \sigma(\iota(w))\urcorner.$$

The first implies that τ is a permutation; while the two together show us that if $\tau(y) = \iota(y)$, then $\tau(\tau(y)) = y = \tau(\iota(y)) = \sigma(\iota(y))$, which is impossible for any y by virtue of (iv) above. In other words, the negation of the sentence (**) is actually provable for this permutation τ. The proof of the relative consistency and independence of (*) is thus complete.

References

[1] BERNAYS, P. A system of axiomatic set theory, Part VII. *Journal of Symbolic Logic*, Vol. 19 (1954), pp. 81–96.

[2] CHURCH, A. *Introduction to Mathematical Logic*. Princeton (1956), ix+378 pp.

[3] KALISH, D., and R. M. MONTAGUE. Remarks on descriptions and natural deduction. *Archiv für Mathematische Logik und Grundlagenforschung*, Vol. 3 (1957), pp. 50–73.

[4] REIGER, L. A contribution to Gödel's axiomatic set theory, I. *Czechoslovak Mathematical Journal*, Vol. 7 (82) (1957), pp. 323–357.

[5] SCOTT, D. Review of [4]. *Journal of Symbolic Logic*, Vol. 23 (1958), pp. 216 f.

[6] QUINE, W. V. New Foundations for Mathematical Logic. *From a logical point of view*, Harvard (1953), pp. 80–101.

[7] QUINE, W. V. *Mathematical Logic* (Revised Edition), Harvard (1952), xii+346 pp.

[8] WANG, H. A formal system of logic. *Journal of Symbolic Logic*, Vol. 15 (1950), pp. 25–32.

TYPICAL AMBIGUITY

ERNST SPECKER

Swiss Federal School of Technology, Zürich, Switzerland

This paper is on simple theory of types and some of its extensions. Simple theory of types is certainly one of the most natural systems of set theory; the reason for this is that it is defined rather by a family of structures than by a system of axioms. In order to describe such a structure let T_0 be a non-empty — finite or infinite — set; elements of T_0 are elements of type 0. T_1 is the set of subsets of T_0; T_2 is the set of subsets of T_1, and in general T_{n+1} is the set of subsets of T_n (n natural number). If the set T_0 is finite, we can write down this tower to any level we want; let us consider the case where T_0 has exactly one element a : T_0 is (a), T_1 is $(\Lambda, (a))$ (Λ is the empty set) T_2 is $(\Lambda, (\Lambda), ((a)), (\Lambda, (a)))$, etc. If T_0 has n_0 elements, the number of elements of T_1 is $n_1 = 2^{n_0}$ and of n_k is the number of elements of T_k, $n_{k+1} = 2^{n_k}$. If T_0 is infinite, these relations still hold if the number n_k of elements of T_k is interpreted as the cardinal of T_k and if powers of 2 are defined in the usual way. In the infinite case such definitions are only possible on the basis of a set theory; as we do not want to presuppose such a theory, we formalize and axiomatize type theory. As to formalization, there are essentially two ways of doing it. The first possibility is to introduce a predicate P_k for each type k: $P_k(a)$ says that a is an element of type k. The second possibility (which will be chosen) is to introduce a separate sequence of variables for each type. (It is well known that these alternatives are equivalent.) We have therefore variables $x_1^0, x_2^0, x_3^0, \cdots$ (to be interpreted as running over elements of type 0), variables $x_1^1, x_2^1, \ldots$ (running over type 1), $x_1^2, x_2^2, \ldots$ (running over type 2), etc. There will be prime formulas of two kinds: formulas as $x_2^0 = x_7^0$, $x_4^3 = x_2^3$ (superscripts of the variables to the left and the right of "$=$" are the same; subscripts are arbitrary); formulas as $x_3^4 \in x_2^5$, $x_6^1 \in x_6^2$ (superscript of the variable to the left of "$\in$" by one unit smaller than superscript of the variable to the right; subscripts arbitrary). From these prime formulas general formulas are built with the help of logical connectives and quantifiers in the usual manner of a first-order calculus. If we want, we can allow the introduction of ι-terms; but we then have to keep in mind that our theory is many-sorted and that every term has therefore its type. (There will, e.g., be an empty set of type 0, 1, etc.)

"Ideal type theory" could now be defined as the set of sentences (formulas without free variables) holding in every structure $(T_0, T_1, \cdots; =, \in)$, where T_{k+1} is the power set of T_k and where "$=$", "$\in$", and the variables are interpreted in the obvious way. Again, such a definition presupposes set theory and it is for this (and other) reasons necessary to axiomatize type

Sponsored in part by the Office of Naval Research under Contract No. NONR 401 (20)–NR 043–167.

theory although one knows beforehand that no recursive axiom system will give us all theorems of the ideal type theory (e.g., by Gödel's incompleteness theorem).

One group of axioms of type theory are the axioms of extensionality; there is one such axiom for every type (except type 0), and it says that two sets are equal if they have the same elements (this is the axiom for type 1):

$$(x_1^1)(x_2^1)[(x_1^0)(x_1^0 \in x_1^1 \leftrightarrow x_2^1 \in x_1^2) \rightarrow x_1^1 = x_2^1)]$$

A second group of axioms are the axioms of comprehension; they are first-order substitutes for the fact that T_{k+1} contains all subsets of T_k as elements. The axioms of comprehension are best given by an axiom scheme for every type; so let C be a formula of our calculus with, e.g., x_1^2 as free variable: $C(x_1^2)$. We then have

$$(Ex_1^3)(x_1^2)[x_1^2 \in x_1^3 \leftrightarrow C(x_1^2)].$$

(The existential quantifier of type 3 must not occur in C; free variables in C other than x_1^2 can be bound in front of the formula.)

The axioms of extensionality and of comprehension are in a certain sense the same for all types. In order to make this more precise we define an operation $+$ which associates a formula F^+ to a formula F: F^+ is obtained from F by raising the superscript of every variable in F by 1. Example: $[(x_3^1)(Ex_1^2)(x_3^1 \in x_1^2)]^+$ is $(x_3^2)(Ex_1^3)(x_3^2 \in x_1^3)$. (If F is a formula of our calculus, so is F^+, and conversely.) The operation $+$ associates to an axiom of extensionality another such axiom and to an axiom of comprehension another such axiom. And as the rules of (many-sorted) first-order logic are obviously not destroyed by the operation $+$, we have the following result: *If S is a theorem of type theory based on axioms of extensionality and comprehension, so is S^+.* This is a first possible meaning of typical ambiguity.

The same invariance of theorems under the operation $+$ holds true for ideal type theory. If $(T_0, T_1, \cdots; =, \in)$ is a structure of the kind as considered for the definition of ideal type theory, so is $(U_0, U_1, \cdots; =, \in)$, where $U_k = T_{k+1}$ and where the relations are defined as before. A sentence S holds in the second structure if and only if S^+ holds in the first; S holds in every structure only if S^+ does: *If S is a theorem of ideal type theory, so is S^+.*

The converse holds neither in ideal type theory nor in type theory based on the axioms of extensionality and comprehension. In fact, the sentence $(Ex_1^1)(Ex_2^1)(x_1^1 \neq x_2^1)$ can be proved from these axioms with the help of the following two instances of the scheme of comprehension: $(Ex_1^1)(x_1^0)(x_1^0 \in x_1^1 \leftrightarrow x_1^0 = x_1^0)$, $(Ex_2^1)(x_1^0)(x_1^0 \in x_2^1 \leftrightarrow x_1^0 \neq x_1^0)$. On the other hand, the sentence $(Ex_1^0)(Ex_2^0)(x_1^0 \neq x_2^0)$ does not even hold in ideal type theory, as there is a structure $(T_0, \cdots; =, \in)$, where T_0 has exactly one element.

We can, however, consistently add to ideal type theory (and *a fortiori* to any weaker system) the following rule: If S^+ is a theorem, so is S. As such a rule is applied in any proof only a finite number of times and as $(S_1 \wedge S_2 \wedge \wedge \cdots \wedge S_m)^+$ is $S_1^+ \wedge \cdots \wedge S_m^+$, it suffices to prove the following special case: S is consistent with ideal type theory if $S^{+\cdots+}$ is a theorem of ideal type theory. ($S^{+\cdots+}$ is obtained from S by raising type superscripts by m.) $S^{+\cdots+}$ being a theorem, it holds in every structure $(T_0, T_1, \cdots; =,)$, where T_{k+1} is the power set of T_k; if $U_k = T_{k+1}$, S holds in $(U_0, U_1, \cdots; =, \in)$, which is of course also a model of ideal type theory.

Type theory with the additional rule "If $\vdash S^+$, then $\vdash S$" is closely connected to Hao Wang's theory of negative types [8]. He considers sequences of variables $x_1^k, x_2^k, \cdots$ for every (positive and negative) integer; axioms are the axioms of comprehension and extensionality (to which of course further axioms might be added). One easily checks that the theorems provable in the type theory based on axioms of extensionality and comprehension (and the additional rule "If $\vdash S^+$, then $\vdash S$") are exactly the theorems of Wang's theory which do not contain negative type superscript. A model of Wang's theory is a structure of the form $(\cdots, M_{-2}, M_{-1} M_0, M_1, \cdots; =, \in)$, where M_k are non-empty sets for every integer k, and "$\in$" is a relation defined between elements of M_k and M_{k+1}. It is obvious that every such model gives rise to a model $(M_0, M_1, \cdots; =, \in)$ of type theory with the additional rule. The converse, however, seems very doubtful; this (presumably open) problem can also be put in the following form: For every model $M = (M_0, M_1, \cdots; =, \in)$ of type theory (based on axioms of extensionality and comprehension) with the additional rule "If $\vdash S^+$, then $\vdash S$", does there exist a model $N = (N_0, N_1, \cdots; =, \notin)$ such that $N_{k+1} = M_k$ and $a \in_M b$ if and only if $a \in_N b$?

The consistency of the additional rule "If $\vdash S^+$, then $\vdash S$" raises the question whether "$S^+ \leftrightarrow S$" (where S is a sentence) might not be added consistently to type theory. Consider models $T = (T_0, T_1, \cdots; =, \in)$ and $U = (U_0, U_1, \cdots; =, \in)$ of type theory, where $U_k = T_{k+1}$ and $a \in_U b$ if and only if $a \in_T b$. S^+ then holds in T if and only if S holds in U; the equivalences "$S \leftrightarrow S^+$" therefore hold in T if and only if the same sentences hold in T and U, i.e., if the structures T and U are elementary equivalent. The structures T and U are certainly elementary equivalent if they are isomorphic; an isomorphism from T to U is a one-to-one map defined on the union of the sets T_k such that the image of T_k is T_{k+1} and that $f(a) \in f(b)$ if and only if $a \in b$. It has been shown in [7] that the existence of such a model of type theory (based on the axioms of extensionality and comprehension) is equivalent to the consistency of Quine's *New Foundations* [3]; the equivalence is shown by a simple model-theoretic argument: If *New Foundations* is consistent, it has a model $(M, =, \in)$; we define a model $(M_0, M_1, \cdots; =, \in')$ of type theory as follows: M_k $(k = 0, 1, \cdots)$ is the set of ordered pairs (a, k), where $a \in M$ and $(a, k) \in' (b, k+1)$ if and only if $a \in b$ holds in M. From the axioms of extensionality and comprehension in *New Foundations*, one easily derives the corresponding axioms in type theory; the map f defined by $f(a, k) = (a, k+1)$ is obviously an isomorphism. If there exists on the other hand such a model of type theory $(M_0, M_1, \cdots; = \in)$, we obtain a model $(M_0, =, \bar{\in})$ by defining $a \bar{\in} b$ as $a \in f(b)$, where f is an isomorphism mapping M_k onto M_{k+1}. The same correspondence between the existence of a model of type theory with "complete typical ambiguity" and the consistency of *New Foundations* holds if additional axioms are added to both theories; such axioms, are e.g., the axiom of infinity and the axiom of choice. In [6] the axiom of infinity has been proved and in *New Foundations* the axiom of choice disproved; it follows therefore that in every model of type theory (based on the axioms of extensionality and comprehension) with complete typical ambiguity the axiom of infinity holds, while the axiom of choice does not hold. (The axiom of choice has been used in [6] in the form that every non-empty set of cardinals has a smallest element; this form can of course be derived in NF from most other forms of an axiom of choice, as for instance from Russel's multiplicative axiom.) A look at the proofs of these theorems shows that they can be carried through in type theory with the additional axiom scheme "$S \leftrightarrow S^+$"; a closer discussion shows that for the proof of the axiom of infinity one instance of this scheme suffices, while for the disproof of the axiom of choice two seem to be necessary.

The question whether every sentence holding in type theory with complete typical ambiguity can be proved from the additional scheme "$S \leftrightarrow S^+$" has been asked in [7] and answered in a footnote to the affirmative; NF is therefore consistent if and only if simple theory of types (based on axioms of extensionality and comprehension) with the additional scheme "$S \leftrightarrow S^+$" is consistent. The rest of this paper will be devoted to the study of the relation of the model-theoretic aspect of typical ambiguity to its proof-theoretic aspect. The theorem we want to prove is the following:

If theory of types (based on axioms of extensionality and comprehension) with the additional scheme "$S \leftrightarrow S^+$" is consistent, then there exists a model $(M_0, M_1, \cdots; =, \in)$ *admitting an isomorphism mapping* M_k *onto* M_{k+1}.

In order to find simple general conditions which give us the above theorem as a corollary, we re-formalize simple theory of types as a one-sorted theory. We therefore introduce type predicates $T_0, T_1, \cdots$; the axioms of the theory are given by the following schemes: $x_1 = x_2 \rightarrow (T_k(x_1) \rightarrow T_k(x_2))$, $x_1 \in x_2 \rightarrow (T_k(x_1) \leftrightarrow T_{k+1}(x_2))$, $k = 0, 1, \cdots$; axioms schemes for axioms of extensionality and comprehension (it is simplest to introduce a type predicate for every variable though this is not necessary). As in the many-sorted theory, we associate to every formula F a formula F^+ defined as follows: F^+ is obtained from F by replacing T_k by T_{k+1}. To an isomorphism mapping M_k onto M_{k+1} corresponds here a one-to-one map of a model M into itself such that $T_k(a)$ if and only if $T_{k+1}(a^+)$ and $a \in b$ if and only if $a^+ \in b^+$ (a^+ is the image of a by the map). The consistency of the scheme "$S \leftrightarrow S^+$" (which has been shown to be necessary for the existence of such a model) is clearly equivalent to the existence of a complete extension of type theory, where every sentence S holds if and only if S^+ holds. (In such an extension "$S \leftrightarrow S^+$" holds; if "$S \leftrightarrow S^+$" is a consistent scheme, every complete extension of this theory has the desired property.)

The existence of models of type theory having a type-raising isomorphism is therefore a corollary of the following theorem:

If it is complete, then a theory with an endomorphism has a model with a corresponding endomorphism.

(With "endomorphism" replaced by "automorphism", this theorem has been given without proof in [7]; simple examples are given there to show that completeness is necessary.)

In the following definition of the notion of endomorphism of a theory we do not aim at generality, as there is a theorem by R. L. Vaught which is still more general.

An endomorphism of a (first-order and one-sorted) theory is a map of its set of formulas into itself such that the following conditions are satisfied: (1) The image F^* of a formula F has the same free variables as F. (2) The map * commutes with logical operations and with change of variables, i.e., $(A \wedge B)^*$ is $A^* \wedge B^*$, etc., $[(\mathrm{E}x_1)A]^*$ is $(\mathrm{E}x_1)A^*$, $(A(x_{k_1}, \cdots, x_{k_m}))^*$ is $A^*(x_{k_1}, \cdots, x_{k_m})$. (Here and in what follows $A(c_1, \cdots, c_m)$ results if we substitute from A the terms c_i for the variables x_i, $i = 1, \cdots, m$.) (3) The image of the identity relation is the identity relation, i.e., $(x_1 = x_2)^*$ is $x_1 = x_2$. (4) The image of a valid sentence, which is a sentence by (1), is valid.

The map induced in the formulas of type theory by replacing T_k by T_{k+1} is clearly an endomorphism in the sense just defined.

If T is a theory with an endomorphism *, a map * of a model M of T into itself is called a corresponding endomorphism if for every primitive predicate R of T the sentence $\tilde{R}^*(e_1^*, \cdots, e_m^*)$ holds in M if and only if $\tilde{R}(e_1, \cdots, e_m)$ holds. (The tilde indicates the passage from a formal predicate to its interpretation; e^* is the image of e under the map * of M; if the theory T contains functions, predicates such as $f(x_1) = x_2$ have to be considered as primitive.)

We sketch the construction of a model admitting a *-endomorphism which follows closely— after a first lemma — a Henkin-type completeness proof; a reduction similar to the one in this lemma occurs in [1].

LEMMA. *Let T be a complete theory with an endomorphism *; let A be a formula with only the free variable x_1; let $P_i (i = 1, \cdots, m)$ be formulas with no other free variables than $x_1, \cdots, x_n$; and let $1 \leq k \leq n + 1$. Then a model M of T contains elements $e_1, \cdots, e_{n+1}$ such that the following sentences hold in M: $(\mathrm{E}x_1)\tilde{A}(x_1) \rightarrow \tilde{A}(e_k)$, $\tilde{P}_i(e_1, e_2, \cdots, e_n) \leftrightarrow \tilde{P}_i^*(e_2, e_3, \cdots, e_{n+1})$, $i = 1, \cdots, m$.*

The proof is by induction on n. For $n = 0$, P_i and P_i^* are sentences, and the equivalences $P_i \leftrightarrow P_i^* (i = 1, \cdots, m)$ hold by condition (4) and the completeness of the theory T; there exists in M an element e_1 such that $(\mathrm{E}x_1)\tilde{A}(x_1) \rightarrow \tilde{A}(e_1)$ holds in M.

For the inductive step, let $P^\varepsilon (\varepsilon = 0, 1)$ be P or $\neg P$ according to whether $\varepsilon = 0$ or $\varepsilon = 1$. We first assume $1 \leq k \leq n$. Consider $Q_{\varepsilon_1, \ldots, \varepsilon_m}$ defined as $(\mathrm{E}x_n) \bigwedge P_i^{\varepsilon_i} (\bigwedge P_i^{\varepsilon_i}$ is the conjunction of $P_1^{\varepsilon_1}, \cdots, P_m^{\varepsilon_m})$; by condition (2) $Q^*_{\varepsilon_1, \ldots, \varepsilon_m}$ is $(\mathrm{E}x_n) \bigwedge P_i^*$. By the hypothesis of the induction, there are elements $e_1, \cdots, e_n$ in M such that the following sentences hold in M for all sequences

$\varepsilon_1, \cdots, \varepsilon_m$: $(\mathrm{Ex}_1)\tilde{A}(x_1) \rightarrow \tilde{A}(e_k)$, $Q_{\varepsilon_1,\ldots,\varepsilon_m}(e_1, \cdots, e_{n-1}) \leftrightarrow \tilde{Q}^*_{\varepsilon_1,\ldots,\varepsilon_m}(e_2, \cdots, e_n)$. Choose $\eta_i (i = 1, \cdots, m)$ in such a way that $\tilde{P}^{\eta_i}_i(e_1, \cdots, e_n)$ holds in M. $\tilde{Q}^*_{\eta_1,\ldots,\eta_m}(e_1, \cdots, e_{n-1})$ then holds in M and so does $\tilde{Q}^*_{\eta_i,\ldots,\eta_m}(e_2, \cdots, e_n)$, which is the same as $(\mathrm{Ex}_n)\Lambda\tilde{P}^{*\eta_i}_i(e_2, \cdots, e_n, x_n)$, i.e., there is an element e_{n+1} such that $\tilde{P}^{*\eta_i}_i(e_2, \cdots, e_{n+1})$ hold $(i = 1, \cdots, m)$ and we have $\tilde{P}_i(e_1, \cdots, e_n) \leftrightarrow \tilde{P}^*_i(e_2, \cdots, e_{n+1})$.

If on the other hand $k = n+1$, consider $R_{\varepsilon_1,\ldots,\varepsilon_m}$ defined as $(\mathrm{Ex}_n)\Lambda P_{\varepsilon_i}(x_n, x_1, \cdots, x_{n-1})$. By the induction hypothesis there are elements $e_2, \cdots, e_{n+1}$ such that $(\mathrm{Ex}_1)\tilde{A}(x_1) \rightarrow \tilde{A}(e_{n+1})$ and $\tilde{R}_{\varepsilon_1,\ldots,\varepsilon_m}(e_2, \cdots, e_n) \leftrightarrow \tilde{R}^*_{\varepsilon_1,\ldots,\varepsilon_m}(e_2, \cdots, e_{n+1})$ hold in M for all sequences $\varepsilon_1, \cdots, \varepsilon_m$. We choose η_i such that $\tilde{P}^{*\eta_i}_i(e_2, \cdots, e_{n+1})$ holds in $M (i = 1, \cdots, m)$, and find an element e_1 such that $P^{\eta_i}_i(e_1, \cdots, e_n)$ holds $(i = 1, \cdots, m)$, whence $\tilde{P}_i(e_1, \cdots, e_n) \leftrightarrow \tilde{P}^*_i(e_2, \cdots, e_{n+1})$.

The proofs of the following two lemmas are now immediate:

(1) Let T be a complete theory admitting an endomorphism *, let A be a formula with the only free variable x_1. Then T can be extended to a complete theory T' having in addition to the constants of T a sequence $a_k (k = 0, \pm 1, \pm 2, \cdots)$ of new individual constants and a new axiom $(\mathrm{Ex}_1)A(x_1) \rightarrow A(a_0)$ such that the following extension of the endomorphism * of T is an endomorphism of T': $[B(x_1, \cdots, x_j, a_{k_1}, \cdots, a_{k_m})]^*$ is $B^*(x_1, \cdots, x_j, a_{k_1+1}, \cdots, a_{k_m+1})$.

(2) Let T be a complete theory admitting an endomorphism *. Then there exists a complete extension T'' of T having as only new constants individual constants a^i_k $(k = 0, \pm 1, \pm 2, \cdots; i \in I$, where I is arbitrary but can be chosen as the set of natural numbers in case of a denumerable theory) such that the following conditions are satisfied: For every formula A of T'' having x_1 as the only free variable, there is an element i of I such that $(\mathrm{Ex}_1) A(x_1) \rightarrow A(a^i_0)$; if Q is a formula of T having no other free variables than $x_1, \cdots, x_m$, the following sentence holds in T'': $Q(a^{i_1}_{k_1}, \cdots, a^{i_m}_{k_m}) \leftrightarrow Q^*(a^{i_1}_{k_1+1}, \cdots, a^{i_m}_{k_m+1})$.

A model of T having an endomorphism * can now be constructed by choosing as set M the set of individual constants a^i_k, by defining the primitive predicates as they are defined in the extension T'' of T, and by putting $(a^i_k)^* = a^i_{k+1}$.

As noted by Dana Scott [5] the existence of such a model may also be deduced as a direct consequence of a theorem of A. Robinson [4].

The same deduction yields even a somewhat stronger theorem of R. L. Vaught (which in turn implies the just mentioned theorem of Robinson as remarked by Vaught). In Vaught's theorem a theory T is (relatively) interpreted in two ways in a theory T'. Such an interpretation is given by a formula K of T' (with one free variable) and formulas F_i of T' for each primitive predicate P_i of T, F_i having the same free variables as P_i. (It is convenient to assume that neither T nor T' contain function symbols.) A formula T is translated into a formula of T' by replacing P_i by F_i and by restricting quantifiers to K; such a translation is an interpretation if $(\mathrm{Ex}_1)K$ holds in T' (assuming that x_1 is the free variable of K) and if every axiom of T is translated into a provable sentence of T'. (A classical example of such an interpretation is the interpretation of non-Euclidean geometry in Euclidean geometry; K holds for the points in the interior of the unit circle.) If a theory T is interpreted in a theory T', there is a natural mapping from models of T' to models of T: The domain of the model of T is given by the elements for which K holds and the predicates P_i are defined by the formulas F_i.

THEOREM (R. L. VAUGHT). *If a complete theory T is interpreted in two ways in a theory T', there exists a model of T' such that the corresponding two models of T are isomorphic.*

In order to derive the theorem on the existence of models having endomorphisms from Vaught's theorem, we simply interpret the theory T in itself in the two following ways: K holds identically in both interpretations and P_i is interpreted as P_i in the one and as P_i^* in the other. (There exists an older unpublished theorem of M. D. Morley which is closely connected: If $(A, R_0, R_1, \cdots; a_0, a_1, \cdots, a_\xi, \cdots)$ and $(A, R_0, R_1, \cdots; b_0, b_1, \cdots, b_\xi, \cdots)$ are elementary equivalent structures and if f is defined on $(a_0, \cdots, a_\xi, \cdots)$ with $f(a_\xi) = b_\xi$, then $(A, R_0, R_1, \cdots)$ can be imbedded in $(A', R_0', R_1', \cdots)$ having an automorphism extending f.)

The reduction (due to Scott) of Vaught's to Robinson's theorem is as follows: One may assume that the theory T' is also complete, that T and T' have no predicates in common and do not contain function symbols. One then defines the disjoint union T^* of two such theories T_1, T_2: Primitive predicates of T^* are the primitive predicates of T_1 and of T_2 and two new one-place predicates K_1, K_2. Axioms of T^* are first the relativized forms of the axioms of T_i to K_i-elements ($i = 1, 2$); then an axiom saying that every element is either a K_1- or K_2-element, that no element is a K_1- and a K_2-element, and that there are elements of both kinds; finally axioms saying that a primitive predicate of T_i holds in T^* only if all the arguments are K_i-elements, $i = 1, 2$.

LEMMA. *The disjoint union of two complete theories is complete.*[1]

A sketch of proof will be given at the end of the paper.

An interpretation of a theory T in the theory T' induces two interpretations of T in the disjoint union of T and T': one is the interpretation where a predicate of T is interpreted as the same predicate in T^*; the other is obtained by interpreting T in T' and T' in T^*. There exist models of T^* such that these two interpretations are isomorphic. In order to see this, we define the disjoint

[1]This is an immediate consequence of a stronger theorem on disjoint unions announced by Solomon Feferman, "Some operations on relational systems", *Bulletin of the American Mathematical Society*, Vol. 61 (1955), p. 172.

union of two structures (relational systems) M_1 and M_2 with no relations in common and disjoint base sets: The base set B^* of the union M^* is the set-theoretic union of B_1 and B_2; relations of M^* are the relations of M_1 and M_2 extended to B^* in the following way: If R is a relation of M_i, then $R(a_1, \cdots, a_m)$ holds if and only if all the a_j are elements of B_i and the relation holds in M_i. If M_i is a model of T_i ($i = 1, 2$), then the disjoint union of M_1 and M_2 (with the obvious definition of K_1, K_2) is a model of the disjoint union of T_1 and T_2, and every model of the union T^* is of this form. Given an interpretation of the theory T in T', consider an arbitrary model M' of T'; the interpretation then defines a model M of T (which may be chosen with disjoint base set); the two interpretations of T in the disjoint union T^* then clearly induce isomorphic models of T in the model M^* of T^*.

Now let T_0^* be the following extension of the disjoint union T^* of T and T': Constants of T_0^* are constants of T^* and a new one-place function symbol f; axioms of T_0^* are axioms of T^* and new axioms saying that f is an isomorphism of one interpretation onto the other. As there exists a model of T^*, where the two interpretations are isomorphic, there exists a model of T_0^*, and this theory is consistent; on the other hand, every model of T_0^* defines a model of T^* where these two interpretations are isomorphic.

Consider now a complete theory T interpreted in two ways in the complete theory T'. Extend the disjoint union T^* in the above manner to two theories T_1^* (new function symbol f_1) and T_2^* (new function symbol f_2) according to the two interpretations. Both these theories are consistent and so is therefore by a theorem of A. Robinson [4] their union (the constants of this union are the constants of T^* and f_1, f_2; axioms are the axioms of T_1^*, T_2^*; it is essential that the common part T^* of both theories is complete.) A model of this union defines a model of T^*, where both interpretations of T in T' are isomorphic to the interpretation of T in T^*; the induced model of T' is therefore a model with isomorphic interpretations of T.

We finally sketch a proof of the lemma that the disjoint union of two complete theories is complete. A theory is complete if and only if all its models are elementarily equivalent. Every model of the disjoint union of two theories is the disjoint union of models of these theories. It suffices therefore to prove the following lemma on disjoint unions of structures: if M_i and N_i are elementarily equivalent structures ($i = 1, 2$), so are the disjoint unions M^* (of M_1 and M_2) and N^* (of N_1 and N_2). This equivalence is an immediate consequence of the characterisation of elementarily equivalent structures given by R. Fraïssé [2].

References

[1] Ehrenfeucht, A., and A. Mostowski. Models of axiomatic theories admitting automorphisms. *Fund Math.*, Vol. **43** (1956), pp. 50–68.

[2] Fraïssé, R. Application des γ-opérateurs au calcul logique du premier échelon. *Z. Math. Logik Grundlagen Math.*, Vol. **2** (1956), pp. 76–92.

[3] QUINE, W. V. New Foundations for Mathematical Logic. *Am. Math. Monthly*, Vol. 44 (1937), pp. 70–80.

[4] ROBINSON, A. A result on consistency and its application to the theory of definition. *Nederl. Akad. Wetensch. Proc. Ser. A 59 = Indag. Math.*, Vol. 18 (1956), pp. 47–58.

[5] SCOTT, DANA. Review of [7]. *Math. Review*, Vol. 21 (1960), p. 1026.

[6] SPECKER, E. The axion of choice in Quine's New Foundations for mathematical Logic. *Proc. Nat. Acad. Sci. USA*, Vol. 29 (1953), pp. 366–368.

[7] SPECKER, E. Dualität. *Dialectica*, Vol. 12 (1958), pp. 451–465.

[8] WANG, HAO. Negative types. *Mind.*, Vol. 61 (1952), pp. 366–368.

SOME PROBLEMS AND RESULTS RELEVANT TO THE FOUNDATIONS OF SET THEORY

ALFRED TARSKI

University of California, Berkeley, California, U.S.A.

Introduction

Numerous problems in set theory and related domains are known which exhibit the following pattern. Each of the problems consists in determining all the (infinite) cardinals which have a given property P. It has been known that the smallest infinite cardinal, ω, does not have this property. It has also been known that all the accessible cardinals, i.e., all those which are not (strongly) inaccessible, have the property P. Until recently, however, the problem had been open whether any, or possibly all, inaccessible cardinals greater than ω have the property in question. It seemed even plausible that the solution of the problem for inaccessible cardinals would require an introduction of some new set-theoretical axioms which would differ essentially in their character not only from the usual axioms of set theory, but also from those hypotheses whose inclusion among the axioms has previously been discussed in the literature (such as the generalized continuum hypothesis or various existential hypotheses which assure the existence of inaccessible cardinals). The significance of many of the problems involved is enhanced by the simplicity of their formulation and the clarity of their mathematical content.[1]

Only now it has turned out that, contrary to expectations, most of the problems discussed can be solved for a large class of inaccessible cardinals without the help of any additional axioms, and that the cardinals involved behave with regard to these problems not like the smallest inaccessible cardinal ω, but like all the accessible cardinals.

In the present paper we wish to report briefly on some results obtained in this direction, reserving detailed proofs (as well as a complete presentation of all the results involved) for a later publication. In Section 1 we concentrate on a metamathematical result which has been recently obtained by William P. Hanf (as a solution of a problem suggested by the author) and which plays an essential part in the later discussion. In Section 2 we take up

---

The results stated in this paper were found when the author was working on a research project in the foundations of mathematics supported by the U. S. National Science Foundation (Grant G–6693).

[1]Some problems of this kind are discussed in [1, pp. 326—329], and implicitly in [8, Sections 3 and 4] (see References at the end of this paper); in both articles references to earlier publications can also be found. A paper containing the full presentation of the results mentioned in [1], *loc. cit.* (in particular those stated on p. 328, footnote 4) will soon appear in print.

certain purely mathematical problems involving inaccessible cardinals, for which a partial solution has recently been found.

As a theoretical basis for our discussion we can choose one of the well-known axiomatic systems of set theory, for instance, the Zermelo-Fraenkel system (with the regularity axiom) or the Bernays system. We assume that the *ordinals* have been introduced in such a way that every ordinal coincides with the set of all smaller ordinals and that the order relation $<$ between ordinals coincides with the membership relation $\in$. The *cardinals* are identified with those ordinals α which have larger power than all smaller ordinals $\xi < \alpha$; thus an ordinal α is a cardinal if and only if α is either finite ($\alpha < \omega$) or of the form $\alpha = \omega_\xi$ for some ordinal ξ. For any given ordinal α we denote by 2^α the cardinal which is of the same power as the family of all subsets of α. The existence of the cardinal 2^α is assured by the well-ordering principle.

An infinite cardinal α is called *singular* if it is confinal with some smaller cardinal β, i.e., it can be represented as the sum of β cardinals smaller than α; otherwise α is called *regular*. We say that α is *accessible* if either it is singular or else there is an ordinal β for which $\beta < \alpha \leqq 2^\beta$; if neither of these two conditions is satisfied, α is said to be (*strongly*) *inaccessible* (cf. [12]). We assume that all the inaccessible cardinals have been arranged in a transfinite increasing sequence $\Theta_0, \Theta_1, \ldots, \Theta_\xi, \ldots$. Thus $\Theta_0 = \omega$, and Θ_ξ is the smallest inaccessible cardinal which is $> \Theta_\zeta$ for every $\zeta < \xi$. As is well known, the existence of a cardinal Θ_ξ with $\xi \geqq 1$ cannot be established in the Bernays or Zermelo-Fraenkel set theory. The existence problem, however, will not intervene in our discussion; all the results stated below which concern cardinals Θ_ξ with $\xi \geqq 1$ are assumed to be provided with a premiss stating that the cardinals involved actually exist.

With every set A we can correlate an ordinal $\rho(A)$, called the *rank* of A, in such a way that $\rho(A)$ is the smallest ordinal which is larger than all the ordinals $\rho(x)$ correlated with elements x of A. The set of all sets whose rank is smaller than a given ordinal γ is denoted by $R(\gamma)$.

Section 1

The first result which has been recently obtained for inaccessible cardinals is not of set-theoretical, but of metamathematical nature; it concerns the so-called compactness problem for predicate logics with infinitely long formulas, which have been briefly discussed by the author in [10].

Let $\mathbf{L}_\omega$ be the ordinary (first-order) predicate logic. For any given regular cardinal α let $\mathbf{L}_\alpha$ be a logical system which differs from $\mathbf{L}_\omega$ in the following respects: (i) There are α *different variables* in $\mathbf{L}_\alpha$ arranged in a transfinite sequence $v_0, v_1, \ldots, v_\xi, \ldots$ ($\xi < \alpha$). (ii) Every formula in $\mathbf{L}_\alpha$ is a sequence of symbols of a type $< \alpha$. (iii) In building compound *formulas* from atomic ones some new operations are admitted (in addition to those available in $\mathbf{L}_\omega$), namely, the formation of the *disjunction* and the *conjunction*,

$$\bigvee_{\xi<\gamma}\phi_\xi \quad \text{and} \quad \bigwedge_{\xi<\gamma}\phi_\xi,$$

of any sequence of formulas $\phi_0, \phi_1, \ldots, \phi_\xi, \ldots$ whose type γ is an arbitrary ordinal $< \alpha$, as well as the *universal* and the *existential quantification,*

$$(\forall v_{\gamma_\xi})_{\xi<\gamma}\phi \quad \text{and} \quad (\exists v_{\gamma_\xi})_{\xi<\gamma}\phi,$$

of a formula ϕ *under any sequence of variables* $v_{\gamma_0}, v_{\gamma_1}, \ldots, v_{\gamma_\xi}, \ldots$ whose type γ is again an arbitrary ordinal $< \alpha$. (It may be noticed that for a singular cardinal α a logic $\mathbf{L}_\alpha$ with all these properties cannot be constructed; in fact, as is easily seen, conditions (ii) and (iii) become then incompatible.)

There is no difficulty in extending basic semantical notions, such as the notions of *satisfaction* and *model,* to logics $\mathbf{L}_\alpha$. For the purposes of the discussion in the present section we can assume that the only non-logical constant in $\mathbf{L}_\alpha$ is a binary predicate ε, and hence every atomic formula is of the form

$$v_\xi = v_\zeta \text{ or } v_\xi \,\varepsilon\, v_\zeta$$

for some ξ, $\zeta < \alpha$. Under this assumption, the models of any given set S of sentences (formulas without free variables) in $\mathbf{L}_\alpha$ are structures of the form $\langle A, E\rangle$, where A is a non-empty set and E is a binary relation between elements of A. Such a structure is referred to as a *set-theoretical model* if E coincides with the relation $\in_A$, i.e., with the membership relation restricted to elements of A. A set-theoretical model $\langle A, \in_A\rangle$ is called *transitive* if the conditions $x \in A$ and $y \in x$ always imply $y \in A$; it is called *natural* if, for some ordinal γ, A coincides with $R(\gamma)$. Clearly, every natural model is transitive.

The *compactness problem* for logics $\mathbf{L}_\alpha$ is the problem of determining all the cardinals α for which the following compactness theorem holds:

If S is any set of sentences in $\mathbf{L}_\alpha$ *and if every subset of S with power* $< \alpha$ *has a model, then S also has a model.*

For lack of a better term we shall refer to the cardinals α for which the compactness theorem holds as *compact cardinals.* The remaining infinite cardinals, including all the singular ones, will be referred to as *incompact.* In particular, a cardinal α will be called *strongly incompact* if either it is singular or there is a set S of sentences in logic $\mathbf{L}_\alpha$ with power α which has no model while every subset of S with power $< \alpha$ has a model.

It is well known that the cardinal ω is compact. It has also been known for some time that all the accessible cardinals are incompact.[2] On the suggestion of the author of this note, Hanf has studied the compactness problem for logics $\mathbf{L}_\alpha$ with inaccessible α's and has established the following result (cf. [2]):

---

[2]It is known that the Property P_0 formulated below in Section 2 applies to every accessible cardinal α; see, e.g., [8, p. 257, Corollary 3.7]. Hence we conclude rather easily that in logic $\mathbf{L}_\alpha$ (and actually in the sentential calculus correlated with this logic) there is a set S of sentences which has no model while every subset of S with power $< \alpha$ has a model. The result is mentioned (implicitly) in [7, p. 170].

THEOREM 1. *Every cardinal α of the form $\alpha = \Theta_\xi$ with $0 < \xi < \alpha$ is strongly incompact.*

We shall outline briefly Hanf's proof of this result, restricting ourselves for simplicity to the case $\alpha = \Theta_1$. Given any ordinal $\xi<\alpha$ we can easily construct a formula ϕ_ξ in $\mathbf{L}_\alpha$, with v_ξ as the only free variable, which defines ξ in the following sense: given any transitive set-theoretical model $\langle A, \epsilon_A\rangle$, an element $x \in A$ satisfies ϕ_ξ in this model if and only if $x = \xi$. We can take, e.g., for ϕ_ξ the following formula:

$$(\exists v_\zeta)_{\zeta<\xi} \bigwedge_{\zeta<\xi+1} (\forall v_{\xi+1})(v_{\xi+1} \,\varepsilon\, v_\zeta \leftrightarrow \bigvee_{\eta<\zeta} v_{\xi+1} = v_\eta).$$

Let $\bar{\phi}_\xi$ be the sentence

$$(\exists v_\xi)\phi_\xi.$$

We can also construct a formula ψ_0, with v_0 as the only free variable, which defines the notion of an ordinal (in terms of the membership relation), in the sense that ψ_0 is satisfied in any transitive model $\langle A, \epsilon_A\rangle$ by those and only those elements $\xi \in A$ which are ordinals; such a formula ψ_0 is known from the literature. Furthermore, we can construct a formula ψ_1, again with v_0 as the only free variable, which has the following properties: (i) Θ_1 does not satisfy ψ_1 in any transitive model $\langle A, \epsilon_A\rangle$ with $\Theta_1 \in A$; (ii) every ordinal $\xi < \Theta_1$ satisfies ψ_1 in every natural model $\langle R(\gamma), \epsilon_{R(\gamma)}\rangle$ with $\gamma > \xi$. To construct ψ_1, we express in a straightforward manner the fact that the element ξ represented by v_0 is an ordinal (i.e., satisfies ψ_0) and either equals 0 or equals ω or else is confinal with some smaller ordinal ζ or, finally, satisfies the condition $\xi \leqq 2^\zeta$ for some smaller ordinal ζ. Let $\bar{\psi}_0$ and $\bar{\psi}_1$ be, respectively, the following two sentences:

$$(\exists v_0)\ (\psi_0 \wedge \neg\ (\exists v_1)(v_0 \in v_1)),$$
$$(\forall v_0)(\psi_0 \rightarrow \psi_1).$$

Finally, let τ_0 be the ordinary extensionality axiom of set theory,

$$(\forall v_0)(\forall v_1)[(\forall v_2)(v_2 \in v_0 \leftrightarrow v_2 \in v_1) \rightarrow v_0 = v_1],$$

and let τ_1 be the regularity or "well foundedness" axiom in the following formulation:

$$(\forall v_\xi)_{\xi<\omega}\ \neg \bigwedge_{\xi<\omega}(v_{\xi+1} \in v_\xi).$$

Consider the set S consisting of all sentences $\bar{\phi}_\xi$ with $\xi < \Theta_1$ and of the four sentences $\bar{\psi}_0, \bar{\psi}_1, \tau_0, \tau_1$. Obviously, S is of power Θ_1. Let X be any subset of S with power $< \Theta_1$. Then there exists an ordinal $\gamma < \Theta_1$ such that $\bar{\phi}_\xi \in X$ implies $\xi < \gamma$ for every ξ; and, as is easily seen, the structure $\langle R(\gamma+1), \epsilon_{R(\gamma+1)}\rangle$ is a natural model of X. On the other hand, it is known from the literature that if the whole set S had a model $\langle A, E\rangle$, it would also have a transitive set-theoretical model $\langle B, \epsilon_B\rangle$ isomorphic with $\langle A, E\rangle$; this is a consequence of the fact that τ_0 and τ_1 are in S (cf. [6], p. 147, Theorem 3). Since $\bar{\phi}_\xi \in S$ for every $\xi < \Theta_1$, B must contain as elements all ordinals $< \Theta_1$. By $\bar{\psi}_0$, B must have a largest ordinal, say, β; hence $\Theta_1 \leqq \beta$, i.e., $\Theta_1 \in \beta$ or $\Theta_1 = \beta$. Since the model $\langle B, \epsilon_B\rangle$ is transitive, it follows that $\Theta_1 \in B$. Therefore, by $\bar{\psi}_1$, Θ_1 satisfies ψ_1, and this is a contradiction. Thus, the set S has no model, and the proof is complete.[3]

Theorem 1 is by no means the strongest result obtained so far in connection with the compactness problem. As was pointed out by Hanf, his construction of the set S depends essentially on two facts: (i) for every regular cardinal $\alpha > \omega$ we can formulate in $\mathbf{L}_\alpha$ the regularity axiom τ_1; (ii) for $\alpha = \Theta_1$ (and, more generally, for $\alpha = \Theta_\xi$ with $\xi < \alpha$) we can, in a certain sense, describe in $\mathbf{L}_\alpha$ the property of being an ordinal $< \alpha$. These two facts apply to a great variety of cardinals α which are not involved in Theorem 1. In the first place, Hanf has proved, for some very comprehensive classes of accessible cardinals, that all cardinals belonging to these classes are not only incompact, but also strongly incompact. This holds in particular for the class of all cardinals α of the forms $\alpha = \omega_{\xi+1}$ and $\alpha = 2^\beta$, where ξ is any ordinal and β is any cardinal; under the assumption of the generalized continuum hypothesis ($2^{\omega_\xi} = \omega_{\xi+1}$ for every ordinal ξ) the result implies that all accessible cardinals are strongly incompact. Secondly, if the transfinite sequence of cardinals $\Theta_0, \Theta_1, \ldots, \Theta_\xi, \ldots$ has any fixed points, i.e., if there are cardinals α for which $\Theta_\alpha = \alpha$, they can again be arranged in an increasing transfinite sequence $\Gamma_0, \Gamma_1, \ldots, \Gamma_\xi, \ldots$, and Hanf has shown that all the cardinals $\alpha = \Gamma_\xi$ with $\xi < \alpha$ are strongly incompact. This procedure can be continued indefinitely. Even stronger results can be obtained by considering certain classes of very large inaccessible cardinals, the so-called *hyper-inaccessible* cardinals of various types, recently discussed in [4]. None of the cardinals Θ_ξ with $\xi < \Theta_\xi$, of the cardinals Γ_ξ with $\xi < \Gamma_\xi$, etc., are hyper-inaccessible cardinals of type 1. Hanf has proved that, in general, every inaccessible cardinal $\alpha > \omega$ which is not hyper-inaccessible of type 1 is strongly incompact, and that this result extends to all inaccessible cardinals $\alpha > \omega$ which are not hyper-inaccessible of type α; he has also obtained the same conclusion for various transfinite sequences of cardinals α which are hyper-inaccessible of type α. The problem whether there exist compact cardinals $\alpha > \omega$ remains open, but we do not know any example of a cardinal $\alpha > \omega$ which would possess a "constructive characterization" (in some very general and rather loose sense of this term) and of which we could not prove that it is incompact and, in fact, strongly incompact.

Section 2

We shall now state a theorem which serves as a bridge in passing from Theorem 1 (and more general metamathematical results mentioned in Section 1) to some purely mathematical consequences.

---

[3]The construction of a set S is analogous to the familiar construction of a set of sentences (in higher-order logic) which is consistent but not ω-consistent; cf. [9, pp. 289 ff.].

The notions of a *Boolean algebra*, of *ideals*, *principal ideals*, and *prime ideals* in such an algebra are assumed to be known. Given any cardinal α, a Boolean algebra $\mathfrak{A}$ is called *α-complete* if, for every set of X of elements of $\mathfrak{A}$ with power $< \alpha$, the sum (join) $\sum_{y \in X} y$ exists; $\mathfrak{A}$ is called *complete* if it is α-complete for every cardinal α. An α-complete Boolean algebra $\mathfrak{A}$ is called *α-distributive* if we have

$$\prod_{i \in I} \sum_{j \in J_i} x_{i,j} = \sum_{f \in F} \prod_{i \in I} x_{i,f(i)},$$

where I and all the J_i's (with $i \in I$) are any sets of power $< \alpha$, F is the Cartesian product of the sets J_i (i.e., the set of all functions f on I such that $f(i) \in J_i$ for $i \in I$), and $x_{i,j}$ (with $i \in I, j \in J_i$) are any elements of the algebra. An ideal I in an α-complete Boolean algebra $\mathfrak{A}$ is called *α-complete* if every sum of less than α elements of I is itself an element of I; it is called *α-saturated* if every set of pairwise disjoint elements of $\mathfrak{A}$ which do not belong to I is of power $< \alpha$. Instead of "ω_1-complete" and "ω_1-distributive" the terms "*countably complete*" and "*countably distributive*" are frequently used. A Boolean algebra in which all elements are sets and the fundamental operations are the familiar set-theoretical operations of forming unions, intersections, and complements is referred to as a *set algebra*; it is called an α-complete set algebra if in addition it is α-complete as a Boolean algebra and if the sums of $< \alpha$ of its elements always coincide with the unions of these elements. (Thus a set algebra may be α-complete as a Boolean algebra without being an α-complete set algebra in our sense.)

THEOREM 2. *Every strongly incompact cardinal α has the following property:*

P_0. *In the set algebra formed by all the subsets of α (or of any set of power α) every α-complete prime ideal is a principal ideal.*

To get an idea of the proof we first notice that P_0 obviously applies to every singular α; we can thus assume that α is regular. It proves convenient to consider the contrapositive form of our theorem: the negation of P_0 implies that α is not strongly incompact; in other words, the statement to the effect that in the set algebra of all subsets of α there is an α-complete non-principal prime ideal implies that the compactness theorem restricted to sets of sentences with power α holds for logic $\mathbf{L}_\alpha$. This implication for $\alpha = \omega$ is known from the literature. Its most direct proof, using the notion of an ultraproduct, is briefly outlined in [5]; some other arguments by means of which the completeness theorem for the ordinary predicate logic $\mathbf{L}_\omega$ is derived from the prime ideal theorem for Boolean algebra can also be adapted to this purpose. By analyzing any one of these proofs, we notice that, with suitable changes, it can be generalized so as to yield the implication discussed for every regular α.

As an immediate consequence of Theorems 1 and 2 we obtain

THEOREM 3. *Every cardinal α of the form $\alpha = \Theta_\xi$ with $0 < \xi < \alpha$ has the property P_0 of Theorem 2.*

This last result, in opposition to Theorems 1 and 2, is of purely mathematical nature, but its proof as outlined above uses of course metamathematical devices. In principle, however, there is no difficulty in translating the proof into mathematical terms. As a matter of fact, it is also possible to replace the metamathematical definition of strongly incompact cardinals by an equivalent mathematical definition, and to dispense with metamathematical terminology in the proofs of Theorems 1 and 2 as well. This can be achieved, for instance, by applying the method developed by the author in [11]. A direct and relatively simple proof of Theorem 3, which is formulated in purely mathematical terms and differs considerably from the argument we have outlined, will be given by Keisler (see [3]).

Numerous properties of infinite cardinals closely related to P_0 have been explicitly or implicitly discussed in the literature. Some of them are of purely set-theoretical nature while others are formulated in terms of metamathematics, algebra, analysis, or topology. Many of these properties can be shown to apply, like P_0, to all strongly incompact cardinals. Without trying to exhaust the topic in the present paper, we give a few samples of such properties in the next theorem.

THEOREM 4. *Every strongly incompact cardinal* α *and, in particular, every cardinal* α *of the form* $\alpha = \Theta_\xi$ *with* $0 < \xi < \alpha$ *has the following properties:*

P_1. *Every function F on the family G of all subsets of* α *to any other family of sets which satisfies the formulas*

$$F(\bigcup_{X\in H}X) = \bigcup_{X\in H}F(X) \text{ and } F(\bigcap_{X\in H}X) = \bigcap_{X\in H}F(X)$$

for every non-empty subfamily H of G with power $< \alpha$ *satisfies the same formulas for every non-empty subfamily H of G independent of its power.*

P_2. *Let G be any family of sets satisfying two conditions:*

(i) *G covers* α *(i.e.,* $\alpha \subseteq \bigcup_{X\in G}X$*);*

(ii) *every family of pairwise disjoint subsets of* α *which do not belong to G is finite.*

Then there is a subfamily H of G with power $< \alpha$ *which also covers* α.

P_3. *In every complete Boolean algebra with at most* 2^α *elements every* α*-complete prime ideal is principal.*

P_4. *There is an* α*-complete and* α*-distributive Boolean algebra which has no* α*-complete prime ideals (and hence is not isomorphic to any* α*-complete set algebra).*[4]

Theorem 4 can be derived from Theorems 1 and 2 (or 2 and 3) by means of a purely mathematical argument. Actually the properties P_0–P_3 are

---

[4] The properties P_1–P_4 are discussed, e.g., in [1, pp. 326 ff.], and [8, pp. 246 ff. (in particular, Theorem 3.4, Corollary 3.7, and Theorem 3.11)]

equivalent to each other for every infinite cardinal α; P_4 is implied by P_0, but it is not known whether the implication in the opposite direction also holds.

The problem naturally arises whether any of the properties P_0–P_4 present not only a necessary but also a sufficient condition for the strong incompactness of α. This problem still remains open. We can show, however, that each of these properties implies, and P_4 is actually equivalent to, the incompactness of α. If, moreover, we insert in P_4 the words "*with α elements*" after "*Boolean algebra*", then the resulting property P'_4 proves to be equivalent to the strong incompactness of α in case α is inaccessible. Thus, under the assumption of the generalized continuum hypothesis, *for an infinite cardinal α to be strongly incompact it is necessary and sufficient that α either be accessible or possess the property P'_4.*

We shall now discuss a property of cardinals, Q_0, which is stronger than P_0 — in the sense that it obviously implies P_0 for every cardinal $\alpha > \omega$, while the implication in the opposite direction is dubious.

THEOREM 5. *For every infinite cardinal β the following two conditions are equivalent*:

(i) *every cardinal α such that $\omega_1 \leqq \alpha \leqq \beta$ has the property P_0 of Theorem* 2;

(ii) *the cardinal $\alpha = \beta$ has the following property*:

Q_0. *In the set algebra formed by all the subsets of α every ω_1-complete prime ideal is principal.*

This theorem remains valid if we replace ω_1, in both its occurrences, by an arbitrary infinite cardinal γ.

The content of Theorem 5 can be equivalently expressed as follows:

If every infinite cardinal $> \omega$ has the property P_0, then every such cardinal has also the property Q_0; if, on the other hand, there are infinite cardinals $> \omega$ for which P_0 fails, and γ is the smallest among them, then Q_0 holds for all those and only those infinite cardinals which are $< \gamma$.

By comparing Theorem 5 with Theorems 1 and 2 and with the known result by which P_0 holds for all accessible cardinals, we obtain at once

THEOREM 6. *If an infinite cardinal α is such that every inaccessible cardinal β with $\omega < \beta \leqq \alpha$ is strongly incompact or, in particular, is such that $\beta \neq \Theta_\beta$ for every cardinal $\beta \leqq \alpha$, then α has the property Q_0.*

The property Q_0 deserves special interest in view of its close connection with the *abstract measure problem* (see, e.g., [8], section 4). By a *countably additive measure in a set A* we understand a function m on the family of all subsets of A to the set of non-negative real numbers satisfying the following conditions:

$m(A) = 1$;

$m(X) = 0$ for every one-element subset X of A;

$m(\bigcup_{\xi<\omega} X_\xi) = \sum_{\xi<\omega} m(X_\xi)$ for every infinite sequence of pairwise disjoint subsets $X_0, X_1, \ldots, X_\xi, \ldots$ of A.

As is easily seen, Q_0 can be equivalently re-formulated as follows:

Q'_0. *A being any set of power* α, *there is no countably additive two-valued measure in* A.

Consider moreover the following two properties of an infinite cardinal α:

R_0. *In the set algebra formed by all the subsets of* α *every* ω_1*-complete and* ω_1*-saturated ideal is principal.*

R'_0. *A being any set of power* α, *there is no countably additive measure in* A.

Clearly, R_0 implies R'_0, while R'_0 implies Q_0 and Q'_0. It is known that, under the continuum hypothesis $2^\omega = \omega_1$ (or under the weaker hypothesis by which every cardinal β with $\omega < \beta \leqq 2^\omega$ is either singular or has an immediate predecessor), all the four properties just mentioned are equivalent to each other.[5] We can thus replace, in Theorems 5 and 6, Q_0 by Q'_0 and, under the continuum hypothesis, also by R_0 or R'_0. In view of these results the possibility of constructing a set A with a countably additive measure defined on all subsets of A seems to be made remote "beyond any imagination".

We can easily formulate three properties of cardinals, Q_1, Q_2, and Q_3, which are in exactly the same relation to P_1, P_2, and P_3 as Q_0 is to P_0. The four properties Q_0–Q_3 prove to be equivalent, so that Theorems 5 and 6 can be referred to any one of them.

The status of the property Q_0 in the present discussion differs in some respects from that of all the properties formulated in Theorems 2 and 4. The properties P_0–P_4 exhibit the pattern described at the beginning of this note; i.e., it has been known that none of them applies to the cardinal ω while all of them apply to every accessible cardinal; and now we have succeeded in showing that they apply to a very comprehensive class of inaccessible cardinals as well. On the other hand, Q_0 trivially holds for $\alpha = \omega$, and until recently it was only known that it holds for every infinite cardinal $\alpha < \Theta_1$. In Theorem 6 this result has been extended to a very comprehensive class of cardinals containing both accessible and inaccessible cardinals. The problem whether Q_0 applies to all accessible cardinals still remains open and, as is seen from Theorem 5, it is equivalent to the problem whether Q_0 applies to all infinite cardinals without exception.

We conclude this paper with two remarks.

(1) There are problems involving infinite cardinals which have been solved for ω in one direction and for all accessible cardinals in the opposite direction, and which still remain open for all inaccessible cardinals $> \omega$. Such are, e.g., the graph problem and the ordering problem formulated

---

[5]To prove this it suffices to show that Q_0 implies R_0 (under one of the hypotheses stated in the text). This can be derived rather easily from the results in [8, Section 3, Theorems 3.1 and 3.8]. The equivalence of Q'_0 and R'_0 was first established in [13, p. 149].

in [1, p. 327]. It seems likely that new results extending partial solutions of these problems to comprehensive classes of inaccessible cardinals will be found in the near future.

(2) For the problems discussed in Section 2 of this paper the results obtained amount to shifting the lower bound of cardinals for which the problems remain open from the smallest inaccessible cardinal $> \omega$ to the smallest inaccessible cardinal $> \omega$ which is not strongly incompact. This undoubtedly presents a considerable progress. For one thing, the belief in the existence of inaccessible cardinals $> \omega$ (and even of arbitrarily large cardinals of this kind) seems to be a natural consequence of basic intuitions underlying the "naive" set theory and referring to what can be called "Cantor's absolute". On the contrary, we see at this moment no cogent intuitive reasons which could induce us to believe in the existence of cardinals $> \omega$ that are not strongly incompact, or which at least would make it very plausible that the hypothesis stating the existence of such cardinals is consistent with familiar axiom systems of set theory. As was pointed out at the end of Section 1, we do not know any "constructively characterized" cardinal $> \omega$ of which we cannot prove that it is strongly incompact and for which therefore the problems discussed remain open. However, in spite of the progress achieved, we see no serious reasons to believe that the methods available will eventually lead to a complete solution of these problems.

We would of course fully dispose of all the problems involved if we decided to enrich the axiom system of set theory by including (so to speak, on a permanent basis) a statement which precludes the existence of "very large" cardinals, e.g., by a statement to the effect that every cardinal $> \omega$ is strongly incompact. Such a decision, however, would be contrary to what is regarded by many as one of the main aims of research in the foundations of set theory, namely, the axiomatization of increasingly large segments of "Cantor's absolute". Those who share this attitude are always ready to accept new "construction principles", new axioms securing the existence of new classes of "large" cardinals (provided they appear to be consistent with old axioms), but are not prepared to accept any axioms precluding the existence of such cardinals — unless this is done on a strictly temporary basis, for the restricted purpose of facilitating the metamathematical discussion of some axiomatic systems of set theory.

References

[1] Erdös, P., and A. Tarski. On families of mutually exclusive sets. *Annals of Mathematics*, Vol. 44 (1943), pp. 315–329.

[2] Hanf, W. P. Models of languages with infinitely long expressions. *International Congress for Logic, Methodology and Philosophy of Science. Abstracts of Contributed Papers*, Stanford, Calif., Stanford University, 1960 (mimeographed), p. 24.

[3] Keisler, H. J. Some applications of the theory of models to set theory. This volume, pp. 80–86.

[4] Lévy, A. Axiom schemata of strong infinity in axiomatic set theory. *Pacific Journal of Mathematics*, Vol. 10 (1960), pp. 223–238.

[5] Morel, A. C., D. Scott, and A. Tarski. Reduced products and the compactness theorem. *American Mathematical Society Notices*, Vol. 5 (1958), pp. 674–675, abstract 550-9.

[6] Mostowski, A. An undecidable arithmetical statement. *Fundamenta Mathematicae*, Vol. 36 (1949), pp. 143–164.

[7] Scott, D., and A. Tarski. A sentential calculus with infinitely long expressions. *Colloquium Mathematicum*, Vol. 6 (1958), pp. 165–170.

[8] Smith, E. C., and A. Tarski. Higher degrees of distributivity and completeness in Boolean algebras. *Transactions of the American Mathematical Society*, Vol. 84 (1957), pp. 230–257.

[9] Tarski, A. *Logic, Semantics, Metamathematics. Papers from 1923 to 1938*. Oxford, Clarendon Press, 1956, XIV+471 pp.

[10] Tarski, A. Remarks on predicate logic with infinitely long expressions. *Colloquium Mathematicum*, Vol. 6 (1958), pp. 171–176.

[11] Tarski, A. Some notions and methods on the borderline of algebra and metamathematics. *Proceedings of the International Congress of Mathematicians, Cambridge, Mass., 1950*, Providence, R.I., American Mathematical Society, 1952, Vol. 1, pp. 705–720.

[12] Tarski, A. Über unerreichbare Kardinalzahlen. *Fundamenta Mathematicae*, Vol. 30 (1938), pp. 68–69.

[13] Ulam, S. Zur Masstheorie in der allgemeinen Mengenlehre. *Fundamenta Mathematicae*, Vol. 16 (1930), pp. 140–150.

COMMON EXTENSION IN EQUATIONAL CLASSES

JERZY ŁOŚ
Mathematical Institute, Warszawa, Poland

The problem of common extension for a class of algebras $\mathfrak{A}_0$ is in finding the necessary and sufficient conditions under which, for two given algebras A and B in $\mathfrak{A}_0$, there exists an algebra C which is also in $\mathfrak{A}_0$ and which contains isomorphic images of A and B.

In the case where $\mathfrak{A}_0$ is an elementary class (i.e., defined by means of elementary sentences) the problem is solved by the theorems given in [3]. The necessary and sufficient condition is the following:

For every open disjunction of the form

$$(1) \qquad \alpha(x_1, \cdots, x_n) \vee \beta(y_1, \cdots, y_m),$$

which is true for every algebra of $\mathfrak{A}_0$, either α or β has to be true for both algebras A and B. Obviously for equational classes (i.e., for classes defined by means of equations) the same condition holds, but it may be expected that in this case a stronger theorem holds too, a theorem restricting the class of all disjunctions of the form (1) to one of its subclasses. The aim of this paper is to give a more detailed solution of the problem for equational classes. First we shall start with two necessary conditions and show, by means of suitable examples, that they are not sufficient. Then we shall discuss a necessary and sufficient condition.

1. Notations and Terminology

Let $\mathfrak{A}$ be the class of all algebras of a fixed similarity type. We shall denote algebras $\langle A, F_1, \cdots, F_n \rangle$ in $\mathfrak{A}$ simply by the symbol of their set A. Let S, O, E be, respectively: the class of all elementary sentences for $\mathfrak{A}$, the class of all open sentences for $\mathfrak{A}$, the set of all equations for $\mathfrak{A}$. We have obviously $E \subset O \subset S$.

For A in $\mathfrak{A}$ we use $S(A)$ to denote the set of all sentences in S that are true for A. Moreover we set $O(A) = S(A) \cap O$, $E(A) = O(A) \cap E$, and for a subclass $\mathfrak{A}_0$ of $\mathfrak{A}$ also

$$S(\mathfrak{A}_0) = \bigcap_{A \in \mathfrak{A}_0} S(A), \; O(\mathfrak{A}_0) = \bigcap_{A \in \mathfrak{A}_0} O(A), \; E(\mathfrak{A}_0) = \bigcap_{A \in \mathfrak{A}_0} E(A).$$

For a subset X of S let $\mathfrak{A}(X)$ denote the set $\{A \text{ in } \mathfrak{A};\ X \subset S(A)\}$.

A subclass $\mathfrak{A}_0$ of $\mathfrak{A}$ is, respectively, elementary, open, or an equational class if $\mathfrak{A}_0 = \mathfrak{A}(S(\mathfrak{A}_0))$, $\mathfrak{A}_0 = \mathfrak{A}(O(\mathfrak{A}_0))$, or $\mathfrak{A}_0 = \mathfrak{A}(E(\mathfrak{A}_0))$.

A conjunction of equations is called a system of equations and will be denoted by $U(x_1, \cdots, x_n)$. We assume that no other variables occur in U

This work was in part carried out at the University of California, Berkeley, on a proj ect supported by the U. S. National Science Foundation (Grant No. G-6693).

except those in the brackets. We assume the same when writing $\alpha(x_1, \cdots, x_n)$, $\beta(y_1, \cdots, y_m)$, and so on.

If in an algebra A there exist elements $a_1, \cdots, a_n$, satisfying $U(x_1, \cdots, x_n)$, then U is called solvable in A.

2. Algebras of Constants

Let $\alpha(x, x_1, \cdots, x_n)$ be a sentence in O. If $\mathfrak{A}_0$ is an equational class and $\sum_x \sum_{x_1} \cdots \sum_{x_n} \alpha(x, x_1, \cdots, x_n) \in S(\mathfrak{A}_0)$, $\alpha(x, x_1, \cdots, x_n) \wedge \alpha(y, y_1, \cdots, y_n) \rightarrow x = y \in O(A_0)$, then α is called an O-definition for $\mathfrak{A}_0$. Every such O-definition points out for every algebra A in $\mathfrak{A}_0$ one and only one element a_α, which, together with the other elements $a_1, \cdots, a_n$ in A, satisfies α. Every such element a_α is called an O-constant of A. The set of all O-constant elements (relative to $\mathfrak{A}_0$) in A will be denoted by $C_{\mathfrak{A}_0}(A)$.

Suppose that τ is a term with only one variable x, and the equation $\tau(x) = \tau(y)$ belongs to $E(\mathfrak{A}_0)$. Then τ is called a constant term. It is easy to see that $\tau(x) = x$ is an O-definition for $\mathfrak{A}_0$. Every element defined in this way is called "defined by a term". Now we will prove that

Every element in $C_{\mathfrak{A}_0}(A)$ is defined by a term.

Suppose a_α to be in $C_{\mathfrak{A}_0}(A)$, then

$$\sum_x \sum_{x_1} \cdots \sum_{x_n} \alpha(x, x_1, \cdots, x_n) \text{ is in } S(\mathfrak{A}_0) = S(\mathfrak{A}(E(\mathfrak{A}_0))).$$

It follows from Herbrand's theorem that a disjunction of the form

$$\bigvee_{i=1}^{k} \alpha(\phi^{(i)}(x), \psi_1^{(i)}(x), \cdots, \psi_n^{(i)}(x)), \tag{2}$$

where $\phi^{(i)}$, $\psi_j^{(i)}$ are terms, belongs to $O(\mathfrak{A}_0)$. Substituting y for x, we obtain

$$\bigvee_{i=1}^{k} \alpha(\phi^{(i)}(y), \psi_1^{(i)}(y), \cdots, \psi_n^{(i)}(y)).$$

But α being an O-definition, it follows that $\alpha(x, x_1, \cdots, x_n) \wedge \alpha(y, y_1, \cdots, y_n) \rightarrow x = y$ belongs to $O(\mathfrak{A}_0)$. Applying this to both of the disjunctions, we obtain

$$\bigvee_{\substack{i=1\\j=1}}^{k} \phi^{(i)}(x) = \phi^{(j)}(y), \tag{3}$$

which belongs to $O(\mathfrak{A}_0)$. As we know, if a disjunction of equations belongs to $O(\mathfrak{A}_0)$, where $\mathfrak{A}_0$ is an equational class, then one member of the disjunction must belong to $E(\mathfrak{A}_0)$. Suppose $\phi^{(i_0)}(x) = \phi^{(j_0)}(y)$ belongs to $E(\mathfrak{A}_0)$; then $\phi^{(i_0)}(x) = \phi^{(i_0)}(y)$ belongs also to $E(\mathfrak{A}_0)$, which shows that $\phi^{(i_0)}$ is a constant term. Now let us substitute in (2) $\phi^{(i_0)}x)$ for x. We get

$$\bigvee_{i=1}^{k} \alpha(\phi^{(i)}(\phi^{(i_0)}(x)), \psi_1^{(i)}(\phi^{(i_0)}(x)), \cdots, \psi_n^{(i)}(\phi^{(i_0)}(x))). \tag{4}$$

This disjunction holds for every algebra in $\mathfrak{A}_0$, especially for A. Then one member (at least) of (4) holds for A. Let us suppose that it is

$$\alpha(\phi^{(j_0)}(\phi^{(i_0)}(x)), \psi_1^{(j_0)}(\phi^{(i_0)}(x)), \cdots, \psi_n^{(j_0)}(\phi^{(i_0)}(x))).$$

But $\phi^{(j_0)}(\phi^{(i_0)}(x))$ is a constant term (by definition of $\phi^{(i_0)}(x)$). It follows that a_α is defined by $\phi^{(j_0)}(\phi^{(i_0)}(x)) = x$.

This theorem shows that we can restrict our considerations to the constant elements defined by terms. It shows also that either $C_{\mathfrak{A}_0}(A)$ is void or it is the least subalgebra of A (i.e., the intersection of all non-void subalgebras of A). It is also easy to see that for two algebras A and B in $\mathfrak{A}_0$ there exists at most one homomorphism which maps $C_{\mathfrak{A}_0}(A)$ into $C_{\mathfrak{A}_0}(B)$. For the problem of common extension we have the following corollary:

A necessary condition for the existence of a common extension of two algebras A and B in $\mathfrak{A}_0$ is the isomorphism of the subalgebras $C_{\mathfrak{A}_0}(A)$ and $C_{\mathfrak{A}_0}(B)$.

The condition of the corollary was conjectured in my paper [2] as being sufficient for the problem of common extension in an equational class. The following example, due to A. Białynicki-Birula, shows that it is not so.

Let $\mathfrak{A}_0$ be the class of all commutative rings with unity. Let R_1 and R_2 be two extensions of the ring of integers $\mathscr{I}$, such that in R_1 the inverse element of 2 exists and in R_2 the number 2 is a divisor of zero. Obviously $C_{\mathfrak{A}_0}(R_1) = C_{\mathfrak{A}_0}(R_2) = \mathscr{I}$. On the other hand, there is no common extension of R_1 and R_2 in $\mathfrak{A}_0$, because there is no element in a ring which can be both an inverse element and a divisor of zero.

3. Algebras of Pseudo-Constants

Let $\mathfrak{A}_0$ be an equational class and let $\alpha(z, x_1, \cdots, x_n)$ be a sentence in O. If the implication

$$\alpha(z_1, x_1, \cdots, x_n) \wedge \alpha(z_2, y_1, \cdots, y_n) \rightarrow z_1 = z_2$$

belongs to $O(\mathfrak{A}_0)$, then α is called an O-pseudo-definition.

Let $PD(\mathfrak{A}_0)$ be the set of all O-pseudo-definitions, and let A be an algebra in $\mathfrak{A}_0$. If $\sum_z \sum_{x_1} \cdots \sum_{x_m} \alpha$ belongs to $S(A)$, then there exists an element $\phi_A(\alpha)$ in A, which with n other elements in A satisfies α. Then ϕ_A maps a part of the set $PD(\mathfrak{A}_0)$ into A. The set of images of ϕ_A will be denoted by $P_{\mathfrak{A}_0}(A)$. The elements of this set will be called pseudo-constants of A.

If A and B were two algebras in $\mathfrak{A}_0$, then we will denote the set $\phi_A[\phi_A^{-1}(P_{\mathfrak{A}_0}(A)) \cap \phi_B^{-1}(P_{\mathfrak{A}_0}(B))]$ by $P_{\mathfrak{A}_0}(A/B)$.

$P_{\mathfrak{A}_0}(A/B)$ is the set of such pseudo-constants of A for which there exist in B "the same" pseudo-constants.

It is very easy to see that $P_{\mathfrak{A}_0}(A)$ and $P_{\mathfrak{A}_0}(A/B)$ are either subalgebras of A or void sets. (In what follows the void sets of two algebras will be considered as isomorphic algebras.)

Suppose now that A and B are subalgebras of an algebra C in $\mathfrak{A}_0$. It is clear that in this case we have $P_{\mathfrak{A}_0}(A/B) = P_{\mathfrak{A}_0}(B/A)$. It shows that:

A necessary condition for having a common extension of two algebras A and B in an equational class $\mathfrak{A}_0$ *is the isomorphism of the subalgebras* $P_{\mathfrak{A}_0}(A/B)$ *and* $P_{\mathfrak{A}_0}(B/A)$.

To show that the condition of the theorem above is not a sufficient one, we shall construct an equational class $\mathfrak{A}_0$ such that $P_{\mathfrak{A}_0}(A)$ is void for every A in $\mathfrak{A}_0$, and show two algebras in $\mathfrak{A}_0$ which have no common extension.

We start with a lemma.

If in an equational class $\mathfrak{A}_0$ *there exists an algebra B with two different one-point subalgebras, then* $P_{\mathfrak{A}_0}(A)$ *is void for every A in* A_0.

For the proof we need some statements concerning free products (see, e.g., [4]).

By the free product of two algebras A and B in $\mathfrak{A}_0$, we understand an algebra C in $\mathfrak{A}_0$, containing isomorphic images A' and B' of A and B and satisfying the following condition:

If D is in $\mathfrak{A}_0$, then for every two homomorphisms h and g, which map, respectively, A' and B' into D, there exists a homomorphism f of C into D which agrees with h and g on A' and B' (f is then a common extension of h and g).

The free product of two algebras in $\mathfrak{A}_0$ does not always exist, because it is a common extension. But if any one common extension of two algebras exist in an equational class, then the free product exists also. It follows that for any equational class $\mathfrak{A}_0$ the free product of two isomorphic algebras is always present.

Now we shall proceed to the proof of our lemma. Suppose D in $\mathfrak{A}_0$ has two different one-point subalgebras, (d_1) and (d_2), and A is an algebra in $\mathfrak{A}_0$ with $P_{\mathfrak{A}_0}(A) \neq 0$. Let B be an algebra isomorphic to A, and let C be the free product of A and B. It may be assumed that A and B are simply subalgebras of C. We obviously have $O \neq P_{\mathfrak{A}_0}(A) = P_{\mathfrak{A}_0}(B) = P_{\mathfrak{A}_0}(A/B) = P_{\mathfrak{A}_0}(B/A) \subset A \cap B$, which shows that A and B are not disjoint. Consider homomorphisms h and g mapping A and B onto (d_1) and (d_2). They cannot have a common extension, because their values on the intersection $A \cap B$, which is not void, are different. This shows that the assumption $P_{\mathfrak{A}_0}(A) \neq 0$ leads to a contradiction.

Let $\mathfrak{A}$ be the class of algebras with one binary "multiplication" and four unitary operations $1(\cdot)$, $L(\cdot)$, $K_1(\cdot)$, $K_2(\cdot)$. $\mathfrak{A}_0$ will be defined as the class of these algebras in $\mathfrak{A}$, in which the following two equalities hold:

$$(*) \qquad \begin{cases} x \cdot 1(y) = x, \\ K_1(x) \cdot L(y) = K_2(x) \cdot L(y). \end{cases}$$

Every algebra, in which the equations $x \cdot y = 1(x) = L(x) = K_1(x) = K_2(x) = x$ hold, belongs, as is clearly seen, to $\mathfrak{A}_0$. In every algebra of this kind every element is a one-point subalgebra; therefore it follows from our lemma that $P_{\mathfrak{A}_0}(A) = 0$ for every A in $\mathfrak{A}_0$. On the other hand, it is easy to see that if in algebra A the equation $L(y) = 1(y)$ has a solution and if in algebra B the equation $K_1(x) \neq K_2(x)$ for some x, then A and B cannot have a common extension. This is true because from (*) and $L(y) = 1(y)$ for some y it follows that $K_1(x) = K_2(x)$ for every x.

Suitable example is easy to construct. Let $A = B$ be the set of rationals with the usual multiplication. Let us set in A

$$1(x) = 1, \; L(y) = 0; \; K_1(x) = 1 - K_2(x),$$

and in B

$$1(x) = L(y) = 1, \; K_1(x) = K_2(x).$$

For the reasons explained above, we do not have a common extension of A and B in $\mathfrak{A}_0$.

4. Necessary and Sufficient Conditions for the Existence of a Common Extension

Let $\mathfrak{A}_0$ be an equational class and $U_1(\mathfrak{x})$, $U_2(z_1, z_2, \mathfrak{y})$ be two systems of equations (where $\mathfrak{x}$ stands for some x_i and $\mathfrak{y}$ for some y_i).

Let us suppose that

$$U_1(\mathfrak{x}) \vee U_2(z_1, z_2, \mathfrak{y}) \rightarrow z_1 = z_2 \tag{5}$$

belongs to $O(\mathfrak{A}_0)$.

If there exist in $\mathfrak{A}_0$ two algebras A and B such that in A the system U_1 is solvable and in B the system U_2 can be solved with $z_1 \neq z_2$, then A and B do not have a common extension in $\mathfrak{A}_0$.

Now we shall show that if A and B, both belonging to an equational class $\mathfrak{A}_0$, do not have a common extension in this class, then an open sentence of the form (5) belongs to $O(\mathfrak{A}_0)$ such that U_1 can be solved in either A or B and U_2 in the remaining one, so that $z_1 \neq z_2$.

We need the following lemma:

If a disjunction of the form

$$\delta_1 \vee \delta_2 \vee \cdots \vee \delta_k$$

belongs to $O(\mathfrak{A}_0)$, where $\mathfrak{A}_0$ is an equational class and δ_i are equations or inequalities, and furthermore if this disjunction is a minimal one (i.e., $\delta_1 \vee \cdots \vee \delta_{i-1} \vee \delta_{i+1} \vee \cdots \vee \delta_k$ does not belong to $O(\mathfrak{A}_0)$, for $i = 1, 2, \cdots, k$), then there is only one equation among δ_i's.

This is a well-known lemma. The essential part of its proof can be found, e.g., in [1].

Let A and B be two algebras without a common extension in $\mathfrak{A}_0$. Then it follows from the theorems in [3] that there exists a sentence

$$\alpha(\mathfrak{x}) \vee \beta(\mathfrak{y}) \tag{1}$$

belonging to $O(\mathfrak{A}_0)$ such that $\alpha(\mathfrak{x})$ do not belong to $O(A)$ and $\beta(\mathfrak{y})$ do not belong to $O(B)$.

First we shall prove that (1) may be assumed to be a disjunction of equations and inequalities. In order to prove this we shall present both α and β in the conjunctive-disjunctive form. Then (1) becomes

$$\bigwedge_{i=1}^{k} \bigvee_{j=1}^{n_i} \delta_{i,j}^{(1)}(\mathfrak{x}) \vee \bigwedge_{r=1}^{l} \bigvee_{s=1}^{m_r} \delta_{r,s}^{(2)}(\mathfrak{y}),$$

where $\delta_{i,j}^{(1)}$ and $\delta_{r,s}^{(2)}$ are equations or inequalities.

By distributing disjunction over the conjunctions we obtain

$$\bigwedge_{i=1}^{k} \bigwedge_{r=1}^{l} \left(\bigvee_{j=1}^{n_i} \delta_{i,j}^{(1)}(\mathfrak{x}) \vee \bigvee_{s=1}^{m_r} \delta_{r,s}^{(2)}(\mathfrak{y}) \right). \tag{6}$$

Every member of the conjunction (6) belongs to $O(\mathfrak{A}_0)$, and it is easy to see that for some member i_0, r_0 the disjunction

$$\bigvee_{j=1}^{n_{i_0}} \delta_{i_0,j}^{(1)}(\mathfrak{x})$$

does not belong to $O(A)$ and

$$\bigvee_{j=1}^{m_{r_0}} \delta_{r_0,s}^{(2)}$$

does not belong to $O(B)$. Therefore, it may be assumed that (1) is a disjunction of equations and inequalities, and it follows from the lemma that one and only one of its members is an equation. Let us suppose that the equation in a member containing the variables $\mathfrak{y}$, which results in (1) being found in the form

$$\varepsilon_1'(\mathfrak{x}) \vee \cdots \vee \varepsilon_k'(\mathfrak{x}) \vee \varepsilon_{k+1}'(\mathfrak{y}) \vee \cdots \vee \varepsilon_{k+l}'(\mathfrak{y}) \vee \varepsilon_{k+l+1}(\mathfrak{y}), \tag{7}$$

where ε_j are equations.

Obviously (7) is equivalent to

$$\bigwedge_{i=1}^{k} \varepsilon_i(\mathfrak{x}) \vee \bigwedge_{j=1}^{l} \varepsilon_{k+j}(\mathfrak{y}) \rightarrow \varepsilon_{k+l+1}(\mathfrak{y}). \tag{8}$$

Now suppose $\varepsilon_{k+l+1}(\mathfrak{y})$ has the form $\tau(\mathfrak{y}) = \vartheta(\mathfrak{y})$, where τ and ϑ are terms; then let us set $U_1(\mathfrak{x})$ for $\bigwedge_{i=1}^{k} \varepsilon_i(\mathfrak{x})$ and $U_2(z_1, z_2, \mathfrak{y})$ for $\bigwedge_{j=1}^{l} \varepsilon_{k+j}(\mathfrak{y}) \vee \tau(\mathfrak{y}) = z_1 \vee \vartheta(\mathfrak{y}) = z_2$.

It may be remarked that (8) implies

$$U_1(\mathfrak{x}) \vee U_2(z_1, z_2, \mathfrak{y}) \rightarrow z_1 = z_2, \tag{9}$$

which therefore also belongs to $O(\mathfrak{A}_0)$. On the other hand, we see that $U_1(\mathfrak{x})$ can be solved in A and that U_2 can be solved in B with $z_1 \neq z_2$.

Now let us summarize the results explained above in the form of a theorem.

For the existence of a common extension for the two algebras A and B in an equational class $\mathfrak{A}_0$ the following condition is sufficient and necessary:

In every implication of the form (6) which belongs to $O(\mathfrak{A}_0)$, if U_1 can be solved in either algebra A or B, then $z_1 = z_2$ for every solution of U_2 in the remaining algebra.

References

[1] McKinsey, J. C. C. The decision problem for some classes of sentences without quantifiers. *Journal of Symbolic Logic*, Vol. 8 (1943), pp. 61–76.

[2] Łoś, J. Quelques remarques, théorèmes et problèmes sur les classes définissable d'algèbres. *Mathematical Interpretation of Formal Systems*, Amsterdam, 1955, pp. 97–113.

[3] Łoś, J., and R. Suszko. On the extending of models (II), Common extensions. *Fund. Math.*, Vol. 42 (1955), pp. 343–347.

[4] Sikorski, R. Products of abstract algebras. *Fund. Math.*, Vol. 39 (1952), pp. 211–233.

Symposium on Metamathematics of Algebra and Geometry

METAMATHEMATICS AND ALGEBRA: AN EXAMPLE

ROGER C. LYNDON

University of Michigan, Ann Arbor, Michigan, U.S.A.

It is well known that applications of algebra to logic and of logic to algebra have enriched both domains. It is also true that, quite apart from any interaction, the two subjects have much in common. I want to illustrate this by comparing two sets of ideas, one from algebra and the other from logic. The ideas from algebra center about the Freiheitssatz, a theorem in group theory stated and proved by Magnus, who attributes it to lectures of Dehn relating to topology. The ideas from logic are typified by an 'Interpolation Theorem', or 'Separation Theorem', of Craig, and by a similar metamathematical result of Beth, in the theory of definition. I think it is clear that the two sets of ideas arose quite independently. But I shall try to point out that the two sets of ideas show a similarity that seems more than mere analogy, and hence suggests a more comprehensive theory containing them both.

The Freiheitssatz is most easily formulated as a theorem about free groups. We recall that a group F is said to be free on a set $X = \{x_1, x_2, \cdots\}$ of generators if every map from X into a group G has a unique extension to a homomorphism from F into G. In other words, the generators x_i are free in the sense that they satisfy only such relations (in the form of equations) as hold for all sets of elements g_i in any group G, that is, only such relations $w(x_1, \cdots, x_n) = 1$ for which $\forall x_1 \cdots \forall x_n w(x_1, \cdots, x_n)$ is a consequence of the group axioms. The existence of free groups, and indeed of free algebras of any class defined by universally quantified equations, is an easy result in the theory of models. But, for group theory, it is often preferable to have a more explicit construction that makes no overt appeal to metamathematical ideas. In fact, in purely algebraic investigations free algebras are often used as a substitute for metamathematical considerations; a free algebra serves as a 'calculus' for a certain part of the first order theory of groups in much the same way as Boolean algebras serve for the sentential calculus.

Elements of the free group F may be represented by 'words' (or 'terms'), that is, by certain expressions built up from (symbols for) the generators x_i by means of (symbols for) the group operations: multiplication, inversion, neutral element. The elements of F can then be identified with equivalence classes of words, or with certain words in canonical form; we shall not find it necessary to distinguish closely between a word and the group element it represents.

An important consequence of the property used to characterize free groups is that every group G is a homomorphic image of a free group F. The words of F can thus serve also as names for the elements of G, although relations $w(x_1, \cdots, x_n) = 1$ will ordinarily hold in G that do not hold in F. The group G can be described by specifying a set of such 'defining relations' from which all others follow; and in practice, especially in topology, it often happens that a group is given to us by just such a 'presentation'. The first question to arise is that of when two words represent the same element of G, or, equivalently, when one relation is a consequence of others. The well known fact that this question is not generally solvable does not render the 'metatheory' of this sort of consequence relation any the less interesting.

The question at hand is easily formulated in purely logical terms: when is a formula $w(x_1, \cdots, x_n) = 1$ a logical consequence of similar formulas $w_i = 1$ together with the axioms of group theory? It can equally be formulated within the theory of free groups: when is w contained in the normal subgroup 'defined' by the w_i, that is, the smallest normal subgroup containing all the w_i? More explicitly, when is w expressible as a product of conjugates $uw_i^{\pm 1}u^{-1}$ of the w_i and their inverses? It is customary to call w, in this case, a 'consequence' of the w_i, and to write $w_1, w_2, \cdots \rightarrow w$.

It will be clear that this consequence relation in free groups will inherit some properties of the relation of logical consequence. It may also be viewed as a non-commutative analog of the familiar linear dependence relation for vector spaces, or modules, although here one must recognize the equal claim of the simpler, but nonetheless interesting and important, dependence relation under which w belongs to the (ordinary) subgroup of F generated by the w_i. All these dependence theories could be subsumed under the study of 'closure algebras' equipped, for the purposes at hand, with certain auxiliary operations.

Magnus rests his proof of the Freiheitssatz on a number of lemmas, whose main content can be phrased as follows.

(1) *Let W be a set of words containing only generators from a set A, U a set of words containing only generators from a set B, and suppose that every*

consequence of either W or U that contains only generators from the set $A \cap B$ is in fact a consequence of both W and U. Then every consequence of $W \cup U$ that contains only generators from the set A is in fact a consequence of W alone.

One derives without great difficulty the following consequence:

(2) *If $\{w_i\} \rightarrow v$ then $\{w_i\} \rightarrow \{w'_h\}$ and $\{w'_h\} \rightarrow v$ for some $\{w'_h\}$ containing only generators that appear both in some w_i and in v.*

The analogy is clear between (2) and the following theorem of Craig.

(3) *If W and V are first order formulas and $W \vdash V$, then $W \vdash W'$ and $W' \vdash V$ for some formula W' containing only those (non-logical) constants that occur both in W and in V.*

The obvious analog (4) of (1) now follows directly from (3). For $W, U \vdash V$ implies $W \vdash U \supset V$, whence (3) gives $W \vdash W'$ and $W' \vdash U \supset V$ where W', as a consequence of W containing only constants from the set $A \cap B$, is also a consequence of U, and it follows that $U \vdash V$. Indeed, this argument establishes the analog for sentences of the following stronger assertion.

(1′) *Let $W \cup U \rightarrow v$. Then there exists W' such that $W \rightarrow W'$, that $W' \cup U \rightarrow v$, and that the words in W' contain only generators that occur in some w from W and also either in v or in some u from U.*

But the example $x^{-1}yxz, y^2 \rightarrow z^2$ shows that (1′) itself does not hold for groups.

Despite the similarity of their content, it does not appear that (1), or even (2), can be obtained directly from (3). One naturally would seek to apply (3) to a language in which the x_i occur as individual constants. If this language admits quantification over individuals, (3) will be satisfied by W' obtained from $w_1 = 1 \,\&\, \cdots \,\&\, w_m = 1$ by replacing with existentially quantified variables all x_i that do not occur in some u_j or in v, and this W' does not provide us with the required w'_h. If, on the other hand, we restrict our language, as is permissible, to one without quantification, we have to admit as hypotheses instances of the group axioms, such as $(x_i x_j)x_k = x_i(x_j x_k)$, which may contain combinations of constants that prevent us from absorbing them harmlessly into either the w_i or the u_j.

In fact, as suggested by Magnus in a footnote, (1) is hardly more than an alternative statement of a basic theorem of Schreier concerning free products. A group G is the free product of its subgroups G_1 and G_2 if it is generated by G_1 and G_2 together, and has the property that any pair of homomorphisms from G_1 and G_2 into a group H that agree on $G_1 \cap G_2$ have a common extension to a homomorphism from G into H. Schreier's theorem asserts the existence of a free product of two arbitrary groups, with prescribed identification of isomorphic subgroups.

(5) *Let there be given isomorphisms κ_1 and κ_2 from a group K into groups G_1 and G_2. Then there exist isomorphisms γ_1 and γ_2 of G_1 and G_2 in a group*

H such that H is the free product of the two images, H_1, H_2, and that $\gamma_1\kappa_1$ and $\gamma_2\kappa_2$ define the same map from K onto the intersection of the two images, $H_1 \cap H_2$.

One can easily reduce the proof of (5) to the following case: $G_1 = F_1/R_1$, $G_2 = F_2/R_2$, $K = F_0/R_0$ where F_1 is free on a set X_1 of generators, F_2 on X_2, F_0 on $X_1 \cap X_2$, and κ_1 and κ_2 are the natural isomorphisms, hence where $R_1 \cap F_2 = R_0 = R_2 \cap F_1$. Then, if the required group K exists at all, we can take it as $H = F/R$ where F is free on $X_1 \cup X_2$ and R is the normal subgroup of F defined by R_1 and R_2 together; it is in fact immediate that all the assertions of the theorem hold except possibly that the natural maps of G_1 and G_2 into H be isomorphisms. We have then to show that, in the present notation,

(6) $R_1 \cap F_2 = R_2 \cap F_1$ *implies* $R \cap F_1 = R_1$ (*and, similarly,* $R \cap F_2 = R_2$).

But this will be recognized as a mere restatement of (1).

That (1) does not follow from (2) as easily as (4) did from (3) is suggested by the above, and becomes clear from the following. Typically, from $w, u \to v$ one can infer that $w \to u_0^{-1}v$ for some consequence u_0 of u; this is an analog of $W \vdash U \supset V$. But, while $U \supset V$ contains only constants occurring in U or in V, one cannot conclude directly that u_0, and therefore $u_0^{-1}v$, contains only generators occurring in u or in v.

It appears that some construction, such as that given by Schreier, or the more explicitly syntactical argument of Magnus, is essential to establish the existential content of (1), or of (5). The situation is similar to Craig's theorem (3), which requires either the essential constructive content of Gödel's Completeness Theorem, or else a rather explicit proof-theoretic analysis. But it is still reasonable to ask for one construction, or at least one general theorem, that would contain both results. The question is presumably that of extending Craig's theorem to a class of theories, with non-logical axioms, in which the formulas are of some restricted form, as, here, that of equations. This is related to the question of extending Schreier's theorem; that it is not true for all equational classes is shown by the following simple example and remark of Higgins. In the theory of semigroups with zero, subject to the further axiom $xyz = 0$, the consequence $xx = y \to yz = 0$ violates (3); and, in general, (3) and (5) will fail if an identity $w(u, v) = (u, v)$ holds, where u and v have no common variables, but not $w(x, y) = w'(x, y)$, for x and y variables.

The question of free products, extensions, and unions of models has of course been studied. Taking the constants in Craig's theorem, as is more usual, to be predicates or relations rather than elements raises similar questions on a higher level.

The use of (1) in the proof of the Freiheitssatz rests upon the following corollary.

(7) *Suppose that* $w, u_1, \cdots, u_m \to v$, *and that* w *has no consequence other than* 1 *containing only generators that occur in some one of* $u_1, \cdots, u_m$ *or* v. *Then* $u_1, \cdots, u_m \to v$.

The possibility of realizing the hypothesis on w is given by the Freiheitssatz itself.

(8) *Let* w *be a cyclically reduced word: a product of generators and their inverses, with no successive factors inverse to each other, and the last factor not inverse to the first. Then every consequence of* w, *other than* 1, *contains every generator that occurs in* w.

This is trivial if w consists of at most one factor, and a device of Magnus enables him to use (7) to carry out an induction on the number of factors. By a similar argument he proves the following.

(9) *Two words are equivalent:* $w \to v$ *and* $v \to w$, *if and only if one is a conjugate of the other, or of its inverse.*

It is clear that every word w is equivalent to a cyclically reduced word w_1, and that every word equivalent to w must contain the set $|w|$ of all generators that occur in such w_1. Thus the Freiheitssatz says that if a generator occurs in every word equivalent to w, then it occurs also in every non-trivial consequence of w.

It follows easily from Craig's theorem that two equivalent formulas are always equivalent to a third formula containing only those constants that they have in common. Hence, for every formula W there is a unique minimal set $|W|$ of constants common to all formulas equivalent to W, and there exists W' equivalent to W containing only these constants. But the analog of the Freiheitssatz does not hold for arbitrary formulas: the sentence $W : k_1 = k_2 \,\&\, k_3 = k_4$ of identity theory is clearly equivalent to no sentence not containing all four constants, but has the non-trivial consequence $k_1{=}k_2$ in which k_3 and k_4 do not appear.

Nevertheless, the question of which sentences contain all (or some) of their constants essentially, in the sense of the Freiheitssatz, has some natural interest. The name of the Freiheitssatz is derived from the following formulation.

(10) *In the group with generators* $x_1, \cdots, x_n$, *defined by a single relation* $w = 1$ *where* w *is a cyclically reduced word containing the generator* x_1, *the subgroup generated by* $x_2, \cdots, x_n$ *is free on these generators.*

Similarly, if a sentence $W(k)$ contains the constant k essentially, and T is the theory obtained from a theory $T(k)$ by dropping the constant k, then, by definition, $W(k)$ has no consequence in the theory T that is not a theorem. Alternatively, every model for T can be extended to contain a 'solution' of the sentence $\exists y \cdot W(y)$; here it hardly needs to be remarked that the primary interest attaches to the case that k does not belong to the range of quantification, since otherwise the sentence $\exists y \cdot W(y)$ of T would have to be a theorem. There should be some interest, in appropriate theories, in which formulas contain all their constants (at least from a prescribed set) essentially, and to what extent a general formula can be resolved into such components.

That the difficulty illustrated by the sentence W: $k_1 = k_2$ & $k_3 = k_4$ is not an insuperable obstacle to the application of the Freiheitssatz is already evident in the treatment of groups defined by two relations, $w_1 = 1$ and $w_2 = 1$. For we may still derive consequences from the fact that, even if there is no single generator common to all non-trivial consequences v of a set of words $w_1, \cdots, w_m$, it may still be the case that the set of generators occurring in a cyclically reduced consequence v is not entirely arbitrary. Thus any consequence of W, above, that does not contain k_1 cannot contain k_2 except trivially. Such a result is embodied in the Hauptform of the Freiheitssatz, of which we give only a simple case.

(11) *Let w_1 and w_2 be cyclically reduced, with x_1 occurring in w_1 but not in w_2, and x_2 in w_2 but not in w_1. If $w_1, w_2 \to v$ and v does not contain x_1, then $w_2 \to v$.*

The analog for logical formulas is clear.

Our current re-examination of the Freiheitssatz arose from an attempt to extend the Hauptform, and related results that we mention below, to more general situations suggested by problems encountered by Papakyriakopoulos in his investigation of the Poincaré conjecture. We have made some progress in such extensions; and it was the observation of how little specific to group theory entered into our reasoning that drew our attention to the analogy with metamathematical questions. We cite here the metamathematical analog of a typical such extension of the Hauptform.

(12) *Let K be a set of constants k_p indexed by a set P of lattice points p in Euclidean space of dimension $n \geqq 1$. If W is any formula, let P_W be the intersection with P of the convex closure of the set of those p for which k_p occurs in W. Let Ω be a set of formulas with the following properties:*

(i) *if p is an extremal point of P_W, $W \in \Omega$, then k_p occurs in every consequence of W that is not a theorem;*

(ii) *no $P_{W_1} \subseteqq P_{W_2}$ for $W_1 \neq W_2$, $W_1, W_2 \in \Omega$;*

(iii) *no extremal point of $P_{W_1} \cup P_{W_2}$ belongs to*

$$P_{W_1} \cap P_{W_2} \quad \text{for} \quad W_1 \neq W_2, W_1, W_2 \in \Omega.$$

Then, if any formula V is a consequence of all W in Ω, it is a consequence of those W alone that contain k_p only for p in P_V.

We conclude with remarks on two sets of results closely related to the Freiheitssatz and its extensions. First, Magnus obtained, by a method of proof very similar to that for the Freiheitssatz, a positive solution of the word problem for groups with a single defining relation; that is, he showed that the relation $w \to v$ is decidable. This suggests, although I have not tried to check it, that, in the situation of (12), the set (normal subgroup) of all v such that $\Omega \to v$ should be recursively reducible to the sets of those v such that $W \to v$, for each W in Ω.

A related matter is the question of whether a word v is obtainable as a consequence of words $w_1, \cdots, w_m$ in various essentially different ways. I have been able to extend to the situation of (12) an earlier 'Identity Theorem' asserting (apart from a minor technicality) that if v is expressible as a product of conjugates $uw_i^{\pm 1}u^{-1}$ of the w_i and their inverses, then this expression is unique apart from reordering of factors and from replacing the u by u' equivalent to them, modulo the w_i, that is, where the w_i have as consequence $u^{-1}u'$. The analogous metamathematical context, that of the 'rearrangement'' of proofs, is familiar enough in general terms, but I am not aware of any definition of 'essential equivalence' of proofs that would provide an interesting formulation of the question analogous to the Identity Theorem: when are all proofs from given premises to a specified conclusion essentially equivalent? Alternatively, if normal subgroups R_1 and R_2 are independent in the current sense, then their intersection contains no more than the *a priori* necessary commutator group (R_1, R_2); when are two sentences W_1 and W_2 independent in the sense of having no common consequence beyond some set, as yet to be specified, of obvious common consequences such as $W_1 \vee W_2$? Although these questions are vague and unanswered, it is hard not to feel that some sense is inherent in the idea of two premises, say from quite unrelated disciplines, being independent in their implications.

We end by noting a situation where the shoe is on the other foot, and known metamathematical results suggest natural and interesting, but unsolved, problems in group theory. Craig's theorem (3) is effective: given a proof $W \vdash V$, his reasoning gives a construction for the required W', and for proofs that $W \vdash W'$ and $W' \vdash V$. Similarly, in the situation analogous to that of (7), from a proof that $W, U_1, \cdots, U_n \vdash V$ we can construct a proof that $U_1, \cdots, U_n \vdash V$. Although a similar 'elimination of premises' can be recognized as playing an important role in certain special arguments in group theory, we still have no proof, or refutation, of the parallel group theoretic conjecture. In its simplest form, given $w_1(x_1)$, $w_2(x_2)$, $v(x_2)$ as in (11), and an expression for v as a product of conjugates of $w_1^{\pm 1}$, $w_2^{\pm 1}$, is there a natural way (in a sense that can be made precise) of transforming this into an expression for v as a product of conjugates of $w_2^{\pm 1}$ alone?

Bibliographical Note. A discussion of Craig's theorem and other metamathematical references will be found in [6]; the remaining papers listed below contain those results to which we have referred from group theory.

[1] M. DEHN, Über unendliche diskontinuerliche Gruppen, *Math. Ann.* Vol. 71 (1911) 116.

[2] O. SCHREIER, Die Untergruppen der freien Gruppen, *Abh. Seminar Hamburgischen Univ.* Vol. 5 (1927) 161.

[3] W. MAGNUS, Über diskontinuerliche Gruppen mit einer definierenden Relation, (Der Freiheitssatz), *J. reine u. angewandte Math.* Vol. 63 (1930) 141.

[4] W. Magnus, Das Identitätsproblem für Gruppen mit einer definierenden Relation. *Math. Ann.* Vol. 106 (1932) 295.

[5] R. C. Lyndon, Cohomology theory of groups with a single defining relation, *Ann. of Math.* Vol 52 (1950) 650.

[6] R. C. LYNDON, Properties preserved under algebraic construction, *Bull. Amer. Math. Soc.* Vol. 65 (1959) 287.

[7] R. C. LYNDON, Dependence and Independence in free groups, *J. reine u. angewandte Math.*, to appear.

DIOPHANTINE EQUATIONS AND NON-STANDARD MODELS OF ARITHMETIC

MICHAEL O. RABIN

Hebrew University, Jerusalem, Israel

In the following paper we apply methods of general model theory to obtain information about questions concerning non-standard models of arithmetic. While non-standard models possess, by definition, all the elementary properties of the system of integers, viewed from the outside they exhibit a markedly different behavior. Thus we prove that for every non-standard model of arithmetic there exists a diophantine equation with coefficients in the model which is not solvable in the model but is solvable in a suitable extension model (Theorem 5, actually a stronger result is proved). This cannot, of course, happen with diophantine equations over the standard model.

An added incentive to the study of non-standard models is the possibility that besides gaining information on their structure, one may be able to deduce results in number theory and axiomatics of arithmetic proper. Thus the result cited above has an application to axiomatics. In Section 2 we establish a close connection between certain questions concerning models and their extensions and the question whether every recursively enumerable predicate is diophantine.

The most striking feature of non-standard models of arithmetic is that they contain elements which may be considered as being, in a certain sense, infinite integers. In studying non-standard models these may serve to represent infinite collections of integers, or sets of integers, etc. Thus we employ here an infinite integer to show that the union of a certain infinite collection of sets of elements of a model is always a *proper* subset of a certain set, this being the main step in the proof of Theorem 5. Further exploration of this device should yield interesting results.

Preliminaries

Let I be the set of non-negative integers and let $\mathscr{X} = \langle I, +, \cdot, \rangle$ be the relational system with $+$ and $\cdot$ being ordinary addition and multiplication of integers. Let L be the first-order language having two function constants $\mathbf{+}$ and $\cdot$, a relation $=$, an infinite list of individual variables $\mathbf{u}, \mathbf{v}, \mathbf{w}, \mathbf{x}, \mathbf{y}, \mathbf{z}, \mathbf{u}_1, \cdots$, and an infinite list of individual constants $\mathbf{0}, \mathbf{1}, \mathbf{2}, \cdots$ (to be called *numerals*). By $\mathbf{T}$ we shall denote the set of all sentences of L satisfied in $\mathscr{X}$ upon interpreting the function constants $\mathbf{+}$ and as addition and multiplication, respectively, interpreting $=$ as equality, and interpreting each numeral $\mathbf{n}$ as the corresponding integer n. $\mathbf{T}$ will be called the set of *true sentences of arithmetic.*

Any system $\mathscr{X}' = \langle I', +, \cdot\rangle$, where $+$ and $\cdot$ are binary functions on I', which is a model of $\mathbf{T}$ (under the obvious interpretation), will be called a *strong model of arithmetic*; strong model for short. Every strong model $\mathscr{L}'$ contains a unique sub-model isomorphic to $\mathscr{L}$. By effecting an appropriate identification, every model may thus be considered an extension of $\mathscr{L}$. If the extension is *proper*, i.e., $I' - I \neq \phi$, we shall call $\mathscr{L}'$ a *non-standard* (strong) model. The model $\mathscr{L}$, and any system isomorphic to it, will be called the *standard* model.

In a non-standard model $\mathscr{L}'$, the elements $\pi \in I' - I$ will be called *infinite integers*. We introduce the relation $<$ by the usual definition. The infinite integers of $\mathscr{L}'$ may then be characterized as those elements $\pi \in I'$ satisfying $i < \pi$ for every actual integer $i \in I \subseteqq I'$.

Notations: The meta-mathematical variables $a, b, i, j, k, m, n, p, q$ range over integers, i.e., elements of I; the corresponding bold-face letters denote numerals. The variables u, v, w, x, y, z will be used metamathematically to denote indeterminates in writing polynomials, range over elements of a given set, etc. Fixed elements of a model will be denoted by Greek letters. Polynomial equations will be written, for the sake of brevity, in the form $P(x) = 0$ even though there is no subtraction in the system. This is permissible because for any polynomial equation $P(x) = 0$ with positive and negative coefficients one can find an equation $P_1(x) = P_2(x)$ in the same indeterminates, with positive coefficients and with the same solutions.

1. Diophantic Equations in Non-Standard Models

1.1. Number-Theoretic Theorems. Let us choose a definite Gödel numbering of all polynomials $P(y_1, \cdots, y_n, x_1, \cdots, x_m)$, where m is fixed but n varies over all positive integers, with positive and negative coefficients. The polynomial having Gödel number i will be denoted by P_i and we assume that every integer is a Gödel number of some polynomial.

LEMMA 1. *The number-theoretic relation $E(i, b, a_1, \ldots, a_m)$ holding if and only if i is a Gödel number of a polynomial P_i in $n + m$ variables, $b = 2^{b_1} \cdots p_{n-1}^{b_n}$ is a Gödel number of a sequence $(b_1, \cdots, b_n)$, and $P_i(b_1, \cdots, b_n, a_1, \cdots, a_m) = 0$, is primitive recursive.* The proof is obvious.

$E(\mathbf{u}, \mathbf{y}, \mathbf{x}_1, \cdots, \mathbf{x}_m)$ will denote a formula of L which numeral-wise represents the primitive recursive predicate E.

REMARK. For an infinite integer η the predicate $(Ey)E(\eta, y, \vec{x})$ has no direct meaning. If, however, $i \in I$, then $(Ey)E(i, y, \vec{x})$ has the intended meaning in the sense that

$$(\vec{\mathbf{x}})[(E\mathbf{y})E(\mathbf{i}, \mathbf{y}, \vec{\mathbf{x}}) \equiv (E\vec{\mathbf{y}})P_i(\vec{\mathbf{y}}, \vec{\mathbf{x}}) = \mathbf{0}] \in \mathbf{T},$$

and $(E\mathbf{y})E(\mathbf{i}, \mathbf{y}, \vec{\mathbf{x}})$ thus represents the relation $(E\vec{y})P_i(\vec{y}, \vec{x}) = 0$ in every model.

LEMMA 2. *Let* $C(\mathbf{x})$ *be any formula of* L. *The sentence*

$$(1)\quad (\mathbf{u})(E\mathbf{v})(\vec{\mathbf{x}})\{(E\mathbf{y})E(\mathbf{v}, \mathbf{y}, \vec{\mathbf{x}}) \equiv (E\mathbf{w})[\mathbf{w} < \mathbf{u} \wedge C(\mathbf{w}) \wedge (E\mathbf{y})E(\mathbf{w}, \mathbf{y}, \vec{\mathbf{x}})]\},$$

where $\vec{\mathbf{x}}$ *abbreviates* $(\mathbf{x}_1, \cdots, \mathbf{x}_m)$ *is a true sentence of arithmetic.*

PROOF. Let i be any integer. The set of integers j satisfying $j < i \wedge C(j)$ is finite and consists of, say, $j_1, \cdots, j_n$. The union of the finite number of (extensionally) diophantine relations $(Eb)E(j_k, b, a_1, \cdots, a_m)$, $1 \leqq k \leqq n$, is, as one can readily see, again a diophantine relation. Let q be the Gödel number of a polynomial $P_q(y_1, \cdots, u_p, x_1, \cdots, x_m)$ for which

$$(\vec{a})[(E\vec{c})P_q(\vec{c}, a_1, \cdots, a_m) = 0 \equiv (Eb)E(j_1, b, \vec{a}) \vee \cdots \vee (Eb)E(j_n, b, \vec{a})].$$

The integer q satisfies

$$(\vec{a})\{(Eb)E(q, b, \vec{a}) \equiv (Ej)[j < i \wedge C(j) \wedge (Eb)E(j, b, \vec{a})]\},$$

in the model $\mathscr{Z}$. The sentence (1) is thus true in the standard model $\mathscr{Z}$, and hence belongs to **T**.

From M. Davis' result [1, p. 113] to the effect that the negation of a diophantine relation is not necessarily a diophantine relation, there follows at once the existence of integers k and n such that the number-theoretic predicate

$$(2)\qquad \sim(Eb_1, \cdots, b_n)\Big[\sum_{0 \leqq i_j \leqq k} a_{i_1 \ldots i_n} b_1^{i_1} \cdots b_n^{i_n} = 0\Big],$$

stating the non-solvability of the diophantine equation

$$(3)\qquad \sum a_{i_1 \ldots i_n} t_1^{i_1} \cdots t_n^{i_n} = 0, \quad 0 \leqq i_j \leqq k,$$

is not diophantine.

Let us assign to each of the $(k+1)^n$ n-tupels a number $i = \nu(i_1, \cdots, i_n)$ so that i runs through the numbers $\leqq (k+1)^n$.

Translating (2) into L we get a formula $\sim D(\mathbf{x}_1, \cdots, \mathbf{x}_m)$:

$$\sim D(\mathbf{x}_1, \cdots, \mathbf{x}_m) = \sim(E\mathbf{z}_1, \cdots, \mathbf{z}_n)\Big[\sum_i \mathbf{x}_{\nu(i_1, \cdots, i_n)} \mathbf{z}_1^{i_1} \ldots \mathbf{z}_n^{i_n} = 0\Big],$$

where $m = (k+1)^n$, and the summation includes all different monomials $\mathbf{z}_1^{i_1} \cdots \mathbf{z}_n^{i_n}$.

We clearly have

LEMMA 3. *The sentence*

$$(4)\qquad (\mathbf{v})(E\vec{\mathbf{x}})[\sim D(\vec{\mathbf{x}}) \not\equiv (E\mathbf{y})E(\mathbf{v}, \mathbf{y}, \vec{\mathbf{x}})]$$

is a true sentence of arithmetic.

COROLLARY. *The sentence*

$$(5)\quad (\mathbf{v})\{(\vec{\mathbf{x}})[(E\mathbf{y})E(\mathbf{v}, \mathbf{y}, \vec{\mathbf{x}}) \supset \sim D(\vec{\mathbf{x}})] \supset (E\vec{\mathbf{x}})[\sim(E\mathbf{y})E(\mathbf{v}, \mathbf{y}, \vec{\mathbf{x}}) \wedge \sim D(\vec{\mathbf{x}})]\}$$

is in **T**.

1.2. A Model-Theoretic Result. We aim at finding elements $\alpha_1, \ldots, \alpha_m$ of the non-standard model $\mathscr{Z}'$ so that on substituting $\alpha_{\nu(i_1,\ldots,i_n)}$ for $a_{i_1,\ldots,i_n}$, the equation (3) is not solvable in $\mathscr{Z}'$ but is solvable in some extension model $\mathscr{Z}''$ of $\mathscr{Z}'$. In other words, $\sim D(\alpha_1, \cdots, \alpha_m)$ should hold in $\mathscr{Z}'$ but not in some extension. When is it *impossible* to change an elementary property of given elements of a model by passing to an extension model? The answer is furnished by the following theorem employed also in [2, § 3.2.]; the reader may consult [2] for a proof.

THEOREM 4. *Let the relational system* $\mathscr{M} = \langle S, R_1, R_2, \ldots \rangle$ *be a model of the set* $\mathbf{T}$ *of sentences of the first-order language* L *and let* $\alpha_1, \cdots, \alpha_m \in S$. *Let* $\sim D(\mathbf{x}_1, \cdots, \mathbf{x}_m)$ *be a formula of* L *with no free variables other than* $\mathbf{x}_1, \cdots, \mathbf{x}_m$ *and assume that* $\sim D(\alpha_1, \cdots, \alpha_m)$ *holds in* $\mathscr{M}$. *A necessary and sufficient condition for* $\sim D(\alpha_1, \cdots, \alpha_m)$ *to hold in every extension model* $\mathscr{M} < \mathscr{M}'$ *of* $\mathscr{M}$ *is that there exists a formula* $E(\mathbf{x}_1, \cdots, \mathbf{x}_m)$ *in prenex form such that*

(i) $E(\mathbf{x}_1, \cdots, \mathbf{x}_m)$ *is existential,*
(ii) $E(\alpha_1, \cdots, \alpha_m)$ *holds in* $\mathscr{M}$,
(iii) $\vdash_{\mathbf{T}} (\mathbf{x}_1, \cdots, \mathbf{x}_m)[E(\mathbf{x}_1, \cdots, \mathbf{x}_m) \supset \sim D(\mathbf{x}_1, \cdots, \mathbf{x}_m)]$.

1.3. The Main Theorem.

THEOREM 5. *For every non-standard model* $Z', = \langle I', +, \cdot \rangle$ *of arithmetic there exist elements* $\alpha_1, \cdots, \alpha_m \in I'$ *and an extension model* $\mathscr{Z}' > \mathscr{Z}''$ *such that on substituting* $\alpha_{\nu(i_1,\ldots,i_n)}$ *for* $\alpha_{i_1,\ldots,i_n}$ *the diophantine equation* (3) *is not solvable in* $\mathscr{Z}'$ *but is solvable in the strong model* $\mathscr{Z}''$.

PROOF. We have to find elements $\alpha_1, \ldots, \alpha_m \in I'$, such that $\sim D(\alpha_1, \ldots, \alpha_m)$ holds in $\mathscr{Z}'$ but does not hold in some extension model of $\mathscr{Z}'$. In view of Theorem 4 we must find elements $\alpha_1, \cdots, \alpha_m \in I'$ such that for *every* existential formula $E(\mathbf{x}_1, \cdots, \mathbf{x}_m)$ satisfying (iii), $\sim E(\alpha_1, \cdots, \alpha_m)$ holds in $\mathscr{Z}'$. The set

$$S_E = \{(\alpha_1, \cdots, \alpha_m) | \alpha_1, \cdots, \alpha_m \text{ satisfy } E(\mathbf{x}_1, \cdots, \mathbf{x}_m) \text{ in } \mathscr{Z}'\},$$

where E satisfies (i) and (iii), is by Lemma 3 always a proper subset of the set $S_{\sim D}$ of all $(\alpha_1, \cdots, \alpha_m)$ satisfying $\sim D(\mathbf{x}_1, \cdots, \mathbf{x}_m)$ in $\mathscr{Z}'$. But this does not preclude, *a priori*, the possibility that the union of the sets S_E equals $S_{\sim D}$. The proof is achieved by employing an infinite integer as follows.

Let $\pi \in {}'I$ be an infinite integer. Let $C(\mathbf{u})$ be the formula

$$C(\mathbf{u}) = (\vec{\mathbf{x}})[(E\mathbf{y})E(\mathbf{u}, \mathbf{y}, \vec{\mathbf{x}}) \supset \sim D(\vec{\mathbf{x}})].$$

The informal meaning of $C(u)$ is that u is the Gödel number of a polynomial giving a diophantine predicate (of $\mathscr{Z}'$) which is a subset of $S_{\sim D}$. By Lemma 2 there exists a $\eta \in I'$ such that

$$(\vec{x})\{(Ey)E(\eta, y, \vec{x}) \equiv (Ew)[w < \pi \wedge C(w) \wedge (Ey)E(w, y, \vec{x})]\}$$

holds in $\mathscr{L}'$. The set of m-tuples $(\beta_1, \cdots, \beta_m) = \vec{\beta}$ satisfying $(Ey)E(\eta, y, \vec{\beta})$ in $\mathscr{L}'$ is the union of the sets of m-tuples $\vec{\beta}$ satisfying $(Ey)E(\sigma, y, \vec{\beta})$, where σ runs through all elements $\sigma < \pi$ satisfying $C(\sigma)$. The set of m-tuples $\vec{\beta}$ satisfying $(Ey)E(\eta, y, \vec{\beta})$ in $\mathscr{L}'$ is, therefore, a subset of $S_{\sim D}$. By the Corollary to Lemma 3 it is a *proper* subset of $S_{\sim D}$. There exist therefore elements $\alpha_1, \cdots, \alpha_m \in I'$ for which

$$\sim(Ey)E(\eta, y, \vec{\alpha}) \wedge \sim D(\vec{\alpha}) \tag{6}$$

holds in $\mathscr{L}'$.

Let $P_i(y_1, \cdots, y_n, x_1, \cdots, x_m)$ be a polynomial with the Gödel number i such that the formula

$$E(\mathbf{x}_1, \cdots, \mathbf{x}_m) = (E\mathbf{y}_1, \cdots, \mathbf{y}_n)[P_i(\mathbf{y}_1, \cdots, \mathbf{y}_n, \mathbf{x}_1, \cdots, \mathbf{x}_m) = \mathbf{0}]$$

satisfies condition (iii) of Theorem 4. For the numeral $\mathbf{i}$ we have, by the Remark following Lemma 1,

$$(\vec{\mathbf{x}})[(E\mathbf{y})E(\mathbf{i}, \mathbf{y}, \vec{\mathbf{x}}) \equiv E(\vec{\mathbf{x}})] \in \mathbf{T}, \tag{7}$$

so that this sentence is certainly satisfied in $\mathscr{L}'$. This implies, since $E(\vec{\mathbf{x}})$ satisfies (iii), that $C(\mathbf{i}) \in \mathbf{T}$. The integer $i \in I \subseteqq I'$ now satisfies $i < \pi$ and $C(i)$ in $\mathscr{L}'$, and the set of m-tuples satisfying $(Ey)E(i, y, \vec{x})$ in $\mathscr{L}'$ is, consequently, a subset of the set of m-tuples satisfying $(Ey)E(\eta, y, \vec{x})$. Equations (6) and (7) imply that $\sim E(\alpha_1, \cdots, \alpha_m)$ holds in $\mathscr{L}'$. The proof is now completed by appealing to Theorem 4.

1.4. An Application to Axiomatics. By applying Theorem 5, we prove a result concerning axiomatics of arithmetic. This result is not new and may also be proved by other methods, e.g., by using Tarski's Theorem to the effect that the set **T** is not arithmetical. The interest in the proof given here lies in the fact that it is purely model-theoretic and avoids the use of arithmetization of syntax.

A sentence B is said to be in form AE if it is in prenex form and all universal quantifiers precede all existential quantifiers. It is quite obvious that if **S** is a (consistent) set of sentences in form AE, then the union of an ascending chain of models of **S** is again a model of **S**.

THEOREM 6. *There does not exist a set* $\mathbf{S} \subset \mathbf{T}$ *of true sentences of arithmetic in form* AE *such that all sentences of* **T** *are logical consequences of sentences of* **S**.

By the previous remark Theorem 6 is an immediate consequence of the following:

THEOREM 7. *There exists as ascending chain* $\mathscr{L}_1 \prec \mathscr{L}_2 \prec \cdots$, *of strong models of arithmetic such that the union* $\mathscr{L}' = \bigcup_i \mathscr{L}_i$ *is not a strong model of arithmetic.*

PROOF. We recall that $D(\mathbf{x}_1, \ldots, \mathbf{x}_m)$ is the formula stating that the diophantine equation (3) with coefficients $a_{i_1,\ldots,i_n} = x_{\nu(i_1,\ldots,i_n)}$ is solvable. Notice that if $D(\alpha_1, \cdots, \alpha_m)$ holds in a model $\mathscr{L}_1$, it holds in every extension model $\mathscr{L}_2$ of $\mathscr{L}_1$.

Let $\mathscr{L}_1 = \langle I_1, +, \cdot \rangle$ be a non-standard model. Let $\mathbf{Z}_1$ be the diagram of $\mathscr{L}_1$ (for the notion of *diagram* see [3, p. 74]). From Zorn's lemma there follows the existence of a set $J_1 \subseteqq I_1^m$ of m-tuples maximal with respect to the property that the set of sentences (of an appropriate extension of the language L)

$$\mathbf{M}_1 = \{D(\alpha_1, \cdots, \alpha_m) | (\alpha_1, \cdots, \alpha_m) \in J_1\}$$

is consistent with $\mathbf{Z}_1 \cup \mathbf{T}$. The consistent set $\mathbf{Z}_1 \cup \mathbf{T} \cup \mathbf{M}_1$ has a model $\mathscr{L}_2$. Clearly $\mathscr{L}_2$ is a strong model of arithmetic and, being a model of $\mathbf{Z}_1$, may be considered an extension of $\mathscr{L}_1$. Notice that $D(\alpha_1, \cdots, \alpha_m)$, for $\vec{\alpha} \in I_1^m$, holds in $\mathscr{L}_2$ if and only if $\vec{\alpha} \in J_1$.

Repeating this construction, we get an ascending chain of models

$$\mathscr{L}_1 < \mathscr{L}_2 < \mathscr{L}_2 < \cdots, \mathscr{L}_i = \langle I_i, +, \cdot \rangle.$$

Consider the union $\mathscr{L}' = \bigcup_i \mathscr{L}_i$. Assume that $\mathscr{L}' = \langle I', +, \cdot \rangle$ is a model of $\mathbf{T}$; then, being an extension of $\mathscr{L}_1$, it must be a non-standard model. By Theorem 5 there exist $\alpha_1, \cdots, \alpha_m \in I'$ so that $\sim D(\vec{\alpha})$ holds in $\mathscr{L}'$ but $D(\vec{\alpha})$ is consistent with $\mathbf{T}$ and with the diagram $\mathbf{Z}'$ of $\mathscr{L}'$.

There exists a model $\mathscr{L}_i$ for which $\vec{\alpha} \in I_1^m$. Now, $\sim D(\vec{\alpha})$ holds in $\mathscr{L}'$ and therefore holds also in $\mathscr{L}_{i+1}$. This implies that $\vec{\alpha} \notin J_i$, and hence that

$$\mathbf{T} \cup \mathbf{Z}_i \cup \mathbf{M}_i \cup \{D(\vec{\alpha})\}$$

is not consistent. But the diagram $\mathbf{Z}'$ contains $\mathscr{L}_i$ and all sentence of $\mathbf{M}_i$ are satisfied in $\mathscr{L}'$ so that $\mathbf{T} \cup \mathbf{Z}' \cup \mathbf{M}_i \cup \{D(\vec{\alpha})\}$ is consistent, a contradiction.

A theorem due to A. Robinson [3, p. 117] states that if a set $\mathbf{A}$ of axioms is such that the intersection of every two submodels of a model of $\mathbf{A}$ is non-empty and a model of $\mathbf{A}$, then the union of every ascending sequence of models of $\mathbf{A}$ is a model of $\mathbf{A}$. Combining this result with Theorem 7, we immediately obtain

THEOREM 8. *There exists a strong model $\mathscr{L}'$ and two submodels $\mathscr{L}_1 < \mathscr{L}'$ and $\mathscr{L}_2 < \mathscr{L}'$ so that $\mathscr{L}_1 \cap \mathscr{L}_2$ is not a strong model of arithmetic.*

2. Cofinal Extensions

We wish to discuss briefly, without proofs, the relation between certain problems concerning strong models and problems of number theory, particularly the question whether every recursively enumerable predicate is diophantine, which is intimately connected with Hilbert's tenth problem.

2.1. Kinds of Extensions. We consider systems $\mathscr{Z}_f = \langle I, +, \cdot, f_1, \ldots \rangle$ which are obtained from $\mathscr{Z}$ by adding certain fixed arithmetical functions $f_1, \cdots$. Let L_f be obtained from L by adding to it function constants $\mathbf{f}_1, \cdots$; and let $\mathbf{T}_f$ be the set of sentences of L_f true in $\mathscr{Z}_f$. A model of $\mathbf{T}_f$ will be called a *strong model of augmented arithmetic*. The set $\{f_1, \cdots\}$ of additional functions is, in what follows, a fixed (possibly empty) set.

DEFINITION. *Let* $\mathscr{Z}_1 = \langle I_1, +, \cdot, f_1, \ldots \rangle$ *and* $\mathscr{Z}_1 < \mathscr{Z}_2 = \langle I_2, +, \cdot, f_1, \ldots \rangle$ *be two strong models of augmented arithmetic. If for every* $\beta \in I_2$ *there exists a* $\beta < \alpha \in I_1$, *we call* Z_2 *a* COFINAL EXTENSION *of* Z_1.

For cofinal extensions we have the following

THEOREM 9. *Every strong non-standard model* $\mathscr{Z}_1$ *of augmented arithmetic possesses a cofinal extension.*

2.2. Models and Recursive Predicates. We wish to study the behavior of recursive predicates under extension of models. As a first step, we obtain information about formulas with bounded quantification.

LEMMA 10. *Let* $B(\vec{\mathbf{x}}, \vec{\mathbf{y}}, \vec{\mathbf{z}})$, *where* $\vec{\mathbf{x}} = (\mathbf{x}_1, \ldots, \vec{\mathbf{x}}_n)$, $\vec{\mathbf{y}} = (\mathbf{y}_1, \ldots, \mathbf{y}_n)$, *and* $\vec{\mathbf{z}} = (\mathbf{z}_1, \cdots, \mathbf{z}_m)$, *be a formula of* L_f; *and let* $\mathscr{Z}_1 = \langle I_1, +, \cdot, f_1, \cdots \rangle$ *be a strong model. Define a relation* $A(\alpha_1, \cdots, \alpha_n, \beta_1, \cdots, \beta_{n-1}, \vec{\gamma})$ *of* I_1 *by*

$$A = (x_1)_{x_1 < \alpha_1}(Ey_1)_{y_1 < \beta_1} \cdots (x_n)_{x_n < \alpha_n}(Ey_n)B(\vec{x}, \vec{y}, \vec{\gamma}),$$

where $\vec{\gamma} = (\gamma_1, \cdots, \gamma_m)$. *Denote the prefix with bounded quantifiers by* Σ. *For every* $\alpha_1, \cdots, \alpha_n$, $\beta_1, \cdots, \beta_{n-1}$, *and* $\gamma_1, \cdots, \gamma_m$ *in* I_1 *there exists a* $\beta_n \in I_1$ *such that*

$$A(\alpha_1, \cdots, \alpha_n, \beta_1, \cdots, \beta_{n-1}, \vec{\gamma}) \equiv \Sigma(Ey_n)_{y_n < \beta_n} B(\vec{x}, \vec{y}, \vec{\gamma})$$

is valid in $\mathscr{Z}_1$. The dual of this theorem is also true.

THEOREM 11. *Let the set* $S = \{+, \cdot, f_1, \ldots\}$ *of functions of* $\mathscr{Z}_f$ *(the standard model) be such that all additional functions* $f_1, \cdots$, *are recursive and every recursive predicate (on* I*) is existentially definable from functions of* S. *If* $\mathscr{Z}_1$ *and* $\mathscr{Z}_2$ *are any strong models of (augmented) arithmetic and* $\mathscr{Z}_2$ *is a cofinal extension of* $\mathscr{Z}_1$, *then* $\mathscr{Z}_2$ *is an elementary extension (in the sense of Tarski-Vaught* [5]*) of* $\mathscr{Z}_1$.

The theorem is proved by obtaining from a formula $F(\mathbf{x})$ and an element $\gamma \in I_1$ such that $F(\gamma)$ holds in $\mathscr{Z}_1$ and $\sim F(\gamma)$ holds in $\mathscr{Z}_2$, a formula $F'(\vec{\mathbf{x}})$ with bounded quantifiers and constants $\gamma_1, \cdots, \gamma_m \in I_1$, so that $F'(\vec{\gamma})$ holds in $\mathscr{Z}_1$ but $\sim F'(\vec{\gamma})$ holds in $\mathscr{Z}_2$.

Using a well-known result of J. Robinson [4] we have as a corollary that *for arithmetic with exponentiation, every cofinal extension model of a strong model is an elementary extension.*

If we can construct a pair of strong models of ordinary arithmetic so that one is a non-elementary cofinal extension of the other, then it would follow that not every recursive predicate is diophantine.

We would like to end by posing the problem whether the converse of Theorem 11 is true.

References

[1] Davis, M. *Computability and Unsolvability*. New York, McGraw-Hill, 1951, xxv+210 pp.

[2] Rabin, M. O. Non-standard models and independence of the induction axiom. *Essays on the Foundations of Mathematics* (Fraenkel's Festschrift). Jerusalem, Magnes Press (to appear).

[3] Robinson, A. *On the Metamathematics of Algebra*. Amsterdam, North-Holland Publishing Co., 1951, ix+195 pp.

[4] Robinson, J. B. The undecidability of exponential diophantine equations. *American Mathematical Society Notices*, Vol. 7 (1960), p. 75.

[5] Tarski, A., and R. L. Vaught. Arithmetical extensions of relational systems. *Compositio Mathematica*, Vol. 13 (1957), pp. 82—101.

ON COMPLETENESS AND DECIDABILITY OF SOME NON-DEFINABLE NOTIONS OF ELEMENTARY HYPERBOLIC GEOMETRY

WOLFRAM SCHWABHÄUSER
Humboldt Universität, Berlin, Germany

In the first part of my address I should like to discuss a proof for completeness of elementary hyperbolic geometry and the existence of a decision method for this theory, making use of Tarski's analogous results for elementary algebra.[1] In the second part I shall discuss a corollary concerning the non-definability of some notions in elementary hyperbolic geometry.[2]

1

By *elementary hyperbolic geometry* (EHG) we will mean a theory formalized within the first-order predicate calculus with three kinds of variables, representing points, straight lines, and planes of the three-dimensional hyperbolic space, the primitive notions being incidence, order, and congruence in the sense of Hilbert [3]. Since, however, we have no symbols for segments and for angles, we will use a relation of rank 4 between points in order to express congruence between segments and one of rank 6 between points in order to express congruence between angles.

The theory is built on axioms which are essentially those of Hilbert, but with the difference that as axioms of continuity we have a scheme like that given by Tarski in [8], and as parallel axioms the negation of the corresponding axiom for Euclidean geometry.

An arbitrary formula Φ we shall call (geometrically) *provable* (we shall write for this $\vdash_g \Phi$) if and only if it can be obtained from these axioms and from logical axioms by performing the usual operations of inference.

We shall call a formula Φ *geometrically valid* (written agg Φ) in case it is valid[3] in Klein's model of EHG, the points of which are the inner points of an ellipsoid which we assume to be the sphere $x_1^2+x_2^2+x_3^2=1$ in analytic geometry over the field R of real numbers, x_1, x_2, x_3 being Cartesian coordinates.

Then the semantical completeness theorem can be formulated as follows:

If agg Φ, *then* $\vdash_g \Phi$.

In the proof we may restrict ourselves to a special class of formulas, built by means of logical operations from formulas of the form $A=B$

[1]Published in detail in German (see [7]).

[2]To be published in German in *Zeitschr. für math. Logik und Grundlagen d. Math*

[3]"Allgemeingültig", i.e., satisfied by each geometrical belegung, with respect to this model (cf. p. 56, footnotes 13, 14).

(equality between points) and AB agl CD (equidistance relation for points, meaning that the distance from A to B equals the distance from C to D), and hence containing only variables for points (for which we use Latin capitals). Formulas of this class we shall therefore call formulas of *punctual geometry*. As is well known, it is sufficient to establish our completeness theorem only for sentences, even for sentences of punctual geometry, since equality for points and equidistance relation can be used as the only primitive notions in developing Euclidean or hyperbolic geometry, so that to each sentence of EHG there can be found an equivalent sentence of punctual geometry.[4]

Now we use the following completeness theorem for arithmetic of real numbers (ARZ), established by Tarski (see [8]).

For each formula Ψ *of* ARZ *the following is true*:

If Ψ *is arithmetically valid* (aga Ψ) (i.e., valid in the ordered field of real numbers), *then* Ψ *is arithmetically provable* ($\vdash_a \Psi$) (i.e., it can be obtained from the axioms of ARZ by using the rules of inference).

To reduce our completeness theorem to Tarski's theorem, we shall correlate with each formula Φ of punctual geometry a formula Rda(Φ) of ARZ — we shall call it the *arithmetical reductum* of Φ — so that the following theorems hold for each sentence Φ of punctual geometry.

THEOREM 1. *If* agg Φ, *then* aga Rda(Φ).

THEOREM 2. *If* $\vdash_a$Rda (Φ), *then* $\vdash_g \Phi$.

The arithmetical reductums are constructed in such a way that Theorem 1 can be established without difficulties. Moreover, we obtain a slightly stronger theorem.

THEOREM 1′. *For each sentence* Φ *of punctual geometry there is* agg Φ *if and only if* aga Rda(Φ).

But the attempt to establish Theorem 2 directly, perhaps by an induction according to the definition of arithmetical provability, is not successful, for, in the formal proof of an arithmetical reductum Rda(Φ), there can appear formulas of ARZ which are not arithmetical reductums of formulas of punctual geometry.

However, we could use such an induction to establish a theorem in which the provability of an arbitrary formula Ψ of ARZ is presumed. Therefore we shall correlate with each formula Ψ of ARZ a formula Rdg(Ψ) of EHG — we shall call it the *geometrical reductum* of Ψ — so that the following theorem can be established by an induction as mentioned above.

THEOREM 2′. *For each formula* Ψ *of* ARZ, *if* $\vdash_a \Psi$, *then* $\vdash_g$ Rdg (Ψ).

---

[4]Cf. Beth and Tarski [2].

Applying this to an arithmetically provable formula of the form Rda(Φ), we obtain that the formula Rdg(Rda(Φ)) (which is not the same as Φ) is geometrically provable. To complete the proof of Theorem 2 (and with it the completeness theorem for EHG), we shall establish a third theorem.

THEOREM 3′. *For each sentence Φ of punctual geometry Φ is equivalent to* Rdg(Rda(Φ)), *i.e.*, $\vdash_g \Phi \leftrightarrow (\mathrm{Rdg}(\mathrm{Rda}(\Phi)))$.

Formerly the completeness of elementary Euclidean geometry has been established by the author in the same manner, i.e., by constructing proper reductums so that Theorems 1′, 2′, and 3′ hold (see [6]). Against that, the construction of the reductums itself, of course, depends essentially on the nature of the formalized theories considered here, namely, EHG and ARZ.

The construction of the arithmetical reductums and the proof of Theorem 1′ aims at describing geometrical facts by means of arithmetic. This will be done by using in Klein's model real coordinates of such a kind that the equidistance relation for points can be expressed in their coordinates by rational operations, which are definable in ARZ. For such coordinates we use the Cartesian coordinates x_1, x_2, x_3 mentioned above. If we join these coordinates to a vector $\mathfrak{x}$, denoting by $\mathfrak{x}$ also the corresponding point of Klein's model (by $\mathfrak{x}\mathfrak{y}$ the inner product of $\mathfrak{x}$ and $\mathfrak{y}$, and by $\mathfrak{x}^2$ the inner product $\mathfrak{x}\mathfrak{x}$), and define the hyperbolic distance $\overline{\mathfrak{x}\mathfrak{y}}$ between points $\mathfrak{x}$ and $\mathfrak{y}$ in the usual way,[5] we can establish

$$\cosh \overline{\mathfrak{x}\mathfrak{y}} = \frac{1-\mathfrak{x}\mathfrak{y}}{\sqrt{(1-\mathfrak{x}^2)(1-\mathfrak{y}^2)}},$$

which leads to a criterion for equidistancy as wanted.

Analogously, in the formalism ARZ we shall denote by fracture types triples $\mathfrak{x}=[x', x'', x''']$ of variables x', x'', x''' (or any terms) for real numbers, by $\mathfrak{x}\mathfrak{y}$ — presumed that $\mathfrak{x} = [x', x'', x''']$ and $\mathfrak{y} = [y', y'', y''']$ — the term $x'y'+x''y''+x'''y'''$, by $\mathfrak{x}^2$ the term $\mathfrak{x}\mathfrak{x}$, and by $\mathfrak{x} = \mathfrak{y}$ the formula $x'=y' \wedge x''=y'' \wedge x'''=y'''$.

Now we correlate with each variable A_i for points a triple $\mathfrak{x}_i = [x_i', x_i'', x_i'''$ of number variables and define the arithmetical reductum by an induction based upon the following conditions:

(1) $\mathrm{Rda}(A_i=A_j) = \mathfrak{x}_i=\mathfrak{x}_j.$
$\mathrm{Rda}(A_iA_j \text{ agl } A_kA_l) = (1-\mathfrak{x}_i\mathfrak{x}_j)^2(1-\mathfrak{x}_k{}^2)(1-\mathfrak{x}_l{}^2)$
$= (1-\mathfrak{x}_k\mathfrak{x}_l)^2(1-\mathfrak{x}_i{}^2)(1-\mathfrak{x}_j{}^2).$

(2) $\mathrm{Rda}(\sim\Phi) = \sim \mathrm{Rda}(\Phi).$
$\mathrm{Rda}(\Phi_1 \wedge \Phi_2) = \mathrm{Rda}(\Phi_1) \wedge \mathrm{Rda}(\Phi_2).$
$\mathrm{Rda}(\exists A_i\Phi) = \exists x_i' \exists x_i'' \exists x_i''' (\mathfrak{x}^2 < 1 \wedge \mathrm{Rda}(\Phi)).$

From (2) one can obtain further conditions for the usual logical connectives, which can be expressed by $\sim$, $\wedge$, $\exists$.

---

[5]See, e.g., Baldus [1, p. 81].

Then Theorem 1′ can be established.[6]

The construction of the geometrical reductums and the proof of Theorem 2′ aims at finding a surrogate for arithmetic within EHG. That was already done by Hilbert (see [4]) in his end-calculus. Since the notion of an end is not expressible in elementary geometry, we replace each end occurring in the calculus by the straight line, connecting this end and the fixed end ∞ introduced by Hilbert. Then the straight lines representing numbers form a pencil of parallel lines, in which a sum, a product, and an order of lines are defined, and which is determined by its null o and its unit e; we shall call it the *arithmetical pencil* determined by o and e. In order that any two straight lines determine an arithmetical pencil, it is necessary and sufficient that they are parallel and distinct. Transferring the results of Hilbert to arithmetical pencils, we can conclude from the axioms of EHG that if straight lines o and e determine an arithmetical pencil, the axioms of ARZ hold in this pencil.

Now we single out two variables o and e for straight lines and correlate with each number variable x_i a line variable b_i (different from o and e).

At first we define a *term reductum* $\mathrm{Rdt}(T)$ for arbitrary terms[7] T of ARZ by an induction as follows:

(1) $\mathrm{Rdt}(0) = o,\ \mathrm{Rdt}(1) = e,\ \mathrm{Rdt}(x_i) = b_i.$

(2) $\mathrm{Rdt}(T_1+T_2) = \mathrm{Rdt}(T_1) \underset{o,e}{+} \mathrm{Rdt}(T_2).$

$\mathrm{Rdt}(-T) = \underset{o,e}{-}\mathrm{Rdt}(T).$

$\mathrm{Rdt}(T_1 \cdot T_2) = \mathrm{Rdt}(T_1) \underset{o,e}{\cdot} \mathrm{Rdt}(T_2).$

Herein the notations $\underset{o,e}{+}, \underset{o,e}{-}, \underset{o,e}{\cdot}$ mean the addition, forming of the inverse, and multiplication of straight lines in the arithmetical pencil determined by o and e. Thus, the terms on the right-hand side of the equations (2) contain also o and e as free variables.

Then we define a *preliminary geometrical reductum* $\mathrm{Rdgp}(\Psi)$ for arbitrary formulas Ψ of ARZ by an induction as follows:[8]

(1) $\mathrm{Rdgp}(T_1=T_2) = \mathrm{Rdt}(T_1=\mathrm{Rdt}(T_2).$

$\mathrm{Rdgp}(\mathrm{pos}\ T) = \mathrm{pos}_{oe}\ \mathrm{Rdt}(T).$

(2) $\mathrm{Rdgp}(\sim\Psi) = \sim \mathrm{Rdgp}(\Psi).$

$\mathrm{Rdgp}(\Psi_1 \wedge \Psi_2) = \mathrm{Rdgp}(\Psi_1) \wedge \mathrm{Rdgp}(\Psi_2).$

$\mathrm{Rdgp}(\exists x_i \Psi) = \exists b_i(\mathrm{Ar}_{oe} b_i \wedge \mathrm{Rdgp}(\Psi)).$

---

[6] Cf. p. 56, footnote 16.

[7] As terms of ARZ we use expressions built from number variables and the constants 0 and 1 by means of the operation signs + (addition), − (forming of the inverse), and · (multiplication).

[8] As atomic formulas we use equations $T_1=T_2$ and expressions of the form pos T (meaning that T is positive).

Herein $\text{pos}_{oe}\, a$ means that a is a positive line in the arithmetical pencil determined by o and e; $\text{Ar}_{oe} c_1 \ldots c_n$ means that o and e determine an arithmetical pencil and (if $n > 0$) $c_1, \ldots, c_n$ are lines of this pencil ($n \geqq 0$).

At last we define the geometrical reductum by

$$\text{Rdg}(\Psi) = \forall o \forall e(\text{Ar}_{oe} a_{i_1} \ldots a_{i_n} \to \text{Rdgp}(\Psi)),$$

where $a_{i_1}, \ldots, a_{i_n}$ are the variables occurring free in $\text{Rdgp}(\Psi)$ except o and e. Roughly speaking, $\text{Rdg}(\Psi)$ is a formula of EHG, meaning that in each arithmetical pencil the statement corresponding to Ψ holds.

Then Theorem 2′ can be established by an induction according to the definition of arithmetical provability.

In establishing Theorem 3′, i.e., the equivalence of an arbitrary sentence Φ and its twofold reductum $\text{Rdg}(\text{Rda}(\Phi))$, our main task is to describe EHG by means of an arithmetical pencil in the same manner as we described Klein's model by means of the field of real numbers. For this purpose we can develop, as we did in Klein's model, a part of hyperbolic trigonometry and correlate with each point three coordinates that are lines of an arithmetical pencil, so that the equidistancy of points can be expressed in their coordinates. This is, I think, also the main task of the completeness proof.

Then we can establish first the following theorem.

THEOREM 3″. *For each formula Φ of punctual geometry there is*

$$\vdash_g \Pi_\Phi \to (\Phi \leftrightarrow \text{Rdgp}(\text{Rda}(\Phi))),$$

where Π_Φ is a premise meaning that the free variables for straight lines, occurring except o and e in $\text{Rdgp}(\text{Rda}(\Phi))$, *are the coordinates of the corresponding free variables for points, occurring in Φ, with respect to any system of coordinates and any arithmetical pencil.*

This theorem can be established by an induction according to the definition of the relation that Φ is a formula of punctual geometry.

Theorem 3′, referring only to sentences, cannot be shown directly by such an induction, but it can be obtained immediately from Theorem 3″.

Thus the (semantical) completeness of EHG is established.

From this we obtain other kinds of completeness, as is well known, especially the classical completeness of EHG:

For each sentence of EHG *there is* $\vdash_g \Phi$ *or* $\vdash_g \sim\Phi$.

Now it is not difficult to transfer also Tarski's *decision method* for ARZ to EHG. For this purpose we can again restrict ourselves to sentences of punctual geometry. According to Theorem 1′ such a sentence is geometrically valid if and only if its arithmetical reductum is arithmetically valid, which can be decided by Tarski's method. Thus, we have a decision method for validity, and hence for provability too, as we know from the completeness theorem. Moreover, if a sentence turns out to be provable, we can construct, in a mechanical way, a formalized proof for this sentence by means of Tarski's decision method and the proof of Theorems 2′ and 3′.

As to *models* of EHG, it is well known from the Löwenheim-Skolem Theorem (cf., e.g., Schröter [5, p. 60, etc.]) that EHG, being formalized within the first-order predicate calculus, is not categorical, i.e., admits models which are not isomorphic to each other. The formulas of EHG which were to be proved in establishing the completeness theorem suffice to obtain from Tarski's analogous result for ARZ the following theorem:

A geometrical structure [9] *is a model of* EHG *if and only if it is isomorphic to a model built in the same way as Klein's model by means of the elements of an arbitrary real closed field instead of real numbers.*

From the classical completeness we obtain the semantical completeness of EHG with respect to any model of EHG:

If a formula Φ *is valid in some model of* EHG, *then it is geometrically provable.*

In this case it is also valid in each model, so that models of EHG are geometrically indistinguishable.

2

In developing a part of hyperbolic trigonometry as was mentioned above, I used the relation that, in the arithmetical pencil determined by o and e, the line a represents the hyperbolic tangent of the distance from A to B, which in Klein's model or any isomorphic model is definable. In such models we have a uniquely determined isomorphism between an arbitrary arithmetical pencil and the ordered field of real numbers, so that we can say a line represents the number corresponding to it in that isomorphism. Now I should like to discuss the fact that the distance between points itself, considered in the same sense as an element of an arithmetical pencil, is not definable in EHG.[10]

To conclude this from Tarski's results concerning definable relations for real numbers, we shall establish the following theorem.

THEOREM 4. *Let* S *be any* n*-ary relation between real numbers. Let* R *be the* $(n+2)$*-ary relation between lines of Klein's model* (*or any isomorphic model*) *of* EHG *which holds for lines* $o, e, a_1, \ldots, a_n$ *if and only if, firstly,* o *and* e *determine an arithmetical pencil containing the lines* $a_1, \ldots, a_n$, *and, secondly, the relation* S *holds for the real numbers represented by* $a_1, \ldots, a_n$ *in this pencil. If* R *is definable* (*in* EHG), *then* S *in also definable* (*in* ARZ).

Suppose that the distance is definable. Then we can define the relation that, in an arithmetical pencil determined by some lines o and e, one line represents the hyperbolic tangent of another line (more precisely, of the number represented by this line) of this pencil. From Theorem 4 we con-

---

[9]Possible realization of EHG in the sense of Tarski [10, p. 8].

[10]This was stated without proof in [7].

clude that the binary relation between real numbers, which holds for numbers x, y if and only if y is the hyperbolic tangent of x, is arithmetically definable. Thus we would have a transcendental function definable in ARZ, which contradicts the following theorem, which can be obtained from Tarski's results.

THEOREM 5. *If a function f is definable in* ARZ, *then f is algebraic.*

Hence, the distance of points cannot be definable in EHG.

The same applies to the distance with respect to an arbitrary (not the usual absolute) unit of length, and also to the measure of angles (with respect to an arbitrary unit), since the sine and the cosine of angles are definable in EHG.

To establish Theorem 4 we use again arithmetical reductums, as we defined for formulas of punctual geometry in the completeness proof for EHG. But now, since arbitrary formulas can be used in representing a definable relation, we have to extend the definition of Rda(Φ) to arbitrary formulas Φ of EHG. This we can do, observing how not only points but also straight lines and planes are described by systems of real numbers in analytic geometry, namely, for straight lines we can use a parameter representation $\mathfrak{x} = \mathfrak{r} + t\mathfrak{p}$ and for planes an equation $\mathfrak{u}\mathfrak{x} + u = 0$ ($\mathfrak{p}, \mathfrak{u} \neq \mathfrak{o}$, where $\mathfrak{o}$ denotes the null vector $[0, 0, 0]$). A straight line or a plane belongs to Klein's model if and only if it contains at least one point of this model, i.e., one point $\mathfrak{x}$ for which $\mathfrak{x}^2 < 1$ holds.

So we correlate with each point variable A_i again a triple $\mathfrak{x}_i = [x_i', x_i'', x_i''']$ of number variables, with each line variable a_i we correlate two triples $\mathfrak{r}_i = [r_i', r_i'', r_i''']$ and $\mathfrak{p}_i = [p_i', p_i'', p_i''']$, and with each variable α_i for planes we correlate a triple $\mathfrak{u}_i = [u_i', u_i'', u_i''']$ and a single number variable u_i. Then we define the arithmetical reductum by an induction as follows:

(1) $\mathrm{Rda}(A_i = A_j) \;\; = \mathfrak{x}_i = \mathfrak{x}_j.$

$\mathrm{Rda}(a_i = a_j) \;\; = \exists s(\mathfrak{r}_j - \mathfrak{r}_i = s\mathfrak{p}_i) \wedge \exists t(\mathfrak{p}_j = t\mathfrak{p}_i).$[11]

$\mathrm{Rda}(\alpha_i = \alpha_j) \;\; = \exists t(\mathfrak{u}_j = t\mathfrak{u}_i \wedge u_j = tu_i).$

$\mathrm{Rda}(\mathrm{Inz}\, A_i a_j) = \exists t(\mathfrak{x}_i = \mathfrak{r}_j + t\mathfrak{p}_j).$[12]

$\mathrm{Rda}(\mathrm{Inz}\, A_i \alpha_j) = \mathfrak{u}_j\mathfrak{x}_i + u_j = 0.$

Further conditions have to be used, which give the arithmetical reductums of the other atomic formulas in the way as the according primitive notions (order and congruence of segments and of angles) for points are expressed by the coordinates of these points.

(2) Conditions (2) from page 161 and:

$\mathrm{Rda}(\exists a_i\Phi) = \exists r_i' \exists r_i'' \exists r_i''' \exists p_i' \exists p_i'' \exists p_i''' (\mathrm{L}(\mathfrak{r}_i, \mathfrak{p}_i) \wedge \mathrm{Rda}(\Phi)).$

$\mathrm{Rda}(\exists \alpha_i\Phi) = \exists u_i' \exists u_i'' \exists u_i''' \exists u_i (\mathrm{P}(\mathfrak{u}_i, u_i) \wedge \mathrm{Rda}(\Phi)).$

---

[11]If $\mathfrak{x} = [x', x'', x''']$, $\mathfrak{y} = [y', y'', y''']$, then, of course, $\mathfrak{x} \pm \mathfrak{y}$ denotes the triple $[x' \pm y', x'' \pm y'', x''' \pm y''']$, $t\mathfrak{x}$ denotes the triple $[tx', tx'', tx''']$.

[12]Inz Aa and Inz $A\alpha$ mean that the point A lies on the straight line a and on the plane α, respectively.

Here we used the abbreviations

$$\mathrm{L}(\mathfrak{r}_i, \mathfrak{p}_i) = \mathfrak{p}_i \neq \mathfrak{o} \wedge \exists t(\mathfrak{r}_i + t\mathfrak{p}_i)^2 < 1$$

("$\mathfrak{r}_i$, $\mathfrak{p}_i$ describe a straight line of Klein's model"),

$$\mathrm{P}(\mathfrak{u}_i, u_i) = \mathfrak{u}_i \neq \mathfrak{o} \wedge \exists x' \exists x'' \exists x''' (\mathfrak{x}^2 < 1 \wedge \mathfrak{u}_i \mathfrak{x} + u_i = 0)$$

("$\mathfrak{u}_i$, u_i describe a plane of Klein's model"),

where $\mathfrak{x} = [x', x'', x''']$, $\mathfrak{o} = [0, 0, 0]$.

A geometrical *belegung* φ with respect to Klein's model[13] and an arithmetical belegung ψ with respect to the field of real numbers[14] we shall call *arithmetically connected* if and only if for each variable v [15] of EHG the values of ψ for the correlated number variables are numbers describing the geometrical object which is the value $\varphi(v)$ of φ for the variable v. Then we obtain the following theorem:

THEOREM 4′. *Let Φ be a formula of* EHG. *Then for each pair of arithmetically connected belegungen φ, ψ, the belegung φ satisfies Φ if and only if ψ satisfies* Rda(Φ).

This can be established by an induction according to the definition of formulas.[16]

Now let the hypothesis of Theorem 4 hold, and let the $(n+2)$-ary relation R be definable; let R be represented, for example, by the formula Φ containing the free variables $o, e, a_1, \ldots, a_n$.

We consider, in Klein's model, a special arithmetical pencil, consisting of the straight lines $\mathfrak{x} = \mathfrak{r} + t\mathfrak{p}_x$, where $\mathfrak{r} = [0, 1, 0]$, $\mathfrak{p}_x = [x, -1, 0]$. Then x is the real number corresponding to the line $\mathfrak{x} = \mathfrak{r} + t\mathfrak{p}_x$ in the isomorphism from this pencil to the field of real numbers (cf. [7, p. 167, etc.]). Let correlated with the line variables o, e be the triples $\mathfrak{r}_o = [r'_o, r''_o, r'''_o]$, $\mathfrak{p}_o = [p'_o, p''_o, p'''_o]$, and $\mathfrak{r}_e = (r'_e, r''_e, r'''_e]$, $\mathfrak{p}_e = [p'_e, p''_e, p'''_e]$, respectively. Let Ψ be the formula which we obtain from Rda(Φ) if we replace the free number variables

a) r'_i, r'''_i, p'''_i by the constant 0, r''_i by 1, p''_i by -1 ($i = o, e, 1, \ldots, n$),
b) p'_o by 0, p'_e by 1,
c) p'_i by x_i ($i = 1, \ldots, n$).

Thus Ψ contains only $x_1, \ldots, x_n$ as free variables. Moreover, Ψ represents the relation S, so that S is definable.

---

[13]I.e., a function defined for all variables of EHG, the values of which are points, lines, and planes of Klein's model, respectively, for point variables, line variables, and plane variables.

[14]I.e., a function defined for all number variables, the values of which are real numbers. It is assumed to be clear, in which case a formula Φ and EHG and Ψ of ARZ is said to be *satisfied* by such a geometrical and arithmetical belegung, respectively. (This conception can be defined by an induction according to the definition of formulas, cf. Tarski [9].)

[15]The notation v can mean a point variable, a line variable, or a plane variable.

[16]We need the same theorem in establishing Theorem 1′, although only for formulas of punctual geometry.

Indeed, let ψ be an arbitrary arithmetical belegung. Let ψ' be an arithmetical belegung for which the following hold:

a) $\psi'(r_i') = \psi'(r_i''') = \psi'(p_i''') = 0$, $\psi'(r_i'') = 1$, $\psi'(p_i'') = -1$, $(i = o, e, 1, \ldots, n)$,

b) $\psi'(p_o') = 0$, $\psi'(p_e') = 1$,

c) $\psi'(p_i') = \psi(x_i)$ $(i = 1, \ldots, n)$,

d) for some geometrical belegung φ the belegungen φ and ψ' are arithmetically connected.

Then the following conditions are equivalent:

1. ψ satisfies Ψ.
2. ψ' satisfies Rda(Φ).
3. φ satisfies Φ (by Theorem 4′).
4. R holds for the lines $\varphi(o)$, $\varphi(e)$, $\varphi(a_1), \ldots, \varphi(a_n)$ (by construction of Φ).
5. S holds for the numbers corresponding to the lines $\varphi(a_1), \ldots, \varphi(a_n)$ in the isomorphism mentioned above, i.e., S holds for the numbers $\psi(x_1), \ldots, \psi(x_n)$ (by hypothesis of Theorem 4).

Thus we have for an arbitrary arithmetical belegung ψ, that ψ satisfies Ψ if and only if $S\psi(x_1) \ldots \psi(x_n)$, which demonstrates that S is represented by the formula Ψ. With this, Theorem 4 is established.

References

[1] Baldus, R., and F. Löbell. *Nichteuklidische Geometrie*. 3rd ed., Berlin, 1953.

[2] Beth, E. W., and A. Tarski. Equilaterality as the only primitive notion of Euclidean geometry. *Indag. Math.*, Vol. 18 (1956), pp. 462–467.

[3] Hilbert, D., and P. Bernays. *Grundlagen der Geometrie*. 8th ed., Stuttgart, 1956.

[4] Hilbert, D. Neue Begründung der Bolyai-Lobatschefskyschen Geometrie. *Math. Ann.*, Vol. 57 (1903), pp. 137–150 (reprinted as Anhang III in [3]).

[5] Schröter, K. Theorie des logischen Schließens II. *Zeitschr. f. math. Logik u. Grundl. d. Math.*, Vol. 4 (1958), pp. 10–65.

[6] Schwabhäuser, W. Über die Vollständigkeit der elementaren euklidischen Geometrie. *Zeitschr. f. math. Logik u. Grundl. d. Math.*, Vol. 2 (1956), pp. 137–165.

[7] Schwabhäuser, W. Entscheidbarkeit und Vollständigkeit der elementaren hyperbolischen Geometrie. *Zeitschr. f. math. Logik u. Grundl. d. Math.*, Vol. 5 (1959), pp. 132–205.

[8] Tarski, A. *A Decision Method for Elementary Algebra and Geometry*. 2nd ed., Berkeley and Los Angeles, 1951.

[9] Tarski, A. Der Wahrheitsbegriff in den formalisierten Sprachen. *Studia philosophica*, Vol. 1 (1936), pp. 261–405.

[10] Tarski, A., A. Mostowski, and R. M. Robinson. *Undecidable Theories*. Amsterdam, 1953.

NEW FOUNDATIONS OF ABSOLUTE GEOMETRY

WANDA SZMIELEW

University of Warsaw, Warsaw, Poland

In 1899 (see [1]) Hilbert constructed a commutative ordered field $\overline{\mathfrak{S}} = \langle \mathbf{S}, +, \cdot, < \rangle$ in a formalized system $\mathscr{E}_0$ of plane *Euclidean geometry* without the axiom of continuity. For our purposes it is more convenient to consider the field $\overline{\mathfrak{S}}$ in a theory $\mathscr{E}$ which is an extension of $\mathscr{E}_0$. This theory is obtained from $\mathscr{E}_0$ by supplementing the axiom system by a statement to the effect that a line passing through an inner point of a circle intersects this circle. In $\mathscr{E}$ the ordered field $\overline{\mathfrak{S}}$ proves to be *Euclidean*. This means that every positive element of $\mathbf{S}$ is a square. The field $\overline{\mathfrak{S}}$ is generated by a *calculus of (free) segments*. Hilbert introduces a rectangular coordinate system over $\overline{\mathfrak{S}}$; the two coordinates of a point p are of the form $\pm X_1, \pm X_2$, where X_1 and X_2 are two segments. From this construction Hilbert derives the linear equation of the line.

In 1903 (see [3]) Hilbert constructed a commutative Euclidean field $\overline{\mathscr{E}} = \langle \mathbf{E}, +, \cdot, < \rangle$ in a formalized system $\mathscr{H}$ of plane *hyperbolic* (*Bolyai-Lobachevskian*) *geometry* without the axiom of continuity. The class $\mathbf{E}$ consists of pencils of parallel half-lines which Hilbert refers to as *ends*. The analytic geometry is based, this time, on a coordinate system for lines, two ends being assigned to a line. From this construction Hilbert derives the linear equation of the point.

From this short description it is clear that the geometrical concepts of the fields $\overline{\mathfrak{S}}$ and $\overline{\mathscr{E}}$ are completely different; also the two analytic geometries, over $\overline{\mathfrak{S}}$ and over $\overline{\mathscr{E}}$, are founded upon completely different bases. In this paper we shall construct a Euclidean commutative field $\overline{\mathfrak{S}}' = \langle \mathbf{S}, +', \cdot', < \rangle$ in the common part $\mathscr{A}$ of the theories $\mathscr{E}$ and $\mathscr{H}$, and thus in a system of *absolute geometry* without the axiom of continuity. Consequently a uniform coordinatization over one and the same field $\overline{\mathfrak{S}}'$ will be achieved in both geometries $\mathscr{E}$ and $\mathscr{H}$. We start with a concise description of the field $\overline{\mathfrak{S}}$; then we shall show how $\overline{\mathfrak{S}}$ should be modified to obtain $\overline{\mathfrak{S}}'$. In fact both the fields $\overline{\mathfrak{S}}$ and $\overline{\mathfrak{S}}'$ will prove to depend upon a segment parameter U and hence in what follows we will denote them by $\overline{\mathfrak{S}}_U$ and $\overline{\mathfrak{S}}'_U$, respectively.

By a *segment* we understand any non-ordered couple pq of two distinct points p and q. We denote by $[pq]$ the equivalence class under the relation of geometrical congruence containing pq, more simply, the set of all segments congruent to pq. We shall refer to such equivalence classes as *free segments* and denote them by the letters X, Y, Z. By $\mathbf{S}$ we denote the class of all free segments. Obviously

$$\mathbf{S} \neq 0. \tag{1.1}$$

The relation $<$ coincides with the usual *less-than* relation for free segments. Let **B** denote the *betweenness* relation of three points on a line. Then $X < Y$ *iff*[1] $\mathbf{B}(pqr)$, $X = [pq]$, *and* $Y = [pr]$, *for some distinct points* p, q, r. As is well known, we can prove in $\mathscr{E}$ (in fact, in $\mathscr{A}$)

(2.1) $$X \text{ non-} < X$$

and

(2.2) $$X = Y \text{ or } X < Y \text{ or else } Y < X.$$

The operation $+$ coincides with the usual *addition* for free segments:

$X + Y = Z$ *iff* $\mathbf{B}(pqr)$, $X = [pq]$, $Y = [qr]$, *and* $Z = [pr]$ *for some distinct points* p, q, r.

Hence $+$ is always performable, which is written as

(3.1) $$\text{if } X, Y \in \mathbf{S}, \text{ then } X + Y \in \mathbf{S}.$$

As is well known, we can prove in $\mathscr{E}$ (in fact, in $\mathscr{A}$)

(3.2) $$X+Y = Y+X,$$

(3.3) $$(X+Y)+Z = X+(Y+Z),$$

and

(3.4) $$X < Z \text{ iff } X+Y = Z \text{ for some } Y \text{ in } \mathbf{S}.$$

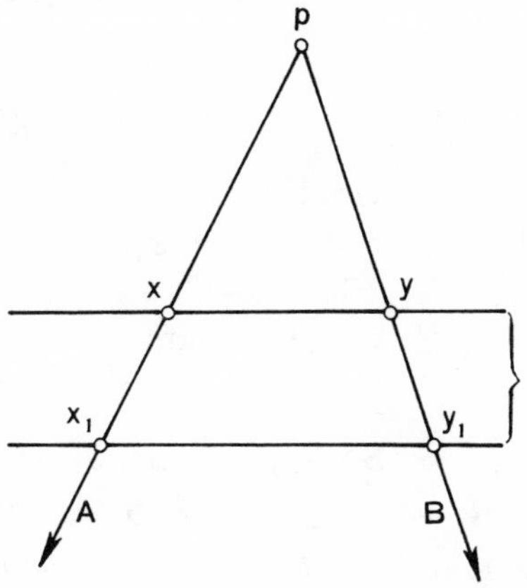

FIG. 1

To define $\cdot$ it is convenient to start with the quaternary relation **P** of *proportion.* We fix an angle AB with a vertex p (Fig. 1). The angle AB is understood here as the non-ordered pair of half-lines A and B which are supposed to be non-collinear and to have the common origin p. Given four free segments X, Y, X_1, Y_1, we take points x, x_1 on A and y, y_1 on B in such a way that

$$X = [px],\ Y = [py],\ X_1 = [px_1], \text{ and } Y_1 = [py_1],$$

[1]We use "*iff*" for "*if and only if*".

and we put

$$\mathbf{P}(XYX_1Y) \quad \textit{iff} \quad \mathbf{L}(xy) \| \mathbf{L}(x_1y_1),$$

provided $\mathbf{L}(pq)$ is the line through p and q, for every two distinct points p and q. It can be proved in $\mathscr{E}$ that the relation $\mathbf{P}$ does not depend on the choice of the angle AB. In particular one can imagine AB to be a right angle. The following properties of $\mathbf{P}$ can be proved in $\mathscr{E}$:

(4.1) $$\mathbf{P}(XYXY),$$

(4.2) $$\textit{if } \mathbf{P}(XYX_1Y_1) \textit{ and } \mathbf{P}(XYX_2Y_2), \textit{ then } \mathbf{P}(X_1Y_1X_2Y_2),$$

(4.3) $$\textit{if } \mathbf{P}(XYX_1Y_1), \textit{ then } \mathbf{P}(XX_1YY_1),$$

(4.4) $$\textit{if } \mathbf{P}(XYX_1Y_1) \textit{ and } X < Y, \textit{ then } X_1 < Y_1,$$

(4.5) $$\textit{if } \mathbf{P}(XYX_1Y_1), \textit{ then } \mathbf{P}(XY(X+X_1)(Y+Y_1)),$$

(4.6) $$\bigwedge_{X,Y,X_1} \bigvee_{Y_1} \mathbf{P}(XYX_1Y_1),$$ [2]

and

(4.7) $$\bigwedge_{X,Z} \bigvee_{Y} \mathbf{P}(XYYZ).$$

Moreover, it follows from (4.1)—(4.4) with the help of (2.2) that in (4.6) the free segment Y_1 (the *fourth proportional* to X, Y, X_1) is uniquely determined by the free segments X, Y, X_1. We now fix an arbitrary element U in $\mathbf{S}$ and put

(4.8) $$X \dot{_U} Y = Z \quad \textit{iff} \quad \mathbf{P}(UXYZ).$$

Thus the operation $\dot{_U}$ is relativized to U.

We consider now the algebraic system $\mathfrak{S}_U = \langle \mathbf{S}, +, \dot{_U}, < \rangle$. From the theorems (1.1), (2.1), (2.2), (3.1)—(3.4), (4.1)—(4.7), and the definition (4.8) we can derive, by a purely algebraic argument, the embedding theorem for $\mathfrak{S}_U$:

THEOREM 1. *System* $\mathfrak{S}_U = \langle \mathbf{S}, +, \dot{_U}, < \rangle$ *can be embedded in a commutative Euclidean field* $\overline{\mathfrak{S}}_U = \langle \overline{\mathbf{S}}, +, \dot{_U}, < \rangle$ *in such a way that* $\mathbf{S}$ *coincides with the set of all positive elements in* $\overline{\mathfrak{S}}_U$. *Moreover,* $\overline{\mathfrak{S}}_U$ *is up to isomorphism uniquely determined by* $\mathfrak{S}_U$ *and* U *is the unit element of the field* $\overline{\mathfrak{S}}_U$.

Let us pass to the absolute geometry $\mathscr{A}$. We wish to construct in $\mathscr{A}$ a commutative Euclidean field. First of all we ask whether the algebraic system $\mathfrak{S}_U$ and consequently the field $\overline{\mathfrak{S}}_U$ can be constructed in $\mathscr{A}$, and thus without using the Euclid axiom. The answer is negative. We can establish in $\mathscr{A}$ all the properties of $<$ and $+$, but we cannot establish in $\mathscr{A}$ all the properties of $\mathbf{P}$. For example, the statement (4.5), which implies the distrib-

---

[2]For abbreviation we express the statements (4.6) and (4.7) by using the universal quantifier $\bigwedge$ (*for every*) and the existential quantifier $\bigvee$ (*there is*).

utivity law for $\dot{_U}$ with respect to $+$ is not valid in $\mathscr{A}$. Hence we have to change the operations $+$ and $\dot{_U}$. Of course, we would like to change them as little as possible.

We start with the relation of proportion. Using the same construction as before, based upon an arbitrarily chosen angle AB, we put now $\mathbf{P}'(XYX_1Y_1)$ if and only if the line through p perpendicular to the line xy coincides with the line through p perpendicular to the line x_1y_1 (Fig. 2), which we write shortly

$$\mathbf{P}'(XYX_1Y_1) \text{ iff } \mathbf{O}(p\mathbf{L}(xy)\mathbf{L}(x_1y_1)).$$

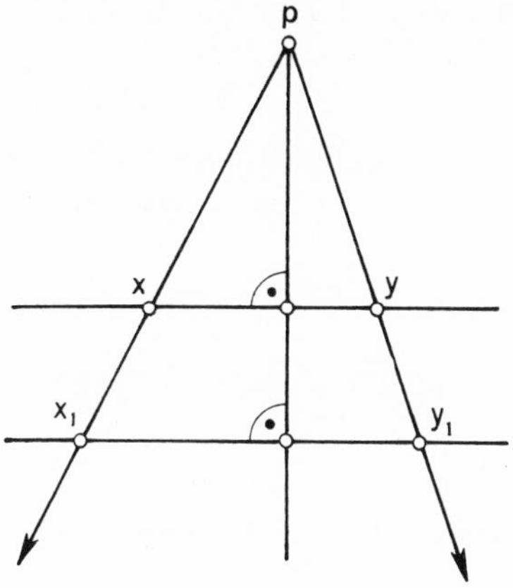

FIG. 2

It can be proved in $\mathscr{A}$ that the relation $\mathbf{P}'$ does not depend on the choice of the angle AB. Clearly, in $\mathscr{E}$ we have $\mathbf{P}' = \mathbf{P}$. This does not hold in $\mathscr{A}$. Nevertheless it can be proved in $\mathscr{A}$ that $\mathbf{P}'$ satisfies all the postulates (4.1) – (4.7) with the exception of (4.5) and (4.6). Thus

(4.1)′ $$\mathbf{P}'(XYXY),$$

(4.2)′ $$\text{if } \mathbf{P}'(XYX_1Y_1) \text{ and } \mathbf{P}'(XYX_2Y_2), \text{ then } P'(X_1Y_1X_2Y_2),$$

(4.3)′ $$\text{if } \mathbf{P}'(XYX_1Y_1), \text{ then } \mathbf{P}'(XX_1YY_1),$$

(4.4)′ $$\text{if } \mathbf{P}'(XYX_1Y_1) \text{ and } X < Y, \text{ then } X_1 < Y_1,$$

(4.7)′ $$\bigwedge_{X,Y} \bigvee_{Z} \mathbf{P}'(XYYZ).$$

We replace (4.6) by a weaker statement

(4.6)′ $$\text{if } \mathbf{P}'(XYX_1Y_1) \text{ and } X_2 < X_1, \text{ then } \bigvee_{Y_2} \mathbf{P}'(XYX_2Y_2),$$

which can be proved in $\mathscr{A}$. In consequence the operation $\dot{_U}'$ defined by

(4.8)′ $$X \dot{_U}' Y = Z \text{ iff } \mathbf{P}'(UXYZ)$$

is not always performable. On the other hand, it follows from (4.1)′ – (4.4)′ and (4.6)′—(4.8)′ that for a given X in $\mathbf{S}$ there is a unique Y in $\mathbf{S}$ such that $Y \dot{_U}' Y = X$. We put $Y = \sqrt[U]{X}'$. Clearly, in $\mathscr{E}$ the operation $\dot{_U}'$ coincides with $\dot{_U}$.

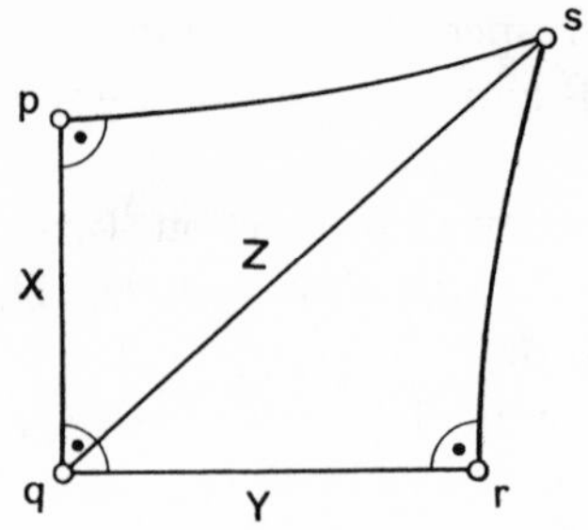

FIG. 3

In the postulate (4.5) the operation $+$ is involved. We change this operation. We start with an auxiliary operation $\oplus$. Given three free segments X, Y, Z, we put $X \oplus Y = Z$ if and only if there is a Lambert quadrangle $pqrs$ with right angles at the vertices p, q, r (Fig. 3) such that $X = [qp]$, $Y = [qr]$, $Z = [qs]$. Clearly, this operation is not always performable. Now we put

$$X +' Y = Z \textit{ iff } \underset{U}{\sqrt{X}'} \oplus \underset{U}{\sqrt{Y}'} = \underset{U}{\sqrt{Z}'}.$$

The operation $+'$ easily proves to be independent of the segment U although its definition involves U. Let us notice that in $\mathscr{E}$ the operation $+'$ coincides with the operation $+$. In fact, by the definition, $X +' Y = Z$ if and only if there is a Lambert quadrangle $pqrs$ with right angles at vertices p, q, r (Fig. 4) such that

$$\underset{U}{\sqrt{X}'} = [qp], \ \underset{U}{\sqrt{Y}'} = [qr], \ \underset{U}{\sqrt{Z}'} = [qs].$$

In $\mathscr{E}$, the quadrangle $pqrs$ is a rectangle, and hence

$$[pr] = \underset{U}{\sqrt{Z}'};$$

moreover the operation $\underset{U}{\cdot}'$ coincides with the operation $\underset{U}{\cdot}$. In consequence, using the Pythagorean formula, we get $X \oplus Y = Z$. In $\mathscr{A}$ the operation $+'$ differs from $+$. In particular, since $+$ is not always performable, $+'$ is not always performable either. Therefore the postulates (3.1) – (3.3) should be replaced now by weaker statements:

(3.1)′ *if* $X +' Y \in \mathbf{S}$ *and* $Z < Y$, *then* $X +' Z \in \mathbf{S}$,

(3.2)′ *if* $X +' Y \in \mathbf{S}$, *then* $X +' Y = Y +' X$,

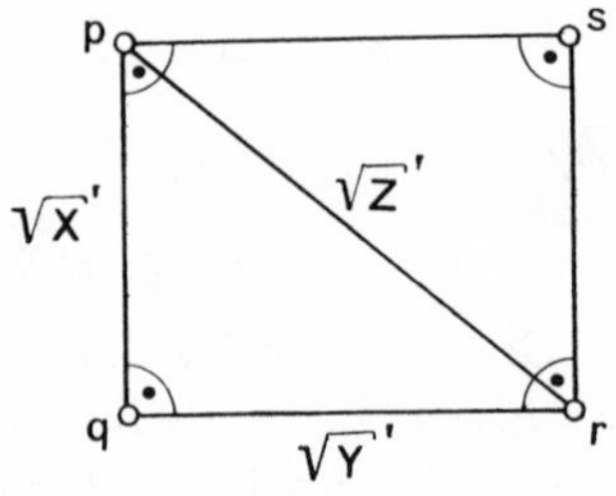

FIG. 4

(3.3)′ *if* $X+'Y,\ (X+'Y)+'Z,\ Y+'Z \in \mathbf{S}$, *then*
$$(X+'Y)+'Z = X+'(Y+'Z).$$

These statements are valid in $\mathscr{A}$; and so is

(3.4)′ $X < Z$ *iff* $X+'Y = Z$ *for some* Y *in* $\mathbf{S}$.

We have also to modify the postulate (4.5) to

(4.5)′ *if* $\mathbf{P}'(XYX_1Y_1)$ *and* $X+'X_1,\ Y+'Y_1 \in \mathbf{S}$, *then*
$$\mathbf{P}'(XY(X+'X_1)(Y+'Y_1)).$$

Statement (4.5)′ proves to be valid in $\mathscr{A}$.

Finally, since both operation $+'$ and $\dot{_U}'$ are not always performable, we have to add one more postulate

(2.3)′ $$\bigwedge_X \bigvee_Y X < Y.$$

Let us consider the algebraic system $\mathfrak{S}'_U = \langle \mathbf{S},\ +',\ \dot{_U}',\ < \rangle$. From the theorems (1.1), (2.1), (2.2), (2.3)′, (3.1)′—(3.4)′, (4.1)′—(4.7)′ and the definition (4.8′) we can derive, by a purely algebraic argument, the embedding theorem for $\mathbf{S}'_U$.

THEOREM 1′. *System* $\mathfrak{S}'_U = \langle \mathbf{S},\ +',\ \dot{_U}',\ < \rangle$ *can be embedded in a commutative Euclidean field* $\overline{\mathfrak{S}}'_U = \langle \overline{\mathbf{S}},\ +',\ \dot{_U}',\ < \rangle$ *in such a way that* $\mathbf{S}$ *coincides with an open interval* $I \subseteqq \overline{\mathbf{S}}$ *(finite or infinite), one end of which is the zero element of the field* $\overline{\mathfrak{S}}'_U$ *and containing* U. *In fact,* $\overline{\mathfrak{S}}'_U$ *is uniquely determined up to isomorphism by* $\mathfrak{S}'_U$ *and* U *is the unit element of the field* $\overline{\mathfrak{S}}'_U$.

Thus a commutative Euclidean field has been constructed in $\mathscr{A}$. We can now fix a perpendicular coordinate system; the two coordinates of a point p are of the form $\pm X_1,\ \pm X_2$ (Fig. 5), where $X_1,\ X_2 \in \mathbf{S}$. In $\mathscr{A}$, as in $\mathscr{E}$, the linear equation of the line can be derived from this construction.

In such a way everything which was done by Hilbert separately and by means of different geometrical ideas in Euclidean geometry $\mathscr{E}$ and in hyper-

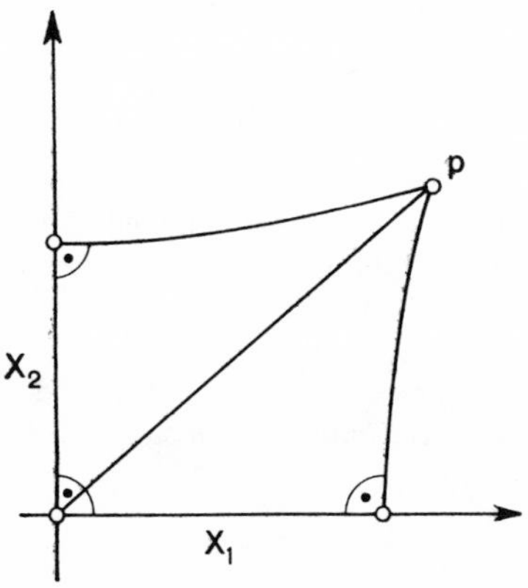

FIG. 5

bolic geometry $\mathscr{H}$ is now obtained in absolute geometry $\mathscr{A}$ and hence simultaneously in $\mathscr{E}$ and $\mathscr{H}$. In fact, we did not change even the operations of the algebraic system $\mathfrak{S}_U$ constructed by Hilbert in $\mathscr{E}$; we changed only the definitions of the operations. As a consequence, in $\mathscr{E}$ the system $\mathfrak{S}'_U$ coincides with $\mathfrak{S}_U$. In $\mathscr{H}$ the field $\overline{\mathfrak{S}}'_U$ is isomorphic to the field $\overline{\mathscr{E}}$ constructed by Hilbert in $\mathscr{H}$ and seems to be very natural for the hyperbolic case. The lack of space prevents our clarifying this point here. For more details see [5], where a *hyperbolic calculus* $\mathfrak{S}'$ *of segments*,[3] very closely related to $\mathfrak{S}'_U$, but independent of any parameter U, is constructed in $\mathscr{H}$, and [4], where the relation between $\mathfrak{S}'_U$ and $\mathfrak{S}'$ is fully established. Compare also [6].

The character of the whole discussion seems to be purely geometrical. Actually, only the form is geometrical; the content is meta-geometrical. To construct an algebraic structure, for instance an ordered field in geometry, is a geometrical problem. However we have constructed in absolute geometry $\mathscr{A}$ the field $\overline{\mathfrak{S}}'_U$ in terms of which all the primitive notions of $\mathscr{A}$ can be expressed (some of them, in fact the metric ones, differently in Euclidean and hyperbolic cases); e.g., the linear equation of the line obviously implies an analytic interpretation of the *incidence* relation. In meta-geometrical language this means that we have arrived at the representation theorem for absolute geometry $\mathscr{A}$, in other words, at a uniform (since based upon one and the same field $\overline{\mathfrak{S}}'_U$) description of all models for both Euclidean geometry $\mathscr{E}$ and hyperbolic geometry $\mathscr{H}$. Again, the lack of space enables us to formulate explicitly the representation theorem. For more details see [4], where, however, the field $\overline{\mathfrak{S}}'_U$ is constructed not in $\mathscr{A}$ but in the full *elementary absolute geometry* $\overline{\mathscr{A}}$,[4] and hence the representation theorem also applies to $\overline{\mathscr{A}}$.

In our discussion absolute geometry has been treated as a common part of Euclidean, that is, *parabolic*, and *hyperbolic* geometries. Absolute geometry can also be treated as a common part of three geometries: *parabolic*, *hyperbolic*, and *elliptic*. The problem of a uniform description of all models of these three theories is still open. We hope that it can be solved by a modification of our construction.

References

[1] Hilbert, D. *Grundlagen der Geometrie.* 1st ed. Leipzig, 1899.

[2] Hilbert, D. *Grundlagen der Geometrie.* 2nd ed. Leipzig, 1903.

[3] Hilbert, D. Neue Begründung der Bolyai-Lobatschefskyschen Geometrie. *Mathematische Annalen,* Vol. 57 (1903), pp. 137–150. Reprinted in [2] as Appendix.

[4] Szmielew, W. Absolute calculus of segments and its metamathematical implications. *Bulletin de l'Académie Polonaise des Sciences,* Série des sci. math., astr. et phys., Vol. 7 (1959), pp. 213–20.

[3] In [5] it is denoted by $\mathfrak{S}$.

[4] In [4] it is denoted by $\mathscr{A}_2$.

[5] SZMIELEW, W. Some metamathematical problems concerning elementary hyperbolic geometry. *The Axiomatic Method*, Proceedings of an International Symposium, University of California, Berkeley, 1957, North-Holland Publishing Co., Amsterdam, 1959. pp. 30–52.

[6] SZMIELEW, W. A new analytic approach to hyperbolic geometry. *Fundamenta Mathematicae*, Vol. 50 (1961), pp. 129–58.

SECTION

III

PHILOSOPHY OF LOGIC AND MATHEMATICS

REMARKS ABOUT FORMALIZATION AND MODELS

PAUL BERNAYS

Federal School of Technology, Zürich, Switzerland

1

The method of formalizing mathematical proofs has given rise to various formal systems in which certain methods of derivation are in a natural way delimited. Within some of these systems we are able to formalize all demonstrations of classical number theory, analysis, and set theory. We can even be content for this purpose with standard formalization, where the means of derivation are the predicate calculus with equality, and a recursive set of axioms given by finitely many formulas and (eventually) finitely many formula-schemata, containing besides the logical symbols (and the variables) other primitive symbols (individual symbols, predicators, functors).

These facts, however, do not mean that we can fully include each domain of classical mathematics in a formal system. This not even the case for number theory. For by one of Gödel's incompleteness theorems we know that there is no consistent formal system allowing us to derive every true arithmetic formula (i.e., every closed formula formed out of the symbols 0, 1, $+$, $\cdot$, $=$, by means of the propositional connectives and the quantifiers, which is true with the ordinary interpretation of the symbols). This can be expressed also by saying that the set of Gödel numbers (for any effective Gödel numbering of the true arithmetic formulas) is not recursively enumerable; or in a less technical formulation: the number-theoretic concept of truth cannot be operatively defined, i.e., the true arithmetic propositions cannot be characterized as those obtained from some explicitly stated propositions and propositional schemata by some rules of procedure given in advance.

It clearly was on the whole the awareness of this circumstance which induced Lorenzen, Schütte, Ackermann, and Stenius to enlarge the concept of formal derivation by admitting infinite induction.

2

As is well known, a complete system (i.e., a system which cannot consistently be extended by adding an axiom which is expressible as a formula of the system) can admit different non-isomorphic models. A simple instance is the axiom system for densely ordered sets with no first and no last element. The axioms can be stated as follows:

$$(x)\neg(x < x),$$
$$(x)(y)(z)(x < y \wedge y < z \rightarrow x < z),$$
$$(x)(y)(z)(\neg(x < y) \wedge \neg(y < z) \rightarrow \neg(x < z),$$
$$(x)(y)(x = y \leftrightarrow \neg(x < y) \wedge \neg(y < x)),$$
$$(x)(y)(x < y \rightarrow (Ez)(x < z \wedge z < y)),$$
$$(x)(Ey)(Ez)(y < x \wedge x < z).$$

The general equality schema can be omitted. Let us denote this system by "$\{<, d\}$". We have here obviously the two models: (1) the natural order of the rational numbers, and (2) that of the real numbers. These models differ already in their power, but they can also be distinguished by the occurrence of gaps (as Dedekind calls them) in the order of the rational numbers, which are excluded in the order of the real numbers.

There is even the general theorem that every formal system in standard form which has an infinite model (i.e., a model with an infinite domain of individuals) admits not only denumerable models but also non-denumerable models of arbitrarily high power. The existence of a denumerable model was indeed observed by Löwenheim, and Skolem noticed first that in the proof of the existence the choice-principle can be dispensed with.

Now with respect to the foregoing example of the system $\{<, d\}$ one could argue, by strengthening the formalist point of view, as follows: Let S be a formal system in standard form sufficient for formalizing analysis and for establishing formally the existence of the two above-mentioned models of the system $\{<, d\}$. By Löwenheim's theorem there exists a denumerable model for S, the existence of which again can be established in a metatheory M. By means of this model we get a one-to-one correspondence in M between the representatives of the rational numbers and those of the real numbers in S; and, by a well-known theorem of set theory, we even obtain an isomorphism between the two with respect to the order relation. Thus the distinctness of the two models for $\{<, d\}$, which can be formally stated in the system S, disappears by passing to the metatheory M.

To this reasoning it can be replied that the isomorphic mapping obtained in M between the two models of $\{<, d\}$ in S comes about only by the restricted character of every formal system S of analysis, which gives rise to the possibility of non-standard models not satisfying fully the Dedekind condition of continuity, but only satisfying this condition with respect to those Dedekind cuts which can be expressed in S. More briefly: the denumerable non-standard model given in M of the continuum as formalized by S does not respresent the continuum for M; for just this reason the model is called non-standard. Generally the possible models of a formal system of the continuum are relative to this system, but the theorem of the non-denumerability of the continuum holds invariantly in every formalizing system.

This is not to be wondered at, for the non-denumerability of the continuum follows rather directly from its characteristic topological properties. Indeed by an argument of Cantor (which seems to be almost forgotten in the newer literature on foundations), from an enumeration of the continuum we would obtain a certain sequence of elements $p_1, p_2, \cdots$ such that $p_{2n-1} < p_{2n+1} < p_{2n+2} < p_{2n}$, for $n = 1, 2, \cdots$. From this a sequence of closed intervals $i_1, i_2, \cdots$ results, where i_{n+1} lies in the interior of i_n, and where there is no common element (point) lying in all the intervals. (p_1 is the first element in the enumeration; p_2 the first point to the right of p_1; p_3 the first between p_1 and p_2; and so on.)

3

One would be wrong to suppose that the reasoning we have applied to the system $\{<, d\}$ could be applied correspondingly to every complete system in standard form. A drastic counter-example is the system, in standard form, of real algebra studied especially by Tarski — let us call it the system T — with the primitive predicators $=$, $<$, the functors $+$, $\cdot$, and the individual symbols 0, 1, whose axioms are those of an ordered field with also the schema of Lückenlosigkeit (by Dedekind):

$$(x)(y)(A(x) \wedge \neg A(y) \rightarrow x < y) \wedge (Ex)A(x) \wedge (Ex) \neg A(x) \rightarrow \\ (Ez)(x)((A(x) \rightarrow (x < z \vee x = z)) \wedge (\neg A(x) \rightarrow (z < x \vee z = x))),$$

which of course has here only a restricted applicability.

For this system there is a minimal model consisting of only the real algebraic numbers which are all nameable in T — whereas in the models of $\{<, d\}$ no element is nameable in that system. This property of the minimal model of T implies that a one-to-one correspondence between this model and any more-embracing model cannot be an isomorphism with respect to T quite independently of the question of power. Generally any two different fields consisting of real numbers which are real closed are non-isomorphic models of T. This is due to the circumstance that each real number is determined uniquely by its order relations with the rational numbers, which are indeed nameable in T; hence, for any two different real numbers a, b there is in T an elementary predicate satisfied by a, but not by b, even as it is stated in the Eudoxean theory of proportions. Hence in particular we have many non-isomorphic *denumerable* models of T. This strong non-categoricity is of course by no means a deficiency of the system T, for this formal system is intended to characterize not just one structure but a kind of structures.

It might be mentioned that from the system T, by merely adding the fundamental predicate $\mathrm{Int}(c)$ ("c is an integer") with the formal axioms

$$\begin{aligned}&\mathrm{Int}(0)\\&\mathrm{Int}(a) \rightarrow \mathrm{Int}(a+1)\\&\mathrm{Int}(a) \wedge \mathrm{Int}(b) \wedge a < b \rightarrow a+1 < b \vee a+1 = b\end{aligned}$$

and then defining $Nm(o)$ ("c is a natural number") by

$$Nm(a) \leftrightarrow \mathrm{Int}(a) \wedge (0 = a \vee 0 < a),$$

we get a system from which the formula

$$0 < a \wedge a < b \rightarrow (Ex)(Nm(x) \wedge b < a \cdot x),$$

expressing the Archimedean axiom, as well as the schema of complete induction

$$A(0) \wedge (x)(A(x) \wedge Nm(x) \rightarrow A(x+1)) \rightarrow (Nm(a) \rightarrow A(a))$$

is derivable. (The following auxiliary formulas are useful for the derivation:

$$\begin{aligned}&\neg Nm(a) \rightarrow (Ex)(0 < x(y)(Nm(y) \rightarrow y+x < a \vee a+x < y)),\\&(x)(x+1 \leqq 0(Ey)(Nm(y) \wedge (x < y \vee x = y) \wedge y < x+1)).\end{aligned}$$

In this extension T_1 of T all means of the usual formal system of number theory in standard form (denoted by "P" in "Undecidable Theories") are available. Also the predicate "r is the number at the k-th decimal place in the infinite decimal expansion of the positive real number a" can be expressed by the formula

$$\begin{aligned}&0 < a \wedge Nm(k) \wedge 0 < k \wedge Nm(r) \wedge r < 10 \wedge (Ex)(Nm(x) \wedge x < a \cdot 10^k\\&\quad \wedge (a \cdot 10^k < x+1 \vee a \cdot 10^k = x+1) \wedge (Ey)(Nm(y) \wedge x = y \cdot 10+r)).\end{aligned}$$

We thus can develop in T_1 the theory of real numbers, though for function theory this system is certainly not sufficient. Of course T_1 is not complete.

4

The view might be defended that every representation of the continuum in which each element is nameable is non-standard. This opinion of course does not conflict with the fact that every real number is uniquely determined by the set of the lower rational numbers (or in other words, by its order relations with the rational numbers); for the set of the rational numbers which are lower than a real number c is in general defined only *with reference* to c, and only in special cases independently definable, as in the case of $\sqrt{2}$ or of π. Brouwer's theory of the continuum, by the introduction of the concept of choice sequence, is in accordance with this view. In classical, non-formalized analysis a corresponding kind of freedom as that afforded by operating with choice sequences is effected, even in a strengthened way, by the unrestricted concept of a set of natural numbers (or a sequence of rational numbers).

Still one other remark: In the theory of real numbers we know, as mentioned before, that any two elements can be distinguished by a property which is expressible (in any sufficient formalizing system) by a predicate that is satisfied by the first but not by the second element (though these elements need not be nameable in the formal system). A corresponding fact, it seems, does not hold for the theory of the second number class and neither for the theory of the class of sets of real numbers.

MATHEMATICS AND LOGIC

ALONZO CHURCH

Princeton University, Princeton, New Jersey, U.S.A.

As the title indicates, this paper concerns, not a contemporary trend in the sense of something that is presently in process, but an old question in regard to which developments have come to a conclusion, or at least a pause. It is not true that opinions now agree. But the cessation of active development means that the matter can be summed up and even that some attempt may be made at adjudication.

There are two senses in which it has been maintained that logic is prior to mathematics. One of these, which I shall call the strong sense, is the doctrine which has come to be known as logicism. And the other, the weak sense, is the sense in which the standard postulational or axiomatic view of the nature of mathematics requires the priority of logic as being the means by which the consequences of a particular system of mathematical postulates are determined.

To take the strong sense first, the logicistic thesis is that logic and mathematics are related, not as two different subjects, but as earlier and later parts of the same subject, and indeed in such a way that mathematics can be obtained entirely from pure logic without the introduction of additional primitives or additional assumptions.

To make this definite, we first require an answer of some sort to the question, What is meant by logic? Certainly not merely traditional logic, i.e., the logic of Aristotle plus further developments in this same immediate context — else the logicistic thesis is obviously false. If we are to take the logicists seriously, we must concede them a broad sense of the term, logic.

As a descriptive account rather than a definition, and assuming the notion of deductive reasoning as already known, from experience with particular instances of it, let us say that logic consists in a theory of deductive reasoning, plus whatever is required in object language or metalanguage for the adequacy, generality, and simplicity of the theory.

That logic does not therefore consist merely in a metatheory of some object language arises in the following way. It is found that ordinary theories, and perhaps any satisfactory theory, of deductive reasoning in the form of a metatheory will lead to analytic sentences in the object language, i.e., to sentences which, on the theory in question, are consequences of any arbitrary set of hypotheses, or it may be, of any arbitrary non-empty set of hypotheses.[1] These analytic sentences lead in turn to certain generalizations; e.g., the infinitely many analytic sentences $A \vee \sim A$, where A ranges over all

[1] We may understand consequence either in the sense of provability or in any other, less effective, sense which the particular metatheory may provide, the distinction being not important for the immediate purpose.

sentences of the object language, lead to the generalization $p \vee \sim p$, or more explicitly $(p) . p \vee \sim p$; and in similar fashion $(F)(y) . (x)F(x) \supset F(y)$ may arise by generalization from infinitely many analytic sentences of the appropriate form. These generalizations are common to many object languages on the basis of what is seen to be in some sense the same theory of deductive reasoning for the different languages. Hence they are considered to belong to logic, as not only is natural but has long been the standard terminology.

Against the suggestion, which is sometimes made from a nominalistic motivation, to avoid or omit these generalizations, it must be said that to have, e.g., all of the special cases $\mathrm{A} \vee \sim \mathrm{A}$ and yet not allow the general law $(p) . p \vee \sim p$ seems to be contrary to the spirit of generality in mathematics, which I would extend to logic as the most fundamental branch of mathematics. Indeed such a situation would be much as if one had in arithmetic $2 + 3 = 3 + 2$, $4 + 5 = 5 + 4$, and all other particular cases of the commutative law of addition, yet refused to accept or formulate a general law, $(x)(y) . x+y = y+x$.

For our present purpose it is convenient to regard a language as being given when we have a set of primitive symbols and formation rules and, in some sense which it is not here necessary to make definite, meanings for the expressions (wffs) of the language. Thus let me speak of the rules of inference, not as constitutive of the language, but rather as belonging to a theory of deductive reasoning for the language — so that there may be different sets of rules of inference for the same language.[2]

There is then another consideration which leads us to count certain generalizations of analytic sentences as belonging to logic. This arises from the idea that logic cannot be taken as exhausted by what is special to particular languages.[3] Abstractly the laws of logic are not dependent on whether, for example, one uses C or $[\supset]$ as sign of implication, or whether one writes $\mathrm{P}(x)$ or $x\mathrm{P}$, the predicate before or after the subject. Thus the metatheoretic principle that from $[\mathrm{B} \supset \mathrm{C}]$ and $[\mathrm{A} \supset \mathrm{B}]$ may be inferred $[\mathrm{A} \supset \mathrm{C}]$ is to be regarded as special to a particular language; and the corresponding general principle of logic is rather something like $(p)(q)(r) . q \supset r \supset . p \supset q \supset . p \supset r$. In this connection the Fregean distinction of two kinds of meaning, the sense and the denotation, has the merit that the abstract general laws of logic may satisfactorily be formulated as extensional, since an intensional aspect of the meaning is still present in the sense. But from the point of view of a Russellian theory of meaning, which denies the sense in favor of the denotation, the variables p, q, r, F, etc., must be taken as intensional varia-

[2]The term, language, is of course often used by logicians in such a sense that a particular language is not determined until inference (or transformation) rules have been determined in addition to the other things named above. There is actually a need for two terms.

[3]Else indeed, since Greek and Latin are different languages, the logic of Aristotle and the logic of Boethius could not be said to have even in part the same content or to treat the same topic.

bles, having propositions, properties, etc., as their values. From this point of view, if one is inclined to minimize the domain allowed to logic, one might even take the extreme position that such assertions as $(p) \centerdot p \vee \sim p$ and $(F)(y) \centerdot (x)F(x) \supset F(y)$, where p and F are extensional variables, having, respectively, truth-values and classes as their range, though they are analytic, do not belong to logic.[4]

Now from the point of view of such an account of what is meant by logic one may see the logicistic attempt to reduce mathematics to logic in its most favorable light. For it could be said that logic is at any rate one prerequisite for mathematics, since deductive reasoning plays so prominent a role in mathematics. This is the weak sense of the priority of logic, which was referred to above. And if we accept it, we may then well say that mathematics would be founded on a minimum basis if it could be reduced to nothing but pure logic.

Historically logicists have not been as explicit as this but have seemed just to assume that the laws of logic have so ultimate and fundamental a character that the reduction to logic is clearly desirable if possible, and that the true nature of mathematics would be revealed by such a reduction.

Now having the case for the logicistic thesis before us, let us proceed immediately to objections. There are three important ones to be cited, and possibly a fourth.

The first objection is simply that the attempted reduction of mathematics to logic has not been more than half successful. The history is well known. Frege — who held the logicistic thesis only for arithmetic as opposed to geometry — did indeed reduce arithmetic to his own formulation of pure logic. Frege's logic includes the extensional as well as the intensional. This is a feature which I do not regard as being a defect in itself. But it is precisely the extensional part of Frege's logic which, despite the immediate appeal of its principles as intuitively sound, leads to its inconsistency. And the historical fact is that Frege, confronted with the Russell paradox, gave up in despair.

To avoid the paradoxes, Russell, and later Whitehead and Russell in *Principia Mathematica,* introduced the theory of types, and this in turn compelled use of the axiom of infinity. The term "axiom of infinity" is due, not to Russell, but to C. J. Keyser. And in an early paper Russell had argued against Keyser that the axiom of infinity is not a special assumption which is required by mathematics above and beyond the laws of logic, because the axiom (or supposed axiom) can be proved on logical grounds alone. Thus when Russell later reversed himself and adopted an axiom of infinity, it is almost his own admission, it might be said, that he thus went beyond pure logic. Indeed the axiom of infinity might be described as half-logical in

[4] I do not advocate this extreme position, and Russell did not do so. But it is worth noticing that it provides a very satisfactory motivation for Russell's avoidance of extensionality by means of his contextual definition of class abstracts which is mentioned below.

character, since it can be stated in the same vocabulary that is used to state the laws of pure logic, but is not analytic according to any known theory of deductive reasoning that I believe can be accepted as adequately and naturally representative of existing standard practice in mathematical reasoning. And though it is known that elementary arithmetic can be obtained without axiom of infinity if based on a set-theoretic rather than a type-theoretic approach, it does not appear that mathematics as a whole can dispense with such an axiom if otherwise based only on a standard and naturally acceptable formulation of pure logic.

An incidental point is that Russell showed the derivability of mathematics from intensional logic, plus axiom of infinity.[5] Or more correctly, Russell's logic is neither extensional nor intensional, but neutral. He assumes no principle of extensionality for his propositional and functional variables. Equally he assumes no different and stricter principle of individuation which would require an intensional range for any of these variables. He simply has no need of such an hypothesis, as he says. In accomplishing this, the role of Russell's elimination of classes by the device of contextual definition is perhaps not as widely appreciated as it should be. And though there may be objections to it which I would urge in a different context, they concern such matters as adequacy for the logic of indirect discourse, and certainly not the adequacy for mathematics.

To return, however, to objections against the logicistic thesis — the second one concerns the question of founding particular branches of mathematics on a minimum basis. If we wish to found the whole of mathematics — or to evade difficulties connected with the Gödel incompleteness theorem and related questions, let us say rather the whole of presently extant mathematics — it does indeed appear that pure logic in an appropriate formulation,[6] plus axiom of infinity, affords at least an approximation to a minimum basis. But for most particular branches of mathematics, and especially for elementary arithmetic, this is not the case. For the Frege-Russell method requires predicate variables of higher order to obtain even elementary arithmetic. Such higher-order variables may well be regarded as belonging to the vocabulary of pure logic, since they arise naturally from even a first-order language if we first generalize from the analytic sentences in the way that has been described, then extend the language by adding the notations required for these generalizations, then formulate an extended theory of deductive reasoning to apply to the extended language, then generalize again from the analytic sentences, and so on. However, the higher-order

---

[5]For a strictly historical account, the axiom of reducibility should also be added. But it is now usual to avoid this by the introduction of simple type theory, and it may therefore be ignored for our present purpose.

[6]This does not hold if we include in the logic assumptions that require intensional values for the propositional and functional variables. However, as already noticed, Russell, and Whitehead and Russell, do not do this, but regard the assumption of intensionality and of extensionality as alike superfluous.

predicate (or functional) variables, together with comprehension principles which are required for them, mean in the presence of an axiom of infinity that even the non-denumerably infinite has been admitted. A more satisfactorily economical basis for elementary arithmetic is provided either by one of the standard formulations of first-order arithmetic employing primitive notations special to arithmetic and special arithmetic postulates, or by a weak set theory which is adequate for the treatment of finite sets but omits all the standard set-theoretic axioms that are not needed for this purpose (including the axiom of infinity).

According to a third objection, it is not logic in the sense of a theory of deductive reasoning that is required for mathematics but only just various concrete instances of deductive reasoning. This third objection might be taken, like the second, as directed against the desirability of deriving mathematics from purely logical primitives, rather than against the success of the logicists in doing so. However, mathematical intuitionists in particular have urged such an objection in a stronger form, maintaining that mathematics is prior to logic in a sense which would make the derivation of mathematics from logic unsound on the ground of circularity. In fact intuitionists go far beyond denying that the strong logic required by Frege and Russell is an acceptable foundation for mathematics, and intend an objection as much against the weak sense of the priority of logic as against the strong sense.

Now it is true that any foundation of either mathematics or logic is in a certain fashion circular. That is, there always remain presuppositions which must be accepted on faith or intuition without being themselves founded. We may seek to minimize the presuppositions, but we cannot do away with them. Whether the minimum of presupposition that remains after reduction is to be called mathematics, or logic, or both, or neither, becomes a question of terminology. But I would remark, in criticism of the intuitionists, that it is at any rate much less than the total content of a mathematics library, or even of a few good mathematical books.

It is not clear to me just how far the intuitionistic denial of priority to logic applies against the use of the logistic method [7] in founding particular theories. For intuitionists, Heyting in particular, have used the logistic method and I think do not dispute its value. In fact it is by the logistic method that those who do not share the intuitionistic intuition are nevertheless able to see, at least in the case of particular mathematical and logical theories, what it is to which the intuitionistic intuition would lead. The crucial point in regard to the intuitionists' use of the logistic method is not whether they proceed by direct application of intuition before reaching the logistic formulation of a theory, but whether having once reached the logistic formulation they then regard it as definitive of the theory in the sense that a change in it or addition to it has to be regarded as a change to a different theory. Since it

---

[7] I.e., the method of metatheoretic statement of the formation and transformation rules of a language.

appears that they do not treat the logistic formulation as characterizing the theory in this way, or even as adequately representing it, we thus have the situation that no theory is ever fully intersubjectively determinate. If intuitionists are to be so understood, it would seem to me that this is the weakest point of their doctrine, and by no means essential to the rest of it. I believe that there is much more to be said in favor of their objections against particular classical theories, and against conventionalistic and "formalistic" aspects of the axiomatic method as classically understood.

From the point of view of the intuitionistic rejection of certain parts of the logic of classical mathematics, one might add as a fourth objection to the program of logicism that it is simply rendered impossible. And indeed this would seem to be the case, even if an axiom of infinity is conceded. Against the contention on behalf of logicism that logic in the broad sense is a natural extension and an essential completion of even the most rudimentary theory of deductive reasoning, there is the intuitionistic contention that the extension has gone too far and in the effort to achieve generality has passed beyond tenability. The objection will carry conviction only for intuitionists. But it agrees with the second objection in emphasizing the strength of the logic required by logicism.

Classically, even if we accept one or more of the first three objections and regard them as cogent, it does not follow that logicism is barren of fruit. Two important things remain. One of these is the reduction of mathematical vocabulary to a surprisingly brief list of primitives, all belonging to the vocabulary of pure logic. The other is the basing of all existing mathematics on one comparatively simple unified system of axioms and rules of inference. Such a reduction of the primitive basis of mathematics might indeed be made differently if one were less exclusively occupied with the logicistic doctrine, but it was nevertheless in the first instance an accomplishment of the logicists.

NOMINALISTIC ANALYSIS OF MATHEMATICAL LANGUAGE

LEON HENKIN

University of California, Berkeley, California, U.S.A.
Dartmouth College, Hanover, New Hampshire, U.S.A.

In a congress where logic and methodology play so prominent a role, it is perhaps permissible to preface one's talk with a brief meta-talk — and even to indulge in a modicum of self-reference.

Let me begin, then, by confessing that although from the beginning of my studies in logic I have been intrigued by philosophical questions concerning the foundations of mathematics, and have often been to greater or lesser extent attracted or antagonized by some particular viewpoint, I have never felt an overwhelming compulsion to decide that any given theory was 'right' or 'wrong'. On the contrary, I have had a strong continuing feeling that 'working mathematics' comes first, and that differing approaches to the foundations of the subject were largely equally possible ways of looking at a fascinating activity and relating it to broader areas of experience.

My interest in foundational theories has rather been directed toward the extent to which these are themselves susceptible of mathematical formulation, and toward the solution of technical problems which may arise from such analyses. In particular, this has characterized my approach to modern efforts to obtain a nominalistic interpretation of mathematical language.

While the nominalistic tradition in philosophy is of course very ancient, a specific concentration of interest in this viewpoint, as applied especially to the analysis of *mathematical* language, can be clearly discerned in the work of the Polish school of logicians during the early decades of this century. The names of Lesniewski, T. Kotarbinski, Chwistek and his student Hepter, and Tarski are all associated with this activity. Among the best known of this work is Kotarbinski's theory of Reism ('Everything that is, is a person or an object') and his efforts to define all categories in terms of one lowest category, and Chwistek's efforts to establish the consistency of mathematics by providing an interpretation wherein all of its assertions could be shown to be truths about physical objects.

Aside from some writings of Russell this interest of the Polish logicians did not seem to be reflected outside of their own country. But with the transplantation of Tarski to the United States in 1938 the concern with nominalism made itself evident in this country, and subsequently in countries of western Europe. From 1940 on there has been a steady series of publications in this

---

This talk was prepared while the author was supported by an NSF research contract with the University of California (Grant No. G-14006). The manuscript was written subsequently while the author was a Visiting Professor at Dartmouth College.

area, including works by Quine, Goodman, Martin, Woodger, Church, Wang, G. Bergmann, Lejewski, Scheffler — and even myself. Nominalistic considerations have made themselves congenial both to some holding a constructivist viewpoint in the foundations of mathematics, and to others who have advanced a formalistic position.

In this paper I wish to begin by considering two rather special pieces of analysis presented by Quine and Goodman in an early joint work.[1] Underlying their analysis is a dual goal which these authors set for a nominalistic re-interpretation of mathematical language:

(*a*) to provide a description of the conditions under which mathematical sentences may be properly affirmed, without reference or appeal to abstract entities of any kind; and

(*b*) to eschew any assumption as to the finitude or infinitude of (physical) things, since this matter is not (and probably cannot) be definitely known and so should not form the basis of the meaning of language.

The first of the Quine-Goodman problems which we wish to consider is that of giving nominalistically acceptable meaning to sentences of the form *A is an ancestor of B*. The solution of these authors is to alter the set-theoretical formulation of this concept, whose idea goes back to Frege, by replacing the member-set relation with the part-whole relation (between physical objects). The result is to construe a statement of the form *A is an ancestor of B* as meaning that *A and B are persons, and everything which contains A as a part, and which is such that all children of any person which is a part of it are also parts of it, has B as a part.* The validity of this analysis depends, of course, on conceiving that physical objects may be scattered in space-time so that, for example, one can speak of the object which is the sum (in the sense of part-whole theory) of a man and his great-great-great-grandson.

As Quine and Goodman indicate, this form of analysis is not adequate to explain the connection between an arbitrary binary relation (holding between pairs of physical objects) and its ancestral (which is another relation of the same type). Its efficacy in the present instance depends upon the fact that no ancestor of a person can have a part in common with that person. And Quine and Goodman indicate that they do not see how to solve the more general problem.

We should like to advance an alternative interpretation for sentences of the form *A is an ancestor of B*, which provides a method of treating the ancestrals of many relations not susceptible of treatment by the Quine-Goodman method. And indeed the interpretation which we put forward is a much more *natural* one than that of Quine and Goodman, for it consists of a description of the method by which the truth of many sentences of the indicated form is in fact established.

Our proposal is to interpret *A is an ancestor of B* as meaning that *there*

---

[1]See [2]. Numbers in brackets refer to References at end of paper.

is a list of inscriptions, of which one is a name of A and a later one is a name of B, such that whenever x and y are successive inscriptions of the list then x denotes some person and y denotes one of his children.

One objection to this proposal which immediately comes to mind is that there are undoubtedly pairs of people, such that we would normally say that one is an ancestor of the other, but such that no one has ever happened to prepare a list which includes their names and those of their intermediate relatives in order of birth. It might thus appear as if the proposed interpretation, instead of specifying the existence of an actual spatio-temporal list, should somehow be weakened so as to require only the existence of a 'possible', or 'potential' list.

A concept of 'possible existence', similar to this, does indeed appear in the work of Chwistek. However, it does not seem likely that such a 'possible list' would qualify as a physical object admitted to the realm of entities of which Quine and Goodman permit themselves to speak (although they are careful to refrain from giving specific criteria for distinguishing these). On the other hand, these authors construe inscriptions (and hence, presumably, would be willing to construe lists of inscriptions) as pieces of matter having certain shapes — even if this matter is in no way differentiated from the surrounding 'background' matter. Under this construction, for example, several copies of every work ever written in any natural language exist as parts of any given blank page (which is not too small). It is rather clear that under this construction anything which one would be likely to call a 'possible list' would, in fact, qualify as an actual list. We can, therefore, allow our original proposal to stand unmodified.

A second objection which comes to mind is that the proposed interpretation involves reference to the semantical concept of denotation, and it is well known that use of this relation can lead to a paradox. However, it appears to be a simple matter to limit the kind of names which may appear on our lists, and so in effect to deal only with a limited portion of the denotation relation and in such a way, it is well known, one can avoid any of the known derivations of paradox.[2]

A moment's reflection will show that our proposed interpretation in terms of lists can be carried over *verbatim* to provide an explication of the

[2]In this connection let it be noted that Quine has himself indicated a willingness to countenance the use of semantical concepts in giving meaning to mathematical statements in which semantical terms do not overtly obtrude — although such willingness was not explicitly acknowledged. Thus, where G is a predicate variable, Quine has considered an interpretation of second-order sentences of the form *for all G, A*, where A is an inscription from which sentences can be formed by replacing G with any predicate-inscription, as follows: *For every predicate P, the result of replacing G by P in A is true.* (See [3].) Although mentioning several objections to this interpretation, and ultimately rejecting it on those grounds, Quine offers no criticism of the proposed interpretation based on its use of the semantical concept of truth. Notice that it is not possible to express this interpretation in the form: *For all G, A* if and only if — — —, where the blank is filled in without use of semantical terms.

ancestral of any relation for which one can form a list of names reaching from any individual who bears the relation to something, to any of his ancestors. The requirement that no individual have a part in common with any ancestor, which limits the application of the Quine-Goodman interpretation, in no way appears.

The second of the Quine-Goodman analyses which we wish to consider is the one which they furnish for the sentence: *There are more dogs than cats.* They first define a *bit* to be anything which is the size of the smallest among all cats and dogs, and then speak of a *bit of* x (where x may be anything) as a part of x which is a bit. Their proposed interpretation for the sentence *there are more dogs than cats* reads as follows: *Everything which contains a bit of each dog as a part of it, is larger than something which has a bit of each cat as a part of it.*

Aside from the charge of ambiguity residing in such notions as *larger* and *size* (which can easily be resolved in any of several ways), the proposed interpretation seems open to the objection that it violates the proscription against assigning meanings which are based upon an assumption of the finitude or infinitude of things. For if it should turn out that the generations of cats continue without cease, and if it should happen that this species evolves in such manner as to produce cats of ever-diminishing size, then the concept of a *bit* would lack realization!

Even if we limit our analysis of sentences of the form *there are more A's than B's*, however, to the case where we know there are only finitely many *A's* and *B's*, it is clear that the Quine-Goodman analysis will not in general be correct if some *A's*, say, are parts of others (as they themselves point out).

As an alternative interpretation, depending neither on an assumption of finitude nor on one of disjointness, we offer the following: *There is no list of inscriptions which contains just one name of each A and each B, and in which each name of an A is followed by a name of B.* As with our earlier analysis, the only limit on the applicability of this interpretation is the possibility that in certain cases we may be talking about things for which we cannot obtain a complete list of names.

Let us turn now to an examination of this limitation.

Quine and Goodman themselves point out that in a world with only finitely many things there will inevitably be many things which have no names (since many of the things of the world have to be used as symbols which are not names, and many different things are often names of the same thing). If we construe lists of inscriptions, like inscriptions themselves, as materials having certain shapes, then it is clear that for lack of matter we may be unable to form or to find some list of which we can conceive, even if all of the objects to be listed do have names.

Ordinarily when we think of a list we visualize it as composed of matter lying in a plane-like region during some segment of time. However, when we consider the problem of enormous lists, which would be needed for our proposed interpretation of such sentences as *there are more dogs than cats*, it is evident that we will have to resolve such problems as whether to have our lists curve about the surface of the earth or go off into space! Furthermore, to insure good-sized lists we should somehow make provision for re-using things in one place many times over, at different moments, for different items on our list.

Actually the use of things having certain shapes for puposes of inscription can be regarded partly as a historical accident (as is evident from a consideration of the case of peoples having no written language), and partly as a matter of convenience in communicating. When, however, inscriptions are to be used not for communication but to give meaning to a variety of sentences in the manner contemplated above, it is natural to seek some other objects which may be better fitted to serve the new purpose. Indeed, just as we now have written and spoken inscriptions for different puposes of communication, we may seek a third type of inscription, perhaps not suitable for communication at all, which could be employed for purposes of nominalistic semantical analysis.

For simplicity, let us suppose that we wish our inscriptions to be recognizable as instances of words formed with a 2-symbol alphabet; it is known, indeed, that such a vocabulary suffices for the expression of propositions formulated in more complex symbolisms. Among the formal requirements for such a system of inscriptions are the following:

(i) There should be indicated a predicate which applies to all and only those things which are to serve as inscriptions.

(ii) Among inscriptions of this kind some are to be distinguished as 'simple-type-A', others as 'simple-type-B', and the remainder as 'compound'. It is desirable to have a 'large' supply (possibly limited by the possible finitude of all things) of each kind of inscription.

(iii) Given any compound inscription z, there should be determined in a unique way an inscription x, and a simple inscription (either of type-A or of type-B) y, so that we can interpret z as the inscription consisting of x 'followed by' z.

(iv) There should be a specification of when two inscriptions are *equiform* (or simply *alike*), in such a way that any two type-A inscriptions are alike, as are any two of type-B, while compound inscriptions z_1 and z_2 are alike if and only if x_1 and x_2 are alike and y_1 and y_2 are alike — where x_j and y_j are the unique inscriptions determined by z_j $(j = 1, 2)$ according to (iii) above.

(v) In so far as limitations imposed by the possible finitude of all things will permit, it is desirable that given any inscription x, one should be able to find an inscription x_A consisting of x (or an inscription which is equi-form with x) 'followed by' a type-A inscription, and an x_B consisting of x (or equi-form inscription) 'followed by' a type-B inscription.

To give an example of such a system, which is rather far removed from the traditional system of shaped lumps of matter arranged in roughly linear pattern, we may consider sums of persons — i.e., thing x such that everything y, which has as a part each person which is a part of x, has x itself as a part of it. Let us call a *p-inscription* any such sum of persons which has no two parts which are persons of the same age (born on the same day, say), and which has a part which is a person younger than any other person who is a part of it. (Of course this last clause would be unnecessary if we were certain of the finitude of mankind.)

As simple *p*-inscriptions of *type-A* we may take all male persons; those of *type-B* would be the other persons; and the *compound* *p*-inscriptions would be all those which are sums of two or more people.

Given any compound *p*-inscription z we can obtain a unique decomposition (of the kind described in (iii) above) by taking y to be the youngest person who is part of z and x to be the remainder of z (i.e., that part of z which has no part in common with y, such that z is the sum of y and it). Then we may consider z to be the *p*-inscription consisting of the *p*-inscription x 'followed by' the simple *p*-inscription y.

To define a suitable notion of equi-form inscriptions we can proceed in a manner similar to the Quine-Goodman definition of like formulas. We first need the notion of an *initial segment* of a given inscription z which we can simply take to be a part y of z which is an inscription such that every person who is a part of y is older than every person who is a part of z but not of y. Then we can call two inscriptions y_1 and y_2 *equally long* if something which has exactly one ounce of matter in common with each person who is part of y_1 weighs the same as something which has exactly one ounce in common with each person who is part of y_2. And finally we say that y_1 and y_2 are *equi-form* if they have the same length and if whenever x_1 and x_2 have the same length and are initial segments of y_1 and y_2, respectively, the youngest person of x_1 and the youngest person of x_2 have the same sex.[3]

Of course the question whether the proposed system of *p-inscriptions* is adequate does not admit a clear-cut answer because of the intrinsic ambiguity expressed in conditions (ii) and (v) above. Its adequacy *would* be clear if we knew that the generation of persons would continue without cease. Lacking this knowledge we might consider adopting the proposition as a working hypothess on the grounds that if events occur which show the

[3]While the Quine-Goodman analysis has served us adequately here, it does not seem to have served as well in their own work. In fact, Definition *D*10 in [2] does not convey the intended sense of one inscription being longer than another, owing to the fact that two parts of an inscription may be charatcers (i.e., have certain shapes), even though one is a part of the other. The difficulty can probably be avoided by amending *D*10 so as to speak of a character which is a *segment* of an inscription wherever Quine and Goodman speak of a character which is a *part* of an inscription. Of course the Quine-Goodman treatment of syntax may be objected to on the grounds that their primitive predicate *C* of concatenation (in terms of which *segment* is defined) in effect presupposes the concept of *inscription*, so that no nominalistic analysis of this concept is provided.

hypothesis to be incorrect they will doubtless cause us to lose interest in all further use of inscriptions!

It is interesting to observe that if we use either the Quine-Goodman interpretation of sentences of the form *there are more A's than B's* or the interpretation suggested above in terms of lists, we are unable to certify the falsity of such a sentence as *there are more things other than the earth than there are things*.

Despite the evident difficulties in providing a nominalistic interpretation for particular sentences such as have been discussed, it is desirable to investigate what possibilities there are for a nominalist to provide a systematic interpretation for all the sentences of some well-defined mathematical language of a kind adequate for most mathematical discourse. If, in fact, there is a system of infinitely many inscriptions, then this is indeed possible, while if there are only finitely many things, then it is certainly not — as I have pointed out elswehere.[4]

References

[1] Henkin, J. Some notes on nominalism. *Journal of Symbolic Logic*, Vol. 18 (1953), pp. 19–29.

[2] Goodman, N., and W. V. Quine. Steps toward a constructive nominalism. *Journal of Symbolic Logic*, Vol. 12 (1947), pp. 105–122.

[3] Quine, W. V. On universals. *Journal of Symbolic Logic*, Vol. 12 (1947), pp. 74–84.

[4] See [1].

AFTER THIRTY YEARS

A. HEYTING

University of Amsterdam, Amsterdam, The Netherlands

In September 1930 the editors of the journal *Erkenntnis* organized a symposium at Köningsberg, where representatives of logicism, formalism, and intuitionism met for the first time. Carnap, Von Neumann, and myself gave lectures about these three conceptions, respectively [1]. The participants in this symposium earnestly tried to understand each other's point of view; yet everyone was convinced that his point of view was the only true one, that no other had a right to the name of mathematics, and that its victory was certain in a near future.

The points of view were clear and precise. Carnap formulated the thesis of logicism as follows: The mathematical notions can be reduced to the logical notions by explicit definition; the mathematical theorems can be deduced from the logical axioms by purely logical deductions. For the foundation of logic he referred to Russell and Whitehead. In the discussion Hahn came back to this point; according to him the theorems of logic were tautologies; the members of a logical identity express the same fact in different ways. Von Neumann defended a more radical formalist point of view than that of Hilbert; he called mathematics a combinatory play with symbols. And in my opinion, at that time, the mathematical intuition left no fundamental problems open.

The problems yet to be solved were more of a technical than of a fundamental nature. This was least true for logicism, where Carnap stressed the difficulty of eliminating the axiom of reducibility without adopting Ramsey's platonism. In formalistic mathematics the consistency proofs were the main problem, in intuitionistic mathematics the actual development of an important part of mathematics. Each of the speakers wished to make constructive mathematics. For Carnap constructivity consisted in the explicit definition of mathematical notions from the basic logical concepts, as opposed to their introduction by means of axioms.

Let me now compare the situation of 1930 with that of today. The spirit of peaceful cooperation has gained the victory over that of ruthless contest. No direction of research has any longer the pretension to represent the only true mathematics. The philosophical importance of research in the foundations of mathematics consists at least partly in the isolation of formal, intuitive, logical, and platonistic elements in the structure of classical mathematics, and in the exact determination of their scope and their limitations. A new form of mathematics is born, in which we know at every moment whether we work on an intuitive basis or not, which part of the work is purely formal, and which platonistic assumptions we make. In this connection I recall a remark made by Hahn in the discussion, namely, that he considered intuitionism and formalism as important investigations inside mathematics, but not as foundations of mathematics. Kreisel made a similar remark in 1953 [2], saying that 'some people develop preferences for certain methods in mathematics and dislikes of others'. Hahn and Kreisel both seem to consider mathematics as something given beforehand, and research of foundations as a special subject inside it. In my opinion this is turning things upside down.

None of the conceptions of mathematics is today as clear-cut as it was in 1930. I shall be short about formalism and logicism. Formalism is the least vulnerable, but for metamathematical work it needs some form of intuitive mathematics. As to logicism, many axiomatic systems of logic and of set theory compete.

It has proved not to be intuitively clear what is intuitively clear in mathematics. It is even possible to construct a descending scale of grades of evidence. The highest grade is that of such assertions as $2 + 2 = 4$. $1002 + 2 = 1004$ belongs to a lower grade; we show this not by actual counting, but by a reasoning which shows that in general $(n + 2) + 2 = n + 4$. Such general statements about natural numbers belong to a next grade. They have already the character of an implication: 'If a natural number n is constructed, then we can effect the construction, expressed by $(n + 2) + 2 = n + 4$'. This level is formalized in the free-variable calculus. I shall not try to arrange the other levels in a linear order; it will suffice to mention some notions which by their introduction lower the grade of evidence.

(1) The notion of the order type ω, as it occurs in the definition of constructible ordinals.

(2) The notion of negation, which involves a hypothetical construction which is shown afterwards to be impossible.

(3) The theory of quantification. The interpretation of the quantifiers themselves is not problematical, but the use of quantified expressions in logical formulas is.

(4) The introduction of infinitely proceeding sequences (choice sequences, arbitrary, functions).

(5) The notion of a species, which suffers from the indefiniteness of the notion of a property. The natural numbers form a species; all species do not. It is doubtful whether all species of natural numbers form a species; therefore I prefer not to use this notion.

It is undeniable that the appreciation of constructivity has considerably fallen since 1930. On the other hand, the notion of constructivity has been made more precise by the creation of the theory of recursive functions. One of the difficulties which Brouwer met when he tried to create a constructive theory of the continuum was that the notion of a sequence of natural numbers determined by a law was completely unmanageable. If recursive functions had been invented before, he would perhaps not have formed the notion of a choice sequence, which, I think, would have been unlucky.

The notion of a recursive function, which had been invented in order to make that of a calculable function more precise, is interpreted by many mathematicians in such a way, that it loses every connection with calculability, because they interpret non-constructively the existential quantifier which occurs in the definition.

Of course, every finite set is primitive recursive. But is every subset of a finite set recursive? Who can calculate the Gödel number of the characteristic function of the set of all non-Fermat exponents less than 10^{10}, or of the set $P_n = \{x \mid x < n \,\&\, (Ey)T_1\,(x, x, y)\}$, where n is a given natural number? The answer depends upon the logic which is adopted. If recursiveness is interpreted non-constructively, then P_n constitutes a counter-example to the converse of Church's thesis. The good habit of distinguishing between results on recursive functions obtained by intuitionistic logic and those which for their proof need classical logic is abandoned in many recent papers and books [3]. I regret this, because thereby the connection of the theory with the notion of effective calculability is obscured.

The theory of recursive functions has made the notion of a calculable function more precise, but not that of a calculable number. However, it is asserted that P_n is recursive for every n. Evidently, its Gödel number is a function of n, say $\varphi(n)$; it seems natural to ask whether this function is recursive. From a constructive point of view a function is well-defined only if it is calculable. Analogously, in the theory of recursive functions, it is natural to consider a function as well-defined only if it is recursive. Then the assertion that $P_n(x)$ is recursive for every n means that $\varphi(n)$ is recursive.

An analogous difficulty occurs with respect to the definition of a recursive real number. There are several definitions which have been proved by many authors to be equivalent, though Brouwer [4] had proved in 1920 from the constructive point of view that they are not.

Let me consider two of these definitions.

I. The real number a is sequence-recursive (s-recursive) if it is the limit of a recursive, recursively convergent sequence of rational numbers; more precisely, if it is given by a sequence $\{a_n\}$ where $a_n = f(n)/2n$ and $(\forall e)$ $(|\, a_{m+p} - a_m| < 2^{-n})$ for $m = g(n)$, where f and g are recursive.

II. The real number a is decimal-recursive (d-recursive) if it is given by a decimal expansion in which the nth digit is a recursive function $h(n)$ of n.

Mostowski proved [5] that the corresponding definitions for recursive sequences of real numbers are not equivalent. The analogues to I and II are:

Ia. The sequence of real numbers $\{a_k\}$ is s-recursive, if there are recursive functions $f(k, n)$, $g(k, n)$, such that a_k is given by the sequence $\{f(k, n)2^{-n}\}$ and $(\forall p)(\,|\, a_{k,m+p} - a_{km}\,| < 2^{-n})$ for $m = g(k, n)$. (Mostowski's definition is different, but the argument applies to his definition as well.)

IIa. The sequence of real numbers $\{a_k\}$ is d-recursive if the nth digit in a decimal expansion of a_k is given by a recursive function $h(n, k)$.

I object that Ia and IIa are not analogues of I and II. The condition that $h(n, k)$ is recursive in both variables implies that its Gödel number as a function of n is a recursive function of k; this is a computability condition which is not postulated in II. Thus IIa is only analogous to II if the latter is interpreted constructively; but then II is not equivalent to I.

To put it otherwise, the equivalence of I and II means, among other things, that, given f and g, we can find h. A natural interpretation of this assertion is that h is recursive in f and g, Mostowski's counter-example shows that this is not the case.

Markov [6] takes an intermediate position. He rejects platonistic assumptions, but he considers that an algorithm π is applicable to a word P, if it is impossible that the process of application of π to P is infinite. This comes to the adjunction of the rule

$$(\forall x)(A \vee \neg A) \;\&\; \neg (\forall x) \neg A \rightarrow (\exists x) A$$

to intuitionistic logic. It would be interesting to know which of the results of his school are independent of this assumption.

As I said before, constructivity is much less appreciated now than it was thirty years ago. Yet effectiveness is a primitive notion, for a proof is only a proof if it is effectively given.

This is also my answer to Church's thesis. If we define the notion of a calculable function as meaning a recursive function, then the definition of the latter notion requires for its interpretation the notion of calculability. Therefore, it is circular to define recursiveness by calculability.

References

[1] Carnap, R. Die logizistische Grundlegung der Mathematik. *Erkenntnis*, Vol. 2 (1931), pp. 91–105. Heyting, A. Die intuitionistische Grundlegung der Mathematik. *Ibid.*, pp. 106–115. Von Neumann, J. Die formalistische Grundlegung der Mathematik. *Ibid.*, pp. 116–121.

[2] Kreisel, G. A variant to Hilbert's theory of the foundations of arithmetic. *British J. Phil. of Science*, Vol. 4 (1953), pp. 107–129; see p. 107.

[3] Davis, M. *Computability and Unsolvability*. New York–Toronto–London, 1958, for instance.

[4] Brouwer, L. E. J. Besitzt jede reelle Zahl eine Dezimalbruchentwicklung? *Proc. Akad. Wet. Amsterdam*, Vol. 23 (1920), pp. 955–965.

[5] Mostowski, A. On computable sequences. *Fundamenta Math.*, Vol. 44 (1956), pp. 37–51.

[6] Markov, A. A. O nepreryvnosti konstruktivnych funkciĭ. *Uspehi. matem. nauk* IX, no. 3 (61) (1954), pp. 226–230.

FOUNDATIONS OF INTUITIONISTIC LOGIC

G. KREISEL

University of Paris, Paris, France

1. Introduction

Intuitionistic mathematics, as developed by Brouwer and Heyting, has two aspects. Its *negative* aspect, which is well known, rejects the basic notions of set-theoretic (or classical) mathematics. The *positive* aspect is this: the notions of 'construction (constructive function)' and 'constructive proof (of equality between two constructions)' are regarded as sufficiently clear for at least a part of mathematics to be built up systematically from some evident assertions about these notions. This aspect has been largely disregarded, probably because of current preoccupation with formal and first-order aspects of mathematics. In particular, when questions of interpretation are ignored, the first-order systems of Heyting can be set out as subsystems of the corresponding classical systems, and so any formal derivation in one of the former systems is also one of the latter. Thus, though Heyting intended his formal rules to be justified in terms of an intuitionistic interpretation they can also be justified on the basis of classical interpretations. Little attention has been paid to Heyting's higher-order systems [6] or, e.g., to Kleene's fragment of intuitionistic analysis [11], although it is only here that specifically intuitionistic notions begin to come into their own: e.g., the consistency of these higher-order systems is evident on their intended meaning, but more or less elaborate reinterpretations like Gödel's [5] or recursive realizability [11] are needed to establish their formal consistency classically. (Since consistency is expressible arithmetically, we have here an arithmetic statement which is proved more shortly by means of the basic intuitionistic notions than by classical ones.)

Our main purpose here is to enlarge the stock of formal rules of proof which follow directly from the meaning of the basic intuitionistic notions but not from the principles of classical mathematics so far formulated.[1] The specific problem which we have chosen to lead us to these rules is also of independent interest: *to set up a formal system, called 'abstract theory of constructions' for the basic notions mentioned above, in terms of which the formal rules of Heyting's predicate calculus can be interpreted.*

In other words, we give a formal semantic foundation for intuitionistic formal systems in terms of the abstract theory of constructions. This is analogous to the semantic foundation for classical systems [18] in terms of

---

Partially supported by the Office of Ordnance Research, Contract DA-04-200-ORD-997.

[1] In particular, the consistency of the new formal rules cannot be proved easily in the usual classical systems, and, perhaps, not at all.

abstract set theory.[2] It should be noted that in both cases the value of the *formal* semantic foundation is primarily technical. Thus, it seems to me, the informal indications of Heyting [7, p. 98] are quite sufficient to convey the meaning of the intuitionistic logical constants with the possible exception of quantifiers over ips, considered in Sec. 8. But, on the technical side, semantic foundations (i) are useful for independence proofs, since they set out minimal properties of the notions needed in the interpretation, and (ii) lead naturally 'beyond' the formal system considered and therefore seemed suited to our main purpose.

For the mathematician, their most useful application is, perhaps, this. Given a formal system, say in the notation of predicate logic, a classical interpretation assigns a set D_0 for the range of the variables and subsets D_i of $D_0^{n_i}$ to the n_i-placed predicate symbols occurring in the axioms of the given system. A 'non-standard' model uses then sets D different from the sets D^* of the intended interpretation; e.g., with (fragments of) arithmetic one uses a set D_0 of 'non-archimedean' integers instead of the set D_0 of natural numbers, but to date no really usable examples of such D_0 are known. In the intuitionistic case we have species[3] $\mathfrak{D}_0$, $\mathfrak{D}_i$ corresponding to D_0, D_i; but, in addition, we have a class of proofs $\mathfrak{P}$ as, roughly speaking, an extra parameter. In the intended interpretation, $\mathfrak{P}^*$ consists of *all* constructive proofs, while in a 'non-standard' interpretation $\mathfrak{P}$ may be any subclass of $\mathfrak{P}^*$ which satisfies the axioms laid down in formal semantics. Thus one gets non-standard models (with an easily described $\mathfrak{P}$, $\mathfrak{P} \neq \mathfrak{P}^*$), where $\mathfrak{D} = \mathfrak{D}^*$. Another application concerns *generalized inductive definitions* (cf., e.g., [17]). On the Dedekind-Frege interpretation of these definitions (as the least class satisfying the defining conditions) these are highly impredicative, since they involve quantification over all subclasses of the class of objects considered. On the intuitionistic interpretation they are much less so, and moreover much 'smaller' species will satisfy a given inductive definition, for now an object α is required to belong to the species defined only if α can be *proved by the restricted means of* $\mathfrak{P}$ to satisfy the premise in the inductive definition considered.

From a more logical point of view the abstract theory of constructions provides a systematic notation for various completeness results on intuitionistic logic (cf. end of Sec. 6). Of course, as pointed out in [13], these are perfectly intelligible from evident properties of proof and construction, and the mere possibility of finding some systematic notation could not have been doubted by anyone who really read Heyting's informal exposition. But the actual details have not been previously written down. Another logically

---

[2]A semantic foundation of a formal system verifies that the formal theorems are valid on the intended interpretation of the symbolism, and a *formal* semantic foundation makes explicit just what properties of the notions which are used in the interpretation, are needed for this verification.

[3]The term is explained in Sec. 4.

interesting application of the work below is that it leads to a considerable simplification of [16].

It should be noted that all these applications are, scientifically speaking, independent of the negative aspect of intuitionistic mathematics. Psychologically it may well be that for many people intuitionistic mathematics becomes more interesting if they believe the alternatives to be ill-conceived.

2. Comparison with Set-Theoretic Foundations (of classical systems)

There is a striking parallelism between foundations based on set-theoretic notions on the one hand and intuitionistic ones on the other. We have a *negative* attitude of set-theoretically-minded logicians who regard the intuitionistic notions as intelligible only when formulated in some formal system.[4] Further, as shown by Gödel (again of course aside from interpretation), first-order classical systems can be formulated as subsystems of the corresponding intuitionistic systems.[5]

Note in passing that the parallelism has a disturbing side to it, since Frege's original formulation of abstract set theory, which corresponds to the abstract theory of constructions below, was inconsistent. Therefore I occasionally formulate below weakened versions of the 'natural' axioms such that a combinatorial consistency proof for the weak axioms can be given by means of hierarchies of formal systems.

3. Comparison with Finitist Foundations

It is clear that a semantic foundation cannot maximize the evidence for (or minimize the presuppositions of) given formal manipulations. The very fact that formal semantic foundations for a given system F need only *some* properties of the basic semantic notions shows that their *full* content is not needed to justify the formal rules of F (though it generally will be needed for the most obvious justification of F and for a well-motivated use of F). Further, the evidence of F is not increased by an explicit formulation of the restricted versions[6] of the semantic notions which satisfy the abstract theory, if, at the same time, one insists on defining these restrictions in terms of the basic semantic notions. Thus, if one is interested in evidence, one is forced to formulate a problem of foundations in terms of a group of notions introduced independently of and (if possible) in a more elementary manner

---

[4]Which they proceed to reinterpret classically, thereby depriving themselves of whatever mathematical fecundity the basic intuitionistic notions may have (except of course their having suggested the reinterpretation).

[5]Naturally, this applies to (first-order) systems where under the intended interpretation the variables range over first-order objects, e.g.. in arithmetic, but not in abstract set theory.

[6]I.e., restrictions of the notions of arbitrary construction and constructive proof in the intuitionistic case, and of the notion of set to a subclass of the collection of all sets in the classical case. 'Evidence (of)' is here used in the sense of the German 'Evidenz', and not of 'evidence (for)'.

than the basic semantic notions. This is evidently the line of reasoning which leads to *Hilbert's programme*.

In conception this does not conflict at all with a semantic foundation since, roughly speaking, Hilbert's programme begins where the semantic foundation leaves off. In practice, however, the remarkable success of Hilbert's programme (applied to first-order arithmetic) undermines an interest in intuitionism, and, all the more, its semantic foundations. For, granted that one is preoccupied with Heyting's first-order systems we have this: (i) as far as results and elegance of proof are concerned the classical rules are just as good and better, (ii) as far as evidence is concerned, finitist foundations make substantially fewer assumptions because they use only constructions applied to spatio-temporal objects, whereas in the intuitionistic case constructions are applied to abstract notions; this distinction was first formulated and stressed by Gödel [5]; and (iii) as far as a mathematically significant analysis of proofs [12] is concerned, Herbrand's theorem and other finitist interpretations have been generally more informative than translations into intuitionistic systems.[7]

The situation is changed when one tries to give a constructive analysis of second-order systems. Even if one's final aim is to avoid the problematic (highly abstract) general notions of construction and proof, as in the modified Hilbert programme [15], these notions are needed for a systematic approach. So to speak, intuitionism is to provide a *general theory of constructivity* which should allow a rational approach to specific problems of constructivity, just as a general theory of equations isolates the significant properties of equations which also help one with special cases. A very encouraging application of this kind is provided by Gödel [5], where, with the help of intuitionistic considerations, the consistency problem of classical arithmetic is broken down into several steps (cf. [15, para. 12]) and thus made much more transparent than, e.g., in [2].

4. The Intuitionistic Position (General Statement)

The *sense* of a mathematical assertion denoted by a linguistic object A is intuitionistically determined (or understood) if we have laid down what constructions constitute a *proof* of A, i.e., if we have a construction r_A such that, for any construction c, $r_A(c) = 0$ if c is a proof of A and $r_A(c) = 1$ if c is not a proof of A: the logical particles in this explanation are interpreted

---

[7]Strictly speaking, if one uses intuitionistic concepts, exceptions can be formulated. Let $\mathfrak{A}$ be a prenex formula $(x_1)(Ey_1)\ldots(x_n)(Ey_n)A(x_1, \ldots, x_n, y_1, \ldots, y_n)$, e.g., of arithmetic, $\mathfrak{A}^-$ its negative version where $\vee$ and (E) are eliminated, $\mathfrak{A}^*$ be the (usual) prenex form of $\neg\mathfrak{A}$, namely, $(Ex_1)(y_1)\ldots(Ex_n)(y_n)\neg A(x_1,\ldots x_n, y_1,\ldots, y_n)$, $\mathfrak{A}^{**}$ the (second-order) prenex form of $\neg\mathfrak{A}^*$. Then intuitionistically, $\mathfrak{A}\rightarrow\neg\neg\mathfrak{A}\rightarrow\mathfrak{A}^-\rightarrow\neg\neg\mathfrak{A}^{**}\rightarrow\neg\mathfrak{A}^*$ but, in general, not conversely. For a classically provable $\mathfrak{A}$, the so-called no-counter-example interpretation yields $\mathfrak{A}^{**}$ (with explicit statement of the functionals involved), while Heyting's arithmetic yields $\mathfrak{A}^-$. But this improvement is not intelligible and certainly not significant unless the intuitionistic notions are adopted for other reasons.

truth functionally, since we are adopting the basic intuitionistic idealization that we can recognize a proof when we see one, and so r_A is decidable. (Note that this applies to *proof*, not *provability*). A *species* of n-tuples of constructions $a_1, \cdots, a_n$ is determined by a construction s where $s(c, a_1, \cdots, a_n) = 0$ if c is a proof that $\langle a_1, \cdots, a_n \rangle$ belong to the species, $s(c, a_1, \cdots, a_n) = 1$ otherwise. A construction c is to be thought of as the object constructed when c is of first order (function of zero arguments), and as a method of construction when c is of higher order. However, we do not make explicit type distinctions following, e.g., Heyting's practice in introducing the logical constants [7, p. 98].

Consider then a formula A of the predicate calculus whose relation symbols are $R_i(x_1, \cdots, x_{n_i})$, $1 \leqq i \leqq k$, where we use variables x in the formal system of Heyting and $a, b, c \cdots$ in the abstract theory of constructions. Suppose we are given 'interpretations' for the R_i, namely, species of n_i-tuples determined by $s_i(c, a_1, \cdots, a_{n_i})$. As Heyting indicated, one then obtains proof conditions for A in terms of s_i. In particular, if A is BoC, where o denotes a logical connective and r_B, r_C determine the senses of B and C, then we obtain r_A from r_B and r_C. In the case of quantifiers it is clear that the idea of an *infinite* range must be regarded as a *façon de parler* (about proof conditions), because intuitionistic mathematics does not recognize infinite extensions. Generally, one must be careful not to take over too mechanically the syntactic formation rules from classical calculi, since syntactic rules are motivated by considerations about the *sense* attached to linguistic objects, and these senses are different in classical and intuitionistic cases.

While the notion of 'proof of a formula A' is defined, the notion 'c is a proof of the extensional equality of the constructions a and b' is taken as primitive in our formulation below, and all assertions are reduced to this special form (for motivation, cf. the Remark on p. 206). In the formal system, $a = b$ is interpreted as essentially intensional[8] equality between a and b; $\pi(c, a, b) = 0$ as 'the construction c is a proof of the equality of a and b', where all three variables a, b, c are permitted to take arbitrary constructions as values.[9]

5. Abstract Theory of Constructions

We give a simultaneous description of *terms*, *formulae*, *axioms*, and *rules of inference*. We indicate the intended meaning of the terms and leave it to

[8] The precise content is made explicit in the axioms below; e.g., if two definitions are convertible into one another in the very elementary manner considered below, the constructions so defined are considered equal, e.g., pair formation and inverses.

[9] This corresponds to the 'mixing' of mathematics and metamathematics stressed in the informal writings of intuitionists. It is to be distinguished from the interplay of protologic and formal rules in operative logic, because, in contrast to the latter, we consider proofs as constructions on constructions and not merely on symbolic expressions. Naturally, except in very elementary first-order contexts, different assertions hold for the intuitionistic and operative notions of construction.

the reader to verify that the axioms and rules hold for this meaning. When comparing the system with, e.g., abstract set theory, one finds that we have more *constant* terms because we do not have quantifiers. Note that the starred rules raise consistency questions.

TERMS. 0,1 (*two distinct first-order objects*); f, g, h. . . . (*distinct variables for constructions*): If a, b, c *are terms, then so are* $*a(b, c, \cdots)$ (*the result of applying the construction represented by* a *to* b, c, $\cdots$ *if this makes sense, i.e., if the number and types of the arguments fit, otherwise it is* a *itself*).

The corresponding unstarred rule permits such formation with variable a only in the context $\pi[c, a(b, c, \cdots), a_1(b_1, c_1, \cdots)]$.

$*\lambda_f\, a$ where f is a variable not bound in a. The corresponding unstarred rule requires that a actually contain f and adds the extra constants 0^1, 0^2, $0^3, \cdots$ with $0^1(a) = 0$, $0^2(a, b) = 0$, $0^3(a, b, c) = 0, \cdots$. Further, only *two-valued* a, introduced below, are permitted.

$d(a, b)$ (the pair of constructions a and b)

$d_1(a)$ (the first element of a if a is a pair, otherwise, e.g., a)

$d_2(a)$ (the second element of a)

$n(a)$ (generalization of truth functional negation, i.e., a construction on a, which, applied to $a = 0$ and $a = 1$, has the value $1-a$)

$k(a, b)$ (generalization of truth functional conjunction)

Abbreviation: $i(a, b)$ for $n\{k[a, n(b)]\}$ (hence generalization of truth functional implication);

$\pi(a, b, c)$ ($= 0 : a$ is a proof that b and c are extensionally equal);

$r_i(c)$, $s_i(c, a_1, \cdots, a_{n_i})$ (constructions determining particular assertions and particular species).

The following terms are not needed in the introduction of logical constants, but only in the proofs that they satisfy Heyting's formal rules.

$a * b$ (concatenation)

$a \circ b$ (particularization: if $\pi[a, \lambda_f c_1(f), \lambda_f c_2(f)] = 0$, then $\pi[a \circ b, c_1(b), c_2(b)] = 0$).

$\pi_0(a, b)$ ('verifiability' of π: if a proves $b = 0$, then $\pi_0(a, b)$ proves $\pi(a, b, 0) = 0$).

$\pi_1(a, b)$ ('contractibility' of π: if a proves $\pi(b, c, 0) = 0$, then $\pi_1(a, b)$ proves $c = 0$).

$r^i(a)$. ('verifiability' of r_i: if $r_i(a) = 0$, then $\pi[r^i(a), r_i(a), 0] = 0$).

$r^{(i)}(a, b)$ ('contractibility' of r_i: if a proves $r_i(b) = 0$, then $r_i[r^{(i)}(a,b)] = 0$).

For any sequence $\mathfrak{p}$ of equations between terms, $\pi_{\mathfrak{p}}$ is a term (if $\mathfrak{p}$ is a formal derivation in our system of $a(f_1, \cdots, f_k) = 0$, then $\pi_{\mathfrak{p}}$ represents an — intuitive — proof of the extensional equality of $\lambda_{f_1,\ldots,f_k} a(f_1, \cdots, f_k)$ and $\lambda_{f_1,\ldots,f_k} 0$).

TWO-VALUED TERMS. 0, 1; *for arbitrary* a, b, c, $r_i(a)$, $s_i(c, a_1, \ldots, a_{n_i})$, $0^1(a)$, $0^2(a, b)$, $\cdots$, $\pi(a, b, c)$; *for two-valued* a, b, $n(a)$, $k(a, b)$ (*two-valuedness expresses decidability*).

Notation: If a and b are two-valued, we write $\sim a$ for $n(a)$, a & b for $k(a, b)$, $a \supset b$ for $i(a, b)$ and $a \cup b$ for $n\{k[n(a), n(b)]\}$.

FORMULAE. *If* a *and* b *are terms,* $a = b$ *is a formula.*
($=$ denotes intensional equality at higher types, extensional equality at lowest type.)

AXIOMS. $[\lambda_f a(f)](b) = a(b)$,
$n(0) = 1, n(1) = 0, n[n(a)] = a$,
$k(0, a) = a, k(1, a) = 1, k(a, b) = k(b, a)$,
$k(\lambda_f a, \lambda_f b) = \lambda_f k(a, b), n(\lambda_f a) = \lambda_f n(a)$,
$d_1[d(a, b)] = a, d_2[d(a, b)] = b, d_1(\lambda_f a) = \lambda_f d_1(a), d_2(\lambda_f a) = \lambda_f d_2(a)$,
$d(\lambda_f a, \lambda_f b) = \lambda_f d(a, b)$.

If $I(A_1, \cdots, A_k)$ *is an identity of the classical propositional calculus* (*in the notation* $\sim$ *and* &) *and* $a_1, \cdots, a_k$ *are two-valued terms,*
$I(a_1, \cdots, a_k) = 0$ *is an axiom.*
$\{\pi(a, b, 0) \supset \pi[\pi_0(a, b), \pi(a, b, 0), 0]\} = 0$,
$\{\pi[a, \pi(b, c, 0), 0] \supset \pi[\pi_1(a, b), c, 0]\} = 0$.

(The corresponding starred rule is $*i[\pi(a, b, 0), b] = 0$, which is obvious on the intended interpretation, but troublesome for the consistency proof. The unstarred rule suffices for the semantic foundation of Heyting's predicate logic.)

$\{r_i(a) \supset \pi[r^i(a), r_i(a), 0]\} = 0$,
$\{\pi[a, r_i(b), 0] \supset r_i[r^{(i)}(a, b)]\} = 0$,
$[\{\pi(a, b, 0)$ & $\pi[a_1, i(b, c), d]\} \supset \pi(a * a_1, c, d)] = 0$,
$\{\pi[a, \lambda_f c(f), d] \supset \pi[a \circ b, c(b), d(b)]\} = 0$.

RULES OF INFERENCE. $a = a$,

$$\frac{a = b}{b = a}, \qquad \frac{a = b, b = c}{a = c}, \qquad \frac{a = b}{a(c) = b(c)}, \qquad \frac{a = b}{c(a) = c(b)}.$$

(The unstarred version of this rule is applied, when c is a π-term only to $\pi(a, a_1, b_1)$, not to $\pi(a_1, a, b_1)$ nor to $\pi(a_1, b_1, a)$. Note that the starred rule is strong; e.g., applied to $\pi(a_1, a, b_1)$, it means that even if the constructions a and b are only convertible into each other, the same construction a_1 proves the equality of a and b_1 and of b and b_1. This would of course not hold if *proof* were regarded in the syntactic sense).

Finally, if a does not contain f and if $\mathfrak{p}$ is a formal derivation of $[a \supset b(f_1, \cdots, f_k)] = 0$, then

$$\pi\{\pi\mathfrak{p}, i[a, \lambda_{f_1,\ldots,f_k} b(f_1, \cdots, f_k)], \lambda_{f_1,\ldots,f_k} 0\} = 0$$

is an axiom.

REMARK. The rules above should be compared with Gödel's axioms and rules [3]. However, as noted already in [16], it is not particularly reasonable to apply truth functional connectives to provability statements. In fact, if $BA \to A$ and other properties of informal provability are assumed, even the consistency of the classical rules is not obvious, since it is not apparent (i) classically that the notion of provability has a well-defined extension, (ii) intuitionistically that it is decidable.

6. Introduction of Logical Constants

With every formula $A(x_1, \cdots, x_k)$ of predicate logic whose free variables are $x_1, \cdots, x_k$ and whose relation symbols are R_i we associate a term $r_A(c, a_1, \cdots, a_k)$ of Sec. 5 above with the following intended meaning: c proves that $a_1, \cdots, a_k$ satisfy $A(x_1, \cdots, x_k)$ if and only if $r_A(c, a_1, \cdots, a_k) = 0$. To avoid excessive subscript we write for r_A

$$\Pi(c, a_1, \cdots, a_k; \ulcorner A(x_1, \cdots, x_k)\urcorner).$$

Also, we generally suppress free variables.

To distinguish (formal) objects of the predicate calculus from those of our system above, we use $\wedge$, $\vee$, $\rightarrow$, $\neg$ for the non-truth functional connectives.

$$\Pi(c, a_1, \cdots, a_{n_i}; \ulcorner R_i(x_1, \cdots, x_{n_i})\urcorner) \text{ is } s_i(c; a_1, \cdots, a_{n_i}).$$

Below we write c_1 for $d_1(c)$ and c_2 for $d_2(c)$.

$$\Pi(c; \ulcorner A \wedge B\urcorner) \text{ is } \Pi(c_1; \ulcorner A\urcorner) \,\&\, \Pi(c_2; \ulcorner B\urcorner),$$

where here and below the use of truth functional connectives is permitted since Π is a two-valued term (by induction).

$$\Pi(c; \ulcorner A \vee B\urcorner) \text{ is } \Pi(c; \ulcorner A\urcorner) \cup \Pi(c; \ulcorner B\urcorner),$$
$$\Pi(c; \ulcorner A \to B\urcorner) \text{ is } \pi\{c_1, \lambda_f \Pi(f; \ulcorner A\urcorner) \supset \Pi[c_2(f); \ulcorner B\urcorner], \lambda_f 0\},$$
$$\Pi(c; \ulcorner \neg A\urcorner) \text{ is } \pi\{c_1, \lambda_f \Pi(f, \ulcorner A\urcorner) \supset \pi[c_2(f), 1, 0], \lambda_f 0\},$$
$$\Pi(c; \ulcorner (\mathrm{Ex}) A(x)\urcorner) \text{ is } \Pi(c_1, c_2; \ulcorner A(x)\urcorner),$$
$$\Pi(c; \ulcorner (x) A(x)\urcorner) \text{ is } \pi\{c_1, \lambda_f \Pi[c_2(f), f; \ulcorner A(x)\urcorner], \lambda_f 0\}.$$

THEOREM. *For every formally derivable A of Heyting's predicate calculus HPC we obtain a term p_A such that $\Pi(p_A; \ulcorner A\urcorner) = 0$ is formally provable in our abstract theory of constructions above.*

COROLLARY. The theorem holds also if the quantifiers in A are relativized to given species of constructions (expressed by A_R), since if $\vdash_{HPC} A$, then also $\vdash_{HPC} A_R$.

For the proof, it is best to use Kleene's system $G3$ (and not e.g., Heyting's axiomatization in [7]). Let $\vdash$ mean provable in the abstract theory of constructions. One establishes, by induction with respect to the length of derivations in $G3$, that if $\vdash_{G3} \Gamma \to A$ and Γ consists of $C_1, C_2 \cdots C_r$, and $x_1, \cdots, x_k$ is a complete list of free variables occurring in Γ and A, then there is a term

$p(g; f_1, \cdots, f_k)$ such that

$$\{\Pi(g, f_1, \cdots, f_k; \ulcorner C_1 \wedge \cdots \wedge C_r \urcorner) \supset \Pi[p(g; f_1, \cdots, f_k), f_1, \cdots, f_k; \ulcorner A \urcorner]\} = 0$$

with the free variables $g, f_1, \cdots, f_k$.

One uses the following facts about our system above.

LEMMA 1. *For every formula A (of the predicate calculus) there is a term $X_A^{(c)}$ such that*

$$\{\Pi(c; \ulcorner A \urcorner) \supset \pi[\chi_A(c), \Pi(c; \ulcorner A \urcorner), 0]\} = 0.$$

(Verifiability of the Π-relation.)

LEMMA 2. *For every formula A there is a term $\psi_A(c, d)$ such that*

$$\{\pi[c, \Pi(d; \ulcorner A \urcorner), 0] \supset \Pi[\psi_A(c, d); \ulcorner A \urcorner]\} = 0.$$

(Contractibility of the Π-relation.)

LEMMA 3. *For every formula A there is a term $\tau_A(c)$ such that*

$$\{\pi(c, 1, 0) \supset \Pi[\tau_A(c); \ulcorner A \urcorner]\} = 0.$$

One uses the following derived rules of the abstract theory of constructions:

$$\frac{n(a) = 0}{a = 1}, \qquad \frac{n(a) = 1}{a = 0}, \qquad i(1, a) = 0, \qquad \frac{a = 0,\ i(a, b) = 0}{b = 0}.$$

REMARK. It is now clear why the relation $\pi(c, a, b) = 0$ is fundamental, and not e.g., $\Pi(c; \ulcorner A \urcorner) = 0$. For, starting with the latter for unanalyzed formulae A_i, $\Pi(c; \ulcorner A \urcorner)$ for composite A is defined from $\Pi(c; \ulcorner A_i \urcorner)$ by means of $\pi(c, a, b)$, but not conversely.

Relation to informal intuitionistic observations. (i) In our interpretation of the connective $\rightarrow$, $c_2(f)$ is totally defined. In contrast, Heyting [8, p. 334] insists on the need for partially defined functions. This need is greatly reduced by explicit use of parameters over proofs, as can be illustrated from the theory of recursively enumerable sets. Let $S = \{n: (\exists x)A(n, x)\}$, $T = \{n: (\exists x)B(n, x)\}$ A and B primitive recursive. For certain S and T, there are partially, but not potentially, recursive p such that $n \in S \rightarrow p(n) \in T$, illustrating a 'need' for partial functions. But if we regard a number m for which $A(n, m)$ holds as a 'proof' of $n \in S$, we eliminate this need in the following sense: there are recursive (and often primitive recursive) $p_1(n, m)$, $p_2(n, m)$ such that $A(n, m) \rightarrow p_1(n, m) \in T$ and, further, $A(n, m) \supset B[p_1(n, m), p_2(n, m)]$. Presumably, partial functions would be needed, if $\pi(c, a, b)$ is not assumed to be decidable, but only be 'verifiable' when it holds. In this case, the meaning of $\rightarrow$ could not be explained in terms of π and our generalizations of the truth functions, but only by having a (positive) logic in the abstract theory of constructions itself ('impredicativity of implication').

(ii) The Theorem above can be reformulated so as to express more directly that A is valid, i.e., that for all species R_i there is a 'proof' of A_R. (The extension to all species R_0 as domain of individuals [13] follows then from the corollary to the Theorem.)

We have to find a term $\chi(c; s_1, \cdots, s_k)$ with the following property: if c proves that s_i *define species*, then $\Pi[\chi(c), \ulcorner A \urcorner]$, where now the s_i are treated as arbitrary constructions. The condition of 'defining a species', i.e., two-valuedness, is not assumed as an axiom for s_i, but formulated in the premise: c_1 proves the equality of $\lambda_{g, f_1, \ldots, f_{n_i}} 0$ and $\lambda_{g, f_1, \ldots, f_{n_i}} \{\pi[c_2(g, f_1, \cdots, f_{n_i}), s_i(g, f_1, \cdots, f_{n_i}), 0] \cup \pi[c_2(g, f_1, \cdots, f_{n_i}), s_i(g, f_1, \cdots, f_{n_i}), 1]$. Thus we have here a (limited) possibility of *quantifying over all species.*

7. Consistency

A finitist consistency proof for the *unstarred* axioms and rules of our theory of constructions is obtained by an interpretation in quantifier-free formal systems. The main observation needed is the following

LEMMA. *Let F be a formal system which includes primitive recursive arithmetic and has a primitive recursive proof predicate (represented in F by a formula) $P(a, b)$ (for which the defining equations can be formally proved in F). Let $\ulcorner A(0^{(n)}) \urcorner$ denote the term $t(n)$ of F which is the canonical representation in F of the Gödel number of the formula obtained by replacing x in $A(x)$ by the nth numeral. Then there is a primitive recursive $p_1(a, b)$ such that:*

(1) $$\vdash_F P[a, \ulcorner P(0^{(b)}, 0^{(c)}) \urcorner] \supset P[p_1(a, b), c].$$

Observe first that, as in [9, pp. 312–324], there is a $q_1(b, c)$ such that

$$\vdash_F \sim P(b, c) \supset P[q_1(b, c), \ulcorner \sim P(0^{(b)}, 0^{(c)}) \urcorner].$$

So, if $\sim P(b, c)$, the proofs in F with numbers a and $q_1(b, c)$ joined together yield a contradiction, and so there is a $q_2(a, b, c)$ which is a proof in F of the formula with number c. *Define* $p_1(a, b) = b$ if $P(b, c)$, and $= q_2(a, b, c)$ if $\sim P(b, c)$ and $P[a, \ulcorner P(0^{(b)}, 0^{(c)}) \urcorner]$, c being determined by a. Hence the lemma.

The function p_1 in (1) provides what is needed to verify the axiom $\{\pi[a, \pi(b, c, 0), 0] \supset \pi[\pi_1(a, b), c, 0]\} = 0$ in the interpretation below. Since (1) is formally proved in F, one does not have to go outside F.[10] The interpretation of the unstarred theory is similar to the one sketched in [16].

---

[10] In particular, one does not need *hierarchies* of systems [16]. In contrast, the stronger axiom $(\pi[a, \pi(b, c, 0), 0] \supset \pi(b, c, 0)) = 0$ would require $P[a, \ulcorner P(0^{(b)}, 0^{(c)}) \urcorner] \supset P(b,c)$, which is not provable in (a consistent) F. Find numerals b_0 and c_0 for which $\sim P(b_0, c_0)$, when we should have $\sim P[a, \ulcorner P(0^{(b_0)}, 0^{(c_0)}) \urcorner]$, i.e., Con F. Similarly, as Gödel pointed out in [3] for his provability interpretation, there we should need:

$$(Ey)P[y, \ulcorner (Ez)P(z, 0^{(c)}) \urcorner] \supset (Ex)P(x, c);$$

take $c = \ulcorner 0 = 1 \urcorner$, and so $(Ey)P(y, \ulcorner \neg \text{Con } F \urcorner) \supset \neg \text{Con } F$, i.e., Con $F \supset \text{Con}(F \cup \{\text{Con } F\})$, contrary to the second incompleteness theorem. Note, however, that hierarchies of systems are needed when induction is included.

The principal difference concerns equations $\pi(a, b, 0) = 0$ when b has the form $\lambda_f b_1(f)$ or $f(b_1)$. Suppose a', $b_1'(f)$, b_1' are the interpretations of a, $b_1(f)$, b_1. We replace *free* variables g in b_1' (but not in a') by $0^{(g)}$; if b is $\lambda_f b_1(f)$, we replace $\pi(a, b, 0) = 0$ by $P[a', \ulcorner b_1'(f, 0^{(g)}) = 0\urcorner]$; and if b is $f(b_1)$, by $P\{a', s[\ulcorner b_1'(0^{(g)})\urcorner, f]\}$, where $s(m, n)$ denotes the Gödel number of the term obtained by replacing the free variable in the nth term by the term with Gödel number m. In short, although the abstract theory does not distinguish between objects and their names, the interpretation reintroduces such a distinction; in fact, the starred rules were excluded just to make this possible.

Independence Proofs. The interpretation sketched above is an example of a 'non-standard' model of the kind mentioned in the introduction, since we have verified that the constructions and proofs *represented* in the formal system F satisfy the (starred part of the) abstract theory. Note that for *finitist* consistency or independence proofs it is necessary to formulate a translation in the syntactic style above, while from an intuitionistic point of view it is more natural to think in terms of informal proofs *represented* by formal derivations in F.

8. Extensions

Undoubtedly the most important open problem is to give a *foundation for the introduction of species by means of* (generalized) *inductive definitions for which the corresponding principles of proof by induction can be derived.* It may be remarked that on the basis of Brouwer's analysis [1] the introduction of linguistic expressions involving variables over ips is reduced to the use of generalized inductive definitions.[11] For according to Brouwer [1], an expression $A(\alpha)$ is well-determined for ips α if and only if the corresponding decision function r_A is in the species C of constructions determined by the following inductive definition:

For an arbitrary numerical constant c and variable f over constructions of N^N, $\lambda_f c \in C$; if, for each n, $r_n \in C$, then so does $\lambda_f r_{f(0)}[\lambda n f(n+1)]$.[12]

Granted this, combinations of such $A(\alpha)$ by means of first-order predicate logic are easily seen to have decision functions which are definable inductively as in C above (with essential use of the π-function of course). General quantification over ips is still obscure.

---

[11]The misgivings about ips because they are 'incomplete' are out of place on the present approach because the sense of an assertion containing *any* variables, whether for ips or not, is determined by proof conditions and not by reference to a 'complete extension'. Note in passing that, for so-called *absolutely* free choice sequences, Theorem 4 of [14, p. 377] gives such conditions explicitly for $(\alpha)A(\alpha)$ when $A(\alpha)$ is of first order.

[12]Gödel has observed that on the *classical* interpretation of these two conditions, C consists of *all* those mappings from N^N to N which are continuous when N^N has the product topology. It was this fact that suggested the interpretation of [1] adopted in the text.

Remark. Even the case of complete induction over the natural numbers requires further investigation along at least two lines: First, by analogy to the Frege-Dedekind method, one may define the *species* of natural numbers $[Z(c; n) : c$ is a proof that n is a natural number$]$ either by (i) c_1 proves (where $\equiv$ denotes extensional equality) if a_1 proves $b(0) = 0$, and a_2 proves $\lambda_f i[b(f), b(f * 1)] \equiv \lambda_f\ 0$, then $c_2(a, b)$ proves $b(n) = 0$; or by (ii) c_1 proves (for any constructions a, a', b, b') if a_1' proves that b is a species, a_1 proves $b(a_2', 0) = 0$, a_2 proves $\lambda_{f,g} i[b(g, f), b\{b'(g, f), f * 1\}] \equiv \lambda_{f,g} 0$, then $c_{21}(a, b, a', b')$ proves $b[c_{22}(a, b, a', b'), n] = 0$. Here (i) corresponds to taking the natural numbers as the intersection of all *decidable* inductive sets, (ii) of *all* inductive sets. These definitions can be straightforwardly framed in the present theory. The justification of the *rule* of induction depends then on *definition by induction*

$$\rho(0) = a, \quad \rho(n * 1) = b[n, \rho(n)],$$

for natural numbers n; but the existence of such a construction ρ is really plausible only if the species of natural numbers is *decidable* (or: a set, in Brouwer's terminology). The second approach would require a modification of the notation of Sec. 5; one would wish to express the idea that a natural number n is obtained by repeated application (iteration) of the operation $*1$, beginning with 0, and that this sequence of operations can be followed out step by step to get a proof of $A(n)$; i.e., a p_n such that $\Pi(p_n, n; \ulcorner A(x) \urcorner) = 0$ when $\Pi(p_0, 0; \ulcorner A(x) \urcorner) = 0$ and

$$\pi\{p_1', \lambda_{gf} \Pi(g, f; \ulcorner A(x) \urcorner) \supset \Pi[p_2'(g, f), f * 1; \ulcorner A(x) \urcorner], \lambda_{gf} 0\} = 0$$

are given.

A more isolated, but interesting, open problem is to formulate on the basis of the present work the question: Are $\wedge$, $\vee$, $\rightarrow$, $\neg$ the only intuitionistic propositional connectives? More generally, *what is an intuitionistic propositional connective*? As is well known, for the classical case the corresponding question has been satisfactorily settled by the identification of propositional connectives with truth functions.

References

[1] Brouwer, L. E. J. Über Definitionsbereiche von Funktionen. *Mathematische Annalen*, Vol. 97 (1927), pp. 60–75.

[2] Gentzen, G. Die Widerspruchsfreiheit der reinen Zahlentheorie. *Mathematische Annalen*, Vol. 112 (1936), pp. 493–565.

[3] Gödel, K. Eine Interpretation des intuitionistischen Aussagenkalküls. *Ergebnisse eines mathematischen Kolloquiums*, Vol. 4 (1932), pp. 39–40.

[4] Gödel, K. Zur intuitionistischen Arithmetik und Zahlentheorie. *Ergebnisse eines mathematischen Kolloquiums*, Vol. 4 (1932), pp. 34–38.

[5] Gödel, K. Über eine bisher noch nicht benützte Erweiterung des finiten Standpunktes. *Dialectica*, Vol. 12 (1958), pp. 280–287.

[6] HEYTING, A. Die formalen Regeln der intuitionistischen Logik. *Sitzungsberichte der Preussischen Akademie der Wissenschaften, Physikalisch-Mathematische Klasse* (1930), pp. 158–169.
[7] HEYTING, A. *Intuitionism. An Introduction.* Amsterdam, North-Holland Pub. Co., 1956, viii+133 pp.
[8] HEYTING, A. Blick von der intuitionistischen Warte. *Dialectica*, Vol. 12 (1958) pp. 332–345.
[9] HILBERT, D., and BERNAYS. *Grundlagen der Mathematik*. Vol. 2, Berlin, Springer, 1939, XII+498 pp.
[10] KLEENE, S. C. *Introduction to metamathematics*. Princeton, Van Nostrand Co, 1950, vi+550 pp.
[11] KLEENE, S. C. Realizability, in *Constructivity in mathematics*, A. Heyting, ed., Amsterdam, North-Holland Pub. Co. 1959, viii+297 pp.
[12] KREISEL, G. Mathematical significance of consistency proofs. *Journal of Symbolic Logic*, Vol. 23 (1958), pp. 26–50.
[13] KREISEL, G. Elementary completeness properties of intuitionistic logic with a note on negations of prenex formulae. *Journal of Symbolic Logic*, Vol. 23 (1958) pp. 317-330. Erratum, *ibid.*, p. vi.
[14] KREISEL G. A remark on free choice sequences and the topological completeness proofs. *Journal of Symbolic Logic*, Vol. 23 (1958), pp. 369–388.
[15] KREISEL, G. Hilbert's programme. *Dialectica*, Vol. 12 (1958), pp. 346–372.
[16] KREISEL, G. Ordinal logics and the characterization of informal concepts of proof Pp. 289–299 in *Proceedings of the International Congress of Mathematicians*, August 14–21, 1958, J. A. Todd,ed., Cambridge, University Press, 1960, lxiv+573 pp.
[17] LORENZEN, P. Logical reflection and formalism. *Journal of Symbolic Logic*, Vol. 23 (1958), pp. 241–249.
[18] TARSKI, A. Der Wahrheitsbegriff in den formalisierten Sprachen. *Studia philosophica*, Vol. 1 (1936), pp. 261–405.

SECTION

IV

GENERAL PROBLEMS OF METHODOLOGY AND PHILOSOPHY OF SCIENCE

PRAXIOLOGICAL SENTENCES AND HOW THEY ARE PROVED

TADEUSZ KOTARBIŃSKI

Polish Academy of Sciences, Warsaw, Poland

By praxiology I mean the science of efficient action. Consequently, the tasks of praxiology are to formulate and to prove recommendations concerning what must be done: what it is advisable to do under definite circumstances in order to attain the intended results in the most efficient way. To put it more briefly, the task of praxiology is to investigate the conditions on which the maximization of efficiency depends. It is superfluous to add that the formulations given above cover both positive recommendations and warnings and the avoidance and elimination of the effects that disagree with our intentions as well as of all shortcomings of efficiency in action.

The task of the present paper is to bring out the specific nature and the various types of praxiological theorems and to describe the ways of proving them in an adequate manner. In our endeavour to set apart praxiological theorems we shall have, first of all, to distinguish the essential theses of that discipline, as opposed to its auxiliary and secondary sentences. Now these essential theses are certain practical directives, that is, directives recommending as appropriate means those which lead to definite results. Not every directive is practical in this sense. For instance, such directives as "Behave honourably" or "Avoid ugliness" are not practical, because they point to objectives, singled out on emotional grounds, but do not indicate the means with which to attain them. On the other hand, the instructions "If you want to protect your child against smallpox, subject him to vaccination" or "The lift is to be set in motion by pressing the button" are practical directives. To leave the sphere of concrete examples, we ask how to formulate the scheme of a simple practical directive. Now here is a sample: "Under circumstances A it is necessary (or it is advisable, or it suffices) to do B in order to cause C". When we say "it is necessary" we point to a condition which is indispensable under circumstances A, that is, one without which C cannot occur in those circumstances. When we say "it suffices" we point to a condition which is sufficient under circumstances A, such that when it is added to circumstances A, then C must occur. When we say "it is advisable" we point to an action which, when added to circumstances A, makes the occurrence of C more probable than it would be without that action.

All simple practical directives are praxiological sentences, since they are recommendations tending to increase the efficiency of actions. They may belong, however, not only to praxiology but also to the various practical abilities or disciplines. For instance, the directive "Under ordinary circumstances, a quantity of water must be heated if it is to boil" belongs to technology as well, and the directive "Under ordinary circumstances, it is sufficient to swallow a tablet of luminal in order to fall asleep" belongs to medicine as well. But any practical discipline is interested in definite directives from a different point of view than that of praxiology, so that a given practical directive occupies in a given practical discipline a different place and a different position in the hierarchy of theorems than it does in the set of praxiological theses. In order to explain that difference, one must examine the concepts of the theoretical and technical foundations of a given practical discipline and the concept of the type of action. Now by the theoretical foundation of a simple practical directive we mean the causal dependence of C on B (see the scheme of a simple technical directive as formulated above), when the type of action is the way of doing that B. In the first of the last two examples the theoretical foundation was the causal dependence of boiling on a previous rise in temperature, and in the second, the theoretical foundation was the causal dependence of sleep on the absorption of luminal by the human body. Yet in the individual cases we appeal in practical directives to causal dependences that are specific either to substances which do not exist in a natural state (e.g., soporific drugs as produced by the pharmaceutical industry), or to instruments with a definite structure and functioning. In the latter case, the directive recommending winding and setting an alarm clock so as to make it sound at a determined time may serve as an example. Such substances and instruments are called the technical base of a practical directive.

Now, advances in the various practical disciplines usually depend in an overwhelming measure either on the application of a theoretical foundation that has been unknown or unused so far, or else on changes in the technological base. On the other hand, the praxiologist is interested above all in the types of movements and directed efforts that are, or should be, resorted to by the agents. It is also on those movements and directed efforts that successes in practical disciplines depend to a certain degree. Thus, this is the point of common interest of the given practical discipline and of praxiology. The difference consists in the fact that what in the eyes of the praxiologist always is the essential point is for the representative of a given practical discipline of greater or lesser importance according to the degree to which advances in that discipline are determined by the mode of action, as opposed to changes in the theoretical foundation or in the technological base. And since the differences in the modes of action consist in the selection and combination of component actions, and the selection and combination of component actions of a complex action are nothing else than the organization of that (complex) action, the sphere of common interest of the various practical disciplines and of praxiology is the vast field of the organization of actions.

The notion of a "selection of actions" requires some explanation. The problem arises: what must be given if one wants to answer the question, "What actions fall within the scope of a given activity?" Are the component actions characterized sufficiently by the indication of who is to perform them, with what parts of his body, and what the movement is to be as regards its route, direction, and effort? I do not mean only *such* a characteristic of the various actions. That characteristic also includes the information on what the movement in question was directed to as its objective, and how the agent imagined the inner course of events which he was to start by his free impulse, and — in the case of mental actions — to what question the act of concentration of attention was directed. But then the doubt arises whether the descriptions of the selection of the component parts of a given action (i.e., praxiological sentences) should not include descriptions of changes in the theoretical foundation or in the technological bases intended or effected by that action. Let that doubt be removed by a distinction between the description of an action undertaken with the intention to bring about a certain fact or state of things by means of a definite course of events in the substance involved, and the description of that course of events. In order to describe an action which has been, or is to be, performed with a view of bringing about such and such A through the process B, one has to engage in the description of that process B only as far as to determine indirectly the parameters of action; namely, who is to act and by means of what instruments, what will be the direction and tension of a given individual movement, etc.

Can it be said then that praxiology is identical to the science of management? I think that one might say so, if work in the textbooks dealing with that discipline were understood as broadly as possible as all types of activity, and not only as professional work in industry, commerce and business and state administration. But it is not so, since these textbooks are usually confined to these types of work only, and it is very rarely and incidentally that they include theses with a more general validity. No concern is usually shown in them about a scale of universality of theorems and in particular about the so-called adequacy of theorems. Thus, it is the task of the praxiologists to write the opening or the concluding chapter of the theory of management, which would contain the most general instructions formulated as so-called adequate theorems.

To explain that concept more precisely a brief historical digression may prove useful. The basic idea comes from Aristotle, who demanded not only that a geometrical theorem should truly ascribe a given property to the individuals that fall under the general subject of the sentence in question, but that the class of those individuals should exhaust the class of all the individuals characterized by that property. Thus, for instance, an exposition of geometry should not contain the theorem that every equilateral triangle has the sum of its inner angles equal to two right angles, since all triangles have that property, and not only the equilateral ones. Consequently, only the theorem that every triangle has the sum of its inner angles equal to two right angles should be a geometrical theorem. Only then may we say the triangle as such has that property, or that that property results from the essence of the triangle. Many centuries later the idea was taken over, through the intermediary of Ramus, by Francis Bacon, who applied it to his own research problems in the paper *Valerius Terminus*, where he discussed the conditions that should be satisfied by a least-restricted rule of behaviour. If we have, for instance, to answer the question, how to impart to a body the property of whiteness, then the following recommendations would be too narrow: "boil" (since this holds probably only for the white of the egg), "beat into foam" (since this holds only for water), "grind into powder" (since this holds only for glass). Only the instruction recommending such a shaping of the surface of the body in question, that that surface should reflect certain light rays, will be adequate in our sense, since every body shaped in that manner and only a body shaped in that manner will have the property of whiteness. In recent times a similar point was raised by Petrażycki, from whom comes the term "adequate theory". Now that idea of Aristotle, Ramus, Bacon, and Petrażycki deserves application in praxiology, which would like to prove its practical directives by statements of causal relations, and the latter can probably be formulated only in adequate theses. For is it not true that if a given result can be attained by means A or means B or means C, then the factor which brings about that result must be something which is common to all those means and with which that result is specifically connected? Moreover, the search for adequate theorems complies with the demand of the economization of actions, since it is more economical to formulate in a single sentence a truth about a class of which a given property is a specific attribute, than to state the same thing in many sentences referring to subclasses of that class. If, e.g., the zoologist states that all cloven-footed Ungulata are empty-horned, in order not to repeat that separately about Oxen, Goats, Sheep, etc., then why should not the praxiologist recommend definite actions jointly with respect to all those cases of which the effectiveness of such actions is characteristic, instead of repeating the same recommendation with reference to each of such cases separately? This concludes the explanation of the concept and the utility of adequacy of a general thesis; it may only be added that the idea contained in the requirement of adequacy (or, practically, in the requirement of adequacy of the subject and the predicate of a general thesis) can in conformity with modern terminology be formulated as a requirement of finding a condition which would be necessary and sufficient at the same time.

The requirement of adequacy, as applied to the justification of practical directives, gives rise to the need to base a number of practical directives on a theoretical foundation in the form of relationships belonging to a theory of events. These relationships are common to the natural sciences and to social sciences. Here are some examples of such relationships. (1) Every object has its own developmental trend, specific to given conditions. Thus, e.g., a fragment of rock, moved about by the current of the stream, pushed from place to place, and worn by contact with the bed and with other stones, gradually acquires a smooth shape and becomes a boulder. Another fragment of rock, e.g., sandstone, exposed to rain, wind, and frost, is eroded gradually, finally to become a heap of crumbled pieces of stone. A seed in fertile ground shoots up and develops into a tree in conformity with the laws of Nature. A clock, when wound, works until the spring uncoils: the hands change their positions regularly, the clock strikes hours at specified moments, and finally ceases to move. A normal person remembers for a certain time the information he has received. A letter, when mailed, follows its normal route to the addressee (provided that the post is functioning). (2) The possibility of a given change precedes that change and comes to an end as soon as what has been possible has actually occurred. Before a blossom develops into a flower it rests in the phase of the possibility to become a flower, which possibility is lost when it has actually turned into a flower. Before a grenade explodes, there is the possibility of its explosion, which ceases when that explosion takes place. (3) A whole which is functioning in a purposive way and has a steering element decomposes when that element is destroyed. In this way a vertebrate dies when its brain is destroyed, a motor vehicle ceases to work when there is a defect in its motor, a tank is paralysed when its driver is killed, a team disbands when its leader perishes. Examples of such relationships, which might be called relationships belonging to the theory of events, might easily be multiplied. They belong to our ordinary experience and very often form the theoretical foundations of ordinary practical directives which are observed by all practical disciplines (along with the directives that are specific to any discipline concerned). Thus praxiology in its endeavour to find out most general directives, and in conformity with the requirements of adequacy of general theses, of necessity formulates theorems that have as their theoretical foundations the various relationships belonging to the theory of events; this is one of the principal differences between praxiology on the one hand and the practical discipline called the theory of management, as understood so far, on the other.

Examples of directives motivated in this manner can easily be combined with the examples of relationships belonging to the theory of events, as formulated above. Thus, (1) it suffices, under given conditions, to bring about an earlier developmental phase of an object in order to cause its later developmental phase, specific to its development trend under the given conditions. Very often the development trend consists just in duration without changes in a given respect. This leads to the directive of bringing about *faits accomplis*: if we want an object to have a certain property at a later date we must cause it to acquire that property at an earlier time, and must do it early enough, when it is still an easy thing to achieve, whereas at a later time it might require considerable effort. By acting in this way we must at the most defend what we already possess instead of struggling for possession, which usually is much more difficult. Applications: store the ice which was produced naturally in winter, instead of making ice in summer; occupy in advance the territory which is to be the object of a controversy; send your potential customer in advance the goods he may need, and when later on the question arises as to whom he is to buy those goods from, they will be already there, and your competitor will have to drive them out, which is more difficult than just to let the goods stay where they are. (2) When we are in a position to bring about a certain state of things, postpone as long as you can making use of your possibility. This is a useful maxim. Suppose that we have at our disposal the last cartridge. As long as we are able to shoot it, we can threaten to do so in various directions and check the approach of several attackers. Thus it is advisable in a battle to retain our possibility of shooting, not just because it defends us to a certain extent against attacks, but because it defends us simultaneously against attacks from various quarters. Once the cartridge is shot, it can in the very act of shooting frustrate the attack more effectively than the mere threat to shoot, but at the same time the shooting puts an end to our possibility of defence, not only against many attacks, but of defence at all. (3) If you want a whole which has a central controlling element to go on functioning purposively, protect above all that central element against destruction; and if you want that purposively functioning whole to collapse, destroy its controlling element: protect the brain, the motor, the leader; strike at the brain, the motor, the leader. Strike at the premises of the proof on which your opponent bases his argumentation.

So far we have remained within the sphere of simple practical directives. But even that limited sphere of examples shows which directives are most interesting to the praxiologist. First of all, they are those directives which lay stress on the choice and order of actions. Next, he must distinguish the more general directives, and above all those based on relationships belonging to the theory of events. But practical directives are not confined to simple ones alone. On the contrary, simple directives give rise to various compound directives, among which the praxiologist must especially single out comparative directives. It is only here that the evaluations of methods of action that bear not only on effectiveness but also on other aspects of efficiency have their say. For the methods of action may also differ in productivity, in the economy of the resources used up, the simplicity of operations, the required level of skill in manipulation, etc. It is important to compare the various possibilities in a certain respect, so that as a result of that comparison one may recommend this, and not that, mode of action. I think such comparative directives are most interesting in the eyes of the praxiologist. Here, e.g., is the recommendation to cumulate the substance worked on; i.e., instead of imparting a certain property to the individual objects separately, to impart it jointly to all of them in a single action. Thus, e.g., instead of rewriting a text on many sheets of paper, one types it in many copies with carbon paper. Instead of repeating the same thing to many persons separately, one prints the instruction or information in question or the recommendation of the optimum order of actions; i.e., perform the action A before the action B, and not vice versa, if A makes it easier to perform B, but B does not facilitate the performance of A.

The distinctions, in a practical directive between the theoretical foundations, the technical base, and the selection and order of actions correspond to the three directions of proving new directives: one notices a relation between events that has not been known so far and formulates a new directive based on the newly discovered relation and justified by that discovery; or one produces an instrument characterized by a new structure (often just by availing oneself of a relation between events so far not utilized for that purpose) and formulates a new directive based on that technical novelty and justified by the innovation in question; or the novelty and the justification of a new directive consist in a new choice and order of operations different from those resorted to thus far and making up a new type of action recommended by that new directive, which — as mentioned before — is for the praxiologist the most interesting case. Here is an example of an improvement of the first kind: in the composition of a medicine the element A is replaced by the element B. As a result a more effective drug is produced. No changes in the structure of instruments and in operations were necessary, and yet the directive recommending the use of B in the production of the medicine in question is better than the directive which recommended the use of A for the same purpose; the explanation of progress in this case consists in making use of a chemical relation other than that which was being utilized before. An example of an improvement of the second kind: a narrow pipe has been replaced by a wide one so that the container can be filled and emptied in a shorter time than before by means of the same manipulations in handling the taps and without resorting to any new mechanical relationships. An improvement of the third kind can be illustrated by the directive how to play a musical instrument, indicating what movements should be performed in what order to obtain in a most effective manner a definite sequence of sounds with the help of an instrument working according to a fixed relationship between events. One might also mention here the directives recommending the order and speed of operations to be performed by members of a team so that the whole should work smoothly, without breaks, and so that earlier operations should in an optimum way prepare later ones. It happens rarely that, following the replacement of an old method by a new one and the corresponding reformulation of the old directive involved, an improvement takes place only in one of the three fields: the theoretical foundations, the technical base, and the organization of operations. Usually changes occur in all these fields jointly: changes in instruments and utilization of new relationships between events are generally followed by a new organization of operations. It is so, for instance, when railway transport is replaced by air transport.

Let me now take a stand regarding critical remarks that question the distinctive nature of praxiology and the need of singling it out as a separate discipline; those criticisms in fact refer to all practical disciplines which are nothing else than sets of practical directives. It is said that the theses of those disciplines, namely, practical directives, are merely trivial transformations of theses belonging to other disciplines. Thus, whenever one justifies an improvement of a mode of action for a given purpose by reference to a new theoretical foundation, all progress consists in proving that under given circumstances, according to the newly discovered relationship, that is, after B_2 and not after B_1, the event C occurs either with a greater probability, or sooner, or with a smaller loss of certain values or properties, etc. To transform that thesis into a comparative directive it suffices to make a trivial reformulation of the recommendation: under given circumstances, C is achieved with a greater probability (or sooner, or with a smaller loss of certain values or properties) if B_2 is achieved first, than if B_1 is achieved first. In general, whenever one can state the relationship B causes C, the following recommendation is justified: if you want to achieve C, make B occur (if only C is suitable to be a goal of action and B is an event which can be brought about by a free impulse). *Mutatis mutandis*, the same can be said with reference to justifying directives for improvements based on changes in the technical base.

When replying to that objection, one has to admit that it is justified to a certain extent. In fact, the practical directives that are common to praxiology and to other practical disciplines would be reducible without any significant remainder to theoretical disciplines, if all the improvements recommended by those directives really had their sources in theoretical disciplines. Thus, e.g., the practical directives of technology would be reducible, without any significant remainder, to theorems of physics; the practical directives of medicine, to theorems of physiology; etc. In particular, the most general practical directives would be reducible, without any significant remainder, to theorems of the theory of events, and the latter theory (so far postulated rather than existing) would be expected to supplement practical directives, based on narrower relationships, with directives generalized to a maximum in conformity with the principle that adequate theses must be striven for. Yet, the invention and justification of improvements refer to something else, namely, to a choice and order of operations differing from that used so far.

But at this point the psychologists and the sociologists claim their rights by stating that if a certain choice and order of operations are more effective than some other choice and order of operations, the difference in effectiveness is often explained not by achievements in the knowledge of substances and materials concerned, but by making use of the regularities prevailing in the sphere of agents, that is, by making use of some new relationships, either psychological or sociological. The corresponding praxiological directives would thus be reducible, without any important remainder, to psychological or sociological theorems. Let us take into account, for instance, the following directive: if you want to acquire more skill in a given manipulation (typewriting, knitting, playing a musical instrument), repeat specified movements while observing the rising scale of difficulty and making necessary intervals. Is it not a trivial transformation of the theorem stating that one acquires manipulative skill by repeating the given operation according to the rising scale of difficulty and making necessary intervals? And this is not a directive, but a psychological law. By analogy, the following directive — increase the efficiency of a team by promoting the spirit of competition — is just a reformulation of the theorem, belonging to sociology, that people are more interested in the results of their work if they strive to prove their superior efficiency. I am willing to agree that on this point too the critics are right, but on a certain condition. I agree that in cases such as those now under consideration practical directives are reducible, without any important remainder, to psychological and sociological theorems, provided that psychology is not understood as the discipline interested solely in the mental aspect of human experiences, disregarding both human gestures and the evaluations of the effects of human pressures on the environment, and that sociology is not understood as the science concerned only with social institutions and mass phenomena. If psychology is understood as a discipline covering the study of human movements, directed to a goal, dynamic and motivated, taking into account the conditions under which the effectiveness of such movements increases, and if sociology is understood as a discipline investigating all relations between members of groups of human agents, taking into account all the relations between persons and the extra-personal environment, then in fact the directives recommending such and such choice and order of component operations of a given action must be considered just reformulations of psychological and sociological laws.

Consequently, if the practical disciplines, that is, such sets of practical recommendations (and praxiology is among them), have a claim to being treated separately as distinct disciplines, that claim is not based on the fact that the sentences belonging to those practical disciplines have the form of directives, since that form turns out to be a rather unimportant trait. The essential point is that the practical disciplines cannot remain satisfied with borrowing from strictly theoretical disciplines their theorems on relationships between events, but must themselves search for those relationships on which their own recommendations are to be based. They are looking, as has been mentioned above, for such C's which might be possible goals of actions and such B's which might be direct effects of free impulses, and at the same time events satisfying the following condition: B together with certain simultaneous events is a sufficient (or, sometimes, necessary) condition of a later C in view of some causal law of sequence of events. Practical disciplines have their own way of proving the relationships they discover and, indirectly, the directives they formulate.

Now, we know that one of the principal methods of proving practical directives used by the praxiologists is the study of actual practice. For if we prove or justify a comparative directive, we usually contrast the innovation we suggest with the practice observed so far. But we study actual practice in these cases too when we endeavour to describe the efficiency of a certain mode of behaviour either to recommend or to reject it regardless of any comparison with other possibilities. An individual case of such investigations consists in ascertaining what was being done in the past when a given activity was crowned with success or ended in failure. It can often be noticed that societies full of initiative often paradoxically lag behind societies of imitators in introducing latest improvements. It is so because the former have introduced certain improvements before the latter; these early pioneer solutions are functioning and have a well-established position later on when improvements on them have been found out. The imitators introduce new institutions or installations already having additional improvements, whereas the initiators are using them in their original form without those additional improvements partly because they succumb to a certain inertia of what already exists and partly because the difference between the original and the improved form is not big enough to justify costly modifications.

Another example of such a historical generalization is provided by the statement that compulsory situations — especially those of the "*aut-aut*" type, that is, situations with a single relatively advantageous way out, and among those in turn critical situations in which that way out may be reached only at the expense of a maximum effort — play a very important motivational role. This is not an occasion for a detailed analysis of the variations of compulsory situations, and I shall therefore confine myself to the explanation that a given agent is in a compulsory situation with respect to a certain need when he must make necessary efforts if that need is to be satisfied. Let it be added that the motivational force of compulsory situations increases according to the degree of importance of the need in question and reaches its maximum when the life or the health of the agent is at stake.

An extremely large number of historical generalizations which are praxiological in nature is provided by the field of changes due to increase either of the number of members of a group, or of resources, or of products, etc. In those cases we usually observe a growth of intermediate actions, that is, multiplication and complication of intervening links between the free impulses of the agents and the ultimate intended results of their actions, and also a process of differentiation of functions of the various elements of such growing groups. It suffices to compare the natural technique of self-transport by walking or swimming with the modern instrumentalized technique of mechanical transport, or direct communication by speech with the modern media of mass communication which practically disregard distance.

Sometimes a comparison of instances of successful practice leads to correct generalizations of what is possible, sufficient, or necessary to be done under given circumstances in order to have one's action improved, e.g., the statement that a team works more efficiently if its members are informed about the final goal of the team's work and are consulted in connection with that goal. Often we are only able to observe certain persevering tendencies of efficiency to increase or to fall after certain changes, although we are not able to realize what circumstances account for the fact. But even such generalizations are useful at least as partial justifications of experimental directives, whether affirmative or negative.

A researcher cannot fail to combine such historical generalizations with the typology of the forms of action currently resorted to, a typology which does not include assessment of actions from the point of view of their efficiency, but offers a general possibility of making use of typological observations for evaluation and formulation of directives. This is concerned with the various possible forms of action, which in turn inevitably leads to analytical observations on the structure of elementary action. By engaging in such observations, one enters the field of a general theory of action, which includes investigations on the essence of agent, efficient act, substance, material, apparatus, means, method, objective, product, intended effect, unintended effect, etc., and the relations between these things and events. This is the proper place to introduce differentiation between simple act, set of acts, compound act, positive co-operation, negative co-operation (struggle or conflict), the relations of assistance, obstruction, facilitation, making difficult, preparation, planning, execution, control, guidance and leadership, organization, etc. Research in that field is partly empirical and partly reflective and speculative, consisting in purely intellectual constructions. Empirical investigations may take the form of observation that the apparatus used includes devices which transfer (sometimes with a change in tension) the impulse of the agent onto substance, and also other devices which transfer (sometimes with a change) stimuli to the receptors of the agent, and also devices which restrict the freedom of movement of things taking part in the process (containers, compartments, etc.). And it would be interesting to verify and to explain the hypothesis, suggested by observation, that animals are able to produce only apparatus of the last-named type, whereas apparatus of the first two types are produced only by men. When observing the various cases of action we notice the obvious difference between analytical action, consisting in working from the whole to detail (e.g., when a sculptor works on a block of stone), and synthetical action, consisting in working from elements to the whole (e.g., when a mosaic-maker puts the stones together). When we study the various types of collective work we observe the existence of teams with varying degrees of dependence of their component parts, with varying degrees of differentiation of functions, etc.

On the other hand, the analysis of the structure of an individual act necessitates a, so to speak, lexicographical work, namely, the construction of concepts. One has to establish and fix the meanings of such terms as those enumerated above (agent, efficient act, substance, method, objective, product, etc.). The ideal solution would be to turn the theory of act, and praxiology as a whole, into a deductive system. This would include the requirement that the terms used in those disciplines must be established by axiomatizing the theory concerned, by adopting certain terms as primitive ones (undefined but determined only by their use in axioms), and, in defining the remaining terms, by referring them to primitive terms. Yet the investigations in the field now under discussion are still remote from such a degree of precision. I think we need now to determine provisionally the meanings of the various terms in order to avoid misunderstandings; and hence, we should refer to the intuitive meanings of these terms as used in ordinary language. Here is an example: "A in view of his free impulse B at the moment t is the agent of the later event C if and only if B is an indispensable element of a sufficient condition, which condition exists at the moment t, of the event C in the light of a causal law of sequence of events". This is an example of a "regulating" definition which establishes the meaning of the term "agent" in conformity with current usage, but makes that meaning clearer, and consequently determines the scope of use of that term with more precision. This also applies to such terms as "free impulse", "moment", "causal law". They are in turn subject to explanations such as that by a free impulse I mean either a pressure exercised on something in order to bring about some external effect or mental effort made with a purpose; by a moment I mean a time segment, e.g., the time segment during which an impulse takes place, etc. Thus, similar definitions belong to the set of praxiological sentences, which set obviously includes sentences conclusively derivable from the former and from knowledge acquired in other ways. For instance, the definition of the agent, as given above, combined with other unquestionable knowledge leads to the conclusion that a person may be the agent of a certain event because of the pressure he has exerted upon his environment at a previous moment, and further, that because of every free impulse a given person is the agent not only of what he intended to bring about (and sometimes precisely not of that), but also of many unintended events, etc.

The presentation of the ways of proving praxiological sentences includes a big gap if one forgets a practice which is very common in this field: one is fully justified in saying that an enormous number of practical directives and other kinds of praxiological sentences are well-known maxims which belong to the common practical wisdom of reasonable and active people. They are formulated as proverbs, maxims, sayings, etc. Everyday intuitive knowledge, often primitive, empirical, formulated in a manner which is far from any theoretical maturity, requires verification and elaboration about its concepts and formulations. The praxiologists have to extract scientific content from such semi-finished material. Here are some examples of such maxims: "*Festina lente*", "*Principiis obsta, sero medicina paratur*", "*Ha dei hemas mathontas poiein, tauta poiuntes manthanomen*", etc. *Homo faber* has the experience of an order of millions of years, and reflections on that experience, clad in a verbal form, go back to the beginnings of human speech. This has given rise to all sorts of analysis of the efficiency of actions. A lot of such observations, differing in the degree of precision, universal validity, and substantiation, is scattered all over the works of novelists, playwrights, essayists, moralists, pedagogues, publicists, economists, experts in business management, authors of textbooks of practical disciplines, historians and theoreticians of politics, law, culture, etc. One can find there bold generalizations concerning the theory of events, e.g., the thesis stating that a system which is in a state of mobile equilibrium when disturbed by an external force develops forces restoring its equilibrium (which suggests that people interested in the equilibrium of that system should restrict their external activity since the system itself tends to regain equilibrium). In other cases we meet with far-reaching recommendations, for instance, such that a maximum specialization is indicated wherever it is possible. Thus the praxiologists face the task of critically examining, fully utilizing, and adequately formulating and substantiating the whole store of such "half-baked" statements.

Finally, I could not imagine a treatise on the effectiveness of actions which would not include numerous metapraxiological statements concerning praxiological sentences. At present it is probably not possible to engage in praxiology without at the same time engaging in the philosophy of praxiology — without investigating the distinctiveness of its subject matter and tasks, the specific nature of its concepts and its characteristic tasks. The present analysis is just an endeavour of such philosophizing on the theory of efficient action.

Symposium on Models in the Empirical Sciences

MODELS IN THE EMPIRICAL SCIENCES

R. B. BRAITHWAITE

University of Cambridge, Cambridge, England

Any science which has passed beyond the interlinked stages of the classification of observable properties and relations, and of the establishment of empirically testable generalizations about these observable concepts, attempts to explain these generalizations by showing that they are logical consequences of more general hypotheses. A *scientific theory* is a deductive system consisting of certain *initial hypotheses* at the summit and empirically testable generalizations at the base. The deductive structure of a theory is shown explicitly by expressing the theory by means of a *formal axiomatic system* or *calculus* consisting of a sequence of sentences (or formulae) in which the initial hypotheses are represented by sentences called *axioms* and what are deduced from these hypotheses by sentences which are the *theorems* of the calculus. The calculus may also have axioms representing propositions, logical or mathematical, of the *basic logic* of the theory: such axioms will not concern us here. The rules of derivation of the calculus correspond to the deductive principles of the theory's basic logic. A theory expressed by a calculus will be called a *formalized theory*. The theory will be called a *semi-formalized theory* if (as is usually the case) it is expressed not by a whole calculus but by the parts of a calculus which provide the steps in the deductions which are not thought to be so obvious that they need not be explicitly stated.

In psychology and the social sciences the word 'model' is frequently used merely as a synonym for a formalized or semi-formalized theory. For example, Richard Stone's *Three Models of Economic Growth*, which he has presented in Section VIII of this Congress, are in fact three alternative theories for explaining the phenomena of economic growth expressed in mathematical form so that mathematical techniques can be used in the deductions. As another example, R. R. Bush and F. Mosteller's book expounding their statistical learning theory is entitled *Stochastic Models for Learning*. There are, I think, three reasons why social scientists tend to use the word 'model' to describe what is in fact a formalized or semi-formalized theory:

1. The theory may seem such a small one, comprising so few deductive steps or covering such a limited topic in the field, that the word 'theory' may seem too grand to apply to it.
2. Theories that are even semi-formalized are so rare in the social sciences (except in economics) that a special term may seem to be appropriate to emphasize that the deductive system of the theory is being, at least in part, explicitly presented.
3. The word 'model' may be used instead of 'theory' to indicate that the theory is only expected to hold as an approximation, or that employing it depends upon various simplifying assumptions. In particular, a system in which the hypotheses and the conclusions deduced from them are all thought only to hold *ceteris paribus* may be called a model to show ignorance of the conditions which would make this qualification unnecessary.

None of these seems to me a good reason for refusing to call a scientific deductive system a theory, even if it holds only for an 'isolated' field and is only a little theory. It would be better to call it a *theoruncula* or (affectionately) a *theorita*, using a Latin or a Spanish diminutive, than to call it a model. In any case, to use the word 'model' instead of 'theory' presents no problems specific to the notion of model.

These problems arise only when 'model' is used in a sense which distinguishes it from the theory for which it is a model. I take this sense to be that in which a *model for a theory* T is another theory M which corresponds to the theory T in respect of deductive structure. By *correspondence in deductive structure* between M and T is meant that there is a one-one correlation between the concepts of T and those of M which gives rise to a one-one correlation between the propositions of T and those of M which is such that if a proposition in T logically follows from a set of propositions in T, the correlate in M of the first proposition in T logically follows from the set of correlates in M of the propositions of the set in T.

Since the deductive structure of T is reflected in M, a calculus which expresses T can also be interpreted as expressing M: a theory and a model for it can both be expressed by the same calculus. Thus an alternative and equivalent explication of *model for a theory* can be given by saying that a model is another interpretation of the theory's calculus. Note that the interpretation need not consist of true propositions: it need not be what Alonzo Church calls a *sound* interpretation. The initial propositions of the model, which are correlated with the initial hypotheses of the theory, need not be true, or thought to be true; all that is required is that the rest of the model propositions must be logical consequences of the set of them. Scientists frequently use quite imaginary models: the nineteenth-century mechanical models for optical theory treated of fluids never found in heaven or earth. Mathematical logicians who use the word 'model' for an interpretation of a calculus restrict it to a sound interpretation, and frequently to a sound interpretation which employs logical concepts only. This is perfectly reasonable for the purposes for which they want the notion, but it is too restrictive for philosophy of science. And consequently the requirements of categoricalness, etc., which play such an important role in mathematical logicians' concern with models have little relevance to models in the scientists' sense.

Sometimes the working of an automatic computing machine is thought of as modelling a scientific theory. When the mode of operation of the computer is irrelevant to such a modelling, the computer is merely being used *qua* 'black box' to provide outputs interpreted as logical consequences of the inputs fed into it. Here, if the deductive apparatus of the theory is already incorporated in the working of the machine, the machine will in fact be operating the calculus representing the theory, the input being the axioms and the outputs the various theorems of the formal axiomatic system. So the working of the machine should be regarded as equivalent more properly to the calculus itself than to an interpretation of the calculus as a theory. Bush and Mosteller's 'stat-rat' is the device of using a computer capable of applying Monte Carlo methods and programming it (among other things) with the probability-parameters which their learning theory attributes to an imagined rat. The output is interpreted as propositions about the long-term or statistical behaviour of rats; but the stat-rat itself corresponds to the Bush-Mosteller formal axiomatic system rather than to the theory expressed by this system by which they would explain a rat's behaviour.

But when the mode of operation of the computer is part of its modelling function, the physical processes in the computer will be regarded not as providing the deductive steps in the scientific theory but as echoing, in temporal sequence, the succession of processes in the field which is the subject-matter of the theory. For example, when a (binary) digital computer is proposed for modelling the working of a brain, the switching operations of the computer are taken as corresponding to the 'firings' of synapses in the brain. Strictly speaking, the computer as a piece of hardware will be a model of a brain in the vulgar sense of, e.g., a clockwork model locomotive: what in my sense is a model for a theory of cerebral functioning will be the theory of the internal functioning of the computer, which will include propositions relating what happens in it at one time to what happens at a later time, corresponding to hypotheses about the temporal relationships of events in the brain.

Let us pass now to the most interesting question about models for scientific theories: why use models at all in scientific thinking?

If the non-logical concepts occurring in the initial hypotheses of the theory are all observable properties or relations, there is no reason whatever for thinking up a model for the theory except either to establish the theory's logical consistency, which finding a sound interpretation for its calculus will do, or for purely didactic purposes. Someone may find it easier to appreciate the deductive structure of the theory in an illustrative model, just as many of us find it helpful to think of spatial diagrams when considering the logical relationships of classes. But usually, and in all interesting cases, the initial hypotheses of the theory will contain concepts which are not purely logical but which are not themselves observable (call these *theoretical concepts*); examples are electrons, Schrödinger wave-functions, genes, ego-ideals. A fundamental problem for philosophy of science is how these theoretical concepts should be understood. One school of thought, represented most prominently by N. R. Campbell, holds that the only way to understand these concepts, and hence to understand the explanatory hypotheses of the scientific theory, is to represent the theory by a model whose deductive arrangement corresponds to that of the theory but in which all the concepts concerned are familiar concepts. (Campbell would also require that the propositions of the model should be, in fact, true propositions.)

Familiar concepts, but not necessarily observable properties or relations. What the modellists (as I shall call them) think necessary is that the correlates, in the model, of the theoretical concepts of the theory should be understood, and they may be understood as being theoretical concepts of a simpler theory which is already understood. Attempts to understand electromagnetic theory by constructing mechanical models for it did not depend upon supposing that all the mechanical concepts involved, e.g., kinetic energy, potential energy, action, were observable, but only that the theory of mechanics using these as theoretical concepts had been previously understood so that all its concepts were familiar. The modellist doctrine of scientific explanation is a stage-by-stage doctrine. Theory T_1 has to be understood by constructing a model for it, all of whose concepts are observable; theory T_2 can then be understood by constructing a model for it with the concepts of theory T_1, and so on.

But the modellist may say more than that understanding the model yields an understanding of the theory and of its theoretical concepts which is in some way fuller than that provided by an understanding based solely on the bare theory. He may say that a model is predictive in a way in which the bare theory is not, in that it yields new generalizations about observable properties which the theory itself does not provide. These new generalizations will be empirically testable, that is, they can be used for making new predictions; so the modelled theory will be a stronger theory than the theory in its bare form. I will discuss this thesis before passing to the more general question of understanding.

Let the observable properties concerned in the generalizations which the old theory was put forward to explain (the *old* generalizations) be A_1, $A_2 \cdots A_n$, and let B_1, $B_2 \cdots B_n$ be the familiar properties which are their correlates in the model. Let L_1, $L_2 \cdots L_m$ be the familiar properties which are correlates in the model of the theoretical concepts of the theory, i.e., the L's are the model-interpretations of the theoretical terms which occur in the axioms of the calculus representing the theory.

There are four ways in which consideration of the model may serve to yield new generalizations about observables in the theory.

1. Considering the initial propositions in the model may show that it is possible to deduce from them propositions concerned with, e.g., B_1, B_2, B_3 which do not correspond to any of the old generalizations occurring in the theory. Then passing from the model to the theory will enable one to assert that the corresponding generalizations about A_1, A_2, A_3 are consequences of the initial propositions of the theory. Since these generalizations are not among those upon which the theory was founded, they will be new generalizations and can be used to make predictions that would otherwise not have been made by the theory. These new generalizations will be concerned with properties which were concerned in the old generalizations. Call this *first-type predictive novelty.*

2. Considering the familiar properties L_1, $L_2 \ldots L_m$ occurring in the initial propositions of the model may show that there is a new familiar property B_{n+1} which is such that generalizations in which it occurs, together with one or more of the old properties B_1, $B_2 \ldots B_n$, follow from the initial propositions of the model, together with a new initial proposition relating B_{n+1} to $L_1, L_2, \ldots L_m$. Passing then from the model to the theory will suggest looking for an observable property A_{n+1}, which is the theory-correlate of the B_{n+1} in the model. If such a property can be found, the addition to the theory's initial hypotheses of one relating A_{n+1} to the theoretical concepts will enable new generalizations to be deduced relating A_{n+1} to some of A_1, $A_2 \ldots A_n$. This *second-type predictive novelty* will yield new generalizations about a new observable property.

3. Considering the familiar properties $L_1, L_2, \ldots L_m$ occurring in the initial propositions of the model may suggest propositions about some of these familiar properties which would, if added to the initial propositions in the model, enable new generalizations about, e.g., B_1, B_2, B_3 to be deduced in the model. Passing then from the model to the theory will suggest that if corresponding new initial hypotheses are added to the theory, the extended theory will yield new testable generalizations about A_1, A_2, A_m. As with the first type this *third-type predictive novelty* will yield new generalizations about properties which were concerned in the old generalizations.

4. So far there has been no extension to $L_1, L_2, \ldots L_m$ or to the corresponding theoretical concepts of the theory. But the model may suggest a new familiar property L_{m+1} which might enter in combination with some of $L_1, L_2, \ldots L_m$ into new initial propositions of the model from which new generalizations about the B's can be deduced. There will usually be no object in adding L_{m+1} unless there can also be added new familiar properties B_{n+1}, B_{n+2}, etc., which enter into the new generalizations. In this case, of course, more initial propositions will have to be added relating the new B's

to some or all of the *L*'s. Passing from the model to the theory will then suggest looking for observable properties A_{n+1}, A_{n+2}, etc., which are such that new generalizations relating them to some of $A_1, A_2, \ldots A_n$ can be deduced from the initial hypotheses of the theory with the addition of new hypotheses corresponding to the new initial propositions of the model which contain L_{n+1}. This *fourth-type predictive novelty* will yield new generalizations about new observable properties by extending the theory to incorporate hypotheses about new theoretical concepts.

The relations between these four types of predictive novelty can be summarized by saying that, in the first type there is no change in the initial hypotheses of the theory; in the second type the change is the addition of an extra hypothesis relating a new observable property to the theoretical concepts; in the third type the change is the addition of extra hypotheses relating together theoretical concepts of the theory; and in the fourth type there is the addition of extra hypotheses containing new theoretical concepts.

I have described these four types of predictive novelty as what might come out of consideration of a model. But how much, in fact, does the employment of a model assist in providing or suggesting any of these types of predictive novelty? For the first type not at all, since there is no addition to the axioms of the calculus which expresses both the model and the theory, and any proposition that can be deduced within the model can be deduced with equal ease within the theory itself without calling upon the model for assistance. And it is almost the same in the case of the second type. For here the only addition to the axioms of the calculus provided by the new initial proposition of the model is one to be interpreted in the theory as relating a new observable property to the theoretical concepts. The difficulty here is almost always that of discovering such an observable property and not in determining the initial hypothesis that would relate it, when found, to the theoretical concepts.

It is with regard to the third and fourth types of predictive novelty that a model may plausibly be claimed to be of genuine assistance. For here there are additions to the axioms of the calculus concerned with relationships between the theoretical terms, and in the fourth type also an addition to the number of the theoretical terms themselves. Since the model interprets the theoretical terms of the calculus as familiar concepts, there may well be propositions (true or false) relating these familiar concepts together (or relating them to new familiar concepts) which are not included in the model's initial propositions, but which thinking of the model immediately brings to mind. The model may then be said to *point* towards its extension in a way which thinking of the calculus in isolation would not do. This pointing will be most striking when the propositions of the model are known to be true (so that the model is known to be a sound interpretation of the calculus): for then there may well be other known relations between the familiar concepts of the model (or between other familiar concepts and those of the model) which point to corresponding relations between the theoretical concepts of the theory (or of an extended theory). In this case the pointing is frequently held to provide an argument — an argument by analogy — for inferring from the known features of the model to unknown features of the theory.[1] Indeed it is sometimes held that analogy provides a good reason for believing that *any* feature of the extended model will be reproduced in the correspondingly extended theory, until an empirically testable generalization, which is a consequence of supposing that the extended theory has this feature, is refuted by experience.

This claim cannot be allowed. Analogy can provide no more than suggestions of how the theory might be extended; and the history of science tells us that while some analogical suggestions have led to valuable extensions of the theory, others have led to dead ends.

The pointing of a model towards extensions of it can only provide suggestions for extensions of the theory (except in the case of first-type novelty, but here the extensions are as latent in the theory as in the model). Whether the theory will bear extensions in its initial hypotheses will have to be decided by testing against experience the testable generalizations deduced in the extended theory, and in this testing a model is of no use whatever. The thesis that a modelled theory has, *ipso facto*, greater predictive power than the bare theory cannot be sustained.

The modellist, however, will retort with a series of questions, which modulate into the crucial question of what it is to *understand* a theory. How can the theory as a whole be empirically tested unless its testable generalizations are known to follow from the initial hypotheses? How can this be known unless the initial hypotheses are understood? How can initial hypotheses concerned with theoretical concepts be understood unless we understand what these theoretical concepts are? And how can theoretical concepts be understood except by taking the theory to correspond with a model all of whose concepts are already familiar?

To answer these questions requires giving an adequate account of the functioning of theoretical concepts which makes no use whatever of models. Such an account (which I will call the *contextualist* account) has been given by many recent writers: Quine in his recent book[2] refers to works by Carnap, Einstein, Frank, Hempel and myself, and this list could be expanded. Briefly, the contextualists hold that the way in which theoretical concepts function in a scientific theory is given by an interpretation of the calculus expressing the theory which works from the bottom upwards. The final theorems of the calculus are interpreted as expressing empirically testable generalizations, the axioms of the calculus are interpreted as propositions from which these generalizations logically follow, and the theoretical terms occurring in the calculus are given a meaning implicitly by their context, i.e., by their place within the calculus. So an understanding of a theoretical

[1]See M. B. Hesse, *Forces and Fields* (1961), p. 27, on the 'surplus content' of models.
[2]W. V. Quine, *Word and Object* (1960), p. 16n.

concept in a scientific theory is an understanding of the role which the theoretical term representing it plays in the calculus expressing the theory, and the empirical nature of the theoretical concept is based upon the empirical interpretation of the final theorems of the calculus.

If such a contextualist account of the meaning of theoretical terms is adequate, thinking of a model for a theory is quite unnecessary for a full understanding of the theory. But we contextualists can easily explain why it is that most people find models so helpful. For the contextualist account makes explicit reference to the calculus expressing the theory; so a full understanding of a theoretical concept requires what Quine calls a "semantic ascent" from thinking of things to thinking of the symbolism or language which represents the things. In the case of explanation by a scientific theory, this requires considering the uninterpreted calculus, which is to express the theory *before* interpreting it to express the theory. Many people find the notion of an uninterpreted calculus difficult to digest. For them it is easier to think of a scientific deductive system by first thinking of a model for it, all of whose concepts are familiar, and then by formalizing (or semi-formalizing) the model by expressing it in a calculus (or part of a calculus). The calculus is thus always thought of as interpreted, the model being its original interpretation. However, to pass from the calculus expressing the model to the same calculus expressing the theory it is necessary first to 'disinterpret' it (to use Quine's felicitous neologism) by ignoring the interpretations of its non-logical terms as standing for familiar concepts, retaining only the interpretations of its logical features. The calculus thus disinterpreted empirically will then be re-interpreted (from the base upwards) to serve to express the scientific theory. The psychological advantage of proceeding through the two stages of disinterpretation and subsequent re-interpretation is that at no point need a completely uninterpreted calculus be considered.

Nevertheless the essential step, philosophically speaking, is the same for the modellist as for the contextualist — to interpret the calculus, from the base upwards, so that it expresses the theory. The modellist does this by re-interpreting an originally interpreted calculus which he has previously disinterpreted; the contextualist does it by interpreting an originally uninterpreted calculus. The modellist does not escape the semantic ascent: he dodges having to speak explicitly of a calculus by talking of model and theory having the same deductive structure, but to understand this presupposes a semantic ascent. So the modellist cannot justly claim that his account provides a deeper understanding of scientific explanation than that provided by the contextualist account, when the use of his model (apart from its psychological function in illustrating the theory) is to approach indirectly a difficulty which the contextualist attacks directly and clearsightedly by talking of his calculus. The philosopher of science, concerned with the problem of how it is that we understand a theory containing theoretical concepts, cannot avoid a semantic ascent.

ON THE STRUCTURAL FORM OF INTERDEPENDENT SYSTEMS

LEONID HURWICZ

University of Minnesota, Minneapolis, Minnesota, U.S.A.

1. Interdependent Systems

In certain fields, notably economics (but also, e.g., electronic network theory), we deal with a set (*configuration*) of objects (*components*) which are interdependent in their behavior.

For purposes of both theoretical analysis and empirical investigation of such situations, the phenomena are often described (in idealized form) by means of a system of simultaneous equations. If $x = (x_1, x_2, \cdots, x_n)$ is a state description of a configuration C whose components are $c_1, c_2, \cdots, c_m$, such a system would typically be of the form

$$(1) \qquad f_i(x_1, x_2, \cdots, x_n) = 0 \quad (i = 1, 2, \cdots, m)$$

where the function f_i depends on the properties of the ith component (but not on the properties of the other components); we shall find it convenient to refer to f_i as the *behavior pattern of the component* c_i.[1]

[In contexts involving the processes of statistical inferences one uses a variant of (1) in which the right-hand members have random variables (disturbances) instead of zeros, thus making the model probabilistic.]

To simplify notation, we sometimes write (1) as

$$(1') \qquad f_i(x) = 0 \quad (i = 1, 2, \cdots, m)$$

or, even more briefly,

$$(1'') \qquad f(x) = 0.$$

The symbol f in (1″) stands for a function vector, sometimes referred to as the *behavior pattern of the configuration* C.

2. Looking for Behavior Patterns

A great deal of effort is devoted in econometrics and elsewhere to attempts at finding the behavior pattern of an observed configuration. Such effort is justified on the grounds that the knowledge of the behavior pattern is needed for purposes of explanation or prediction. The merits of this justification will be examined below. At this point we shall consider certain difficulties encountered in the process of looking for the behavior patterns.

To facilitate exposition, we shall confine ourselves to the case of *linear*

Work supported in part by the Office of Naval Research at the University of Minnesota.

[1] It is convenient to think of each x_j as a vector; its dimensionality is irrelevant here. Similarly, the range of f_i is vectorial. Some or all of the variables might be restricted to integral values.

behavior patterns where the equation system corresponding to (1) may be written as

$$\sum_{j=1}^{n} a_{ij}x_j - b_j = 0 \qquad (i = 1, 2, \cdots, m) \tag{2}$$

or, in matrix notation (corresponding to (1″)),

$$Ax - b = 0. \tag{2″}$$

[The behavior pattern f of the configuration is specified by the augmented matrix (A, b).]

The equation system (2) imposes a restriction on the possible states of the system: more explicitly, it defines a set (in the space $\mathfrak{X}$ of the x's) outside of which the conditions of (2) would be violated. In fact, the configuration may not have gone through all of these possible states, but we shall assume that it has, in order to show that even under most favorable conditions certain basic difficulties are bound to appear. We shall refer to this maximal set of past states of the configuration as its *history* and denote it by h. I.e., $h = \{x \in \mathfrak{X}: Ax - b = 0\}$.[2]

The difficulty experienced by the researcher looking for the behavior pattern (A, b) of the configuration on the basis of its history h is simply due to the fact that alternative behavior patterns might also have "generated" the same history h. More specifically, h might equally well have been generated by the behavior pattern (C, d), provided there exists a non-singular m by m matrix P such that

$$C = PA \quad \text{and} \quad d = Pb. \tag{3}$$

Under such circumstances we shall say that the two behavior patterns $[(A, b)$ and $(C, d)]$ are *equivalent* [3] and we may then restate the nature of the difficulty by saying that history fails to distinguish between equivalent behavior patterns. In the jargon of econometrics one says that the system is *not identifiable.*

3. The Price and Value of Identifiability

Clearly, history alone will not enable us to determine the behavior pattern of the configuration,. but this does not mean that the task is hopeless. For, quite frequently, we are in possession of additional information which is not incorporated in the general form of (2). This information is typically obtained deductively from axiom systems or theories believed to be of relevance to the behavior pattern of the configuration, usually with the help of empirical information other than the history of the configuration; hence the term customarily applied to it, *a priori information,* is somewhat misleading;

---

[2] A more informative, but heavier, symbol for h might be $X_{(A,b)}$. This would correspond to the use of X_f in section 4 below.

[3] In the notation of the preceding footnote, $X_{(A,b)} = X_{(C,d)}$.

nevertheless, we shall conform to this tradition in the interest of preserving continuity of terminology.

The most usual form of a priori information tells us that some particular variable, say x_r, does not appear in the behavior pattern of a specified component, say c_s; in the linear model (2), this is equivalent to saying that the coefficient a_{sr} equals zero; however, it should be stressed that a priori information sometimes comes in a form other than that concerning the presence or absence of zeros in the matrix A.

Now if something is known about the location of zeros in A (to take the typical case of a priori information), we would be able to reject as false some of the behavior patterns equivalent to the true (A, b), namely, those behavior patterns (C, d) which fail to satisfy the a priori conditions. Thus the effect of a priori information is to prohibit certain ones among the transformation matrices P in (3). If enough a priori information is available, it might happen that the only *permissible* P's (i.e., P's yielding behavior patterns (C, d) compatible with the a priori information) would be diagonal. But if P is diagonal, we can say that (A, b) is the same as (C, d) except for (or, up to) normalization. With slight inaccuracy of language, therefore, we shall say that in such a case the behavior pattern is *uniquely* determined by history (together with the a priori information) and that the system is *identifiable.*

We see that one can think of a (non-quantitative) *degree of identification* in terms of the class of P's permissible with respect to the given a priori information.

At best, this class, to be denoted by $\mathscr{P}_I$ (where I refers to a priori information), consists only of diagonal matrices and we have *complete identifiability*; on the other hand, when no a priori information is available, it contains all non-singular P's of appropriate dimension, and we lack identifiability. It is clear, however, that many intermediate possibilities may arise. In particular, it may happen that the a priori information is sufficient to identify, say, the ith behavior pattern (so that the ith row of (C, d) is the same as the ith row of (A, b)), but not all of the other behavior patterns; we then speak of the ith behavior pattern as identifiable.

The a priori information is the *price* we pay for identifiability. Often the price is quite onerous, in the sense that trustworthy a priori information may be hard to come by. It is therefore natural to ask just what the *value* of identifiability is. True enough, without identifiability we cannot acquire unambiguous knowledge of the behavior pattern of the configuration (though we might still be able to find the behavior patterns for some of the components). But do we really need the knowledge of the behavior pattern of the configuration?

This question is quite fundamental in econometrics, but is also of relevance to philosophical investigations concerned with the problem of the *natural law* (scientific law, lawlike) *status* of past regularities and with the problem of *causality.* It will be approached here from the viewpoint of prediction.

That is, the word "need" in the above question will be understood as "need for purposes of prediction."

Now it is clear that the knowledge of the behavior pattern is not required for all types of prediction situations. In particular, if it is assumed that the future behavior pattern will be the same as that in the past, the set of permissible points in the x-space remains the same, and prediction amounts to the description of this set on the basis of past experience; the knowledge of the history of the configuration is obviously sufficient for the purpose and there is no need for further information on the behavior patterns.

But the situation is different if one is required to make predictions on the assumption that the behavior pattern itself will have undergone a change (planned, expected, or hypothetical) as compared with the past during which the historical information was obtained. We shall see that under such circumstances more or less knowledge of the behavior patterns may be required.

4. Predicting for a Modified Structure

Let us denote by X_f the set of possible states of a configuration given the behavior pattern f.[4]

If f^* is the behavior pattern during the historical period (during which the configuration was observed) and f^{**} is the behavior pattern in the period for which prediction is to be made (to be called the *modified* behavior pattern), the problem of *prediction* of the consequences of the modification is considered to be that of determining the modified set $X_{f^{**}}$ of possible states of the configuration.

Such prediction would, of course, be impossible without some information linking the modified pattern f^{**} to the past properties of the configuration. But the conditions under which the prediction is to be made are typically such that the modified behavior pattern of each component can be found if its old behavior pattern is known. This can be expressed by a set of relations

$$f_i^{**} = \phi_i(f_i^*) \quad (i = 1, 2, \cdots, m) \tag{4}$$

where the *modification functions* ϕ_i for the components are known to the forecaster. (4) can be written more briefly as

$$f^{**} = \phi(f^*), \tag{5}$$

again with ϕ (the modification function for the configuration) regarded as known.

In practice, we are typically interested in predicting the consequences not just of one particular modification, but of some set of alternative modifications. Hence in asking about the need for a priori information, it is proper to couch the questions in terms relative to the *class* of modifications under

[4] I.e., $X_f = \{x \in \mathfrak{X} : f(x) = 0\}$, with the behavior pattern given by (1″) above.

consideration, or, equivalently, in terms of the class Φ of modification functions.

We have already seen that the extreme case where Φ is a one-element set, this element being a vector of identities ($f^{**} = f^*$), no a priori information is required; i.e., the set $\mathscr{P}_I$ of permissible transformations P is maximal.

On the other hand, there are well-known examples in econometrics and other fields where Φ is sufficiently large to create the need for complete identifiability, thus reducing $\mathscr{P}_I$ to its minimal size (diagonal P's only).

This suggests the presence of a relationship between the "size" of the anticipated modification class and the need for a priori information, and this relationship will now be explored.

5. Determinability by Hypothetical Modifications

Again, we shall confine ourselves to the linear case (2″). Here the modifications of the behavior pattern amount to changes in the entries of (A, b). It is convenient to introduce a new variable w which is responsible for the modifications, so that $A = A(w)$, $b = b(w)$. The old pattern (historically observed) f^* is given by $A^* = A(w^*)$, $b^* = b(w^*)$, where w^* is the "historical" value of the modifying variable w. Typically, w is multidimensional. In a configuration of separately modifiable components, we may think of w as being also m-dimensional, say $w = (w_1, w_2, \cdots, w_m)$, with independent variability of the w_i's, and with the changes in w_i affecting only the behavior pattern of the ith component of the configuration. This, however, is only one special case.

As a counterpart of the modification equations (4), we may now write

$$(6) \qquad A(w) = \phi[A^*, b^*, w] \qquad\qquad b(w) = \psi[A^*, b^*, w]$$

with the functions ϕ and ψ regarded as known. (The counterpart of (4) can be written similarly in terms of matrix rows.) The class of anticipated modifications is then specified by stating the domain W over which the variable w is permitted to roam.

To make a prediction for some specified value of w amounts to finding the set X_w in the x-space compatible with the anticipated modification,

$$(7) \qquad X_w = \{x\colon A(w)x - b(w) = 0\}.$$

If the true old behavior pattern (A^*, b^*) were known, (6) could certainly be used to obtain the prediction specified by (7). But, as before, there may well be another (false) behavior pattern (A', b'), related to the true one by the transformation

$$(8) \qquad A' = RA^* \quad \text{and} \quad b' = Rb^*,$$

yielding the same prediction X_w as the true behavior pattern. On the other hand, for some matrices R, the resulting false behavior pattern might yield false predictions. Hence from among patterns equivalent to the true one, the modification variable value w picks out a subclass of patterns which are *acceptable for predicting the consequences* of using w. Let F_w denote the set of all patterns so selected by w. The intersection of such sets, for w varying over the domain W, to be denoted by F_W, tells us how much we must know to predict the consequences of all the modifications of the behavior pattern while w varies over the domain W. In particular, W might be rich enough (as happens when each component can be modified while the rest of the configuration remains unchanged), so that F_W is a one-element class (up to normalization). At the other extreme, when W is a one-element set consisting of w^* (i.e., $f^{**} = f^*$, no change in pattern anticipated), F_W consists of all the patterns equivalent to the true one.

The situation is clearly analogous to that arising in connection with identifiability, where the given a priori information I determines a class of behavior patterns, say F_I, which are compatible with I.

This parallelism enables us to give a simple answer to the question posed in section 3 above. *The need for knowledge of the behavior pattern* of the configuration is not absolute, but *relative to* the *modification domain* W (or, equivalently, the class of modification functions Φ). More specifically, the class of behavior patterns F_I compatible with a priori information I must be contained in the class of behavior patterns F_W permitted by the anticipated modification domain W. I.e., the requirement is that

$$F_I \subseteqq F_W. \tag{9}$$

If the class of permissible transformations in (8) (i.e., transformations harmless for prediction purposes over W) is denoted by $\mathcal{R}_W$, the relationship between anticipated modifications and required a priori information may also be written as

$$\mathcal{P}_I \subseteqq \mathcal{R}_W. \tag{10}$$

When F_W is (up to normalization) a one-element set, this element is called the *structure* of the system and the corresponding equation system is said to be in *structural form with respect to* W. Similarly, an individual equation of the system is said to be in structural form with respect to W if all elements of F_W are alike with regard to this equation. Thus these relations require identifying information if the anticipated modifications define their structural forms, but not otherwise.

It should be noted at this point that there seems to be a close relationship between the status of an equation as a natural law in some philosophers' terminology and its status as a structural equation in the terminology of the present paper.

6. On the Concept of Structural Form

In view of the final remark of the preceding section, it may not be out of place to point out some special features of the concept of structure as here defined. It will be seen later that these features are of importance in connection with applications to the concept of causality.

The most important point is that the *concept* of structure *is relative to the domain of modifications anticipated.* In particular, the structure is not necessarily defined for every domain W. Hence a certain equation of a system may be in structural form relative to some W' but not relative to W''. If two individuals differ with regard to modifications they are willing to consider, they will probably differ with regard to the relations accepted as structural. An analogous situation seems to arise in Braithwaite's discussion of the Case of Two Hooters [1, pp. 306–8] where p and q, but not r, are entitled to lawlike (in our language, structural) status if modifications violating t are permitted; if such modifications were prohibited, the formulation of the present paper would lead us to say that the system lacks structural form and the status of p and q is no different from that of r. It is to be noted that from prediction viewpoint there is no need for distinguishing between the status of r as against that of p and q if t cannot be modified; there is such a need, however, if t loses its inviolability. [p: every sounding of hooter at factory $a \cdots$ followed by workers leaving a; q: the corresponding statement for b; r: hooting at $a \cdots$ followed by workers leaving b; t: the simultaneity of hooting at the two factories.]

It should also be emphasized that this relativity of the concept of structure is due to the fact that it represents *not a property of the material system under observation,* but rather a property of the anticipations of those asking for predictions concerning the state of the system.

Finally, it is by no means necessary that the system under consideration should be a configuration of independently modifiable components. Other systems may well be considered, since the concepts introduced in no way depend on such interpretation. The importance of the special case of such a configuration lies in the fact that the availability of a priori information and the possibility of anticipated modifications determining a structure become fairly plausible.

7. Structural Form and Causality

Although the following remarks might apply to most explications of causality, we shall relate them only to that of Simon [3]. Given a system of equations (we take the very simple case where $m = n = 2$)

$$(11) \qquad x_1 + a_{12}x_2 - b_1 = 0 \qquad\qquad a_{21}x_1 + x_2 - b_2 = 0,$$

Simon would say [3, p. 18, Def. 3.7] that x_1 is directly causally dependent on x_2 if and only if $a_{21} = 0$, $a_{12} \neq 0$. But, as Simon himself recognizes, the latter property is not invariant under linear transformations, so that there are what we have called equivalent forms of (11) in which the coefficient of x_1 in the second equation does not vanish, even though $a_{21} = 0$. Hence the system must be in structural form in order to make its causal properties meaningful. This, in turn, requires that a sufficiently rich class of modifications be implicit (or explicit) in the model; Simon indeed proceeds along those lines, although somewhat informally.[5] In particular, his material system is a configuration of independently modifiable components. This approach was also characteristic of the Cowles Commission work on the problem of identification and prediction [2] and can be traced back to Frisch.

From the viewpoint of the present paper, the following is of interest. If, for any reason, one were so to narrow down the class of anticipated modifications as to make the structural form undefined, it would no longer be possible to speak meaningfully of the direction of causality in Simon's sense. But again, the knowledge of this direction would be unnecessary for purposes of prediction.

8. Structural Form and A Priori Information

In section 5 above, we define the structural form of a system on the basis of modifications implicit in the prediction problem. It often happens that the prediction problem itself is not explicitly stated. However, where structural form is nevertheless defined, the hypothetical modifications can be shown to be implicit in the reasoning underlying what we have called a priori information. Hence, as before, the structural form is defined relative to a class of modifications.

References

[1] Braithwaite, R. B. *Scientific Explanation.* Cambridge, Cambridge University Press, 1953.

[2] Koopmans, T. C., ed. *Statistical Inference in Dynamic Economic Models.* Wiley, 1950.

[3] Simon, H. "Causal Ordering and Identifiability". *Models of Man.* New York, Wiley, 1957. (Reprinted from the original version published in 1953.)

[4] Simon, H. "Causality and Econometrics: Comment". *Econometrica,* Vol. 23 (1955), 193–95.

[5] Wold, H. "Causality and Econometrics". *Econometrica,* Vol. 22 (1954), 162–77.

---

[5] In particular, see Simon's comment 1 [4, p. 193] on Wold's definition of non-experimental causality [5, p. 166, lines 7–10].

WHAT THEORIES ARE NOT

H. PUTNAM

Princeton University, Princeton, New Jersey, U.S.A.

The announced topic for this symposium was the role of models in empirical science; however, in preparing for the symposium, I soon discovered that I had first to deal with a different topic, and this different topic is the one to which this paper actually will be devoted. The topic I mean is the role of *theories* in empirical science; and what I do in this paper is attack what may be called the 'received view' on the role of theories — that theories are to be thought of as 'partially interpreted calculi' in which only the 'observation terms' are 'directly interpreted' (the theoretical terms being only 'partially interpreted', or, some people even say, 'partially understood').

To begin, let us review this received view. The view divides the non-logical vocabulary of science into two parts:

OBSERVATION TERMS	THEORETICAL TERMS
such terms as 'red', 'touches', 'stick', etc.	such terms as 'electron', 'dream', 'gene', etc.

The basis for the division appears to be as follows: the observation terms apply to what may be called publicly observable things and signify observable qualities of these things, while the theoretical terms correspond to the remaining unobservable qualities and things.

This division of terms into two classes is then allowed to generate a division of statements into two[1] classes as follows:

OBSERVATIONAL STATEMENTS	THEORETICAL STATEMENTS
statements containing only observation terms and logical vocabulary	statements containing theoretical terms

Lastly, a scientific theory is conceived of as an axiomatic system which may be thought of as initially uninterpreted, and which gains 'empirical meaning' as a result of a specification of meaning *for the observation terms alone*. A kind of partial meaning is then thought of as drawn up to the theoretical terms, by osmosis, as it were.

i) *The observational-theoretical dichotomy.* One can think of many distinctions that are crying out to be made ('new' terms vs. 'old' terms, technical

[1]Sometimes a *tripartite* division is used: observation statements, theoretical statements (containing *only* theoretical terms), and 'mixed' statements (containing both kinds of terms). This refinement is not considered here, because it avoids none of the objections presented below.

terms vs. non-technical ones, terms more-or-less peculiar to one science vs. terms common to many, for a start). My contention here is simply:

(1) The *problem* for which this dichotomy was invented ('how is it possible to interpret theoretical terms?') does not exist.

(2) A basic reason some people have given for introducing the dichotomy is false: namely, justification in science does *not* proceed 'down' in the direction of observation terms. In fact, justification in science proceeds in any direction that may be handy — more observational assertions sometimes being justified with the aid of more theoretical ones, and vice versa. Moreover, as we shall see, while the notion of an *observation report* has some importance in the philosophy of science, such reports cannot be identified on the basis of the vocabulary they do or do not contain.

(3) In any case, whether the reasons for introducing the dichotomy were good ones or bad ones, the double distinction (observation terms — theoretical terms, observation statements — theoretical statements) presented above is, in fact, completely broken-backed. This I shall try to establish now.

In the first place, it should be noted that the dichotomy under discussion was intended as an explicative and not merely a stipulative one. That is, the words 'observational' and 'theoretical' are not having arbitrary new meanings bestowed upon them; rather, pre-existing uses of these words (especially in the philosophy of science) are presumably being sharpened and made clear. And, in the second place, it should be recalled that we are dealing with a double, not just a single, distinction. That is to say, part of the contention I am criticizing is that, once the distinction between observational and theoretical *terms* has been drawn as above, the distinction between theoretical statements and observational reports or assertions (in something like the sense usual in methodological discussions) can be drawn in terms of it. What I mean when I say that the dichotomy is 'completely broken-backed' is this:

(A) If an 'observation term' is one that cannot apply to an unobservable, then there are no observation terms.[2]

(B) Many terms that refer primarily to what Carnap would class as 'unobservables' are not theoretical terms; and at least some theoretical terms refer primarily to observables.

(C) Observational reports can and frequently do contain theoretical terms.

(D) A scientific theory, properly so-called, may refer only to observables. (Darwin's theory of evolution, as originally put forward, is one example.)

To start with the notion of an 'observation term': Carnap's formulation in *Testability and Meaning* [1] was that for a term to be an observation term

[2] I neglect the possibility of trivially constructing terms that refer only to observables: namely, by conjoining 'and is an observable thing' to terms that would otherwise apply to some unobservables. 'Being an observable thing' is, in a sense, highly theoretical and yet applies only to observables!

not only must it correspond to an observable quality, but the determination whether the quality is present or not must be able to be made by the observer in a relatively short time, and with a high degree of confirmation. In his most recent authoritative publication [2], Carnap is rather brief. He writes, 'the terms of Vo [the 'observation vocabulary' — H.P.] are predicates designating observable properties of events or things (e.g., 'blue', 'hot', 'large', etc.) or observable relations between them (e.g., 'x is warmer than y, 'x is contiguous to y', etc.)' [2, p. 41]. The only other clarifying remarks I could find are the following: 'The name 'observation language' may be understood in a narrower or in a wider sense; the observation language in the wider sense includes the disposition terms. In this article I take the observation language Lo in the narrower sense' [2, p. 63]. 'An observable property may be regarded as a simple special case of a testable disposition: for example, the operation for finding out whether a thing is blue or hissing or cold, consists simply in looking or listening or touching the thing, respectively. Nevertheless, *in the reconstruction of the language* [italics mine — H.P.] it seems convenient to take some properties for which the test procedure is extremely simple (as in the examples given) as directly observable, and use them as primitives in Lo' [2, p. 63].

These paragraphs reveal that Carnap, at least, thinks of observation terms as corresponding to qualities that can be detected without the aid of instruments. But always so detected? Or can an observation term refer sometimes to an observable thing and sometimes to an unobservable? While I have not been able to find any explicit statement on this point, it seems to me that writers like Carnap must be *neglecting* the fact that *all* terms — including the 'observation terms' — have at least the possibility of applying to unobservables. Thus their problem has sometimes been formulated in quasi-historical terms — 'How could theoretical terms have been introduced into the language?' And the usual discussion strongly suggests that the following puzzle is meant: if we imagine a time at which people could only talk about observables (had not available any theoretical terms), how did they ever manage to *start* talking about unobservables?

It is possible that I am here doing Carnap and his followers an injustice. However, polemics aside, the following points must be emphasized:

(1) Terms referring to unobservables are *invariably* explained, in the actual history of science, with the aid of already present locutions referring to unobservables. There never was a stage of language at which it was impossible to talk about unobservables. Even a three-year-old child can understand a story about 'people too little to see'[3] and not a single 'theoretical term' occurs in this phrase.

---

[3]Von Wright has suggested (in conversation) that this is an *extended* use of language (because we first learn words like "people" in connection with people we *can* see). This argument from "the way we learn to use the word" appears to be unsound, however (cf. [4]).

(2) There is not even a single *term* of which it is true to say that it *could not* (without changing or extending its meaning) be used to refer to unobservables. 'Red', for example, was so used by Newton when he postulated that red light consists of *red corpuscles*.[4]

In short: if an 'observation term' is a term which *can*, in principle, only be used to refer to observable things, then *there are no observation terms*. If, on the other hand, it is granted that locutions consisting of just observation terms can refer to unobservables, there is no longer any reason to maintain *either* that theories and speculations about the unobservable parts of the world must contain 'theoretical (= non-observation) terms' *or* that there is any general problem as to how one can introduce terms referring to unobservables. Those philosophers who find a difficulty in how we understand theoretical terms should find an equal difficulty in how we understand 'red' and 'smaller than'.

So much for the notion of an 'observation term'. Of course, one may recognize the point just made — that the 'observation terms' also apply, in some contexts, to unobservables — and retain the class (with a suitable warning as to how the label 'observation term' is to be understood). But can we agree that the complementary class — what should be called the 'non-observation terms' — is to be labelled 'theoretical terms'? No, for the identification of 'theoretical term' with 'term (other than the 'disposition terms', which are given a special place in Carnap's scheme) designating an unobservable quality' is unnatural and misleading. On the one hand, it is clearly an enormous (and, I believe, insufficiently motivated) extension of common usage to classify such terms as 'angry', 'loves', etc., as 'theoretical terms' simply because they allegedly do not refer to public observables. A theoretical term, properly so-called, is one which comes from a scientific *theory* (and the almost untouched problem, in thirty years of writing about 'theoretical terms' is what is *really* distinctive about such terms). In this sense (and I think it the sense important for discussions of science) 'satellite' is, for example, a theoretical term (although the things it refers to are quite observable[5] and 'dislikes' clearly is not.

---

[4]Some authors (although not Carnap) explain the intelligibility of such discourse in terms of logically possible submicroscopic observers. But (a) such observers could not see single photons (or light corpuscles) even on Newton's theory; and (b) once such physically impossible (though logically possible) 'observers' are introduced, why not go further and have observers with sense organs for electric charge, or the curvature of space, etc.! Presumably because *we* can see *red*, but not *charge*. But then, this just makes the point that we *understand* 'red' even when applied outside our normal 'range', even though we learn it ostensively, without *explaining* that fact. (The explanation lies in this: that understanding any term — even "red" — involves at least two elements: internalizing the syntax of a natural language, and acquiring a background of ideas. Overemphasis on the way 'red' is *taught* has led some philosophers to misunderstand how it is *learned*.)

[5]Carnap might exclude 'satellite' as an observation term, on the ground that it takes a comparatively long time to verify that something is a satellite with the naked

Our criticisms so far might be met by re-labelling the first dichotomy (the dichotomy of terms) 'observation vs. non-observation', and suitably 'hedging' the notion of 'observation'. But more serious difficulties are connected with the identification upon which the second dichotomy is based — the identification of 'theoretical statements' with statements containing non-observation ('theoretical') terms, and 'observation statements' with 'statements in the observational vocabulary'.

That observation statements may contain theoretical terms is easy to establish. For example, it is easy to imagine a situation in which the following sentence might occur: 'We also *observed* the creation of two electron-positron pairs'.

This objection is sometimes dealt with by proposing to 'relativize' the observation-theoretical dichotomy to the context. (Carnap, however, rejects this way out in the article we have been citing.) This proposal to 'relativize' the dichotomy does not seem to me to be very helpful. In the first place, one can easily imagine a context in which 'electron' would occur, in the same text, in *both* observational reports and in theoretical conclusions from those reports. (So that one would have distortions if one tried to put the term in either the 'observational term' box or in the 'theoretical term' box.) In the second place, for what philosophical problem or point does one require even the relativized dichotomy?

The usual answer is that sometimes a statement A (observational) is offered in support of a statement B (theoretical). Then, in order to explain why A is not itself questioned in the context, we need to be able to say that A is functioning, in that context, as an observation report. But this misses the point I have been making! I do not deny the need for some such notion as 'observation report'. What I deny is that the distinction between observation reports and, among other things, theoretical statements, can or should be drawn on the basis of vocabulary. In addition, a relativized dichotomy will not serve Carnap's purposes. One can hardly maintain that theoretical terms are only partially interpreted, whereas observation terms are completely interpreted, if no sharp line exists between the two classes. (Recall that Carnap takes his problem to be 'reconstruction of the language', not of some isolated scientific context.)

ii) *Partial interpretation*. The notion of 'partial interpretation' has a rather strange history — the term certainly has a technical ring to it, and someone encountering it in Carnap's writings, or Hempel's, or mine[6] certainly would be justified in supposing that it was a term from mathematical logic whose

---

eye, even if the satellite is close to the parent body (although this could be debated). However, 'satellite' cannot be excluded on the quite different ground that many satellites are too far away to see (which is the ground that first comes to mind) since the same is true of the huge majority of all *red* things.

[6] I used this notion uncritically in [5]. From the discussion, I seem to have had concept (2) (below) of 'partial interpretation' in mind, or a related concept. (I no

exact definition was supposed to be too well known to need repetition. The sad fact is that this is not so! In fact, the term was introduced by Carnap in a section of his monograph [3], without definition (Carnap *asserted* that to interpret the observation terms of a calculus is automatically to 'partially interpret' the theoretical primitives, without explanation), and has been subsequently used by Carnap and other authors (including myself) with copious cross references, but with no further explanation.

One can think of (at least) three things that 'partial interpretation' could mean. I will attempt to show that none of these three meanings is of any use in connection with the 'interpretation of scientific theories'. My discussion has been influenced by a remark of Ruth Anna Mathers to the effect that not only has the concept been used without any *definition*, but it has been applied indiscriminately to *terms*, *theories*, and *languages*.

(1) One might give the term a meaning from mathematical logic as follows (I assume familiarity here with the notion of a 'model' of a formalized theory): to 'partially interpret' a theory is to specify a non-empty class of intended models. If the specified class has one member, the interpretation is *complete*; if more than one, properly *partial*.

(2) To partially interpret a *term* P could mean (for a Verificationist, as Carnap is) to specify a verification-refutation procedure. If $\bar{a}_1$ is an individual constant designating an individual a_1 (Carnap frequently takes space-time points as the individuals, assuming a 'field' language for physics), and it is possible to verify $P(\bar{a}_1)$, then the individual a_1 is in the extension of the term P; if $P(\bar{a}_1)$ is refutable, then a_1 is in the extension of $\bar{P}$, the negation of P; and if the existing test procedures do not apply to a_1 (e.g., if a_1 fails to satisfy the antecedant conditions specified in the test procedures) then it is *undefined* if a_1 is in or out of the extension of P.

This notion of partial interpretation of *terms* immediately applies to terms introduced by reduction sentences[7] (Carnap calls these 'pure disposition terms'). In this case the individual a_1 is either in the extension of P or in the extension of $\bar{P}$, provided the antecedant of at least one reduction sentence 'introducing' the term P is true of a_1, and otherwise it is *undefined* whether $P(a_1)$ is true or not. But it can be extended to theoretical primitives in a *theory* as follows: If $P(\bar{a}_1)$ follows from the postulates and definitions of the theory and/or the set of all true observation sentences, then a_1 is in the extension of P; if $\bar{P}(\bar{a}_1)$ follows from the postulates and definitions of the theory and/or the set of all true observation sentences, then a_1 is in the extension of $\bar{P}$; in all other cases, $P(\bar{a}_1)$ has an *undefined* truth-value.

---

longer think *either* that set theory is helpfully thought of as a 'partially interpreted calculus' in which only the 'nominalistic language' is directly interpreted, *or* that mathematics is best identified with set theory for the purposes of philosophical discussion, although the idea that certain statements of set theory, e.g., the continuum hypothesis, do not have a defined truth-value does have a certain appeal, given the unclarity of our notion of a 'set'.)

[7]For the definition of this concept, see [1].

(3) Most simply, one might say that to partially interpret a formal *language* is to *interpret part* of the language (e.g., to provide translations into common language for some terms and leave the others mere dummy symbols).

Of these three notions, the first will not serve Carnap's purposes, because it is necessary to use theoretical terms in order to specify even a *class* of intended models for the usual scientific theories. Thus, consider the problem of specifying the intended values of the individual variables. If the language is a 'particle' language, then the individual variables range over 'things' — but things in a *theoretical* sense, including mass points and systems of mass points. It is surely odd to take the notion of a 'physical object' as either an observational or a purely logical one when it becomes wide enough to include point-electrons, at one extreme, and galaxies at the other. On the other hand, if the language is a 'field' language, then it is necessary to say that the individual variables range over *space-time points* — and the difficulty is the same as with the notion of a 'physical object.'

Moving to the predicate and function-symbol vocabulary: consider, for example, the problem of specifying either a unique intended interpretation or a suitable class of models for Maxwell's equations. We must say, at least, that E and H are intended to have as values vector-valued functions of *space-time points*, and that the norms of these vectors are to measure, roughly speaking, the velocity-independent force on a small test particle per unit charge, and the velocity-dependent force per unit charge. One might identify force with mass times (a suitable component of) acceleration, and handle the reference to an (idealized) test particle via 'reduction sentences', but we are still left with 'mass', 'charge', and, of course, 'space-time point'. ('Charge' and 'mass' have as values a real-valued function and a non-negative real-valued function, respectively, of space-time points; and the values of these functions are supposed to measure the intensities with which certain *physical magnitudes* are present at these points — where the last clause is necessary to rule out flagrantly unintended interpretations that can never be eliminated otherwise.)

(One qualification: I said that *theoretical* terms are necessary to specify even a *class* of intended models — or of models that a realistically minded scientist could accept as what he has in mind. But 'physical object', 'physical magnitude' and 'space-time point' are not — except for the last — 'theoretical terms', in any idiomatic sense, any more than they are 'observation terms'. Let us call them for the nonce simply 'broad spectrum terms' — noting that they pose much the same problems as do certain meta-scientific terms, e.g., 'science' itself. Of them we might say, as Quine does of the latter term [6], that they are not defined in advance — rather science itself tells us (with many changes of opinion) what the scope of 'science' is, or of an individual science, e.g., chemistry, what an 'object' is, what 'physical magnitudes' are. In this way, these terms, although not theoretical terms, tend eventually to acquire technical senses via theoretical definitions.)

A further difficulty with the first notion of 'partial interpretation' is that theories with false observational consequences have *no* interpretation (since they have no model that is 'standard' with respect to the observation terms). This certainly flies in the face of our usual notion of an interpretation, according to which such a theory is *wrong*, not *senseless*.

The second notion of partial interpretation that we listed appears to me to be totally inadequate even for the so-called 'pure disposition terms', e.g., 'soluble'. Thus, let us suppose, for the sake of a simplified example, that there were only one known test for *solubility* — immersing the object in water. Can we really accept the conclusion that it has a *totally undefined* truth-value to say of something that is never immersed in water that it is soluble?

Let us suppose now that we notice that all the sugar cubes that we immerse in water dissolve. On the basis of this *evidence* we *conclude* that all sugar is soluble — even cubes that are never immersed. On the view we are criticizing, this has to be described as 'linguistic stipulation' rather than as 'discovery'! Namely, according to this concept of partial interpretation, what we do is *give* the term 'soluble' the *new* meaning 'soluble-in-the-old-sense-of-sugar'; and what we ordinarily describe as evidence that the un-immersed sugar cubes are soluble should rather be described as evidence that our new meaning of the term 'soluble' is compatible with the original 'bilateral reduction sentence'.

Also, although it will now be true to say 'sugar is soluble', it will still have a totally undefined truth-value to say of many, say, lumps of *salt* that *they* are soluble.

Ordinarily, 'change of meaning' refers to the sort of thing that happened to the word 'knave' (which once meant 'boy'), and 'extension of meaning' to the sort of thing that happened in Portugal to the word for family ('familhia'), which has come to include the servants. In these senses, which also seem to be the only ones useful for linguistic theory, it is simply *false* to say that in the case described (concluding that sugar is soluble) the word 'soluble' underwent either a change or an extension of meaning. The *method of verification* may have been extended by the discovery, but this is only evidence that method of verification is not meaning.

In any case, there does not seem to be any reason why we cannot agree with the customary account. What we meant all along by 'it's soluble' was, of course, 'if it *were* in water, it would dissolve'; and the case we described can *properly* be described as one of drawing an inductive inference — to the conclusion that all these objects (lumps of sugar, whether immersed or not) are soluble in *this* sense. Also, there is no reason to reject the view, which is certainly built into our use of the term 'soluble', that it has a definite (but sometimes unknown) truth-value to say of anything (of a suitable size and consistency) that it is soluble, whether it satisfies a presently-known test condition or not. Usually the objection is raised that it is 'not clear what it means' to say 'if it *were* in water, it would dissolve'; but there is no *linguistic* evidence of this unclarity. (Do people construe it in different ways? Do they ask for a paraphrase? Of course, there is a philosophical problem having to do with 'necessary connection', but one must not confuse a word's being connected with a philosophical problem with its possessing an unclear meaning.)

Coming now to theoretical terms (for the sake of simplicity, I assume that our world is non-quantum mechanical): If we want to preserve the ordinary world-picture at all, we certainly want to say it has a definite truth-value to say that there is a helium atom inside any not-too-tiny region X. But in fact, our test conditions — even if we allow tests implied by a theory, as outlined above under (2) — will not apply to small regions X in the interior of the sun, for example (or in the interior of many bodies at many times). Thus we get the following anomalous result: it is *true* to say that there are helium atoms in the sun, but it is neither true nor false that one of these is inside any given tiny subregion X! Similar things will happen in connection with theoretical statements about the very large, e.g., it may be 'neither true nor false' that the average curvature of space is positive, or that the universe is finite. And once again, perfectly ordinary scientific discoveries will constantly have to be described as 'linguistic stipulations', 'extensions of meaning', etc.

Finally, the third sense of 'partial interpretation' leads to the view that theoretical terms have *no meaning at all,* that they are mere computing devices, and is thus unacceptable.

To sum up: We have seen that of the three notions of 'partial interpretation' discussed, each is either unsuitable for Carnap's purposes (starting with observation terms), or incompatible with a rather minimal scientific realism; and, in addition, the second notion depends upon gross and misleading changes in our use of language. Thus in *none* of these senses is 'a partially interpreted calculus in which only the observation terms are directly interpreted' an acceptable model for a scientific theory.

iii) *'Introducing' theoretical terms.* We have been discussing a proposed solution to a philosophical problem. But what *is* the problem?

The problem is sometimes referred to as the problem of 'interpreting', i.e., giving the meaning of theoretical terms in science. But this cannot be much of a *general* problem (it may, of course, be a problem in specific cases). Why should not one be able to give the meaning of a theoretical term? (Using, if necessary, *other* theoretical terms, 'broad spectrum' terms, etc.) The problem might be restated — to give the meaning of theoretical terms, *using only observation terms.* But then, why should we suppose that this is or ought to be possible?

Something like this may be said: suppose we make a 'dictionary' of theoretical terms. If we allow theoretical terms to appear both as 'entries' and in the *definitions,* then there will be 'circles' in our dictionary. But there are circles in every dictionary!

We perhaps come closer to the problem if we observe that, while dictionaries are useful, they are useful only to speakers who already know a good deal of the language. One cannot learn one's native language to begin with from a dictionary. This suggests that the problem is really to give an account of how the use of theoretical terms is *learned* (in the life-history of an individual speaker); or, perhaps, of how theoretical terms are 'introduced' (in the history of the language).

To take the first form of the problem (the language-learning of the individual speaker): It appears that theoretical terms are learned in essentially the way most words are learned. Sometimes we are given lexical definitions (e.g., 'a *tiglon* is a cross between a tiger and a lion'); more often, we simply imitate other speakers; many times we combine these (e.g., we are given a lexical definition, from which we obtain a rough idea of the use, and then we bring our linguistic behavior more closely into line with that of other speakers via imitation).

The story in connection with the introduction of a new technical term into the *language* is roughly similar. Usually, the scientist introduces the term via some kind of paraphrase. For example, one might explain 'mass' as 'that physical magnitude which determines how strongly a body resists being accelerated, e.g., if a body has twice the mass it will be twice as hard to accelerate'. (Instead of 'physical magnitude' one might say, in ordinary language, 'that property of the body', or 'that *in* the body which . . .'. Such 'broad-spectrum' notions occur in every natural language; and our present notion of a 'physical magnitude' is already an extreme refinement.) Frequently, as in the case of 'force' and 'mass', the term will be a common-language term whose new technical use is in some respects quite continuous with the ordinary use. In such cases, a lexical definition is frequently omitted, and in its place one has merely a statement of some of the differences between the usual use and the technical use being introduced. Usually one gains only a rough idea of the use of a technical term from these explicit metalinguistic statements, and this rough idea is then refined by reading the theory or text in which the term is employed. However, the role of the explicit metalinguistic statement should not be overlooked: one could hardly read the text or technical paper with understanding if one had neither explicit metalinguistic statements or previous and related uses of the technical words to go by.

It is instructive to compare here the situation with respect to the logical connectives, in their modern technical employment. We introduce the precise and technical senses of 'or', 'not', 'if-then', etc., using the imprecise 'ordinary language' *or, and, not,* etc. E.g., we say 'A v B shall be true *if* A is true, *and* true *if* B is true, *and* A v B shall be false *if* A is false *and* B is false. In particular, A v B shall be true *even if* A *and* B are *both* true.' Notice that no one has proposed to say that 'v' is only 'partially interpreted' because we use 'and', 'if', etc., in the ordinary imprecise way when we 'introduce' it.

In short, we can and do perform the feat of using imprecise language to introduce more precise language. This is like all use of tools — we use less-refined tools to manufacture more-refined ones. Secondly, there are even ideas that can be expressed in the more precise language that could not be intelligibly expressed in the original language. Thus, to borrow an example due to Alonzo Church, a statement of the form $(((A \rightarrow B) \rightarrow B) \rightarrow B)$ can probably not be intelligibly rendered in ordinary language — although one can understand it once one has had an explanation of '$\rightarrow$' in ordinary language.

It may be, however, that the problem is supposed to be *this*: to *formalize* the process of introducing technical terms. Let us try this problem out on our last example (the logical connectives). Clearly we *could* formalize the process of introducing the usual truth-functional connectives. We would only have to take as primitives the 'ordinary language' *and*, *or*, *not* in their usual (imprecise) meanings, and then we could straightforwardly write down such characterizations as the one given above for the connective 'v' But if someone said: 'I want you to introduce the logical connectives, quantifiers, etc., without having any *imprecise* primitives (because using imprecise notions is not 'rational reconstruction') and also without having any *precise* logical symbols as primitives (because that would be 'circular')', we should just have to say that the task was impossible.

The case appears to me to be much the same with the 'theoretical terms'. If we take as primitives not only the 'observation terms' and the 'logical terms', but also the 'broad-spectrum' terms referred to before ('thing', 'physical magnitude', etc.), and, perhaps, certain imprecise but useful notions from common language — e.g., '*harder* to accelerate', 'determines' — then we can introduce theoretical terms without difficulty:

(1) Some theoretical terms can actually be explicitly defined in Carnap's 'observation language'. Thus, suppose we had a theory according to which everything consisted of 'classical' elementary particles — little-extended individual particles; and suppose no two of these were supposed to touch. Then 'elementary particle', which is a 'theoretical term' if anything is, would be explicitly definable: X is an elementary particle ≡ X cannot be decomposed into parts Y and Z which are not contiguous — and the above definition requires only the notions 'X is a part of Y' and 'X is contiguous to Y'. (If we take *contiguity* as a reflexive relation, then 'part of' is definable in terms of it: X is a part of Y ≡ everything that is contiguous to X is contiguous to Y. Also, Y and Z constitute a 'decomposition' of X if (i) nothing is a part of both Y and Z; (ii) X has no part which contains no part in common with either Y or Z. However, it would be perfectly reasonable, in my opinion, to take 'part of' as a *logical* primitive, along with 'is a member of' — although Carnap would probably disagree.)

We note that the, at first blush surprising, possibility of defining the obviously theoretical term 'elementary particle' in Carnap's 'observation language' rests on the fact that the notion of a *physical object* is smuggled into the language in the very interpretation of the individual variables.

(2) The kind of characterization we gave above for 'mass' (using the no-

tion 'harder to accelerate') could be formalized. Again a broad-spectrum notion ('physical magnitude') plays a role in the definition.

But once again, no one would normally want to formalize such obviously informal definitions of theoretical terms. And once again, if someone says: 'I want you to introduce the theoretical terms using *only* Carnap's *observation terms*', we have to say, apart from special cases (like that of the 'classical' notion of an elementary particle), that this seems impossible. But why should it be possible? And what philosophic moral should we draw from the impossibility? — Perhaps only this: that we are able to have as rich a theoretical vocabulary as we do have because, thank goodness, we were never in the position of having *only* Carnap's observation vocabulary at our disposal.

References

[1] Carnap, R. Testability and meaning. Pp. 47–92 in *Readings in the Philosophy of Science,* H. Feigl and M. Brodbeck, eds., New York, Appleton-Century-Crofts, 1955, x+517 pp. Reprinted from *Philosophy of Science,* Vol. 3 (1936) and Vol. 4 (1937).

[2] Carnap, R. The methodological character of theoretical concepts. Pp. 1–74 in *Minnesota Studies in the Philosophy of Science,* I., H. Feigl *et al.*, eds., Minneapolis, University of Minnesota Press, 1956, x+517 pp.

[3] Carnap, R. *The Foundations of Logic and Mathematics.* Vol. 4, no. 3 of the International Encyclopedia of Unified Science, Chicago, University of Chicago Press, 1939, 75 pp.

[4] Fodor, J. Do words have uses? Submitted to *Inquiry.*

[5] Putnam, H. Mathematics and the existence of abstract entities. *Philosophical Studies,* Vol. 7 (1957), pp. 81–88.

[6] Quine, W. V. O. The scope and language of science, *British Journal for the Philosophy of Science,* Vol. 8 (1957), pp. 1–17.

MODELS OF DATA

PATRICK SUPPES

Stanford University, Stanford, California, U.S.A.

1. Introduction

To nearly all the members of this Congress the logical notion of a model of a theory is too familiar to need detailed review here. Roughly speaking, a model of a theory may be defined as a possible realization in which all valid sentences of the theory are satisfied, and a possible realization of the theory is an entity of the appropriate set-theoretical structure. For instance, we may characterize a possible realization of the mathematical theory of groups as an ordered couple whose first member is a non-empty set and whose second member is a binary operation on this set. A possible realization of the theory of groups is a model of the theory if the axioms of the theory are satisfied in the realization, for in this case (as well as in many others) the valid sentences of the theory are defined as those sentences which are logical consequences of the axioms. To provide complete mathematical flexibility I shall speak of theories axiomatized within general set theory by defining an appropriate set-theoretical predicate (e.g., "is a group") rather than of theories axiomatized directly within first-order logic as a formal language. For the purposes of this paper, this difference is not critical. In the set-theoretical case it is convenient sometimes to speak of the appropriate predicate's being satisfied by a possible realization. But whichever sense of formalization is used, essentially the same logical notion of model applies.[1]

It is my opinion that this notion of model is the fundamental one for the empirical sciences as well as mathematics. To assert this is not to deny a place for variant uses of the word "model" by empirical scientists, as, for example, when a physicist talks about a physical model, or a psychologist refers to a quantitative theory of behavior as a mathematical model. On this occasion I do not want to argue for this fundamental character of the logical notion of model, for I tried to make out a detailed case at a colloquium in Utrecht last January, also sponsored by the International Union of History and Philosophy of Science [3]. Perhaps the most persuasive argument which might be singled out for mention here is that the notion of model used in any serious statistical treatment of a theory and its relation to experiment does not differ in any essential way from the logical notion of model.

The focus of the present paper is closely connected to the statistical

---

The writing of this paper was partially supported by the Group Psychology Branch of the Office of Naval Research.

[1]For a detailed discussion of axiomatization of theories within set theory, see Suppes [2, Chap. 12].

analysis of the empirical adequacies of theories. What I want to try to show is that exact analysis of the relation between empirical theories and relevant data calls for a hierarchy of models of different logical type. Generally speaking, in pure mathematics the comparison of models involves comparison of two models of the same logical type, as in the assertion of representation theorems. A radically different situation often obtains in the comparison of theory and experiment. Theoretical notions are used in the theory which have no direct observable analogue in the experimental data. In addition, it is common for models of a theory to contain continuous functions or infinite sequences although the confirming data are highly discrete and finitistic in character.

Perhaps I may adequately describe the kind of ideas in which I am interested in the following way. Corresponding to possible realizations of the theory I introduce possible realizations of the data. Models of the data of an experiment are then defined in the customary manner in terms of possible realizations of the data. As should be apparent, from a logical standpoint possible realizations of data are defined in just the same way as possible realizations of the theory being tested by the experiment from which the data come. The precise definition of models of the data for any given experiment requires that there be a theory of the data in the sense of the experimental procedure, as well as in the ordinary sense of the empirical theory of the phenomena being studied.

Before analyzing some of the consequences and problems of this viewpoint, it may be useful to give the ideas more definiteness by considering an example.

2. Example from learning theory

I have deliberately chosen an example from learning theory because it is conceptually simple, mathematically non-trivial and thoroughly probabilistic. More particularly, I consider linear response theory as developed by Estes and myself [1]. To simplify the presentation of the theory in an inessential way, let us assume that on every trial the organism in the experimental situation can make exactly one of two responses, A_1 or A_2, and after each response it receives a reinforcement, E_1 or E_2, of one of the two possible responses. A possible experimental outcome in the sense of the theory is an infinite sequence of ordered pairs, where the nth term of the sequence represents the observed response — the first member of the pair — and the actual reinforcement — the second member of the pair — on trial n of the experiment.

A possible realization of the theory is an ordered triple $\mathscr{X} = <X, P, \theta>$ of the following sort. The set X is the set of all sequences of ordered pairs such that the first member of each pair is an element of some set A and the second member an element of some set B, where A and B each have two elements. The set A represents the two possible responses and the set B the two possible reinforcements. The function P is a probability measure on the smallest Borel field containing the field of cylinder sets of X; and θ, a real number in the interval $0 < \theta \leqq 1$, is the learning parameter. (Admittedly, for theories whose models have a rather complicated set-theoretical structure the definition of possible realization is at points arbitrary, but this is not an issue which affects in any way the development of ideas central to this paper.)

There are two obvious respects in which a possible realization of the theory cannot be a possible realization of experimental data. The first is that no actual experiment can include an infinite number of discrete trials. The second is that the parameter θ is not directly observable and is not part of the recorded data.

To pursue further relations between theory and experiment, it is necessary to state the axioms of the theory, i.e., to define models of the theory. For this purpose a certain amount of notation is needed. Let $A_{i,n}$ be the event of response A_i on trial n, $E_{j,n}$ the event of reinforcement E_j on trial n, where $i, j = 1,2$, and for x in X let x_n be the equivalence class of all sequences in X which are identical with x through trial n. A possible realization of the linear response theory is then a model of the theory if the following two axioms are satisfied in the realization:

Axiom 1. *If* $P(E_{i,n}A_{i',n}x_{n-1}) > 0$, *then*
$$P(A_{i,n+1} | E_{i,n}A_{i',n}x_{n-1}) = (1-\theta)\, P(A_{i,n} \mid x_{n-1}) + \theta.$$

Axiom 2. *If* $P(E_{j,n}A_{i',n}x_{n-1}) > 0$ *and* $i \neq j$, *then*
$$P(A_{i,n+1} \mid E_{j,n}A_{i',n}x_{n-1}) = (1-\theta)\, P(A_{i,n} \mid x_{n-1}).$$

The first axiom asserts that when a response is reinforced, the probability of making that response on the next trial is increased by a simple linear transformation. The second axiom asserts that when a different response is reinforced, the probability of making the response is decreased by a second linear transformation. To those who are concerned about the psychological basis of this theory it may be remarked that it is derivable from a much more complicated theory that assumes processes of stimulus sampling and conditioning. The linear response theory is the limiting case of the stimulus sampling theory as the number of stimuli approaches infinity.

For still greater definiteness it will be expedient to consider a particular class of experiments to which the linear response theory has been applied, namely, those experiments with simple contingent reinforcement schedules. On every trial, if an A_1 response is made, the probability of an E_1 reinforcement is π_1, independent of the trial number and other preceding events. If an A_2 response is made, the probability of an E_2 reinforcement is π_2. Thus, in summary for every n,

$$P(E_{1,n} \mid A_{1,n}) = \pi_1 = 1 - P(E_{2,n} \mid A_{1,n}),$$
$$P(E_{2,n} \mid A_{2,n}) = \pi_2 = 1 - P(E_{1,n} \mid A_{2,n}).$$

This characterization of simple contingent reinforcement schedules has been made in the language of the theory, as is necessary in order to compute theoretical predictions. This is not possible for the finer details of the experiment. Let us suppose the experimenter decides on 600 trials for each subject. A brief description (cf. [4, pp. 81–83]) of the experimental apparatus might run as follows.

> The subject sits at a table of standard height. Mounted vertically in front of the subject is a large opaque panel. Two silent operating keys (A_1 and A_2 responses) are mounted at the base of the panel 20 cm. apart. Three milk-glass panel lights are mounted on the panel. One of these lights, which serves as the signal for the subject to respond, is centered between the keys at the subject's eye level. Each of the other two lights, the reinforcing events E_1 and E_2, is mounted directly above one of the keys. On all trials the signal light is on for 3.5 sec.; the time between successive signal exposures is 10 sec. A reinforcing light comes on 1.5 sec. after the cessation of the signal light and remains on for 2 sec.

It is not surprising that this description of the apparatus is not incorporated in any direct way at all into the theory. The important point is to take the linear response theory and this description as two extremes between which a hierarchy of theories and their models is to be fitted in a detailed analysis.

In the class of experiments we are considering, the experimenter records only the response made and reinforcement given on each trial. This suggests the definition of the possible realizations of the theory that is the first step down from the abstract level of the linear response theory itself. This theory I shall call the *theory of the experiment*, which term must not be taken to refer to what statisticians call the theory of experimental design—a topic to be mentioned later. A possible realization of the theory of the experiment is an ordered couple $\mathcal{Y} = < Y, P >$, where (i) Y is a finite set consisting of all possible finite sequences of length 600 with, as previously, the terms of the sequences being ordered pairs, the first member of each pair being drawn from some pair set A and correspondingly for the second members, and (ii) the function P is a probability measure on the set of all subsets of Y.

A possible realization $\mathcal{Y} = < Y, P >$ of the theory of the experiment is a model of the theory if the probability measure P satisfies the defining condition for a simple contingent reinforcement schedule. Models of the experiment thus defined are entities still far removed from the actual data. The finite sequences that are elements of Y may indeed be used to represent any possible experimental outcome, but in an experiment with, say, 40 subjects, the observed 40 sequences are an insignificant part of the 4^{600} sequences in Y. Consequently, a model closer to the actual situation is needed to represent the actual conditional relative frequencies of reinforcement used.

The appropriate realization for this purpose seems to be an N-tuple Z of elements from Y, where N is the number of subjects in the experiment. An N-tuple rather than a subset of Y is selected for two reasons. The first is that if a subset is selected there is no direct way of indicating that two distinct subjects had exactly the same sequence of responses and reinforcements — admittedly a highly improbable event. The second and more important reason is that the N-tuple may be used to represent the time sequence in which subjects were run, a point of some concern in considering certain detailed questions of experimental design. It may be noted that in using an N-tuple as a realization of the data rather than a more complicated entity that could be used to express the actual times at which subjects were run in the experiment, we have taken yet another step of abstraction and simplification away from the bewilderingly complex complete experimental phenomena.[2]

The next question is, When is a possible realization of the data a model of the data? The complete answer, as I see it, requires a detailed statistical theory of goodness of fit. Roughly speaking, an N-tuple realization is a model of the data if the conditional relative frequencies of E_1 and E_2 reinforcements fit closely enough the probability measure P of the model of the experiment. To examine in detail statistical tests for this goodness of fit would be inappropriate here, but it will be instructive of the complexities of the issues involved to outline some of the main considerations. The first thing to note is that no single simple goodness of fit test will guarantee that a possible realization Z of the data is an adequate model of the data. The kinds of problems that arise are these: (i) (*Homogeneity*) Are the conditional relative frequencies (C.R.F.) of reinforcements approximately π_i or $1-\pi_i$, as the case may be, for each subject? To answer this we must compare members of the N-tuple Z. (ii) (*Stationarity*) Are the C.R.F. of reinforcements constant over trials? To answer this practically we sum over subjects, i.e., over members of Z, to obtain sufficient data for a test. (iii) (*Order*) Are the C.R.F. of reinforcements independent of preceding reinforcements and responses? To answer this we need to show that the C.R.F. define a zero order process — that serial correlations of all order are zero. Note, of course, that the zero order is with respect to the conditional events E_i given A_j, for $i, j = 1,2$. These three questions are by no means exhaustive; they do reflect central considerations. To indicate their essentially formal character it may be helpful to sketch their formulation in a relatively classical statistical framework. Roughly speaking, the approach is as follows. For each possible realization Z of the data we define a statistic $T(Z)$ for each question. This statistic is a random variable with a probability distribution — preferably a distribution that is (asymptotically) independent of the actual C.R.F. under the null hypothesis that Z is a model of the data. In statistical terminology, we "accept" the null hypothesis if the obtained value of the statistic $T(Z)$ has a probability equal to or greater than some significance level α on the assumption that indeed the null hypothesis is true.

---

[2]The exact character of a model $\mathscr{Y}$ of the experiment and a model Z of the data is not determined uniquely by the experiment. It would be possible, for instance, to define $\mathscr{Y}$ in terms of N-tuples.

For the questions of homogeneity, stationarity, and order stated above, maximum likelihood or chi-square statistics would be appropriate. There is not adequate space to discuss details, but these statistics are standard in the literature. For the purposes of this paper it is not important that some subjectivists like L. J. Savage might be critical of the unfettered use of such classical tests. A more pertinent caveat is that joint satisfaction of three statistical tests (by "satisfaction" I mean acceptance of the null hypothesis with a level of significance $\geqq .05$) corresponding to the three questions does not intuitively seem completely sufficient for a possible realization Z to be a model of the data.[3] No claim for completeness was made in listing these three, but it might also be queried as to what realistic possibility there is of drawing up a finite list of statistical tests which may be regarded as jointly sufficient for Z to be a model of the data. A skeptical non-formalistic experimenter might claim that given any usable set of tests he could produce a conditional reinforcement schedule that would satisfy the tests and yet be intuitively unsatisfactory. For example, suppose the statistical tests for order were constructed to look at no more than fourth-order effects, the skeptical experimenter could then construct a possible realization Z with a non-random fifth-order pattern. Actually the procedure used in well-constructed experiments makes such a dodge rather difficult. The practice is to obtain the C.R.F. from some published table of random numbers whose properties have been thoroughly investigated by a wide battery of statistical tests. From the systematic methodological standpoint it is not important that the experimenter himself perform the tests on Z.

On the other hand, in the experimental literature relevant to this example it is actually the case that greater care needs to be taken to guarantee that a possible realization Z of the data is indeed a model of the data for the experiment at hand. A typical instance is the practice of restricted randomi-

---

[3]For use at this point, a more explicit definition of models of the data would run as follows. Z is an N-fold model of the data for experiment $\mathcal{Y}$ if and only if there is a set Y and a probability measure P on subsets of Y such that $\mathcal{Y} = \langle Y, P \rangle$ is a model of the theory of the experiment, Z is an N-tuple of elements of Y, and Z satisfies the statistical tests of homogeneity, stationarity, and order. A fully formal definition would spell out the statistical tests in exact mathematical detail. For example, a chi-square test of homogeneity for E_1 reinforcements following A_1 responses would be formulated as follows. Let N_j be the number of A_1 responses (excluding the last trial) for subject j, i.e., as recorded in Z_j — the jth member of the N-tuple Z, and let ν_j be the number of E_1 reinforcements following A_1 responses for subject j. Then

$$\chi^2_H(Z) = \sum_{j=1}^{N} \frac{(\nu_j - N_j\pi_1)^2}{N_j\pi_1} + \frac{(N_j - \nu_j - N_j(1-\pi_1))^2}{N_j(1-\pi_j)}$$

$$= \sum_{j=1}^{N} \frac{(\nu_j - N_j\pi_1)^2}{N_j\pi_1(1-\pi_1)},$$

and this χ^2 has N degrees of freedom. If the value $\chi^2_H(Z)$ has probability greater than .05 the null hypothesis is accepted, i.e., with respect to homogeneity Z is satisfactory.

zation. To illustrate, if $P(E_{1,n} \mid A_{1,n}) = .6$, then some experimenters would arrange that in every block of 10 A_1 responses exactly 6 are followed by E_1 reinforcements, a result that should have a probability of approximately zero for a large number of trials.[4]

The most important objection of the skeptical experimenter to the importance of models of the data has not yet been examined. The objection is that the precise analysis of these models includes only a small portion of the many problems of experimental design. For example, by most canons of experimental design the assignment of A_1 to the left (or to the right) for every subject would be a mistake. More generally, the use of an experimental room in which there was considerably more light on the left side of subjects than on the right would be considered mistaken. There is a difference, however, in these two examples. The assignment of A_1 to the left or right for each subject is information that can easily be incorporated into models of the data — and requirements of randomization can be stated. Detailed information about the distribution of physical parameters characterizing the experimental environment is not a simple matter to incorporate in models of data and is usually not reported in the literature; roughly speaking, some general *ceteris paribus* conditions are assumed to hold.

The characterization of models of data is not really determined, however, by relevant information about experimental design which can easily be formalized. In one sense there is scarcely any limit to information of this kind; it can range from phases of the moon to I.Q. data on subjects.

The central idea, corresponding well, I think, to a rough but generally clear distinction made by experimenters and statisticians, is to restrict models of the data to those aspects of the experiment which have a parametric analogue in the theory. A model of the data is designed to incorporate all the information about the experiment which can be used in statistical tests of the adequacy of the theory. The point I want to make is not as simple or as easily made precise as I could wish. Table 1 is meant to indicate a possible hierarchy of theories, models, and problems that arise at each level to harass the scientist. At the lowest level I have placed *ceteris paribus* conditions. Here is placed every intuitive consideration of experimental design that involves no formal statistics. Control of loud noises, bad odors, wrong times of day or season go here. At the next level formal problems of experimental design enter, but of the sort that far exceed the limits of the particular theory being tested. Randomization of A_1 as the left or right response is a problem for this level, as is random assignment of subjects to different experimental groups. All the considerations that enter

[4]To emphasize that conceptually there is nothing special about this particular example chosen from learning theory, it is pertinent to remark that much more elaborate analyses of sources of experimental error are customary in complicated physical experiments. In the literature of learning theory it is as yet uncommon to report the kind of statistical tests described above which play a role analogous to the physicists' summary of experimental errors.

TABLE 1

Hierarchy of Theories, Models, and Problems

Theory of	Typical Problems
Linear response models	Estimation of θ, goodness of fit to models of data
Models of experiment	Number of trials, choice of experimental parameters
Models of data	Homogeneity, stationarity, fit of experimental parameters
Experimental design	Left-right randomization, assignment of subjects
Ceteris paribus conditions	Noises, lighting, odors, phases of the moon

at this level can be formalized, and their relation to models of the data, which are at the next level, can be made explicit — in contrast to the seemingly endless number of unstated *ceteris paribus* conditions.

At the next level, models of the experiment enter. They bear the relation to models of the data already outlined. Finally at the top of the hierarchy are the linear response models, relatively far removed from the concrete experimental experience. It is to be noted that linear response models are related directly to models of the data, without explicit consideration of models of the experiment. Also worth emphasizing once again is that the criteria for deciding if a possible realization of the data is a model of the data in no way depend upon its relation to a linear response model. These criteria are to determine if the experiment was well run, not to decide if the linear response theory has merit.

The dependence is actually the other way round. Given a model of the data we ask if there is a linear response model to which it bears a satisfactory goodness of fit relation. The rationale of a maximum likelihood estimate of θ is easily stated in this context: given the experimental parameters π_1 and π_2 we seek that linear response model, i.e., the linear response model with learning parameter $\hat{\theta}$, which will maximize the probability of the observed data, as given in the model of the data.

It is necessary at this point to break off rather sharply discussion of this example from learning theory, but there is one central point that has not been sufficiently mentioned. The analysis of the relation between theory and experiment must proceed at every level of the hierarchy shown in Table 1. Difficulties encountered at all but the top level reflect weaknesses in the experiment, not in the fundamental learning theory. It is unfortunate that it is not possible to give here citations from the experimental literature of badly conceived or poorly executed experiments that are taken to invalidate the theory they presume to test, but in fact do not.

3. The theory of models in the empirical sciences

I began by saying that I wanted to try to show that exact analysis of the relation between empirical theories and relevant data calls for a hierarchy of models of different logical type. The examination of the example from learning theory was meant to exhibit some aspects of this hierarchy. I would like to conclude with some more general remarks that are partially suggested by this example.

One point of concern on my part has been to show that in moving from the level of theory to the level of experiment we do not need to abandon formal methods of analysis. From a conceptual standpoint the distinction between pure and applied mathematics is spurious — both deal with set-theoretical entities, and the same is true of theory and experiment.

It is a fundamental contribution of modern mathematical statistics to have recognized the explicit need of a model in analyzing the significance of experimental data. It is a paradox of scientific method that the branches of empirical science that have the least substantial theoretical developments often have the most sophisticated methods of evaluating evidence. In such highly empirical branches of science a large hierarchy of models is not necessary, for the theory being tested is not a theory with a genuine logical structure but a collection of heuristic ideas. The only models needed are something like the models of the experiment and models of the data discussed in connection with the example from learning theory.

Present statistical methodology is less adequate when a genuine theory is at stake. The hierarchy of models outlined in our example corresponds in a very rough way to statisticians' concepts of a sample space, a population, and a sample. It is my own opinion that the explicit and exact use of the logical concept of model will turn out to be a highly useful device in clarifying the theory of experimental design, which many statisticians still think of as an "art" rather than a "science." Limitations of space have prevented working out the formal relations between the theory of experimental design and the theory of models of the data, as I conceive it.

However, my ambitions for the theory of models in the empirical sciences are not entirely such practical ones. One of the besetting sins of philosophers of science is to overly simplify the structure of science. Philosophers who write about the representation of scientific theories as logical calculi then go on to say that a theory is given empirical meaning by providing interpretations or coordinating definitions for some of the primitive or defined terms of the calculus. What I have attempted to argue is that a whole hierarchy of models stands between the model of the basic theory and the complete experimental experience. Moreover, for each level of the hierarchy there is a theory in its own right. Theory at one level is given empirical meaning by making formal connections with theory at a lower level. Statistical or logical investigation of the relations between theories at these different levels can proceed in a purely formal, set-theoretical manner. The more explicit the analysis the less place there is for non-formal considerations. Once the empirical data are put in canonical form (at the level of models of data in Table 1), every question of systematic evaluation that arises is a formal one. It is important to notice that the questions to be answered are formal but not mathematical — not mathematical in the sense that their answers do not in general follow from the axioms of set theory (or some other standard framework for mathematics). It is precisely the fundamental problem of scientific method to state the principles of scientific methodology that are to be used to answer these questions — questions of measurement, of goodness of fit, of parameter estimation, of identifiability, and the like. The principles needed are entirely formal in character in the sense that they have as their subject matter set-theoretical models and their comparison. Indeed, the line of argument I have tried to follow in this paper leads to the conclusion that the only systematic results possible in the theory of scientific methodology are purely formal, but a general defense of this conclusion cannot be made here.

References

[1] Estes, W. K., and P. Suppes. Foundations of linear models. Chap. 8 in *Studies in Mathematical Learning Theory*, R. R. Bush and W. K. Estes, eds., Stanford, Calif., Stanford Univ. Press, 1959, 432 pp.

[2] Suppes, P. *Introduction to logic*, Princeton, Van Nostrand, 1957, 312 pp.

[3] Suppes, P. A comparison of the meaning and uses of models in mathematics and the empirical sciences, *Synthese*, Vol. 12 (1960), 287–301.

[4] Suppes, P., and R. C. Atkinson. *Markov Learning Models for Multiperson Interactions*, Stanford, Calif., Stanford Univ. Press, 1960, xii+296 pp.

DETERMINISM AND INDETERMINISM IN A NEW "LEVEL" CONCEPTION OF MATTER

J. P. VIGIER

Institute Henri Poincaré, Paris, France

The question of determinism in any given physical theory can only be discussed within the frame of its basic postulates. To understand it within the frame of quantum mechanics let us first briefly review the basic postulates of classical Mechanics.

We know classical mechanics rests on five basic philosophical postulates.

A. The world exists objectively, independently of any observer.

B. Any motion in nature can be described in the frame of the space-time "Arena". This implies that we can describe such motions by successive positions occupied at different times.

C. One can consider any physical system as an assembly of "material points" without dimensions; points endowed with a finite number of properties (mass, etc.).

D. The motion of these points results from "forces" independent of these points; forces that are governed by differential equations which represent the laws of nature. In other terms these "laws" exist independently of any object and if we know all initial positions, velocities, and forces of a given material system, we can predict its evolution for all subsequent time.

E. This system of laws is "complete": meaning the laws of nature are in finite number and well determined. This implies that if we knew all initial positions and velocities in nature, we could predict the future with absolute certainty.

This set of postulates (especially the last two) constitute what is called "Newtonian (or Laplacian) determinism". In their frame there is no such thing as objective probability, since all statistical laws (the gas laws, for example) result in reality from very complex motions (due to uncorrelated collisions) which one could in principle analyse in detail. All such laws should be derivable from the basic determinist laws.

The progress of physics has exploded this beautiful scheme in two steps.

I) Starting from the Michelson-Morley experiment, Einstein proposed a theory (relativity) which deeply modified postulates B, C, and D.

Conserving postulate A, he first introduced the idea that the "arena" and the matter moving within were not independent. More precisely he unifies B and C by stating that nature is a field (describable by a non-Riemannian geometry); matter being constituted therein by singularities. This is a very important step, since it suggests for the first time that the elements of matter do not conserve their material identity in the course of motion and can be compared in a sense to vortices moving within a liquid.

This conference is a synthesis of the views of many physicists among whom are Professors de Broglie, Yukawa, and especially Professor Bohm. No attempt will be made here to distinguish between their respective contributions.

Einstein's second step is to unify C and D. He considers the forces (and the laws which govern their behaviour) as reflecting the local properties of the field considered as a whole (including its singularities); so that the singularity's behaviour is completely determined and results from field behaviour. Finally Einstein conserves postulate E.

II) The second step corresponds to quantum mechanics.

Starting from the "black-body" radiation, the "probabilistic interpretation of quantum mechanics developed by Bohr, Born, Heisenberg, and others, implies an even more radical modification of the five classical postulates:

a) The probabilistic interpretation of quantum mechanics first rejects postulate A. It assumes there is no objective existence outside of observation, and no statement is valid which does not take into account the simultaneity, observable-observer.

b) It also rejects postulate B, namely, the possible description within the space-time "arena". As a consequence of Heisenberg's uncertainty relations, Professor Bohr describes particles as "unsharply defined beings within the frame of space and time". As a result they can only be described by distribution probabilities.

c) Professor Bohr's next step is to accept without modification the classical picture of point-like particles devoid of internal structure but endowed with mass.

d) He also accepts the classical idea of "law", but changes its significance. The laws will apply deterministically to probability distributions and govern their behaviour in space-time. We note here that the relation between (c) and (d) is more complex than in classical mechanics because of the complementarity principle. The particle is either a wave or a point; it is never both at the same time.

e) The last step in the probabilistic interpretation is to accept E but to interpret the "completeness" in terms of probabilities. This is expressed in von Neumann's famous theorem which states that all we will ever know and all there is to know about a particle is expressed in its wave function and in the laws of quantum mechanics.

This implies two important consequences. The first is that probability in the quantum mechanical sense has nothing to do with the classical "objective" probability. By definition it cannot be explained in terms of "hidden" parameters or deeper motions. It constitutes an *a priori* limitation to scientific knowledge. It is absolute probability.

The second is that quantum mechanics is a final step in scientific knowledge, since its laws are complete and finite. In that sense the probabilistic interpretation could be called "Newtonian (or Laplacian) indeterminism", since it accepts all basic assumptions of classical mechanics reinterpreted in terms of probabilities.

Now such positions (in particular the assumption that one has reached a final stage in research) have always been contradicted by the history of science itself. Moreover, we know there is already some trouble with quantum mechanics, not only mathematical (the famous divergencies) but also physical, since it does not account for the variety and transformation laws of elementary particles.

The question raised is therefore to see whether it is not possible to build a "deeper" theory (valid at distances $< 10^{-13}$ cm.) which would yield quantum mechanics as a limiting case.

This has led to the development of the so-called "level" theory, an attempt which I will try to summarize in the following way.

A′) We propose to come back to postulate A, that is, to accept the idea that particles exist independently of any observer. The qualitative difference between macroscopic and microscopic bodies will be in their relation with experiments. No real observation can be performed on microobjects which does not perturbate them in a significant way.

B′) We propose to drop the classical point-like description of the particle and assume it has, effectively, an extended structure (and therefore an infinite number of degrees of freedom) within the frame of an Einstein-like space-time. This means particles have simultaneously singular and wave-like aspects and should be considered as different types of excitations of universal fundamental field.

C′) We propose to drop the "completeness" postulate and accept as a starting point the idea that nature contains an infinite number of "levels", so that no theory corresponding to a given level can claim to explain the totality of nature.

To make things clearer we say there are no such things as points in space or instants in time but only cells and intervals. For distances $> 10^{-8}$ cm (and the corresponding time intervals) we can abstract certain collective parameters which will objectively satisfy classical mechanics. For distances 10^{-13} cm $< x < 10^{-8}$ cm new properties appear which imply quantum mechanics. If we go deeper, new mechanics may appear to be associated with finer "hidden" properties we are not able to measure at present.

In that sense the new quantum numbers (isobaric spin, etc.) associated with elementary particles may well correspond to real variables describing their internal structure.

In principle there should be no limit to such an analysis. Any seemingly stable structure would recover motions at a deeper level. Nothing would be stable, since stability would only recover periodic deeper behavior.

In this scheme both deterministic and probability laws would be necessary. Determinism would recover statistical behavior which in its turn could be analyzed as uncorrelated deeper motion, and so on ad infinitum. In principle, new mechanics would be needed as we descend step by step into the infinitesimal world or ascend into higher and higher energy domains.

This leads to a scheme and conceptions which strongly recall the fundamental ideas introduced by Heroditus in philosophy. In the "level theory" matter and motion cannot be separated. Each element of nature has its own specific history. There is no limit to the complexity of any specific phenomena, no *a priori* limit to the development and to possible progress of human knowledge.

Symposium on Theoretical and Empirical Aspects of Science

THE CONTROVERSY: DEDUCTIVISM VERSUS INDUCTIVISM

JANINA KOTARBIŃSKA
University of Warsaw, Warsaw, Poland

1

Inductivism is the view, universally known and almost universally adopted, which recognizes the inductive method to be the basic method in the empirical sciences. Deductivism is upheld by Professor K. Popper, whose standpoint originated in his criticism of inductivism [4]. His criticism is quite revolutionary, since it calls for the elimination of induction from the so-called inductive sciences and for its replacement by the deductive method as the only one which does not sin against the requirements of logical correctness and which makes it possible, in general, to avoid the difficulties encountered by induction. It is Professor Popper's conviction that the deductivist theory has succeeded in working out a detailed program of such a method. As indicated by the title, the purpose of this paper is to examine the issues emerging from the controversy between deductivism and inductivism.

2

Without entering into details, it can be said that both deductivism and inductivism endeavor to solve the same major problems. In both cases the point is to indicate a method which would make it possible to justify general statements pertaining to an indefinite number of cases—in other words, statements of universal generality—on the strength of individual statements of a certain distinguished type (basic statements, as Popper calls them) and at the same time to establish for the justified statements both an empirical character and a sufficient cognitive value. Discussion is focused, above all, on the issues pertaining to the specific distinct properties of empirical statements, i.e., the criterion of empiricism, and to the conditions on which the cognitive value of such statements depends, i.e., the criterion of their acceptability. The first issue has been widely examined in the literature of the subject, so I confine myself to discussing more significant divergences, devoting attention mainly to the second issue.

When it comes to empiricism, the two theories have a common starting point, which consists in the assumption that certain statements, namely basic statements, are empirical in nature regardless of their relation to other statements, and that precisely those (basic) statements determine the empirical character of all other statements. The empirical statements include, on the one hand, the basic statements, and on the other, all and only such statements which bear a certain definite logical relation to the basic statements. But both the basic statements and the logical relations involved are interpreted in different ways.

In the case of inductivism, basic statements are usually characterized as individual statements of the type "A is B" which describe observable phenomena. In the case of deductivism they are characterized as individual existential statements, that is, statements of the type "There is such and such an object in such and such a place and at such and such time", which describe phenomena that are observable intersubjectively.[1]

More important is another difference, which is revealed in the different characterizations of the empirical non-basic statements. Although the inductivists see, according to Popper, the empirical character of the non-basic statements in the fact that they are subject both to verification and to falsification with the aid of finite and non-contradictory sets of basic statements, Prof. Popper drops the conditions of verifiability and makes the empirical character of statements depend solely on whether they admit the possibility of being falsified by means of basic statements. Many times in the literature attention has been drawn to the difficulties connected with these views.

3

The problem of the criterion of acceptability of empirical statements is usually examined separately with reference to the basic statements and the remaining empirical statements.

If the only requirement with respect to the basic statements is that they must have a certain definite outward form and describe observable or intersubjectively observable phenomena — and only such a requirement has been taken into consideration in the case of the interpretations discussed so far — then one obtains an infinite number of statements satisfying these conditions, including contradictory statements. Among those statements which Prof. Popper sometimes calls "possible basic statements" (this terminology will be used hereafter) one only has to choose the basic statements in the proper sense of the word; that is, choose those which in

[1]It would be well to mention that in the vocabulary of the deductionist the term "observable" in contrariety to "observed" is a non-psychological term.

the empirical sciences would decide the acceptance or rejection of all the remaining statements without being themselves justified by any other statements. What would be the criterion of choice of such basic statements in the proper sense of the word?

The inductivists usually ascribe this role to perceptual statements as statements which are justified directly by perceptual experiences, and as such require no further justification. To this Professor Popper raises the objection of psychologism which, in his opinion, is not admissible in the field of methodology. He compares it with his own view, which is a different one and which he himself calls conventionalism with reference to the basic statements. According to his standpoint the basic statements, like all statements in general, may be justified exclusively by means of other statements. And since such a process of justification cannot be continued indefinitely, one has to stop sooner or later at some statements as the basic statements (in the proper sense of the term), in spite of the fact that they in principle require a justification and may be falsified as a result of further investigations. Now the selection of such basic statements is always arbitrary and in that sense conventional, since we just accept them by virtue of our decision, as there are no logical reasons which would force us to stop at these statements and not at others.

The intentions behind conventionalism conceived in this way are not quite clear. It is opposed to psychologism, but in what interpretation of that term? Does the psychologism stigmatized here consist in the fact that the choice of the proper basic statements depends on their perceptual nature, in the requirement that such basic statements should state phenomena which not only are observable but have actually been observed by someone? Or does it consist only in the fact that the perceptual nature of the proper basic statements is considered to be the criterion of their complete validity, the reliable guarantee of their being true statements? The critical argument used by Prof. Popper is aimed almost entirely at the second version of psychologism, which is much more far-reaching and, let it be added here, not accepted by all inductivists. But his own suggestions and conclusions, reached as a conclusion of his considerations, seem to testify to much more radical tendencies, which oppose any demands to make the choice of the basic statements depend on psychological criteria. And that probably is Prof. Popper's true intention.

If so, then the methodological program of conventionalism, and consequently of deductivism, of which conventionalism is one of the component parts, leads to extremely paradoxical results: it is programmatically not required when laying the foundations of the empirical sciences to refer to actual observational experience, a freedom of choice being left in that respect. Thus it is admitted that in principle the empirical sciences may become completely independent of the results of observations and experiments, the methodological role of which becomes incomprehensible in conventionalism. The connection between the empirical sciences and experience is confined to the fact that the basic statements of those sciences speak of observable phenomena, and as such are couched in empirical terms. That condition excludes metaphysical fantasy, but does not suffice to exclude fantasy expressed in an empirical language. This is probably no less grave a sin than that with which Prof. Popper reproached inductivism (that criticism being a misdirected one) and which is said to consist in obliterating the demarcation line between science and metaphysics. Here the demarcation line is obliterated between honest empirical knowledge and something else which is not knowledge. Responsibility for that, in the opinion of the present author, rests with the too radical, anti-psychological tendencies revealed by Popper in his treatment of methodology as a branch of logic in the narrower sense of the term, that is, as a discipline concerned with statements solely from the point of view of the logical relations between them.[2]

4

We now come to the issue which is the focal point in the controversy between deductivism and inductivism, namely, the criterion of acceptability of the non-basic empirical statements, in particular statements of universal generality, i.e., nomological statements, which are of exceptional importance in science. Following Prof. Popper, the present author will confine herself to a discussion of the controversy with reference to the nomological statements interpreted in this way.

Both parties agree that the acceptability of such statements is decided by the method of justifying them. But whereas inductivism recommends accepting the nomological statements which are sufficiently justified by inductive inference, deductivism rejects induction as a method devoid of all justifying value and generally useless from the point of view of the needs of science, and at the same time points to another method, the deductive one (also called the method of criticism of hypotheses or the trial-and-error method), which is claimed to have none of the shortcomings that are said to disqualify the inductive method.

Professor Popper's arguments require a more detailed examination. Let us begin with the justifying value. According to him induction cannot be used as a justifying method, since it is a faulty inference from the logical point of view; the conclusion of an induction is not deducible from its premises, and may prove false even if all the premises are true.

The method recommended by the deductivist program is in Prof. Popper's opinion not subject to this criticism. The starting point here always is some

---

[2] [4], pp. 30–32, 99 *et passim*. This is perhaps a good opportunity to mention that Prof. Popper is not always consistent in putting this into effect. For example, a certain breach is made by the assumption, important for deductivism, that the verification of a hypothesis has a justifying value only if it has been made in an honest and thorough way, with the desire to exhaust all the available tests that might be dangerous for the given hypothesis. (Cf. [4], p. 267 *et passim*.)

hypothesis, and the procedure consists in a critical examination of the hypothesis being justified, that is, in drawing from it by deduction logical consequences in the form of basic statements and in investigating whether one of these consequences is not a false statement. If a false consequence is found, the given hypothesis is rejected as false, again as a result of deductive inference. But if all the consequences prove true and, moreover, satisfy certain additional conditions, the given hypothesis is accepted provisionally until a false consequence is found in the course of further investigations. It is claimed that the deductive character of the types of reasoning used in this method and the merely hypothetical acceptance of justified statements make the method correct from the point of view of logical validity. This, according to Prof. Popper, puts an end to the so-called problem of induction with which the theory of induction has been grappling at least since Hume without any prospects for its solution ([5], pp. 33, 42, 265–66).

Let us stop here for a moment. What should one think about the correctness of the view presented above? The answer depends, above all, on the interpretation of induction, against which criticism is leveled, and on the criteria of evaluation of its validity.

Now when referring to induction, Popper, as he explains it at the outset of his analysis ([4], p. 27), has in mind its traditional interpretation, which he believes is extremely common up to this day among those who are in favor of induction. In the case of such an interpretation, "inference is called inductive if it consists in a transition from individual statements (sometimes also called singular statements) such as reports on observations or experiments to universal statements such as hypotheses or theories." Inference is here identified with "transition" from statements to some other statements, and the peculiarity of inductive inference is seen in the type of the statements from which and to which that "transition" takes place.

The vagueness of this formulation is well known. "Transition" from some statements to some other statements, for instance from the statements $A_1, \ldots,$ A_n to the statement B, can be interpreted in at least three ways: either (1) we derive the statement B from the statements $A_1, \ldots, A_n$ as their logical consequence; or (2) we derive the statement B from the statements $A_1 \ldots,$ A_n, already previously accepted, as their logical consequence, and we accept, besides, in the final phase of the whole procedure the statement B; or else (3) we accept the statement B simply because the statements $A_1, \ldots, A_n$ had been accepted before, "acceptance" being interpreted either in the stronger sense of the word, marked by complete certainty about the truth of the statement in question, or in the weaker sense, which covers hypothetical acceptance, without the certainty that the accepted statement is true.

Which of these interpretations is taken into account by Popper when he argues against induction? No comments to that effect are to be found in the text. His objections to induction seem to indicate that he usually understands "transition" in the second sense above; this is the narrowest interpretation in which the term "inference" does not differ in meaning from the term "deductive inference" in its usual sense. In such an interpretation induction is in fact a type of inference that is incorrect from the logical point of view, and consequently does not contribute to the justification of statements obtained as a result of its application.

But this is not the only interpretation of the term "induction" and not even the most common one. Among logicians another interpretation, corresponding to that described under point (3) above, is at least equally frequent. In such an interpretation of the term "inference", induction is understood as a mental process consisting of hypothetically accepting a nomological statement on the basis of individual statements that are its particular cases ([1–3], [6]). It seems that in some parts of his analysis Popper means precisely such an interpretation of induction; at least it is only in the case of such an interpretation that some of the objections he raises can be explained.

The question arises whether, in the light of Prof. Popper's opinion, induction understood in such a way would have to be refused all justifying value. The answer to the question is negative. The method of the criticism of hypotheses is a deductive method only in the sense which singles out deduction because of the chronological sequence of the steps of reasoning and not because of the logical relationship between the conclusion and the premises. From this standpoint the method of criticism of hypotheses is, properly speaking, nothing else than a variation of inductive inference, satisfying certain special conditions. The controversy between deductivism and inductivism becomes then, at least to a certain extent, a purely verbal controversy arising from linguistic misunderstandings.

5

According to Popper, one of the most serious shortcomings of induction is the fact that it does not provide criteria that would make it possible to distinguish between hypotheses which have some scientific value and those which are pseudoscientific and devoid of all cognitive value. The rules of inductive justification admit of the acceptance of a hypothesis as sufficiently justified simply if a certain number of facts that are in conformity with that hypotheses have been found and if no facts to the contrary have been encountered. These requirements are so weak that they can be satisfied with respect to almost every hypothesis. On the other hand, the deductivist rules are much more exacting: before a hypothesis is accepted, it must be examined critically, facts must be sought which would testify against it rather than in its favor, and arguments must be looked for which would speak against the hypothesis in question rather than against rival hypotheses. A hypothesis which does not stand such an examination does not deserve even a provisional acceptance in science.

At first, such an interpretation must seem astonishing. It would appear that the operation consisting in seeking confirmation of a hypothesis does not differ from the operation consisting in submitting that hypothesis to falsification tests, since both operations are in fact reducible to drawing consequences from the hypothesis being verified and to examining whether those consequences are true statements, i.e., conforming with reality, or false statements.

But Professor Popper probably means not the mental procedure as such, but the conditions which are to be satisfied by the consequences obtained if they are to be given a justifying value. Now in Prof. Popper's opinion inductivism rests satisfied with the condition of truth. On the contrary, deductivism assumes that true consequences justify a hypothesis only if there exist "proper (severe) tests", i.e., if the probability of the truth of these consequences is comparatively small in the light of existing knowledge, possible with a provisional assumption of falseness of the hypothesis being verified.

In connection with such a conception of the matter, there may arise doubts as to whether it conforms with the state of things. The principle which ascribes to the facts that agree with the hypothesis being verified the greater justifying value the lesser the probability of the occurrence of such a fact in the light of existing knowledge is often met with, and has been so before, also in the theory of induction, so that there is no need to involve deductivism in these matters.

6

The concept of falsification, which in the deductivist system has played so important a role in the analysis described above (the concept of empirical statement, the theory of criticism of hypotheses), comes to the forefront again in Prof. Popper's analysis of the criterion of differentiation between rival hypotheses from the point of view of their cognitive value; this is the criterion which should guide the choice of that hypothesis which under given circumstances is the most suitable for provisional acceptance. Now according to Professor Popper, the greater or lesser cognitive value of the rival hypotheses depends on the degree of falsification: that hypothesis which is easier to falsify is more valuable, and that hypothesis which is more difficult to falsify is less valuable. That criterion is supposed to be connected with the deductivists' concept of justification. Since the degree of justification of a hypothesis depends on the severity of the tests used, those hypotheses which admit of more severe tests are better. In Popper's opinion — which, let it be noted, is far from obvious — these are precisely the hypotheses which are easier to falsify and which are thus more exposed to disproval.

The question arises, of course, What does it mean to say that one hypothesis is easier to falsify than another? Professor Popper explains this question only partially with respect to some particular cases of generalizations which have the same predicate but whose subjects differ as to extension (one of them is narrower than the other): the more general one is easier to falsify than the less general, because it is false if, but not only if, that narrower generalization is also false. Analogously, from two generalizations which have the same subject but whose predicates differ in the same way as to extension it is easier to falsify the more definite generalization which has the narrower predicate.

It might seem that this point reveals one of the most important differences between the standpoint taken by Prof. Popper and the theory which he opposes, that it is only here that truly essential differences can be seen: when a choice is to be made between four rival hypotheses, differing in the degree of generality or the degree of determinacy and up to now non-abolished, the deductivist prefers the more general and at the same time the more determinate hypothesis as the one which is easier to disprove, whereas the inductivist, as is stressed by Popper himself, would choose the other hypothesis. In the inductivist's striving for knowledge as well justified as possible and in identifying the degree of justification with the degree of certainty, he would accept the least risky hypothesis, which in the least degree goes beyond observation data and consequently is least exposed to falsification, i.e., which is less general.

In the eyes of Popper, that difference of opinion is an extremely important argument in favor of his view. He emphasizes that it is a fact that the natural sciences strive for the most general and most determinate laws and that as science progresses more, such laws are introduced. For instance, in mechanics Newton's law of gravitation long ago replaced Kepler's laws, which have turned out to be special cases. And if more general and more determinate laws are of a lesser value, as it is usually assumed in the theory of induction, then why do we always strive to formulate them? In the opinion of Professor Popper, the theory of inductive justification leads just to such consequences, which are in glaring disagreement with the actual state of science, whereas his own idea adequately explains the trend in the natural sciences: in science we strive for increasingly general and increasingly determinate laws because such laws can more easily be falsified, and that is precisely why they are more valuable.

Is Professor Popper right in making his claim? What he says is rather suggestive, but it is difficult to resist the impression that he simplifies the issue too much and consequently triumphs easily over his adversary. For instance, there are two generalizations: "All planets attract one another with force inversely proportional to the square of the distance between them" and "All bodies attract one another with force inversely proportional to the square of the distance between them"; the scientist verifies those two generalizations exclusively with respect to planets (both will, of course, be confirmed, since Mars, Venus, etc., are both planets and bodies) and then faces the choice between the less general and the more general. Should the scientist in such circumstances always choose the more general one, Popper's objection would be justified, since in view of the inductivist assumptions a more general law would not be as well justified with respect to given observations as a less general law with respect to *the same* observations. But it seems that in fact the situation is somewhat different. In the natural sciences, a more general law is accepted only when observations have been made which exceed the scope of applicability of the less general law and can be explained by the more general law, e.g., the universal law of gravitation replaced Kepler's laws only when Newton noticed that it is not only planets, but various other bodies as well, which gravitate. Thus the law of gravitation is justified on the strength of a different scope of observation than were Kepler's laws. If, moreover, such additional observations are very numerous and much differentiated, then in the light of the traditional theory of induction — just as in the light of Popper's theory — it may be said correctly that Newton's law — in spite of the fact that it is more general and perhaps even just because it is more general — is better justified than Kepler's laws. It might even be said, and not without justice, that as a rule less general (and also less determinate) laws come to be replaced by more general (or more determinate) laws only on the condition that the latter are better justified than were the former. And should it be really so, then we would have to question, at least in part, both the objections raised by Popper against induction and his own theory as well.

Moreover, it seems that a consistent deductivist would object to drawing from his assumption those conclusions which Popper has drawn. The theory of criticism of hypotheses makes the adoption of hypotheses depend not only on the degree of their falsifiability, i.e., their relation to possible basic statements, but also (and perhaps even principally) on the degree of their justification, which is determined by the number, variety, and strictness of the tests used in their verification, that is, by the number and kind of the accepted basic statements used as premises. A greater degree of falsifiability does not necessarily accompany a greater degree of justification. If it does, then the deductivist, too, will not always recognize as better a statement that is more general and more determinate compared with a less general and a less determinate one. He will do so only when these additional conditions are satisfied, conditions which — let it be remarked parenthetically — do not differ from those by which the inductivist is guided in the choice of hypotheses. Thus both of them, the deductivist and the inductivist alike, will probably make the same choice.

7

Such are Professor Popper's more important arguments intended to discredit the inductive method and to pave the way for the method of criticism of hypotheses, built on deductivist principles. It has been my intention to demonstrate that Popper's endeavors have failed, either because his objections against induction were misdirected, or because they referred only to some variations of the theory of induction, mainly those that are most simplified and quite obsolete today, or because they aimed not only at the theory of induction but also at the rival method of criticism of hypotheses.

Moreover, analysis has shown that if induction is interpreted in a certain manner that is rather common today, the method of criticism of hypotheses satisfies all the conditions imposed on induction and thus turns out to be just a special case of the latter.

Thus Professor Popper's investigations have failed in their principal purpose, yet they have nevertheless succeeded in bringing other valuable results. Such a wealth of detailed methodological recommendations as is contained in Popper's work is probably not to be found elsewhere; the same applies to the great number of pertinent and penetrating observations concerning the errors, shortcomings, and abuses that often mark actual inductive procedures, and to the strong emphasis laid on the need for caution and criticism even in the case of a provisional acceptance of hypotheses. It must be borne in mind that these are matters of primary importance both for research practice and for a rational attitude in collective life.

His critical analysis concerned with the various concepts of probability and with the endeavors to apply them in the theory of justification of hypotheses also deserves special mention. I have not raised these subjects here, since their discussion would take too much time and yet, so it seems, would not affect my conclusions. Besides, Professor Popper's opinions in these matters have undergone certain essential modifications that are to find expression in the second volume of *The Logic of Scientific Discovery*, already announced but not yet published.

References

[1] Jevons, S. *The Principles of Science*, new ed., New York, 1958.

[2] Lalande, A. *Vocabulaire technique et critique de la philosophie*, 5th ed., 1947.

[3] *Philosophical Writings of Pierce*. Selected and edited by J. Buchler, New York, 1955.

[4] Popper, K. *The Logic Scientific Discovery*, London, 1959.

[5] Popper, K. Philosophy of Science. A personal report, in *British Philosophy in the Mid-Century*, London, 1957, pp. 182–83.

[6] Stebbing, L. *A Modern Introduction to Logic*, 4th ed., London, 1945.

THE THEORETICAL AND EMPIRICAL ASPECTS OF SCIENCE

HENRYK MEHLBERG

University of Chicago, Chicago, Illinois, U.S.A.

1. Introduction

Let me begin by surveying some significant theoretical and empirical aspects of science. This procedure can establish a frame of reference for the subsequent discussion of our Symposium and it is therefore likely to be of use, no matter how sketchy my survey must be in view of its time-limit, and no matter how personal this survey is bound to be, since philosophy is involved.

I take it that only those who are blind to man's present situation can fail to realize that by now science has become both a universally decisive and universally unfamiliar feature of this situation. Of course, the main reason for man's present unfamiliarity with the information, the methods, the equipment which the scientists got hold of in the last few thousand years, and, particularly, in the last three centuries, is the increasing specialization of scientific activity, indispensable for the increasing speed of the advance of science. Auguste Comte anticipated this situation over a century ago and felt that a study of this comparatively novel feature of the philosophical landscape which now goes by the name of the "philosophy of science", i.e., a philosophical and broad-minded science of science, is the sole thing man can do about this predicament of an increasingly important and increasingly unfamiliar science.

The topic of this Symposium is obviously concerned with a single pivotal issue in the philosophy of science. In this branch of philosophy, as elsewhere, we have to simplify and to oversimplify in order to get started at all. I shall therefore deal, in the opening address of this Symposium, with contemporary science as reducible to the class of all contemporary scientific theories. I realize, of course, that there is more to science than the class of all the theories which pertain to it. Thus, interdependent systems of scientific theories are no less important in the logical structure of science than single scientific theories, as I have tried to show elsewhere. However, since we have to start with a simplified version of science, let me discuss the only problem on our agenda, i.e., the relationship between empirical and theoretical aspects of science, on the simplifying assumption that these two aspects refer only to single scientific theories. And, first of all, let us try to make it sufficiently clear what is meant by a scientific theory and, in particular, by the distinction between the empirical and the theoretical aspects of such a theory.

To begin with, let us explain what is meant by a scientific theory, e.g., Newtonian mechanics. Well, such a theory is a finitely axiomatizable deductive system of law-like statements which involve a few specific concepts associated with this theory, provided that the truth of these law-like statements be reliably established by available observational results. For instance, the statements of the theory of mechanics involve only the concepts of force and of mass in addition to kinematic concepts like rest, motion, frame of reference, etc. All the law-like statements pertaining to mechanics and shown to be true within the latter are termed mechanical laws.

Similarly, in regard to any other theory T, it is always possible to indicate the specific concepts of T, the deductively organized laws of T which involve some or all of these specific concepts and make up T. Given T, it is also possible to indicate the particular facts described by the instances of the laws of T, or, as the saying goes, governed by the laws of T. A basic scientific achievement is the ability to establish universal and practically non-controversial scientific laws, like those of mechanics; such laws are items of relevant and reliable information. Another, even more fundamental scientific achievement, is the ability to offer, in scientific theories, packages of infinitely numerous laws, each of which governs, in turn, an infinity of facts.

2. Empirical Aspects of a Theory

(a) The Summarizing Function of a Theory. The preliminary question we have now to discuss is the precise meaning to be attached to the *empirical* and *theoretical* aspects of any scientific theory that fits the description just given, say in the case of mechanics. At a later stage, we shall define theoretical aspects in terms of the *empirical* ones. Accordingly, we have to characterise the empirical aspects of a theory first, and we shall soon realize that these aspects are determined, in substance, by a few essential functions discharged by any scientifically acceptable theory within the scientist's over-all activity. In the case of mechanics, e.g., as in any other theory, one of its essential functions is summarizing an infinite number of mechanical laws and thereby making an infinite set of laws manageable. The conciseness achieved by the physicist in this respect is unparalleled. The whole theory of mechanics can be condensed into a single variational principle (e.g., the Law of Least Action) expressible in a few letters. Yet, the consequences derivable from this variational principle are not only co-extensive with other formulations of mechanics; they are also infinitely numerous in a genuine sense, since there is an infinity of mechanical laws, no two of which are logically equivalent to each other.

This achievement of mechanics is so striking that some outstanding philosophers of physics, like Kirchhoff and Mach, felt that the ability to condense a potentially infinite set of informative, law-like statements into a single, manageable formula is the only function of a scientific theory. We do not have to share their belief in the monopoly of the summarizing function of theories in order to appreciate this function and to list it among the principal functions which an acceptable theory is expected to discharge.

(b) The Predictive Function of a Theory. A question arises here naturally: does the theory T, say mechanics, only summarize mechanical laws and facts already established, or must the theory also predict all mechanical laws and facts which may be established on some future occasion? There is no crystal-clear answer in Mach's writings and this historical query is anyway of no concern to us at this juncture. The important fact is that, since the summarizing function of a theory is usually confined to what has already been established, then, to be acceptable, the theory is also expected to *predict* any mechanical law which could possibly come to be discovered; by the same token, the theory must also predict any mechanical fact which would be observed under any specifiable circumstances. As you well know, the predictive success of mechanics is even more spectacular than its summarizing success. For astronomy, say of the solar system, is just a subsystem of mechanics, and the astronomer's ability to predict, say, that a solar eclipse will occur exactly so many years, days, minutes, and seconds from the present moment has so impressed several philosophers of science as to induce them to grant a monopoly to the predictive function of scientific theories similar to the monopoly of their summarizing function which Mach had defended so eloquently. "Savoir c'est prévoir," declared A. Comte, the father of the philosophy of science. Quite a few of our contemporary leading philosophers of science still seem to hold the same view of the role of prediction in scientific theories.

However, let us make the same observation once more: while being very appreciative of the import of the predictive function of scientific theories, we fail to see any conclusive argument in support of granting a monopoly to this function. To put it otherwise: on closer analysis, it seems inevitable at present to part company with both Comte and Mach in so far as their respective monopolistic attitudes towards the predictive and the summarizing functions of scientific theories are concerned. But we do have to admit that summarizing and predicting deserve to be listed among those essential functions which a satisfactory theory is expected to perform.

(c) **The Controlling and Explanatory Functions of a Theory.** Our refusal to grant a monopoly either to the summarizing or to the predictive function of scientific theories is corroborated by another requirement which any acceptable theory must admittedly meet: any theory of this sort should enable us to bring about desirable changes in our environment by following procedures which the theory indicates, or, to put it otherwise, an acceptable theory must provide for the control of our environment. I have little doubt that the *controlling* function of scientific theories is as important as their summarizing and predictive functions. However, once more, I am not prepared to grant a monopoly to the controlling function of a theory by identifying this function with the truth of the theory, as William James implied in his pragmatist version of the concept of truth.

So far I have tried to show that, while summarizing, predicting, and controlling can be fully appreciated as pertaining to the essential functions discharged by any acceptable theory, there is no conclusive reason for granting a monopoly to any of these three functions. As a matter of fact, explanation is another as yet unlisted essential function of any acceptable theory. Apart from providing for a control of relevant phenomena, apart from condensing knowledge achieved in the past and from predicting knowledge to be acquired in the future (whether this knowledge be of a particular fact, or of a universal law, or of another theory derivative from T), the theory T should also determine *why* a fact known to have taken place actually did so, why a law known to be valid in its proper realm of phenomena is actually valid there, why another theory derivative in regard to T contains valid laws only. The explanatory function of scientific theories was almost completely banned during the nineteenth century, when most philosophers of science, influenced by Comte, maintained that a scientist can know what is the case, or what was or will be the case, whereas the very logic of his method allegedly prevented him from determining why things were, are, or will be the way they actually were, are, or will be. This ban on scientific explantion is far from being extinct at present.

However, owing to investigations of several philosophers of science carried out in the last three decades, the logical status of scientific explanation has changed radically.[1] We know today that the predictive and the explanatory functions of a scientific theory are inseparable from each other: a theory cannot be predictively successful unless its explanatory function is satisfactorily discharged, and vice versa. Hence, in view of this result of the logical analysis of scientific explanation, we do not have to repeat the dogma of early nineteenth-century positivism to the effect that while condensed description and prediction are within the province of science, explanation is not. One of the leading works in the philosophy of science published in the current decade (by Professor R. B. Braithwaite) has the significant title *Scientific Explanation*.

(d) The Informational Function of a Theory. Another essential function of scientific theories, which should actually be placed at the top of our list, consists in the fact that such theories provide us with socially relevant and dependable information about objects which are observable by man, on the understanding that the dependability of this information is due to its being backed up by the outcome of other observations carried out by human investigators. In other words, scientific theories provide us with *knowledge* of things observable because that is what socially relevant and reliable information about such things comes to. This fifth, *informational* or *cognitive* function carried out by scientific theories in respect of things observable by man satisfies one of man's strongest needs, viz., the need to know about his

[1]K. R. Popper, *Die Logik der Forschung*, Vienna, Springer, 1935. Subsequent essential contributions to the problem of explanation are contained in C. G. Hempel and P. Oppenheim, "The Logic of Explanation", *Philosophy of Science*, Vol. 15, 1948.

observable environment. The need is obviously similar to the powerful exploratory drive of higher animals, a drive the strength of which has been objectively measured and proved inferior only to the strongest animal drives of maternal protection and thirst.

Let us add that no enigmatic meaning is attached to the concept of empirical knowledge provided by scientific theories which we have just referred to as the fifth essential function of science. A piece of information P, expressed in a statement S of a language L is said to be part of the empirical knowledge possessed by an individual I who speaks L, if S is true in L, and I is induced to believe in S by adequate empirical evidence available to him. This explanation of an item of empirical knowledge does not amount to a full-fledged definition because the explanation contains the troublesome concepts of empirical truth and of "adequate empirical evidence," which themselves call for an additional definition.

These two gaps must be filled. Let us start with the meaning of "empirical truth" which, in my mind, differs from the meaning of truth as applied to statements in the logico-mathematical field. What it means to be true for a statement pertaining to logic or mathematics has been clarified in Tarski's pioneering work on the "Concept of Truth in the Languages of Deductive Sciences." The meaning of empirical truth, however, differs so much from the meaning of truth envisaged by Tarski that the former requires a considerable modification of the "semantic method" applied so successfully by Tarski in the field he envisaged. For instance, the Law of Excluded Middle, valid for languages which Tarski has investigated, has to be abandoned when empirical truth is involved, and quite a few other departures from his "semantical approach" to the meaning of truth in the logico-mathematical field turn out to be inevitable. I have tried to show elsewhere that the meaning of empirical truth can nevertheless be satisfactorily defined, without attributing to this type of truth any enigmatic qualities. Here, I shall have to confine myself to this reference concerning the meaning of empirical truth because of the shortage of time.

What about the other locution we used in tentatively explaining what empirical knowledge is, and which is not self-explanatory either? We resorted to the phrase "adequate empirical evidence" in support of a piece of information P in order to state that an individual who speaks the language L in which P is expressed by the statement S can be credited with knowing empirically that S is the case if this individual is induced to believe in S (which happens to be true in L) by some "adequate empirical evidence" available to him. "Empirical evidence" is very much the same as a set Σ of empirical statements such that all the statements in Σ are true and empirical, that Σ guarantees, or nearly guarantees, the truth of the piece of information P, and that the human investigator under consideration is induced to believe in S because he believes in all the statements in Σ. But when shall we classify a statement S under the heading "empirical"? In the simplest cases when S ascribes a directly observable property to a directly observable object, or asserts a directly observable relation among several directly observable objects, the singular statement having such a content may certainly be considered empirical, or, perhaps, more specifically, directly empirical. In the general case, we can define S' as empirical if and only if S' is a logical consequence of a set of directly empirical statements (on the understanding that the general, model-theoretical sense of logical consequence is involved).

I think that, at this juncture, the comment I just gave should suffice to make the cognitive function discharged by scientific theories as unenigmatic as their summarizing, predictive, controlling, and explaining functions are. We can see now why a scientific theory's ability to exercise any one of the aforementioned functions may be viewed as an empirical aspect of this theory. In respect to the informational function, the answer is straightforward: this function is discharged by a theory T if and only if T provides its users with empirical knowledge (the phrase "empirical knowledge" being construed as just explained). The remaining four essential functions of a scientific theory are, all of them, based on its cognitive function exercised under special circumstances characteristic of the special function under consideration. Thus, the summarizing function is simply the cognitive function exercised by T in regard to an individual X at a moment t when X already knows empirically the set Σ of laws and facts to be summarized, provided that T exercises, in addition, the function of condensation or abbreviation on Σ. A similar explanation applies obviously to prediction and control. Only the explanatory function of T may raise some doubts when classified under the heading of an empirical aspect of T. However, such doubts will tend to disappear once it is realized that the explanatory and the predictive functions of T are co-extensive in regard to any set of statements, since either both functions are performable on the set, or neither is.

3. The Theoretical Aspects of Scientific Theories

We shall now try to show that scientific theories could not discharge the aforementioned five essential functions implied in their empirical aspects, if these theories were not provided with a set of at least three different components which do not correspond directly to the empirical aspects of any theory but on closer analysis turn out to be nevertheless indispensable.

The three components of a scientific theory T which make up its theoretical aspect can be designated as (a) the mathematical formalism of T, (b) the logical formalism of T, and (c) the metaphysical formalism of T. Let us start with component (a), which is likely to be the least controversial.

(a) The Mathematical Formalism of a Theory. To begin with, let us consider briefly von Neumann's axiomatic system for quantum mechanics. This system consists, in substance, of Schrödinger's (time-dependent) partial differential equation and of Born's "Rule of Statistical Interpretation." Yet, although von Neumann's work is entitled *The Mathematical*

Foundations of Quantum Mechanics, the entire first half of his work deals neither with Schrödinger's equation nor with Born's Statistical Rule. Instead, it concentrates exclusively on the mathematical theory of functional spaces called Hilbert-spaces, which have, all of them, a denumerably infinite number of dimensions, that consist of square-integrable functions, but display nevertheless a strange similarity to ordinary, Euclidean, three-dimensional space. The theory of such functional spaces has become, ever since von Neumann's work, the central mathematical tool of quantum mechanics. In the case of the hydrogen atom, for example, which consists, practically speaking, of an ordered pair of material points with opposite electrical charges, this mathematical tool is vitally important because it is necessary to associate the hydrogen system with an appropriate, infinitely-dimensional Hilbert-space in order to provide for the applicability of quantum-mechanical laws to it.

Nevertheless, the theory of Hilbert-spaces, usually referred to as the "mathematical formalism" of quantum mechanics, is but a theoretical aspect of this empirical theory. What is involved in classifying the Hilbert-spaces under the heading of a theoretical aspect of quantum theory? Well, first of all, the theory of these functional spaces does not discharge any of the essential functions which an acceptable empirical theory should be able to perform according to our previous discussion. But there is another, more easily applicable criterion to show that the Hilbert-spaces are merely a theoretical aspect of quantum-mechanics. The point is that the mathematical theory of these spaces is interchangeable in principle and has often been interchanged with another mathematical theory, within the framework of quantum mechanics, viz., with the theory of infinite matrices, without affecting any one of the empirical functions of quantum mechanics and, in particular, without affecting the observational consequences of quantum theoretical axioms. To use the official terminology, the theory of Hilbert-spaces and the theory of infinite matrices are simply two alternative mathematical formalisms of the same empirical theory. In our more general terminology related to the empirical and the theoretical aspects of a given empirical theory, we can simply say that Hilbert-spaces constitute a theoretical aspect of quantum mechanics because the substitution of a Hilbert-space for a theory of infinite matrices leaves invariant the empirical functions of quantum mechanics.

We thus obtain a first significant class of the theoretical properties of a particular empirical theory, viz., the class of all alternative mathematical formalisms of this theory. Another example of the mathematical formalism of an empirical theory is provided by the use of tensor calculus in Einstein's general theory of relativity.

(b) The Logical Formalism of a Theory. The logic implicit in an empirical theory constitutes a more fundamental theoretical aspect of the latter. We shall term this aspect the logical *formalism* of the theory under consideration. The more fundamental nature of the logical aspect of a theory is made apparent by the fact that the substitution of two alternative mathematical formalisms in a theory would not be viewed in general as affecting the theory itself; whereas the question of whether quantum mechanics stands to gain or to lose if we were to replace its conventional logical formalism with an alternative one would be intrinsically interesting and would be evaluated with a good deal of suspicion and concern.

This applies, e.g., to the von Neumann-Birkhoff result that some purely physical assumptions of quantum mechanics could be dropped without affecting any empirical function of this theory, provided that the classical logic used in conventional presentations of quantum mechanics (and based, usually, on the sentential and the predicate calculi developed by Whitehead and Russell) is replaced by an appropriately modified logical calculus of sentences. A similar observation can be made apropos of the numerous suggestions that we introduce into quantum mechanics, some non-classical, multi-valued logic of the sort created by Lukasiewicz and Post, e.g., a three-valued logic envisaged in von Weizsäcker's earlier version of quantum theoretical formalism. Von Weizsäcker's more recent idea that in quantum mechanics the manifold of truth-values ascribable to any statement has the cardinality and order of a two-dimensional continuum, provides a more striking example of an alternative logical formalism which may suit quantum mechanics. I shall here skip logical formalisms involving a ramified theory of types, a simplified theory of types, a cumulative one, one involving transfinite types, or one which does without types at all. I shall also skip logical formalisms involving modal vs. non-modal calculi, extensional vs. intensional calculi, formalisms with finite or recursively or non-recursively infinite vocabularies, lists of axioms, and lists of rules of inference (the latter referring possibly to infinitely long proofs characterized by a specifiable transfinite ordinal number).

The possibility of using, in quantum mechanics, any one of these infinitely numerous and distinct logical formalisms has disturbed several outstanding investigators, and has induced some of them to reject the age-long belief in the impossibility of observationally refuting a logical truth and quite a few other equally classical assumptions. Yet it is hardly the case that any conclusive argument has been produced against the use, within quantum mechanics, of any logical formalism chosen from an ever-increasing array of logics produced today on the assembly line. The only sensible conclusion to be drawn from this situation is that the logical formalism of an empirical theory (say, of quantum mechanics) simply exemplifies another theoretical aspect of this theory. We may grant that the theoretical aspect which corresponds to a particular logical formalism is in many ways less familiar and more disturbing than any mathematical aspect of this theory. However, all the logical and the mathematical formalisms of a particular empirical theory share the privilege or the calamity (no matter how one feels about it) of being merely a theoretical aspect of the theory.

(c) The Metaphysical Formalism of a Theory. Let us now comment briefly on a third type of formalism which may be associated with an empirical theory, and so may form a new, theoretical aspect of the latter. I have in mind the distinctive role played in all advanced axiomatized scientific theories by axioms which are undecidable on logico-mathematical grounds and are not susceptible to any observational test either. We shall refer to the class of such assumptions as the "metaphysical formalism of the theory" and shall without reservation admit that the logical status of the metaphysical formalism of any theory has seemed very suspicious, to say the least, ever since the emergence of the so-called pragmatist "Verifiability Theory of Meaning." For, according to this theory, an assumption which is undecidable on mathematico-logical and observational grounds has no meaning. On the European continent, this attitude towards the metaphysical formalism of empirical theories seems to have been independently re-discovered by Viennese neo-positivists like the early Carnap and Wittgenstein, and to have then been very successfully sold to a considerable fraction of the world's present philosophical population, perhaps mainly by A. J. Ayer.

Within my time limits, I cannot afford to show in detail that the metaphysical formalism of advanced scientific theories is both meaningful and indispensable. I have tried to do it to the best of my ability in *The Reach of Science.* Nor shall I spell out some of the interesting consequences of the presence of a metaphysical formalism in all advanced scientific theories. The question why the assumptions of a particular theory which are undecidable either on mathematico-logical or on observational grounds should be considered as an integral part of the theoretical aspect of this theory, like the mathematical and the logical aspects of it, is easily answered. In my aforementioned volume, I have tried to prove that assumptions pertaining to the metaphysical formalism of a theory, while meaningful and indispensable, are nevertheless devoid of any truth-value. No wonder, therefore, that such assumptions can always be replaced by others which also transcend the possibilities of logico-mathematical proof or of an observational verification and are, therefore, devoid for similar reasons of any definite truth-value. In other words, the metaphysical formalism of a theory shares with the mathematical and logical formalisms the inability to perform any of the essential empirical functions of the theory, the interchangeability with alternative formalisms which leaves the empirical functions unaltered, and finally, meaningfulness and indispensability. Some of the metaphysical formalisms are extremely versatile, almost omnipresent. This holds, e.g., of Euclidean and similar geometries, since the simplest geometrical assumptions (say, to the effect that between any two distinct points there is at least one more point) proved to be undecidable on logico-mathematical and on observational grounds. The concepts which occur essentially in such assumptions, e.g., that of a geometrical point, are responsible for the essential undecidability of these assumptions and are usually referred to as "theoretical constructs."

This shows also what is essentially the interrelation between the empirical and the theoretical aspects of a theory. No theoretical aspect of a theory is able to discharge any of the theory's essential functions of summarizing, explaining, predicting, controlling, or informing. But, on closer examination, it turns out that none of these essential functions of an advanced theory could possibly be discharged without the theory's theoretical aspects, i.e., if the theory were not associated with a mathematical, a logical, and a metaphysical formalism. This interconnection between the empirical and theoretical aspects of a theory has several implications which may be of interest in the context of our discussion. One of these implications points to the legitimacy of metaphysical, epistemological, and ethical investigations, no matter what any verifiability theory of meaning may adduce against such legitimacy. Another implication shows the legitimacy of several unorthodox interpretations of quantum theory which disagree with the Copenhagen interpretation. In particular, the De Broglie-Bohm-Vigier interpretation of quantum mechanics as well as the Landé interpretation, prove to be as legitimate as the one manufactured in Copenhagen if the interrelation of the empirical and the theoretical aspects of quantum mechanics is duly taken into account.

SOME COMMENTS ON TRUTH AND THE GROWTH OF KNOWLEDGE

K. R. POPPER

University of London, London, England

What I have in mind when I speak of the growth of scientific knowledge is the repeated overthrow of scientific theories and their replacement by better ones — rather than the accumulation of observations or of 'data'. While in most fields of human endeavour there is change, but not progress, it is my thesis that *in science we have a criterion of progress*.

In other words, we *know* what a good scientific theory should be like, and what kind of theory would be better still — even before it has been tested — provided it passes certain crucial tests. It is my thesis that this (meta-scientific) knowledge makes it possible to speak of progress in science, and of a rational choice between theories.

This is due to the fact that in science, we can learn from our mistakes. I assert that it is the method of critical discussion and the critical attitude (as opposed to that of looking for positive justification[1]) which makes progress in science possible — that is, the choice of better theories. This critical method constitutes the rationality of science. One may also say: if scientific knowledge ceases to grow, if science ceases to progress, it will lose its rational and its empirical character; for the rational and empirical character of science lies in the way it makes progress — and this means, the way in which we discriminate between theories and choose the better theory.

I

I have said that we may know of a theory, even before it has been tested, that *if* it passes certain tests it will be better than some other theory. Thus I assert that we have a criterion of relative potential satisfactoriness, or of potential progressiveness, which can be applied to a theory even before we know whether or not it will turn out, by the passing of some crucial tests, to be satisfactory in fact.

This criterion of relative satisfactoriness (which I introduced some time ago[2]) allows us sometimes to *grade* certain theories according to their degree of relative satisfactoriness. It is an extremely simple and intuitive criterion. It states that we should prefer a theory which tells us more, that is to say, which contains the greater amount of information; which is logically stronger; which has the greater explanatory and predictive power; and which can there-

---

[1]See especially [6] and [7].

[2]See the discussion of degree of testability, empirical content, corroborability, and corroboration in [4] and [5], especially sections 31–46, 82–85, and in appendix * ix in [5]; also the discussion of degrees of explanatory power in this appendix, and the comparison of Einstein's and Newton's theories in [5] note 7 on p. 401.

fore be more severely tested by comparing predicted facts with observations. In short, we prefer an interesting and a daring and a highly informative theory to a trivial one.

All these properties which we desire in a theory can be shown to amount to one and the same thing: to a higher *degree of empirical content,* or of *testability.*[3]

II

My study of the *content* of a theory (or of any statement whatsoever) was based on the simple and obvious idea that the content of a *conjunction* of two statements will always be greater than, or equal to, that of any of its components. Writing $Ct(a)$ for 'the content of the statement a', and 'ab' for the conjunction of a and b, we have

(1) $$Ct(a) \leqq Ct(ab) \geqq Ct(b).$$

Now this reminds us at once of the monotony law of probability theory,

(2) $$P(a) \geqq P(ab) \leqq P(b),$$

where the unequality signs are inverted. Together, these two laws state that, with increasing content, probability decreases; or, in other words, that content increases with increasing *im*probability.

It is an inescapable consequence of the trivial fact that, if growth of knowledge means theories of increasing content, it also must mean theories of decreasing probability. Thus, if our aim is the advancement, the growth of knowledge, then a high probability cannot possibly be our aim also; for these two aims would be incompatible.

I found this trivial yet fundamental result about thirty years ago, and I been preaching it ever since. Yet the prejudice that a high probability must be something desirable is so deeply ingrained that my trivial result is still held by many to be paradoxical;[4] and all kinds of more or less sophisticated theories have been designed to get over it.[5] I believe I have shown that none of these is, or can be, successful.[6] But, what is more important, they are quite unnecessary. The simple fact has to be accepted that the property which we cherish in theories and which we may perhaps call 'verisimilitude' or 'truthlikeness' is *not* a probability — in the sense of the calculus of probability of which (2) is an inescapable theorem.

Thus if we aim, in science, at a high informative content — if the high content of a theory indicates progress or growth — then we have to admit that we also aim at a low probability, in the sense of the calculus of probability. And since a low probability means a high probability of being falsified, it follows that a high degree of falsifiability, refutability, or testability is

---

[3]See [4], [5], section 35; and [1], p. 406.

[4]See for example [2].

[5]See for example [1], pp. 5725–73, and 574–575.

[6]See for example [4], [5], [7].

one of the aims in science — in fact it is precisely the same aim as a high informative content.

The criterion of potential satisfactoriness is thus testability, or improbability: it is only a highly testable or improbable theory which we find worth testing, and which we actually find satisfactory if it stands up to severe tests — those tests to which we could point as crucial for the theory before they were ever undertaken.

III

The severity of our tests can be objectively compared; and if we like, we can define a measure of their severity as follows.

Let h be the hypothesis to be tested; let e be the test statement (the evidence), and b the 'background knowledge', that is to say, all those things which we accept (tentatively) as unproblematic while we are testing the theory (b may also contain statements of the character of initial conditions). Let us assume, to start with, that e is a logical consequence of h and b (this assumption will be later relaxed), so that $P(e, hb) = 1$. For example, e may be a statement of a predicted position of the planet Mars, derived from Newton's theory h and our knowledge of past positions which forms part of b.

We then can say that if we take e as a test of h, the severity of this test will be the greater the less probable e is, given b alone (without h); that is to say, the smaller is $P(e, b)$, the probability of e given b.

There are in the main two methods[7] of defining the severity

$$S(e, b)$$

of the test e, given b. One starts from the idea of content as the *complement* of probability

(3) $$Ct_1(a) = 1 - P(a);$$

the other starts from the idea of content as the *reciprocal* of probability

(4) $$Ct_2(a) = 1/P(a).$$

The first suggests a definition like $S_1(e, b) = 1 - P(e, b)$ or, better,

(5) $$S_1(e, b) = (1 - P(e, b))/(1 + P(e, b)),$$

that is to say, it suggests that we measure the severity of the test by Ct_1 or, better, by something like a 'normalized' Ct_1 (using $1 + P(e, b)$ as a normalizing factor). The second suggests that we measure the severity of the test simply by Ct_2:

(6) $$S_2(e, b) = Ct_2(e, b) = 1/P(e, b).$$

We may now generalize these definitions by relaxing the demand that e logically follows from h and b, or even the weaker demand that

$$P(e, hb) = 1.$$

Instead we now assume that there is some probability $P(e, hb)$, which may or may not be equal to 1. (Thus e need no longer be fully predicted by hb.)

---

[7]See especially note *1 to section 83, p. 270, of [5]

This suggests that, in order to obtain a generalization of (5) and (6), we substitute in both these formulae the more general term '$P(e, hb)$' for '1'. We thus arrive at the following generalized definitions of the severity of the test e as a supporting evidence of the theory h, given the background knowledge b.

(7) $$S_1(e, h, b) = (P(e, hb) - P(e, b))/(P(e, hb) + P(e, b)),$$

(8) $$S_2(e, h, b) = P(e, hb)/P(e, b).$$

These are our measures of the severity of tests, *qua* supporting evidence. There is little to choose between them since the transition from the one to the other is order-preserving;[8] that is to say, the two are topologically invariant. (The same holds, if we replace the measures Ct_2 and S_2 by their logarithms[9] — for example by $\log_2 S_2$ — in order to make these measures additive.)

IV

Having defined a measure of the severity of our tests, we can now use the same method to define the explanatory power $E(h, e, b)$ of a theory h (and, if we like, in a somewhat similar way, the degree of corroboration[10] of h) with respect to e, in the presence of b:

(9) $$E_1(h, e, b) = S_1(e, h, b),$$

(10) $$E_2(h, e, b) = S_2(e, h, b).$$

These definitions indicate that the explanatory power of a theory h (with respect to some explicandum e) is the greater the more severe is e if taken as a test of the theory h.

It can now be shown quite easily that the maximum degree of the explanatory power of a theory, or of the severity of its tests, depends upon the (informative or empirical) content of the theory.

Thus our criterion of progress or of the potential growth of knowledge will be the increase of the informative content, or the empirical content, of our theories and, at the same time, the increase of their testability.

The thesis that the criterion here proposed actually dominates the progress of science can easily be illustrated with the help of historical examples. Kepler's and Galileo's theories were unified and superseded by Newton's stronger and better testable theory, and similarly Fresnel's and Faraday's theories by Maxwell's. Newton's and Maxwell's theories, in their turn, were unified and superseded by Einstein's. And in each of these cases, the progress made was towards a stronger and therefore logically less probable theory: towards a more severely testable theory because it made predictions which, in a purely logical sense, could be more easily refuted.

---

[8] See [5], p. 104.
[9] *Ibid.*, pp. 402–406.
[10] *Ibid.*, pp. 400–402.

V

So far I have spoken about science — its progress, and its criterion of progress — without even mentioning *truth*. It is possible to do this, and without falling into pragmatism (or instrumentalism). It is even possible to argue in favour of the intuitive satisfactoriness of the criterion of progress in science without mentioning truth. In fact, before I became acquainted with Tarski's theory of truth,[11] it appeared to me safer and more economical to discuss the criterion of progress without getting too deeply involved in the highly controversial problem of truth.[12]

All this was changed by Tarski's theory of truth, and of the correspondence of a statement with the facts.[13] Tarski's greatest achievement, and the real significance of his theory for the philosophy of the empirical sciences, lies, I believe, in the fact that he re-established a correspondence theory of absolute or objective truth which showed that we are free to use the intuitive idea of truth as correspondence with the facts. The view that his theory is only applicable to formalized language is, I think, mistaken. It is applicable to any consistent and (more or less) 'natural' language — as long as we manage to learn from Tarski's analysis to dodge the antinomies.

Although I may assume in this assembly some familiarity with Tarski's theory of truth, I may perhaps remind you of the way in which it can be regarded, from an intuitive point of view, as a simple elucidation of the idea of *correspondence with the facts*. I shall have to stress this almost trivial point because, in spite of its triviality, it will be crucial for my argument. Moreover, it seems that the highly intuitive character of Tarski's ideas becomes more evident if we first decide to take 'truth' as a synonym of 'correspondence with the facts', and only as a second step proceed to *define the idea of 'correspondence with the facts'* in the Tarskian manner, rather than its synonym 'truth'.

Thus we shall first consider (in a metalanguage) under what conditions a certain assertion (of an object language) corresponds to the facts.

(1) The statement, or the assertion, '*Snow is white*' corresponds to the facts if and only if snow is, indeed, white.

(2) The statement, or the assertion, '*Grass is red*' corresponds to the facts if and only if grass is, indeed, red.

These formulations (in which the word 'indeed' is only inserted for ease, and may be omitted) sound, of course, quite trivial. But it was left to Tarski to discover that, in spite of their apparent triviality, they contained the solution of the apparently insoluble problem of explaining correspondence with the facts and, with it, truth.

I believe that it is only the idea of truth which allows us to speak sensibly of mistakes and of rational criticism, and which makes rational discussion

---

[11]See [7].

[12]See [4] and [5], especially section 84, and [5] note *1 on p. 274.

[13]See [8–11].

possible — that is to say, critical discussion in search of mistakes with the serious purpose of eliminating as many of these mistakes as we can, in order to get nearer to the truth. Thus the very idea of error — and of fallibility — involves the idea of an objective truth as the standard of which we may fall short.[14] (It is in this sense that the idea of truth may be called a *regulative* idea.)

VI

Yet it is clear that we do not merely want truth — we want more truth, and new truth. We are not content with 'twice two equals four', even though it is true: we do not resort to reciting the multiplication table if we are faced with a problem in topology or in physics. Mere truth — or even more truth — is not enough; what we look for is *an answer to our problem*. The point has been well put by the German humorist and poet Busch, of Max-and-Moritz fame, in a little nursery rhyme — I mean a rhyme for the epistemological nursery:[15]

> Twice two equals four: 'tis true,
> But too empty, and too trite.
> What I look for is a clue
> To some matters not so light.

Only if it is a clue, an answer to a problem — a difficult, a fertile problem, a problem of some depth — does truth, or a conjecture about the truth, become relevant to science.

Yet besides this aim of getting more information, and more relevant and more interesting information (and in this way proceeding in the direction towards what people mean when they speak of '*the whole truth*'), there is another important aim and another way in which the idea of truth plays a regulative role in the growth of knowledge.

Looking at the progress of scientific knowledge, many people have been moved to say that — even though we do not and cannot know how near or far we are from the truth — we can and do *approach more and more closely to the truth*. I myself have sometimes said such things in the past, but always with a twinge of bad conscience. Not that I believe that we should be over-fussy about what we say: as long as we do not pretend that what we say is exact or well established if it is not, and as long as we do not try to derive exact consequences from vague intuitive premises, there is no harm whatever in vagueness, or in voicing once upon a time our feelings and general impressions about things. Yet whenever I said something about the progress of science as a kind of approach to truth, I felt that I really ought to be writing 'Truth' with a capital 'T', in order to make quite clear what a vague and highly metaphysical notion was here involved, in contradistinction to

---

[14] See [6], esp. sections x, xvi, and xvii.

[15] My attention was drawn to this rhyme by my late friend Julius Kraft, who quoted it in [3], p. 262. My translation makes it perhaps more of a nursery rhyme than Busch intended.

Tarski's 'truth', which we can with a clear good conscience write in the ordinary way, with small letters.

It was only quite recently that I set myself to consider whether the idea of Truth here involved was really necessarily vague and metaphysical. Almost at once I found that it was not, and that there was no particular difficulty in applying Tarski's fundamental idea to it.

For we may say of a theory, without any particular vagueness or any other difficulty, that it *corresponds better to the facts* than another. This simple initial step makes everything clear: we speak about our theories in a metalanguage (and, no doubt, in a 'semantical' metalanguage). Admittedly, expressions like 'this theory corresponds (or agrees) better to the facts' or 'comes closer to the facts' need not always be applicable or to the point; but that does not matter at this stage. The main thing is that the barrier has fallen between what at first appeared to be Truth with a capital 'T' and truth in a Tarskian sense.

A little consideration suggests that we might try to differentiate between a number of variants of the idea of approaching or approximating truth, and also that we might have to operate here with a number of *relative* ideas, as opposed to the Tarskian idea of *absolute* truth. Yet we certainly need not give up that objectivity which characterizes Tarski's ideas.

Let us survey some of these relative notions of a better correspondence, or a better agreement, with the facts, confining ourselves to explanatory theories. We consider two theories, an earlier theory T_1 and a later theory T_2 which, we assume, corresponds better to the facts than T_1, in some sense or other.

We shall have in mind such ideas as these:

(1) The theory T_2 takes account of, and explains, more facts than the theory T_1.

(2) T_2 explains the facts in more detail than T_1.

(3) T_2 makes more precise assertions than T_1. (It is, therefore, a 'better approximation' in the most usual sense.)

(4) T_2 has stood up to tests which T_1 failed to pass.

(5) T_2 has led to new and hitherto unexpected tests — where 'hitherto unexpected' means unexpected in the light of T_1, and of our *background knowledge* (that is, knowledge accepted as unproblematic — either for the time being, or for the purpose in hand; for example, for making our tests).

(6) T_2 has actually stood up to these new and hitherto unexpected tests.

(7) T_2 has unified or connected various hitherto unrelated problems or theories.

There does not seem any difficulty in making the ideas in this list as precise as might be required for any application. It would also be easy to construct formalized model languages with respect to which we can give some more precise definitions. But I do not think that there is much point in doing this, for a wealth of physical theories is at our disposal to illustrate the various relations of better correspondence or better agreement with the facts.

In all the seven senses here listed of approximation to the truth, the idea of content (partly in the form of degree of testability or of severity of tests actually passed, that is, of corroboration) plays a decisive role. This is very clear in the cases (1) and (4–7), that is to say, when we are aiming at a more comprehensive theory — one capable of explaining more facts, or a wide *range of facts*. In such cases as (2), and especially (3), it is perhaps less immediately obvious. How these cases, too, are related to the question of increasing contents of theories is briefly explained in section 37 of [4] and [5].

It will be seen that, for the purposes of this discussion of *approaching or approximating truth*, the idea of truth as correspondence with the facts provides us with all that is needed: there is no need to introduce another idea or conception of truth. It will be seen, however, that our analysis of the idea of approximation to the truth makes it possible to see (*pace* Busch) how the two aims or regulative ideas — of truth, and of a richer content — may be brought together, as indeed they ought to be. The idea of *approximation to truth* — or '*verisimilitude*' or '*truthlikeness*' — may thus be contrasted to that of *probability* (which, one might say, represents the idea of approaching truth through *lack* of content).[16]

References

[1] Carnap, Rudolf. *Logical Foundations of Probability*, Chicago, Ill., University of Chicago Press, 1950, xvii+607 pp.

[2] Harsanyi, John C. Popper's improbability criterion for the choice of scientific hypotheses, *Philosophy*, Vol. 35 (1960), pp. 332–340.

[3] Kraft, Julius. Ueber Philosophisches in Wilhelm Busch's "Schein und Sein", pp. 261–268 in *Erziehung und Politik — Minna Specht zu ihrem 80. Geburtstag*, H. Becker *et al.*, eds., Frankfurt am Main, Verlag Oeffentliches Leben, 1960, 416 pp.

[4] Popper, Karl R. *Logik der Forschung*, Vienna, Springer Verlag, 1934 (1935), vi+248 pp.

[5] Popper, Karl R. *The Logic of Scientific Discovery*, New York, Basic Books, 1959, and London, Hutchinson, 1959, 1960, 480 pp.

[6] Popper, Karl R. *On the Sources of Knowledge and of Ignorance*, London, published for the British Academy by Oxford University Press, 1961, 33 pp.; also in *Proceedings of the British Academy*, Vol. 46 (1960), pp. 39–71.

[7] Popper, Karl R., *Conjectures and Refutations*, London, Routledge & Kegan Paul and New York, Basic Books (to be published 1962).

[8] Tarski, Alfred. Der Wahrheitsbegriff in den Sprachen der deduktiven Disziplinen, *Anzeiger der Akademie der Wissenschaften*, Vol. 69 (1932), pp. 23–25.

[9] Tarski, Alfred. Der Wahrheitsbegriff in den formalisierten Sprachen, *Studia Philosophica*, Vol. 1 (1936), pp. 261–405.

[10] Tarski, Alfred. The semantic conception of truth and the foundations of semantics, *Philosophy and Phenomenological Research*, Vol. 4 (1944), pp. 341–376.

[11] Tarski, Alfred. *Logic, Semantics, Metamathematics*, tr. by J. H. Woodger, Oxford, Clarendon Press, 1956.

---

[16] A fuller treatment of the questions here discussed, and a definition of verisimilitude in terms of truth and of content, will be found in [7, chapter 10].

ABSTRACTION IN NATURAL SCIENCE

J. H. WOODGER

University of London, London, England

The following statement occurs in an article by an eminent geneticist:

> It is well known how the introduction of an organized assembly of genes in the form of a goat onto an oceanic island may completely change its flora, fauna and physiography.

This is an astonishing statement to find in a scientific book; for science is supposed to be the pursuit of truth, and this statement is palpably false. The effect of introducing an organized assembly of genes in the form of a goat onto an oceanic island cannot possibly be well known because the experiment has never been performed; and it has never been performed for the very good and sufficient reason that there is no such thing as an organized assembly of genes in the form of a goat. We could speak sensibly and truly of goats' being assemblies of genes only if goats were *composed* of genes in the same sense in which a lump of sulphur is believed to be composed of sulphur atoms. But genes are supposed to be parts of chromosomes, and even chromosomes have parts which are neither genes nor parts of genes; chromosomes again are parts of cell nuclei, but such nuclei have parts which are neither chromosomes nor parts of chromosomes; nuclei in their turn are parts of cells, but cells have parts which are not nuclei, neither are they parts of nuclei; finally some cells are parts of goats, but goats have parts which are not cells and are not parts of cells. Thus goats are very complicated objects and cannot be identified with assemblies of genes, however well organized they may be. Now the geneticist who wrote the above passage was doubtless perfectly familiar with these facts about goats. Why, then, did he make the above assertion, which suggests that he regards all parts of goats which are not genes as of so little consequence that they need not be mentioned? In the following pages an attempt is made to provide a clear answer to this question. A similar tendency is exhibited in the following statement by another well-known geneticist:

> So we may differ from one another either because the genes we have received from our parents are not the same or because our environments have not been alike — or by reason of both causes acting at once.

Here we notice the same disregard for biological objects other than genes which was so conspicuous in the first passage quoted, but here reference is made to a relation which was not explicitly mentioned there, namely, the relation of sameness or likeness. Both passages illustrate one result of what is called *abstraction* in natural science, in one sense, at least, of that word. Our first task is to discover in what sense the notion of identity is used here and what part this relation plays in abstraction.

In order to distinguish this kind of identity from other kinds it will here be called *indistinguishability in a functional system.* It is a relation between classes, not between individuals. It is well known that physics — contrary to the teaching of Francis Bacon and J. S. Mill — is a search not for causes but for *functional relations.* But this insight has not yet penetrated into biology to any great extent. Roughly speaking, a functional system (as here understood) is a set of functional relations together with a relation which is required for formulating statements involving these functional relations. What is meant will become clearer after two examples have been given.

My first example is a purely fictitious one constructed for the purpose of illustration. In what is called dog racing the competing units are dogs, but in horse racing, in spite of the name, the competing units are not horses: they are composite objects, each consisting of a horse and a man who sits on its back and rides and guides it. But we appear to have no name for these composite objects. If it is asked (in the language of the Turf): 'What won the Derby?' the answer is always given by uttering the name of a horse. This is a rare instance of modesty on the part of members of the species *Homo sapiens,* and shows to what lengths they are prepared to go, and what sacrifices they are willing to make, in the interests of linguistic brevity and simplicity. But for the purpose of this illustration it is necessary to have a name for these composite objects, and I shall call them *equomos* (from *equus* and *homo*). An equomo is any object composed exclusively of one man and one horse when the man is riding the horse. Equomos provide an interesting contrast to the more common objects of everyday life in being continuous in time for only relatively short periods. When a jockey *a* mounts a horse *b* an equomo *c* comes into existence; and when, after a period of exercise, *a* dismounts and goes into an inn for liquid refreshment, while *b* is taken round the corner to receive a feed of hay, *c* ceases to exist. If *a* mounts *b* again, an equomo *c′* comes into existence which is distinct from *c* and is not continuous with *c* in time.

Now suppose that a man keeps a racing stable with two horses and two jockeys. We are not concerned with these horses and jockeys when they are, so to speak, off duty and not forming parts of equomos. Let us therefore use '$\mathbf{H}_1$' to denote the set of all time-stretches of one horse when it forms part of an equomo, and '$\mathbf{H}_2$' to denote the corresponding set of time-stretches of the other horse.[1] Similarly, '$\mathbf{J}_1$' will denote the set of all time-stretches of one jockey when he forms part of an equomo, and '$\mathbf{J}_2$' will denote the corresponding set of time-stretches of the other jockey. The owner of the racing stable will be able to construct equomos of four classes: $\mathbf{E}_1$ will be the class of all equomos when the horse belongs to class $\mathbf{H}_1$ and the jockey to $\mathbf{J}_1$; $\mathbf{E}_2$ will be the class of all equomos having the horse belonging to $\mathbf{H}_2$ and the jockey to $\mathbf{J}_1$; $\mathbf{E}_3$ will be the class of all equomos with its horse belonging to $\mathbf{H}_1$ and the jockey to $\mathbf{J}_2$, and finally $\mathbf{E}_4$ will be the class of all equomos having

[1]Letters printed in bold type are constants; those printed in italic are variables.

the horse belonging to $\mathbf{H}_2$ and the jockey to $\mathbf{J}_2$. Further, we shall suppose that there are available four *race courses* for training and racing. Here again we shall be concerned with these courses only at times when they are being used by equomos belonging to our four classes. Accordingly we shall let '$\mathbf{C}_1$' denote the class of time-stretches when one of the courses is being used, '$\mathbf{C}_2$' will denote the corresponding class for another of the courses, and '$\mathbf{C}_3$' and '$\mathbf{C}_4$' will denote corresponding classes for the remaining two of the four courses. In the interests of brevity and simplicity we shall make the highly artificial assumption that these courses are not affected by seasonal changes; nor are the equomos affected, during the period under consideration, by the passage of time; so that it suffices to let a member of a given equomo class run once over a course belonging to one of the four classes in order to determine something called the speed of that class of equomos on that class of courses. We shall denote the speed of an equomo class X over a course of class Y by '$\mathbf{Sp}(X, Y)$'. For the present purpose it is a matter of no interest what the actual speeds are in miles per hour, we are not even interested in whether one speed is greater than another; we are concerned only with whether one speed *differs or not* from another. We shall therefore use the figures: 1, 2, 3, 4, and 5 as arbitrary designations of the speeds of the equomo classes concerned on the available classes of courses. We shall suppose that trials have revealed the speeds on the courses mentioned to be as they are depicted on the following matrix. Where a figure occurs at the intersection

Sp	$\mathbf{E}_1$	$\mathbf{E}_2$	$\mathbf{E}_3$	$\mathbf{E}_4$
$\mathbf{C}_1$	4	2	4	2
$\mathbf{C}_3$	3	1	3	1
$\mathbf{C}_3$	5	3	5	3
$\mathbf{C}_4$	1	2	1	2

of a row and a column, that figure designates the speed for the equomo class whose name occurs at the top of the column, on the class of courses whose name occurs at the left-hand end of the row. It will be noticed that if we consider the set $\mathbf{S} = \{=, \mathbf{Sp}, \mathbf{E}_1, \mathbf{E}_2, \mathbf{E}_3, \mathbf{E}_4, \mathbf{C}_1, \mathbf{C}_2, \mathbf{C}_3, \mathbf{C}_4, 1, 2, 3, 4, 5\}$, it forms a closed system in the sense that if we choose any one of the equomo classes and any one of the classes of courses, there will be one and only one of the five speeds which is the speed for that equomo class on that class of courses. It therefore provides a simple example of what we are calling a functional system. It will also be seen that in the matrix for this particular system all the rows are distinguishable; no two of them have the same figures in all corresponding columns. The columns, on the other hand, are not all distinguishable in this sense. Columns headed by $\mathbf{E}_1$ and $\mathbf{E}_3$ are distinguishable only by their headings, and the same applies to those headed by $\mathbf{E}_2$ and $\mathbf{E}_4$.

Now since columns headed by $\mathbf{E}_1$ and $\mathbf{E}_3$ in the matrix are indistinguishable, we can say that the equomo classes $\mathbf{E}_1$ and $\mathbf{E}_3$ are indistinguishable in the system **S**, because, as far as obtaining speed 4 is concerned, it is a matter of complete indifference — provided we use courses of class $\mathbf{C}_1$ — whether we use an equomo belonging to $\mathbf{E}_1$ or one belonging to $\mathbf{E}_3$. This does not mean, of course (and this is an important point in the present context), that the horses concerned have the same coat colour or the jockeys the same body weight. All that is asserted is that $\mathbf{E}_1$ and $\mathbf{E}_3$ are indistinguishable in **S**, and in **S** there is no mention of coat colour or body weight. And this is because within that system if there is diversity of coat colour and body weight, this can be ignored within its limitations. Corresponding remarks apply to the equomo classes $\mathbf{E}_2$ and $\mathbf{E}_4$. In consequence of the indistinguishability of the two columns for each of these pairs of equomo classes, the matrix can be reduced to one with only two columns by replacing the separate designations for the indistinguishable classes by single designations denoting their sums:

Sp	$\mathbf{E}_1 \cup \mathbf{E}_2$	$\mathbf{E}_2 \cup \mathbf{E}_2$
$\mathbf{C}_1$	4	2
$\mathbf{C}_2$	3	1
$\mathbf{C}_3$	5	3
$\mathbf{C}_4$	1	2

If all the equomo classes were indistinguishable in **S**, the matrix would be reduced to one with only a single column and there would be no need for designations for equomo classes at all—at least as far as obtaining any given speed is concerned. Corresponding remarks apply to the rows. If all the classes of courses were indistinguishable in **S**, it would be as though only one class were available as far as speed was concerned, and the owner of the stable would not need to mention the name of any particular course in giving orders concerning **S** to his jockeys. It will be seen below that something exactly analogous to this happens in the traditional functional systems of genetics; and this will help to explain the tendency, illustrated by the passages quoted above, for references to certain factors connected with such systems to be dropped out and not mentioned.

We now turn to the question: Why is $\mathbf{E}_1$ distinguishable from $\mathbf{E}_2$ in **S**? One method of seeking an answer is provided by the following rule: If two equomo-classes (in the senses here used) are distinguishable in a racing system *S*, then either the classes of jockeys concerned or the classes of horses concerned are in some way distinguishable. In order to decide between these two alternatives in the present case we must refer to the information given above about the composition of members of $\mathbf{E}_1$ and $\mathbf{E}_2$. There we are told that $\mathbf{E}_1$ is the class of all equomos in which the horse belongs to $\mathbf{H}_1$ and the jockey to $\mathbf{J}_1$, and $\mathbf{E}_2$ is the class of all equomos in which the horse belongs to $\mathbf{H}_2$ and the jockey to $\mathbf{J}_1$. Applying the above rule, we find that $\mathbf{E}_1$ and $\mathbf{E}_2$ are distinguishable in **S** because $\mathbf{H}_1$ and $\mathbf{H}_2$ are distinguishable in **S**.

Next we ask: Why is it that $\mathbf{E}_1$ and $\mathbf{E}_3$ are *in*distinguishable in **S**? Reference to composition shows us that $\mathbf{E}_3$ is the class of all equomos in which the horse belongs to $\mathbf{H}_1$ and the jockey to $\mathbf{J}_2$, so that members of $\mathbf{E}_1$ resemble those of $\mathbf{E}_3$ as far as the horse is concerned, but the former have $\mathbf{J}_1$ whilst the latter have $\mathbf{J}_2$. In this case, therefore, we must say that $\mathbf{J}_1$ and $\mathbf{J}_2$ are indistinguishable in **S**. This is confirmed by the consideration of $\mathbf{E}_2$ and $\mathbf{E}_4$, which also are indistinguishable in **S**. We thus have a situation in which on every course the horses are distinguishable but the jockeys are not. We can in fact construct a speed-matrix which makes no reference to jockeys:

Sp	$\mathbf{H}_1$	$\mathbf{H}_2$
$\mathbf{C}_1$	4	2
$\mathbf{C}_2$	3	1
$\mathbf{C}_3$	5	3
$\mathbf{C}_4$	1	2

This means that to obtain a given speed we must attend to the horse and the course, but it is a matter of indifference which jockey we choose within the system **S**. Naturally this does *not* mean that we can dispense with jockeys altogether! It only means that within our imaginary system **S** *which* of the available jockeys we choose is of no consequence. For that reason it is most important that statements concerning the elements of a functional system should always be *relativized* to the system in question.

We can now raise questions of the above type on a different level; we can ask: Why are $\mathbf{H}_1$ and $\mathbf{H}_2$ distinguishable? In order to answer this question we must notice that what we have called horses are themselves composite objects. In addition to the naked or biological horses there are such parts as bridles, saddles, and horse-shoes to be taken into consideration as possible vehicles of diversity or distinguishability. We must therefore devise some means of discovering which of these components are distinguishable in the system **S**. Suppose, for example, we denote the classes of time-stretches of the two biological or naked horses by '$\mathbf{h}_1$' and '$\mathbf{h}_2$', and suppose that we have two sets of horse-furniture (using this as a collective term to cover bridle, saddle, and horse-shoes) and call them $\mathbf{f}_1$ and $\mathbf{f}_2$; then we have the possibility of four types of composite horses equipped for racing: $\mathbf{H}_1$ composed from members of $\mathbf{h}_1$ and $\mathbf{f}_1$; $\mathbf{H}_2$ composed from members of $\mathbf{h}_2$ and $\mathbf{f}_1$; $\mathbf{H}_3$ composed from members of $\mathbf{h}_1$ and $\mathbf{f}_2$, and finally $\mathbf{H}_4$ composed from members of $\mathbf{h}_2$ and $\mathbf{f}_2$. Omitting reference to the jockeys — as our last matrix showed that we could in the system **S** — let us suppose that we obtain the following matrix for composite horses and courses:

Sp	H_1	H_2	H_3	H_4
C_1	4	2	4	2
C_2	3	1	3	1
C_3	5	3	5	3
C_4	1	2	1	2

This shows that switching the horse-furniture from $\mathbf{h}_1$ to $\mathbf{h}_2$ has no effect on the speed; $\mathbf{f}_1$ is therefore indistinguishable from $\mathbf{f}_2$ in **S** and reference to horse-furniture can be omitted as far as **S** is concerned, although of course this does not mean that we do not need horse-furniture in training and racing horses. The speed matrix can thus be reduced to one with two columns only, one headed by '$\mathbf{h}_1$' and the other by '$\mathbf{h}_2$'. We now ask: How does $\mathbf{h}_1$ differ from $\mathbf{h}_2$ in **S**? The answer is one for physiology to provide. It will be clear (and this is a point of some importance) that the success of this method of analysis within a functional system largely depends upon having, at each step, just *one* pair of alternatives, one of which can be eliminated, on the data obtainable.

We must now turn from our fictitious example to actual functional systems in genetics. To begin with we shall require the statement-forming functor '$\subseteq$' instead of '$=$' and the name-forming functor '**Fil**', associated with two variables. By **Fil** (X, Y) will be meant the set of all offspring from pairs of parents when one of the parents belongs to the class X and the other belongs to Y. By way of abbreviation we write:

$$\mathbf{Fil}^2(X, Y) = \mathbf{Fil}(\mathbf{Fil}(X, Y), \mathbf{Fil}(X, Y))$$

A Mendelian experiment begins by taking a class **A**, which is a subclass of some species and is included in a class **P** called a phenotype because membership of **P** is discoverable by direct inspection. Then we take another set **B**, which is included in the same species as **A** but in a phenotype **Q**, which has no members in common with, and is distinguishable from, **P**. By observing the results of breeding members of these sets together, the relation (inclusion or exclusion) of the classes $\mathbf{Fil}(\mathbf{A}, \mathbf{A})$, $\mathbf{Fil}^2(\mathbf{A}, \mathbf{A})$, $\mathbf{Fil}(\mathbf{B}, \mathbf{B})$, $\mathbf{Fil}^2(\mathbf{B}, \mathbf{B})$, $\mathbf{Fil}(\mathbf{A}, \mathbf{B})$, and $\mathbf{Fil}^2(\mathbf{A}, \mathbf{B})$ to **P** and **Q** is determined. If $\mathbf{Fil}\ (\mathbf{A}, \mathbf{B}) \subseteq \mathbf{P}$, then **P** is said to be dominant to **Q**, and if $\mathbf{Fil}(\mathbf{A}, \mathbf{B}) \subseteq \mathbf{Q}$, then **Q** is said to be dominant to **P**. In some cases a third phenotype **R**, having no members in common with **P** or **Q**, appears such that $\mathbf{Fil}(\mathbf{A}, \mathbf{B}) \subseteq \mathbf{R}$. The result in a typical Mendelian system is shown in the following matrix[2] in which it will be noticed that **A** and $\mathbf{Fil}(\mathbf{A}, \mathbf{A})$ are indistinguishable in the system,

[2]It should be mentioned that one datum has been omitted, namely the proportions in which members of **P**, **Q**, and **R** occur when more than one is represented in a class of offspring. This is done purely for brevity because it is not essential for the purpose of this example. The system with dominance is derivable from the above by putting $\mathbf{P} = \mathbf{R}$ or $\mathbf{Q} = \mathbf{R}$, as the case may be.

Fil	**A**	**Fil (A, A)**	**B**	**Fil (B, B)**	**Fil (A, B)**
A	**P**	**P**	**R**	**R**	**P** ∪ **R**
Fil (A, A)	**P**	**P**	**R**	**R**	**P** ∪ **R**
B	**R**	**R**	**Q**	**Q**	**Q** ∪ **R**
Fil (B, B)	**R**	**R**	**Q**	**Q**	**Q** ∪ **R**
Fil (A, B)	**P** ∪ **R**	**P** ∪ **R**	**Q** ∪ **R**	**Q** ∪ **R**	**P** ∪ **Q** ∪ **R**

and the same applies to **B** and **Fil**(**B**, **B**). The system is thus reducible to the set {⊆, **Fil**, **A**, **B**, **Fil**(**A**, **B**), **P**, **Q**, **R**}. Another point to notice is that no reference is made to the environments concerned. This is not because environments are of no consequence (no animal or plant will survive immersion in boiling oil), but because precautions are taken to ensure that the classes of environments involved are all indistinguishable in the system. A third point to notice is that no mention is made of the sex of the parents. If in the matrix we suppose those in the top row to be all male, and those represented in the left-hand column to be all female, we shall see that the matrix is perfectly symmetrical about the main diagonal. This is usually expressed by saying that reciprocal crosses give the same result. In such a system the sexes are therefore indistinguishable and reference to them is not necessary.

We now pass to the question: Why is **A** distinguishable from **B**? Here we must pause to consider in more detail how **A** and **B** and their progeny are produced. Each member of any of these classes begins by the union of two cells (called gametes), one from one parent and one from the other. The object resulting from this union develops in an environment and eventually reaches a condition when it is recognizable as belonging to **P** or **Q** or **R**. We therefore require a new functor which will be associated with three variables; thus '**D**(α, β, E)' will denote the class of all lives which begin with the union of a member of α with a member of β and which develop in an environment belonging to the class E. We also require a functor associated with two variables; thus '**G**(X, K)' will denote the class of all gametes which are produced by members of the class X of lives and which have an environment belonging to the class K. With the help of these two functors we can now define the filial functor for the general case when account is taken of the environment classes (using **Fil′** with prime to distinguish this from the symbol already used):

$$\mathbf{Fil}'_{K,M,E}(X, Y) = \mathbf{D}(\mathbf{G}(X, K), \mathbf{G}(Y, M), E).$$

If we now use **G′**(**A**) for the class of gametes produced by members of **A**, and **D′**(**G′**(**A**), **G′**(**A**)) for the lives which develop from united pairs from **G′**(**A**) for our example in which abstraction from the environment classes occurs, we can define the original filial functor thus:

$$\mathbf{Fil}(\mathbf{A}, \mathbf{A}) = \mathbf{D}'(\mathbf{G}'(\mathbf{A}), \mathbf{G}'(\mathbf{A}))$$

with corresponding expressions for **A**, **B**, (**A**, **B**) and (**B**, **B**), and obtain a **D**′-matrix thus:

D′	**G**′(**A**)	**G**′(**Fil**(**A**, **A**))	**G**′(**B**)	**G**′(**Fil**(**B**, **B**))	**G**′(**Fil**(**A**, **B**))
G′(**A**)	**P**	**P**	**R**	**R**	$\mathbf{P} \cup \mathbf{R}$
G′(**Fil**(**A**, **A**))	**P**	**P**	**R**	**R**	$\mathbf{P} \cup \mathbf{R}$
G′(**B**)	**R**	**R**	**Q**	**Q**	$\mathbf{Q} \cup \mathbf{R}$
G′(**Fil**(**B**, **B**))	**R**	**R**	**Q**	**Q**	$\mathbf{Q} \cup \mathbf{R}$
G′(**Fil**(**A**, **B**))	$\mathbf{P} \cup \mathbf{R}$	$\mathbf{P} \cup \mathbf{R}$	$\mathbf{Q} \cup \mathbf{R}$	$\mathbf{Q} \cup \mathbf{R}$	$\mathbf{P} \cup \mathbf{Q} \cup \mathbf{R}$

From this we see that **G**′(**A**) is indistinguishable from **G**′(**Fil**(**A**, **A**)) and **G**′(**B**) from **G**′(**Fil**(**B**, **B**)), but **G**′(**A**) is distinguishable from **G**′(**B**) in this system and both are distinguishable from **G**′(**Fil**(**A**, **B**)).

We can now see what we must do in order to pass from this set of experiments yielding an instance of a Mendelian system to the generalized system of which it is an instance. Let '**a**' denote the class that is the sum of all classes of gametes which are not distinguishable from **G**′(**A**) in any system, and let '**b**' denote the corresponding sum for those classes which are not distinguishable from **G**′(**B**). Then we shall have $\mathbf{A} \subseteq \mathbf{D}'(\mathbf{a}, \mathbf{a})$; $\mathbf{G}'(\mathbf{A}) \subseteq \mathbf{G}'(\mathbf{D}'(\mathbf{a}, \mathbf{a}))$ and $\mathbf{Fil}(\mathbf{A}, \mathbf{B}) \subseteq \mathbf{D}'(\mathbf{a}, \mathbf{b})$, etc. But if we assume that $\mathbf{G}'(\mathbf{D}'(\mathbf{a}, \mathbf{a})) \subseteq \mathbf{a}$, we should have a system in which, as far as **D**′(**a**, **a**) is concerned, no evolution is possible. This is one of the disadvantages of dropping the reference to the environment classes, and hence one of the disadvantages of incautious abstraction. In order to have the possibility of evolution we need at least two distinct classes of environments, $\mathbf{E}_1$ and $\mathbf{E}_2$, such that we have $\mathbf{G}(\mathbf{D}'(\mathbf{a}, \mathbf{a}), \mathbf{E}_1) \subseteq \mathbf{a}$ but *not* $\mathbf{G}(\mathbf{D}'(\mathbf{a}, \mathbf{a}), \mathbf{E}_2) \subseteq \mathbf{a}$; we need a distinct class **c** of gametes such that $\mathbf{G}(\mathbf{D}'(\mathbf{a}, \mathbf{a}), \mathbf{E}_2) \subseteq \mathbf{c}$ and $\mathbf{D}'(\mathbf{c}, \mathbf{c}) \subseteq \mathbf{T}$, where **T** is distinguishable from **P**.

Now we turn to the next question which is: Why is **a** distinguishable from **b**? In order to answer this it is necessary to know that every gamete, being a cell, is composed (like an *equomo*) of two major parts: a nucleus enclosed by a cytoplasm. Consequently there is the possibility that **a** is distinguishable from **b** because the class of nuclei of members of **a** is distinguishable from the class of nuclei of members of **b**, or because the corresponding classes of cytoplasms are distinguishable; or both may be distinguishable. Then there is a further complication which has not yet been explicitly mentioned: the fact, namely, that gametes are of two kinds, male and female, and that when two unite to form the beginning of a new life one is always male and the other female. Let us denote the nuclei of the male members of **a** by '$\mathbf{n}_1$' and those of the female members by '$\mathbf{n}_2$', the cytoplasms of the male members by '**c**' and those of the female members by '**C**'; correspondingly let '$\mathbf{m}_1$' denote the nuclei of male members of **b** and '$\mathbf{m}_2$' those of the female members, and '**d**' the cytoplasms of the male and '**D**' those of the female members of **b**. With these designations we can now construct another **D**′-matrix as follows:

D′	$\mathbf{n_1c}$	$\mathbf{m_1d}$
$\mathbf{n_2C}$	**P**	**R**
$\mathbf{m_2D}$	**R**	**Q**

From this we learn that the class of cells which we can call ($\mathbf{n_1c}$; $\mathbf{n_2C}$) formed by the union of male members of **a** with female members of **a**, is distinguishable from the class ($\mathbf{m_1d}$; $\mathbf{n_2C}$) formed by the union of male members of **b** with female members of **a**; consequently male members of **a** are distinguishable from male members of **b**. We also learn that the class ($\mathbf{m_1d}$; $\mathbf{n_2C}$) is distinguishable from the class ($\mathbf{m_1d}$; $\mathbf{m_2D}$), so that female members of **a** are distinguishable from female members of **b**. We see further that the class ($\mathbf{n_1c}$; $\mathbf{m_2D}$) is *in*distinguishable from the class ($\mathbf{n_2C}$, $\mathbf{m_1d}$) in this system. Now in the process of union of ($\mathbf{n_1c}$) with ($\mathbf{m_2D}$) combined nuclei ($\mathbf{n_1m_2}$) and combined cytoplasms (**cD**) are formed; and in the process of union of ($\mathbf{n_2C}$) with ($\mathbf{m_1d}$) combined nuclei ($\mathbf{m_1n_2}$) and combined cytoplasms (**Cd**) are formed; and since these cell-classes are indistinguishable, the class ($\mathbf{n_1m_2}$) of nuclei is indistinguishable from the class ($\mathbf{m_1n_2}$), and the class (**cD**) of cytoplasms is indistinguishable from the class (**Cd**). We also know from microscopical observation that **c** is distinguishable from **C** and **d** from **D**; consequently we must have **c** indistinguishable from **d** and **C** from **D**. Now since ($\mathbf{n_1c}$) is distinguishable from ($\mathbf{m_1d}$), we must have $\mathbf{n_1}$ distinguishable from $\mathbf{m_1}$; and correspondingly, from the distinguishability of ($\mathbf{n_2C}$) from ($\mathbf{m_2D}$) and the indistinguishability of **C** from **D**, we find that $\mathbf{n_2}$ is distinguishable from $\mathbf{m_2}$. Thus we can learn from this that male members of **a** are distinguishable from male members of **b** by their nuclei and the same applies to the female members of these two classes. But because these cytoplasmic classes are indistinguishable in Mendelian systems, the assumption that they are indistinguishable in all functional systems involving cytoplasmic classes is not justified; neither is the assertion that 'the cytoplasm plays no part in heredity'. When the spectacular events which take place in the nuclei of cells when they undergo division and when they prepare to form gametes were studied at the beginning of the present century, they suggested the hypothesis that the chromosomes are the nuclear parts which are primarily concerned with the genetic distinguishability of gamete classes in Mendelian systems. This hypothesis has proved itself to be extremely successful, although it does not exclude the possibility that there may be genetical systems in which nuclear parts which are neither chromosomes nor parts of chromosomes have to be taken into consideration.

What lessons for the methodology of science are to be learned from these examples? First, they show how abstraction can be taken for granted and forgotten. It should surely be part of the task of methodology to search out the characteristic modes of abstraction of the several sciences and to study their consequences. The effects of the notion of composition are especially important. A. N. Whitehead has written:

> The disadvantage of exclusive attention to a group of abstractions, however well-founded, is that, by the nature of the case, you have abstracted from the remainder of things. In so far as the excluded things are important in your experience, your modes of thought are not fitted to deal with them. You cannot think without abstractions; accordingly, it is of the utmost importance to be vigilant in critically revising your *modes* of abstraction.[3]

Another point is that when one science (e.g., physics) is applied in another (e.g., biology) the applied science will automatically impose its modes of abstraction on the science in which it is applied, and this will inhibit the independent discovery of new modes of abstraction suitable to the latter science. Finally, in applied set-theory it is clearly important to keep in mind the distinction between class identity (mutual inclusion) and distinguishability in a functional system.

[3]A. N. Whitehead: *Science and the Modern World*, 1927, p. 73. The whole of Chapter IV of this book is worth reading in this connexion.

SECTION

V

FOUNDATIONS OF PROBABILITY AND INDUCTION

THE AIM OF INDUCTIVE LOGIC

RUDOLF CARNAP

University of California, Los Angeles, California, U.S.A.

By inductive logic I understand a theory of logical probability providing rules for inductive thinking. I shall try to explain the nature and purpose of inductive logic by showing how it can be used in determining rational decisions.

I shall begin with the customary schema of decision theory involving the concepts of utility and probability. I shall try to show that we must understand "probability" in this context not in the objective sense, but in the subjective sense, i.e., as the degree of belief. This is a psychological concept in empirical decision theory, referring to actual beliefs of actual human beings. Later I shall go over to rational or normative decision theory by introducing some requirements of rationality. Up to that point I shall be in agreement with the representatives of the subjective conception of probability. Then I shall take a further step, namely, the transition from a quasi-psychological to a logical concept. This transition will lead to the theory which I call "inductive logic".

We begin with the customary model of decision making. A person X at a certain time T has to make a choice between possible acts $A_1, A_2, \cdots$. X knows that the possible states of nature are $S_1, S_2, \cdots$; but he does not know which of them is the actual state. For simplicity, we shall here assume that the number of possible acts and the number of possible states of nature

The author is indebted to the National Science Foundation for the support of research in inductive probability.

are finite. X knows the following: if he were to carry out the act A_m and if the state S_n were the actual state of nature, then the outcome would be $O_{m,n}$. This outcome $O_{m,n}$ is uniquely determined by A_m and S_n; and X knows how it is determined. We assume that there is a utility function U_X for the person X and that X knows his utility function so that he can use it in order to calculate subjective values.

Now we define the *subjective value* of a possible act A_m for X at time T:

(1) DEFINITION.

$$V_{X,T}(A_m) = \sum_n U_X(O_{m,n}) \times P(S_n),$$

where $P(S_n)$ *is the probability of the state* S_n, *and the sum covers all possible states* S_n.

In other words, we take as the subjective value of the act A_m for X the *expected utility* of the outcome of this act. (1) holds for the time T before any act is carried out. It refers to the contemplated act A_m; therefore it uses the utilities for the possible outcomes $O_{m,n}$ of act A_m in the various possible states S_n. [If the situation is such that the probability of S_n could possibly be influenced by the assumption that act A_m were carried out, we should take the conditional probability $P(S_n|A_m)$ instead of $P(S_n)$. Analogous remarks hold for our later forms of the definition of V].

We can now formulate the customary *decision principle* as follows:

(2) Choose an act so as to maximize the subjective value V.

This principle can be understood either as referring to *actual* decision making, or to *rational* decisions. In the first interpretation it would be a psychological law belonging to *empirical* decision theory as a branch of psychology; in the second interpretation, it would be a normative principle in the theory of *rational* decisions. I shall soon come back to this distinction. First we have to remove an ambiguity in the definition (1) of value, concerning the interpretation of the probability P. There are several conceptions of probability; thus the question arises which of them is adequate in the context of decision making.

The main conceptions of probability are often divided into two kinds, objectivistic and subjectivistic conceptions. In my view, these are not two incompatible doctrines concerning the same concept, but rather two theories concerning two different probability concepts, both of them legitimate and useful. The concept of *objective* (or statistical) *probability* is closely connected with relative frequencies in mass phenomena. It plays an important role in mathematical statistics, and it occurs in laws of various branches of empirical science, especially physics.

The second concept is *subjective* (or personal) *probability*. It is the probability assigned to a proposition or event H by a subject X, say a person or a group of persons, in other words, the degree of belief of X in H. Now it seems to me that we should clearly distinguish two versions of subjective probability, one representing the *actual* degree of belief and the other the *rational* degree of belief.

Which of these two concepts of probability, the objective or the subjective, ought to be used in the definition of subjective value and thereby in the decision principle? At the present time, the great majority of those who work in mathematical statistics still regard the statistical concept of probability as the only legitimate one. However, this concept refers to an objective feature of nature; a feature that holds whether or not the observer X knows about it. And in fact, the numerical values of statistical probability are in general not known to X. Therefore this concept is unsuitable for a decision principle. It seems that for this reason a number of those who work in the theory of decisions, be it actual decisions or rational decisions, incline toward the view that some version of the subjective concept of probability must be used here. I agree emphatically with this view.

The statistical concept of probability remains, of course, a legitimate and important concept both for mathematical statistics and for many branches of empirical science. And in the special case that X knows the statistical probabilities for the relevant states S_n but has no more specific knowledge about these states, the decision principle would use these values. There is general agreement on this point. And this is not in conflict with the view that the decision principle should refer to subjective probability, because in this special situation the subjective probability for X would be equal to the objective probability.

Once we recognize that decision theory needs the subjective concept of probability, it is clear that the theory of *actual* decisions involves the first version of this concept, i.e., the *actual* degree of belief, and the theory of *rational* decisions involves the second version, the *rational* degree of belief.

Let us first discuss the theory of *actual* decisions. The concept of probability in the sense of the *actual* degree of belief is a psychological concept; its laws are empirical laws of psychology, to be established by the investigation of the behavior of persons in situations of uncertainty, e.g., behavior with respect to bets or games of chance. I shall use for this psychological concept the technical term "*degree of credence*" or shortly "credence". In symbols, I write '$Cr_{X,T}(H)$' for "the (degree of) credence of the proposition H for the person X at the time T". Different persons X and Y may have different credence functions $Cr_{X,T}$ and $Cr_{Y,T}$. And the same person X may have different credence functions Cr_{X,T_1} and Cr_{X,T_2} at different times T_1 and T_2; e.g., if X observes between T_1 and T_2 that H holds, then $Cr_{X,T_1}(H) \neq Cr_{X,T_2}(H)$. (Let the ultimate possible cases be represented by the points of a logical space, usually called the probability space. Then a proposition or event is understood, not as a sentence, but as the range of a sentence, i.e., the set of points representing those possible cases in which the sentence holds. To the conjunction of two sentences corresponds the intersection of the propositions.)

On the basis of credence, we can define *conditional credence*, "the credence of H with respect to the proposition E" (or "$\cdots$ given E"):

(3) DEFINITION.

$$Cr'_{X,T}(H|E) = \frac{Cr_{X,T}(E \cap H)}{Cr_{X,T}(E)},$$

provided that $Cr_{X,T}(E) > 0$. $Cr'_{X,T}(H|E)$ *is the credence which* H *would have for* X *at* T *if* X *ascertained that* E *holds.*

Using the concept of credence, we now replace (1) by the following:

(4) DEFINITION.

$$V_{X,T}(A_m) = \sum_n U_X(O_{m,n}) \times Cr_{X,T}(S_n).$$

As was pointed out by Ramsey, we can determine X's credence function by his betting behavior. A bet is a contract of the following form. X pays into the pool the amount u, his partner Y pays the amount v; they agree that the total stake $u+v$ goes to X if the hypothesis H turns out to be true, and to Y if it turns out to be false. If X accepts this contract, we say that he bets on H with the total stake $u+v$ and with the betting quotient $q = u/(u+v)$ (or, at odds of u to v). If we apply the decision principle with the definition (4) to the situation in which X may either accept or reject an offered bet on H with the betting quotient q, we find that X will accept the bet if q is not larger than his credence for H. Thus we may interpret $Cr_{X,T}(H)$ as the highest betting quotient at which X is willing to bet on H. (As is well known, this holds only under certain conditions and only approximately.)

Utility and credence are psychological concepts. The utility function of X represents the system of valuations and preferences of X; his credence function represents his system of beliefs (not only the content of each belief, but also its strength). Both concepts are theoretical concepts which characterize the state of mind of a person; more exactly, the non-observable micro-state of his central nervous system, not his consciousness, let alone his overt behavior. But since his behavior is influenced by his state, we can indirectly determine characteristics of his state from his behavior. Thus experimental methods have been developed for the determination of some values and some general characteristics of the utility function and the credence function ("subjective probability") of a person on the basis of his behavior with respect to bets and similar situations. Interesting investigations of this kind have been made by F. Mosteller and P. Nogee [13], and more recently by D. Davidson and P. Suppes [4], and others.

Now we take the step from empirical to *rational decision theory*. The latter is of greater interest to us, not so much for its own sake (its methodological status is in fact somewhat problematic), but because it is the connecting link between empirical decision theory and inductive logic. Rational decision theory is concerned not with actual credence, but with *rational* credence. (We should also distinguish here between actual utility and rational utility; but we will omit this.) The statements of a theory of this kind are not found by experiments but are established on the basis of requirements of rationality; the formal procedure usually consists in deducing theorems from axioms which are justified by general considerations of rationality, as we shall see. It seems fairly clear that the probability concepts used by the following authors are meant in the sense of rational credence (or rational credibility, which I shall explain presently): John Maynard Keynes (1921), Frank P. Ramsey (1928), Harold Jeffreys (1931), B. O. Koopman (1940), Georg Henrik von Wright (1941), I. G. Good (1950), and Leonard J. Savage (1954). I am inclined to include here also those authors who do not declare explicitly that their concept refers to rational rather than actual beliefs, but who accept general axioms and do not base their theories on psychological results. Bruno De Finetti (1931) satisfies these conditions; however, he says explicitly that his concept of "subjective probability" refers not to rational, but to actual beliefs. I find this puzzling.

The term "subjective probability" seems quite satisfactory for the actual degree of credence. It is frequently applied also to a probability concept interpreted as something like rational credence. But here the use of the word "subjective" might be misleading (comp. Keynes [9, p. 4] and Carnap [1, § 12A]). Savage has suggested the term "personal probability".

Rational credence is to be understood as the credence function of a completely rational person X; this is, of course, not any real person, but an imaginary, idealized person. We carry out the idealization step for step, by introducing *requirements of rationality* for the credence function. I shall now explain some of these requirements.

Suppose that X makes n simultaneous bets; let the ith bet ($i = 1, \cdots, n$) be on the proposition H_i with the betting quotient q_i and the total stake s_i. Before we observe which of the propositions H_i are true and which are false, we can consider the *possible* cases. For any possible case, i.e., a logically possible distribution of truth-values among the H_i, we can calculate the gain or loss for each bet and hence the total balance of gains and losses from the n bets. If in *every* possible case X suffers a net loss, i.e., his total balance is negative, it is obviously unreasonable for X to make these n bets. Let X's credence function at a given time be Cr. By a (finite) betting system in accordance with Cr we mean a finite system of n bets on n arbitrary propositions H_i ($i = 1, \cdots, n$) with n arbitrary (positive) stakes s_i, but with the betting quotients $q_i = Cr(H_i)$.

(5) Definition. *A function Cr is coherent if and only if there is no betting system in accordance with Cr such that there is a net loss in every possible case.*

For X to make bets of a system of this kind would obviously be unreasonable. Therefore we lay down the *first requirement* as follows:

R1. *In order to be rational, Cr must be coherent.*

Now the following important result holds:

(6) A function Cr from propositions to real numbers is coherent if and only if Cr is a normalized probability measure.

(A real-valued function of propositions is said to be a probability measure if it is a non-negative, finitely additive set function; it is normalized if its value for the necessary proposition is 1. In other words, a normalized probability measure is a function which satisfies the basic axioms of the calculus of probability, e.g., the axioms I through V in Kolmogoroff's system [10, § 1].)

The first part of (6) ("... coherent if ...") was stated first by Ramsey [15] and was later independently stated and proved by De Finetti [5]. The much more complicated proof for the second part ("... only if ...") was found independently by John G. Kemeny [8, p. 269] and R. Sherman Lehman [12, p. 256].

Let Cr' be the conditional credence function defined on the basis of Cr by (3). As ordinary bets are based on Cr, conditional bets are based on Cr'. The concept of coherence can be generalized so as to be applicable also to conditional credence functions. (6) can then easily be extended by the result that a conditional credence function Cr' is coherent if and only if Cr' is a normalized conditional probability measure, in other words, if and only if Cr' satisfies the customary basic axioms of conditional probability, including the general multiplication axiom.

Following Shimony [17], we introduce now a concept of coherence in a stronger sense, for which I use the term "strict coherence":

(7) DEFINITION. *A function Cr is strictly coherent if and only if Cr is coherent and there is no (finite) system of bets in accordance with Cr on molecular propositions such that the result is a net loss in at least one possible case, but not a net gain in any possible case.*

It is clear that it would be unreasonable to make a system of bets of the kind just specified. Therefore we lay down the *second requirement*:

R2. *In order to be rational, a credence function must be strictly coherent.*

We define *regular credence function* (essentially in the sense of Carnap [1, § 55A]):

(8) DEFINITION. *A function Cr is regular if and only if Cr is a normalized probability measure and, for any molecular proposition H, $Cr(H) = 0$ only if H is impossible.*

By analogy with (6) we have now the following important theorem; its first part is due to Shimony, its second part again to Kemeny and Lehman:

(9) A function Cr is strictly coherent if and only if Cr is regular.

Most of the authors of systems for subjective or logical probability adopt only the basic axioms; thus they require nothing but coherence. A few go one step further by including an axiom for what I call regularity; thus they require in effect strict coherence, but nothing more. Axiom systems of both kinds are extremely weak; they yield no result of the form "$P(H|E) = r$", except in the trivial cases where r is 0 or 1. In my view, much more should be required.

The two previous requirements apply to any credence function that holds for X at any time T of his life. We now consider two of these functions, Cr_n for the time T_n and Cr_{n+1} for a time T_{n+1} shortly after T_n. Let the proposition E represent the observation data received by X between these two time points. The *third requirement* refers to the transition from Cr_n to Cr_{n+1}:

R3. (a) *The transformation of Cr_n into Cr_{n+1} depends only on the proposition E.*

(b) *More specifically, Cr_{n+1} is determined by Cr_n and E as follows: for any H, $Cr_{n+1}(H) = Cr_n(E \cap H)/Cr_n(E)$ (hence $= Cr'_n(H|E)$ by definition* (3)).

Part (a) is of course implied by (b). I have separated part (a) from (b) because X's function Cr might satisfy (a) without satisfying (b). Part (a) requires merely that X be rational to the extent that changes in his credence function are influenced only by his observational results, but not by any other factors, e.g., feelings like his hopes or fears concerning a possible future event H, feelings which in fact influence the beliefs of all actual human beings. Part (b) specifies exactly the transformation of Cr_n into Cr_{n+1}; the latter is the conditional credence Cr'_n with respect to E. The rule (b) can be used only if $Cr_n(E) \neq 0$; this condition is fulfilled for any possible observational result, provided that Cr_n satisfies the requirement of strict coherence.

Let the proposition E_{n+2} represent the data obtained between T_{n+1} and a later time point T_{n+2}. Let Cr_{n+2} be the credence function at T_{n+2} obtained by R3b from Cr_{n+1} with respect to E_{n+2}. It can easily be shown that the same function Cr_{n+2} results if R3b is applied to Cr_n with respect to the combined data $E_{n+1} \cap E_{n+2}$. In the same way we can determine any later credence function Cr_{n+m} from the given function Cr_n either in m steps, applying the rule R3b in each step with one datum of the sequence $E_{n+1}, E_{n+2}, \cdots, E_{n+m}$, or in one step with the intersection $\bigcap_{p=1}^{m} E_{n+p}$. If m is large so that the intersection contains thousands of single data, the objection might be raised that it is unrealistic to think of a procedure of this kind, because a man's memory is unable to retain and reproduce at will so many items. However, since our goal is not the psychology of actual human behavior in the field of inductive reasoning, but rather inductive logic as a system of rules, we do not aim at realism. We make the further idealization that X is not only perfectly rational but has also an infallible memory. Our assumptions deviate from reality very much if the observer and agent is a natural human being, but not so much if we think of X as a robot with organs of perception, data processing, decision making, and acting. Thinking about the design of a robot will help us in finding rules of rationality. Once found, these rules can be applied not only in the construction of a robot but also in advising human beings in their effort to make their decisions as rational as their limited abilities permit.

Consider now the whole sequence of data obtained by X up to the present time T_n: $E_1, E_2, \cdots, E_n$. Let K_{X,T_n} or, for short, K_n be the proposition representing the combination of all these data:

(10) DEFINITION.

$$K_n = \bigcap_{i=1}^{n} E_i.$$

Thus K_n represents, under the assumption of infallible memory, the total observational knowledge of X at the time T_n. Now consider the sequence of X's credence functions. In the case of a human being we would hesitate to ascribe to him a credence function at a very early time point, before his abilities of reason and deliberate action are sufficiently developed. But again we disregard this difficulty by thinking either of an idealized human baby or of a robot. We ascribe to him a credence function Cr_1 for the time point T_1; Cr_1 represents X's personal probabilities based upon the datum E_1 as his only experience. Going even one step further, let us ascribe to him an *initial credence function* Cr_0 for the time point T_0 before he obtains his first datum E_1. Any later function Cr_n for a time point T_n is uniquely determined by Cr_0 and K_n:

(11) For any H, $Cr_n(H) = Cr'_0(H|K_n)$, where Cr'_0 is the conditional function based on Cr_0.

$Cr_n(H)$ is thus seen to be the *conditional initial credence of* H given K_n.

How can we understand the function Cr_0? In terms of the robot, Cr_0 is the credence function that we originally build in and that he transforms step for step, with regard to the incoming data, into the later credence functions. In the case of a human being X, suppose that we find at the time T_n his credence function Cr_n. Then we can, under suitable conditions, reconstruct a sequence $E_1, \cdots, E_n$, the proposition K_n, and a function Cr_0 such that (a) $E_1, \cdots, E_n$ are possible observation data, (b) K_n is defined by (10), (c) Cr_0 satisfies all requirements of rationality for initial credence functions, and (d) the application of (11) to the assumed function Cr_0 and K_n would lead to the ascertained function Cr_n. We do not assert that X actually experienced the data $E_1, \cdots, E_n$, and that he actually had the initial credence function Cr_0, but merely that, under idealized conditions, his function Cr_n could have evolved from Cr_0 by the effect of the data $E_1, \cdots, E_n$.

For the conditional initial credence (Cr'_0) we shall also use the term "*credibility*" and the symbol '*Cred*'. As an alternative to defining '*Cred*' on the basis of 'Cr_0', we could introduce it as a primitive term. In this case we may take the following universal statement as the main postulate for the theoretical primitive term '*Cred*':

(12) Let *Cred* be any function from pairs of propositions to real numbers, satisfying all requirements which we have laid down or shall lay down for credibility functions. Let H and A be any propositions (A not empty). Let X be any observer and T any time point. If X's credibility function is *Cred* and his total observational knowledge at T is A, then his credence for H and T is $Cred(H|A)$.

Note that (12) is much more general than (11). There the function *Cred* (or Cr'_0) was applied only to those pairs H, A, in which A is a proposition of the sequence $K_1, K_2, \cdots$, and thus represents the actual knowledge of X at some time point. In (12), however, A may be any non-empty proposition. Let A_1 be a certain proposition which does not occur in the sequence K_1, $K_2, \cdots$, and H_1 some proposition. Then the statement

$$Cr_T(H_1) = Cred(H_1|A_1)$$

is to be understood as a counterfactual conditional as follows:

(13) If the total knowledge of X at T had been A_1, then his credence for H_1 at T would have been equal to $Cred(H_1|A_1)$.

This is a true counterfactual based on the postulate (12), analogous to ordinary counterfactuals based on physical laws.

Applying (12) to X's actual total observational knowledge $K_{X,T}$ at time T, we have:

(14) For any H, $Cr_{X,T}(H) = Cred_X(H|K_{X,T})$.

Now we can use credibility instead of credence in the definition of the subjective value of an act A_m, and thereby in the decision rule. Thus we have instead of (4):

(15) DEFINITION.

$$V_{X,T}(A_m) = \sum_n U_X(O_{m,n}) \times Cred_X(S_n|K_{X,T}).$$

(If the situation is such that the assumption of A_m could possibly change the credence of S_n, we have to replace '$K_{X,T}$' by '$K_{X,T} \cap A_m$'; see the remark on (1).)

If *Cred* is taken as primitive, Cr_0 can be defined as follows:

(16) DEFINITION. *For any* H, $Cr_0(H) = Cred\ (H/Z)$, *where* Z *is the necessary proposition (the tautology).*

This is the special case of (12) for the initial time T_0, when X's knowledge K_0 is the tautology.

While $Cr_{X,T}$ characterizes the momentary state of X at time T with respect to his beliefs, his function $Cred_X$ is a trait of his underlying permanent intellectual character, namely his permanent disposition for forming beliefs on the basis of his observations.

Since each of the two functions Cr_0 and *Cred* is definable on the basis of the other one, there are two alternative equivalent procedures for specifying a basic belief-forming disposition, namely either by Cr_0 or by *Cred*.

Most of those who have constructed systems of subjective or personal probability (in the narrower sense, in contrast to logical probability), e.g., Ramsey, De Finetti, and Savage, have concentrated their attention on what we might call "adult" credence functions, i.e., those of persons sufficiently developed to communicate by language, to play games, make bets, etc., hence persons with an enormous amount of experience. In empirical decision theory it has great practical advantages to take adult persons as subjects of investigation, since it is relatively easy to determine their credence functions on the basis of their behavior with games, bets, and the like. When I propose to take as a basic concept, not adult credence but either initial credence or credibility, I must admit that these concepts are less realistic and remoter from overt behavior and may therefore appear as elusive and dubious. On the other hand, when we are interested in *rational* decision theory, these concepts have great methodological advantages. Only for these concepts, not for credence, can we find a sufficient number of requirements of rationality as a basis for the construction of a system of inductive logic.

If we look at the development of theories and concepts in various branches of science, we find frequently that it was possible to arrive at powerful laws of great generality only when the development of concepts, beginning with directly observable properties, had progressed step by step to more abstract concepts, connected only indirectly with observables. Thus physics proceeds from concepts describing visible motion of bodies to the concept of a momentary electric force, and then to the still more abstract concept of a permanent electric field. In the sphere of human action we have first concepts describing overt behavior, say of a boy who is offered the choice of an apple or an ice cream cone and takes the latter; then we introduce the concept of an underlying momentary inclination, in this case the momentary preference of ice cream over apple; and finally we form the abstract concept of an underlying permanent disposition, in our example the general utility function of the boy.

What I propose to do is simply to take the same step from momentary inclination to the permanent disposition for forming momentary inclinations also with the second concept occurring in the decision principle, namely, personal probability or degree of belief. This is the step from credence to credibility.

When we wish to judge the morality of a person, we do not simply look at some of his acts, we study rather his character, the system of his moral values, which is part of his utility function. Single acts without knowledge of motives give little basis for a judgment. Similarly, if we wish to judge the rationality of a person's beliefs, we should not simply look at his present beliefs. Beliefs without knowledge of the evidence out of which they arose tell us little. We must rather study the way in which the person forms his beliefs on the basis of evidence. In other words, we should study his credibility function, not simply his present credence function. For example, let X have the evidence E that from an urn containing white and black balls ten balls have been drawn, two of them white and eight black. Let Y have the evidence E' which is similar to E, but with seven balls white and three black. Let H be the prediction that the next ball drawn will be white. Suppose that for both X and Y the credence of H is $\frac{2}{3}$. Then we would judge this same credence $\frac{2}{3}$ to be unreasonable for X, but reasonable for Y. We would condemn a credibility function *Cred* as non-rational if $Cred(H|E) = \frac{2}{3}$; while the result $Cred(H|E') = \frac{2}{3}$ would be no ground for condemnation.

Suppose X has the credibility function *Cred*, which leads him, on the basis of his knowledge K_n at time T_n to the credence function Cr_n, and thereby, with his utility function U, to the act A_{mi}. If this act seems to us unreasonable in view of his evidence K_n and his utilities, we shall judge that *Cred* is non-rational. But for such a judgment on *Cred* it is not necessary that X is actually led to an unreasonable act. Suppose that for E and H as in the above example, K_n contains E and otherwise only evidence irrelevant for H. Then we have $Cr_n(H) = Cred(H|K_n) = Cred(H|E) = \frac{2}{3}$; and this result seems unreasonable on the given evidence. If X bets on H with betting quotient $\frac{2}{3}$, this bet is unreasonable, even if he wins it. But his credence $\frac{2}{3}$ is anyway unreasonable, no matter whether he acts on it or not. It is unreasonable because there are possible situations, no matter whether real or not, in which the result $Cred(H|E) = \frac{2}{3}$ would lead him to an unreasonable act. Furthermore, it is not necessary for our condemnation of the function *Cred* that it actually leads to unreasonable *Cr*-values. Suppose that another man X' has the same function *Cred*, but is not led to the unreasonable *Cr*-value in the example, because he has an entirely different life history, and at no time is his total knowledge either E or a combination of E with data irrelevant for H. Then we would still condemn the function *Cred* and the man X' characterized by this function. Our argument would be as follows: if the total knowledge of X' had at some time been E, or E together with irrelevant data, then his credence for H would have had the unreasonable value $\frac{2}{3}$. The same considerations hold, of course, for the initial credence function Cr_0 corresponding to the function *Cred*; for, on the basis of any possible knowledge proposition K, Cr_0 and *Cred* would lead to the same credence function.

The following is an example of a requirement of rationality for Cr_0 (and hence for *Cred*) which has no analogue for credence functions. As we shall see later, this requirement leads to one of the most important axioms of inductive logic. (The term "individual" means "element of the universe of discourse", or "element of the population" in the terminology of statistics.)

R4. *Requirement of symmetry. Let a_i and a_j be two distinct individuals. Let H and H' be two propositions such that H' results from H by taking a_j for a_i and vice versa. Then Cr_0 must be such that $Cr_0(H) = Cr_0(H')$.* (In other words, Cr_0 must be invariant with respect to any finite permutation of individuals.)

This requirement seems indispensable. H and H' have exactly the same logical form; they differ merely by their reference to two distinct individuals. These individuals may happen to be quite different. But since their differences are not known to X at time T_0, they cannot have any influence on the Cr_0-values of H and H'. But suppose that at a later time T_n, X's knowledge K_n contains information E relevant to H and H', say information making H

more probable than H' (as an extreme case, E may imply that H is true and H' is false). Then X's credence function Cr_n at T_n will have different values for H and for H'. Thus it is clear that R4 applies only to Cr_0, but is not generally valid for other credence functions $Cr_n (n > 0)$.

Suppose that X is a robot constructed by us. Because H and H' are alike in all their logical properties, it would be entirely arbitrary and therefore inadmissible for us to assign to them different Cr_0-values.

A function Cr_0 is suitable for being built into a robot only if it fulfills the requirements of rationality; and most of these requirements (e.g., R4 and all those not yet mentioned) apply only to Cr_0 (and *Cred*) but not generally to other credence functions.

Now we are ready to take the step to *inductive logic*. This step consists in the transition from the concepts of the Cr_0-function and the *Cred*-function of an imaginary subject X to corresponding purely logical concepts. The former concepts are quasi-psychological; they are assigned to an imaginary subject X supposed to be equipped with perfect rationality and an unfailing memory; the logical concepts, in contrast, have nothing to do with observers and agents, whether natural or constructed, real or imaginary. For a logical function corresponding to Cr_0, I shall use the symbol '$\mathscr{M}$' and I call such functions (inductive) measure functions or $\mathscr{M}$-functions; for a logical function corresponding to *Cred*, I shall use the symbol '$\mathscr{C}$', and I call these functions (inductive) confirmation functions or $\mathscr{C}$-functions. I read '$\mathscr{C}(H|E)$' as "the degree of confirmation (or briefly "the confirmation") of H with respect to E" (or: ". . . given E"). An $\mathscr{M}$-function is a function from propositions to real numbers. A $\mathscr{C}$-function is a function from pairs of propositions to real numbers. Any $\mathscr{M}$-function $\mathscr{M}$ is supposed to be defined in a purely logical way, i.e., on the basis of concepts of logic (in the wide sense, including set-theory and hence the whole of pure mathematics). Therefore the value $\mathscr{M}(A)$ for any proposition A depends merely on the logical (set-theoretic) properties of A (which is a set in a probability space) but not on any contingent facts of nature (e.g., the truth of A or of other contingent propositions). Likewise any $\mathscr{C}$-function is supposed to be defined in purely logical terms.

Inductive logic studies those $\mathscr{M}$-functions which correspond to rational Cr_0-functions, and those $\mathscr{C}$-functions which correspond to rational *Cred*-functions. Suppose $\mathscr{M}$ is a logically defined $\mathscr{M}$-function. Let us imagine a subject X whose function Cr_0 corresponds to $\mathscr{M}$, i.e., for every proposition H, $Cr_0(H) = \mathscr{M}(H)$. If we find that Cr_0 violates one of the rationality requirements, say R4, then we would reject this function Cr_0, say for a robot we plan to build. Then we wish also to exclude the corresponding function $\mathscr{M}$ from those treated as admissible in the system of inductive logic we plan to construct. Therefore, we set up axioms of inductive logic about $\mathscr{M}$-functions so that these axioms correspond to the requirements of rationality which we find in the theory of rational decision making about Cr_0-functions.

For example, we shall lay down as the basic axioms of inductive logic those which say that $\mathcal{M}$ is a non-negative, finitely additive, and normalized measure function. These axioms correspond to the requirement R1 of coherence, by virtue of theorem (6). Further we shall have an axiom saying that $\mathcal{M}$ is regular. This axiom corresponds to the requirement R2 of strict coherence by theorem (9).

Then we shall have in inductive logic, in analogy to the requirement R4 of symmetry, the following:

(17) Axiom of Symmetry. *$\mathcal{M}$ is invariant with respect to any finite permutation of individuals.*

All axioms of inductive logic state relations among values of $\mathcal{M}$ or $\mathcal{C}$ as dependent only upon the logical properties and relations of the propositions involved (with respect to language-systems with specified logical and semantical rules). Inductive logic is the theory based upon these axioms. It may be regarded as a part of logic in view of the fact that the concepts occurring are logical concepts. It is an interesting result that this part of the theory of decision making, namely, the logical theory of the $\mathcal{M}$-functions and the $\mathcal{C}$-functions, can thus be separated from the rest. However, we should note that this logical theory deals only with the abstract, formal aspects of probability, and that the full meaning of (subjective) probability can be understood only in the wider context of decision theory through the connections between probability and the concepts of utility and rational action.

It is important to notice clearly the following distinction. While the *axioms* of inductive logic themselves are formulated in purely logical terms and do not refer to any contingent matters of fact, the *reasons* for our choice of the axioms are not purely logical. For example, when you ask me why I accept the axiom of symmetry (17), then I point out that if X had a Cr_0-function corresponding to an $\mathcal{M}$-function violating (17), then this function Cr_0 would violate R4, and I show that therefore X, in a certain possible knowledge situation, would be led to an unreasonable decision. Thus, in order to give my reasons for the axiom, I move from pure logic to the context of decision theory and speak about beliefs, actions, possible losses, and the like. However, this is not in the field of empirical, but of rational decision theory. Therefore, in giving my reasons, I do not refer to particular empirical results concerning particular agents or particular states of nature and the like. Rather, I refer to a *conceivable* series of observations by X, to conceivable sets of possible acts, of possible states of nature, of possible outcomes of the acts, and the like. These features are characteristic for an analysis of *reasonableness* of a given function Cr_0, in contrast to an investigation of the *successfulness* of the (initial or later) credence function of a given person in the real world. Success depends upon the particular contingent circumstances, rationality does not.

There is a class of axioms of inductive logic which I call *axioms of invariance*. The axiom of symmetry is one of them. Another one says that $\mathcal{M}$

is invariant with respect to any finite permutation of attributes belonging to a family of attributes, e.g., colors, provided these attributes are alike in their logical (including semantical) properties. Still another one says that if E is a proposition about a finite sample from a population, then $\mathscr{M}(E)$ is independent of the size of the population. These and other invariance axioms may be regarded as representing the valid core of the old *principle of indifference* (or principle of insufficient reason). The principle, in its original form, as used by Laplace and other authors in the classical period of the theory of probability, was certainly too strong. It was later correctly criticized by showing that it led to absurd results. However, I believe that the basic idea of the principle is sound. Our task is to restate it by specific restricted axioms.

It seems that most authors on subjective probability do not accept any axioms of invariance. In the case of those authors who take credence as their basic concept, e.g., Ramsey, De Finetti, and Savage, this is inevitable, since the invariance axioms do not hold for general credence functions. In order to obtain a stronger system, it is necessary to take as the basic concept either initial credence or credibility (or other concepts in terms of which these are definable).

When we construct an axiom system for $\mathscr{M}$, then the addition of each new axiom has the effect of excluding certain $\mathscr{M}$-functions. We accept an axiom if we recognize that the $\mathscr{M}$-functions excluded by it correspond to non-rational Cr_0-functions. Even on the basis of all axioms which I would accept at the present time for a simple qualitative language (with one-place predicates only, without physical magnitudes), the number of admissible $\mathscr{M}$-functions, i.e., those which satisfy all accepted axioms, is still infinite; but their class is immensely smaller than that of all coherent $\mathscr{M}$-functions. There will presumably be further axioms, justified in the same way by considerations of rationality. We do not know today whether in this future development the number of admissible $\mathscr{M}$-functions will always remain infinite or will become finite and possibly even be reduced to one. Therefore, at the present time I do not assert that there is only one rational Cr_0-function.

I think that the theory of the $\mathscr{M}$- and $\mathscr{C}$-functions deserves the often misused name of "*inductive logic*". Earlier I gave my reasons for regarding this theory as a part of logic. The epithet "inductive" seems appropriate because this theory provides the foundation for inductive reasoning (in a wide sense). I agree in this view with John Maynard Keynes and Harold Jeffreys. However, it is important that we recognize clearly the essential form of inductive reasoning. It seems to me that the view of almost all writers on induction in the past and including the great majority of contemporary writers, contains one basic mistake. They regard inductive reasoning as an *inference* leading from some known propositions, called the premisses or evidence, to a new proposition, called the conclusion, usually a law or a singular prediction. From this point of view the result of any particular inductive reasoning is the *acceptance* of a new proposition (or its rejection, or its suspension until further evidence is found, as the case may be). This seems to me wrong. On the basis of this view it would be impossible to refute Hume's dictum that there are no rational reasons for induction. Suppose that I find in earlier weather reports that a weather situation like the one we have today has occurred one hundred times and that it was followed each time by rain the next morning. According to the customary view, on the basis of this evidence the "inductive method" entitles me to accept the prediction that it will rain tomorrow morning. (If you demur because the number one hundred is too small, change it to one hundred thousand or any number you like.) I would think instead that inductive reasoning about a proposition should lead, not to acceptance or rejection, but to the assignment of a number to the proposition, viz., its $\mathscr{C}$-value. This difference may perhaps appear slight; in fact, however, it is essential. If, in accordance with the customary view, we accept the prediction, then Hume is certainly right in protesting that we have no rational reason for doing so, since, as everybody will agree, it is still possible that it will not rain tomorrow.

If, on the other hand, we adopt the new view of the nature of inductive reasoning, then the situation is quite different. In this case X does not assert the hypothesis H in question, e.g., the prediction "it will rain tomorrow"; he asserts merely the following statements:

(18) (a) At the present moment T_n, the totality of X's observation results is K_n.
(b) $\mathscr{C}(H|K_n) = 0.8$.
(c) $Cred_X(H|K_n) = 0.8$.
(d) $Cr_{X,T_n}(H) = 0.8$.

(a) is the statement of the evidence at hand, the same as in the first case. But now, instead of accepting H, X asserts the statement (c) of the *Cred*-value for H on his evidence. (c) is the result of X's inductive reasoning. Against this result Hume's objection does not hold, because X can give rational reasons for it. (c) is derived from (b) because X has chosen the function $\mathscr{C}$ as his credibility function. (b) is an analytic statement based on the definition of $\mathscr{C}$. X's choice of $\mathscr{C}$ was guided by the axioms of inductive logic. And for each of the axioms we can give reasons, namely, rationality requirements for credibility functions. Thus $\mathscr{C}$ represents a reasonable credibility function. Finally, X's credence value (d) is derived from (c) by (14).

Now some philosophers, including some of my empiricist friends, would raise the following objection. If the result of inductive reasoning is merely an analytic statement (like (b) or (c)), then induction cannot fulfill its purpose of guiding our practical decisions. As a basis for a decision we need a statement with factual content. If the prediction H itself is not available, then we must use a statement of the *objective* probability of H. In answer to this objection I would first point out that X has a factual basis in his evidence, as stated in (a). And for the determination of a rational decision neither the acceptance of H nor knowledge of the objective probability of H

is needed. The rational subjective probability, i.e., the credence as stated in (d), is sufficient for determining first the rational subjective value of each possible act by (15), and then a rational decision. Thus in our example, in view of (b) X would decide to make a bet on rain tomorrow if it were offered to him at odds of four to one or less, but not more.

The old puzzle of induction consists in the following dilemma. On the one hand we see that inductive reasoning is used by the scientist and the man in the street every day without apparent scruples; and we have the feeling that it is valid and indispensable. On the other hand, once Hume awakens our intellectual conscience, we find no answer to his objection. Who is right, the man of common sense or the critical philosopher? We see that, as so often, both are partially right. Hume's criticism of the customary forms of induction was correct. But still the basic idea of common sense thinking is vindicated: induction, if properly reformulated, can be shown to be valid by rational criteria.

References

[1] Carnap, R. *Logical foundations of probability.* Chicago, 1950.

[2] Carnap, R. *The continuum of inductive methods.* Chicago, 1952.

[3] Carnap, R. Inductive logic and rational decisions. (This is an expanded version of the present paper.) To appear as the introductory article in: *Studies in probability and inductive logic,* Vol. I, R. Carnap, ed. Forthcoming.

[4] Davidson, D., and P. Suppes. *Decision making: An experimental approach.* Stanford, 1957.

[5] De Finetti, B. La prévision: ses lois logiques, ses sources subjectives. *Annales de l'Institut Henri Poincaré,* Vol. 7 (1937), pp. 1–68.

[6] Good, I. J. *Probability and the weighing of evidence.* London and New York, 1950.

[7] Jeffreys, H. *Theory of probability.* Oxford (1939), 2nd ed. 1948.

[8] Kemeny, J. Fair bets and inductive probabilities. *Journal of Symbolic Logic,* Vol. 20 (1955), pp. 263–273.

[9] Keynes, J. M. *A treatise on probability.* London and New York, 1921.

[10] Kolmogoroff, A. N. *Foundations of the theory of probability.* New York (1950), 2nd ed. 1956.

[11] Koopman, B. O. The bases of probability. *Bull. Amer. Math. Soc.,* Vol. 46 (1940), pp. 763–774.

[12] Lehman, R. S. On confirmation and rational betting. *Journal of Symbolic Logic,* Vol. 20 (1955), pp. 251–262.

[13] Mosteller, F. C., and P. Nogee. An experimental measurement of utility. *Journal of Political Economy,* Vol. 59 (1951), pp. 371–404.

[14] Neumann, J. von, and O. Morgenstern. *Theory of games and economic behavior.* Princeton (1944), 2nd ed. 1947.

[15] Ramsey, F. P. *The foundations of mathematics and other logical essays.* London and New York, 1931.

[16] Savage, L. J. *The foundations of statistics.* New York and London, 1954.

[17] Shimony, A. Coherence and the axioms of confirmation. *Journal of Symbolic Logic,* Vol. 20 (1955), pp. 1–28.

[18] Wright, G. H. von. *The logical problem of induction.* Oxford and New York (1941), 2nd ed., 1957.

Symposium on Current Views of Subjective Probability

SUBJECTIVE PROBABILITY AS THE MEASURE OF A NON-MEASURABLE SET

I. J. GOOD

Admiralty Research Laboratory, Teddington, Middlesex, England

1. Introduction

I should like to discuss some aspects of axiom systems for subjective and other kinds of probability. Before doing so, I shall summarize some verbal philosophy and terminology. Although the history of the subject is interesting and illuminating, I shall not have time to say much about it.

2. Definition

In order to define the sense in which I am using the expression "subjective probability" it will help to say what it is not, and this can be done by means of a brief classification of kinds of probability [16, 11, 8].

Each application of a theory of probability is made by a communication system that has apparently purposive behaviour. I designate it as "you". It could also be called an "org", a name recently used to mean an organism or organization. "You" may be one person, or an android, or a group of people, machines, neural circuits, telepathic fields, spirits, Martians and other beings. One point of the reference to machines is to emphasize that subjective probability need not be associated with metaphysical problems concerning mind (compare [7]).

We may distinguish between various kinds of probability in the following manner.

(i) Physical (material) probability, which most of us regard as existing irrespective of the existence of orgs. For example, the "unknown probability" that a loaded, but symmetrical-looking, die will come up 6.

(ii) Psychological probability, which is the kind of probability that can be inferred to some extent from your behaviour, including your verbal communications.

(iii) Subjective probability, which is psychological probability modified by the attempt to achieve consistency, when a theory of probability is used combined with mature judgment.

(iv) Logical probability (called "credibility" in [19] for example), which is hypothetical subjective probability when you are perfectly rational, and therefore presumably infinitely large. Credibilities are usually assumed to have unique numerical values, when both the proposition whose credibility is under consideration and the "given" proposition are well defined. I must interrupt myself in order to defend the description "infinitely large".

You might be asked to calculate the logical probabilities of the Riemann, Fermat, and Goldbach conjectures. Each of these probabilities is either 0 or 1. It would be cheating to wait for someone else to produce the answers. Similarly, as pointed out in [17, p. x], you cannot predict the future state of society without first working out the whole of science. The same applies even if you are satisfied with the logical probabilities of future states of society. Therefore a rational being must have an infinite capacity for handling information. It must therefore be infinitely large, or at any rate much larger than is practicable for any known physical org. In other words, logical probabilities are liable to be unknown in practice. This difficulty occurs in a less acute form for subjective probability than for logical probability.

Attempts have been made [2, 10] to define logical probability numerically, in terms of a language or otherwise. Although such a programme is stimulating and useful, the previous remarks seem to show that it can never be completed and that there will always remain domains where subjective probability will have to be used instead.

(In Carnap's contribution to this Congress he has shifted his position, and now defines logical probability to mean what I call numerically completely consistent subjective probability. He permits more than one consistent system of probabilities. Thus his present interpretation of logical probability is a consistent system within a "black box" in the sense of Section 3 below.)

Physical probability automatically *obeys* axioms, subjective probability *depends* on axioms, psychological probability neither obeys axioms nor depends very much on them. There is a continuous gradation, depending on the "degree of consistency" of the probability judgments with a system of axioms, from psychological probability to subjective probability, and beyond, to logical probability, if it exists. Although I cannot define "degree of consistency", it seems to me to have very important intuitive significance. The notion is indispensable.

In my opinion, every *measure* of a probability can be interpreted as a subjective probability. For example, the physical probability of a 6 with a loaded die can be estimated as equal to the subjective probability of a 6 on the next throw, after several throws. Further, if you can become aware of the value of a logical probability, you would adopt it as your subjective probability. Therefore a single set of axioms should be applicable to all kinds of probability (except psychological probability), namely the axioms of subjective probability.

Superficially, at least, there seems to be a distinction between the axiom systems that are appropriate for physical probability and those appropriate for subjective probability, in that the latter are more often expressed in terms of inequalities, i.e., comparisons between probabilities. Theories in which inequalities are taken seriously are more general than those in which each probability is assumed to be a precise number. I do not know whether physical probabilities are absolutely precise, but they are usually assumed to be, with a resulting simplification in the axioms.

3. A Black-Box Description of the Application of Formalized Theories

I refer here to a "description", and not to a "theory", because I wish to avoid a discussion of the theory of the application of the black-box theory of the application of theories [4, 5, 6]. The description is in terms of the block diagram of Fig. 1 in which observations and experiments have been omitted. It consists of a closed loop in which you feed judgments into a black box and feed "discernments" out of it. These discernments are made in the black box as deductions from the judgments and axioms, and also, as a matter of expediency, from theorems deduced from the axioms alone. If no judgments are fed in, no discernments emerge. The totality of judgments at any time is called a "body of beliefs". You examine each discernment, and if it seems reasonable, you transfer it to the body of beliefs. The purpose of the deductions, in each application of the theory, is to enlarge the body of beliefs, and to detect inconsistencies in it. When these are found, you attempt to remove them by means of more mature judgment.

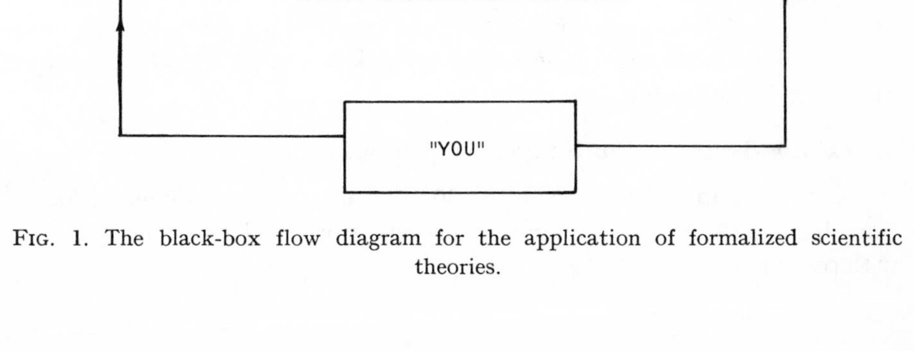

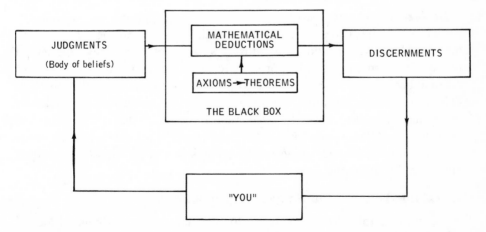

FIG. 1. The black-box flow diagram for the application of formalized scientific theories.

The particular scientific theory is determined by the axioms and the rules of application.

The rules of application refer to the method of formalizing the judgments, and of "deformalizing" the mathematical deductions. For example, in a theory of subjective probability the standard type of judgment might be a comparison of the form

$$P'(E|F) \geqq P'(G|H),$$

where $P'(E|F)$ is the intensity of conviction or degree of belief that you would have in E if you regarded F as certain. The P''s are not necessarily numerical, and what is meaningful is not a P' by itself, but a comparison of intensities of conviction of the above type. These judgments are plugged into the black box by simply erasing the two dashes. Likewise, discernments can be obtained by taking an output inequality, $P(E|F) \geqq P(G|H)$, and putting dashes on it. The P's are assumed to be numbers, even if you can never discover their values at all precisely. This is the reason for the expression "black box". The black box may be entirely outside you, and used like a tame mathematician, or it may be partially or entirely inside you, but in any case you do not know the P's precisely.

Following Keynes and Koopman, I assume that the P''s are only partially ordered.

Apart from the axioms and rules, there are in practice many informal suggestions that you make use of, such as the need to throw away evidence judged to be unimportant, in order to simplify the analysis, and yet to avoid special selection of the evidence. (In spite of all the dangers, objectivistic methods in statistics invariably ignore evidence in order to achieve objectivity. In each application a subjective judgement is required in order to justify this device. Compare the idea of a "Statistician's Stooge" in [9].) But in this paper I am more concerned with axioms and rules of application than with "suggestions".

De luxe black boxes are available, with extra peripheral equipment, so that additional types of judgment and discernment can be used, such as direct judgments of odds, log-odds, "weights of evidence", numerical probabilities, judgments of approximate normality, and (for a theory of rational behaviour) comparisons of utilities and of expected utilities [5 or 6]. (There are numerous aids to such judgments, even including black-box theorems, such as the central limit theorem, and a knowledge of the judgments of other orgs. All such aids come in the category of "suggestions".) But, as we shall see shortly, for the simplest kind of black box, a certain kind of output must not be available.

4. Axiom Systems for Subjective Probability

See, for example, [18, 3, 13, 14, 4, 20] and, for similar systems for logical probability, [12, 10]. The axioms of subjective probability can be expressed in terms of either

(i) comparisons between probabilities, or preferences between acts, or
(ii) numerical probabilities.

Koopman's system [13, 14] was concerned with comparisons between probabilities, without reference to utilities or acts. Although it is complicated it is convincing when you think hard. From his axioms he deduced numerical ones for what he called *upper* and *lower* probabilities, P^* and P_*. We may define $P_*(E|F)$ and $P^*(E|F)$ as the least upper bound and greatest lower bound of numbers, x, for which you can judge or discern that $P'(E|F) > x$ or $< x$. Here $P'(E|F)$ is not a number, although x is. The interpretation of the inequality $P'(E|F) > x$ is as follows. For each integer n, perfect packs of n cards, perfectly well shuffled, are imagined, so that for each rational number, $x = m/n (m < n)$, there exist propositions, G and H, for which $P(G|H)$ would usually be said to be equal to x. The inequality is then interpreted as $P'(E|F) > P'(G|H)$.

Note that $P_*(E|F)$ and $P^*(E|F)$ depend on the whole body of beliefs. Also note that $P_*(E|F)$ is not the least upper bound of all numbers, x, for which you can *consistently* state that $P'(E|F)>x$: to assume this interpretation for more than one probability would be liable to lead to an *in*consistency.

If $P_* = P^*$, then each is called P, and the usual axioms of probability are included in those for upper and lower probability. The analogy with inner and outer measure is obvious. But the axioms for upper and lower probability do not all follow from the theory of outer and inner measure. It is a little misleading to say that probability theory is a branch of measure theory.

In order to avoid the complications of Koopman's approach, I have in the past adopted another one, less rigorous, but simpler. I was concerned with describing how subjective probability should be used in as simple terms as possible more than with exact formal justification. (I gave an informal justification which I found convincing myself.) This approach consisted in assuming that a probability *inside the black box* was numerical and precise. This assumption enables one to use a simple set of axioms such as the following set (axioms C).

C1. *$P(E|F)$ is a real number.* (Here and later, the "given" proposition is assumed not to be self-contradictory.)

C2. $0 \leqq P(E|F) \leqq 1$.

Definition. *If $P(E|F) = 0$ (or 1), then we say that E is "almost impossible" (or "almost certain") given F.*

C3. *If $E.F$ is almost impossible given H, then*

$$P(E \vee F|H) = P(E|H) + P(F|H) \text{ (addition axiom).}$$

C4. *If H logically implies E, then E is almost certain given H (but not conversely).*

C5. *If $H\cdot E$ and $H\cdot F$ are not self-contradictory and $H\cdot E$ implies F and $H\cdot F$ implies E, then*

$$P(E|H) = P(F|H) \text{ (axiom of equivalence).}$$

C6. $P(E\cdot F|H) = P(E|H)\cdot P(F|E\cdot H)$ (product axiom).

C7. (Optional.) *If $E_i \cdot E_j$ is almost impossible given H ($i < j$; $i, j = 1, 2, 3, \cdots$ ad inf.), then*

$$P(E_1 \vee E_2 \vee \cdots |H) = \sum_i P(E_i|H) \text{ (complete additivity).}$$

(The above axioms are not quite the same as axiom sets A and B of [4].)

C8. (The Keynes-Russell form of the principle of cogent reason. Optional. See [19, p. 397], [4, p. 37].) *Let ϕ and ψ be propositional functions. Then*

$$P(\phi(a)|\psi(a)) = P(\phi(b)|\psi(b)).$$

I describe this axiom as "optional" because I think that in all those circumstances in which it is judged to be (approximately) applicable, the judgment will come to the same thing as that of the equation itself, with dashes on.

It follows from axiom C1, that $P(E|F) <, >$, or $= P(G|H)$, but we do not want to deduce that $P'(E|F)$ and $P'(G|H)$ are comparable. There is therefore an artificial restriction on what peripheral equipment is available with *de luxe* black boxes. This artificiality is the price to be paid for making the axioms as simple as possible. It can be removed by formulating the axioms in terms of upper and lower probabilities. To use axioms C is like saying of a non-measurable set that it really has an unknowable ("metamathematical") measure lying somewhere between its inner and outer measures. And as a matter of fact there is something to be said for this paradoxical-sounding idea. If you will bear with me for a moment I shall illustrate this in a non-rigorous manner.

Suppose A and B are two non-intersecting and non-measurable sets. Write m for the unknowable measure of a non-measurable set, and assume that

$$m(A+B) = m(A)+m(B).$$

Then

$$m(A+B) \leqq m^*(A)+m^*(B), \quad m(A+B) \geqq m_*(A)+m_*(B).$$

Therefore (for elucidation, compare the following probability argument)

$$m^*(A+B) \leqq m^*(A)+m^*(B), \quad m_*(A+B) \geqq m_*(A)+m_*(B),$$

and these inqualities are true. Similarly,

$$m(A) = m(A+B)-m(B) \leqq m^*(A+B)-m_*(B).$$

Therefore

$$m^*(A) \leqq m^*(A+B)-m_*(B),$$

which is also true.

The same metamathematical procedure can be used, more rigorously, in order to derive without difficulty, from axioms C together with the rules of application, a system of axioms for upper and lower probability. These are the axioms D listed below. As an example, I shall prove axiom D6(iii). We have

$$P(E \cdot F|H) = P(E|H) \cdot P(F|E \cdot H).$$

Therefore, if $P(F|E \cdot H) \neq 0$,

$$P(E \cdot F|H)/P(F|E \cdot H) = P(E|H).$$

But $P^*(E \cdot F|H) \geqq P(E \cdot F|H)$, since, in this system, $P^*(E \cdot F|H)$ is defined as the greatest lower bound of numbers, x, for which it can be discerned that $x > P(E \cdot F|H)$. Similarly,

$$P_*(F|E \cdot H) \leqq P(F|E \cdot H).$$

Therefore

$$P^*(E \cdot F|H)/P_*(F|E \cdot H) \geqq P(E|H).$$

Therefore

$$P^*(E \cdot F|H)/P_*(F|E \cdot H) \geqq P^*(E|H).$$

Q.E.D.

The main rule of application is now that the judgment or discernment $P'(E|F) > P'(G|H)$ corresponds to the black-box inequality $P_*(E|F) > P^*(G|H)$. Koopman derived most, but not all, of axioms D1 – D6 from his non-numerical ones, together with an assumption that can be informally described as saying that perfect packs of cards can be imagined to exist. His derived axioms for upper and lower probability do not include axiom D6(iii) and (iv). (D7 and D9 were excluded since he explicitly avoided complete additivity.) I have not yet been able to decide whether it is necessary to add something to his non-numerical axioms in order to be able to derive D6(iii) and (iv). Whether or not it turns out to be necessary, we may say that the present metamathematical approach has justified itself, since it leads very easily to a more complete set of axioms for upper and lower probability than were reached by Koopman with some difficulty.

The axioms D will now be listed. I have not proved that the list is complete, i.e., that further independent deductions cannot be made from axioms C.

D1. $P_*(E|F)$ *and* $P^*(E|F)$ *are real numbers.* (Here and later the given proposition is assumed not to be self-contradictory.)

D2. $0 \leqq P_*(E|F) \leqq P^*(E|F) \leqq 1.$

DEFINITION. *If* $P^* = P_*$, *each is called* P. *The previous definitions of "almost certain" and "almost impossible" can then be expressed as* $P_* = 1$ *and* $P^* = 0$.

D3. *If* $E \cdot F$ *is almost impossible given* H, *then* (addition axiom)

$$P_*(E|H)+P_*(F|H) \leqq P_*(E \vee F|H) \leqq P_*(E|H)+P^*(F|H) \leqq P^*(E \vee F|H) \leqq P^*(E|H)+P^*(F|H).$$

D4. *If* H *logically implies* E, *then* E *is almost certain given* H *but not conversely.*

D5. *If* $H \cdot E$ *implies* F, *and* $H \cdot F$ *implies* E, *then* (axiom of equivalence)

$$P_*(E|H) = P_*(F|H), \quad P^*(E|H) = P^*(F|H).$$

D6. (Product axiom.)

(i) $$P_*(E \cdot F|H) \geqq P_*(E|H) \cdot P_*(F|E \cdot H);$$
(ii) $$P^*(E \cdot F|H) \geqq P_*(E|H) \cdot P^*(F|E \cdot H);$$
(iii) $$P^*(E \cdot F|H) \geqq P^*(E|H) \cdot P_*(F|E \cdot H);$$
(iv) $$P_*(E \cdot F|H) \leqq P_*(E|H) \cdot P^*(F|E \cdot H);$$
(v) $$P_*(E \cdot F|H) \leqq P^*(E|H) \cdot P_*(F|E \cdot H);$$
(vi) $$P^*(E \cdot F|H) \leqq P^*(E|H) \cdot P^*(F|E \cdot H).$$

D7. (Complete super- and sub-additivity. Optional.)

If $E_i \cdot E_j$ *is almost impossible given* $H(i < j;\ i, j = 1, 2, 3, \cdots$ *ad inf.*), *then*

(i) $$P_*(E_1|H)+P_*(E_2|H) + \cdots \leqq P_*(E_1 \vee E_2 \vee \cdots |H);$$
(ii) $$P^*(E_1|H)+P^*(E_2|H)+ \cdots \geqq P^*(E_1 \vee E_2 \vee \cdots |H).$$

D8. (Cogent reason. Optional.) *Let* ϕ *and* ψ *be propositional functions. Then*

$$P_*(\phi(a)|\psi(a)) = P_*(\phi(b)|\psi(b)), \quad P^*(\phi(a)|\psi(a)) = P^*(\phi(b)|\psi(b)).$$

D9. (Complete super- and sub-multiplicativity. Optional.) *For any (enumerable) sequence of propositions,* $E_1, E_2, \cdots$.

(i) $$P_*(E_1|H)P_*(E_2|E_1 \cdot H)P_*(E_3|E_1 \cdot E_2 \cdot H) \cdots \leqq P_*(E_1 \cdot E_2 \cdots |H);$$
(ii) $$P^*(E_1|H)P^*(E_2|E_1 \cdot H)P^*(E|_3E_1 \cdot E_2 \cdot H) \cdots \geqq P^*(E_1 \cdot E_2 \cdots |H).$$

The corresponding result in the C system is a *theorem*. (See Appendix.)

I have not been able to prove that

$$P^*(E \vee F)+P^*(E \cdot F) \leqq P^*(E)+P^*(F),$$

even though the corresponding property is true of Lebesgue outer measure, and I suspect that it does not follow by the above methods. It would be possible to prove it (compare [1, p, 14]) provided that we assumed:

D10. (Optional.) *Given any proposition,* E, *and a positive number,* ε, *there exists a proposition,* G, *which is implied by* E, *and has a precise probability* $P(G) < P^*(E)+\varepsilon$. (This axiom may be made conditional on another proposition, H, in an obvious manner.)

I cannot say that D10 has much intuitive appeal, although the corresponding assertion is true in the theory of measure.

It seems that the theory of probability is not quite a branch of the theory of measure, but each can learn something from the other.

Incidentally, random variables can be regarded as *isomorphic* with arbitrary functions, not necessarily measurable. I understand that this thesis is supported by de Finetti. Also upper and lower expectations can be defined by means of upper and lower integrals in the sense of Stone [21].

5. Higher Types of Probability

A familiar objection to precise numerical subjective probability is the sarcastic request for an estimate correct to twenty decimal places, say for the probability that the Republicans will win the election. One reason for using upper and lower probabilities is to meet this objection. The objection is however raised, more harmlessly, against the precision of the upper and lower probabilities. In [5], and in lectures at Princeton and Chicago in 1955, I attempted to cope with this difficulty by reference to probabilities of "higher type". When we estimate that a probability $P'(E|H)$ lies between 0.2 and 0.8, we may feel that 0.5 is *more likely to be rational* than 0.2 or 0.8. The probability involved in this expression "more likely" is of "type II". I maintain that we can have a subjective probability distribution concerning the estimate that a perfectly rational org would make for $P'(E|H)$ a subjective probability distribution for a credibility. *If* this probability distribution were sharp, then it could be used in order to calculate the expected credibility precisely, and this expectation should then be taken as our subjective probability of E given H. But the type II distribution is not sharp; it is expressible only in terms of inequalities. These inequalities themselves have fuzziness, in fact the fuzziness obviously increases as we proceed to higher types of probability, but it becomes of less practical importance.

It seems to me that type II probability is decidedly useful as an unofficial aid to the formulation of judgments of upper and lower probabilities of type I. I would not myself advocate even the unofficial use of type III probability for most practical purposes, but the notion of an infinite sequence of types of probability does have the philosophical use of providing a rationale for the lack of precision of upper and lower probabilities.

Appendix. Continuity.

(See the remark following D9.) There is a well-known strong analogy between the calculus of sets of points and the calculus of propositions. In this analogy "E is contained in F" becomes "E implies F"; $E+F$ becomes $E \vee F$; $E-F$ becomes $E \cdot \bar{F}$; $E \cap F$ becomes $E \cdot F$; "E is empty" becomes "E is impossible"; "all sets are contained in E" becomes "E is certain"; $E_n \nearrow$ becomes $E_1 \supset E_2 \supset E_3 \supset \cdots$; $E_n \searrow$ becomes $\cdots E_3 \supset E_2 \supset E_1$.

Accordingly we can define, for an infinite sequence of propositions, $\{E_n\}$,

$$\lim\sup E_n = (E_1 \vee E_2 \vee \cdots) \cdot (E_2 \vee E_3 \vee \cdots) \cdot (E_3 \vee E_4 \vee \cdots) \cdots,$$
$$\lim\inf E_n = (E_1 \cdot E_2 \cdots) \vee (E_2 \cdot E_3 \ldots) \vee (E_3 \cdot E_4 \cdots) \vee \cdots.$$

If these are equal, each is called lim E_n. The limit of a monotonic increasing (or decreasing) sequence of propositions is

$$E_1 \vee E_2 \vee \cdots \text{ (or } E_1 \cdot E_2 \cdots).$$

The other definitions and arguments given, for example in [15, pp. 84–85] can be at once adapted to propositions, and we see that complete additivity is equivalent to continuity, i.e., lim $P(E_n) = P$ (lim E_n) if $\{E_n\}$ is a monotonic sequence of propositions. It can then be proved that, for example,

$$P(E_1 \cdot E_2 \cdots) = P(E_1) \cdot P(E_2|E_1) \cdot P(E_3|E_1 \cdot E_2) \cdots,$$

i.e., we have "complete multiplicativity". The axiom D9 is derived from this theorem by means of the metamathematical argument of Section 4.

The analogy between propositions and sets of points is imperfect. For the analogy of a point itself should be a logically possible proposition, E, that is not implied by any other distinct proposition that is logically possible. It is not easy to think of any such proposition E, unless the class of propositions has been suitably restricted. Fortunately the notion of a point is inessential for the above analysis: the algebra of sets of points makes little use of the notion of a point.

References

[1] Burkill, J. C. *The Lebesgue Integral*, Cambridge, University Press, 1951.

[2] Carnap, R. *Logical Foundations of Probability*. Chicago, University of Chicago Press, 1950.

[3] Finetti, B. de. La prévision: ses lois logiques, ses sources subjectives. *Annales de l'Inst. Henri Poincaré*, Vol. 7 (1937), pp. 1–68.

[4] Good, I. J. *Probability and the Weighing of Evidence*, London, Griffin; New York, Hafner; 1950.

[5] Good, I. J. Rational decisions. *Journal of the Royal Statistical Society, Series B*, Vol. 13 (1952), pp. 107–114.

[6] Good, I. J. Chapter 3 of *Uncertainty and Business Decisions*, 2nd ed., Liverpool, University Press, 1957. (Ed. by Carter, Meredith and Shackle.)

[7] Good, I. J. Could a machine make probability judgments? *Computers and Automation*, Vol. 8 (1959), pp. 14–16 and 24–26.

[8] Good, I. J. Kinds of probability. *Science*, Vol. 129 (1959), pp. 443–447.

[9] Good, I. J. The paradox of confirmation. *British Journal of the Philosophy of Science*, Vol. 11 (1960), pp. 145–149; Vol. 12 (1961), pp. 63–64.

[10] Jeffreys, H. *Theory of Probability*. Oxford, University Press, 1939.

[11] Kemble, E. C. The probability concept. *Philosophy of Science*, Vol. 8 (1941), pp. 204–232.

[12] Keynes, J. M. *A Treatise on Probability*, London, Macmillan, 1921.

[13] Koopman, B. O. The axioms and algebra of intuitive probability, *Annals of Mathematics*, Vol. 41 (1940), pp. 269–292.

[14] Koopman, B. O. The bases of probability. *Bulletin of the American Mathematical Society*, Vol. 46 (1940), pp. 763–774.

[15] Loève, M. *Probability Theory*, Toronto, New York, London, van Nostrand, 1955.

[16] Poisson, S. D. *Recherches sur la Probabilité des Jugements*, Paris, Bachelier, 1837.

[17] Popper, K. R. *The Poverty of Historicism*, London, Routledge and Kegan Paul, 1957.

[18] Ramsey, F. P. Chapters 7 and 8 of *The Foundations of Mathematics*, London, Routledge and Kegan Paul, 1931.

[19] Russell, B. *Human Knowledge, its Scope and Limits*, London, George Allen, 1948.

[20] Savage, L. J. *The Foundations of Statistics*. New York, Wiley; London, Chapman and Hall, 1954.

[21] Stone, M. H. Notes on integration, I, II, III, IV. *Proceedings of the National Academy of Sciences*, Vols. 34 and 35 (1948).

REMARKS ON THE EPISTEMOLOGY OF SUBJECTIVE PROBABILITY

G. H. VON WRIGHT

Helsingfors University, Helsingfors, Finland

In the present paper I have set myself two aims. First, I wanted to indicate my reasons for holding that subjective probabilities cannot be *defined*, as Ramsey thought they could, in terms of values and attitudes in options, since the formation of the relevant attitudes requires previous assignments of probabilities. Second, I shall try to outline a conception of probability which, as far as I can see, combines some features of a subjectivist and some of an objectivist view of this notion. It goes without saying that on a number of points I shall have to content myself with only a rough statement of my position, either omitting or cutting short arguments by which I would support it in a fuller treatment.

1

By "subjective probability" I here understand the conception of probability as a *degree of belief* or as a *partial belief*. This conception may be said to face two main epistemological problems.

The first is the problem of *measuring* partial beliefs. This problem again falls in two parts, viz., the question of assigning comparative or relative measures to degrees of belief, and the question of assigning numerical values to them. In this paper I shall discuss *numerical* probabilities only.

By the second main problem I mean the question of the *justification* of the laws (axioms and theorems) of the calculus of probability under a subjectivist conception of the basic notion of this calculus.

As is well known, the calculus of probability can be developed in a purely abstract, axiomatic manner. The axioms of this abstract calculus are remarkably simple, considering the complexity and wealth of their consequences. Two assumptions about the mathematical properties of a two-place functor $P(/)$ taking some "proposition-like" entities as its arguments and possessing a unique, non-negative value are substantially sufficient. The one is an assumption of complementarity $P(E/O)+P(\sim E/O)=1$. The other is the rule for multiplying probabilities $P(E_1 \,\&\, E_2/O) = P(E_1/O) \cdot P(E_2/O \,\&\, E_1)$. By calling the arguments of the functor "proposition-like", I mean that they are some entities which are amenable to truth-functional operations. From the point of view of the abstract calculus it is irrelevant whether we think of these entities as propositions or propositional functions or properties or sets (classes).

It follows from what has just been said that the question of justifying the laws of the calculus is substantially identical with the question of justifying the two axioms of complementarity and of multiplication. If it can be shown that a definition of probability as a partial belief satisfies these two axioms, the definition will *a fortiori* satisfy the theorems of the calculus too.

2

The question may be raised: If a probability is a degree of belief, what is the object of this belief?

Probability is attributed to a wide variety of things, from theories of cosmology to characters in a novel or play. *One* category of things, however, may be said to hold a central position, at least as far as the calculus and its applications are concerned. This is the category of *events*. Numerical probabilities, I would say, are primarily attributed to events. (This need not be true of non-numerical probabilities.)

One may distinguish between *generic* and *individual* events. A generic event is, e.g., rainfall. An individual event is, e.g., the falling of rain at a certain place and time.

An individual event can be characterized as the happening or occurrence of a generic event on an individual *occasion*.

Two or more generic events may happen on the same occasion. For example: the tossing of a coin and the turning up of "head". Then it is sometimes convenient to speak of one of the events as determining a *type* of occasion for the happening of the other event. For example: the tossing of a coin is a type of occasion on which "head" may turn up.

I shall now qualify my statement that (numerical) probabilities are primarily attributed to events by saying that they are primarily attributed to *generic* events on *types* of occasion. Some of my reasons for holding this view will, I hope, become apparent later in the paper.

The symbol $P(E/O)$ may henceforth be read: the probability of the (generic) event E on the (type of) occasion O.

3

A method of measuring partial beliefs was devised by Ramsey and seems to have gained acceptance among later researchers in the field. The method can be regarded as a refinement of the old-established way of measuring a person's belief by proposing a bet and observing the lowest odds he will accept.

A bet can be regarded as an option between goods, and accepting lowest odds as a reflection of an attitude of indifference in an option. Ramsey's method is an application of a rudimentary logic of preferences and indifferences in options for the particular purpose measuring partial beliefs.

The logic of options is of great importance to any science which studies valuations, such as economics or ethics. This branch of logical study is still very insufficiently investigated. We cannot here discuss its principles. Nor can we discuss the notion of *a good* which is fundamental to it.

It is useful to distinguish between *simple* and *conditioned* options. In a simple option the subject is offered a choice between two or more goods "on a tray" as it were. For example: His option is between goods G_1 and G_2, of which he can have either without further ado. In a conditioned option the subject can have the goods only on condition that something else, which is not known for certain, turns out to be the case. For example: The option is between G_1 if p is the case *and* G_2 if q is the case, or as we could also put it between G_1 consequent upon p *and* G_2 consequent upon q.

Ramsey's method of measuring partial belief evolves in three steps.[1] In the first, an attitude of preference in a simple option in combination with an attitude of indifference in a conditioned option is used to *define* what is meant by degree of belief $\frac{1}{2}$ in an arbitrary proposition p. In the second step, the holding of a partial belief of degree $\frac{1}{2}$ in a proposition p combined with an attitude of indifference in a certain option conditioned by p is used to *define* what is meant by saying that the difference in value between two goods, G_1 and G_2, is equal to the difference in value between two other goods, G_3 and G_4.

The notion of equality of differences in value, thus defined, in combination with the laws governing options, enables us to correlate one-to-one real numbers with goods as the measures of their value. I shall use the symbol "$V(\ )$" for the value- or utility-functor. This is a one-place functor taking some proposition-like entities ("goods") as arguments.

In the third and final step in Ramsey's procedure, an attitude of indifference in a certain conditioned option is used to *define* what is meant by saying that a person's degree of belief in an arbitrary proposition is such and such. It should be stressed that Ramsey himself regarded this as a *definition* of degree of belief.[2] This makes his theory of subjective probabilities especially interesting — but also debatable.

The conditioned options which figure in Ramsey's procedure can all be regarded as special cases of the following more general option: On the one hand G_1 consequent upon p and G_2 upon $\sim p$, and on the other hand G_3 consequent upon p and G_4 upon $\sim p$. If the subject, when faced with a choice between these two alternatives, professes to be indifferent, his attitude — on Ramsey's theory — is interpreted as implying that his degree of belief in p equals the ratio

$$\frac{V(G_4)-V(G_2)}{V(G_1)-V(G_3)+V(G_4)-V(G_2)}.$$

Accepting the presuppositions involved in Ramsey's procedure — in particular the laws governing options — we have solved the first main problem which I said confronted the subjectivist conception of probability, or the problem of measuring partial beliefs.

Accepting this solution to the first problem, we immediately obtain a

---

[1]For a full description see [2, pp. 177–180].

[2]See especially [2, p. 179].

solution to the second main problem as well, viz., the problem of justifying the laws of the calculus.

The same conditioned option which fixes the degree of belief in p at

$$\frac{V(G_4)-V(G_2)}{V(G_1)-V(G_3)+V(G_4)-V(G_2)}$$

also fixes the degree of belief in $\sim p$ at

$$\frac{V(G_3)-V(G_1)}{V(G_2)-V(G_4)+V(G_3)-V(G_1)}.$$

The sum of the two degrees of belief is 1. Herewith is shown that Ramsey's definition of degrees of belief satisfies the complementarity principle of probabilities.

The definition also satisfies the multiplication principle. I shall not reproduce here the calculation showing this.[3]

This solution to the problem of justification determines a sense in which the laws of the calculus can be called "laws of consistent (or coherent) partial beliefs". A distribution of partial beliefs, which is not in accordance with the principles of the calculus, is inconsistent *in the sense* that it conflicts with the assumed principles of the logic of options.[4] (As I have said, we have not here investigated what these principles are.)

There is also a second sense in which the laws of the calculus can be said to provide a standard of consistency in beliefs. It is that a distribution of beliefs in accordance with the laws will exclude a so-called Dutch book from being made against the subject in betting. But this standard of consistency, as observed by Ramsey,[5] is derived from the more fundamental standard provided by the laws governing options.

4

Ramsey's procedure takes for granted that it is clear what it *is* to have an attitude of preference or of indifference in a conditioned option —i.e., that the formation of such attitudes does not present a problem which is relevant to the definition of degrees of belief. If we wish to criticize Ramsey's definition, we must raise doubts at this very point.

Assume that we proposed an option of the general type involved in Ramsey's procedure to a man who takes some interest in the four goods in question and also has some opinion of the truth of the uncertain proposition conditioning the option, but who has no particular knowledge of economics or probability theory. We give, say, a farmer an option between being given

---

[3]For Ramsey's derivation of the multiplication principle from his definition of degree of belief see [2, p. 181 f.].

[4][2, p. 182]: "Any definite set of degrees of belief which broke them (*sc.*, the laws of probability) would be inconsistent in the sense that it violated the laws of preference between options, such as that preferability is a transitive asymmetrical relation . . . "

[5][2, p. 182 f.].

a horse if it is raining and a sheep if it is not raining tomorrow *or* being given a cow if it is raining and a hog if it is not raining tomorrow.

If our man says that he is indifferent, this may be but another way of confessing to us that he cannot make up his mind on the question which of the two alternatives is more advantageous to him. He, in other words, has *no reason* at hand, that he should prefer the one to the other, and *therefore* he is indifferent.

This attitude of indifference must be distinguished from another attitude of indifference in which the subject (positively) judges the two alternatives equally advantageous and therefore *has* a reason for *not* preferring the one to the other. I shall call the first an *unreasoned* and the second a *reasoned* attitude of indifference.

An unreasoned attitude of indifference cannot, in combination with assessments of value, be used to define probabilities. This is so, because we have then no guarantee that the probabilities, thus defined, will satisfy the requirement of uniqueness — even for the same subject at a given moment. If our man is just too ignorant or too stupid to form an opinion on the matter, his attitude of indifference may easily be invariant under changes in the values of the goods which, if we accept Ramsey's definition, affect the probabilities.

When the subject has a reasoned attitude of indifference, he judges the alternatives presented for consideration in the option equally good (advantageous) for him. Equality of goodness means the equality of value of two (or more) goods. We therefore ask: Which are the goods that are judged value-equal when the subject has a reasoned attitude of indifference in a conditioned option of the kind under discussion?

These goods cannot be the things he will get depending upon his choice and the truth of p, for these are the four goods G_1–G_4, no two of which need be the same value. Thus it would not be true to say that the subject expects an equal advantage to result from either choice and that *this* is the reason that he is indifferent.

Although the four goods G_1–G_4 are individually of unequal value to the optioning agent, it could of course very well be the case that, say, receiving $2G_1$ and $5G_2$ is thought by him to be as valuable as receiving $2G_3$ and $5G_4$ (irrespective of the order in which he receives the goods and the time over which their reception is spread). This judgment of equality of values of goods can be represented as a judgment of indifference in a simple option, i.e., one not conditioned by the truth of some unknown proposition. The option is between the "accumulated" and the "composite" goods: $2G_1$ and $5G_2$ on the one hand, and $2G_3$ and $5G_4$ on the other hand. The value judgment corresponding to the attitude of indifference is: $V(2G_1 \text{ and } 5G_2) = V(2G_3 \text{ and } 5G_4)$.

I shall now put forward the following suggestion: When a person has what is here called a reasoned attitude of indifference in a conditioned option, he expects that a repetition of the same choice on a number of occasions for making it would result in an *accumulation* of goods of roughly the same value to him as the accumulation which would result from an alternative choice. It is not suggested that he expects this balance of accumulated goods *with certainty*. It is only suggested that he expects this accumulation *rather* than any other particular accumulation.

The suggestion presupposes that the conditioned option which we are discussing can be repeated. This presupposition again is fulfilled if the proposition p which conditions the option is to the effect that some generic event E takes place on some type of occasion O.

For all multiples k let the accumulation of $m \cdot k$ goods G_1 and $n \cdot k$ goods G_2 be judged equal in value to the accumulation of $m \cdot k$ goods G_3 and $n \cdot k$ goods G_4. Then to say that, in repeated options conditioned by the happening of E on O, a subject expects a roughly value-equal accumulation of goods rather than a value-unequal accumulation is tantamount to saying that he expects E to happen with a relative frequency near $m/(m+n)$ on repeated occasions O rather than with any other relative frequency. This *most expected frequency* of the event on repeated occasions for its occurrence is the *probability* we assign to it on the single occasion of an option, in which we judge the alternatives presented for consideration equally good.

To sum up: It is not possible, without circularity, to *define* subjective probabilities in terms of values of goods and attitudes in options. This is due to the fact that not just *any* attitude of indifference in a conditioned option of the relevant kind will serve the purpose of measuring probabilities. The attitude of indifference will serve this purpose only when it entails a judgment of equality of value in a simple option between accumulated amounts of the goods which figure in the conditioned option. This value-judgment again is entailed only when the optioning subject expects that the proposition which conditions the option would, on repeated occasions, come true in a certain proportion of cases rather than in any other proportion. To have this expectation is tantamount to believing in the truth of the proposition to a degree answering to this proportion. Thus in the formation of the attitudes of indifference which are relevant to the measurement of degrees of belief, subjective probabilities are already presupposed. Ramsey's definition procedure begs the question.

5

If subjective probabilities cannot be defined in terms of values of goods and attitudes in options, what then is their epistemological status?

A numerical probability, I shall say, is a *hypothetical magnitude*. Primarily, this magnitude is associated with generic events on types of occasions for their occurrence. Secondarily, it may also become associated with individual events and with general propositions. What I mean by this I shall now try briefly to explain.

There is a danger in calling a probability a hypothetical magnitude. By a "hypothesis" we often mean an assumption or conjecture about an unknown state of affairs. A probability statement, in my view, is *not* a hypothesis in this sense. It is not anything which either an objective state of nature — such as the approximation of a relative frequency towards a limit — or some facts of logic — say about ratios of measures of ranges — would, if known, make true or false.

The term "subjective probability", on the other hand, seems to me misleading. It suggests, by contrast, the existence of some other kind of probability which is *not* "subjective" but "objective". I would contest this dualistic view (of numerical probabilities). The words "subjective" and "objective" in probability theory do not signify a dichotomy of concepts, but rather two aspects of the conception of probabilities as hypothetical magnitudes.

One can distinguish between a *subjective significance* and an *objective significance* of assignments of probabilities. Such assignments are subjectively significant, I shall say, as expressions of certain beliefs and expectations of those who make them. The objective significance of assignments of probability again consists in the facts — if there be such facts — which *justify* us in making the assignments.

I shall further distinguish between a *retrospective* and a *prospective* justification of probabilities. The first is on the basis of facts which become known after the assignments of probabilities have been made; the second on the basis of *reasons* or *evidence* which guide us in making the assignments.

6

Assignments of probability are retrospectively justified when, or better, as long as, they need not become revised in the light of new data of a statistical nature.

There is a characteristic procedure of revising hypothetical probabilities on a statistical basis, and thus indirectly also of justifying such probabilities retrospectively. This procedure is intimately connected with the group of theorems of the calculus of probability known as Laws of Great Numbers. These laws enable us — provided certain conditions are fulfilled — to use our hypothetical assignments of probabilities to events for the purpose of predicting frequencies of those events with *high* probability. Already James Bernoulli had suggested a methodological rule to the effect that a probability near the maximum value should be regarded or treated as a *practical certainty.*[6] This means that if an event does not happen with a frequency with which, assuming a certain probability for this event, it is practically certain to occur, then we may reject or revise our probability assumption. Our practical certainty in highly probable frequencies thus functions as a check on the probabilities, i.e., hypothetical magnitudes associated with generic events on types of occasions. We can not, of course, here attempt to give a detailed description of the functioning of this statistical check on hypothetical probabilities.

---

[6] [1, p. 217].

7

The epistemological problems connected with the prospective justification of probabilities are much more difficult than those connected with their retrospective justification. Traditional discussion of the topic can be divided in two parts. To the first belongs the discussion of the Principle of Non-Sufficient Reason and the Principle of Indifference. To the second belongs the discussion of Bayes's Theorem and other principles of so-called Inverse Probability. I shall here make a shortcut through the entire discussion and only quite briefly state my view of the problem of justification.

This view is that the sole prospective justification of probabilities is knowledge of frequencies which would also constitute a retrospective justification of them. To take but a single example: No one would maintain that the observation of 2 "heads" and 3 "tails" justified us to regard the two outcomes in tossing as unequally probable. But the observation of 200 "heads" and 300 "tails" in 500 tosses does justify this. The reason that the two observations are differently relevant to the prospective justification of the assignment of unequal probabilities is that the second but not the first would constitute a retrospective justification of this assignment. Two "heads" and 3 "tails" are by no means highly improbable if "head" and "tail" are equally probable. But 200 "heads" and 300 "tails" *are* highly improbable and would therefore compel us to abandon an assignment of equal probability to the two outcomes as being unjustified.

The two types of justification are thus provided by exactly the same type of empirical data. The difference between them is only that the retrospective justification follows upon a prediction of frequencies on the basis of assigned probabilities, whereas the prospective justification leads to an assignment of probabilities on the basis of observed frequencies. Neither type of justification, however, is a trivial matter of "reading off" probabilities from frequencies. In both use is made of principles of the calculus of probability, and considerable mathematical knowledge and skill may be required to decide whether such and such statistical data justify such and such probability hypotheses or not.

8

What I have had to say about numerical probability has so far been restricted to attributions of probability to generic events on types of occasions for their occurrence. I shall conclude my paper with some remarks on the question of whether this restriction can be removed.

The question can conveniently be divided into two sub-questions. The first is whether probability can be attributed to singular propositions, i.e., to propositions to the effect that an individual event will occur or that an individual state of affairs obtains. The second is whether probability can be attributed to general propositions, e.g., to so-called Laws of Nature. I shall here briefly touch upon the first problem only.

Consider, e.g., the proposition that he will arrive here tomorrow — "he" being a named individual, "here" a fixed location in space, and "tomorrow" a fixed location in time. And suppose we say that we consider this proposition very probable.

Saying thus we *could*, of course, be saying some such thing as that the *generic* (and thus repeatable) event named "his arrival here" has a high probability on a *type* of occasion which is going to be instantiated tomorrow. (Tomorrow is, say, my birthday). If this is what we mean, then our strong belief in the individual event is but a reflection of our belief in the high relative frequency of the generic event in question on occasions of the type in question.

Although this *could be* the pattern of a true account of what we mean by calling the individual event very probable, it *need not* be. We may be completely unwilling to attribute any particular probability to any generic event, of which the individual event in question is an instantiation, and yet profess a strong belief in this individual event "in itself", considered as unique. When this is the case, and then only, I shall speak of the attribution of probability to the individual event as an *individual probability*.

Can an individual probability be evaluated numerically? It would indeed sound odd, if we were to say "straight away" that there is at least a $\frac{7}{8}$ chance that he will come tomorrow. And it would hardly be practicable to arrive at this estimate by an introspective comparison of our partial belief in the individual event and our belief in some event, to which we agree to assign the probability $\frac{7}{8}$. But the following method of comparison may be practicable, and has in fact often been suggested:

Let i be the individual event and E some event with agreed probability $\frac{7}{8}$, e.g., some outcome in a certain game of chance. Further, let G_1 and G_2 be goods, of which the first is (greatly) preferred to the second. The following option is proposed: G_1 consequent upon i and G_2 upon E, or G_1 consequent upon E and G_2 upon i. Assume that we prefer, without hesitation, the first alternative. This would entitle us to say that the individual probability, i.e., that the degree to which we believe in i, is greater than $\frac{7}{8}$.

Observe that this option is possible only provided that the occasion on which the individual event is expected to take place is an occasion of a type on which the generic event E may also take place. This in no way contradicts the unique character of i. But the uniqueness of i entails that the option is not repeatable.

Since the option is not repeatable, how can its use for comparing probabilities be legitimate? I have tried to argue that only such attitudes of preference and indifference in conditioned options which depend logically upon attitudes in simple options between accumulated goods can be used in combination with utilities to measure probabilities. And the accumulation of goods presupposes that the conditioned option is repeatable, which the option now under consideration is not.

The non-repeatability of the option is a fact worth serious consideration. The proper conclusion to be drawn here is *not*, however, that strictly individual probabilities defy numerical evaluation — as some supporters of a frequency theory of probability may wish to say. *Nor* is it that repeatability is inessential to the notion of a numerical probability — as some extreme subjectivists in probability theory would perhaps maintain. The proper conclusion, to my mind, is that individual events can be assigned numerical probabilities in an *analogical* or *secondary* sense only. The secondary nature of numerical individual probabilities lies in the fact that they are obtained from a comparison with some other numerical probabilities and ultimately with probabilities of some generic events on some types of occasion. They logically presuppose familiarity with numerical probability assignments to generic events — in games of chance and similar situations in which repeatable occasions for events are provided.

Numerical probabilities which are attributed to generic events possess objective significance thanks to the fact that they can be justified, retrospectively and/or prospectively, on the basis of statistical experience. Numerical individual probabilities have no such justification. This follows from the uniqueness, i.e., the non-repeatable nature of the event, to which they are ascribed. Therefore the significance of numerical individual probabilities is bound to be *purely subjective*. And the same holds good, I would maintain, for assignments of numerical probabilities to general propositions, e.g., to laws of nature.

References

[1] Bernoulli, J. *Ars conjectandi*, Baal, 1713, 239 pp.
[2] Ramsey, F. P. *The Foundations of Mathematics and other Logical Essays*. London, Kegan Paul, 1931, xviii+292 pp.

SECTION

VI

METHODOLOGY
AND PHILOSOPHY
OF PHYSICAL
SCIENCES

Symposium on the Role of Mathematics in the Formulation of Physical Theories

---

ANALYSE MATHÉMATIQUE DU „PRINCIPE DE CONTINUITÉ" EN PHYSIQUE

ALEXANDRE FRODA

Institutul de Matematica al Academiei R.P.R., Bucharest, Rumania

L'influence des idées fondamentales de Cantor, pleinement affirmée en mathématiques pures, à partir de la fin du dernier siècle, est loin d'avoir épuisé ses effets en physique. Ce retard relatif est dû à la complication des phénomènes à étudier, qui exigea d'abord l'élaboration des disciplines mathématiques nécessaires au développement déductif de la physique théorique.

Quant à l'avantage parallèle de la théorie des ensembles sur la méthamathématique, en philosophie des sciences, il a été dûment souligné dès 1955, par McKinsey et P. Suppes [12].

Nous nous proposons, dans ce qui suit, à illustrer la fécondité en physique théorique de la méthode cantorienne et de la théorie des fonctions réelles qui s'y rattache, en présentant l'aspect mathématique d'une analyse des fondements de la mécanique classique du point matériel, que nous avons entreprise il y a quelques années [2] et reprise en 1957 au symposiom de

Berkeley sur la méthode axiomatique en géométrie et en physique [6].

La physique théorique classique fut fondée sur les conceptions newtoniennes, dominantes jusqu'au début de ce siècle. Les grandeurs variables, susceptibles de mesure, qu'on y envisageait, devaient être: continues et continument différentiables. Malgré ce soi-disant *principe de continuité*, il restait sous-entendu qu'un état physique différent, tout en restant possible à des instants exceptionnels, ne pouvait être qu'instable et transitoire. L'analyse mathématique classique attachée à cette conception s'y était aisément adaptée.

Le préjugé du principe de continuité en physique ne fut entamé, comme on sait, qu'avec Planck, en 1900 et ce fut la nécessité de consistence de la théorie avec l'expérience, qui y mena. On dut admettre, à côté de la conception infinitésimale, traditionnelle, la conception finitiste et l'on trouva finalement un moyen de les concilier (de Broglie, 1925).

Parallèlement et malgré cette évolution évidente des idées en physique, qu'il nous suffit de rappeler en passant, le principe de continuité continua à se maintenir en mécanique rationnelle. Hamel, en le formulant, l'inclut explicitement parmi ses axiomes (1908), tout en lui opposant l'impossibilité d'une vérification expérimentale ou d'une justification théorique [7]. Même récemment, le système d'axiomes de McKinsey, Sugar, et Suppes [11] dût en accepter les conséquences.

La mécanique classique admet, en effet, qu'un point matériel en mouvement possède à tout instant une accélération, comme l'exige la seconde loi de Newton, qu'on ne peut mettre en question.

En mécanique newtonienne, tout mouvement μ d'un point matériel M de masse constante m peut être rapporté aux repères de l'espace et du temps absolus et ce point de vue est aussi accepté par la mécanique classique.

Soit O un point fixe de l'espace tri-dimensionnel $\mathscr{E}^3$. Le vecteur $\mathbf{r} = \mathbf{OM}$ de $\mathscr{E}^3$, qui indique la position de M à l'instant t, donne la définition cinématique de μ, qu'on écrit

$$\mathbf{r} = \mathbf{r}(t), \tag{1}$$

où $\mathbf{r}(t)$ est une fonction vectorielle continue de la variable réelle t.

En posant, comme d'habitude[1]

$$\mathbf{v}(t) = \lim_{\Delta t \sim 0} \frac{1}{\Delta t} \cdot \Delta \mathbf{r}(t), \tag{2}$$

$$\mathbf{A}(t) = \lim_{\Delta t \sim 0} \frac{1}{\Delta t} \cdot \Delta \mathbf{v}(t), \tag{3}$$

---

[1]On convient d'écrire, pour tout vecteur $\boldsymbol{\lambda}(t)$ de $\mathscr{E}^3$, fonction de t,

$$\Delta \boldsymbol{\lambda}(t) = \boldsymbol{\lambda}(t+\Delta t) - \boldsymbol{\lambda}(t).$$

on définit en mécanique classique la vitesse et l'accélération du point matériel M.

Ces formules (2), (3) n'ont pourtant un sens, que si l'on suppose que la limite qui définit $\mathbf{v}(t)$ existe et est une fonction vectorielle continue de t et que la limite qui donne $\mathbf{A}(t)$ existe. Faute d'un principe de continuité en physique, ces suppositions resteraient en l'air et l'on ne pourrait les justifier, semble-t-il, que par des raisons de commodité de l'analyse mathématique à appliquer à l'étude du mouvement.

Tant que Weierstrass n'avait pas encore mis en évidence l'existence de la classe des fonctions continues non-dérivables pour aucune valeur de t (1875), on pouvait encore admettre que la physique n'avait pas à se préoccuper des instants exceptionnels, où les formules (2), (3) auraient pu n'avoir plus de sens. Mais dès qu'on se rendit compte de la possibilité ouverte par la découverte de Weierstrass, la question de savoir à quoi cela pouvait correspondre en physique s'imposait d'elle-même. Appell et Janaud [1] signalèrent assez tôt ce fait, qu'ils estimèrent être „de grande importance pour les fondements de la physique mathématique et de la mécanique rationnelle". Mais leur essai d'en tirer des implications de quelque conséquence pour la physique fut assez imparfait, justement par suite du manque de développement de la théorie des fonctions réelles à l'époque (1881).

La divergence entre les points de vue mathématique et physique à cet égard est encore plus manifeste aujourd'hui que leur consistence logique est jugée indispensable.

C'est ce qui explique aussi notre essai de répondre à cette exigence, à l'aide des résultats et méthodes de la théorie actuelle des fonctions vectorielles d'une variable réelle, tels qu'on les trouve, par exemple, dans les traités de Bourbaki [2] et de Hobson [9], dont nous avons extrait, rapproché et complété certains résultats.

On commence par exprimer cinématiquement le mouvement μ par l'égalité (1), où $\mathbf{r}(t)$ est une fonction vectorielle continue de t, définie dans les conditions les plus générales de l'analyse. Sous quelles conditions supplémentaires ce mouvement est-il physiquement réalisable?

La réponse à cette question n'est pas du tout simple.

Avant de l'aborder, nous admettrons que le mouvement μ d'un point matériel M appartient au domaine $\mathscr{C}$ des mouvements considérés en mécanique classique, lorsque M fait partie d'un système de points matériels. Par définition de $\mathscr{C}$, il faudra que μ n'appartienne ni au domaine propre à la mécanique quantique, ni à celui de la relativité et que toute force (passive) liée à une dégradation de l'énergie [3] soit exclue de nos considérations.

On est loin d'avoir épuisé ainsi toutes les difficultés qui peuvent se présenter, mais il ne faut pas oublier qu'une théorie complètement satisfaisante de la mécanique générale reste encore à désirer.

L'essentiel de notre but, c'est de nous dispenser de l'hypothèse invérifiable du principe de continuité, sans avoir à restreindre encore plus le domaine $\mathscr{C}$ défini ci-dessus. On y est arrivé en [5], [6] en ajoutant aux axiomes usuels, convenablement exprimés, deux axiomes de *finitude*, indiqués (et vérifiables) par l'expérience et que nous allons formuler, à l'aide d'une brève terminologie auxiliaire.[2]

Axiomes de finitude:

(F) Lorsqu'un mouvement $\mu \in \mathscr{C}$ est physiquement réalisable dans un laps de temps fini δ, il satisfait aux conditions:

1. Parmi les suites de mouvements réguliers, physiquement réalisables, ayant pour limite cinématique le mouvement μ, il existe (au moins) une suite de mouvements $\mu_1, \mu_2, \cdots, \mu_p, \cdots$, telle que les forces $\mathbf{F}_p(t)$ qui les produisent,

$$\mathbf{F}_p(t) = m\mathbf{A}_p(t),$$

soient bornées dans leur ensemble, en δ.

2. La force $\mathbf{F}(t)$, qui produit le mouvement μ ne peut changer d'orientation une infinité de fois en aucune suite indéfinie d'instants successifs (allant en croissant ou en décroissant) dans le laps δ.

La consistence de ces axiomes de finitude avec l'expérience a été examinée dans nos travaux antérieurs, cités. En les ajoutant à d'autres axiomes classiques dûment formulés, nous y avons prouvé le théorème suivant.

($\mathscr{P}$): *Tout mouvement μ d'un point matériel, ayant lieu dans les conditions $\mathscr{C}$ de la mécanique classique, est la succession d'un nombre fini de mouvements réguliers, en tout laps de temps fini.*

La démonstration $\mathscr{D}$ de cette propriété (visiblement conforme à l'expérience) utilise l'instrument de la théorie des fonctions vectorielles $\boldsymbol{\lambda}(t)$ d'une variable réelle t. Leurs propriétés se déduisent sans difficulté des propriétés des fonctions réelles de t : $\lambda_x(t)$, $\lambda_y(t)$, $\lambda_z(t)$, dont les valeurs représentent les composantes scalaires du vecteur $\boldsymbol{\lambda}(t)$ de $\mathscr{E}^3$ dans un système orthogonal d'axes fixes Ox, Oy, Oz de l'espace.

Nous ne pouvons songer à reproduire ici, puisque ce serait trop long, la démonstration $\mathscr{D}$, mais afin de donner quelque idée du genre de notions qu'on y rencontre, nous allons exposer en toute rigueur les diverses espèces de limites de vecteurs variables avec t, qui y interviennent.

Soit $\boldsymbol{\lambda}(t)$ un vecteur de $\mathscr{E}^3$, fonction de la variable réelle $t \in \delta = (t', t'')$. En faisant tendre t vers t_0, on montre — en s'appuyant au fond sur le principe

---

[2]*Définitions.* Un mouvement μ est *régulier*, dans un laps de temps $\delta = (t', t'')$, lorsqu'il possède une accélération $\mathbf{A}(t)$ continue à chaque instant t de δ. Un mouvement μ est *limite cinétique* de mouvements $\mu_n (n = 1, 2, \ldots)$, définis par $\mathbf{r} = \mathbf{r}_n(t)$, lorsqu'en (1) on a $\mathbf{r}(t) = \lim \mathbf{r}_n(t)$, pour $n \sim \infty$. Un vecteur tri-dimensionnel $\mathbf{W}(t)$ *change d'orientation une infinité de fois*, lorsque ses projections $w_a(t)$ sur (au moins) un axe $\mathbf{O}a$ de $\mathscr{E}^3$, changent de sens une infinité de fois. Des vecteurs $\mathbf{W}_p(t)$, $p = 1, 2, \ldots$ sont *bornés dans leur ensemble en* δ s'il existe un $b > 0$, tel que $|(\mathbf{W}_p(t)| < b$ pourtout indice p et tout $t \in \delta$. Un mouvement μ de $\mathscr{C}$ est *physiquement réalisable* s'il peut en exister des réalisations physiques approchées, c.-à.-d. des mouvements réels μ_n, qui s'en approchent indéfiniment (μ limite cinématique des μ_n).

de Bolzano-Weierstrass — qu'il existe au moins une suite σ de $t_j (j = 1, 2, \cdots)$ tendant vers t_0 et un vecteur $\boldsymbol{\lambda}_\sigma$, tels qu'on ait

$$\lim_{j \sim \infty} \boldsymbol{\lambda}(t_j) = \boldsymbol{\lambda}_\sigma$$

et l'on dit que $\boldsymbol{\lambda}_\sigma$ est un des *vecteurs-limite* de $\mathbf{y}(t)$.

Désignons l'ensemble de ces $\boldsymbol{\lambda}_\sigma$ par

$$\left\{ \overline{\overline{\lim_{t \to t_0}}}\, \boldsymbol{\lambda}(t) \right\}. \tag{4}$$

Lorsque cet ensemble se réduit à un seul vecteur $\boldsymbol{\lambda}$, ce qui peut parfois (mais pas toujours) avoir lieu, on dit que $\boldsymbol{\lambda}(t)$ tend vers $\boldsymbol{\lambda}$, lorsque $t \to t_0$. On écrit alors

$$\lim_{t \to t_0} \boldsymbol{\lambda}(t) = \boldsymbol{\lambda}$$

et l'on retrouve ainsi *la limite vectorielle*, au sens classique.

En introduisant, de plus, la condition $t > t_0$ (resp. $t < t_0$), on restreint l'ensemble des vecteurs-limite de (4) et l'on en obtient un sous-ensemble, qu'on peut désigner par

$$\left\{ \overline{\overline{\lim_{t \to t_0}}}_{+}\, \boldsymbol{\lambda}(t) \right\}, \quad \text{resp.} \quad \left\{ \overline{\overline{\lim_{t \to t_0}}}_{-}\, \boldsymbol{\lambda}(t) \right\}.$$

Lorsque ce sous-ensemble se réduit à un seul vecteur, ce qui peut parfois (mais pas toujours) avoir lieu, on dit que $\boldsymbol{\lambda}(t)$ tend *prospectivement* (resp. *rétrospectivement*) vers $\boldsymbol{\lambda}$ et s'écrit

$$\lim_{t \to t_0}{}_{+} \boldsymbol{\lambda}(t) = \boldsymbol{\lambda}, \quad \text{resp.} \quad \lim_{t \to t_0}{}_{-} \boldsymbol{\lambda}(t) = \boldsymbol{\lambda}.$$

On est conduit, en vertu de ces considérations, à attacher au mouvement μ du point M en $\delta = (t', t'')$ des grandeurs cinématiques, qui étendent (2), par les formules

$$\mathbf{v}_+(t) = \lim_{\Delta t \sim 0}{}_{+} \frac{1}{\Delta t} \cdot \Delta \mathbf{r}(t), \quad \text{resp.} \quad \mathbf{v}_-(t) = \lim_{\Delta t \sim 0}{}_{-} \frac{1}{\Delta t} \cdot \Delta \mathbf{r}(t), \tag{5}$$

qui définissent *la vitesse prospective*, resp. *rétrospective*, lorsque les limites, qui y figurent ont un sens. Si l'on avait aussi, de plus, $\mathbf{v}_+(t) = \mathbf{v}_-(t)$ leur valeur commune ce serait la vitesse $\mathbf{v}(t)$, au sens classique. En supposant qu'on se trouve dans ce dernier cas et que $\mathbf{v}(t)$ soit, de plus, continue, on étend aussi (3), par les formules

$$\mathbf{a}(t) = \lim_{\Delta t \sim 0}{}_{+} \frac{1}{\Delta(t)} \cdot \Delta \mathbf{v}(t), \quad \text{resp.} \quad \boldsymbol{\alpha}(t) = \lim_{\Delta t \sim 0}{}_{-} \frac{1}{\Delta t} \cdot \Delta \mathbf{v}(t), \tag{6}$$

qui définissent *l'accélération prospective*, resp. *rétrospective*, lorsque les limites qui y figurent ont un sens. Si l'on avait aussi, de plus, $\mathbf{a}(t) = \boldsymbol{\alpha}(t)$ leur valeur commune ce serait l'accélération $\mathbf{A}(t)$, au sens classique.

Cette analyse rend compte de la complexité des notions cinématiques fondamentales vitesse et accélération, lorsqu'on accorde à la définition du mouvement μ de $\mathscr{C}$ en (1) toute sa généralité analytique.

En revenant à la propriété ($\mathscr{P}$) ci-dessus, on comprend mieux maintenant les difficultés, que doit rencontrer sa démonstration $\mathscr{D}$. Comme on n'a plus recours au principe de continuité, la démonstration s'appuiera nécessairement sur des propriétés physiques fondamentales du mouvement. On invoquera donc d'une part les propriétés exprimées par les axiomes de finitude, de l'autre celle exprimée par la seconde loi de Newton. Cette dernière sera formulée comme suit, afin de ne rien préjuger des résultats à atteindre par le raisonnement:

,,À tout instant $\tau \in \delta$, où l'accélération prospective $\mathbf{a}(\tau)$ a un sens, on a l'égalité

$$\mathbf{F}(\tau) = m\mathbf{a}(\tau),$$

où $\mathbf{F}(\tau)$ est la force qui produit le mouvement μ à l'instant $\tau \in \delta$, et m est la masse (constante) de M, indépendante du mouvement μ considéré".

Nous avons expliqué ailleurs [6] les raisons qui conduisent à remplacer $\mathbf{A}(\tau)$ par $\mathbf{a}(\tau)$ dans la loi de Newton et n'y reviendrons pas maintenant.

Pour la démonstration de ($\mathscr{P}$) on se sert aussi de la loi classique de composition des mouvements et l'on applique des propriétés de l'analyse vectorielle des fonctions d'une variable réelle, où la notion de limite intervient au sens étendu, ci-dessus.

En évitant tout détail, voici comment on procède à la démonstration [5]:

On prouve d'abord que le point M, qui effectue le mouvement μ (de $\mathscr{C}$) en δ possède une vitesse $\mathbf{v}(t)$ à tout instant t de δ.[3] Cette vitesse est une fonction vectorielle continue de t et l'on démontre que le point M possède aussi une accélération prospective $\mathbf{a}(t)$ à tout instant t de δ.

La continuité de l'accélération prospective $\mathbf{a}(t)$ a aussi lieu à tout instant, sauf peut-être en un nombre fini d'instants τ_j et alors la fonction vectorielle $\mathbf{a}(t)$ présente une discontinuité de première espèce (un saut).

Soit E l'ensemble des $\tau_j (j = 1, 2, \cdots)$, qui peut être parfois vide. Aux instants $\tau_j \in E$, l'accélération $\mathbf{A}(\tau_j)$ n'a pas de sens et l'on a $\mathbf{a}(\tau_j) \neq \boldsymbol{\alpha}(\tau_j)$.

En partant des mêmes prémisses, la même voie conduit aussi à d'autres propriétés physiques des mouvements de $\mathscr{C}$ auxquelles nous ne nous arrêterons pas. Mais voici pour conclure, des réflexions d'un caractère plus général, concernant la méthode employée.

La théorie des fonctions vectorielles d'une variable réelle, qui s'appuie en essence sur les résultats fondamentaux de Cantor, Borel, Baire et Lebesgue, peut être considérée aujourd'hui comme achevée, du moins dans ses grandes lignes, mais ses applications à la physique n'ont pas encore pris assez de développement. C'est que la finesse des résultats de la théorie mathématique

---

[3]Cela semble contredit par le cas du choc (parfaitement élastique en $\mathscr{C}$), mais seulement lorsqu'on admet que la durée d'un choc est nulle, contrairement à la réalité.

dépasserait-semble-t-on génèralement croire — les nécessités actuelles de la physique théorique.

Cette croyance n'est nullement justifiée, lorsqu'on se place du point de vue de la rigueur logique, du moins pour une étude des fondements.

Le symposiom de Berkeley sur la méthode axiomatique a dernièrement bien mis cela en évidence. Je vais pourtant citer, à ce propos, ce qu'en pensent Tarski, Henkin, et Suppes:

"Much foundational work in physics is still of the programmatic sort and it is possible to maintain that the status of axiomatic investigations in physics is not yet past the preliminary stage of philosophical discussion expressing doubt as to its purpose and usefulness" [8].

On peut consulter tout traité de physique théorique, comme celui de Joos [10], et l'on verra qu'aucune part de la théorie des fonctions réelles n'y est prise en considération. Et pourtant ce traité même ne manque pas d'attirer l'attention sur l'imparfait ajustement aux réalités physiques de l'analyse classique qui lui sert d'instrument. L'avantage sur cette dernière de la théorie des fonctions réelles, en physique, a été depuis longtemps déjà souligné par Denjoy [4] et notre thème ne fait qu'y apporter de nouveaux arguments.

Il est vrai, qu'il est bien plus compliqué de mettre en oeuvre ce nouvel instrument mathématique en physique théorique. Mais "la nature ne se soucie pas des difficultés analytiques" affirmait Fresnel [13] et ce qui précède peut de nouveau donner à réflechir la-dessus. En tout cas, puisqu'il n'y a pas de voie commode pour explorer la nature des choses, cela peut bien excuser les difficultés de la méthode, qu'on vient de signaler et qui semble indispensable à l'analyse des fondements de la physique théorique.

Bibliographie

[1] Appell, P. et Janaud, Remarque sur l'introduction des fonctions continues n'ayant pas de dérivée dans les éléments de la mécanique. *Comptes rendus des séances de l'Académie des Sciences*, Paris, t. 93 (1881), pp. 1005–1008.

[2] Bourbaki, N. *Fonctions d'une variable réelle*, Livre IV, Paris (1949), chap. I–II.

[3] Bruhat, G. *Thermodynamique*, Paris (1947), p. 141.

[4] Denjoy, Arnaud. *Introduction à la théorie des fonctions de variables réelles*, Paris (1947), I, pp. 8–9.

[5] Froda, A. Sur les fondements de la mécanique des mouvements réalisables du point matériel (en roumain), *Studii si cercetari matematice*, Bucuresti, t. III, 1952, pp. 321–356.

[6] Froda, A. La finitude en mécanique classique, ses axiomes et leurs implications. *Studies in Logic and the Foundations of Mathematics. The Axiomatic Method, with special reference to Geometry and Physics*, Amsterdam (1959), pp. 238–249.

[7] Hamel, G. Die Axiome der Mechanik, *Handbuch der Physik*, Berlin (1927), Bd. 5, pp. 1–42.

[8] Henkin, L., P. Suppes, and A. Tarski (editors). The Axiomatic Method with special reference to Geometry and Physics. *Proceedings of an International Symposium held at Berkeley December 5th, 1957, January 4th, 1958*, Amsterdam (1959), p. viii.

[9] HOBSON, E. W. *The theory of functions of a real variable and the theory of Fourier's series.* Cambridge, 2 vol., 1926–1927.

[10] JOOS, G. *Lehrbuch der theoretischen Physik,* Leipzig (1956), 9e Ed.

(11) MCKINSEY, J. C. C., A. C. SUGAR and P. SUPPES. Axiomatic Foundations of classical particle matter, *Journal of Rational Mechanics and Analysis* (1953), Vol. 2, no. 2, pp. 253–272.

[12] MCKINSEY, J. C. C. and PATRICK SUPPES. On the notion of invariance in classical mechanics, *The British Journal for the Philosophy of Science,* Vol. V, no. 20 (1955), pp. 290–302.

[13] POINCARÉ, H. *La Science et l'Hypothèse,* p. 173.

IS THE MATHEMATICAL EXPLANATION OF PHYSICAL DATA UNIQUE?

HENRY MARGENAU

Yale University, New Haven, Connecticut, U.S.A.

1. The Function of Mathematical Explanation in Physical Science

Within cognitive experience, traditional philosophy and common sense distinguish two polar epistemological components: those called *data* and the rational elements called *concepts*. The former are used as protocol (P) experiences and are taken as authoritative, as the last instances of appeal of any theory; the latter owe their genesis to reason rather than observation, we feel a rational responsibility concerning them and modify them with some freedom. They are *constructed* as counterparts to data in order to provide a larger measure of coherence and intelligibility than P-experiences alone contain. Whether concepts, originally constructed to satisfy inductive suggestions coming from observations, are ultimately accepted and retained as valid explanations of datal experience depends on the way in which they meet a set of complicated requirements. Primary among these requirements is empirical confirmation, the need for conclusions drawn from theory (which is itself a set of constructs joined by logical and mathematical relations) to be confirmed within a certain tolerance by observations. Other requirements, more vague in their formulation, demand simplicity, mathematical elegance, extensibility, causality in the theoretical transcription of data.

The connection between primary data (for which I shall henceforth use the symbol P) and the field of constructs (symbolized by C) is made in a variety of ways. In some instances one passes by long inurement automatically from a complex of data to a corresponding construct. This occurs when we 'reify' a group of immediate sensations into an external object. For the purposes of this paper the process of reification will be ignored or, more specifically, will be included within P-experience. Most important in science is a connection established by instrumental operations, operations which are often claimed to be the definitions of a construct in terms of data. I shall not discuss the propriety of the claim made by operationalists that such passages are definitions, nor the accompanying suggestion that all good scientific definitions must be of this type. My point is that they form a useful link between P and C. They form, as shown elsewhere [1], one type of a very general epistemological relation called rules of correspondence, epistemic correspondences. To cite examples, the measurement of temperature by means of thermometers, force by the extension of springs, psychological responses by j.n.d. (just noticeable differences) reactions, public sentiment by statistical opinion polls are instrumental operations leading from vague,

Supported by a grant from the National Science Foundation.

subjective P-experiences to rational constructs. The latter can then bejoined and modified further by purely theoretical procedures which may take the scientist's concern far into the abstract domains of the C-field.

This situation is represented pictorially in Fig. 1. Circles are drawn for 'individual' constructs even though it is clear to the logician that a concept is not often a discrete entity but, like any idea, is capable of 'decomposition' in many ways. The envelope around several connected concepts represents a theory T. Double lines are epistemic correspondences, whereas single lines are logico-mathematical relations, postulated for, or implied by, the concepts. For example, the constructs force, mass, and acceleration would appear as circles on the diagram; their operational definitions as double lines linking them with P, and Newton's law, $F = ma$, would form single-line connections between F, m, and a.

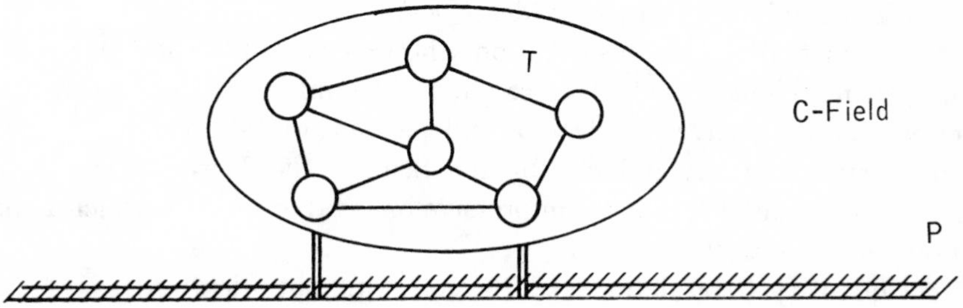

FIG. 1

2. Epistemic Correspondences

Instrumental correspondences render many constructs (usually called quantities or attributes in contradistinction to systems or substances) measurable. This permits the assignment of numbers to some of the lower-order C's, namely, all those connected with P by double lines, and mathematical treatment becomes possible. Numbers lead to functions, functions to operators, and so on, so that ultimately, as we proceed up into the C-field, almost all the devices of mathematics are carried into play. The question we wish to answer is whether their play is unique or can be expected to be unique at some future time.

To secure the answer we must note first a crucial fact about the epistemic correspondences: they are *not* implied or rigidly entailed by P- and C-experiences. They often *seem* to be, and we cite a few examples in which this appearance is strong.

The concept of number is very directly suggested by the operation of counting concrete and distinct objects, not clouds or ideas, to be sure, but fingers, toes, and pebbles. The story that some primitives take off their shoes to do arithmetic beyond the number 10 lends evidence to the contention that numbers are practically and perhaps uniquely determined by P-experience. Furthermore, historically, psychologically, ontogenetically, the process of counting is very probably prior to the number concept. None of these circumstances, however, shed light on the logical or epistemological relation.

The mathematical ideas — point, line, square, triangle — were doubtless all gleaned from immediate observation of natural objects which appear to hold, as it were, the epistemic correspondence between triangular aspect and the construct triangle within their essence. There could be no doubt about the association of what looks like a line and the mathematical construct line; the correspondence seems implied. Similar remarks apply to simple functions which are almost directly and unambiguously suggested by trajectories of moving bodies, waves, etc. Even derivatives appear on the scene of science, in Newton's work at least, as gleanings from imageful experience; they were fluxions, visual properties of moving object, which the 'pricked symbol' ($\dot{X}$) merely 'describes'.

Over against all such considerations, however, stands the clear record of modern mathematics which is capable of defining number, point, line, function, and derivative in a fashion independent of P-experience (though perhaps psychologically induced by it). Schlick and Hermann Weyl call such definitions implicit; a most impressive one is that of area, which I shall set down here as an illustration.

Let a quantity Q be defined by the following specifications:

1. Q is a positive number.
2. If a 'piece' is dissected into two parts by line segments in its interior, then Q for the whole 'piece' is equal to the sum of the Q's for the parts.
3. Congruent 'pieces' have the same Q.

(For convenience, Q will be thought of as associated with a piece of surface, to which the definitions above refer as the 'piece'!)

Remarkably, these simple propositions, devoid of reference to anything existing, give rise to a Q which has all the analytic properties of measurable areas. They form a constitutive definition of the construct *area*. Experience shows that by establishing an epistemic correspondence, which associates Q with the number of cm^2 contained in actual surfaces, one obtains a valid scientific theory. The constitutive definition alone gives no assurance that it will find application in the world. Logically, its success is a miracle.

Or take the implicit definition of π as the ratio of circumference to diameter of an ideal circle. It certainly does not imply the correctness of the following observations. 'If two numbers are written down at random, the probability that they will be prime to each other, i.e., will have no common factor, can be shown to be $6/\pi^2$. In a trial when fifty students wrote down five pairs each, it was found that 154 pairs were prime to each other: so from this trial we should get $6/\pi^2 = 154/250$, which gives $\pi = 3.12$. A trial on a much larger scale would doubtless give a much better approximation to the π of Archimedes' [2].

To establish the connection between the implicit definition of π and its appearance as the square root of 6 divided by the probability that any two numbers will be prime to each other, one needs certain postulates of probability theory, plus the epistemic correspondence expressed in the frequency theory of probability. None of these are obvious, implied by constructs or enforced by data.

There are many instances in which formal or implicit treatments of sets of constructs *preceded* their application to observational science. Notable are Hilbert's elegant theory of function space, group theory, Boolean and matrix algebra. These have found profitable use in modern physics. Arising in science as formal constructs unconnected with the *P*-domain, they acquired epistemic connections as time went on. Yet no one would say that there is anything intuitively obvious or necessary about the association of vectors in Hilbert space with a set of points on a photographic plate which mark the incidence of an atomic particle. The lesson we draw is simple: epistemic correspondences are not entailed by mathematics or uniquely specified by observations. The picture drawn in Fig. 1 can therefore lose and regenerate the double legs on which the constructs stand. It is precisely because the connections between *P* and *C* are not entailed by the theoretical components of the epistemological system that the success of mathematics in explaining physical facts so often seems like magic [3]. The phrase, God was a mathematician, partially expresses part of our present contention.

3. The Limitation of Mathematical Theories

Mathematical theories are limited in application through their rules of correspondence. Either this limitation is recognized from the beginning (a) or it develops with progressive refinement of observations (b).

(a) Instances in which the limitation was known — and the practical use of constructs outside the limitation was deliberately practiced in spite of it — are easy to find throughout formalized science. Boyle's law was always regarded as an idealization, corrections for the behavior of real gases, designed to extend its range of validity, were made at an early date. This means that the theory, like *T* in Fig. 1, had double lines extending only into a certain limited part of the *P*-domain, beyond which double lines rose to some other theory, although again, of course, the division of the domains is never sharp.

The concept of number and the theory of arithmetic were never invented to accommodate the flux of continuous phenomena; hence even this very fundamental and seemingly universal idea encounters limitations in its use.

Special relativity is based upon the postulate of the invariance of the speed of light in inertial systems, sometimes expressed by the equation $x^2 + y^2 + z^2 - c^2t^2 = 0$, where the symbols are conventional. Now many students and some writers have registered great surprise upon learning that c is the speed of light, and that the equation is not true when it is taken to be the speed of sound, for example. The point is simply that *this* aspect of the theory cannot be applied to the propagation of sound; even relativity has certain fundamental limitations. In another sense its very restriction to the velocity of light makes it applicable to the propagation of all signals, but in another form.

The recognition of limits for the valid use of mathematical ideas is not only of historical interest; lack of it can plague contemporary theory as well. I apologize for reiterating here a point already made at greater length in previous publications, maintaining however that it is relevant and still noteworthy. In his famous treatise [4] von Neumann introduced a mathematical operator, sometimes called a statistical matrix, sometimes a projection operator, ρ. This operator can be shown to have only two eigenvalues, 1 and 0, and it seemed admirably suited to represent the physical measuring process which interrogates nature through instruments and receives the answers yes (1) or no (0). This epistemic correspondence was most suggestive, and it has been accepted by many authors. Unfortunately, however, the definition of ρ can be shown to entail another property besides the convenient one of possessing eigenvalues 1 and 0. When applied to a Hilbert state, it projects that state in a direction corresponding to the measured observable. If we hold to the rule of correspondence between ρ and measurement, this latter fact can only be interpreted by saying that a measurement, when performed on the state of a physical system, leaves that system in an eigenstate, specified by the measured observable. This is clearly not generally true, for one can easily name many good measurements which do not produce that result. It is also possible to show that the infamous reduction of the wave packet, so widely misunderstood in quantum mechanics, arises from the retention of this rule of correspondence. To rectify the situation it is necessary to remember that an interesting and simple operator like ρ may nevertheless have limited application to P-experience.

(b) We now cite instances where restrictions, unknown when constructs were introduced; developed in response to finer and richer observations. The first example is hackneyed and will be briefly recorded. Newton's inverse-square law of gravitation was thought to be universally valid; it was indeed called the law of universal gravitation. In our century, the deviationist motion of the planet Mercury, the precession of its perihelion, was discovered. Newton's law became inapplicable to Mercury; its limitations were recognized. At the same time a new construct, the metric of non-Euclidean space, was introduced. The correct features of Newton's theory became incorporated in it and a higher theory arose with wider rules of correspondence.

Until about 30 years ago chemical valence was explained in terms of electron bonds, a concept thought to be of universal scope. But certain ambiguities evolved, best remembered in connection with the benzene ring. Here, the simple concept of electron bond, single or double, could not be applied, and its range had to be restricted. But again a higher construct, the idea of quantum resonance, appeared, and its success, methodologically speaking, was twofold. It modified the simple bond theory slightly and it

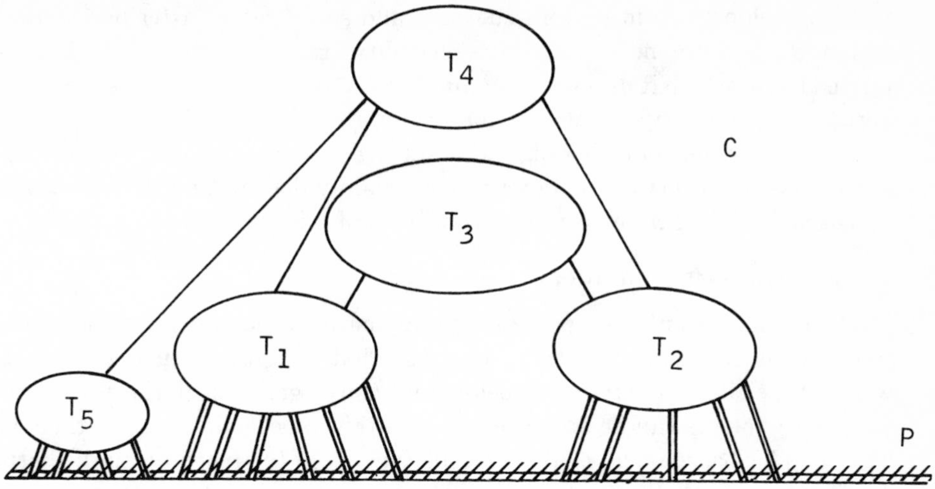

FIG. 2

joined the conforming and the discrepant observations into consequences of a single theory with new rules of correspondence.

A third example, frequently discussed by philosophers of science, and only mentioned here, is provided by the transformation of Newtonian mechanics into special relativity. Limited applicability of the former was recognized in rapidly moving particles. A 'higher' theory arose which modified and unified the ingredients of classical mechanics.

Perhaps the most impressive evolution of this sort took place in physics during the last few decades, when quantum mechanics gained general acceptance. Classical mechanics, like the theory T_1 in Fig. 2, was related satisfactorily to a certain part of P, and Bohr's theory of atoms (T_2) to another. Quantum mechanics, symbolically T_3, joined T_1 and T_2, *modifying each in some respects*. It did this without changing the double lines to an appreciable extent, that is to say, it did *not* require new operational definitions of the low-order constructs which both the Bohr theory and classical mechanics involved. This is not always true; relativity theory, mentioned in the previous example, required a redefinition of mass and force.

A simpler, last example, may epitomize and extend the situation represented in Fig. 2. Let us think of T_1 as Galileo's theory of falling bodies, clearly limited to observations near the surface of the earth. T_2 depicts Kepler's laws of planetary motion, designed to explain entirely different phenomena. Hence at this stage T_1 and T_2 are unconnected. T_3 is Newton's law of gravitation; it fuses T_1 and T_2 into a single theory but with attendant changes, slight to be sure, in both T_1 and T_2. In addition the latter are further illuminated and made more accurate. To be explicit, T_1 and T_2 in Fig. 2 should be relabelled T_1' and T_2' after their merger in T_3. So far what has happened here is formally the same as the union of classical mechanics and quantum mechanics in the former example. But we have had a longer time to watch developments in the present case, and so we can register one further fusion. T_4 is the general theory of relativity. It also united T_1 and T_2, is related to T_3, which it implies approximately, and it accommodates a certain very low level descriptive theory concerning the motion of Mercury.

We summarize our findings by stating the conclusion: *historically*, uniqueness of mathematical description certainly does not exist, and *methodologically* it is not necessary for the success of science.

4. Uniqueness as an Ideal

There remains only the possibility that mathematical explanation tends toward uniqueness as science advances, that diagrams such as Fig. 2 will in time show concrescence below and convergence near the top. Very serious arguments can be advanced against this expectation. One of them is logical and is based on a peculiar interplay between the truth of mathematical theories and the span of the correlations with which they are equipped. More simply, a theory cannot be judged correct before it has a universal range of application; indeed it can be said to be erroneous if it is incomplete.

Consider Fig. 3. If T_1 and T_2 are incompatible though not contradictory, i.e., have separate ranges of application, there will always be a region of P labeled X, which remains unexplained. At the present time relativity and quantum mechanics are two such theories; X contains observations on reactions between particles moving with speeds near that of light. I know of no case where T_1 and T_2 are separate and yet where X is empty, that is to say, where theories manage neatly to coexist without incompatible claims on data. I believe one can prove that such situations cannot occur; that in the realm of science, at least, coexistence under incompatible premises is impossible.

Suppose now that T_1 and T_2 are joined into a supertheory T_3, as is the universal tendency we have discussed in section 3b. Now T_3 can cause X

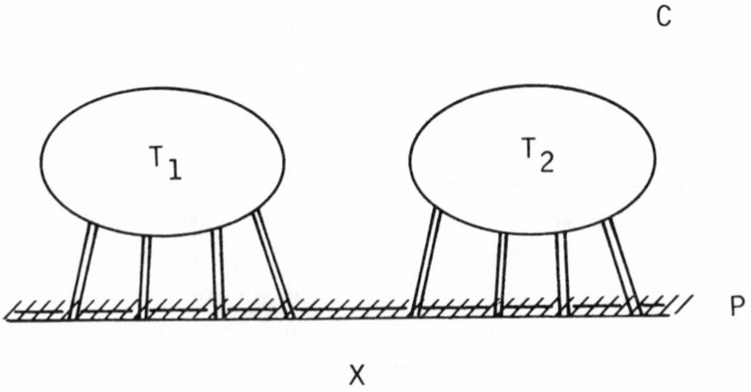

FIG. 3

to vanish, but as we have seen, only at some sacrifice of truth in both T_1 and T_2. Each of them is modified. *Concrescence therefore destroys validity.* So long as we have separate, incompatible theories we can be fairly sure that they are wrong.

Because of this interplay between completeness and validity, the growth of science is not a simple process of continual accommodation; it is like the growth of a pile of large rocks when new ones are added at the top. Its structure suffers discontinuous readjustments of the entire pile at certain times, and it is difficult to assess its growth in terms of convergence to any rigorous sort of limit.

But these difficulties are aggravated by more general philosophical considerations. The continual enrichment of the P-domain by new observations cannot be described in clear and finite fashion. Wholly unexpected experiences may arise from the fertile ground of being. At the same time the C-field grows without limit, for there is no end to mathematical imagination. The creative drive of science will here primarily assert itself.

The dynamics of the scientific enterprise are therefore improperly described as a matching of a completable class of P-experiences against a finite class of theoretical constructs; it is not even like the solving of a giant picture puzzle with ever increasing boundaries. For the pieces we have placed do not stay put; moreover, they disappear and multiply, and the places themselves have the fluidity of ideas rather than the rigidity of geometric patterns. Science is an *open* field, and I see no way of understanding its convergence if it did occur, nor do I expect it. Indeed its threat would fill me with dismay.

References

[1] Margenau, Henry. *The Nature of Physical Reality*, McGraw-Hill Book Company, Inc., New York (1950).

[2] Whittaker, E. *Eddington's Principle in the Philosophy of Science*, Cambridge University Press, p. 17 (1951).

[3] E. Wigner speaks of this feature as the 'unreasonable effectiveness of mathematics in the natural sciences'. See his paper under this title in *Comm. on Pure and Applied Mathematics*, Vol. 13, p. 1 (1960).

[4] Von Neumann, John. *Mathematische Grundlagen der Quantenmechanik*, Springer, 1932.

THE PERNICIOUS INFLUENCE OF MATHEMATICS ON SCIENCE

J. SCHWARTZ
New York University, New York, New York, U.S.A.

Our announced subject today is the role of mathematics in the formulation of physical theories. I wish however to make use of the license permitted at philosophical congresses, in two regards: in the first place, to confine myself to the negative aspects of this role, leaving it to others to dwell on the amazing triumphs of the mathematical method; in the second place, to comment not only on physical science but also on social science, in which the characteristic inadequacies which I wish to discuss are more readily apparent.

Computer programmers often make a certain remark about computing machines, which may perhaps be taken as a complaint: that computing machines, with a perfect lack of discrimination, will do any foolish thing they are told to do. The reason for this lies of course in the narrow fixation of the computing machine 'intelligence' upon the basely typographical details of its own perceptions — its inability to be guided by any large context. In a psychological description of the computer intelligence, three related adjectives push themselves forward: single-mindedness, literal-mindedness, simple-mindedness. Recognizing this, we should at the same time recognize that this single-mindedness, literal-mindedness, simple-mindedness also characterizes theoretical mathematics, though to a lesser extent.

It is a continual result of the fact that science tries to deal with reality that even the most precise sciences normally work with more or less ill-understood approximations toward which the scientist must maintain an appropriate skepticism. Thus, for instance, it may come as a shock to the mathematician to learn that the Schrodinger equation for the hydrogen atom, which he is able to solve only after a considerable effort of functional analysis and special function theory, is not a literally correct description of this atom, but only an approximation to a somewhat more correct equation taking account of spin, magnetic dipole, and relativistic effects; that this corrected equation is itself only an ill-understood approximation to an infinite set of quantum field-theoretical equations; and finally that the quantum field theory, besides diverging, neglects a myriad of strange-particle interactions whose strength and form are largely unknown. The physicist, looking at the original Schrodinger equation, learns to sense in it the presence of many invisible terms, integral, integrodifferential, perhaps even more complicated types of operators, in addition to the differential terms visible, and this sense inspires an entirely appropriate disregard for the purely technical features of the equation which he sees. This very healthy self-skepticism is foreign to the mathematical approach.

Mathematics must deal with well-defined situations. Thus, in its relations with science mathematics depends on an intellectual effort outside of mathematics for the crucial specification of the approximation which mathematics is to take literally. Give a mathematician a situation which is the least bit ill-defined — he will first of all make it well defined. Perhaps appropriately, but perhaps also inappropriately. The hydrogen atom illustrates this process nicely. The physicist asks: 'What are the eigenfunctions of such-and-such a differential operator?' The mathematician replies: 'The question as put is not well defined. First you must specify the linear space in which you wish to operate, then the precise domain of the operator as a subspace. Carrying all this out in the simplest way, we find the following result . . .' Whereupon the physicist may answer, much to the mathematician's chagrin: 'Incidentally, I am not so much interested in the operator you have just analyzed as in the following operator, which has four or five additional small terms — how different is the analysis of this modified problem?' In the case just cited, one may perhaps consider that nothing much is lost, nothing at any rate but the vigor and wide sweep of the physicist's less formal attack. But, in other cases, the mathematician's habit of making definite his literal-mindedness may have more unfortunate consequences. The mathematician turns the scientist's theoretical assumptions, i.e., convenient points of analytical emphasis, into axioms, and then takes these axioms literally. This brings with it the danger that he may also persuade the scientist to take these axioms literally. The question, central to the scientific investigation but intensely disturbing in the mathematical context — what happens to all this if the axioms are relaxed? — is thereby put into shadow.

In this way, mathematics has often succeeded in proving, for instance, that the fundamental objects of the scientist's calculations do not exist. The sorry history of the δ-function should teach us the pitfalls of rigor. Used repeatedly by Heaviside in the last century, used constantly and systematically by physicists since the 1920's, this function remained for mathematicians a monstrosity and an amusing example of the physicists' naïveté — until it was realized that the δ-function was not literally a function but a generalized function. It is not hard to surmise that this history will be repeated for many of the notions of mathematical physics which are currently regarded as mathematically questionable. The physicist rightly dreads precise argument, since an argument which is only convincing if precise loses all its force if the assumptions upon which it is based are slightly changed, while an argument which is convincing though imprecise may well be stable under small perturbations of its underlying axioms.

The literal-mindedness of mathematics thus makes it essential, if mathematics is to be appropriately used in science, that the assumptions upon which mathematics is to elaborate be correctly chosen from a larger point of view, invisible to mathematics itself. The single-mindedness of mathematics reinforces this conclusion. Mathematics is able to deal successfully only with the simplest of situations, more precisely, with a complex situation only to the extent that rare good fortune makes this complex situation hinge upon a few dominant simple factors. Beyond the well-traversed path, mathematics loses its bearings in a jungle of unnamed special functions and impenetrable combinatorial particularities. Thus, the mathematical technique can only reach far if it starts from a point close to the simple essentials of a problem which has simple essentials. That form of wisdom which is the opposite of single-mindedness, the ability to keep many threads in hand, to draw for an argument from many disparate sources, is quite foreign to mathematics. This inability accounts for much of the difficulty which mathematics experiences in attempting to penetrate the social sciences. We may perhaps attempt a mathematical economics — but how difficult would be a mathematical history! Mathematics adjusts only with reluctance to the external, and vitally necessary, approximating of the scientists, and shudders each time a batch of small terms is cavalierly erased. Only with difficulty does it find its way to the scientist's ready grasp of the relative importance of many factors. Quite typically, science leaps ahead and mathematics plods behind.

Related to this deficiency of mathematics, and perhaps more productive of rueful consequence, is the simple-mindedness of mathematics — its willingness, like that of a computing machine, to elaborate upon any idea, however absurd; to dress scientific brilliancies and scientific absurdities alike in the impressive uniform of formulae and theorems. Unfortunately however, an absurdity in uniform is far more persuasive than an absurdity unclad. The very fact that a theory appears in mathematical form, that, for instance, a theory has provided the occasion for the application of a fixed-point theorem, or of a result about difference equations, somehow makes us more ready to take it seriously. And the mathematical-intellectual effort of applying the theorem fixes in us the particular point of view of the theory with which we deal, making us blind to whatever appears neither as a dependent nor as an independent parameter in its mathematical formulation. The result, perhaps most common in the social sciences, is bad theory with a mathematical passport. The present point is best established by reference to a few horrible examples. In so large and public a gathering, however, prudence dictates the avoidance of any possible *faux pas*. I confine myself, therefore, to the citation of a delightful passage from Keynes' *General Theory*, in which the issues before us are discussed with a characteristic wisdom and wit:

"It is the great fault of symbolic pseudomathematical methods of formalizing a system of economic analysis . . . that they expressly assume strict independence between the factors involved and lose all their cogency and authority if this hypothesis is disallowed; whereas, in ordinary discourse, where we are not blindly manipulating but know all the time what we are doing and what the words mean, we can keep 'at the back of our heads' the necessary reserves and qualifications and adjustments which we shall have to make later on, in a way in which we cannot keep complicated partial differentials 'at the back' of several pages of algebra which assume they all vanish. Too large a proportion of recent 'mathematical' economics are mere concoctions, as imprecise as the initial assumptions they rest on, which allow the author to lose sight of the complexities and interdependencies of the real world in a maze of pretentious and unhelpful symbols."

The intellectual attractiveness of a mathematical argument, as well as the considerable mental labor involved in following it, makes mathematics a powerful tool of intellectual prestidigitation — a glittering deception in which some are entrapped, and some, alas, entrappers. Thus, for instance, the delicious ingenuity of the Birkhoff ergodic theorem has created the general impression that it must play a central role in the foundations of statistical mechanics.[1] Let us examine this case carefully, and see. Mechanics tells us that the configuration of an isolated system is specified by choice of a point p in its phase surface, and that after t seconds a system initially in the configuration represented by p moves into the configuration represented by $M_t p$. The Birkhoff theorem tells us that if f is any numerical function of the configuration p (and *if* the mechanical system is metrically transitive), the time average

$$\frac{1}{T}\int_0^T f(M_t p)\, dt$$

tends (as $T \to \infty$) to a certain constant; at any rate for all initial configurations p not lying in a set e in the phase surface whose measure $\mu(e)$ is zero; μ here is the (natural) Lebesgue measure in the phase surface. Thus, the familiar argument continues, we should not expect to observe a configuration in which the long-time average of such a function f is not close to its equilibrium value. Here I may conveniently use a bit of mathematical prestidigitation of the very sort to which I object, thus paradoxically making an argument serve the purpose of its own denunciation. Let $\nu(e)$ denote the probability of observing a configuration in the set e; the application of the Birkhoff theorem just made is then justified only if $\mu(e) = 0$ implies that $\nu(e) = 0$. If this is the case, known result of measure theory tells us that $\nu(e)$ is extremely small wherever $\mu(e)$ is extremely small. Now the functions f of principal interest in statistical mechanics are those which, like the local pressure and density of a gas, come into equilibrium, i.e., those functions for which $f(M_t p)$ is constant for long periods of time and for almost all initial configurations p. As is evident by direct computation in simple cases, and as the Birkhoff theorem itself tells us in these cases in which it is applicable, this means that $f(p)$ is close to its equilibrium value except for a set e of configurations of very small measure μ. Thus, not the Birkhoff theorem but the simple and generally unstated hypothesis '$\mu(e) = 0$ implies $\nu(e) = 0$' necessary to make the Birkhoff theorem relevant in any sense at all tells us why we are apt to find $f(p)$ having its equilibrium value. The

[1]This dictum is promulgated, with a characteristically straight face, in Dunford-Schwartz, *Linear Operators*, Vol. I, Chap. 7.

Birkhoff theorem in fact does us the service of establishing its own inability to be more than a questionably relevant superstructure upon this hypothesis.

The phenomenon to be observed here is that of an involved mathematical argument hiding the fact that we understand only poorly what it is based on. This shows, in sophisticated form, the manner in which mathematics, concentrating our attention, makes us blind to its own omissions — what I have already called the single-mindedness of mathematics. Typically, mathematics knows better what to do than why to do it. Probability theory is a famous example. An example which is perhaps of far greater significance is the quantum theory. The mathematical structure of operators in Hilbert space and unitary transformations is clear enough, as are certain features of the interpretation of this mathematics to give physical assertions, particularly assertions about general scattering experiments. But the larger question here, a systematic elaboration of the world-picture which quantum theory provides, is still unanswered. Philosophical questions of the deepest significance may well be involved. Here also, the mathematical formalism may be hiding as much as it reveals.

CURVED EMPTY SPACE-TIME AS THE BUILDING MATERIAL OF THE PHYSICAL WORLD: AN ASSESSMENT

JOHN A. WHEELER

Princeton University, Princeton, New Jersey, U.S.A.

1. Space-time: Arena or Everything?

Is the physical world in which we live a purely mathematical construct? Put the question in another way: Is space-time only an arena within which fields and particles move about as "physical" and "foreign" entities? Or is the four-dimensional continuum all there is? Is curved empty geometry a kind of magic building material out of which everything in the physical world is made: (1) slow curvature in one region of space describes a gravitational field; (2) a rippled geometry with a different type of curvature somewhere else describes an electromagnetic field; (3) a knotted-up region of high curvature describes a concentration of charge and mass-energy that moves like a particle? Are fields and particles foreign entities immersed *in* geometry, or are they nothing *but* geometry?

It would be difficult to name any issue more central to the plan of physics than this: whether space-time is only an arena, or whether it is everything. Einstein from an early day was animated by the hope for a purely geometrical description of nature. He in turn derived inspiration from previous thinkers, among them Riemann and the Clifford to whom we owe the Clifford numbers of Dirac's theory of the electron. In 1870 Clifford [1] put the issue before the Cambridge Philosophical Society in a more explicit form than anyone ever had before — or anyone was to do for many decades: " I hold in fact (1) that small portions of space *are* in fact of a nature analogous to little hills on a surface which is on the average flat; namely, that the ordinary laws of geometry are not valid in them; (2) that this property of being curved or distorted is continually being passed on from one portion of space to another after the manner of a wave; (3) that this variation of the curvature of space is what really happens in that phenomenon which we call the motion of *matter*, whether ponderable or ethereal; (4) that in the physical world nothing else takes place but this variation, subject (possibly) to the law of continuity."

The vision of Clifford and Einstein can be summarized in a single phrase, "a geometrodynamical universe": a world whose properties are described by geometry, and a geometry whose curvature changes with time — a *dynamical* geometry.

This concept of a geometrodynamical universe is almost a century old, and the equations which Einstein discovered to describe such a universe are more than half a century old. Therefore it might seem reasonable to have arrived by now at a definite verdict for or against this description of nature. However, the past seven years have seen an extraordinary spurt of new development in "general relativity" or "geometrodynamics" and an entirely new assessment of our present position is required. Let me therefore recall the basic ideas of geometrodynamics, then review the recent developments, then list outstanding problems, and finally appraise the purely geometrical picture of nature considering especially in this connection the fascinating picture it offers for the first time as to the nature of electricity.

2. Geometrodynamics [14, 18, 20, 21]

One is most uncomfortable in his first contact with the idea of curved space-time. One is especially ill at ease when he is told that according to Einstein's principle of equivalence it makes no difference what coordinates, what labels, what numbers one uses to distinguish one point from another. One feels a little like a man in a rowboat upon a tossing sea endeavoring with a precision rule to establish to the accuracy of a millimeter the dimensions of a whale! To find one's way out of this chaos—compounded in four dimensions—one seizes upon two basic concepts from Einstein: (1) event and (2) invariant distance. The collision of two particles appears in space-time as the contact—or near contact and bending—of two world lines. It establishes an event, a point in space-time, identifiable by all observers regardless of all questions of coordinate systems. An event, in other words, can be pictured as the interation of two straws in the great haystack of world lines that thread through space-time. The four-dimensional manifold is filled by such events.

Between any two events there is a well-defined distance in space-time, the Einstein "interval". These intervals can be compared, one with another, by way of light rays and tracks of particles through purely geometrical procedures (Lorentz and Marzke). In this kind of geometry the two traditional tools of compass and ruler are abandoned. Neither does one need to make any use of the clocks and meter sticks of familiar textbook discussions. They bring in ideas of atomic structure and the quantum of action that are foreign to the spirit of classical general relativity. Instead the two tools of the geometrodynamicist are the tracks of light rays and test particles. With their help one can find the interval between any two events C and D in terms of the interval between two chosen events A and B. These two events define by their separation the standards of length and time throughout all space and for all time—and this despite the fact that A and B are, for example, merely two successive sparks, two successive flashes of light, that took place fifty years ago. If their separation defines the geometrodynamical standard meter, then in terms of this meter one measures not only all distances but also all times. If one wants to introduce the "speed of light" into the discussion, he can do so just as one brings 5,280 into the planning of a walk—merely as a human and conventional factor of conversion from one unit of interval to another, and nothing more.

Between n events there are evidently $n(n-1)/2$ distances—an enormous mass of data. If the events are peppered about sufficiently densely through space-time, they specify the geometrical structure of the four-dimensional manifold. Look at a table of the airline distances between the principal airports of the world—Athens, Bombay, Cairo, Detroit, · · ·. Try to chart these out on a flat piece of paper. Nothing one can do in relocating the points on the paper will make their separations agree with airline distances. One is *compelled* to go to a curved sphere to make a proper map. The distances themselves tell one just how this map must be constructed. They contain in nutshell form all that is known about the geometry of the curved space. In nutshell form? Not quite! If in passing from New York to San Francisco the shortest air route passes over Chicago, it is evidently enough to know the New York–Chicago distance and the Chicago–San Francisco mileage to find the length of the entire route. In other words, not all distances need be known, only the separation between every pair of *nearby* points. What a saving in the cost of printing our table of distances! One can dispense even with this abbreviated table if one can find a formula to take its place. For this purpose coordinates are useful—for example, the familiar angles θ and ϕ that distinguish one point on a sphere, or on a sphere-like surface, from another. Then the distance between two points with coordinates (θ, ϕ) and $(\theta + d\theta, \phi + d\phi)$ is

$$ds = \{a^2[(d\theta)^2 + \sin^2\theta\,(d\phi)^2]\}$$

on a sphere of radius a and is

$$ds = \{g_{\theta\theta}\,d\theta\,d\theta + 2g_{\theta\phi}\,d\theta\,d\phi + g_{\phi\phi}\,d\phi\,d\phi\}^{\frac{1}{2}}$$

on a deformed sphere. In four dimensions $d\theta$ and $d\phi$ are replaced by four coordinates, $x^\alpha = (x^0, x^1, x^2, x^3)$. The square of the interval is

$$(ds)^2 = g_{\alpha\beta}\,(x)\,dx^\alpha \cdot dx^\beta.$$

(Summation convention! The repetition of any index is understood to imply that summation is to be carried out over that index!) The way the $16 - 6 = 10$ independent "metric coefficients" $g_{\alpha\beta}(x)$ depend upon position—if known in formula form—summarizes all information about distances between nearby points, and therefore tells all that need be known about the geometry.

The geometry of space near the sun, and the curvature of this geometry, in Einstein's theory took the place of gravitation as explanation for the tracks followed by the planets in their yearly motions.

Upon the concepts of "event" and "interval" Einstein thus based general relativity. Yet his theory seemed to fall short of his dreams in one important respect. Electromagnetic fields—or light rays—and material particles still appeared as foreign entities traveling *in* space-time, not as objects constructed *out* of geometry. Not only the structure of these entities but also the law for their movements or changes with time had to be taken as additional to general relativity.

To accept unexplained concepts from outside and to do the best one can with them is a familiar experience for theoretical physics, and not only in the domain of general relativity! In elementary particle physics today, for example, one is almost as far as ever from explaining the internal constitution and stability of elementary particles. Yet the so-called dispersion theory of elementary particle reactions supplies a mathematical connection between rates of very different reactions, some typically already known from experiment, others predicted and then checked to high accuracy by other experiments.

3. Equations of Motion Derived from the Field Equations

This empirical approach — to accept the existence of particles even if one could not explain them — led to an important advance in the long period of general relativity between the early days and the recent developments. Einstein and Grommer, Infeld and Hoffmann succeeded in deriving the equation of motion of masses out of the geometrical equations of general relativity [2, 3, 9, 20]. They no longer needed to consider the Newtonian law of motion, or rather its relativistic generalization, as a separate postulate brought in from outside.

Consider by way of illustration a physicist who has been dragged away in the night and wakes up in the morning to find himself at the top of a tower. Looking down through the mist he sees dark objects moving on straight lines. Occasionally two by accident come close and he sees them deflect each other. He has much time on his hands. He studies the law of interaction between these dark objects and derives for them an equation of motion. Then the weather clears and he discovers that he has been looking at the surface of a pond, and following the progress of small eddies or vortices across its surface. He recalls his knowledge of hydrodynamics. He returns to his pencil and paper. He discovers that he can *derive* his equation of motion of "dark objects" from the laws of hydrodynamics.

There is one important difference between the achievement of the prisoner and the work of Einstein and his collaborators. The analysis from the tower gave a complete description of an apparently discrete object in terms of the dynamics of a continuous medium, the water. In contrast, the Einstein-Grommer-Infeld-Hoffmann theory of motion of masses was incomplete. They did not derive the existence and stability of the mass, they assumed it. But once they assumed that masses *do* exist and hold together, they were able to *derive* the equation of motion of these masses. As for vortices, so here the law of motion of apparently discrete objects came out of the equations of a continuum. Einstein's geodesic equation of motion for a particle now came out of the equations of general relativity for the rate of change with time of the geometry *surrounding* the mass. In the long lull that followed the first exciting days of general relativity no development did more than this EGIH derivation to keep alive the vision of a universe of pure geometry.

4. The Initial Value Problem

The first step into the new era of geometrodynamics was made by Lichnerowicz [10–13] and Mme. Fourès-Bruhat [7, 8]. They asked and answered the question, How much information has to be given about the geometry at one instant—or in relativistic language, on "one space-like three-dimensional hypersurface", or in other words, on one "slice" through space-time—to make it possible to predict the entire past and future? In other words, what are the *initial data* for geometrodynamics? The corresponding question had long before received attention in particle dynamics and in electromagnetism. For a particle moving in a known field of force it is well known to be sufficient to specify its initial position and initial velocity in order to be able to predict its entire future and past. Similarly, to forecast the complete evolution in time of the electromagnetic field it is sufficient to give at the initial moment—everywhere on the initial three-dimensional space-like hypersurface—the values of the electric and magnetic field strengths. In geometrodynamics Fourès-Bruhat and Lichnerowicz found that one must give (1) the three-dimensional geometry *intrinsic* to the initial three-dimensional space-like hypersurface and (2) the *extrinsic* curvature of this hypersurface, telling how it is to be embedded in the not-yet-calculated four-dimensional geometry. Once this double collection of initial-value data has been specified, then Einstein's field equations predict the evolution of the geometry in time, and therefore determine the entire *four*-dimensional geometry.

The distinction between intrinsic and extrinsic geometry is best illustrated by drawing on a sheet of paper a right triangle with the ratio of sides 3 : 4 : 5 and then bending this piece of paper. The geometry intrinsic to the two-surface remains flat; lengths and angles are unchanged; the intrinsic curvature happens in this example to be zero. Not so the extrinsic curvature! Its value at any point is governed by the radius of curvature at that point. It tells how the two-geometry is imbedded in three-space.

How much information it is necessary to have to predict the future is compared and contrasted in Table 1 for geometrodynamics, particle mechanics, and electrodynamics.

5. Electromagnetism as an Aspect of Geometry

General relativity or geometrodynamics as described thus far is still a mixed theory, employing geometry to describe gravitation but using a foreign field immersed *in* the geometry to characterize electromagnetism. In 1956 Misner [14] rediscovered a feature of Einstein's theory that had lain forgotten since Rainich [16, 17] had found it thirty two years before. The second-order differential equations of electromagnetism can be combined with the second-order differential equations of general relativity to give one set of purely geometrical equations of the fourth order. The idea is easily described in physical terms (Fig. 1). It provides a unification of

TABLE 1

SPECIFICATION OF INITIAL VALUE DATA COMPARED AND CONTRASTED FOR THREE KINDS OF DYNAMICAL THEORY

	Initial value data	From this predict:	Any conditions on initial value data?
Dynamics of a single particle	t_0 and x_0 (position) and p_0 (momentum) at t_0	$x(t)$ and $p(t)$	No
Electro-dynamics	Space-like 3-hypersurface in a preexisting already known 4-manifold. Values of **E** (electric field vector) and **H** (magnetic field vector) at every point *on* this 3-hypersurface.	Electromagnetic field at *every* point in *space-time*	div $\mathbf{E} = 0$; div $\mathbf{H} = 0$ (electric and magnetic lines of force never end).
Geometro-dynamics	The 3-geometry intrinsic to some space-like 3-hypersurface* and the extrinsic curvature of this hypersurface as imbedded in a yet to be constructed 4-manifold.	The geometry of the 4-manifold itself	Four conditions at each point, one connecting the difference between intrinsic and extrinsic curvature with the energy density; the other connecting the space rate of change of extrinsic curvature with the density of flow of energy.

* The choice of the space-like hypersurface in electrodynamics corresponded to — and was the relativistic generalization of — the choice of the initial time in particle dynamics. There was a clean distinction between the choice *of* this surface and the specification of the physical data — **E** and **H** — *on* this surface. No such distinction appears in geometrodynamics between the choice of the *time* and of the *geometrical data at this time*; the two kinds of information are inextricably tied together in and specified by the specification of the intrinsic 3-geometry itself.

gravitation and electromagnetism within the framework of familiar Riemannian geometry and Einstein's standard 1916 theory of general relativity.

Unaware of Rainich's early work, Einstein had tried for many years, up to his death, to invent some new kind of geometry [4] which would have sufficient richness to describe both gravitation and electromagnetism. However, the so-called unified field theory, which he had published in his later years, had this unhappy property: it predicted (references in [20]) that a charged object should move as if electrically neutral, no matter how great the amount of the charge piled upon its back. If this unified field theory were correct, no cyclotron could operate! Einstein was aware of this difficulty. He nevertheless persisted in his efforts because out of some kind

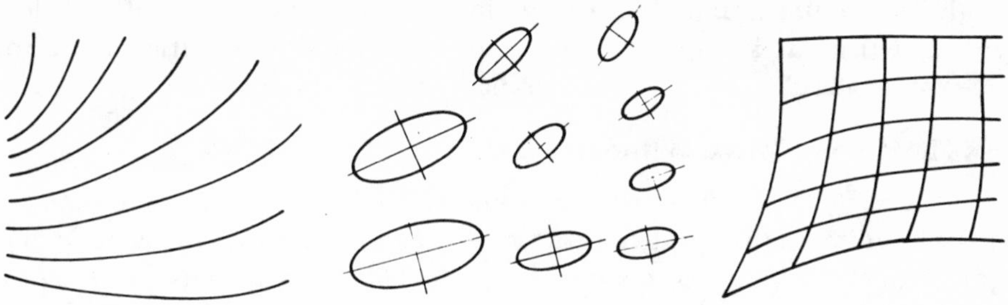

Fig. 1 The electromagnetic field leaves footprints on the geometry of space-time so characteristic that from them one can read back to everything that one can know, or that one wants to know, about the electromagnetic field. Thus one can in effect say that these footprints *are* the electromagnetic field. The lines in the left-hand portion of the diagram symbolize electric or magnetic lines of force. The regions of closer spacing of lines of force correspond to greater density of energy and stress, as suggested by the relative size of the ellipsoids of stress and energy shown in the middle diagram. Energy, however, according to Einstein implies mass; and mass is the source of a gravitational field, or a bending of space. Thus arises the distorted geometry in the right-hand figure. The curvature of that geometry can in principle be detected by purely *geometrical* measurements. From such measurements one can then work back to deduce the electromagnetic field. In other words, the content of Maxwell's equations for the electromagnetic field can be expressed in terms of statements about the curvature of space — and the derivatives of that curvature — and nothing more.

of classical geometry he wanted to see come not only electromagnetism but also quantum theory itself. However, almost all physicists today think of the quantum principle as added *to* a classical theory from outside, not to be derived *from* that theory. In addition, the work of Rainich and Misner has removed the motive artificially to unify electromagnetism with gravitation and geometry. We have an *already unified* field theory — we have at long last come to appreciate — in Einstein's standard 1916 theory.

In the "already unified" phrasing of geometrodynamics due to Rainich and Misner, it is sometimes impossible, as very recently shown by Penrose and Witten, completely to specify the past and future by giving purely geometrical data upon a preselected initial *spacelike* 3-hypersurface. In these cases one has his choice either (1) to specify the geometry, alone (including derivatives) upon some *other* slice through space-time or (2) to give the geometry *and* — for example — the magnetic field upon the *original* space like hypersurface itself. In either case one still treats electromagnetism in principle as an aspect — a sophisticated aspect — of geometry. However, in practice it is often more convenient to adjure a purely geometrical discussion of the dynamics and to use words that come from the lexicons of both geometry and electromagnetism. Only to this limited extent is it wise to concede to Pauli's earlier joking assessment of unified field theory: "Let not man join together what God has put asunder."

If we summarize the earliest achievement of general relativity as gravitation without gravitation, and the results of EGIH in the intermediate period as equations of motion without equations of motion, then we can count the analysis of Rainich and Misner as giving us electromagnetism without electromagnetism, and can turn now to the recent *geon* ("gravitational-electromagnetic entity") [18, 5, 6, 15] and mass without mass.

6. The Geon: Mass Without Mass

The gravitational pull of the sun is known to deflect starlight. In principle a sufficiently massive and compact object can deflect electromagnetic and gravitational radiation into a circular path. This radiation possesses energy and therefore mass. Sufficiently intense, the circulating beam can itself provide all the gravitational attraction that is needed to hold it into circular form for a long period of time. This ball of light, or geon, behaves like a mass: (1) At a distance such an object, like the sun and other astronomical bodies, exerts a gravitational attraction of its own. (2) Under the gravitational attraction of any distant massive entity the geon moves along a curved orbit of its own like any other mass.

Thus studied from outside, the geon appears like any other mass. Internally, however, it consists of nothing but radiation. Nowhere inside is there a place to which one can point and say, "Here there is some 'real mass'." In the geon one has for the first time a *model* for mass in terms of simpler concepts (electromagnetism, gravitation) which on the whole one does understand.

The geons subject to classical analysis have masses greater than 10^{39}g, radii greater than 10^{11}cm ($\sim$ the radius of the sun), and field strengths less than the critical limit at which electron pairs are produced out of the vacuum in great numbers. Geons with lesser dimensions and greater internal fields conceivably exist in principle, but their properties are completely unknown. There is no reason to believe they are stable. Neither is there the slightest evidence that they have any *direct* connection with the world of elementary particles.

In principle one could construct large geons if one were granted sufficiently grandiose radiation sources and other facilities on an astronomical scale. In practical terms there is not the least indication that one will ever be able to reach up to this scale of operations or want to. Geons today are pencil and paper constructs principally of value because they show one way to *build mass out of pure geometry.*

7. Electricity as a Property of Curved Empty Space

Charge too can be constructed in principle out of empty curved space and nothing more [18, 14]. Let the geometry as it changes with time lead to a direct joining together (Fig. 2, upper left-hand diagram) of two regions of space previously connected with each other only through an intervening region. Then electric lines of force which thread through this region become trapped in the topology of a multiply connected space. A "wormhole" comes into existence. One mouth of the wormhole appears as a positive charge, because out of it emerge electric lines of force. The other mouth appears to

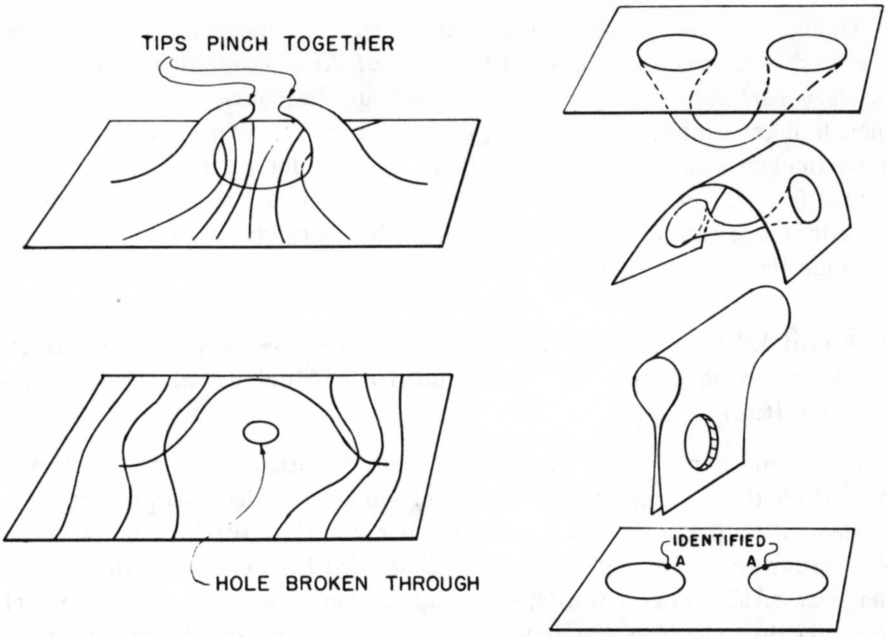

Fig. 2 Trapping of lines of force in the topology of a multiply connected space; and the wormhole picture of electric charge. *Upper left*: Two regions of space of high curvature which are about to pinch together and trap electric lines of force. After this join up has occurred, the space is multiply connected in this sense: there are two inequivalent ways to connect a string between a point A in the space and another point B. One goes through the throat of the newly formed "wormhole", the other outside. *Lower left*: A way to arrive at the same topology by a dynamical development of the geometry which does not allow opportunity for trapping lines of force. *Right-hand column of pictures*: Different ways of regarding the same wormhole showing that the length of the throat need not have any simple connection with the distance between the mouths of the wormhole. The mouths may be very far apart in the surrounding nearly Euclidean space. The lines of force which enter into one mouth emerge out of the other one. To an observer with equipment of poor resolving power the one mouth appears to bear a positive charge and the other an equal and opposite negative charge. Yet nowhere is there anything but curved empty space.

an observer unendowed with microscopic vision as a negative charge of equal magnitude. Onto it from all directions converge electric lines of force. If the observer had means for closer inspection he would see that nowhere is there any "real" electric charge. Watching the geometry change with time, he may see the mouths, the equal and opposite charges, move very far away from each other. During these movements, however complicated, the charge cannot change because there is no way for lines of force to break. Only if the mouths again come together to annihilate the wormhole, or if the topology changes in some other way, can these lines of force escape. Already in pure geometrodynamics, in other words, opposite charges can annihilate each other to produce free radiation.

The geometrodynamical kind of electricity is evidently a property *of* curved empty space, not a mystical magical jelly immersed *in* space.

Though *the mouth of a wormhole* is endowed with charge and energy — and therefore with mass — it *has not the slightest direct connection with an elementary particle.* There is a specificity about the connection between one mouth of a wormhole and another, between a particular positive charge and a particular negative charge, which is quite different from anything observed for elementary particles. In addition the geometrodynamical kind of electric charge can take on any value, whereas the electrical charges in nature are quantized to multiples of the electronic charge.

8. Foam-Like Structure of Those Geometries which Contribute Most Importantly to the Quantum Mechanical Probability Amplitude

When one surveys the consequences of quantizing general relativity, he realizes that wormholes are reasonably to be regarded as a property, not of elementary particles, but of all space [19, 21]. Quantized geometry shows fluctuations quite analogous to the well-studied fluctuations of the electromagnetic field. In other words, space can be compared with an ocean which looks flat to an aviator who flies high above it. Yet regarded more and more closely, it shows more and more agitation, until — so quantum geometrodynamics predicts — at distances of the order of

$$10^{-33}\ \text{cm} \sim \frac{\begin{pmatrix}\text{Newton's constant}\\ \text{of gravitation}\end{pmatrix}^{\frac{1}{2}} \cdot \begin{pmatrix}\text{Planck's quantum}\\ \text{of action}\end{pmatrix}^{\frac{1}{2}}}{(\text{speed of light})^{3/2}},$$

the entire structure is seen to be impermeated every which way with wormholes. If the theory is correct, it forces on all space this foam-like character.

The multiply connected structure is virtual in the sense of quantum theory. There is not a unique topology at a given time. Instead, there is a certain probability of this degree of multiple connectedness, a certain probability of that one, and so on. The flux of lines of force, being trapped as new wormholes are formed, and being released as the local topology momentarily simplifies, describes pairs of positive and negative charges being created and annihilated. This goes on throughout all space. The agitation everywhere is violent. If these consequences of the quantum version of geometrodynamics have any relevance to the problem of elementary particles, they are to be compared and identified with the "vacuum fluctuations" of the standard and well-accepted modern relativistic quantum theory of the electron that has been so well tested by experiment. In that description of nature, too, all space is the seat of virtual creations and annihilations of pairs of so-called "undressed electrons" going on all the time. Thus the "undressed electron" is to be identified, on this picture, with the elementary "wormhole". The experimental electron is understood as a region of space where the concentration of undressed electrons — of wormholes — is percentagewise a tiny bit more than the average. On this view the dynamics of the vacuum is even more central to physics than the constitution of elementary particles; they represent so to speak only regions where the virtual foam-like structure is a little denser than elsewhere.

9. Electric Charge Viewed as Evidence for a Multiple Connectedness of Space

The geometrodynamical picture of charge is out of the question in a world free of all wormholes. Therefore a central issue demands consideration. Is the physical world simply connected or is it multiply connected? In the past there was no occasion to raise this issue. The Euclidean topology of physics was taken for granted. No suspicion arose that electricity could have anything to do with topology. Electricity was studied in its own right. Sources of electricity had to be postulated as extra terms in Maxwell's otherwise beautifully homogeneous equations of electromagnetism. Or those equations had to be assumed to break down in the immediate vicinity of a charge. Now we find that those postulates were not necessary. We do not have to assume that there exists a special kind of jelly with magical properties, otherwise called electricity. Neither do we have to assume that there is some subtle difference between the points in space such that Maxwell's equations are satisfied at some points and not at others. We can abandon the magic jelly and we can uphold Maxwell's equations everywhere, provided only that at the same time we give up the assumption — the pure assumption — that the world is simply connected. To admit the possibility of a multiply connected space is to admit the possibility of a purely topological description of charge.

Imagine the history of physics relived in another order. The new race is extraordinarily interested in distance measurements of enormous precision. They find space-time is curved. They discover the two independent kinds of curvature, one describing electromagnetic waves, the other, gravitational waves. They find the Einstein-Maxwell equations — all the laws of geometrodynamics — but they have never heard of the idea of charge. However, their topologists, reincarnations of Hodge and deRham, become interested in their equations. These mathematical friends point out that in a space endowed with many wormholes the flux through each throat is a constant of the motion, despite all the other changes that go on in the geometry as time advances. They know that no one has yet seen the mouth of a wormhole. Nevertheless they explain to their physicist colleagues that they have a way to search for wormholes even if they are much too small to be seen.

It is only necessary, they point out, to draw a sphere — even a large sphere — around the region where one is searching; to measure at each point of the surface a certain property that can be found from the curvature of space (the normal component of the electric field, they call it); and to integrate the values of this field over the entire surface. If the integral differs from zero then inside there is the mouth of a wormhole.

The suggested experiment is performed. The electric flux is found to be different from zero. Everyone concludes that space is multiply connected, as the topologists suggested might be possible. In other words, from this point of view *the existence of electric charges in nature can be taken as experimental proof that space is multiply connected.* It can be said to be an accident of the history of science that we have not always looked at electric charge as evidence of a multiply connected topology. Or does electric charge supply such evidence?

Cannot one consider a universe where the curvature evolves in time according to the field equations but where all electric charge is due to "real" charge in the traditional sense of "electric jelly". No! The curvature here and there will develop waves strong enough to crest and change the local topology. Inevitably occasions will occur where otherwise free lines of force will be trapped in the topology. Charge of purely geometrodynamical origin will come into being. The universe will then contain two kinds of charge—one made out of geometry, the other out of jelly. But it is a familiar working rule of physics, not to use two explanations of a phenomenon where one will do. Yet the geometrodynamical type of charge can hardly be escaped if one believes general relativity. Therefore it would seem necessary to believe that *all charge is connected with the topology of space.*

If we accept this conclusion, we can say that the existence of electric charge is the most compelling reason we have today to believe in a description of our physical world in terms of curved empty space. It is of course a very long way from that general conclusion to any specific analysis of elementary particle constitution along such lines. Many surprises are undoubtedly in store. But at least we would seem to be looking in a reasonable direction when we raise up our eyes to the ancient vision of a universe of pure geometry.

Appreciation is expressed to Charles Misner and David Sharp and other colleagues for discussions leading to the formulation of the present report.

APPENDIX

SOME LINES FOR FURTHER INVESTIGATION

1. Can nucleons be crushed out of existence under the gravitational pressure at the center of a sufficiently dense and massive star?
2. What objects does the "geometrodynamical zoo" admit besides gravitational waves, electromagnetic waves, geons, and wormholes?
3. Does a closed universe always develop in the course of time regions of infinitely sharp curvature, analogously to the crest of an ocean wave which breaks up into foam?
4. Is there any analog in gravitation physics of the concept of line or tube of force which is so useful in electrodynamics?

5. What is the algebra of the coordinate and momentum variables of geometrodynamics?
6. If a "propagator" is a mathematical quantity that tells how a given state of a field will evolve in time, and if the singularities of the propagator of the electromagnetic field have yielded insight into the nature of this field, what are the singularities of the propagator of the geometrodynamical field?
7. What replaces the "observer" of standard quantum theory when he comes to deal with a closed universe, outside of which there is no platform on which for him to stand?
8. What is the mathematical expression for the fluctuations in the geometry of space which occur at very small distances, according to quantum geometrodynamics?
9. Does a closer study of these fluctuations give a deeper insight into the question of why the world *has* four dimensions — or give a higher standpoint that rises above the question of dimensionality?
10. What has such a wider look to contribute to an understanding of the spin and other symmetries of elementary particles?

References

[1] Clifford, W. K. On the space theory of matter. Cambridge Philosophical Society, Proceedings, Vol. 2 (1876), pp. 157–158. See *Mathematical Papers* by *William Kingdon Clifford*, R. Tucker, ed., London, Macmillan, 1882 for this paper and for Clifford on Riemann's famous lecture of 1854.

[2] Einstein, A., and J. Grommer. Allgemeine Relativitätstheorie und Bewegungsgesetz. *Preussische Akademie der Wissenschaften, Phys.-math. Klasse, Sitzungsberichte*, Vol. 2 (1927), pp. 2–13 (see also pp. 235–245).

[3] Einstein, A., L. Infeld, and B. Hoffmann. Gravitational equations and the problem of motion. *Annals of Mathematics*, Vol. 39 (1938), pp. 65–100.

[4] Einstein, A. *The Meaning of Relativity*. Princeton, New Jersey, Princeton Univ. Press, 5th ed., 1955, pp. 79 — 108; see last section for Einstein's unified field theory.

[5] Ernst, F. J., Jr. Variational Calculations in Geon Theory. *Physical Review*, Vol. 105 (1957) pp. 1662–1664.

[6] Ernst, F. J., Jr. Linear and Toroidal Geons. *Physical Review*, Vol. 105 (1957), pp. 1665–1670.

[7] Fourès-Bruhat, Y. Sur l'intégration des équations de la relativité générale. *Journal of Rational Mechanics and Analysis*, Vol. 5 (1956), pp. 951–966.

[8] Fourès-Bruhat, Y. Théorème d'existence pour certains systèmes d'équations aux dérivées partielles non linéaires. *Acta Mathematica*, Vol. 88 (1952), pp. 141–225.

[9] Infeld, L., and J. Plebanski. *Motion and Relativity*. Warsaw, Panstwowe Wydawnictwo Naukowe and New York, Pergamon Press, 1960, 229 pp.

[10] Lichnerowicz, A. *Problèmes globaux en méchanique relativiste*. Paris, Hermann et cie., 1939.

[11] Lichnerowicz, A. L'intégration des équations de la gravitation relativiste et le problème des n. corps. *Jr. math. pures et appl.*, Séries 9, Vol. 23 (1944), pp. 37–63.

[12] LICHNEROWICZ, A. Problèmes globaux en méchanique relativiste. Paris, Hermann et cie., 1939.

[13] LICHNEROWICZ, A. *Théories relativistes de la gravitation et de l'électromagnetisme.* Paris, Masson et cie., 1955, xii+298 pp.

[14] MISNER, CHARLES W., and JOHN A. WHEELER. Classical physics as geometry: gravitation, electromagnetism, unquantized charge, and mass as properties of curved empty space. *Annals of Physics,* Vol. 2 (1957), pp. 525–603.

[15] POWER, E. A., and J. A. WHEELER. Thermal geons. *Reviews of Modern Physics,* Vol. 29 (1957), pp. 480–495.

[16] RAINICH, G. Y. Electrodynamics in the General Relativity Theory. National Academy of Sciences of the United States of America, *Proceedings,* Vol. 10 (1924), pp. 124–126.

[17] RAINICH, G. Y. Electrodynamics in the General Relativity Theory. *Transactions of the American Mathematical Society,* Vol. 27, (1925), pp. 106–136.

[18] WHEELER, J. A. Geons. *Physical Review,* Vol. 97 (1955), pp. 511–536.

[19] WHEELER, JOHN A. On the nature of quantum geometrodynamics. *Annals of Physics,* Vol. 2 (1957), pp. 604–614.

[20] WHEELER, J. A. Geometrodynamics and the problem of motion. *Reviews of Modern Physics,* Vol. 33 (1961), pp. 63–78.

[21] WHEELER, J. A. Neutrinos, gravitation and geometry. *Rendiconti Scuola Internazionale,* Enrico Fermi, XI Corso (1960), pp. 67–196. See also J. A. WHEELER, *Geometrodynamics,* New York, Academic Press (in publication).

Note added in proof: The references to the initial-value problem [7], [8], [10], [11], [12], [13], should be supplemented by CARTAN, Ê. Sur les équations de la gravitation d'Einstein, *J. Math. pures et appl.,* Vol. 1 (1922), pp. 141–203.

SECTION

VII

METHODOLOGY AND PHILOSOPHY OF BIOLOGICAL AND PSYCHOLOGICAL SCIENCES

THE SCIENTIFIC STATUS OF PSYCHOANALYSIS

ERNEST R. HILGARD

Stanford University, Stanford, California, U.S.A.

Psychoanalysis is, first of all, a medical psychology, concerned with the treatment of human suffering, and as such represents the procedures used by those trained in it as they treat the patients who come to them for help. It is also a general psychology, with its interpretations of human development, memory, thought processes, creativity, social behaviour — fitting all of the subject matter of psychology into its categories. Finally, it presents a general view of man's place in nature, of how man may live with his heritage of unconscious processes if he is to be at peace with himself, and if he is to be as rational as he can be in planning for the future of human society. The influence of psychoanalysis upon literature and drama rests upon this implied *Weltanschauung*.

Every young science goes through a number of stages in its development from naturalistic observation, through the detection of areas of lawfulness and construction of more limited theories, to more comprehensive, parsimonious, and elegant theories. While these states can be assigned some sort of historical order, observations are guided by theories, theories are modified by observations, and some theories of very wide scope may be proposed early, to be supplemented later by less ambitious models. Hence any particular body of scientific material can be assessed only according to its history, its achievements along the way, the course of revision, and its promise for the future.

Psychoanalysis has a special history because it was dominated so long by Sigmund Freud, a man of great genius, who made most of the observations upon which psychoanalysis is built, who began theory construction at the very start of his career, and fought the social battles for recognition against a hostile clientele. He thus defined the field of inquiry, invented the techniques of investigation, proposed the theories, and set the stage for the fervent social interactions that have characterized psychoanalysis as a profession. He continued to think, to change his mind, to propose new ways of looking at things, throughout a long life. Despite the changes in detail, there is a remarkable unity to his thinking, if one looks for the guiding ideas rather than for the changing metaphors that expressed them. One guiding idea is the *continuity of development* from earliest infancy; new ways of behaving are built on earlier ways through subtle transformations and shifts, in which the old and outgrown ways are somehow carried along, also, on occasion becoming manifest. This idea has had a profound influence upon general psychology. The notion that these residues from earlier experience affect behaviour *unconsciously* is a second guiding idea. The nature of the active unconscious, the number of fundamental drives, the nature of repression, may be matters of some dispute, but some equivalent of unconscious motivation, of the regulation of what man does by thought-like processes that are out of awareness, is now part of general psychological thinking. A third guiding idea, that present behaviour is often a resultant of *conflict* and exhibits ways of meeting, resolving, or compromising issues, brings the results of the past into the present. This feature of Freud's teaching has also become a commonplace of academic psychology. There are many other guiding ideas, such as the distinction between impulse-driven thinking, called primary process thinking, and more rational or conceptual thinking, called secondary process thinking. This distinction has not yet been fully domesticated in academic psychology, but it is influential in current research. The special processes assigned to the dreamwork (condensation, displacement, symbolization) are significant original formulations. Thus far I have not discussed the contributions of the psychoanalytic method. Again, to Freud we owe free association, the role of interpretation, and the very important problems of transference and countertransference.

Most of these ideas were spelled out in the seventh chapter of *The Interpretation of Dreams* (1900) [5], Freud's major announcement of his theory, but they had already been worked out in 1895 in his "Project for a scientific psychology" that came to light only recently with the Fliess papers [6]. It is significant that Freud was searching for a theoretical framework for his ideas before the turn of the century, and had four more decades in which to develop them before his death in 1939.

For philosophers of science, the history of psychoanalysis provides a unique opportunity to study the evolution of a science. It of course had many roots and was influenced by the *Zeitgeist*, but it would not have been the same without Freud. We know now the kinds of germinal ideas he had as early as 1895. Many of these were imaginative, novel, inventive, but they were not weird or fantastic, and they foreshadowed developments in neurophysiology as well as in psychoanalysis. Freud built upon the available methods and scientific ideas that were current, molding them honestly and courageously on the basis of his careful observations of himself and of his patients. Frenkel-Brunswik [4] assessed his inferred variables from the point of view of the logic of science, and she found that *in principle*, he was doing what any conceptualizer of science does. He was aware of the problems of scientific logic; while he often used metaphor when events were too difficult to systematize more precisely, he would have preferred to abandon metaphor for better anchored concepts. The interaction between creative imagination, on the one hand, and careful observations, on the other, as exemplified in Freud, bears dispassionate study. His speculations doubtless outran his data at some points, but this is perhaps essential if a young science is to grow.

We are now considering where psychoanalysis stands today, twenty years after Freud's death. As students of the history of science, we need to recognize the personal and social problems that faced psychoanalytic practitioners and theorists following his death. There had been defections from the ranks during his lifetime by such early favorites as Adler, Jung, and Rank, so that the central core of psychoanalysis was both defined and dominated by Freud. During his lifetime a unity within a developing theory could be maintained by accepting his leadership; after his death those who wished to remain within the tradition then had to retain a kind of unity that would be social as well as intellectual. That is, those who now remained within the mainstream of psychoanalysis had to be free to modify their views (as Freud would have done were he still alive), but they felt some obligation to show that they followed Freud's main teachings both as to method and theory, enough at least to preserve unity among themselves. This has inevitably resulted in a certain amount of in-group rigidity and out-group antagonism, understandable in view of the social history of psychoanalysis during Freud's lifetime. Seldom has a man with a new scientific message been greeted with as much antagonism and hostility as Freud met, from both medical and non-medical groups. This is part of the social history that we have to understand if we are to study the evolution of psychoanalysis as a science. Post-Freudian psychoanalysis has its own social history, too, with in-group and out-group relations internal to psychoanalysis. The nature of these relationships, in the light of their history, will some day contribute an interesting chapter to the sociology of knowledge. There is no point at present in passing judgment on these matters, except to note that there is flux. For example, in several large cities psychoanalytic institutes have fissioned into separate groups differing on some matters of doctrine, yet leaders at the national level have managed to keep these factions united within the American Psychoanalytic Association, with graduates of the separate institutes validated as psychoanalysts. Thus the groundwork exists for the eventual reduction of the barriers between the groups that now find themselves somewhat in conflict.

In order to proceed with an assessment of the status of psychoanalysis as a science today, some choices have to be made. I have chosen to discuss what the analysts call their *metapsychology* rather than their theory and technique of psychoanalytic treatment of patients. There fortunately exist two papers providing information about contemporary psychoanalytic thinking within the social tradition of classical psychoanalysis. One is a long chapter by David Rapaport in Koch's *Psychology: A Study of a Science* [12]. The chapter is entitled "The structure of psychoanalytic theory: a systematizing attempt" [17]. Prepared after this chapter, but appearing in print at about the same time, is a paper also by Rapaport, in collaboration with Merton Gill, entitled "The points of view and assumptions of metapsychology" [18]. These papers are serious efforts to state the structure of psychoanalysis "from the inside," and can be taken as a fair specimen of the best of current thinking among those who feel themselves at home within the classical Freudian tradition, while yet ready for new developments ahead. My initial task becomes a review and commentary upon these statements. I shall lean primarily upon the paper by Rapaport and Gill [18].

Psychoanalytic Metapsychology

In undertaking their formal statement of the propositions of metapsychology, Rapaport and Gill begin by distinguishing four kinds of propositions within psychoanalysis: empirical propositions, specific psychoanalytic propositions, propositions of the general psychoanalytic theory, and propositions stating the metapsychological assumptions. Their own examples follow.

Empirical Propositions. "Around the fourth year of life boys regard their fathers as rivals."

This is empirical in the sense that it could be investigated directly by available methods, and is thus either demonstrably true or false on the basis of directly relevant evidence.

Specific Psychoanalytic Propositions. "The solution of the Oedipal situation is a decisive determinant of character formation and pathology."

This is a step removed from direct empirical study because it implies some substantiated theory regarding the Oedipus complex, character formation, and pathology. It is specific in that its reference is to a set of events taking place at one time in the life cycle. Even though the proposition were confirmed, its explanatory value would be limited to this set of events.

General Psychoanalytic Proposition. "Structure formation by means of identifications and anticathexes explains theoretically the consequence of the 'decline of the Oedipus complex.'"

Note that this proposition says something more about the preceding one, placing it in the larger context of identification and cathexes, that will be used to explain other events as well. Hence this proposition is of more general scope.

Metapsychological Proposition. "The propositions of the general psychoanalytic theory which explain the Oedipal situation and the decline of the Oedipus complex involve dynamic, economic, structural, genetic, and adaptive assumptions."

This is, of course, the most general statement of all.

In their paper, Rapaport and Gill attempt to limit themselves to the metapsychological propositions in relation to general psychoanalytic propositions, avoiding the two levels of specific psychoanalytic propositions and the empirical propositions. The metapsychological theory that they present, already hinted at in the illustration, can be restated as follows: *The psychoanalytic explanation of any psychological phenomenon must include propositions reflecting the dynamic, economic, structural, genetic, and adaptive points of view.*

Those familiar with psychoanalytic theory will recall that Freud formulated three metapsychological points of view, which he called dynamic, topographic, and economic. Rapaport and Gill, in order to make explicit what was implicit in Freud, and to include current developments within psychoanalytic ego psychology, accepted the three points of view of Freud (modifying topographic to structural, in view of changes during Freud's lifetime), and added two points of view (genetic and adaptive). These five points of view are in some respects five separate models. Let us see how each of them is characterized.

1. *The Dynamic Point of View.* This is perhaps the most widely understood aspect of psychoanalysis, and gives psychoanalysis its designation as a dynamic psychology. The general psychoanalytic propositions of the dynamic point of view employ the concepts of *unconscious forces and conflicts,* and the concept of *drive or instinct.* Contemporary psychoanalysts commonly refer only to the two specific innate drives of sex and aggression; other drives (if any) are thought to be derivatives of these.

The metapsychological assumptions within this point of view are thus summarized by Rapaport and Gill:

The *dynamic* point of view demands that the psychoanalytic explanation of any psychological phenomenon includes propositions concerning the psychological forces involved in the phenomenon.

The major assumptions are:

a. There are psychological forces.
b. The effect of simultaneously acting psychological forces may be the simple resultant of the work of each of these forces.
c. The effect of simultaneously acting psychological forces may not be the simple resultant of the work of each of these forces.

It is evident that these assumptions are a mere scaffolding upon which a more precise theory has to be built. For example, the third assumption as stated negates the second, so that the two can be combined into this statement: "The effect of simultaneously acting psychological forces may *or may not* be the simple resultant of the work of each of these forces." In this form the statement is a mere truism, but of course there is more intended. The third assumption actually implies something like this: under some circumstances the effect of simultaneously acting forces is modified by drive fusion and overdetermination; under these circumstances the effect is not a simple resultant of the work of each of these forces. This statement draws in, however, some notions from general psychoanalytic theory (e.g., drive fusion and overdetermination), and hence belongs with a next elaboration of the theory rather than with the metapsychological assumptions at the level of generality that Rapaport and Gill seek to hold.

2. *The Economic Point of View.* This is the point of view that all behaviour is regulated by psychological energy, and concerns the principles by which psychological energy is disposed of. The term "economic" means "economical," that is, that psychological energies operate along paths of least effort, leading toward tension reduction and homeostasis.

Psychoanalytic theory when approached from this point of view has to do with the processes by which tension is reduced by energy discharge either directly or through devious means, or by suspending energy discharge until conditions are more favourable. The basic concepts here are primary and secondary process, wish fulfilment, cathexis and countercathexis. There are additional related concepts of binding and neutralization of psychological energy. The level of concepts represented by primary and secondary processes and cathexes belongs, however, to the general psychoanalytic theory, rather than to the metapsychological assumptions.

The metapsychological assumptions are that there are psychological energies, that they follow laws of conservation and entropy, and that these energies are subject to transformations that increase or decrease their entropic tendency.

The use of physical analogies in the assumptions of both the dynamic and economic points of view requires discussion, to which we shall return.

3. *The Structural Point of View.* The structural point of view replaced the earlier topographic one when Freud introduced the tripartite division of id, ego, and superego to displace (or supplement) the emphasis upon unconscious, preconscious, and conscious topography. More recently there has developed within classical psychoanalysis an emphasis known as ego-psychology in which various kinds of structure are proposed: e.g., defense-, control-, and means-structures. The control- and means-structures are considered to be relatively autonomous structures within the ego, and thus part of the conflict-free sphere [8].

I shall not repeat the formal language of the assumptions with respect to structure. The main points are that structures are configurations with a slow rate of change, that these structures have a hierarchical order, and that mental processes take place within, between, and by means of these structures.

4. *The Genetic Point of View.* The course of individual development is very important within psychoanalytic theory, and emphasis upon early

childhood is one of the most influential contributions of psychoanalysis to general psychology. The developmental point of view was so taken for granted within psychoanalysis that it has not traditionally been separately formulated as parallel to the dynamic, economic, and structural viewpoints. The general theory of psychosexual development is well known, in which the child passes through the anal, oral, phallic, latency, and genital stages on the way to maturity. This aspect of the theory is the source of some controversy between those who insist that the crises related to these stages are primarily rooted in the nature of the organism (the more classical position), and those who attribute a major influence to the impact of the culture in which the child is reared (the more dissident position). The terminology is somewhat unfortunate, because "genetic" means ontogenetic or epigenetic, and not gene-controlled as in the more familiar current use of the term. However, we may continue here to use the term as synonymous with developmental.

The metapsychological assumptions of the genetic point of view are that all psychological phenomena have an origin and development, originating in innate givens that mature according to an epigenetic ground plan. The earlier forms of a psychological phenomenon, though superseded by later forms, remain potentially active; at any point in psychological history the totality of potentially active forms codetermines all psychological phenomena.

It may be noted, in passing, that the level of generality of these assumptions is such that the content of general psychoanalytic theory could be greatly changed without violating them. For example, psychosexual development could be replaced by some other content without violating any of these assumptions.

5. *The Adaptive Point of View.* This relative newcomer to psychoanalytic theory permits statements that cover most of the ground familiar to functional psychology, and frees the psychoanalyst from the need to find a libidinal explanation for all behaviour. Among the conceptions are the organism's preparedness (through evolution) for an average expectable environment, "apparatuses" that are essentially abilities by which to cope with the environment, dependence upon external stimulation, achieved relative autonomy from the environment.

The adaptive assumptions include statements concerning adaptation to internal states, to the physical and social environment, and the mutual adaptations between man and environment.

This completes the listing of the five points of view and their assumptions, according to Rapaport and Gill. This summarization cannot do justice to their treatment, which at many points includes reservations, nor to the sources they have used in arriving at the assumptions. They illustrate each of the assumptions by reference to the psychoanalytic theory of affects; for the sake of brevity, these references have been ignored in my summary. Only a reading of their original paper can fill in these gaps.

Rapaport and Gill concluded their paper by a statement of confidence that the five points of view are likely to prove necessary and sufficient "to a degree which recommends that they should be accepted — for the time being — as the framework of psychoanalytic metapsychology." They felt less sure about their assumptions: "It is not yet possible to assess whether all these assumptions are necessary, and whether this set of assumptions is sufficient — when coupled with observational data — to yield the existing body of psychoanalytic propositions."

Five Models or One?

What is implied in the assertion that a psychoanalytic explanation requires a minimum of one proposition from each of the five points of view? It could mean that this is a five-dimensional system, with the coordinates of any event being the five yielded by the dimensions. The dimensions are not of this kind, however, and this interpretation can be rejected. A second possibility is that there are five independent models. An event can be explained according to *any one* of the models, but the explanation has not become exhaustive until it has been explained according to *every* model. That this is possibly the intent of Rapaport and Gill appears to be demonstrated in the empirical use of the five-model scheme in the interpretation of hypnotic phenomena by Gill and Brenman [7]. Each point of view in turn serves for the characterization of what happens within hypnosis; the story is completed when the last of the five points of view has been discussed. The models of course overlap, and references to other points of view are not excluded when a given view provides the background for discussion. The manner of the interaction is not specified, however, and this is one of the weaknesses of the Rapaport and Gill presentation. It is not clear, for example, whether non-interchangeable kinds of information emerge from each model, or whether, by appropriate transformations, the yield of one of the models could be made more powerful by using information from the others.[1]

We have Rapaport saying of the points of view:

"The 'points of view' seem to be the equivalents of 'principles' in psychoanalytic theory. Yet their form shows that the time to examine them one by one, for their long-range significance, has not yet arrived. Instead of formal principles we will present here a few general conceptions, which compound the various points of view, and which seem likely to survive whatever the fate of the more specific ingredients of the psychoanalytic theory should prove to be" [17, p. 152]. His discussion then proceeds at a level quite different from that of the Rapaport-Gill paper.

The vacillation between the points of view as models, as principles, as components to be compounded, is understandable in view of the complexity and looseness of contemporary psychoanalytic formulations.

It is in accordance with good scientific practice to seek for principles of

---

[1]A statement that "*all* psychoanalytic propositions involve *all* metapsychological points of view" does not clarify the status of the separate points of view.

unification, and I have therefore examined the five viewpoints to see if some sub-grouping might be plausible. One principle that appears to be a possible guide for combining the five models into a smaller number is the *time-span* of the processes to which the models refer. The reference of the dynamic and economic models is to events which have primarily a *short* time-span: the resolution of forces, and the transformation of energy into work. The reference of the other models is to events with a *long* time-span: genetic, structural, and adaptive models refer to processes developing over the life-span, changing slowly, and leading in the end to the contemporary situation which the dynamic-economic model is called upon to explain. A first step in simplification would be to unite the dynamic-economic models into one and the genetic-structural-adaptive models into a second one.[2]

If there are just two models, one historical covering a long time-span, one historical covering a short time-span in the present, then both the independence and the interrelationship of the models are easier to comprehend. Let me give an analogy from problem-solving. The *historical* understanding of problem-solving requires that we know what the problem-solver brings to the situation from his past learning, what relevant information he has, what techniques he knows, what attitudes he has toward himself as a problem-solver. We can make certain assertions or predictions on the basis of this knowledge. The *ahistorical* understanding of problem-solving requires that we know the manner in which our problem-solver makes use of his past experience in relation to the present, how he analyzes the problem, selects the relevant information and techniques, how the present display of the problem influences what he is able to do. There are many relationships here that cannot be discussed in purely historical terms. One way of putting this is that sufficient past experience to solve a problem does not guarantee that the subject will solve the problem, unless the present demands upon him are made in an appropriate manner, and unless he has his past experiences available in a form suitable for use.

Translating this example into the language of the clinic, we might say that an individual's relations to his parents in childhood were such as to produce an abiding structure of anxiety-dependency. Now he takes a job in which the boss reminds him (unconsciously) of his father, the anxiety (based on the dynamics of transference) overwhelms him, and he develops neurotic symptoms. The abiding structure is a historical fact, to be explained by the genetic-structural-adaptive model; the breakdown with the present boss is to be explained by the dynamic-economic model. Obviously the two interact in that we understand the individual's present behaviour in relation both to his life history and to the provocative circumstances of the present.

The separation of the two models is a practical convenience because data

---

[2]Hartmann and Kris [9] have also recognized that the explanatory propositions of psychoanalysis classify chiefly into two groups: genetic and dynamic.

come both from the life-history and from the present, though as a scientific enterprise the two models should be combined. If a single equation is written to describe what is happening in the present, it can have terms in it that represent the residues from the past, as well as terms that represent the present. Thus Hull's equations for reaction potential [11] include the simultaneous interactions of habits (including generalized habits) built up in the past, along with the drive state, stimulus dynamisms, and so on, in the present. There is no formal obstacle to including historical and ahistorical data in the same equation.

For convenience, we may discuss the five Rapaport-Gill models as though they were two, turning aside from the problem of their eventual integration into one.

The Dynamic-Economic Model

Some contemporary model of this kind is needed to deal with the problem of conflict and its resolution, and the energetics of behaviour, including facilitation, inhibition, distortion, symbolization.

The physical metaphors as used at present are unsatisfactory, but perhaps they can be built upon to do what the models are intended to do. The physics is not literal: there is no mass for force to accelerate, there is no distance by which to determine how much work a force has done, there is no dissipation of energy into unavailable heat by which to make precise the meaning of entropy; when energy is transformed it is not changed from potential to kinetic [19]. Non-psychoanalytic psychologists have also used physical metaphors, such as threshold and drive, not out of the vocabulary of systematic physical science, or force, distance, direction, as by Kurt Lewin, with more of the flavour of systematic physics. When the vocabulary remains too close to that of strictly physical science, the metaphors are strained and the result has usually been unsatisfactory [14, 16].

Uneasiness with the quantitative concepts of the dynamic-economic model has been expressed by psychoanalysts. Thus Kubie [13] states:

> "Assumptions as to changes in quantities of energy are admissible only if alterations in the pattern of intrapsychic forces are ruled out. A failure to recognize this has made all so-called economic formulations a species of ad hoc speculative allegory in quantitative terms."

Note that this statement of Kubie's not only is critical of the economic theory, but indicates clearly that the dynamic-economic models must be thought of at one and the same time.

Colby [1] has given thoughtful consideration to these problems. He finds the hydraulic analogy used to describe psychological energy (i.e., a reservoir with pipes to regulate the flow) entirely unsatisfactory, and builds his own cyclic-circular model. He recognizes that his energy concept is actually far removed from the physicist's concept: "Our psychic energy provides a synoptic way of talking about activity and change" [1, p. 27f.]. While energy within his system has some descriptive characteristics (pulsation, period, synchrony, etc.), it is transported through the system essentially as a modifiable message, and its "energetic" aspects are minimal. He is struggling with genuine problems within the psychoanalytic description of events and processes, and finds some sort of "feedback" model essential. Without going into his solution of the problems, we can here merely indicate that this is a serious effort to find an alternative to the classical model. It supports the position that the status of the dynamic-economic metapsychology of contemporary psychoanalysis is very provisional.

The Structural-Genetic-Adaptive Model

Freud's tripartite structure — id, ego, superego — is a heuristic convenience in the discussion of typical intrapsychic conflicts. The impulsivity of the id, the intellectual realism of the ego, and the moral flavour of the superego epitomize ways of talking about stresses within the person that are familiar in the Hebraic-Christian tradition. Thus the spirit may be willing while the flesh is weak, one may start out on a course of action but be troubled by a nagging conscience. Anyone raised in Western culture can easily understand the id-ego-superego conflicts, at least in their broad outlines.

This simplicity, while an initial advantage, rises up as an obstacle when the parts of the personality become reified as almost three persons, the id telling the ego what to do, the ego actively fighting the id, the superego being a party, too, to the internal battles. Actually, as Colby says, "its simplicity (i.e., that of the tripartite scheme) makes it insufficient to conceptualize specifically enough the manifold functions of psychic activity" [1, p. 77].

The id, ego, superego structural divisions have been supplemented more recently chiefly by differentiations within the ego. The ego-psychology of Hartmann has multiplied the structures within the ego, calling them "ego-apparatuses." Some of these apparatuses are said to rest on constitutional givens (e.g., perception, motility, intelligence) [8]. Other secondary apparatuses develop through interaction with the environment; both kinds may be relatively autonomous, that is, free of control through the instinctual drives. These ego-apparatuses and structures are very numerous, and I have not found a systematic list of them, if indeed, such a list is possible. Apparently some primary-process defense mechanisms such as displacement, condensation, substitution, symbolization, repression, isolation, reaction formation, and projection, can be included among ego-apparatuses or structures [17, p. 154]. Other structures include control- and means-structures, which are not defenses.

The acceptance of conflict-free ego structures has been viewed as a great advance within classical psychoanalysis, permitting not only the greater differentiation of the structural viewpoint, but the addition of the adaptive viewpoint. The psychoanalyst no longer faces the burden of explaining everything in terms of one or two primordial drives; he can now accept the drive theory as he has always done, but can supplement it with the structures of the conflict-free ego sphere, and thus comprehend the problems of perception, problem-solving, esthetics, play, that were forced into a somewhat artificial perspective when everything had to be derived from drive. The concept of sublimation no longer has to be stretched to cover everything that appears on the surface to be non-sexual. While the multiplication of apparatuses and structures within the ego gives this new freedom, some of the unifying value of the older structural theory has been sacrificed. This is probably inevitable when a theory is in transition, and seeks to encompass new facts under new assumptions.

Because the structural conceptions relate to enduring aspects of the personality, aspects with slow rates of change, these conceptions are intimately bound to the developmental ones represented by the genetic and adaptive viewpoints. Erikson [3] has combined the psychosexual states of classical psychoanalysis with adaptive crises associated with each of these stages, thus integrating the genetic and the adaptive viewpoints as these are characterized by Rapaport and Gill.

While Erikson takes off from Freud, accepting the psychosexual stages associated with the prominence of certain body orifices as the individual matures, he attempts to go beyond Freud and to meet the problem of interaction with the environment, showing how the resolution of each developmental crisis affects the manner in which later crises are met. He introduces some stages beyond the Freudian genital stage, or perhaps as differentiations within it, with the three successive polarities in adolescence and adult life of ego identity vs. role diffusion, generativity vs. self-absorption, and integrity vs. despair and disgust.

Erikson's proposals are insightful, sensitive to the human situation, and provide important supplements to the encapsulated and intrapsychic flavor of the more traditional psychosexual theory of psychogenesis. Yet from the point of view of a logical or systematic plan of human development, intended to hold across cultures, it lacks criteria by which its stages are distinguished and according to which the major problems associated with each stage have been identified.

In general, examination of the structural-genetic-adaptive model indicates that, like the dynamic-economic model, it is a very provisional one, although useful in giving direction to the kind of tighter theory eventually to be achieved.

The Validation of Psychoanalytic Propositions

There have been many attempts to submit theoretical propositions from psychoanalysis to experimental tests, either of a quasi-clinical sort (as in projective tests and hypnosis) or in non-clinical tests (as in studies of memory, animal behaviour, child development in other cultures, etc.). While indeed many of these have come out rather favourably to psychoanalytic conceptions, the general attitude of the classical psychoanalyst has often been one of skepticism, if not of hostility, to these attempts. Why should this be?

1. The first reason for a negative attitude by the psychoanalyst toward these attempts is his confidence that the psychoanalytic method is the only appropriate method for revealing some of the relationships. A depth psychology, it is said, requires a depth method for its study. The only person qualified to interpret evidence is the one who has himself been through a psychoanalysis, and is thus familiar first-hand with the phenomena. Thus psychoanalysis is needed to produce the phenomena and a psychoanalyst is needed to interpret them.

We may accept this objection to studies by non-psychoanalysts, but with two qualifications. First, it applies to *some* aspects of the psychoanalytic theory only. We need to become clearer about which aspects require the analyst and the analytic method, and which do not. Second, when a psychoanalyst obtains the data and assists in its interpretation, then third persons (including non-psychoanalysts as well as other psychoanalysts) may be helpful in arranging for critical hypothesis testing.

2. The second reason for a negative attitude by some psychoanalysts toward empirical attempts at testing psychoanalytic propositions is the complexity of psychoanalytic theory, and hence the fear that tests of separate propositions will be either trivial or irrelevant. According to Rapaport, most of those who try to test the theory either do not understand it, or they ignore what they know. "The overwhelming majority of experiments designed to test psychoanalytic propositions display a blatant lack of interest in the meaning, within the theory of psychoanalysis, of the propositions tested" [17, p. 142].

This second argument has some force, but it can be overstated. To be sure there have been those who interpreted the Freudian theory of forgetting to mean that unpleasant things are forgotten and pleasant things remembered; then they went about constructing lists of words including quinine (unpleasant) and sugar (pleasant) to test the Freudian theory. This sort of thing has not happened much in the last few years, as the knowledge of psychoanalytic theory has become more sophisticated.

The reason that the argument may be overstated is that psychoanalytic propositions at all levels lack the tightness of conceptual integration that makes the very general test possible. Hence more low-level propositional testing is in order before the larger system can be tightened up for a testing within this larger network of theory.

The empirical propositions to be tested are not necessarily trivial, and they usually imply some of the special or general psychoanalytic propositions as these are outlined by Rapaport and Gill. For example, it is not easy to get good evidence as to the age ranges within which boys are especially rivalrous with their fathers. This information (and other of the same general sort) is important to test some of the inferences from the more general theory.

We are led into a paradox when we insist that the superstructure of psychoanalytic theory (including metapsychology) ought to be accepted before we attempt to test theory. Sophistication demands that we do test theory.

The idea that a single hypothesis can be disconfirmed by evidence, but not confirmed, is logically sound, but scientifically trivial. A single hypothesis, embedded in a theory, can be neither confirmed nor disconfirmed in any important sense without knowing more about the theory. That is, one needs to know the interactions: for example, under one circumstance praise will improve learned performance, under another it will handicap performance. The proposition "praise improves performance" is thus not established by a score-card, in which it more often improves than handicaps, but rather by additional propositions which specify when it does one and when it does the other. Thus we test what Cronbach and Meehl [2] call the *nomothetic network*; we do not test one proposition at a time, or, if we do, we do not draw our conclusions from these tests in isolation from each other. The paradox arises because the psychoanalytic theory is not quite good enough for systematic testing. Hence the best we can do is some theory construction, integrating a few of the propositions that appear consonant with the general theory. Then it is *these* propositions that we test. These smaller models, or miniature systems, as Hull called them, will not reconcile the devotee to the whole system, but is the best that can be done at this stage.

Who is to do the testing? For some purposes the psychoanalytic interview is the best source. It may yield inferences that can be checked in other ways, however, and if experimental and clinical evidence agrees, so much the better all around. For example, the adult consequences of loss of a parent in childhood [10] can be studied through interviews with the adult, but these will raise conjectures about what went on at the time of parent loss. These conjectures can be studied by doing some investigations of children who have recently lost a parent. Thus the nature of the hypotheses being tested will often rule on the best method of studying them. There need be no *a priori* decision that the best method will be the psychoanalytic interview, or observational studies of children, or experimental studies. The nature of the hypotheses, and availability of methods and of facilities, will guide investigations within psychoanalysis as they do in any other field of science.

There are some inhibiting factors within professional psychoanalysis that tend to reduce the research productivity of the analysts themselves. One is the long course of training, so that training is typically completed at about age 40, when families are established, obligations are great, and research initiative is on the decline. Another is the nature of a practice involving long and expensive commitments to aid the suffering, so that the analyst must have faith in what he is doing. This leads to a conservative tendency with respect to change of doctrine or method, which, while not to be condemned, is less favourable to research than a situation lacking such commitments. The training institutes have tended to neglect research in their training programs; in the recent report on training in psychoanalysis [15] covering 460 pages, but four pages were devoted to research. Only three of the 14 institutes bring research at all prominently into the training pattern. The job of consolidating psychoanalysis as a science will continue to call for the collaboration of others if it is to move ahead with any rapidity.

The reconstruction of psychoanalytic theory can be expected to take time. It would be undesirable to throw present formulations aside, and to start all over again, for too much would be lost, even though some communication today is by way of rather loose metaphor. The gradual reconstruction may in time produce drastic revisions, but that possibility does not mean that these revisions have to be made all at once. The theory has enough body that investigators can choose segments of the theory within which to work out smaller models to be coordinated with others as the work advances. There are a number of avenues available to them besides those that open up only within the psychoanalytic interview. Among these are the study of child development and child rearing (including studies by anthropologists), studies of perception, learning, and memory (especially where there is ambiguity and perhaps conflict), projective tests, hypnosis, and the study of sleep and dreams. A great many pertinent investigations are now under way in these fields, and we have every reason to expect a reconstruction of psychoanalysis to emerge from them. It will be a reconstruction rather than a validation, for the very act of validation requires reconstruction. In the process a better science will emerge, with firmer data encompassed within a more elegant system.

References

[1] Colby, K. M. *Energy and Structure in Psychoanalysis.* New York: Ronald Press, 1955.

[2] Cronbach, L. J., and P. E. Meehl. Construct validity in psychological tests. *Psychological Bulletin,* Vol. 52 (1955), pp. 281–302.

[3] Erikson, E. H. Identity and the life cycle. *Psychological Issues,* 1, No. 1. New York: International University Press, 1959.

[4] Frenkel-Brunswik, Else. Psychoanalysis and the unity of science. *Proceedings of the American Academy of Arts and Sciences,* Vol. 80 (1954), pp. 271–350.

[5] Freud, S. *The Interpretation of Dreams,* 1900. New York: Basic Books, 1955.

[6] Freud, S. *The Origins of Psychoanalysis: Letters to Wilhelm Fliess, Drafts, and Notes:* 1887–1902. New York: Basic Books, 1954.

[7] Gill, M. M., and Margaret Brenman. *Hypnosis and Related States: Psychoanalytic Studies in Regression.* New York: International University Press, 1959.

[8] Hartmann, H. *Ego Psychology and the Problem of Adaptation,* 1939. New York: International University Press, 1958.

[9] Hartmann, H., and E. Kris. The genetic approach in psychoanalysis. In *The Psychoanalytic Study of the Child.* Vol. 1. New York: International University Press, 1945, pp. 11–29.

[10] Hilgard, Josephine R., Martha F. Newman, and Fern Fisk. Strength of adult ego following childhood bereavement. *American Journal of Orthopsychiatry,* Vol. 30 (1960). pp. 788–798.

[11] Hull, C. L. *A Behavior System.* New Haven: Yale University Press, 1952.

[12] Koch, S. *Psychology: A Study of a Science.* Vol. 3. *Formulations of the Person and the Social Context.* New York: McGraw-Hill, 1959.

[13] Kubie, L. S. The fallacious use of quantitative concepts in dynamic psychology. *Psychoanalytic Quarterly,* Vol. 16 (1947), pp. 507–518.

[14] LEEPER, R. *Lewin's Topological and Vector Psychology: A Digest and a Critique.* Eugene, Oregon: University of Oregon Press, 1943.

[15] LEWIN, B. D., and HELEN ROSS. *Psychoanalytic Education in the United States.* New York: Norton, 1960.

[16] LONDON, I. D. Psychologists' misuse of the auxiliary concepts of physics and mathematics. *Psychological Review,* Vol. 51 (1944), pp. 266–291.

[17] RAPAPORT, D. The structure of psychoanalytic theory: a systematizing attempt. In Koch, S. (Ed.), 1959, pp. 55–183. (Also in *Psychological Issues,* 2, No. 6, 1960.)

[18] RAPAPORT, D., and M. M. GILL. The points of view and assumptions of metapsychology. *The International Journal of Psychoanalysis,* Vol. 40 (1959), pp. 153–162.

[19] SKINNER, B. F. Critique of psychoanalytic concepts and theories. In FEIGL, H., and M. SCRIVEN (Eds.) *The Foundations of Science and the Concepts of Psychology and Psychoanalysis.* Minneapolis: University of Minnesota Press, 1956, pp. 77–87.

Symposium on Alternative Approaches to the Theory of Choice

A STOCHASTIC MODEL FOR THE ACT OF CHOICE

R. J. AUDLEY
University College, London, England

I would like to preface my remarks by thanking the organizers of this symposium for asking me to participate in it. My pleasure in receiving the invitation is enhanced by the fact that I am only required to present an approach to the theory of choice, implying the discussion of intentions rather than achievements. This is a requirement which nicely matches the present state of my speculations.

To turn first to the general notions and beliefs which appear to motivate the present approach. These can be crudely summarized in the proposition that the basic unit of observation in psychology is a single act of choice by a given subject. This is a bald and perhaps naïvely worded proposition which requires some commentary and qualification. One might say that it was a trite statement, but a glance at psychological literature is sufficient to disabuse one of such an optimistic notion.

Firstly, a word or two as to the emphasis upon individual subjects. There is nothing particularly novel in this. Many writers have argued for a greater study of data obtained from individual subjects. The core of the argument is that if one is going to establish general laws of behaviour, it is necessary to validate these upon the individual members of the population under investigation. This is not to deny the value of studies where, for many technical reasons, groups of experimental subjects under different conditions are compared by statistical procedures. Such group-measure comparisons are indispensable in determining what variables are important in the control of behaviour. But where relations between different variables are under consideration, and especially where quantitative theoretical predictions, purporting to be of the nature of general laws, are involved, the group measure comparisons may be inadequate and misleading. It must be granted that there are great technical limitations on the extent to which suitable individual data can be obtained and reliably summarized for inferential purposes, but this does not validate attempts to establish general laws upon the basis of inappropriate group measures. It merely sets limits to the kinds of statements and inferences which can be made in these trying circumstances.

Turning now to the single act of choice. The earlier somewhat dogmatically formulated proposition was not intended to imply that a given choice act is not capable of finer empirical analysis and in fact, later in this paper, possible ways of carrying out such an enterprise will be discussed. Nor is it supposed that a whole sequence of temporally discrete acts by an individual may not together constitute a meaningful unit for the descriptive summary of behaviour. The point of the remark is that in our search for an understanding of the organization of behaviour, the experimental study of this organization invariably requires it to be approached by means of some act of choice on the part of the experimental subject. Thus in making the organization explicit, we use as a kind of measuring instrument an act of choice, and the properties of this instrument are not sufficiently well understood.

It is not, of course, suggested that an act of choice is outside the general organization of behaviour, nor that all choice situations will necessarily exhibit the same properties. The point is that the common use of a choice situation imposes upon the data features which must be rather specific to this commonly selected experimental agent.

As an illustration of the role played by acts of choice in experimentation, two studies by Shipley [5, 6] and collaborators seem apposite. In the first, subjects were presented with pairs of colours and were asked upon each presentation to select the colour they most preferred. Among other findings, the authors report that the time taken to make a choice was inversely related to the general preference for the pair of colours presented. Subjects, that is, were quicker at deciding between two generally preferred colours than between a pair whose members were low on their scale of preference. This result might, of course, be a function only of the affective level of the material for a subject, but then again it might be purely reflecting judgmental processes. In a second experiment, the authors asked subjects to choose the least-preferred colour. Under these new circumstances, speed of choice was again related to the general level of preference for each colour-pair, but the relation was the reverse of that found in the first experiment. Choices were made more rapidly in the presence of two generally unpreferred colours. In this very simple example, the importance of considering the nature of the choice act demanded of a subject is clearly demonstrated.[1] Similar types of observational problems may also be found in the earlier literature on the use of two- and three-category psychophysical procedures for studying human sensory discrimination.

[1] Subsequent to the symposium, it has been found that similar results may be found in simple discrimination tasks. For example, in discriminating two stimuli of differing brightness, subjects were quicker at reporting which was the lighter of two bright stimuli than they were in reporting which was the darker, and this difference in speed diminished as the average brightness level of the stimuli was reduced.

Furthermore, when theoretical propositions are formulated concerning any kind of behaviour it is necessary to include hypotheses concerning the nature of the processes of choice. It is surprising to discover how arbitrary and little-considered these hypotheses can be. Yet they undoubtedly play a very important role in the nature of theoretical predictions. What in fact is being argued here is that our theorizing should be more complete and fully extend to explicit statements concerning the nature of the situations in which our subjects are experimentally studied. It is not good enough to make some general prediction, and test it in terms of some arbitrarily adopted measurement. The theory should also specify the nature of the measurement.

This preliminary polemic serves to introduce the main section of the present paper and was intended to make this appear a not entirely esoteric endeavour. For the present work is not immediately directed towards providing a conceptual scheme relating variations in stimulus conditions to the ensuing variations in observed responses, which is the classical approach of the psychologist. Rather, at the present stage in speculation, the intention is to outline a possible description of behaviour at a choice point with specific emphasis upon the relations between the various types of measure which can be observed in human and animal choice behaviour.

Thus the approach is concerned with the extent to which it is possible to explore, both conceptually and experimentally, the nature of the processes involved in a choice between alternatives where it can be assumed that neither the subject nor the environment is changing in any way. This, it must be admitted, is an ideal situation not likely to be met in experimental reality, but perhaps approximations to this ideal can be found, and it serves as a suitable starting place for speculating about the theoretical description of behaviour. In short, the question asked is "What can be said about a single act of choice?"

In describing choice behaviour there are several variables which are usually available. These might be said to fall into two categories. Firstly, those involved in the description of the primary response to a choice situation, the alternative selected. Secondly, descriptions of the responses which the subject makes to his primary choice, or which accompany this. The first kind are most commonly employed, the three principal ones being as follows:

(a) Relative response frequency — the proportion of occasions on which a particular alternative is selected.

(b) Response time — the time taken for a definite choice to be made.

(c) The number of vicarious trial and error responses (VTE's) — the number of vacillations between the alternatives before a definite choice is made.

In the second category, where the descriptor is often a verbal statement by the subject there are such variables as (a) confidence in the correctness of a given choice, and (b) an assessment of the subjective difficulty of the choice problem.

Now it is reasonable to assume as a starting point that these variables are all functions of a single underlying process. The simple stochastic model which is to be presented is only intended as an initial working hypothesis to assist in the exploration of this possibility and its consequences. It is not expected that the simple assumptions upon which the model is based will alone suffice to provide a satisfactory description of behaviour in a diversity of choice situations. Each situation will have unique properties which have to be taken into account before this can be achieved, and in any case the point of the present approach is to investigate the unique as well as the common properties of choice situations. For this reason derivations from the model have been restricted to a certain class of situations, where one might expect the least need for an abundance of specific assumptions. This class consists of experiments where outside knowledge of the outcome or correctness of a response is not available to the subject at all, or not until after the choice has been made. Thus, for example, most ordinary disjunctive reaction time studies are not considered, because the subject in these experiments can match his response with a known requirement. The class is, however, not a trivial one and includes among others discrimination experiments, including most psychophysical procedures and also studies of preference and conflict.

The following remarks concern the hypothetical events which are supposed to take place during a single act of choice.

It is first assumed that *for given stimulus and organismic conditions, there is associated with each possible choice response a single parameter. This determines the probability that in a small interval of time* $(t, t+\Delta t)$ *there will occur what has been termed an "implicit" response of the kind with which the parameter is associated.*

This, in essence, supposes each response is being emitted in implicit form at a characteristic mean rate. If there were, for example, two alternative responses A and B, then there would be implicit responses, say, a and b, with associated rates of responding α and β. No specific interpretation is given to the term "implicit response," which is left conveniently open to alternative interpretations.

The second assumption is that *an overt choice response occurs when a run of* k *"implicit" responses of a given kind appears, this run being uninterrupted by occurrences of implicit responses of other kinds.*

For example, if $k = 2$, then the events supposed to be going on during a choice between overt responses, A and B, might be as shown in Fig. 1.

The original conception of the model was as a kind of behavioural synapse, with the uninterrupted sequence of implicit responses mimicking temporal and perhaps spatial summation.

There seems no point in presenting the mathematical derivations of the various properties of the model, which, at least for the case when $k = 2$, have been committed to paper elsewhere [1]. It will suffice to make some general comments about these derivations.

The probabilities of the overt occurrence of each alternative response, and the distribution of response times associated with each response may be readily derived. Furthermore, if the implicit responses are identified with

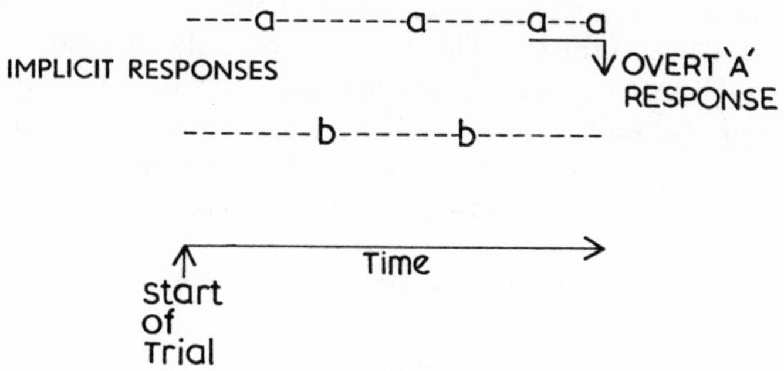

FIG. 1

some kind of orientating or preparatory response, then the distribution of VTE's which would be expected to precede the appearance of each type of overt response can also be determined. It is also suggested that the sequence of implicit responses preceding an overt choice might serve as a basis for the analysis of a subject's judgment of confidence in his selected response. For example, it would seem likely that perfect confidence in a judgment might arise in trials where implicit responses of only one kind emerged and one seems to be almost tautological in suggesting that doubt might reflect a considerable amount of vacillation between the various implicit alternatives before the overt response occurs. Again, the distributions of the descriptors of the first kind to be expected to accompany the various degrees or categories of confidence are fully specified. In short, although this is a very elementary model it does determine the nature of the distribution of several response variables and provide predictions concerning the relations between them.

To turn then to empirical evidence on these matters. There are several general kinds of predictions which can be considered. The first kind is concerned with the description of the results obtained from sequences of near-identical trials, for example a near-threshold discrimination between two stimuli. This is initially the type of empirical problem with which the present approach to choice behaviour is particularly concerned. Qualitatively, the model is in reasonable agreement with data from these situations. For example, the most frequent response is expected to have the quickest response time, and confident responses are expected to be quicker and more accurate than others, expectations which find support in the literature and for which the speaker has also obtained confirmatory data.

The second kind of prediction which can be made concerns the way in which the various response measures change with each other as stimulus conditions are altered. For example, data obtained from sets of discrimination problems of various levels of difficulty. Again, qualitatively the properties of the model are in reasonable agreement with experimental data. In this type of prediction, complications arise in the comparison of time measures, and additional assumptions are required concerning the variation in parameter values with a changing situation. Yet even assuming only a monotonic relation between these values and the independent variable of an experiment suffices to give promising results.

Yet another kind of prediction is available, but the consequences of this have not been greatly scrutinized. This concerns possible variations in the task instructions given to a subject which might lead to k's acting as a variable parameter. Thus a high value of k might be expected to accompany a set for accuracy. It would be predicted that with emphasis upon accuracy, this would be achieved with response times being longer and the general level of confidence reduced.

However, although the qualitative results are encouraging, the justification of the model for the present enterprise must depend upon more detailed quantitative investigations. So far only preliminary investigations of human choice reactions under near-identical conditions have been carried out. These indicate considerable discrepancies between certain of the quantitative predictions and the experimental data, especially in connection with the extent of the differences in response times between various alternatives. This is not surprising, nor unduly alarming at this early stage in the investigation. It may be remarked in parenthesis that a remarkably high degree of consistency was obtained over a sequence of successive experimental sessions on individual subjects for accuracy, frequency of usage of various confidence levels, and accuracy within confidence levels. Response time distributions, however, were not so gratifying in this respect.

In the case of the predictions concerned with variations in the different response variables as stimulus conditions are changed, both human and animal experiments are planned, the human ones being under way. Some of the predictions, for example, those relating expected number of VTE's and the probability of a correct response, are of particular interest in so far as under certain circumstances they should be valid not only for a given subject over a set of different discriminations but also for the results of a number of subjects on one problem. This happens because the same parameters are involved in the hypothetical descriptions of both response measures.

This is a convenient state in the paper to admit that an examination of the literature on choice behaviour suggests that the characterization of a two-choice situation as a competition between just two alternative tendencies must be too gross an oversimplification. It seems much more likely that the model as it stands, when interpreted as a behavioural synapse in the manner originally imagined by the speaker, is more appropriate for situations where there is only one major response available and the decision concerns whether to make this choice or reject it. For example, an animal in the single-door jumping stand situation of Schlosberg and Solomon [4], where the choice is between jumping or not-jumping in the presence of a given stimulus card. This of course raises the delightful problem of an adequate experimental analysis of what is meant by a response of "not-jumping" when this is treated as a definite response and not just the absence of any activity. Perhaps, and an experiment is under way in this connection, the unmodified model may be applicable to situations resembling the psychophysical method of single stimuli, where a subject is presented with a series of stimuli and is asked to categorize each one as it appears. If for example the stimuli be weights, he has to label them as heavy or light.

The least that can be said is that on the first interpretation of the model it seems surprising that it should ever satisfactorily describe the results in a choice between two actual positive alternatives, as in the comparison of two stimuli, or the usual animal jumping stand with two doors. Much of the experimental work of the 30's and 40's indicates that something like a double approach-avoidance model is required. And one might conclude from this work that the two choice situation should perhaps be characterized by something like the diagram in Fig. 2:

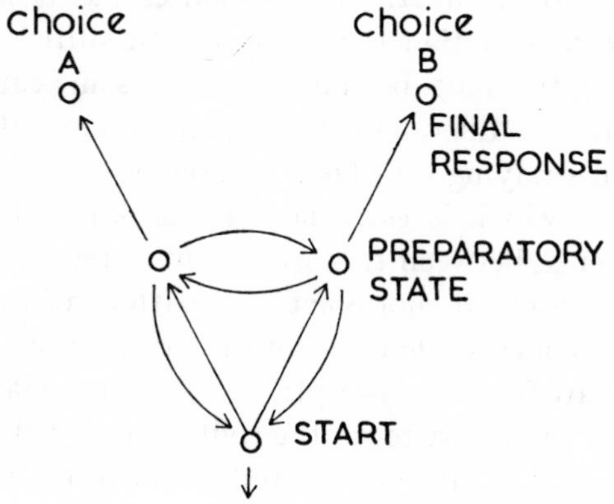

FIG. 2

The circles indicate successive states in choice behaviour and the arrows indicate possible transitions between them. These transitions may be purely approach-and-avoidance tendencies or they may involve processes related to statements like "A looks larger than B", "A looks smaller than B", and so on. Perhaps even enquiries are involved such as "Is A larger than B?"

Now it is interesting to note that the simple model presented earlier can be viewed as an elementary version of this more elaborate scheme. For suppose we consider the model ensuing when $k = 2$, then the diagram can be produced to represent it (Fig. 3), where $\mathrm{p} = \alpha/\alpha+\beta$ and $\mathrm{q} = \beta/\alpha+\beta$, α and β are the hypothetical rates of responding originally associated with the implicit alternatives a and b.

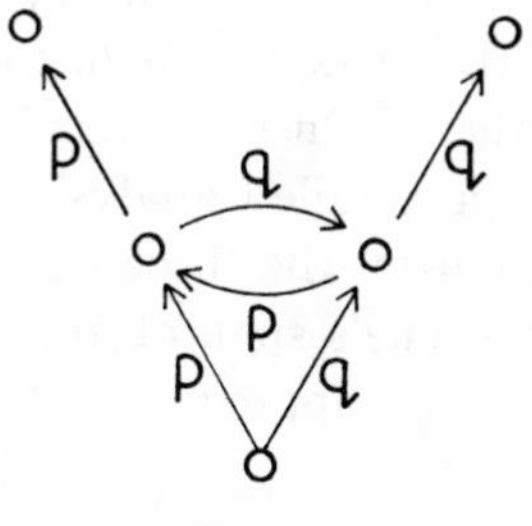

FIG. 3

This interpretation of the model makes it very similar to that proposed by Bower [2] for the description of VTE's at a choice point. A personal communication from him on this point has had an obvious influence upon my speculations, and I am pleased to have the opportunity of acknowledging this both publicly and personally at the same time. I only hope he doesn't consider that I am giving his paper.

This second kind of interpretation of the model suggests that it may be profitable to make more detailed observations of both human and animal choice behaviour with a view to determining the complete sequence of activities involved in a single act of choice. Thus much of what is hypothetical in the choice model which has been presented in this paper may become unnecessary because the competition of responses may be already sufficiently explicit if the choice situation is observed with sufficient ingenuity. The possibilities of doing this have been indicated by some earlier work, notably that of Brown, Mowrer, Miller, and others. More recently it has been attempted by Bower [2] in studying the choice behaviour of rats, although not for individual subjects, which is essential for this kind of study.

The basic difference between this second interpretation and the first lies in the treatment of a given choice act as a pattern of interlocking simpler acts of choice. It is conceivable that both interpretations of the model may be involved in a satisfactory description of choice behaviour. On the one hand, a description of the pattern of activities involved in the selection of one response from a set of alternatives and on the other, a description of the competition involved in moving from one element of the pattern to another.

Having established close contact with Bower's approach it seems worth attempting to make explicit the similarities and differences between the present approach and that elaborated by Luce [3] in his monograph entitled "Individual Choice Behaviour". It is to be hoped that this will not involve a misrepresentation of Luce's intentions.

The similarities seem to stem from the common use of a probabilistic approach and particularly from the fact that Luce's 'v' scale and the present speaker's notation of hypothetical rates of responding are very similar. Divergences occur because Luce develops his scale from a more general axiom and considers predictions concerning such matters as the transitivity of preferences. The basic difference appears to be one of general strategy. Luce appears to be attempting a general theory of choice behaviour in the grand manner of the S—R theorists, although to use his own words his approach is "orthogonal" to theirs. On the other hand the present speaker is much more concerned with a detailed analysis of behaviour in particular choice situations and mistrusts the broader generalizations. However, this may be only a matter of one's span of apprehension for axioms and a common cause is evident in the approaches of Bower, Luce, and myself.

References

[1] Audley, R. J. A Stochastic Model for Individual Choice Behaviour. *Psychol. Rev.* (1960), Vol. 67, pp. 1–15.

[2] Bower, G. H. Choice Point Behavior. Chapter 6 in *Studies in Mathematical Learning Theory* (1959). R. R. Bush and W. K. Estes (eds.), Stanford University Press.

[3] Luce, R. D. *Individual Choice Behavior*. A Theoretical Analysis (1959). New York, Wiley.

[4] Schlosberg, H., and R. L. Solomon. Latency of Response in a Choice Discrimination. *J. Exp. Psychol.* (1943), Vol. 33, pp. 22–39.

[5] Shipley, W. C., J. I. Coffin, and K. C. Hadsell. Affective Distance and other Factors Determining Reaction Time in Judgements of Colour Preferences. *J. Exp. Psychol.* (1945), Vol. 35, pp. 206–215.

[6] Shipley, W. C., E .D. Norris, and M. L. Roberts. The Effect of Changed Polarity of Set on Decision Time of Affective Judgements. *J. Exp. Psychol.* (1946), Vol. 36, pp. 237–243.

RESPONSE STRENGTHS AND CHOICE PROBABILITY: A CONSIDERATION OF TWO COMBINATION RULES

GORDON H. BOWER

Stanford University, Stanford, California, U.S.A.

The area of preferential choice behavior has long been a focus of much interest and activity among experimental psychologists. To people of my persuasion, simple choice experiments are to be thought of as placing into competition two or more instrumental responses, each of which may vary independently in its strength. To handle these situations, the theorist must propose some solution to the following question: Given two competing responses with known strengths, how are we to use this knowledge to predict choice between the two; that is, what is the composition, or combination, rule by which choice probability is related to the strengths of the separate responses?

Within this area of reference, there are today two major theories. One theory is due to Thurstone [11], and it assumes that the probability of choosing response A over B is an increasing function of the difference in strengths of the two responses. The second major theory, which has been proposed by Luce [7], assumes that the choice of A over B is determined by the ratio of their strengths; thus, if A and B have equal strengths, then A is chosen half the time; if A is three times stronger than B, then A will be chosen three-quarters of the time, and so on.

The natural testing grounds for both of these theories has been the experimental arrangement we call 'paired comparisons'. An experiment on paired comparisons has a simple structure. A number of commodities are presented to the subject a pair at a time, and choice probabilities are obtained for all possible pairs. The result of this experiment is a matrix of pairwise choice probabilities, and the test of a theory is how well it can reproduce this matrix after the response strengths have been estimated. A number of experiments like this have been carried out comparing the two theories. The upshot of these theoretical considerations has been essentially this: if the data are based on large sample sizes so that the estimates of pairwise preference are reasonably reliable, then both theories fit the data about equally well and it is difficult to discriminate between them. The two sets of predictions generally differ by less than one percentage point so that it would take literally thousands of observations on each pairwise choice

---

This paper is the text of a speech given in the Symposium on alternative approaches to the theory of choice, at the 1960 meetings of the International Congress for Logic, Methodology, and Philosophy of Science. Financial support for the author's research reported here was provided by a research grant, M-3849, from the National Institutes of Mental Health, United States Public Health Service. The research has also been supported in part by the Group Psychology Branch of the Office of Naval Research.

probability to gain sufficient reliability to accept one theory and reject the other.

Since for practical purposes the two theories do not differ in their account of such results, we must look elsewhere to find reasons for favoring one or the other. Lacking any further constraints, the choice between the two alternatives would seem to be determined by considerations of ease, convenience, and parsimony of assumptions. On these terms alone, the ratio rule would be favored, since (*a*) it is easier to work with mathematically, and (*b*) Luce has shown that it follows from a single assumption about choice behavior, whereas the Thurstone theory requires a number of assumptions, some of which appear unrealistic for finite sets of choice alternatives.[1] Moreover, if a subject's choices among a set of alternatives satisfy Luce's axiom, then we can assign numerals (strengths, utilities) to these alternatives which reflect his choices and which are unique except for multiplication by a positive constant (i.e., ratio measurement is guaranteed).

An alternative line of approach to selection between the Luce and Thurstone rules would be to seek further constraints which a suitable composition rule must satisfy. Such extra constraints could arise from two different sources. One source might be highly confirmed behavioral laws relating response strength to experimental variables. Given such laws for single responses, then the various combination rules may be differentiated by their predictions about certain choice experiments. To cite one example, if we had a well-confirmed law that drive and incentive motivation interact multiplicatively in determining response strength, as Hull [6] has supposed, then the Thurstone rule would imply that choice between alternative rewards would be an increasing function of drive level, whereas the Luce rule would predict no effect of drive level on choice probability in this situation. Other examples of this sort could be cited, but in each case the validity of the test presumes the prior existence of valid theoretical laws about the strengths of single instrumental responses. However, there is some doubt even among behavior theorists whether such well-confirmed theoretical laws can be provided in the near future.

The second source of extra constraints could arise from a more detailed analysis and representation of the component behaviors of a subject during the act of choosing, and it is to this task that we now turn. In the remainder of this paper, we present a detailed representation (model) of what goes on during a single act of choice by an individual, we discuss some direct empirical support for this model, and finally we show that Luce's ratio rule falls out directly as a theorem from this representation of the behavior of a subject at a choice point.

The model [2] began as a rather modest attempt to describe the behavior of a rat at the choice point of a *T*-maze, so let us turn our attention to this

---

[1]This brief sentence suffices here for complex issues, but can be unpacked by the interested reader by referring to Luce [7], Adams and Messick [1], and Marschak [8].

furry rodent as he putters about in the maze. The maze has right and left pathways leading off from the choice point; to be concrete, suppose the left alley is painted white and the right one is painted black. As any seasoned rat-watcher can tell you, the animal's relevant behaviors at the choice point can be categorized, more or less exhaustively, into two classes; orienting to, or looking at, or noticing the alternative choice stimuli, and finally approaching one of the stimuli he is looking at. The animal may spend a good deal of time looking back and forth between the two pathways before he finally approaches one. For reasons indigenous to experimental psychologists, this looking back and forth at the choice point has been labeled vicarious trial-and-error behavior, or VTE for short.

In abstract terms, we may think of our rat at the choice point as being at any time in one of several orienting states: looking straight ahead, looking to the right at the black arm of the maze, or looking to the left at the white arm. When he is oriented toward, say, the black alley, he either reorients or he approaches it, and thus the trial terminates. The original idea of this model was to consider the subject to be performing a random walk over these orienting states before he finally approaches one of the stimuli. In the language of random walks, there would be two absorbing states here, approaching the black or approaching the white, since either of these events terminates the trial. A diagram of the process is shown at the top of Fig. 1. This diagram is supposed to be a skeleton of the animal's behavior at the choice point; indeed, I've laid out the skeleton so that it still resembles a *T*-maze.

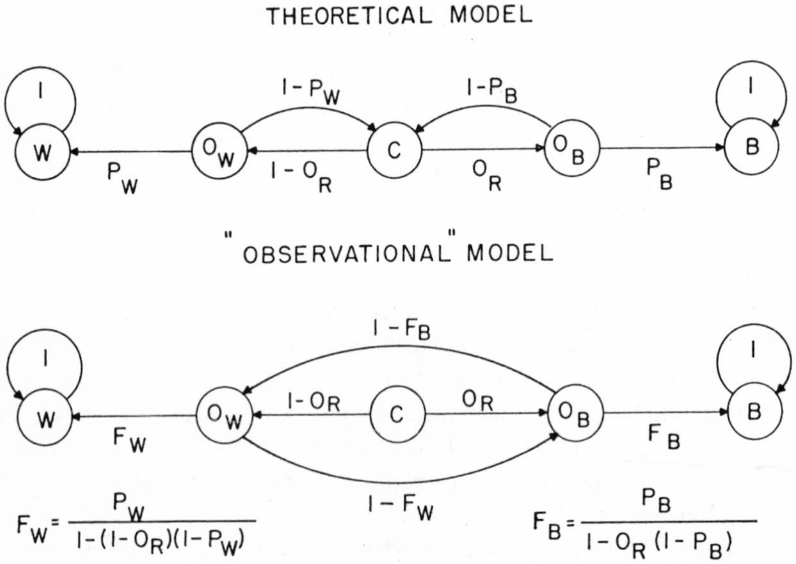

FIG. 1 State diagrams of the random walk process. The probabilities of the various transitions among states are indicated beside the appropriate transition arrow. The observational model at the bottom is derived from the theoretical model at the top of the figure. (See text for explanation.)

The animal begins the trial in the center state, C, oriented straight ahead. With probability o_R he orients to the right, where he sees the black alley; he is then in state O_B. When oriented to the black alley, he may approach it with probability p_B, but with probability $1 - p_B$ he reorients back to the center and the random walk continues. It continues, in fact, until the subject approaches the black or white alley, and thus terminates the trial. 'Choosing the black alley' is to be identified with absorption of the process in state B after a random walk over the transient states. According to this conception, then, the subject's eventual choice is regarded to be the outcome of the interaction of a number of molecular behaviors that go on at the choice point. If we knew the transition probabilities between these states, then in principle we would know everything about the subject's behavior at the choice point. In particular, we can calculate the probability that the subject ends the trial by choosing the black alley rather than the white one. Of more immediate interest here is the fact that the model predicts the distribution of the number of transitions between the various orienting states before absorption occurs. It is the empirical accuracy of these predictions which I propose to offer as independent support for this model of choice behavior.

Suppose we concentrate on the number of times the subject switches his orientation between the black and white stimuli; this would be the number of VTE's on a given trial. One can easily derive the expected distribution of this random variable and if we knew the values of the underlying transition probabilities we could compare our predictions with the data. However, one practical problem with this strategy is that we cannot hope to estimate directly the underlying approach probabilities from watching the rat. The practical difficulty is that we probably would be unable to detect all transitions of a 'loop' form, say, from O_B to C and back to O_B, and these would be necessary to obtain accurate estimates of the approach probabilities. The only behaviors we can hope to record reliably are the complete shifts in orientation from one side of the maze to the other side. These movements are gross enough to be seen and recorded without serious error.

For puposes of VTE predictions, then, it is of practical advantage to replace temporarily the underlying model with what I have called the 'observational' model in the lower part of Fig. 1. The observational model is derived strictly from the one above it, except that here we are considering the probability of an eventual shift between the two orienting states. For example, $1 - F_B$ represents the probability of eventually switching over to the white alley after the subject starts out by orienting to the black alley. The formulas at the bottom of Fig. 1 give the expressions for F_B and F_W calculated from the underlying model.

From this representation, the distribution of the number of VTE's is easily derived as a function of F_B and F_W; since these latter quantities can be estimated from the data, we are in a position to predict the distribution of VTE's.

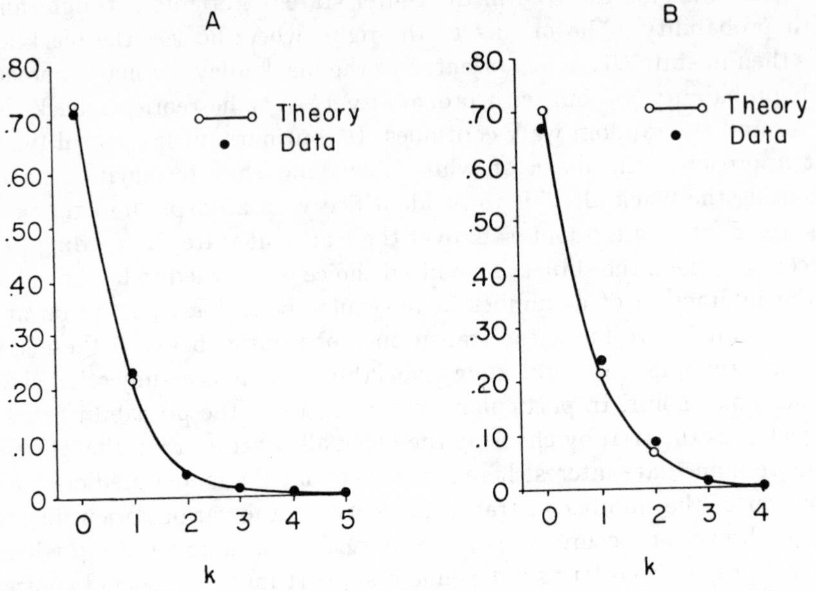

FIG. 2 Observed and predicted distributions on the number of VTE's in two experiments with rats in a *T*-maze.

In Fig. 2 are shown some predicted and obtained distributions from two groups of 15 rats learning *T*-maze problems. These data were collected during the middle course of learning and the basic probabilities were estimated from the data. It is clear from Fig. 2 that the model accurately predicts the VTE distributions obtained in these experiments. We have conducted several other experiments in which the predicted VTE distributions fit as well as or better than in these two studies. Since the model has performed well on a number of such occasions, there is little doubt that some kind of random-walk process is the appropriate model for choice point behavior.

As a bonus for the model's accounting for VTE's, it also gives a reasonably good account of choice times. In several experiments with rats we have obtained correlations in the high nineties between average choice time and VTE's, suggesting that decision time measures are almost redundant when VTE's are recorded. Another nice feature here is that the model delivers the correct prediction that choices of the more probable response are generally quicker than choices of the less probable response.

The previous remarks apply to observations of choice behavior taken over a single experimental trial during which we may assume that the basic transition probabilities remain constant. We have a static model, telling us what will be observed when the response tendencies are such and so. The model can be applied, of course, to those dynamic situations in which the response tendencies are changing from trial to trial as the result of experimental manipulations. An obvious example of a dynamic situation is a learning experiment in which the subject is rewarded or not depending upon which alternative he chooses. The model makes a number of unique predictions about the results of some learning experiments. Space limitations do not permit a full discussion here of many of these cases, but we shall briefly discuss two cases to illustrate the type of predictions derivable from the model.

The first condition to be discussed is that in which the subject is learning to choose, say, the black alley as it is shifted from side to side in the maze; this condition is contrasted with that in which the black-white cues are in fixed spatial positions (right or left of the choice point). The second case to be discussed is that in which, following initial learning, the reward significance of the two brightness cues is reversed.

Consider first the learning of a brightness discrimination in which approaches to the black alley are rewarded while approaches to the white alley are not rewarded. The result of these contingencies will be an increase over successive trials in the subject's tendency to approach the rewarded black alley and a decrease in his tendency to approach the non-rewarded white alley. If the rewarded black alley is shifted from right to left at random in the maze, then over successive trials the subject's orientation probability, o_R, will not vary appreciably from one-half because he has not been consistently reinforced for looking right or left at the choice point. However, if the rewarded black alley is always on the right side of the maze ('position' learning), then orientations to the right are consistently reinforced and o_R would be expected to increase to unity under such conditions. It is this latter fact which differentiates position learning from stimulus discrimination learning.

In Fig. 3 are shown some hypothetical curves illustrating the qualitative differences to be expected for these two cases. The solid curves are for position learning and the dashed curves for stimulus discrimination learning conditions. For both conditions we have plotted the probability of the correct response (upper curves, to be referred to the right ordinate) and the average or expected number of VTE's (lower curves, to be referred to the left ordinate). For this illustration, it has been assumed, as in previous work [2], that reward and nonreward increase and decrease, respectively, the approach probabilities by linear transformations.[2]

The first thing to notice in Fig. 3 is that the probability of the correct response is expected to increase faster in conditions of position learning, and this is a well-established qualitative result in animal learning [10]. The expected difference here is due to the fact that, in position learning, the subject not only is learning which stimulus to approach and which to avoid, but is also learning which way to orient at the choice point to expose himself to the rewarded stimulus. Corresponding to the expected changes in the orienting and approach probabilities, the average number of VTE's for

---

[2]Fortunately, the qualitative results given in Figs. 3 and 4 do not depend to any great extent upon the form or details of the conditioning laws we use in transforming the basic probabilities following the reward-nonreward outcomes.

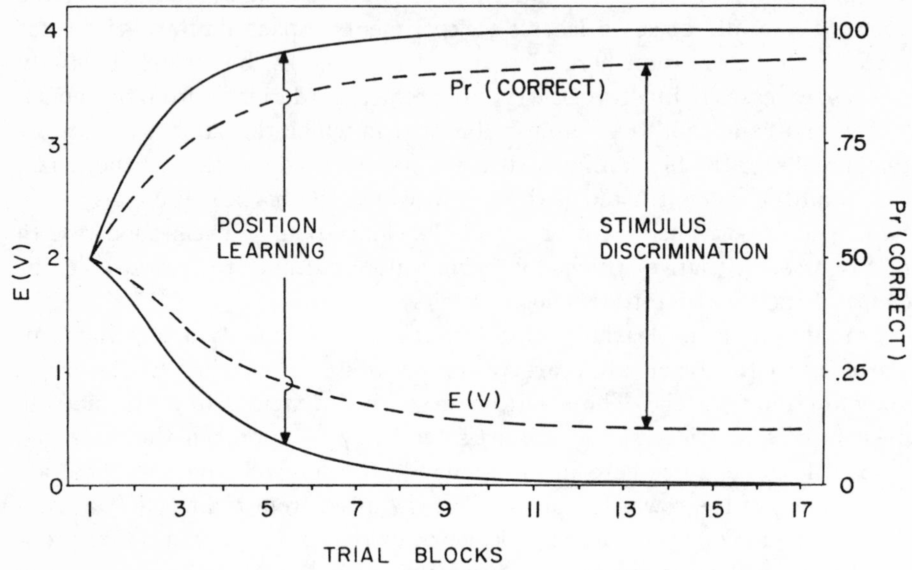

FIG. 3 Hypothetical curves comparing VTE (left ordinate) and choice probability (right ordinate) for conditions of position learning (solid curves) and stimulus discrimination learning (dashed curves). Successive blocks of training trial are plotted on the abscissa.

position learners is expected to drop rapidly to zero. By contrast, the initial orientation at the choice point of the subjects in the stimulus discrimination conditions will continue to be random, so that at asymptote their initial orientation on half the trials will be to the nonrewarded white alley, and one VTE will occur on such trials. Hence, the asymptote of E(V) is .50 for these conditions, and this result is well-established empirically.

According to the theory, the exact path of the VTE curve during learning will depend considerably upon the initial strengths of the approach tendencies to the alternative choice stimuli. For the cases shown in Fig. 3 it was assumed that the initial values of p_B and p_W were low and equal. A completely different course of learning and VTE is expected for those conditions in which the approach tendency to the incorrect stimulus is initially higher than that to the correct stimulus. Such conditions might be expected to obtain in the stimulus discrimination problem, for example, if the reward values of the black and white alleys are reversed after the subject has learned previously to approach one and avoid the other. In Fig. 4 are shown the expected results for reversal learning under two conditions: in one condition, depicted by the dashed lines, the subject simply receives no reward for incorrect choices (and is not permitted to correct his errors); in the other condition, shown in solid curves, the subject is punished, say, by an electric shock every time he makes an error. In terms of conditioning assumptions, the punishment is conceived simply as reducing more rapidly the subject's tendency to approach the incorrect stimulus.

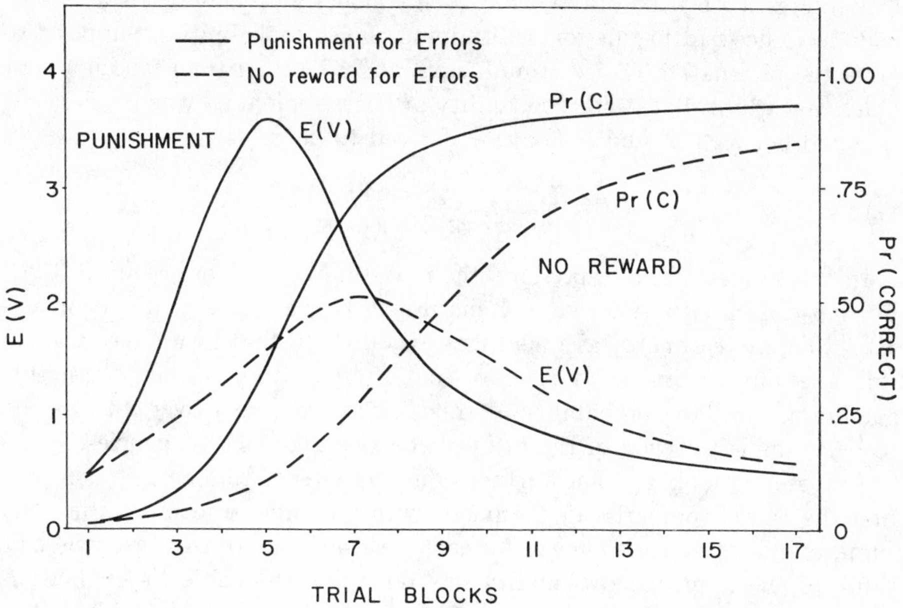

FIG 4. Hypothetical curves showing VTE and choice probability during reversal of a previously learned stimulus discrimination. Two conditions are compared: no reward for errors (dashed curves); and no reward plus punishment for errors (solid curves).

There are several features of Fig. 4 which may be noted. First, the curve for the probability of the correct response during reversal learning is expected to be *S*-shaped rather than negatively accelerated as it was during initial learning when the two responses begin at nearly equal strengths. Secondly, the course of VTE during reversal learning differs from that in initial learning; the E(V) rises to a maximum as the strong incorrect response tendency is reduced, and then falls off as the correct response is strengthened. Finally, the effect of punishment for incorrect responses, as compared with just nonreward for errors, is to increase the absolute amount of VTE behavior and to lead to faster learning of the new correct response.

The qualitative aspects of these last predictions seem to be in general accord with the scant amount of VTE data that have been collected during reversal learning. An experiment by Davenport [4] has demonstrated in rats the hump-shaped VTE curve during reversal learning. Punishment for errors during reversal learning is well-known to increase the rate of learning; VTE during punished reversal learning has not been compared with that using nonreward only, but relevant comparisons during original learning [9] have shown that punishment results in increased levels of VTE behavior.

The previous discussion has provided what I consider to be independent empirical support for this model of choice point behavior. Let us now return to the earlier discussion of different combination rules for determining choice probability given the respective strengths of the competing responses.

One interesting feature of the choice point model is that it yields as a special case Luce's ratio rule for determining choice probabilities. Suppose we label the alternative choice stimuli as S_1 and S_2, rather than talking about black and white alleys. The probability of absorption at S_1 when a choice is required between S_1 and S_2 may be derived to be

$$(1) \qquad P\{1|1,\ 2\} = \frac{o_1 p_1}{o_1 p_1 + (1-o_1) p_2}.$$

In this expression, o_1 represents the initial probability of orienting to S_1. For most of the situations we shall discuss, in particular for paired comparisons, we may reasonably assume that o_1 is one-half; that is, we may assume that the subject orients at random to the alternative stimuli. With this condition, then, the probability of choosing alternative 1 over 2 turns out to be a simple function of the ratio of the two approach tendencies.

Suppose we look at some further consequences of this model. Consider first the paired-comparison experiment with a number of commodities, the subjects indicating their choices for each possible pair. In this case, we may think of the approach probabilities as reflecting the subject's evaluation of the commodities. The first result to be discussed concerns the relationship among the pairwise choice probabilities for any three commodities, say i, j, and k. Suppose we take the ratio of the probability of choosing i over j to the probability of choosing j over i. The value of this ratio, which we may call w_{ij}, is

$$(2) \qquad w_{ij} = \frac{P(i|i,\ j)}{P(j|i,\ j)} = \frac{p_i}{p_j}.$$

Using these w_{ij} numbers, we may prove a theorem which Estes [5] has called the product rule and which Luce [7] calls the triple condition. The theorem is

$$(3) \qquad w_{ik} = w_{ij} \cdot w_{jk}.$$

PROOF:

$$\frac{p_i}{p_k} = \frac{p_i}{p_j} \cdot \frac{p_j}{p_k}.$$

The product rule may be regarded as a probabilistic form of transitivity: it says that if we know the probabilities that i is chosen over j, and j is chosen over k, then we can predict the probability that i is chosen over k.

Some experimental results on the product rule are shown in Table 1. At the top are the results of two rat studies done in T-mazes, the first one by P. T. Young [12] and the second one by the author, and at the bottom are some results of two studies with human subjects in a mock consumer survey, the first of these done by Estes [5] and the second one by the author. In the study by Young, rats' preferences for sugar, wheat, and casein were determined by pairing each substance with the other two in independent compar-

TABLE 1

EXPERIMENTAL TESTS OF THE PRODUCT RULE

	w_{ij}	w_{jk}	predicted w_{ik}	observed w_{ik}
Young (rats)	$W_{SW} = \frac{.55}{.45}$	$W_{WC} = \frac{.70}{.30}$	$W_{SC} = \frac{.74}{.26}$	$\frac{.738}{.262}$
Bower (rats)	$W_{62} = \frac{.992}{.008}$	$W_{24} = \frac{.040}{.960}$	$W_{64} = \frac{.835}{.165}$	$\frac{.833}{.167}$
Estes (humans)	$W_{RB} = \frac{.71}{.29}$	$W_{BY} = \frac{.73}{.27}$	$W_{RY} = \frac{.87}{.13}$	$\frac{.89}{.11}$
Bower (humans)	$W_{GB} = \frac{.65}{.35}$	$W_{BY} = \frac{.55}{.45}$	$W_{GY} = \frac{.70}{.30}$	$\frac{.71}{.29}$

isons. The rats chose sugar over wheat 55 per cent of the time, and wheat over casein 70 per cent of the time. By the product rule, we may predict that sugar will be chosen over casein 74 per cent of the trials, and this prediction compares favorably with the observed percentage of 73.8 shown in the brackets to the side. The study by the author compared rats' asymptotic probability of choosing different amounts of food reward, 6, 4, or 2 tiny food pellets. Three groups of rats were run, one group corresponding to each of the three possible pairs. The results predicted here by the product rule are again quite accurate: 83.5 predicted versus 83.3 observed as the per cent choice of 6 over 4 pellets. In the mock consumer studies with college students, the subjects were asked to indicate their preferences among different pairs of color-combinations for automobiles. For example, in the first study, by Estes, the specific color-combinations compared were red-white, blue-gray, and yellow-black. Comparing the predicted and observed values in the bottom two studies, we see that the product rule performs about as well with the human subjects as it did with the rats. These data strongly suggest that the product rule may be regarded as a low-level law about choice probabilities in this type of situation.

As a final illustration of this model, let us consider its implications for situations in which the subject is required to choose from among more than two alternatives at a time. As one example of this, we may extend the ordinary paired comparisons experiment by having the subjects also indicate their first choices from among all possible sets of three commodities, from among all possible sets of four commodities, and so on. Unfortunately, theoretical and experimental treatment of such multiple choice problems has been seriously neglected in the history of psychology, so the data in this area are quite meager. This neglect has been partly due to the fact that prior to the appearance of Luce's axiom the Thurstone theory was the only usable choice axiom known to psychologists, and that theory has never extended to the multiple choice situation. I might add that the problems in so extending Thurstone's theory seem a bit formidable at the present.

Fortunately, extension of the choice-point model to the multiple choice case is a relatively easy matter. In fact, if we can assume that the subject orients at random to the alternative stimuli in the set presented to him, then the choice probabilities are a simple function of the ratios of the alternative approach tendencies. This result is shown in Equation 4.

$$(4)\quad P\{i|1,\ 2,\ \ldots,\ N\} = \frac{p_i}{p_1 + p_2 + \ldots + p_N} = \frac{1}{w_{1i} + w_{2i} + \ldots + w_{Ni}}.$$

When N stimuli are presented, the probability that the first choice is alternative i is given by p_i divided by the sum of the N approach tendencies. If we were to divide this expression by p_i then it is clear that it's just a function of the ratios of p_k to p_i. These ratios we have met before in the two choice problem where we called them w_{ki} and so forth. The implication of this simple result is that first choices from higher sets of alternatives should be predictable in a straightforward manner from pairwise choice probabilities, since all the w_{ki} can be estimated from pairwise choices. If the theory is correct, then it is enormously productive in terms of the number of predictions it can make. For example, with 6 alternative stimuli, there are 57 possible combinations or choice sets (pairs, triples, fours, etc.) which may be presented to the subject.[3] To describe the distribution of responses in all 57 choice sets would require 129 numbers. If the theory is right, then we can use 5 pairwise choice probabilities to estimate the ratios of the response tendencies, and then predict the other 124 probabilities. We would be getting roughly 25 predictions for each bit of data we use in estimating our parameters, and that is a fairly good operating characteristic for a theory.

One simple way by which part of this grandiose scheme may be tested is shown in Equation 5.

$$(5)\quad w_{ij} = \frac{P(i|1,\ 2,\ \ldots,\ N)}{p(j|1,\ 2,\ \ldots,\ N)} = \frac{p_i}{p_j}.$$

Again let us take the ratio of the probability that the subject's first choice is alternative i when he chooses among N stimuli to the probability that his first choice is alternative j. The summation in the denominators of both probabilities cancels out and we are left simply with the ratio of p_i to p_j, which is the same as that given in Equation 2 for ratios of pairwise probabilities. The important point here is that this ratio is not affected by the number of alternatives that are added on to the choice set in addition to i and j. This constant ratio rule is often regarded as one version of Luce's choice axiom and we see that it also follows from the random walk model.

Empirical tests of the constant ratio rule are particularly scanty. There is one psychophysical experiment by Clarke [3] which gave generally confirmatory results. We attempted to test the constant ratio rule in a mock con-

[3]In general, for N alternatives, there will be $2^N - N - 1$ possible choice sets and $N-1$ free parameters (the w_{ij}'s) to be estimated from the data.

sumer survey, some of the data of which were reported in Table 1. There were 4 choice objects, in this case color-combinations for automobiles. With 4 objects you can construct 6 pairs, 4 triples, and the one set containing all 4 objects. Each of 170 subjects was required to indicate a first choice for each of these choice sets. From this data there are 6 independent probability ratios, and for each of these ratios we calculated the values for choice sets of size 2, 3, and 4. As one might have expected from sampling theory, ratios of probability estimates based on only 170 observations show considerable variability. However, to indicate the overall trend for these six series of probability ratios, I have taken the average ratios for pairs, for triples, and for the one quartet, and these values are shown in Table 2. Although one can't make a definite statistical statement about whether the slight discrepancies from constancy could have occurred by chance, I have accepted, for the moment at least, the conclusion that these ratios are constant, and that the observed deviations can be attributed to chance sampling error. Although this is not a particularly resounding conclusion, we can at least be assured that the data have not entirely defeated our expectations on the constant ratio rule.

TABLE 2

Average Values of Probability Ratios for Choice Sets of Size 2, 3, and 4

N	average w_{ij}
2	2.15
3	2.21
4	2.19

What the previous discussion has attempted to show is that there are extra constraints on the decision about suitable ways (rules) by which alternative response strengths may be combined to yield choice probabilities. The extra constraints arise from a more detailed analysis and representation of the (pre-decision) behaviors the subject engages in during the act of choice, and we have provided independent empirical support for this representation. The important result of interest here was that this model for choice behavior dictated a ratio rule for combining competing response strengths to determine choice probability. The result in this case is the same as that obtained by Luce through his axiomatic approach to choice behavior.

References

[1] Adams, E., and S. Messick. An axiomatization of Thurstone's successive intervals and paired comparisons scaling models. Applied Mathematics and Statistics Laboratory, *Technical Report* 12, Stanford University, 1957.

[2] Bower, G. Choice-point behavior. In Bush, R. R., and Estes, W. K. (eds.): *Studies in mathematical learning theory*. Stanford Univ. Press, 1959.

[3] CLARKE, F. R. Constant-ratio rule for confusion matrices in speech communication. *J. acoust. Soc. Amer.*, 1957, Vol. 29, pp. 715–720.

[4] DAVENPORT, J. W. Analysis of a simple selective learning situation involving differential magnitude of reinforcement. *J. comp. physiol. Psychol.*, 1959, Vol. 52, pp. 349–352.

[5] ESTES, W. K. A random-walk model for choice behavior. In Arrow, K. J., Karlin, S., and Suppes, P. (eds.): *Mathematical methods in the social sciences*, 1959. Stanford Univ. Press, 1960.

[6] HULL, C. L. *Essentials of behavior*. New Haven: Yale Univ. Press, 1951.

[7] LUCE, R. D. *Individual choice behavior*. New York: Wiley, 1959.

[8] MARSCHAK, J. Binary choice constraints and random utility indicators. In Arrow, K. J., Karlin, S., and Suppes, P. (eds.): *Mathematical methods in the social sciences*, 1959. Stanford Univ. Press, 1960.

[9] MUENZINGER, K. F. Vicarious trial and error at a point of choice. I. A general survey of its relation to learning efficiency. *J. genet. Psychol.*, 1938, Vol. 53, pp. 75–86.

[10] RESTLE, F. Discrimination of cues in mazes: a resolution of the 'place-vs-response' question. *Psychol. Rev.*, 1957, Vol. 64, pp. 217–228.

[11] THURSTONE, L. L. A law of comparative judgment. *Psychol. Rev.*, 1927, Vol. 34, pp. 273–286.

[12] YOUNG, P. T. Studies of food preference, appetite and dietary habit. VII. Palatability in relation to learning and performance. *J. comp. physiol. Psychol.*, 1947, Vol. 40, pp. 37–72.

THEORIES OF CHOICE AND THE STIMULUS-RESPONSE FRAMEWORK

J. A. DEUTSCH

Stanford University, Stanford, California, U.S.A.

The philosopher and economist interested in psychological theories of choice have probably noticed that many of the mathematically elaborate approaches to this subject share certain presuppositions which are not discussed within the framework of these theories. These presuppositions are inherited from the now classical S-R (or Stimulus-Response) theories. Such theories suppose (*a*) that performance consists of a sequence of stimulus response pairs, (*b*) that any response at any one time is the outcome of stimulation at the preceding moment, and (*c*) that learning consists of the coupling together of a stimulus and a response whenever these are followed by some third event (a reward, for instance) so that when the stimulus occurs again it will procude that response. It is of this type of theory that Lashley [6] said over thirty years ago, "I believe that it is now becoming an obstacle rather than a help to progress." Lashley himself marshalled an impressive amount of evidence against this kind of theory. Since he spoke, the volume of such evidence has become overwhelming. Nevertheless, the S-R approach continues to command an ever increasing number of adherents, and most of the serious and rigorous thinking in psychology is done within its framework.

What I wish to say about S-R theory will of necessity have to be brief, and therefore it is bound to sound dogmatic. In my summary of the argument against it I shall try to stress especially evidence with implications for a different point of view.

Let us begin with the the notion implicit in most S-R theories that a response of an organism when it is performing some action is the outcome of stimulation at a preceding moment. By this is meant that when an organism makes any sort of movement, such a movement is caused by something which the organism saw, heard, smelled, and so on, at an instantly preceding moment.

However, an experimental analysis of simple activities fails to bear out such suppositions. An example of this kind which is familiar to me is that of singing [7]. It may surprise many people to be told that when they are instructed to sing a steady note their voice shows a characteristic wobble in pitch. It rises and falls quickly many times a second. It has been possible to establish that this wobble is the result of a quick-acting corrective mechanism. Every time the voice strays from the pitch the subject is attempting to maintain, it is brought back. Methods for establishing the nature of this mechanism include, for instance, the delay of the message that the voice has strayed or an artificial interference with the singer's ability to discriminate small differences in pitch. A stimulus-response analysis of these phenomena is only superficially plausible. It is true that the wandering from a certain note may be held to constitute the stimulus and the corrective movement the response. However, closer analysis will reveal that the response which eventuates is determined not only by what the singer hears but also by what note he is attempting to sing but does not hear. That is, a certain heard note may be the stimulus either for a correction downwards (if the heard note is higher than the note to be sung) or upwards (if it is lower). That is, a most important ingredient of such a simple activity is the target or goal which the organism has set itself and this cannot elegantly be included in an S-R formulation. One of the more general implications of this study is that behavior is guided by the difference between the incoming stimuli and the targets or goals which have been set in the animal at any given moment. One of the appeals of S-R theory to the mechanically less sophisticated is that it seemed to banish such things as goals from psychology. However, the type of system which has been uncovered in the above-mentioned case of singing is quite readily interpreted in terms of a mechanism made of hardware or in neurophysiological terms.

A part of what I have said already applies equally to the second proposition which I said described the viewpoint to which S-R adherents would subscribe. This was that any response at any one time is the outcome of stimulation at the preceding moment. On this view, if we knew the linkages of the stimuli at a choice point, as determined by learning or by built-in factors, we should be able to predict the choice of the organism at that point. Here S-R theory is embarrassed by predicting not only that rats are stupider than they turn out to be, but also that they are cleverer. The cases where animals are not so stupid as we would expect from S-R theory are of the following nature. In the first example, an animal is allowed to explore a T-maze with two distinctive goal boxes invisible from the choice-point. It is then made hungry and placed directly in one of the goal boxes where it is then fed. After this, it is placed at the entrance of the T-maze and turns correctly to the goal box where it has just been fed. The response of turning to this goal box cannot have been connected to the stimuli at the choice-point. The animal must presumably be making its choice with reference to a certain goal rather than through a response to the stimuli impinging at the choice-point.

A second type of experiment [8, 9] shows that animals run both hungry and thirsty in a T-maze and rewarded by food on one side and water on the other are capable of running correctly to either the food or the water when they are made separately hungry or thirsty. Such a result is also embarrassing to S-R theory because it supposes the stimuli of hunger and thirst to become connected equally to both the food and water response sequences. However, such results are again consistent with the belief that an important ingredient is being left out in the S-R analysis and that animals can be guided by the anticipated outcomes of their actions as well as by the stimuli which impinge on them at the choice-point.

Where animals are stupider than S-R theory would expect is in the case of single goal box drive discrimination. If a rat has to run two different ways to the same goal box, depending on whether it is trying to obtain water or food, it finds this problem almost impossible to learn [10–12]. If, on the other hand, an identical procedure is followed, the animal being made thirsty one day and hungry the next, with food in one goal box and water in the other, animals learn quickly [11, 13, 14]. The stimulus conditions at the choice-point can be made identical as in my own study [12], but yet there is a very great difference in the difficulty of the task to the rat, depending on the goal box situation. Stimulus-Response theory finds this perplexing. Again this difficulty occurs in a situation which is concerned with the factors of the end of activity for the animal in a choice situation. Such findings may, in my opinion, be explained if we take proper cognizance of the role of such goals or targets in choice behavior.

Here also I find that some of the evidence I have quoted about the second proposition could equally well be marshalled against the third. This was the tenet that learning consists of the coupling together of stimulus and response events whenever these are followed by some third event (a reinforcement, for instance).

Against this type of belief it has been shown that animals do not necessarily need to make the response upon observing, which we should later on conclude that they had learned. Various studies have recently shown that rats riding various kinds of vehicles learn mazes without running them. Direct electroencephalographic evidence as well as behavioral work has shown that sequences of stimuli are learned where it would be fanciful in the extreme to imagine any responses worthy of the name.

Following another line of attack, it has been possible to show that if one response has been learned, the animal will change to an alternative means of achieving the same goal without further learning. Some of the experiments of Lashley illustrate this point admirably [6]. I am sorry that it has not been possible, before turning to the second part of the paper, to give a more complete and comprehensive account of the evidence and arguments. (The interested reader is referred to my recent book [2] for a fuller discussion.) I have, in what follows, attempted to narrow the issues and discuss an experiment somewhat more intensively.

In this second part of the paper, I wish to discuss the implications of a simple experiment for statistical learning theory. This theory shares the S-R assumptions of its predecessors. Not only does it not evade the general objections to the S-R class of theories, but it encounters fresh difficulties of its own, as I hope to show.

Let me, therefore, start with a simple experiment I have chosen [1, 2]. We have a maze with a single choice-point. There is a starting alley which then divides into two alleys. One alley leads right and the other left. They then continue around an outline square and converge on to a single goal box. At the start of the maze we place some hungry rats. They are then rewarded with an equal amount of food in the goal box whether they turn left or right—that is, whichever choice they make.

On the face of it, such an experiment would not show us anything about choice or learning. The animals being rewarded for whatever they choose can hardly be expected to learn even on common-sense grounds. If we take the statistical learning theory [3], it seems that no learning should occur. This theory is a modern variant of the S-R theories discussed above. In it, stimuli become attached to responses during learning, and what response is made is a result of the stimuli at the choice-point through their attachment to the responses between which the choice lies. If the outcome is determined by the number of stimulus elements which are attached to such responses, the choice-point is conceived as an ensemble of stimulus elements. However, at each choice there impinges on the animal only a sample of the ensemble of stimulus elements. That is, the theory differs from its more classical predecessors in considering that there is only a certain chance that any given stimulus at the choice-point will be attached to a response followed by a reinforcement. The number of the stimulus elements sampled will remain constant from trial to trial. If the response the animal makes is rewarded, then those stimuli which preceded this response will evoke it when they occur again. If the response is unrewarded, then no change occurs in attachment of stimulus elements. The occurrence of a response on any one trial will be determined by whether the majority of the sample of stimuli impinging on that trial has been attached to it. When the animal's response by going to one side is rewarded, some of the stimulus elements in the situation will be attached to that response and removed from the alternative. On the other hand, when next it goes to the other and is rewarded for doing so, some stimulus elements will be attached to the response of going to this other side. As we see the animals alternating their choices and so being rewarded equally for both responses, presumably an animal which has been trained for a long time in this situation should not reveal any more learning than a very naïve one.

But are we right to assume that nothing has been learned by these animals? How, then, do we know or how can we deduce anything about the animals' learning in this simple situation? The way Mr. Clarkson and I attempted to find out was simply to insert a block in the alleys just before the goal box. The animal would then make a choice and run up against the block, unaware, of course, of the other. It would then be picked out and placed again at the starting point. If it had learned nothing about the two alternatives then the proportion of choices of the other side, the first trial after the block had been introduced, should be the same as on the preceding trials. The average number of choices of the opposite had been 8.8 out of 19, so we have a baseline for comparison. However, on the very next trial we find 17 out of 19 animals going to the opposite side to that in which they had met the block. They could not see the block from the choice-point, so it follows they must have learned to distinguish the two sides. But this is not the only embarrassment to the statistical theory. As has been stated above, a non-rewarded trial according to the statistical learning theory does not cause a redistribution of attachment between stimulus elements and responses. Therefore, any change in the number of reponses to a side which has not been rewarded should occur only after some other alternative response has been rewarded. Second, even if the theory was amended to postulate changes occurring after a non-rewarded trial, there would be another difficulty left. Any change in the average shift of responding must be gradual. In order to explain the gradualness of learning, it is assumed that only a small proportion of the stimulus ensemble at the choice-point is sampled on each trial. There is, therefore, the extraordinary speed of reversal to be considered. Suppose we grant that some learning had taken place (though it is difficult to see what this could have consisted of if we think in terms of the statistical learning theory), such sudden reversal in one trial presents a difficulty. Must we think in terms of stimulus samples increasing to become almost as large as the ensemble? Does the size of the samples increase with continued exposure to the situation?

Dr. Restle in [4] has suggested something which attempts to explain one trial learning in situations where the animal learns to learn. This is roughly that the stimuli which on being sampled sometimes lead to reward and sometimes to non-reward are excluded from the process of sampling — a kind of device for excluding the irrelevant. However, it seems that this cannot be the explanation of such behavior in our situation. Every stimulus sampled is always rewarded in our situation and therefore this device for norrowing the ensemble will not help us.

Nevertheless, the experiments which Restle has theorized about are of interest to us. Harlow [4], in an extensive and admirable series of investigations, has shown that animals, when taught a series of discriminations, learn progressively faster until they will learn a problem on the information provided by one trial. By careful analysis of the records as the animal learned, he was able to show that the apparently gradual learning early in the series of discriminations was due to the intrusion of systematic irrelevant tendencies which led to errors and that these error tendencies gradually dropped out as further discriminations were learned. These error tendencies, when averaged, give the kind of picture which could mistakenly be thought to support stimulus-sampling theory. It does not seem sound to suppose that the only motivation which a naïve animal has in the maze is that which the experimenter has imposed on it, such as hunger. It should not be forgotten that other unwanted tendencies may either mask or completely obliterate the motivation the experimenter has tried to produce. For instance, it is exceptional for a 24-hour hungry, naïve rat to eat in a maze when first given the opportunity, and its seemingly irrelevant antics in the maze, even after moderate familiarity has set in, tax the patience of most experimenters. It seems to me that it is with such considerations in mind rather than those of stimulus sampling that we ought to look at the probabilistic growth curves we find in learning experiments. In this way, we would escape some of the perplexities into which we have been led by our simple experiment. We could then say that learning was initially a virtually one-trial phenomenon in a simple T-maze where distinctive cues are available and that this is masked initially by various irrelevant tendencies such as fear, exploration, stimulus preferences, and so on. One of the ways of showing this would be to allow the animal to explore and to overcome its fears of a simple T-maze before we introduce the reward. When we do this with well-differentiated goal boxes we do not even have to make the animal make the response of turning left or right to display learning in one trial. Placing the animal hungry in one of the goal boxes and feeding it there, where it has never been fed and has only explored, is sufficient to make it turn to that goal box when it is next placed hungry at the start, as has been mentioned above.

If I may be permitted yet another digression, this last experiment raises other difficulties for the statistical theory. A response appears which has never been rewarded. The animal acts in the way it does presumably because in some way it infers it will be rewarded if it makes that response and not because it has been rewarded for making this response. I apologize for the mentalistic overtones, but I have made a machine that displays this kind of behavior, so I do not regard this vocabulary as indicating an explanation but only as setting the theoretical problem [5, 2].

This ramble brings me to my next point about the experiment I began to describe. Now you will remember that after the rats had been running the maze for some time, sometimes choosing the left side and sometimes the right to go to the same goal, a block was inserted in the maze. The animals being prevented from reaching the goal by one route, on the next trial chose the other route. So it looks as if the animal, when it makes a response which is unrewarded, is less likely to make it the next time. "Time, of course, is no news," you will say. "We knew this already." But this is where you are wrong, because this reminds me that I should have said from the start that there was another condition in this experiment which shows this to be untrue. As you will see, this was an important omission. The other condition was that the animals having been trained, the goal box was simply left empty, so that if an animal turned right, its response would be unrewarded just as if there had been a block in the right alley. So, given the belief that simple non-reward of a response decreased its probability, we would expect the proportion of choices to the other side on the next trial to be the same as in the same as in the block condition — something like 17 out of 19. But it was not. The number of choices of the other side was very like that normally made. Instead of 8.8 (the previous average), it was 9. So you see, non-reward of a response makes it less likely to occur only as a special case. It seems to depend entirely on the expectation which the animal has about the outcome of the line of action. If one route to the food is blocked, then it is best to take the alternative. If, on the other hand, there is no food, and one has to choose, either alternative is as good as the other.

In case I have by now succeeded in persuading you that the rat is really a bewitched fairy prince, let me hasten to say that this was not my intention. I started off by attempting to show that the notion of trying to explain learning curves by assumptions of sampling stimuli which are attached to subsequently rewarded responses was implausible. I then made my case even stronger. I argued that we could not explain choice behavior by assuming that the response at the choice-point was determined solely by the stimuli impinging on the organism at the choice-point, which belief stimulus-sampling theory has inherited from older types of S-R theory. As long as we restrict ourselves to measuring simple choices in a T-maze with a reward in it, this basic notion can be made to fit. What is needed is an experimental analysis of the situation where different basic notions are deliberately put to the test by placing the animals in a whole variety of situations. When we look at experimental evidence on this point, which these methods have revealed, the notion that response can be explained by assuming various amounts or strengths of stimuli at the choice-point and that learning consists in an attachment of stimuli to a response, becomes extremely dubious. I have quoted only a very small part of the evidence against this notion.

There are, of course, always some facts which can be quoted against a working theory such as the statistical learning theory. Some of these will be outside the class of events which the theory was designed to explain. Others will be experiments where the theory cannot make a clear-cut prediction because the situation is not a good one to test the theory. The outcome of other experiments yet will not be predictable from the theory as it stands, but some development, addition, or modification of the theory would accommodate the results. However, the type of evidence I have stressed in criticism cannot be brought under these headings and cannot therefore be shrugged off by saying that the theory is undeveloped. On the contrary, if they are accepted we should have to say that however inchoate the theory is, it is possible already to say that it is on the wrong track.

Now I do not wish to deny that the stimuli which the animal sees at the choice-point have anything to do with its choice. Its choice is in a partial sense determined by the stimuli facing it. Even stimulus sampling may play an important part in the animal's choice under special conditions. But these considerations must be included in a model which is capable of explaining other features of choice behavior also.

Such a theoretical model has been put forward by me in a recent book, *The Structural Basis of Behavior* [2]. The maze experiment which I have been discussing was designed to test this theory, and the theory successfully predicted its outcome as it did for many other experiments which were chosen because a somewhat paradoxical outcome was predicted. It is evidently impracticable to attempt to give anything more than a very cursory sketch here of that part of the system which is relevant to the evidence under discussion.

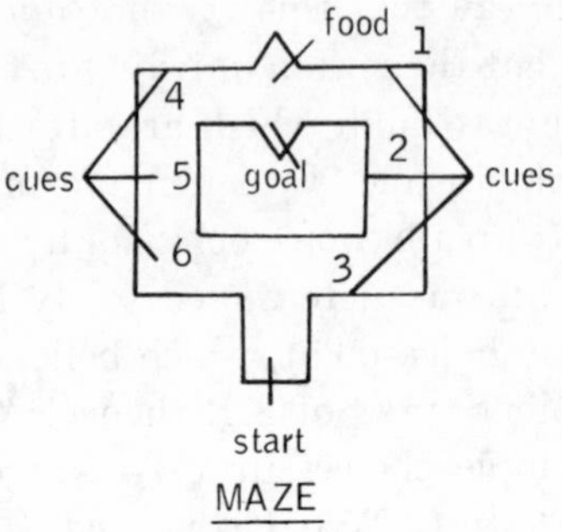

FIG. 1

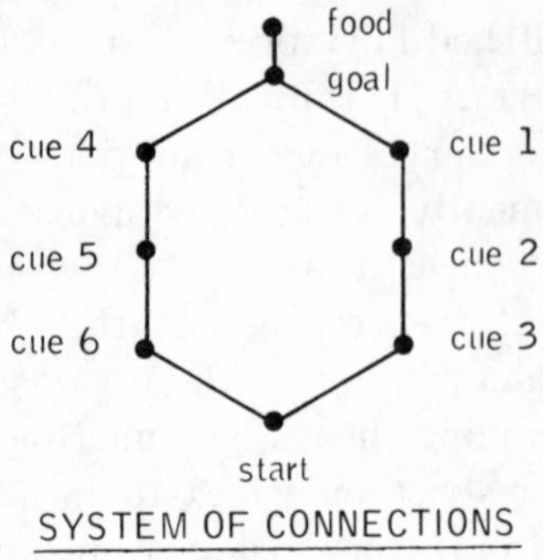

FIG. 2

In the experiment which I have been discussing, the following situation confronts the animal: There is a starting point and then two alleys leading to the same goal (Fig. 1). The theory assumes that each separate cue in the maze excites a corresponding unit in the animal's nervous system. As the animal traverses the maze, such units are connected in the order in which the cues in the maze occur. Therefore, the order of cues in the maze is represented by an order of units in its nervous system. When the animal has run the maze, we assume that the system of connections in Fig. 2 has been set up in its nervous system.

When the animal is hungry, we assume that the food unit is biochemically excited and that this excitation is passed on from this unit to its neighbor, and from this to its neighbors, until it reaches the unit labelled "start" (Fig. 3). Further, it is explained how the arrival of this excitation at a given unit causes the animal to steer toward the cue which this unit represents when it appears. In the case where two cues impinge simultaneously, as when the animal faces both cues 6 and 3 at the choice-point, that cue will be steered toward whichever has the greater amount of excitation arriving from the "food" unit.

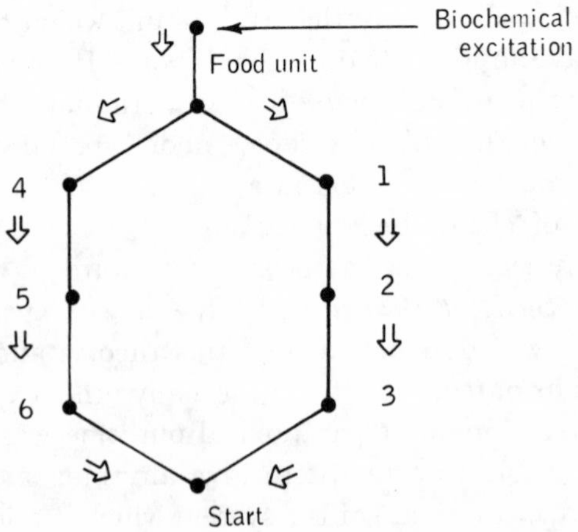

FIG. 3

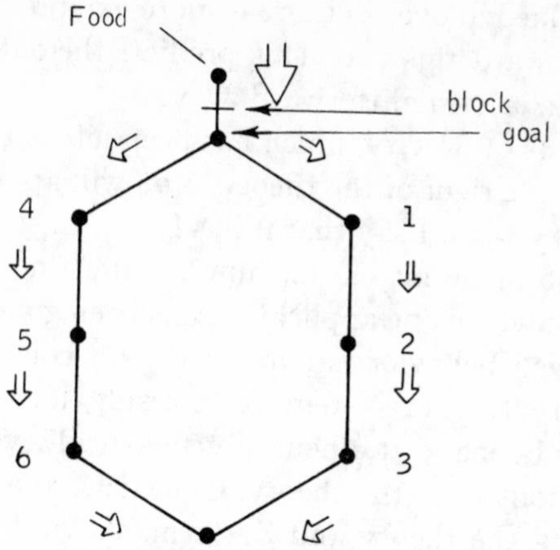

FIG 4.

Another property which this system is postulated to have is this: As the animal is steering, say, toward cue 6 when cue 5 signals its presence, then cue 5 stops transmitting the excitation passed on to it for a time. Therefore, no more excitation will arrive at cue 6 and, as a result, only cue 5 will be steered toward. In this way a hungry animal will approach the food in the goal box.

While a repeated presentation of two cues in succession is held to increase the amount of excitation transmitted from one unit to another, a failure of this succession of two cues is postulated to cut down the amount of excitation transmitted from one to the other. If, for instance, we show the animal the goal box and no food in it, then the excitation from the food unit to the goal box unit is lessened. As the goal box unit transmits such excitation to both cues 3 and 6 (through the mediation of cues 1 and 2, and 4 and 5, respectively) there will be no change in the relative tendency to choose 3 or 6 (Fig. 4).

However, if the goal box cue does not follow cue 1, for instance (if we place a block in that arm of the maze in front of the goal box), only excitation flowing to cue 3 at the choice point will be affected (Fig. 5).

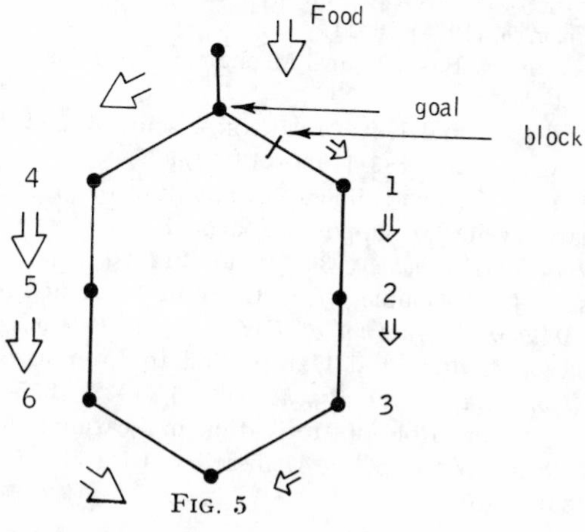

FIG. 5

As was explained above, as there is more excitation arriving at 6, the animal will steer toward this cue. This predicts the outcome of the experiment we examined in a straightforward way.

In the interests of brevity, much has been left out and the exposition fails to do justice to the rigor of the theory. You will appreciate that it is, in fact, a rigorous theory when I say that it has been translated by me into a network of relays and so made into a machine manifesting rat behavior [5, 2].

The theory of which one application has been given is of a structural type. That is, observed behavior is explained as a consequence of a postulated mechanism, structure, or system. As a result, identification of elements of the system can be made at a neurophysiological level and this used to make further predictions from the theory. One such example of this was a prediction made using the theory and Zotterman's work on the chorda tympani nerve. From this it was possible to predict the paradoxical fact that though hypotonic saline would be drunk in greater quantity when the animal was allowed to choose between unlimited quantities of this solution and water, water would actually be more rewarding in a situation where the amounts of water and saline given were equal and limited [15, 2].

My thanks are due to Professor Gordon Bower and to my wife for valuable criticism and discussion.

References

[1] Deutsch, J. A., and J. K. Clarkson. A Test of the Neo-Behavioristic Theory of Extinction, *Quarterly Journal of Experimental Psychology*, 3 (1959), 143–149.

[2] Deutsch, J. A. *The Structural Basis of Behavoir*, Chicago, University of Chicago Press (1960).

[3] Estes, W. K. The Statistical Approach to Learning Theory in Psychology, *A Study of a Science*, Vol. 2 (Ed., Sigmund Koch), New York, McGraw-Hill Book Co., Inc. (1959), 380–491.

[4] Harlow, H. F. Learning Set and Error Factor Theory in Psychology, *ibid.*, 492–537.

[5] Deutsch, J. A. A Machine with Insight, *Quarterly Journal of Experimental Psychology*, 6 (1954), 6–11.

[6] Lashley, K. S. Basic Neural Mechanisms in Behavior, *Psychological Review*, 37 (1930), 1–24.

[7] Deutsch, J. A., and J. K. Clarkson. Nature of the Vibrato and the Control Loop in Singing, *Nature*, 183 (1959) 167–168.

[8] Kendler, H. H. The Influence of Simultaneous Hunger and Thirst Drives Upon the Learning of Two Opposed Spatial Responses of the White Rat, *Journal of Experimental Psychology*, 36 (1946), 212–20.

[9] Deutsch, J. A. Double Drive Learning Without Previous Selective Reinforcement, *Quaterterly Journal of Experimental Psychology*, 10 (1958), 207–10.

[10] Hull, C. L. Differential Habituation to Internal Stimuli in the Albino Rat, *Journal of Comparative Psychology*, 16 (1933), 255–73.

[11] Leeper, R. The Role of Motivation in Learning: A Study of the Differential Motivational Control of the Utilisation of Habits, *Journal of Genetic Psychology*, 46 (1935), 3–40.

[12] Deutsch, J. A. The Hull-Leeper Drive Discrimination Situation — A Control Experiment, *Quarterly Journal of Experimental Psychology*, 11 (1959), 155–63.

[13] Bolles, R. and L. Petrinovich. A Technique for Obtaining Rapid Drive Discrimination in the Rat, *Journal of Comparative Physiological Psychology*, 47 (1954), 378–80.

[14] Deutsch, J. A., and W. Anthony. Blocking the Incorrect Alley in a Two Drive Learning Situation, *Quarterly Journal of Experimental Psychology*, 10 (1958), 22–28.

[15] Deutsch J. A., and A. D. Jones. Diluted Water: an Explanation of the Rat's Preference for Saline, *Journal of Comparative Physiological Psychology*, 53 (1960), 122–127.

A DESCRIPTIVE APPROACH TO THE DYNAMICS OF CHOICE BEHAVIOR

W. K. ESTES

Indiana University, Bloomington, Indiana, U.S.A.

For the philosopher, social scientist, or other "outsider" who would gain an acquaintance with theories of choice behavior, the number and variety of current approaches must be overwhelming. The situation is little better even for the psychologist, accustomed though he is to a multiplicity of theories competing for attention in relation to almost every problem. For one must be prepared not only to accommodate a diversity of viewpoints, but to muster a not inconsiderable technical background. In some instances, current theories of choice involve rather formidable mathematical apparatus; in some instances they are associated with extensive programs of experimental research. I would, if it were possible, wish to proceed in this paper, first to answer the natural question as to why such a patchwork of choice theories should have arisen and flourished, then to show how all will ultimately be combined into a harmonious and manageable whole. What I shall actually attempt is first to organize the array of contemporary theories in terms of the kinds of questions they try to answer, then to offer some reasons to believe that continued development of one type of theory may eventually lead to simplification by eliminating the *raison d'être* for some of the currently fashionable varieties of choice theory.

Alternative Approaches to Choice Behavior

To provide an initial overview of the area we may assemble the various approaches in outline. In all instances the object of attention is the behaviour of an individual in choosing among alternative courses of action. But questions of very different sorts may be raised about the act of choice, and these give rise to quite different kinds of investigation. Questions as to how choices ought to be made have led to systems of the normative type. Calls for explanations of choice behaviour have led, initially at least, to models representing observed choices as the resultant of postulated mental or neurophysiological events. Interest in the prediction of choice has instigated development of psychological scales and other models relating choice probabilities to behavioral correlates and to observed independent variables. Thus we have

I. Normative theories
   A. Moral (ethics)
   B. Rational (theory of games and statistical decision)

II. Quasi normative theories (minimization of regret, maximization of expected value)

III. Hypothetical models
   A. Cognitive and purposive (faculty psychology)
   B. Analogical (physical models, computer simulation)
   C. Neurophysiological

IV. Descriptive theories
   A. Static (scaling and linear programming models)
   B. Dynamic (single and multiple process learning theories)

Perhaps because man's need to replace the apparent capriciousness of human actions with some kind of order so long preceded the availability of techniques for the scientific study of behaviour, it has been a conspicuous characteristic of disciplines dealing with human choices that the elaboration of theory has far outrun the front line of empirical investigation. The precedent set by the great deductive systems of ethics has been more than upheld in the modern systems of game theory and statistical decision theory. These latter are presented formally as purely normative theories, designed to yield rules for optimal decision making, given specific assumptions as to the state of nature and criteria for determining optimality (see, e.g., [20]).

The popularity of normative theories is doubtless due in part to the notion of free will firmly ingrained in our everyday language. If an individual's choices were free of any external influence and if he knew the rules for best making decisions so as to achieve his purposes, then no further theory would be required to account for his choices. But only a few theorists well versed in counterfactual conditionals are able to entertain this possibility seriously. Aside from the difficulty that the premises are sharply contrary to both biological and psychoanalytic psychology, a theory limited to normative assumptions could not even attempt an interpretation of the obvious fact that a great proportion of human choices are far from optimal as judged by any recognized standard of values.

Nevertheless, people, theorists included, like to maintain the belief that they are basically rational even though their actions may not always appear so. When an individual's choices are not optimal, it may be that he has been conforming faithfully to the decision rules of a normative theory but has gone astray because of imprecision in his assignment of probabilities to uncertain events or of values to possible outcomes of his choices. Following this line of thought, social scientists have found it easy to generate plausible choice models almost *ad infinitum* by means of minor emendations of well elaborated normative theories [7], [27]. One popular branch of this family of models stems from the assumption that individuals make choices so as to maximize the expected value of their outcomes in the long run (e.g., [8]). Other variants are based on principles of minimum regret (e.g., [9]), minimax regret (e.g., [24]), and so on. In each case the individual is conceived to function as a modernized version of the rational man of classical economics. His choices simply reflect his persistent efforts to maximize or minimize the expected value of some quantity or combination of quantities. The necessary empirical slack is provided by defining expected value in terms of the individual's subjective scales of utility or probability. The question as to how the individual makes use of past experience in achieving his goals of maximizing or minimizing has not been dealt with by theorists in the normative tradition until very recently. In an unpublished study by Radlow and Siegel [23], an attempt is made to answer the question by assuming that subjective probability develops in accordance with the axioms of statistical learning theory.

Even more sharply than the normative approach, if this be possible, the more clearly hypothetical models illustrate the extent to which theories of choice are determined by the background of the theorist rather than by factual considerations. With the growing popularity of computer simulation of mental processes, it is only to be expected that the older conceptualizations of choice in terms of mental faculties will be supplanted by computer models. A development of this sort is Toda's "Brain-computer" model [29] which combines computer simulation with normative considerations. Although the notion is understandably foreign to social scientists, some biologically oriented theorists (e.g., Deutsch, [5]) maintain that the only legitimate function of a behavioral theory is to yield information about underlying structures. Reflecting this view Deutsch proposes to account for observed choice behavior in terms of hypothetical neurophysiological processes [6].

Although the custom in treating choice behavior has been first to select a preferred type of theory and then to seek some kind of empirical support for it, there would seem to be no logical reason why one could not proceed as with more neutral phenomena, beginning with experimental analysis and introducing, as needed, assumptions and concepts of whatever type prove suitable for describing and predicting empirical data. In fact, an important example of the descriptive approach appeared as early as 1946 in Thurstone's application of the Law of Comparative Judgment to the prediction of choice [28]. Owing to their strictly static character, Thursone's models could not by themselves attempt a generally satisfying interpretation of choice behavior, but they have provided the basis for the scales of subjective probability and utility that provide some link between the normative theories and observed phenomena. Several currently active lines of research are like Thurstone's in that the models generated serve efficiently the function of data-reduction for certain types of choice experiments but do not attempt to relate choice behaviour to antecedent conditions (e.g., [4], [19]).

A descriptive theory as closely geared to data as the scaling models but capable of representing relationships between changes in choice tendencies and determining variables would fill the one conspicuous gap in the array of choice theories. Current trends within the area of choice and decision-making do not, however, appear congenial to any such development. Learning theories are by their nature equipped to deal with changing response probabilities, but they have been developed primarily in conjunction with simple conditioning situations; and learning axioms stated in terms of stimulus and response probabilities cannot lead directly to statements about optimal strategies, utility scales or other like concepts prominent in the literature of choice and decision.

Against the weight of tradition are two recent developments pointing to possible links between learning and choice theory. One of these is Luce's demonstration that the existence of such psychological scales as that of utility can be derived from axioms stated solely in terms of response probabilities [19]. The other is the application of statistical learning models to situations in which the individual is confronted with repeated opportunities to choose among a given set of alternatives, learning being manifested by systematic changes in choice probabilities over trials as a function of values or probabilities of the trial outcomes [2], [10], [15], [26]. In the remainder of this paper, we shall explore the potentialities of this kind of development by summarizing the assumptions of one of these learning models and illustrating some results of its application to binary choice experiments.

Elements of a Learning Theory for Binary Choices

The particular theory to be discussed represents an interpretation of the simplest of the statistical learning models, the "pattern model" [2, ch. 1]. In this theory, a series of choice trials is conceptualized in terms of the stimulus situation (pattern) which can prevail at the beginning of a trial, the response alternatives among which the subject must choose, and the trial outcomes, whose reinforcing effects serve to establish learned associations between stimulus patterns and responses.

For our first illustrative interpretation we shall consider a situation which involves uncertainty with respect to trial outcomes, but no differences in utility for different outcomes, viz., the familiar experiment on simple predictive behaviour or verbal conditioning [11], [15], [21]. The subject's task is simply to choose between two response alternatives, e.g., to operate one of two response keys or to say one of two designated words at the beginning of each trial, attempting to be "correct" as often as possible. The trial terminates with a signal indicating to the subject which response was "correct" according to the experimenter's protocol. Typically the sequence of signals is programmed by the experimenter so that one response has some fixed probability π and the other probability $1-\pi$ of being correct on any trial.

In conceptualizing this experimental situation, we assume that the experimental conditions determine a set of N stimulus patterns any one of which may be present at the beginning of any trial, and all of which are equally likely to occur. A stimulus pattern includes any instruction or other signal given by the experimenter to indicate the initiation of a trial, and may include also whatever aspects of the preceding sequence of trial outcomes the subject has been able to verbalize and recall. Designating the response alternatives by A_1 and A_2, we may categorize trial outcomes into two classes, those that reinforce A_1 and those that reinforce A_2. The principal assumptions concerning the learning process are as follows.

1. Each stimulus pattern is at any time associated with ("connected to") exactly one of the responses A_1 or A_2.

2. When a trial begins with a stimulus pattern connected to A_i, A_i is chosen by the subject with probability one.

3. When a trial begins with a stimulus pattern connected to A_i and the outcome is one which reinforces A_i (indicates A_i was correct), the connection of the pattern to A_i remains unchanged.

4. When a trial begins with a stimulus pattern connected to A_i and the outcome is one which reinforces $A_j (j \neq i)$, then with probability c the pattern becomes connected to A_j, while with probability $1-c$ its connection to A_i remains unchanged.

Probability Matching

It is an obvious theorem that if k of the N patterns are associated with A_1, the probability of A_1 is equal to k/N. Not quite so obvious, but still quite easily derived [2, ch. 1], [10], is the "matching theorem", which states that over a series of trials in which the probability of outcomes that reinforce A_1 is constant and equal to π, the probability of an A_1 choice on the part of the subject approaches π asymptotically. In other words, probability of choosing a given alternative tends to match its probability of reinforcement. There is, to be sure, an element of ambiguity in interpreting the notion of an asymptote with respect to any aspect of human behavior, for even in the best controlled experiment, the conditions influencing the subject's behaviour cannot be held constant indefinitely. Nevertheless, the matching theorem has received rather striking confirmation in a number of experiments.

To give a concrete indication of the degree of confirmation, I have pooled the results reported for 18 groups of human subjects run in six experiments by different groups of experimenters during the period 1939–1956 [11], [14], [15], [16], [17], [21]. The π values for the more frequently reinforced response ranged from .50 to 1.00 with a mean of .76. The mean asymptotic probability of the more frequently reinforced response, estimated by the arithmetic mean of the response proportions for the terminal trial block in each experiment, was .76. The standard deviation of the distribution of differences between π values and mean response proportions was less than .02.

This phenomenon of "probability matching" has excited considerable general interest, partly, no doubt, simply because parameter-free[1]

[1]By "parameter-free" we refer to predictions which do not depend on the evaluation of free parameters from data, but only on experimenter-determined parameters, as π in the present instance.

quantitative predictions have rarely been attempted, let alone confirmed in psychology. Another source of interest has been the disparity between the matching result and the common preconception (evidently based partly on intuition and partly on injudicious extrapolation of game theory) that behavior in the two-choice situation should always conform to a normative principle of maximizing the expected frequency of correct responses. Unfortunately, the question of "matching vs. maximizing" cannot be answered simply by the examination of asymptotic data from choice experiments. Concerning the conclusion of the experiments cited in the preceding paragraph, the criticism was immediately offered that the experiments, typically involving learning series of 100 to 200 trials, might have been terminated too soon and that the observed matching of response and reinforcement frequencies might depend on a fortuitious selection of series duration. In several more recent studies (e.g., [1], [3], [13], [18], [22]) learning series have been more than doubled in length (running from 300 to 450 trials) with no appreciable departures from the previous pattern of results. If one claimed that the asymptote of two-choice learning had now been evaluated, the same criticism could be raised again. It would, however, be hard to dispute the conclusion that over at least the initial stages of simple two-choice learning, probabilities of response tend to approach their probabilities of reinforcement.

Description of Sequential Data

Current research in this area is not by any means preoccupied with the matter of asymptotic probability matching. Emphasis is, rather, shifting to the more ambitious task of accounting for detailed quantitative properties of behavior throughout the course of learning. If the assumptions of the statistical model are sound, it should be possible to predict probabilities of a given choice following any specified sequence of preceding responses and reinforcing events at any stage of learning. One illustration of the level of accomplishment now attainable is given in Table 1. The data come from a

TABLE 1

OBSERVED AND THEORETICAL PROPORTIONS OF MORE FREQUENTLY REINFORCED RESPONSE IN TWO-CHOICE LEARNING EXPERIMENT WITH .80 : .20 REINFORCEMENT PROBABILITIES

	Initial Block		Final Block	
	Obs.	*Th.*	*Obs.*	*Th.*
$p_{11}(1)$	.38	.38	.59	.58
$p_{21}(1)$	.17	.18	.10	.08
$p_{12}(1)$	.06	.07	.13	.12
$p_{22}(1)$	.04	.03	.02	.02
$p_{11}(2)$	.13	.13	.07	.06
$p_{21}(2)$	.12	.12	.04	.07
$p_{12}(2)$	.06	.05	.04	.04
$p_{22}(2)$	.04	.04	.02	.02

study of simple two-choice learning reported by Friedman *et al* [12], in which a group of 80 college student subjects, after having extensive preliminary training with a variety of different reinforcement probabilities (π values), was run through a series of 288 trials with $\pi = .80$. An entry $p_{ij}(k)$ represents the probability of response k on a given trial following the combination of response i and reinforcement j on the preceding trial averaged over trials 1—12 (initial block) or 241—288 (final block). The theoretical values (expressions for which are given in [2, ch. 1]) are those predicted by the pattern model described above after the parameters of the model have been estimated from the data by a modified least squares procedure. Considering that the number of parameters is small relative to the number of degrees of freedom in the data, and that the value of c/N is the same for both blocks, a fairly stringent test of this aspect of the model is provided.

Extension of the Pattern Model to Paired Comparison Learning

Since the assumptions of the statistical model include no direct mention of values or costs, it is not particularly suprising to find that when differential monetary incentives and risks are introduced into the two-choice situation, choice probabilities deviate from the theoretically predicted values. In studies by Siegel and Goldstein [25] and by Suppes and Atkinson [26], among others, monetary rewards have been given for correct choices and fines for incorrect ones. The result, relative to asymptotic behavior, has been a tendency for terminal choice proportions to overshoot matching values, the amount of the disparity being directly related to the magnitudes of the incentives or risks. One interpretation of this finding is that the dynamics of the learning process are basically different in the situation with incentives and risks. A second possibility is that there are two kinds of learning going on in this situation: (1) changes in association between responses and stimulus patterns, produced by the individual trial outcomes in accordance with the assumptions of the pattern model; and (2) changes in habits or hypotheses controlling behaviour over longer sequences of trials, arising from the individual's response to the larger swings in his cash balance. If the latter interpretation is correct, then we might expect to find, somewhat paradoxically, that the simple model will again provide correct predictions if we go to a still more complex incentive-risk situation in which the subjects cannot readily identify and verbalize the relationships between their courses of action and mean values of outcomes over series of trials.

A timely opportunity to test this last suggestion is provided by a "paired comparison" learning experiment conducted in Professor Patrick Suppes' laboratory at Standord University (for a brief description see [26]). In this experiment the subject was offered a choice from a subset of three objects on each trial. Designating the three alternatives as A, B, and C, the combinations AB, AC, BC, and ABC were each presented on 100 trials of the 400 series in random sequence. The experimenter's program, unknown to the subject, assigned A, B, and C, respectively, probabilities of 0.67, .40, and .20

that a choice of the given alternative would be "correct" on any trial on which it was offered. For one group of 48 subjects each correct choice was rewarded with one cent and each incorrect choice cost the subject one cent; for a second group of 48 subjects, each correct choice was rewarded with five cents and each incorrect choice cost the subject five cents.

To apply the pattern model to this situation, we assume that each of the four presentation sets, AB, AC, etc. constitutes a stimulus pattern and that associations of choice responses with any one pattern are learned, over the sequence of trials on which that pattern is present, in accord with the model. As in the simpler case considered above, the model predicts asymptotic probability matching; but there is a complication in that the matching value is now under the joint control of the experimenter and the subject. Consider, for example, the pattern AB. Letting π_a and π_b represent the probabilities that choices of A and B, respectively, will be correct on any trial, one can show by a simple probabilistic argument (see, e.g., [2, ch. 1], [26], [27, chs. 8, 9]) that asymptotically the probability of a choice of A will match its probability of reinforcement[2] only if both are equal to $1-\pi_b/(2-\pi_a-\pi_b)$ (which, of course, reduces to π in the special case, previously considered, where $\pi_{-a} = 1-\pi_{-b} = \pi$). In Table 2 asymptotic choice probabilities computed from this expression are compared with observed proportions over trials 301–400 for the one cent and five cent groups.[3] Although a full evaluation of the predictive power of the model for this situation must wait upon more detailed analysis, including sequential statistics of the data (currently in progress), the results for terminal choice proportions in the binary subsets appear quite promising.

TABLE 2

Observed and Predicted Terminal Choice Proportions for Paired-comparison Learning Experiment

	Observed		Predicted
	1 *c Cr.*	5 *c Cr.*	
$p_{AB}(A)$	.65	.70	.64
$p_{BC}(B)$	.56	.56	.57
$p_{AC}(A)$	.70	.71	.71

Concluding Remarks

In view of recent developments of the sort sketched in the preceding section, it can scarcely be doubted that encroachments of learning theory into the area of choice and decision will continue, probably on a steadily expanding scale. The potentialities and limitations of this approach can scarcely be gauged at the present stage. The denouement which I, personally,

[2]In this situation, a given choice response is said to be reinforced if it occurs and is correct or if the alternative response occurs and is incorrect.

[3]I am indebted to Professor Suppes for making available these unpublished data.

find most congenial to contemplate is an ultimate simplification of the currently motley array of overlapping theoretical efforts into two main kinds: strictly normative theory, essentially a branch of applied mathematics; and a system of descriptive models based on concepts and laws of learning and behavior theory — the latter subsuming the function of the current quasi-normative, faculty, and analogical models.

At best, progress toward such an outcome would necessarily be slow, for in this area theories which must make their way solely on their ability to describe and predict empirical data face resistance in depth from entrenched conceptions of man as a rational decision-maker, as well as from some rather anachronistic views of theory which are prevalent among social and behavioral scientists. Typical of these last is the view expressed by Deutsch [5], [6], which would relegate to second-class citizenship theories which simply describe and predict data. While sharing Deutsch's admiration for theories which generate inferences about underlying structures, one can doubt the wisdom of our straining so hard for interpretation in terms of structure that we fail to discover the "laws of motion." If a functional, descriptive theory of choice proves dependable in helping us to analyze and anticipate the outcomes of new situations, we will probably find that it simultaneously satisfies our demand for an intuitive understanding of choice phenomena.

References

[1] Anderson, N. H., and R. E. Whalen. Likelihood judgments and sequential effects in a two-choice probability learning situation. *Journal of Experimental Psychology,* Vol. 60 (1960), 111–20.

[2] Bush, R. R., and W. K. Estes. *Studies in Mathematical Learning Theory.* Stanford, Calif., Stanford Univ. Press, 1959, viii+432 pp.

[3] Cotton, J. W., and A. Rechtschaffen. Replication report: Two and three choice verbal-conditioning phenomena. *Journal of Experimental Psychology,* Vol. 56 (1958), 96.

[4] Davidson, D., P. Suppes, and S. Siegel. *Decision Making: An Experimental Approach.* Stanford, Calif., Stanford Univ. Press, 1957, 121 pp.

[5] Deutsch, J. A. Learning-behavior-information. *Contemporary Psychology,* Vol. 5 (1960), 147–50.

[6] Deutsch, J. A. The implications of an experiment for theories of choice. *Proceedings of the* 1960 *International Congress for Logic, Methodology and Philosophy of Science.* Stanford, Calif., Stanford Univ. Press, 1961.

[7] Edwards, W. The theory of decision making. *Psychological Bulletin,* Vol. 51 (1954), 380–417.

[8] Edwards, W. The prediction of decisions among bets. *Journal of Experimental Psychology,* Vol. 50 (1955), 201–14.

[9] Edwards, W. Reward probability, amount, and information as determiners of sequential two-alternative decisions. *Journal of Experimental Psychology,* Vol. 52 (1956), 177–88.

[10] Estes, W. K. Of models and men. *American Psychologist,* Vol. 12 (1957), 609–17.

[11] Estes, W. K., and J. H. Straughan. Analysis of a verbal conditioning situation in terms of statistical learning theory. *Journal of Experimental Psychology,* Vol. 47 (1954), 225–34.

[12] FRIEDMAN, M. P., C. J. BURKE, M. COLE, W. K. ESTES, and R. B. MILLWARD. Extended training in a non-contingent two-choice situation with shifting reinforcement probabilities. Paper given at 1960 meetings of the Psychonomic Society.

[13] GARDNER, R. A. Probability-learning with two and three choices. *American Journal of Psychology*, Vol. 70 (1957), 174–85.

[14] GOODNOW, J. J., and L. POSTMAN. Probability learning in a problem solving situation. *Journal of Experimental Psychology*, Vol. 49 (1955), 16–22.

[15] GRANT, D. A., H. W. HAKE, and J. P. HORNSETH. Acquisition and extinction of a verbal conditioned response with varying percentages of reinforcement. *Journal of Experimental Psychology*, Vol. 42 (1951), 1–5.

[16] HUMPHREYS, L. G. Acquisition and extinction of verbal expectations in a situation analogous to conditioning. *Journal of Experimental Psychology*, Vol. 25 (1939) 294–301.

[17] JARVIK, M. E. Probability learning and a negative recency effect in the serial anticipation of alternative symbols. *Journal of Experimental Psychology*, Vol. 41 (1951), 291–97.

[18] LABERGE, D. Effect of preliminary trials on rate of conditioning in a simple prediction situation. *Journal of Experimental Psychology*, Vol. 57 (1959), 20–24.

[19] LUCE, R. D. *Individual Choice Behavior*. New York: Wiley, 1959, xii+153 pp.

[20] LUCE, R. D., and H. RAIFFA. *Games and Decisions*. New York: Wiley, 1958, xix+509 pp.

[21] NEIMARK, E. D. Effects of type of non-reinforcement and number of alternative responses in two verbal conditioning situations. *Journal of Experimental Psychology*, Vol. 52 (1956), 209–20.

[22] NEIMARK, E. D., and E. H. SHUFORD. Comparison of predictions and estimates in a probability learning situation. *Journal of Experimental Psychology*, Vol. 57 (1959), 294–98.

[23] RADLOW, R., and S. SIEGEL. Decision making and learning. Department of Psychology Research Bulletin No. 6 (mimeographed), State College, Pa., Pennsylvania State University, 1960.

[24] SAVAGE, L. J. The theory of statistical decisions. *Journal of the American Statistical Association*, Vol. 46 (1951), 55–67.

[25] SIEGEL, S., and D. A. GOLDSTEIN. Decision-making behavior in a two-choice uncertain-outcome situation. *Journal of Experimental Psychology*, Vol. 57 (1959) 37–42.

[26] SUPPES, P., and R. C. ATKINSON. *Markov Learning Models for Multiperson Interactions*. Stanford, Calif., Stanford Univ. Press, 1960, xii+296 pp.

[27] THRALL, R. M., C. H. COOMBS, and R. L. DAVIS (Eds.). *Decision Processes*. New York: Wiley, 1954, viii+332 pp.

[28] THURSTONE, L. L. The prediction of choice. *Psychometrika*, Vol. 10 (1945), 237–53.

[29] TODA, M. "Brain-computer" model approach to the theory of choice. This volume, pp. 434–41.

"BRAIN-COMPUTER" APPROACH TO THE THEORY OF CHOICE

MASANAO TODA

Hokkaido University, Sapporo, Japan

The *brain-computer* is an imaginary computer, which is, by assumption, a simulator of most of the major functions of man. Suppose that a psychologist is asked to give a general design for this simulator. He is supposed to gather psychological findings which are fairly well established, accumulate psychological theories which are well confirmed, and then attempt to integrate them into a consistent unity, since no computer can be built with inconsistent design and no computer can be run with inconsistent program. Furthermore, the psychologist must start new research to cover the area where the available information is insufficient, since a computer cannot be a satisfactory simulator with incomplete information.

Thus, the brain-computer is a *test*; it tests the internal consistency of psychology as a unitary science. The brain-computer is also *heuristic*; it guides the psychologist how to direct his new research. Further, the brain-computer is a *challenge* to the psychologist if he can build such a machine, and thus will increase his motivation toward the synthesizing of psychology.

In what follows I shall briefly outline my response to this challenge, the main emphasis being placed on the problem of a plausible program of brain-computer to solve decision problems.

The environment surrounding man undergoes a continual change. It exerts certain influences upon the state of man, and man can act back upon the environment. Here it is assumed that by controlling his act and manipulating the environment, man tries to keep his state within a set of certain desirable states. Among this set of desirable states, it is also assumed that there are differences in the desirability of states. Hereby, I wish to introduce a term *adaptance* to represent the degree of desirability of each state. Adaptance is a concept comparable to the concept of utility in the context of the contemporary decision theories, so that adaptance, like utility, is unidimensional and unique up to a linear transformation [3].

The role of the concept of adaptance in the present model might be stated this way: The brain-computer is basically programmed so as to maximize the adaptance integral over its lifetime. However, the brain-computer should consist of finite material, as does man, so that it would not be a perfect machine, and therefore might not be able actually to maximize the adaptance integral every time. Yet the assumption that the brain-computer is programmed this way should mean something definite if an appropriate interpretation is given to adaptance. As apparent from the name of adap-

---

The author wishes to thank Drs. Leon Festinger and Stanley Schachter for their many valuable suggestions.

tance, a connotation of adaptation or survival has been given to the concept; whatever state which is good for survival is of high adaptance value, and this may be a reasonable first approximation.

My first tentative model computer is to be constructed on the basis of this assumption, i.e., it is a survival machine. Furthermore, it is a rational machine — rational in the sense that it is the best machine for maximizing adaptance *under given constraining conditions*. Some of these constraining conditions are already known in psychology and physiology, e.g., fixed memory span for immediate recall, fixed impulse transmission speed through a nerve fiber, and so on, but most of them are yet unknown. In the present approach, however, these unknown constraining conditions are considered as yet undetermined variables. Obviously, any behavior of an organism can be said to be rational if an appropriate set of constraining conditions are assumed, however irrational the behavior may appear to our common sense. A blind man may walk very slowly, but this behavior is not irrational if we know his blindness. A more trivial but suggestive example may be given by the story of a crow who mocked at the rabbit who failed to run away from a wolf: "Why didn't the rabbit fly away from the wolf?"

Likewise, the rationality of a machine is defined only jointly by the purpose of the machine *and* the constraining conditions under which the machine operates. So, conversely, if man is assumed to be a rational machine, any observed human behavior defines a class of admissible sets of constraining conditions that allow a rational interpretation of the observed behavior. The main purport of the present approach is to find a parsimonious set of constraining conditions that make most of the typical human behaviors rational. One particular merit of this approach is obviously that, once such a set of constraining conditions is obtained, it can be tested in any given situation, since a given situation and the constraining conditions should jointly define a rational behavior.

The purpose of the brain-computer is to maximize the adaptance integral as assumed above. In order to attempt it, the brain-computer will be required to be capable of at least the following four functions: First, the measuring of adaptance at a given moment; second, the measuring of some of the basic features of the environment at a given moment; third, the memorizing of both the results of these measurements and the records of its own past acts in a certain systematic way which allows further processing of the stored information; and fourth, the processing of the stored and the currently given information. This final stage should further split into two phases: The processing of redundancies embedded in the stored information for the purpose of prediction, and the solving of maximization problems by utilizing the redundancies already processed.

Before laying down further specifications for the brain-computer, it would be necessary and pertinent here to discuss to some extent the meaning of adaptance integral maximization. Under ordinary circumstances, this maximization problem is not directly solvable, since the adaptance integral is a joint function of behavior, or *act*, and the *state of the world*, and the complete information about the latter is not ordinarily available. To overcome the difficulty, many suggestions have been made among which the following two seem to be most widely accepted, i.e., the minimax solution and the Bayes solution [e.g., 4, 7]. These two suggested solutions are both hard to be subjected to a satisfactory rationalization. So, the reason I prefer the Bayes solution here is not that it is rational but that it better explains experimental results. That is, I adopt the Bayes solution as one of the constraining conditions that man is bound to follow.

Then it is possible to show that, at least in principle, the brain-computer can maximize the *expected* adaptance integral if every bit of its ignorance is represented by a subjective probability distribution. Here, let me lay down a few definitions: An *act* (or a course of action) is defined by a temporal locus of a vector $X(x_1(t), x_2(t), \cdots)$ where $x_1, x_2, \cdots$ are the output variables of the brain-computer which the brain-computer can directly control. The *state of the world* is also represented by a vector $S(s_1(X, t), s_2(X, t), \cdots)$. A *decision* is defined by *any* constraints imposed upon X; e.g.,

$$D_1 = \{x_1(0) = a_1, x_2(0) = a_2, \cdots\}, \quad D_2 = \{x_i(t) = b, \text{ if } S(t)\varepsilon\bar{S}\}, \text{ etc.,}$$

where $a_1, a_2, \cdots$, and b are constants, and $\bar{S}$ is a particular subset of vectors S. The decisions of the type of D_2 will properly be called strategies. *Adaptance* $U(X, S)$ is a numerical function defined over all the possible pairs of X and S. Let $f_D(X, S, t)dt$ be the subjective probability that X and S obtain during the period $[t, t+dt]$, given decision D.

Then the expected adaptance integral given D_i, $V(D_i)$ is expressed as

$$V(D_i) = \int_0^\infty \sum_{X,S} U(X, S) f_{D_i}(X, S, t)dt.$$

This $V(D_i)$ may not necessarily converge, but the difference between any pair of expected adaptance integrals will generally converge if we restrict D within a class of reasonable decisions:

$$V(D_i - D_j) = \int_0^\infty \sum_{X,S} U(X, S)\{f_{D_i}(S, S, t) - f_{D_j}(X, S, t)\}dt.$$

The *optimal decision* D^0 is defined as such a decision for which $V(D^0 - D_i) \geqq 0$ for every alternative D_i.

Thus, the maximization problem is formally solvable, but *not necessarily so in practice*. The number of alternative S must be enormous even if finite, and no computer with limited capacity can compute every $V(D_i - D_j)$ within a reasonable time. Furthermore, there is one constraining condition that considerably complicates the problem, i.e., the *cost of computation*. One thing that should be noted about the real brain is the difficulty in trouble-shooting when it has trouble, and it may easily have trouble if it does not take rest after hard work or long work or both. For the brain-computer to be a simulator of the brain, it should have this characteristic which may most intuitively be expressed as the high cost of computation. To put it more precisely, adaptance is heavily dependent upon the well-being of the brain-computer, and the longer and/or the harder it works, the lower is the adaptance of its state. One of the obvious consequences of this constraining condition is that, paradoxically speaking, it is not ordinarily the optimal act for the brain-computer to attempt to find out the precise optimal decision. Therefore, the computation strategy in solving decision problems should be characterized by the use of a flexible approximation program; the degree of approximation to be adopted in each case depends, roughly speaking, on the importance of the individual decision problem.

First, let me consider the approximation techniques which man is apparently using. The role of science, for example, is said to be the discovery of empirical laws of theories which work. The role of empirical law or theory is obviously to provide a good *approximation* technique, since no science has ever succeeded in predicting the future with absolute certainty. But if a theory is used as if it is predicting the future with certainty, it would enormously reduce the trouble of computing the expected adaptance integral, since it tells us that most f's are simply null. The strong motivation of scientists for deterministic and parsimonious theories may be explained in this context. Also, the same kind of explanation may apply to the broader area of personal beliefs, rules of thumb, and stereotyped opinions, by means of which people make their decisions easily. Although most of these personal beliefs may appear utterly irrational, they could still be conceived as rational, if the criterion for rationality is taken as the maximizing of the adaptance integral, since adaptance is very sensitive to the cost of computation as assumed before.

The perception of "thing" as thing would be another illustration of the same principle. A thing is a package of spatial and temporal redundancy, so that once one obtains the concept of a certain thing as an object, one can draw from it various derivations. Not only the concept of a thing, but every concept and every theory, scientific or not, works in the brain-computer as if it is subroutine; whenever the circumstances are perceived to have come to the point where one of these routine submechanisms for derivation becomes available, it is used, and the cost of computation will considerably be reduced.

The economists' notion of utility, which involves, in effect, the assumption that the value of a certain amount of certain goods is constant, may be considered as another example of expedient means for approximation. Undoubtedly, the value of an object cannot be constant. Possessing an object defines a subset of states characterized by the possession, within which adaptance can take various different values. For example, possessing a piece of food will differently appeal to a person, depending on his state of hunger, on the conditions under which the food is given, and so on. I have conducted an experiment on this, in which a hungry subject is asked to state his *demand price*, i.e., the highest possible amount of money which he is willing to pay, for each of the various amounts of food listed on the given answer sheet. The amount of food to be sold to the subject and the price he must pay for it are then randomly determined by throwing dice. If the randomly determined price is higher than the subject's demand price for the amount of food also randomly determined, no sale is made and he must wait three hours more without food. But if the price turns out lower than or equal to his demand price, the subject buys the food for that price and eats it. The immediate consumption of the food is compulsory.

My hypothesis was that the curve of the demand price plotted against the amount of food would initially increase with negative acceleration, reach a maximum and then decrease very rapidly. The hypothesis was generally confirmed, but an interesting case was found for one subject who did not show this pattern. After the experiment he told me that he simply could not get rid of the idea that the food, which was crackers, was a penny, say, a piece. Incidentally, the dice randomly selected a large amount of food, which he had to eat, and he got sick.

Apparently, the necessary immediate consumption condition imposed upon subjects in this experiment is extremely stringent, rarely confronted in everyday situations. In a sense, we could say that the economic and the related systems of our society have tended to stabilize the utility of an object probably as a consequence of increasing exchangeability. This has certainly served people to develop concepts like a fixed value for each object, which concepts actually work as expedient means for approximation, in so far as they are correctly applied in appropriate situations.

Now, finally, I shall turn to the problem of the general approximation program in search of the optimal act. It is to be noted first that the list of alternative acts would usually be tremendously long if they are tabulated only on the basis of physical possibility. To narrow down the list, the first approximation the brain-computer should employ would be the classification of the environment into discrete categories [2].

Once the classification of the environment is made, some of the environmental categories will be found frequently to recur. These recurrent environments may very often be *small worlds*; that is, under the circumstances, it is expected that the effect of the choice among acts does not extend beyond the immediate outcome of the act. The brain-computer should, and could, have some efficient subprograms to deal with these *familiar* small-world decision-problems just because of their frequency and small-worldness.

When the recurrency and the small-worldness of an environmental category is established, the only thing that the brain-computer needs to do is to pick up a few responses which have been successful in the past and to subject them to a certain subprogram of learning. This subprogram may be a very simple one such as changing the response probabilities depending on the history of adaptance payoffs. It is easily shown that the average adaptance payoff can be improved this way when the environmental conditions are stationary and recurrent. Most of the current stochastic learning theories are of this type, and it would be very easy to rig up this kind of subprogram within the brain-computer, if, as I believe, the brain-computer is basically a stochastically controlled machine[1] for the reasons stated by von Neumann and others [6].

This is not the whole story, however. It is unlikely that we need the whole complex mechanism of the brain to deal only with this kind of fairly unsophisticated mechanism. The real problem is how to make a decision when the environmental category is unfamiliar, even though categorization may be possible because of similarities to known categories. Let me take two examples: The choice of a dish from the menu at a restaurant when one is visiting a foreign country; and the choice of one's profession when one is old enough to make it. In the former example, the foreigner may first look for information from a waiter or from the person sitting next to him. This state still belongs to categorization; he is establishing similarities between this environment and the known categories. The given information will probably be insufficient so that the choice will be made according to the principle of *expected* adaptance integral maximization with subjective probabilities derived from available information. In this case, the choice will probably be a small-, or quasi-small-, world choice, since whatever he may eat there will make little difference after a couple of hours of digestion. Even if this is not true, as, for instance, the foreigner was warned that one of the dishes would cause him stomach trouble, the choice situation is practically closed unless he is supplied with further information about which dish is bad. This kind of choice situation may be called the *small-world by forced ignorance.*

This concept implies a kind of paradox. If ignorance makes choice virtually a small-world choice, and if the more ignorant one is, the easier one's choice, then why does one look for information? To explain this, we must realize that a choice under forced ignorance is equivalent to a choice under forced use of a certain degree of approximation. It is obvious that one has to have an estimate of the probable error characteristics of each approximation procedure in order to use various approximation procedures properly in each decision situation. The optimality of the act obtained by the use of a certain approximation procedure would be guaranteed only if the expected adaptance integral of the alleged optimal act exceeds all the others beyond this probable error. This requirement may not be satisfied under certain ignorance situations, and one should look for information, if possible, to adopt a finer approximation.

The next example is the choice of a profession; an example of an apparently non-small-world choice. Such a choice will continue to affect one's state on and on for a person's whole life-length. A small-world type of approxi-

---

[1] I am inclined to believe, more specifically, that the type of calculation employed by the brain-computer is essentially a kind of Monte Carlo. If this conjecture is right, then it is quite likely that the probabilities are borne by processes similar to Audley's model [1].

mation cannot be employed here. One of the approximations to be used here is the one I have briefly mentioned concerning the utility of possessing an object. The utility of possessing a certain object will be redefined here as the average expected adaptance integral averaged over the subset of states characterized by the possession of the object and over the subset of acts that one will perform when he is within the subset of states. Coming back to the boy who is going to choose his profession, let us suppose that going into business is one of his possible acts. If so, he will probably consider the possibility of being an executive of a big business. Also, probably, his information will be quite insufficient for him to discriminate among the various possible states within this subset of being an executive of a big business. So, he has no choice but to count this subset and all other similar subsets as units, attaching to each of them a utility, or average adaptance integral, and replacing individual states by subsets of states in his calculations. Assuming this to be taken for granted, a good strategy for an approximation of this kind would be obtained by minimizing the total error while keeping the cost of computation constant. For the sake of simplicity, let me assume that the cost is proportional to the number of subsets used. Then our problem turns out to be a search for a plausible partitioning of the whole set of states which minimizes the total estimation error, keeping the number of alternative subsets, or categories, constant. In words more familiar to psychologists, this is the problem of a plausible articulation of one's life-space.

Since this is a quite complicated problem, let me give here only a crude sketch of a plausible program, which is intuitively very simple. The areas of the state-space which should be partitioned into larger than average subsets are those places which are characterized by (1) more homogeneous subjective probability distribution, (2) more homogeneous adaptance distribution, (3) less sensitivity of subjective probability to the chosen act, and (4) smaller subjective probability of getting at the area of the state-space. In terms of the articulation of the life-space, this program may be summarized as follows: Finer articulation for those areas of the life-space which are important, manipulable, rich in information, and likely to be encountered in the near future.

As mentioned before, if the alleged optimal act does not exceed all the others in its expected adaptance beyond the error characteristics of the approximation procedure used, one should employ finer approximation and recalculate at least a part of the former calculation. The strategy to be adopted here is probably very close to the strategy for sequential decision-making as formulated by Wald [7].

Before concluding this loose outline of a brain-computer model I would like to add one further remark on its relevance to some other fields of psychology. Let us consider a person's concept of self. As obvious from the above discussion, it is necessary for a person to have a set of (conditional) subjective probabilities concerning his own act $X(t)$ given S, in order to calculate the expected adaptance integral over a fairly long extension of time. To do so, one has to develop a concept of one's self and ability just as one should develop concepts of external objects. Therefore, any information about one's self would never fail to be important. A prediction to be derived from the brain-computer model hitherto discussed would be like this: A person would in general be less willing to accept information which might force him to decrease his ability estimate than that which would increase the ability estimate. A decreased ability estimate will usually imply the necessity of immediate reworking of his whole scheme developed for calculating expected adaptance integral, since, for example, a decreased ability estimate may deprive a person of the hope of getting into a certain type of profession. There are many such barriers in our life, and a decreased ability estimate may often drastically change one's prospects for the future. On the other hand, an increased ability estimate would not usually give rise to this kind of difficulty. The expected adaptance integral calculated with the old ability estimate would continue to work as an approximation. One could probably be at least as well off as before. Then, the maximization scheme can be corrected afterward by running the brain-computer at its cheap normal activity level.

References

[1] Audley, R. J. A stochastic model for individual choice behavior. *Psychological Review,* Vol. 67 (1960), 1–15.

[2] Bruner, J. S., J. J. Goodnow, and G. A. Austin. *A study of thinking.* New York, Wiley, 1956.

[3] Edwards, W. The theory of decision making. *Psychological Bulletin.* Vol. 51 (1954), 380–417.

[4] Savage, L. J. *The foundation of statistics.* New York, Wiley, 1954.

[5] Toda, M. A computer model of human decision making mechanism: I. Designing brain computer. Experimental Psychology Laboratory Memorandum Report No. 8, Sapporo, Hokkaido, Hokkaido Univ., 1958.

[6] Von Neumann, J. *The computer and the brain.* New Haven, Yale University Press, 1958.

[7] Wald, A. *Statistical decision functions.* New York, Wiley, 1950.

SECTION

VIII

METHODOLOGY AND PHILOSOPHY OF SOCIAL SCIENCES

MODELS FOR THE ANALYSIS OF BALANCE OF POWER IN SOCIETY

JOHN C. HARSANYI

Australian National University, Canberra, Australia

Now at Wayne State University, Detroit, Michigan, U.S.A.

The purpose of my present paper is to survey certain recent developments in game-theoretical bargaining models, which now, I believe, have cleared the way for more extensive fruitful applications of the theory of games in the social sciences. In particular, these developments open the way for what I propose to call a *bargaining-equilibrium analysis* of social behaviour — that is, for explaining social institutions and social practices in terms of the *balance of power* or *bargaining equilibrium* among the interested social groups or individuals.

Apart from their applications in the social sciences, these bargaining models, I think, also have interesting philosophical implications, in that they throw new light on the concept of *rational behaviour*, and on the relationship between rational behaviour and *moral* behaviour.

1. Explanation in Terms of Conflicting Social Interests

One way of explaining the social institutions of a given society is in terms of the *common interests* that these institutions serve for the society as a whole. In sociology and cultural anthropology the present popularity of *functionalistic* ideas has given considerable currency to this type of explanation. There is of course no denying of its usefulness for certain purposes. But, as has often been pointed out, as a general explanation of social institutions it has very serious limitations.

For instance, admittedly, many features of the present American educational system can be explained in terms of the common social needs that this educational system has to serve — such as the need for trained man power in economic and other social organizations, and the need by all social institutions for participants socialized into society's basic values and rules of behaviour.

But evidently these common social needs cannot account for many empirical features of the American educational system. They surely cannot account at least for the shortcomings that this educational system displays in the very service of these social needs. Moreover, and this is more important for our present purposes, the American educational system, just as any other social institution, is under constant pressure by different and often conflicting *sectional interests* — such as student, parent, and teacher interests; employer, trade union, and professional interests; religious, ethnic, and political interests, etc. For a detailed explanation of why the present American educational institutions are such as they are, and why they differ from educational institutions existing in other countries, or from those that existed in America itself in earlier periods, we have to look to *all* these more or less conflicting social interests, and not only to the *common* interests of the society as defined by an impartial observer.

2. The Bargaining Problem vs. the Problem of Dominant Loyalties

Though analysis of social institutions in terms of an interaction among a variety of different social interests has a long history, all such analytical attempts in the past suffered from the fundamental logical defect that no clear theoretical model had been available to explain or predict the outcome of such an interaction among groups or individuals with more or less conflicting interests.

Such an interaction always involves two different, though of course interrelated, analytical problems. One is a problem in social psychology: given free choice, to what extent will people in various situations give priority firstly to their *individual interests* in the narrowest sense; secondly to the *sectional interests* of their own family, or business firm, or occupational group or social class, or ethnic community, or any other social group they happen to belong to; and thirdly to the *general interests* of the society as a whole at the national or international level. This may be called the problem of *dominant loyalties*. It is essentially a question about the nature of each individual's (or social group's) *utility function*, about how much weight this utility function gives to individual, sectional, or general considerations.

The other question belongs to a rather different level of analysis. Now we assume that all participants' utility functions are *given*, including their tastes for commodities, their value attitudes, their willingness to take risks, as well as the relative priorities they assign to their own personal interests, to the sectional interests of the various social groups they belong to, and to the general interests of society as a whole. Our question now is that, given all these utility functions, what factors will determine the relative influence of the various participants' utility functions (or interests) on the final outcome? This problem is known as the *bargaining problem*, because conflicts of interests, if they are settled at all, are typically settled by some form of explicit or implicit bargaining.

3. The Bargaining Problem in Classic Economics

Classic economic theory raised the bargaining problem in several contexts, most importantly in the theory of bilateral monopoly, and in the theory of duopoly or, more generally, of oligopoly. But, in spite of attempts by the best names in the history of economics, no satisfactory solution was achieved. For instance, it is now commonly agreed that the famous duopoly models of Cournot, Bertrand, and Edgeworth are all subject to fatal objections — most importantly to the objection that at one stage or another they attribute quite unacceptably irrational behaviour to the two duopolists.

However, some important partial results did emerge. These do not define a unique solution for the bargaining problem but at least specify certain *necessary conditions* that any rational solution must satisfy. More particularly, it has been pointed out by Edgeworth and others that in the case of

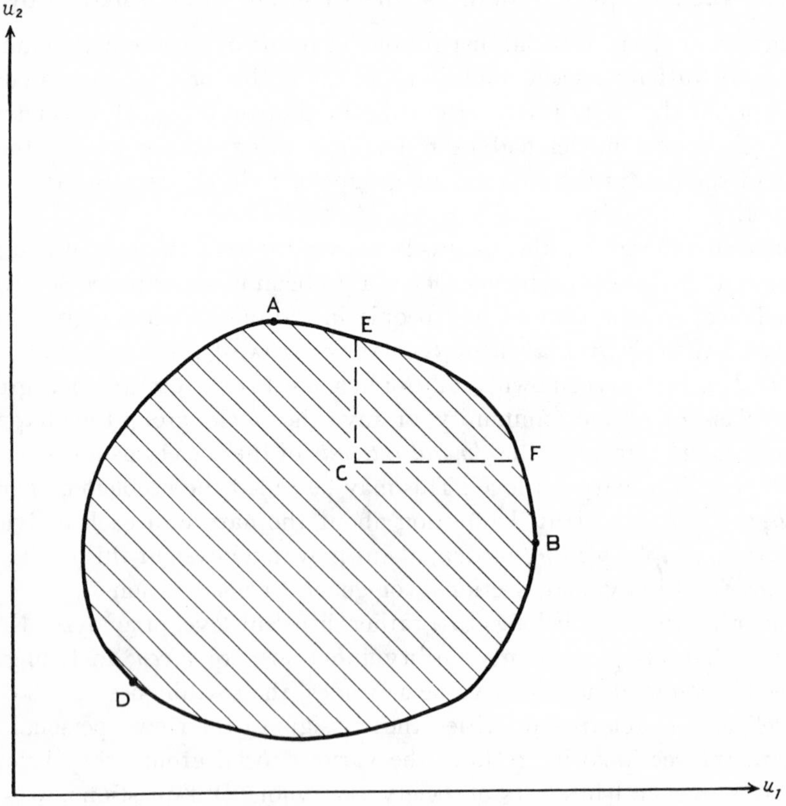

FIG. 1

bargaining between two individuals, (1) the solution must be *individually efficient*, that is, it must be preferable for each party to the conflict situation that would result if no agreement were reached; and (2) the solution must be *jointly efficient* (Pareto-optimal), that is, the agreement reached must not admit of improvement to *both* parties' mutual advantage. (For, if such improvement had been possible, rational bargainers would have made full use of it in concluding their agreement.)

Diagrammatically these two requirements can be represented as follows (see Fig. 1).

Let the two bargainers' utility payoffs u_1 and u_2 be measured along the two axes, and let the area $AEFBD$ represent the *prospect space*, i.e., the set of all utility pairs (u_1, u_2) that the two parties can achieve by any joint strategy available to them. Let C be the *conflict point* representing the utilities the two parties would obtain if they could not reach an agreement. Then, requirement (1) says that the solution (i.e., agreement point) must lie *in* the prospect space *above* and *to the right* of C, that is, in the triangle EFC.

Requirement (2) says that the solution must lie on the *upper-right boundary* of the prospect space, that is, on the curve $AEFB$. Taken in conjunction, the two requirements entail that the solution must lie on the arc EF. But from these two requirements nothing more specific can be inferred about where the solution will actually lie between E and F.

4. The Analytical Tasks of Game-Theoretical Bargaining Models

As the main objection to earlier treatments of the bargaining problem was the fact that they attributed quite implausibly irrational behaviour to the participants, it was a natural next step to attempt developing more satisfactory bargaining models by asking the question, what sort of behaviour would represent *perfectly rational* behaviour on the part of people involved in bargaining situations? This is precisely the question through which the theory of games approaches the bargaining problem.

Thus game-theoretical bargaining models are not based on direct *empirical* generalizations concerning bargaining behaviour, but are rather based on the *normative* concept of 'perfectly' rational behaviour. All the same, one of the main aims of these models is to serve as analytical tools for the study of empirical social behaviour, for explanation and prediction. Experience has shown in economics and in other social sciences that models based on the assumption of perfectly rational behaviour often yield remarkably good predictions about the outcome of real-life social behaviour, at least as a matter of good first approximation.

To be sure, we should be able eventually to obtain more realistic behavioural models of even greater predictive and explanatory value, by using what Herbert A. Simon [20–22] calls models of *limited rationality*, which explicitly specify the limitations to which all human information-processing and decision-making behaviour is always subject, and which also explicitly specify how humans tend to *adjust* to these limitations in their own intellectual abilities. For instance, one will have to make it clear how people, in view of their own computational limitations, tend to approximate the solution of complex and difficult mathematical or logical problems, by solving some much simpler and easier problems instead.

Yet, it seems to me that it will be a great help towards the difficult task of developing acceptable descriptive bargaining models based on some notion of limited rationality, if we set up normative models of perfectly rational bargaining behaviour, and then confront these models with the empirical facts to see what specific restrictions have to be imposed on our rationality postulates. As the example of such powerful minds as Cournot, *et al.*, shows, it is virtually impossible to develop bargaining models of some intrinsic plausibility, and not open to the most damaging objections from the very start, if we do not possess a reasonably clear normative idea of what rational behaviour really amounts to in bargaining situations.

However, even before such more realistic descriptive models become available, our present game-theoretical bargaining models based on normative rationality postulates seem to provide quite useful approximations to the actual results emerging from interaction between various social pressures and counter-pressures in a wide variety of social situations.

But even in cases where they might not supply sufficiently realistic predictions, they still can serve an important analytical purpose. Though they may not indicate the actual outcome of the bargaining process, they do define the outcome that would correspond to the theoretical *balance of power* between the parties, i.e., the outcome that *would* arise *if* all parties made fullest use of their strategical possibilities, i.e., always acted in a perfectly rational manner.

To sum up, game-theoretical bargaining models serve three main analytical purposes, viz., (1) *conceptual clarification* of the notion of rational behaviour as applied to bargaining situations; (2) *explanation* and *prediction* of the outcome of real-life bargaining behaviour; and (3) definition of a bargaining equilibrium point or solution, corresponding to the theoretical *balance of power* between the participants.

5. Bargaining Models and Arbitration Models

Though game-theoretical *bargaining models* are based on a normative concept of rational behaviour, they must be clearly distinguished from normative models of another sort, whose aim is to apply moral or political value judgements to bargaining situations, such as Raiffa's [17] and Braithwaite's [1] *arbitration models*. (These latter belong to ethics or welfare economics, rather than to game theory in the usual sense.) Failure to keep these two apart has given rise to a good deal of confusion in the literature.

Bargaining models are concerned with moral or political value judgements only to the extent to which any particular bargaining party's utility function happens to incorporate such moral or political preferences, But, once all participants' utility functions are given, no use is made of moral or political value judgements in deriving the solution. This is so because, unlike arbitration models, which try to define a morally or politically *fair* solution, bargaining models proper try to define the solution that would arise from a *rational pursuit* of *self-interest* by all parties (or, more generally, from a rational pursuit of individual 'utility', which, as we have seen, may include unselfish considerations). That is, the latter are concerned with bargaining situations in which the parties make concessions, not because they regard it as *fair* to make them, but because they regard it as too *risky* to refuse making them.

I shall argue later (Section 15) that arbitration models and bargaining models proper not only differ in their conceptual interpretation but also have to differ in their mathematical structure — which makes it all the more important to keep a clear distinction between them.

6. The von Neumann-Morgenstern Theory and the Bargaining Problem

When von Neumann and Morgenstern's *Theory of Games and Economic Behavior* [16] was first published in 1944, many social scientists entertained high hopes about the new possibilities that the theory of games would open up for the analysis of the balance of power in society. Most of these hopes, however, met with disappointment — at least in the short run.

In effect, von Neumann and Morgenstern did provide some excellent conceptual tools for the analysis of game situations and more generally for the study of rational behaviour, such as the concepts of cardinal utility, of strategy in general and mixed strategy in particular, of the extensive and the normalized forms of a game, of dominance, of coalitions, and many others. Some of these concepts had very important applications also outside game theory, for instance in statistics and in operations research.

But, like most pioneering efforts, the von Neumann-Morgenstern theory had serious limitations. It did offer a very satisfactory solution for *two-person, zero-sum* (or constant-sum) *games*, in which the two players' interests are exactly opposite to each other. But it did not define a unique solution for *two-person bargaining games* (non-zero-sum games), in which the two players' interests are partly competitive and partly complementary. Nor did it define a unique solution for *n-person games*.

In the analysis of bargaining games in particular the von Neumann-Morgenstern theory did not go beyond the conclusions of classic economic theory, viz., the requirements of individual efficiency and joint efficiency (Section 3 above).

As a result, von Neumann and Morgenstern's theory succeeded in giving new analytical foundations only to one of the social sciences, viz., the science of military strategy and tactics — as war is in the main a two-person, zero-sum game. But their theory had little impact on economics and all the other social sciences which deal with non-zero-sum games and, to a large extent, with *n*-person games.

7. Nash's Theory of the Two-Person Bargaining Game

A few years later, however, a very satisfactory game-theoretical solution to the two-person bargaining problem was suggested by John F. Nash [**13**].

He pointed out that the bargaining problem has an obvious solution at least in the special case of games completely *symmetric* with respect to the two players. For, clearly, if a symmetric game is to have a unique solution at all, this solution must assign the same payoffs to the two players.

To obtain a solution also for non-symmetric bargaining games, Nash argues that the solution of a bargaining game should be invariant with respect to certain mathematical transformations. He then shows that these symmetry and invariance requirements fully determine the solution of the game. If u_1 and u_2 denote the two players' utility functions while C denotes the conflict point, then the only solution point satisfying Nash's requirements will be the unique point S at which the product

$$\pi = [u_1(S) - u_1(C)] \cdot [u_2(S) - u_2(C)]$$

is maximized over the whole of the prospect space.

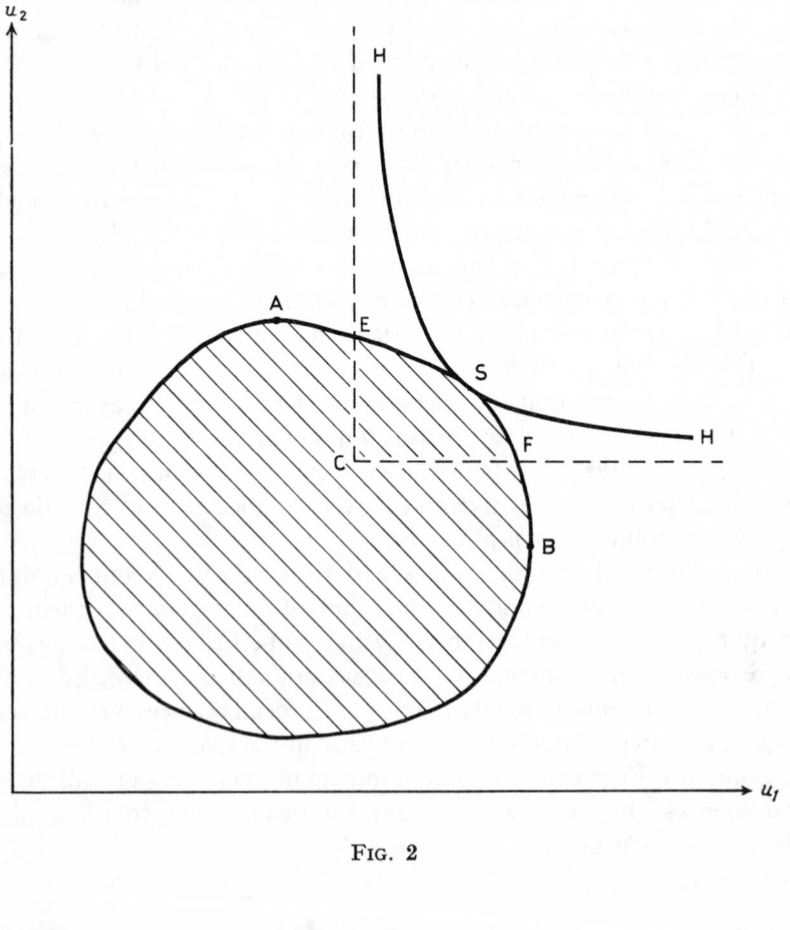

FIG. 2

Geometrically this means (see Fig. 2) that the solution point S is the point of tangency between AB (the upper-right boundary of the prospect space) and HSH (the rectangular hyperbola asymptotic to the vertical and horizontal lines drawn through the conflict point C, i.e., to the lines EC and CF).

Nash also suggested a solution for the more general case of bargaining games, where the position of the conflict point C is *not* simply *given,* but rather depends on the retaliatory strategies the two players would actually use against each other if they could not reach an agreement [15]. He uses a model in which at the beginning of the game both players have to state their *threat strategies*, i.e., the retaliatory strategies they would use against each other in a conflict situation. He then defines each player's *optimal* threat strategy, i.e., the threat strategy which will maximize his final payoff in the bargaining game. (Intuitively, a given player's optimal threat strategy is the strategy which represents the best possible compromise between the aim of *maximizing* the costs of a conflict to his opponent, and the aim of *minimizing* the costs of a conflict to himself.)

If one tries out Nash's solution on various specific bargaining situations, including the classical problems of duopoly and bilateral monopoly, one finds that it is quite generally in excellent agreement with one's common-sense intuitive ideas of what outcome to expect between rational bargainers in each particular bargaining situation, in accordance with the relative strength of the two parties' bargaining positions [12, 6].

In general the Nash solution assigns to any given party a larger payoff

1. the larger this party's *willingness to risk* a conflict rather than making concessions to his opponent;
2. the smaller the *other* party's willingness to risk a conflict;
3. the larger the *damage* that in case of a conflict the first party could cause to the second party, at a given cost to himself; and
4. the smaller the damage that the *second* party could cause to the first party at a given cost to himself.

8. Zeuthen's Decision Rule

Interestingly enough, Nash's solution (though without the concept of optimal threats) was essentially anticipated by the Danish economist Frederic Zeuthen in 1930 [23, Chap. IV]. Though Zeuthen's method of deriving the solution is mathematically less elegant (of course at the time he had no access to game-theoretical ideas), for many purposes his approach is actually preferable, and in general supplements Nash's approach in a very useful way.

In modern terminology, Zeuthen essentially asks the question, what would be the most rational *decision rule* for any given bargaining party to decide at any particular stage of the bargaining process whether he himself should make the next concession or should rather wait for his opponent to make it.

The answer that Zeuthen gives to this question is as follows. Let S_1 and

S_2 denote the last offers of players 1 and 2, respectively, at some given moment. Let C again denote the conflict situation that would arise if no agreement were reached.

Finally, let u_1 and u_2 denote the two players' utility functions. Then, assuming that each player tries to maximize the expected value (actuarial value) of his utility, it is easy to show that the greatest risk (the greatest probability of a conflict) player 1 would be willing to face, rather than accepting his opponent's last offer S_2, would be

$$p_1 = \frac{u_1(S_1) - u_1(S_2)}{u_1(S_1) - u_1(C)}.$$

Similarly, the greatest risk player 2 would be willing to face, rather than accepting his opponent's last offer S_1, would be

$$p_2 = \frac{u_2(S_2) - u_2(S_1)}{u_2(S_2) - u_2(C)}.$$

Now, Zeuthen's decision rule says that player 1 should make the next concession if $p_1 < p_2$ and player 2 should make the next concession if $p_1 > p_2$. (In the case $p_1 = p_2$ both should make a concession.)

It can be shown that, if both players follow Zeuthen's rule, they will end up at the Nash solution of the game, so that Zeuthen's and Nash's models are *mathematically equivalent* [6].

Zeuthen himself proposed his decision rule on intuitive grounds, without offering any detailed justification for it. But it can be shown that his decision rule is in actual fact the *only one* consistent with certain very natural general postulates of rational behaviour.

I cannot go now into the details of the proof, which I have discussed on other occasions [6, 8]. But the main point is this. If I am a rational bargainer and am also facing a rational opponent, then I cannot expect that my opponent will follow a bargaining strategy *less rational* than I myself would follow in his place. This means that I cannot expect, or act on the expectation, that my opponent will make a concession in a situation in which I myself, following my own criteria of rational behaviour, would refuse to make a concession.

This consideration imposes a strong symmetry requirement on the bargaining strategies (or decision rules) that rational bargainers can use against rational opponents. This symmetry requirement, together with some other very natural rationality postulates, as can be shown, directly entails Zeuthen's decision rule.

9. The Theoretical Importance of Zeuthen's Rule

Zeuthen's decision rule turns out to be a principle of very wide applicability and of great analytical usefulness, whose relevance goes far beyond the theory of two-person bargaining games, for which it had been originally formulated. In effect, it seems to me, it represents the solution (or at any rate the major part of it) for *the* fundamental analytical problem of game theory as a whole.

Game theory envisages a rational player faced with rational opponents. If he knew in advance what strategies his opponents would follow, his problem would reduce to straightforward utility maximization. But the real difficulty is that in general he *does not* know in advance what strategies his opponents are going to use. All he knows is that his opponents' strategies will depend on what strategy *they* expect *him* to follow, in the same way as his own strategy depends on what strategies *he* expects *them* to follow. Thus there appears to be a vicious circle here; and the main task of game theory is to break this circle — which requires offering criteria to decide what *rational expectations* the players can entertain about one another's strategies.

But what Zeuthen's decision rule does is precisely to offer a rational criterion for deciding, over a wide range of situations, what expectations rational players can consistently entertain about one another's behaviour.

We shall see that the Zeuthen-Nash solution for two-person bargaining games (two-person cooperative games) can be generalized for *n-person cooperative games*. Indeed, Zeuthen's decision rule can be extended even to *two-person* and *n-person non-cooperative games*, and defines a unique solution also for these non-cooperative games, with the exception of some rather special cases.

10. A Bargaining Model for the n-Person Cooperative Game

As most social situations involve more than two participants, it is obviously desirable to define a determinate solution (or equilibrium payoff vector) also for n-person cooperative games.

Such a solution, with some very attractive mathematical properties, was suggested by L. S. Shapley [19]. I later proposed a certain modification to it, with a view to making it a more accurate representation of the various players' mutual threat possibilities [7, pp. 353–355].

But the Shapley solution,[1] even in its modified form, is restricted to games with *transferable utility*.[2] (This means that, if one player makes a payment to another, the payer's loss exactly equals the payee's gain. This requires that money or other values should be transferable from one player to another without cost or profit, and that all players' utilities should be linear in money or in some other means of payment. It is clearly a very restrictive assumption, seldom met in empirical social situations.)

I have suggested a bargaining model for the n-person cooperative game, which does not require transferable utility [9] (for an earlier version of my

---

[1]The payoffs that the Shapley solution defines for the various players are often referred to as the *Shapley values* of the game.

[2]This restriction the Shapley approach inherits from the von Neumann-Morgenstern theory, on which it relies for certain mathematical tools.

model, see [7]). The model is conceptually a generalization of the Zeuthen-Nash solution for the two-person case to the *n*-person case. But it turns out to contain not only the Zeuthen-Nash solution, but also the modified Shapley solution, as special cases.

The von Neumann-Morgenstern theory of the *n*-person cooperative game is based on the assumption that the *n* players will split up into two (or possibly more) *coalitions* having no common members. But the theory makes no attempt to supply criteria for predicting *which* particular coalitions will come into existence in any given game, out of the usually very large number of possible coalitions among the players. This of course seriously limits the predictive and explanatory value of the theory.

More fundamentally, it seems to me that a splitting up of the players into disjoint coalitions should not be included *a priori* in the very *definition* of rational behaviour in cooperative *n*-person games. For, any particular group of players can always improve their bargaining positions by cooperating in promoting their common interests and in protecting these common interests against the rest of the players. Therefore, in my view, the definition of rational behaviour in cooperative games should include cooperation, within *every* possible subset or coalition of the players, in all matters concerning the members' common interests and protection of these interests against all other players. Assuming rational behaviour, such a cooperation among a given group of players can fail only if the physical limitations imposed upon the players (e.g., restrictions on communication) or their personal preferences (e.g., their mutual dislikes) make this cooperation impossible or prohibitively expensive. (But such conditions can always be represented in the model by an appropriate adjustment of the payoff function for the game.)

For instance, in a three-person game we should assume that, in protecting their common sectional interests, players 1 and 2 will cooperate against 3, players 1 and 3 will cooperate against 2, and players 2 and 3 will cooperate against 1 — whereas all three players will cooperate in matters concerning the common interests of all three of them.

To represent this idea mathematically my model makes the assumption that the members of any possible subset of the players (I call these subsets *syndicates*[3]) guarantee certain payoffs called *dividends*, to all members of that particular syndicate, and agree to cooperate in securing these dividends against any possible resistance by the other players. The final payoff of each player is simply the *sum* of the dividends he receives from all syndicates of which he is a member (including the grand syndicate consisting of all players).

The dividend-guaranteeing ability of each sectional syndicate, on the other hand, is assumed to depend on the power it could muster in a conflict

[3]I am using the term 'syndicate' rather than the term 'coalition' of von Neumann and Morgenstern as a reminder of the difference in the assumptions made.

situation, or — more exactly — on the payoffs that the members of that syndicate could secure for themselves in a conflict against the resistance of all other players.

Within each syndicate, the distribution of the dividends is assumed to be a matter of bargaining among the members of that particular syndicate. It is here that we make use of the Zeuthen-Nash theory of two-person bargaining. We assume that the members of any particular syndicate will be in *multilateral* bargaining equilibrium if and only if any *pair* of players that can be formed out of the members of this syndicate are in *bilateral* bargaining equilibrium according to the Zeuthen-Nash theory. For instance, in a syndicate consisting of players 1, 2, and 3, there will be a full equilibrium situation only if there is bargaining equilibrium (in the sense of there being no effective pressure for dividend redistribution) between players 1 and 2, between players 1 and 3, and again between players 2 and 3.

The solution furnished by this model appears to inherit the desirable properties both of the Zeuthen-Nash solution and of the Shapley solution. Applications to specific cases have given intuitively very satisfactory results. Just as the Zeuthen-Nash solution yields models for duopoly and for bilateral monopoly, this *n*-person solution yields models for oligopoly and for various combinations of oligopoly with bilateral monopoly (e.g,. bilateral oligopoly) as well as for many other bargaining situations with more than two participants. Apart from economics, it has applications in political science, international relations, organization theory, sociology, and other fields. Though its direct applications are of course restricted to bargaining situations which can be described in *quantitative* terms (in particular, to those which allow quantitative assumptions about the participants' utility functions), it does seem to throw light on bargaining situations which at present can be described only in *qualitative* terms, by providing instructive quantitative analogues for these situations.

For instance, the model brings out very clearly how the bargaining position of any given social unit versus some other social unit always depends on both these units' bargaining positions vis-à-vis all *other* social units: for example, how the bargaining position of any Western nation, say Germany, versus the United States will depend on what alternative alliances Germany on the one hand, and the United States on the other, could conclude with third partners, and on the terms that Germany or the United States could obtain in all these alternative alliances.

Again, the model shows very well how the bargaining position of any particular social group in society depends on the possibilities of communication, organization, and cooperation within that particular group: for example, how the bargaining position of the working class in a given society will be weakened if cooperation between different sections of the working class is made difficult by ethnic, religious, or political differences, etc.

More fundamentally, being a generalization of the Zeuthen-Nash model for the two-person case, the model shows how any party's bargaining position depends on his willingness to risk a conflict, and on the damages he could cause to his opponents in case of a conflict.

In simpler cases, of course, these conclusions do not go essentially beyond our common-sense understanding of social situations — though in more complex cases they certainly do — but at any rate it seems to be helpful to possess a general theory which systematically generates all these conclusions, instead of having to introduce them anew on an *ad hoc* basis in each particular case.

11. Non-cooperative Games

Besides his important work in the theory of cooperative games, Nash was also the founder of the theory of non-cooperative games [14]. The very concepts of cooperative and of non-cooperative games in their present forms are due to him.

By a *cooperative game* (or bargaining game) we mean a game in which it is both *possible* and *profitable* for all players to agree on a joint strategy. By a *non-cooperative game* we mean a game in which this is impossible and/or unprofitable.

Zero-sum (constant-sum), two-person games are always non-cooperative because the two players can never benefit by agreeing on a joint strategy as they do not have any common interests they could promote by cooperation. (The same is true of certain 'degenerate' zero-sum, n-person games, called 'inessential games' — but it is not true of other zero-sum, n-person games.) All other games can be played *both* cooperatively *and* non-cooperatively, depending on the situation.

But, as agreement on a joint strategy will enable the players to reach a jointly efficient (Pareto-optimal) solution, rational players will play such games non-cooperatively *only* if

(CASE 1) there is *no* possibility of *enforcing* agreements once concluded; or if

(CASE 2) there is *no* possibility of negotiating agreements for lack or costliness of *communication* facilities between the players; or if

(CASE 3) the players are *ignorant* or *misinformed* about one another's (or even about their own) *utility functions* and/or *strategical possibilities*, which makes them insist, as a price of their cooperation, on excessive demands that could not *all* be satisfied at the same time.

But even these conditions are not always absolute obstacles to cooperation. Even in the absence of facilities for enforcing agreements, some possible agreements may be self-enforcing, or the players may trust one another to keep agreements without direct enforcement, owing to prestige or even to straightforward moral considerations.

Again, inter-player communication can be dispensed with if there is no need for *coordination* between the different players' strategies — e.g., because there is only *one* possible efficient joint strategy within the game, which every player can readily recognize by himself;[4] or because the results of each player's activities are sufficiently *independent* of those of other players.

Finally, ignorance or misconceptions about one another's utility functions and/or strategical possibilities may in fact make the players more *modest* in their demands rather than the other way round, and may actually facilitate, rather than hinder, cooperation among them.

12. Criteria for Rational Behaviour in Non-cooperative Games

What are the criteria for rational behaviour in a non-cooperative game?

I shall deal only with the case where the necessity of playing the game non-cooperatively arises from the impossibility of enforcing agreements, but where the players know one another's utility functions and strategical possibilities. I also assume that they can communicate (or at least that coordination of their strategies poses no special problem). But our argument can be extended to the other cases as well.

The payoff a given player can achieve even against the most unfavourable combination of strategies by the other players is called his *maximin payoff* (while the strategy by which he can ensure this payoff for himself is called his maximin strategy). Clearly, even in a non-cooperative game, a rational player will always obtain at least this payoff. But in general, if all players act rationally, they will be able to obtain more than this — though in general they will not be able to obtain an efficient (Pareto-optimal) payoff vector as they always can in a cooperative game.

An important *necessary* condition for rational behaviour in a non-cooperative game was pointed out by Nash [14]. Every player tries to maximize his own payoff. Hence, in equilibrium every player's strategy must satisfy the requirement that it maximizes that particular player's payoff if all other players' strategies are kept constant. That is, every player's strategy must represent the *best* possible *reply* to the strategies used by the other players. This requirement is called the requirement of *mutual optimality*. A set of strategies, for the *n*-players, such that all of them satisfy this requirement, Nash calls an *equilibrium point* of the game. He has also shown that every non-cooperative game possesses *at least one* such equilibrium point, though usually it will possess more than one.

As we want to reserve the term 'equilibrium point' for a narrower concept satisfying certain stronger postulates, we shall describe a set of strategies satisfying the requirement of mutual optimality as a *semi-equilibrium point*.

It seems to me that in addition to this requirement of mutual optimality, rational behaviour in a non-cooperative game must also satisfy essentially the same requirements of joint *efficiency* and of the *Zeuthen decision rule*

---

[4] Schelling [18] has pointed out that even in the case of several equally rational joint strategies, intelligent players may be able to guess each other's intentions, and may manage to coordinate their strategies without explicit communication.

which we used in cooperative games — except that in the case of non-cooperative games the application of these last two requirements must be *restricted* to the set of semi-equilibrium points of the game. It can be shown that in general these two criteria will pick a *unique* semi-equilibrium point as the solution of the game. Uniqueness fails only in a small class of games (with measure zero), where there is so much symmetry between the strategical positions of two or more players as to make it logically impossible to find a rational criterion for choosing between two or more semi-equilibrium points favoured by different players. (In such cases the players may possibly have no better way out than falling back upon their maximum strategies because agreement on any better solution may become impossible.)

This unique semi-equilibrium point selected by the efficiency requirement and by Zeuthen's decision rule we shall call the *solution* or (full) *equilibrium point* of the game. It can be shown that the solution (bargaining equilibrium point) we have defined for the cooperative game is just a special case of our new solution concept. (It corresponds to the special case where agreements between the players are effectively enforced — that is, where *any* possible joint strategy once agreed upon by the players becomes a semi-equilibrium point, from which no player will have interest to depart because of the penalties attached to violating agreements — so that *all* possible joint strategies, including the whole set of Pareto-optimal strategies, become available to the players.)

To illustrate the use of the efficiency requirement and of Zeuthen's decision rule in non-cooperative games, consider the following two simple examples.

	B_1	B_2
A_1	(2, 2)	(0, 0)
A_2	(0, 0)	(1, 1)

EXAMPLE 1

	B_1	B_2
A_1	(2, 1)	(−1, −100)
A_2	(0, 0)	(1, 2)

EXAMPLE 2

In both examples, player 1 has two strategies, denoted by A_1 and A_2. Player 2 also has two strategies, denoted by B_1 and B_2. In each cell the two figures in parentheses show the payoffs associated with the relevant combination of strategies by the two players.

In the first example, there are two semi-equilibrium points, viz., (A_1, B_1) and (A_2, B_2). What the *efficiency requirement* says is that rational players will choose the *first* semi-equilibrium point because it makes *both* of them better off. Hence, player 1 will use strategy A_1 and player 2 will use strategy B_1.

In the second example, there are again two semi-equilibrium points, viz., (A_1, B_1) and (A_2, B_2). But now in terms of the efficiency requirement there is no choosing between them, as the first is preferable to player 1 while the second is preferable to player 2. All the same, I claim that rational players will choose the *first* semi-equilibrium point. For, consider what would happen if both players insisted on using the strategy associated with their own favourite semi-equilibrium points, i.e., if player 1 used strategy A_1 while player 2 used strategy B_2. Clearly, player 2 would suffer a much heavier loss. Hence, both players will know that player 1 can afford to stick to strategy A_1, in defiance of player 2, much more easily than player 2 could afford to stick to strategy B_2, in defiance of player 1.

What Zeuthen's decision rule does is to formalize this argument in more precise terms. If player 1 uses A_1, he incurs the risk that player 2 may nevertheless use B_2. Assuming that player 1 tries to maximize his expected utility, it can be shown that he will use A_1 only if the subjective probability he attaches to this risk is not greater than $p_1 = \frac{1}{3} = .33$. On the other hand, if player 2 uses B_2, he incurs the risk that player 1 may use A_1. Again, it can be shown that player 2 will use B_2 only if the subjective probability he attaches to this risk is not greater than $p_2 = \frac{1}{102} = .01$. Hence p_1, the *greatest risk* that player 1 is prepared to face, is much higher than p_2, the greatest risk that player 2 is prepared to face. Zeuthen's decision rule now says that under such conditions it will be player 2 who has to *yield* and accept the semi-equilibrium point favoured by his opponent.[5]

To sum up, we have argued that rational behaviour in a non-cooperative game must satisfy Nash's requirement of mutual optimality. But, subject to this overriding requirement, there remains even in a non-cooperative game a certain limited scope for *rational cooperation* among the players, governed by the efficiency requirement and by Zeuthen's decision rule. These two principles in general select a unique solution out of all possible sets of mutually optimal strategies (semi-equilibrium points) of the game.

13. Applications of the Theory

It seems to me that this theory of non-cooperative games, by making explicit the cooperative element inherent even in non-cooperative games, captures an important aspect of real-life social situations.

Virtually no social situation is fully devoid of some degree of agreed cooperation, at least to the extent of excluding some particularly obnoxious strategies by mutual consent. Even in total wars some conventions and customary restraints go on, to be observed by all parties. In general, intensive competition in some fields may very well go together with persistent cooperation in other fields.

For instance, as W. J. Fellner has pointed out [2], business firms in oligopolistic industries may engage in intensive competitive advertising, quality competition, or competitive research and development, without ceasing to cooperate in avoiding price competition or some other particularly damaging

---

[5]The problem illustrated by our second example, which we propose to solve by using Zeuthen's rule, has already been discussed by Luce and Raiffa [10, p. 110]. But they do not offer a formal criterion for solving it. The use of Zeuthen's rule in the case of non-cooperative games is justified by the same general rationality postulates as in the case of cooperative games; cf. [6, 8].

forms of competition. To explain non-cooperative (competitive) strategies by rival firms, Fellner mainly relies on their ignorance in detail of one another's future strategical possibilities. Each firm tends to judge the future effectiveness of its planned activities in research, advertising, etc., more favourably than its rivals do, and this makes it difficult for them to reach an agreement on the *terms* of some collusive arrangement as to mutual restriction of these competitive activities. Thus, according to Fellner's theory the non-cooperative behaviour observed comes under Case 3 of Section 11 above.

14. Incentive Games

An important application of this theory of non-cooperative games involving strong cooperative elements is to what we shall call *incentive games.* In a cooperative game proper the players agree on full cooperation in performing some specified courses of action (strategies) in return for certain fixed payoffs. If any player fell short of complete fulfilment of his contractual obligations, a conflict situation would arise and the player concerned would lose all his rights to the stipulated payoff.

In contrast, in an incentive game each player may retain a right to *choose* between various degrees of cooperation, but his payoff is made dependent, according to an agreed *sliding scale,* on his actual degree of cooperation, i.e., on the actual services he chooses or manages to perform. What is more, his payoff may be made dependent, not only on his actual behaviour (on his actual strategy) but also on his 'results', which may be importantly affected by factors beyond his control; and/or on some other *indirect indicators* of his activities (e.g., his apparent 'industry', his deference to superiors or his 'experience', etc.) which may be only imperfectly correlated with his actual performance.

As a class of non-cooperative games, incentive games come under both Cases 1 and 3 of Section 11. They come under Case 1, because the need for a sliding scale of payoffs arises mainly from the fact that the various players' *strategical possibilities* (their abilities and skills, as well as the temporary conditions affecting their performance at any given moment) are only *imperfectly known* in advance. If the players had to agree on fully specific strategies in advance, *either* they could stipulate only such a level of performance by each player as he is known for *sure* to be able to reach, without giving him any incentive to do better than that, *or,* if they stipulated higher levels of performance, they would have to accept the risk of incurring the social costs of a full-scale conflict in case some of the players happened to fall short of the standards agreed upon. The sliding scale of payoffs makes it possible to motivate the players for good performance, without leading to a disaster in case of less-than-perfect performance.

But incentive games come also under Case 3. For, the use of the players' results or of other indirect criteria in determining the payoffs is made necessary by the sheer impossibility or the prohibitive costs of *enforcing* payoff schedules that would require completely detailed direct supervison and evaluation of the players' actual strategies in terms of theoretically more adequate criteria.

These differences from fully cooperative games seem to provide the main explanations for the — presumably often unavoidable — *inefficiencies* in the incentive structures of empirical societies. The facts that the players are not committed to fully specific strategies, and that their payoffs are made dependent on factors beyond their control, introduce certain elements of unpredictability and uncertainty into social arrangements, which may result in disutilities to some individuals, and may make it necessary to include special risk premiums into their payoffs. More importantly, the dependence of the payoffs on certain indirect criteria, only imperfectly correlated with the socially useful aspects of each player's performance, may lead to a misallocation of human effort to socially undesirable goals (e.g., to mere simulation of effort, etc.).

The more general model of incentive games seems to provide a more suitable theoretical tool for the analysis of the distribution of income and power between different social classes than the model of strictly cooperative bargaining games does. For instance, in a capitalistic society the limits to each social class's bargaining power are essentially defined by the requirement that no social policy can be adopted that would destroy entrepreneur, investor, or saver incentives and cooperation on the one hand, or worker and in general employee incentives and cooperation on the other hand. In either direction, mere compulsion would be a very imperfect, and in the long run unworkable, substitute for more positive incentives.

Since Adam Smith and earlier, differences in the economic performance of alternative systems of economic organization — such as slavery, serfdom, and free labour, or again private enterprise and government enterprise — have been explained to a considerable extent in terms of the different incentive structures associated with these alternative economic systems. But we are still far from possessing any general theory for the analysis of these differences. Our model of incentive games is meant to be one step towards such a theory.

15. Similarities and Differences Between the Postulates of Game Theory and Ethics

To conclude, I should like to say a few more words about the relationship between the *theory of games* and the *theory of morality* (ethics).

Though game theory is concerned with *rational* behaviour defined in mere *expediency* terms, whereas ethics is concerned with the very different concept of *morally right* behaviour, there are interesting formal similarities between the postulates of the two theories, and consequently also between bargaining models and arbitration models (see Section 5 above), which apply the postulates of these two theories to bargaining situations. But there are also important formal differences.

More particularly, the postulates of joint *efficiency* (Pareto-optimality) and of *symmetry* among individuals are common to game theory and to ethics (as well as to welfare economics). Though there is some disagreement between moral philosophers about the precise scope of these two postulates, all of them seem to agree that, at least under normal conditions, whatever serves the interests of *all* individuals in the society is morally right behaviour, and that the basic moral rights and duties of different individuals are the same.[6]

One may even go further and argue that both game theory and ethics are branches of the *same* general theory of rational behaviour. Game theory deals with *rational strategies*, that is, with rules of behaviour that a rational individual would follow if he were concerned only with maximizing *his own* utility (on rational assumptions concerning the other individuals' behaviour). Ethics deals with *moral rules*, that is, with rules of behaviour that a rational individual would recommend for general observance if he gave *equal* weight to the utilities of *all* individuals concerned. As I have argued elsewhere [4, 5], a choice among alternative moral (or welfare-economic) codes can be technically regarded as the maximization of one's utility in an imagined risky situation — that is, as a choice between alternative social arrangements for a given society of n individuals where one chooses *as if* one had the same chance of $\frac{1}{n}$ for being put in the place of *any* one of the n individuals.

But in any case game theory and ethics are very *different* branches of the theory of rational behaviour, and there is at least one important formal difference between their postulates. Whereas moral choices (as well as policy choices based on welfare-economic considerations) cannot avoid *interpersonal comparisons of utility* assessing the relative intensity or urgency of different individuals' needs, game theory has no reason to make such comparisons. According to the von Neumann-Morgenstern-Marschak theory of rational choice [16, pp. 617–628; and 11], a rational individual's behaviour would not change if the utility to him of all available alternatives increased or decreased by the same amount or in the same proportion (*invariance* with respect to order-preserving *linear transformations* of the utility function). With Zeuthen's decision rule, it can be shown that this invariance property carries over also to bargaining situations (and in general to game situations), where each participant is concerned only with expediency considerations. For instance, under the Zeuthen-Nash theory of

[6]Indeed, the similarity goes even further. Zeuthen's decision rule in game theory and Kant's *universalizability* requirement in ethics are formally identical applications of the symmetry postulate in deciding what expectations are logically admissible concerning other people's behaviour. The former says that one cannot *rationally expect* different treatment by another rational individual from what one would oneself provide for him under similar conditions. The latter says that one cannot *morally expect* or require different treatment by another moral agent from what one would oneself provide for him under similar conditions. (For an interesting discussion of the use of the Kantian principle in utilitarian ethics, see [3].)

two-person bargaining games it would make no difference to the solution if suddenly a given player's utility for everything increased twofold in intensity (while the other player's utility for everything remained unaltered). This is so because, by assumption, the utility to him of any possible agreement would increase in the same proportion, and so would the utility (or disutility) to him of the conflict situation — hence, all these effects together would cancel out. (In particular, there would not be any change in his willingness to risk a conflict in any given situation.) In contrast, for any ethical choice as to which individual's interests should be given priority, a large increase in one individual's utility would make a good deal of difference.

Apart from these formal similarities and differences, there are also important points of contact between game theory and the theory of morality on the substantive side. Clearly, the image of conflicts of interests decided by social groups or individuals only with a view to their own sectional or individual interests is an unrealistic abstraction. On the one hand, the bargaining parties themselves may be influenced by moral or other more general social considerations (see Section 5). On the other hand and more importantly, social conflicts are often decided by the intervention of 'neutral' parties, i.e., social groups other than the parties with direct interests in the issue. That is why all parties attach that much importance to winning over the 'neutral' elements in society. The behaviour of these 'neutrals', however, tends to be governed by moral and other more or less disinterested value judgements. Obviously, the analysis of such situations can greatly benefit from a clear theory on what considerations in general tend to enter into people's moral value judgements.

But analysis of these situations would also require a theory of the social-psychological problem which we have called the problem of *dominant loyalties*, i.e., a theory of what factors make people give priority to their individual interests, to the sectional interests of various social groups, or to the general interests of society. However, discussion of this most interesting problem is beyond the scope of this paper.

References

[1] Braithwaite, R. B. *The Theory of Games as a Tool for the Moral Philosopher.* Cambridge University Press, 1955, 76 pp.

[2] Fellner, W. J. *Competition Among the Few.* New York, N.Y., Alfred A. Knopf, 1949, ix+328+iii pp.

[3] Harrod, R. F. Utilitarianism revised. *Mind.* N.S., Vol. 45 (1936), pp. 137–156.

[4] Harsanyi, J. C. Cardinal utility in welfare economics and in the theory of risk-taking. *Journal of Political Economy,* Vol. 61 (1953), pp. 434–435.

[5] Harsanyi, J. C. Cardinal welfare, individualistic ethics, and interpersonal comparisons of utility. *Journal of Political Economy,* Vol. 63 (1955), pp. 309–321.

[6] Harsanyi, J. C. Approaches to the bargaining problem before and after the theory of games: a critical discussion of Zeuthen's, Hicks', and Nash's theories. *Econometrica,* Vol. 24 (1956), pp. 144–157.

[7] HARSANYI, J. C. A bargaining model for the cooperative n-person game. Chap. 17 in *Contributions to the Theory of Games*, Vol. 4, A. W. Tucker and R. D. Luce (eds.), Princeton, N.J., Princeton University Press, 1959, vii+453 pp.

[8] HARSANYI, J. C. On the rationality postulates underlying the theory of cooperative games. *Journal of Conflict Resolution*, Vol. 5 (1961), pp. 179-196.

[9] HARSANYI, J. C. A simplified bargaining model for the n-person cooperative game. Paper read at the summer meeting of the Econometric Society in Stanford, August, 1960. (To be published.)

[10] LUCE, R. D., and H. RAIFFA. *Games and Decisions*. New York, N. Y. John Wiley & Sons, 1957, xi+509 pp.

[11] MARSCHAK, J. Rational behavior, uncertain prospects, and measurable utility. *Econometrica*, Vol. 18 (1950), pp. 111–141.

[12] MAYBERRY, J. P., J. F. NASH, and M. SHUBIK. A comparison of treatments of a duopoly situation. *Econometrica*, Vol. 21 (1953), pp. 141–154.

[13] NASH, J. F. The bargaining problem. *Econometrica*, Vol. 18 (1950), pp. 155–162.

[14] NASH, J. F. Non-cooperative games. *Annals of Mathematics*, Vol. 54 (1951), pp. 286–295.

[15] NASH, J. F. Two-person cooperative games. *Econometrica*, Vol. 21 (1953), pp. 128–140.

[16] VON NEUMANN, J., and O. MORGENSTERN. *Theory of Games and Economic Behavior*. Princeton, N.J., Princeton University Press, rev. ed. 1953, xx+641 pp.

[17] RAIFFA, H. Arbitration schemes for generalized two-person games. Chap. 21 in *Contributions to the Theory of Games*, Vol. 2, H. W. Kuhn and A. W. Tucker (eds.), Princeton, N.J., Princeton University Press, 1953, viii+395 pp.

[18] SCHELLING, T. C. Bargaining, communication, and limited war. *Journal of Conflict Resolution*, Vol. 1 (1957), pp. 19–36.

[19] SHAPLEY, L. S. A value for n-person games. Chap. 17 in *Contributions to the Theory of Games*, Vol. 2, H. W. Kuhn and A. W. Tucker (eds.), Princeton, N.J., Princeton University Press, 1953, viii+395 pp.

[20] SIMON, H. A. A behavioral model of rational choice. Chap. 14 in H. A. Simon, *Models of Man, Social and Rational*, New York, N.Y., John Wiley & Sons, 1957, xiv+287 pp.

[21] SIMON, H. A. Rational choice, and the structure of environment. Chap. 15 in H. A. Simon, *Models of Man, Social and Rational*, New York, N.Y., John Wiley & Sons, 1957, xiv+287 pp.

[22] SIMON, H. A. Theories of decision-making in economics and behavioral science, *American Economic Review*, Vol. 49 (1959), pp. 253–283.

[23] ZEUTHEN, F. *Problems of Monopoly and Economic Warfare*. London, George Routledge & Sons, 1930, xv+152 pp.

PHILOSOPHY OF SCIENCE AND EMPIRICAL SOCIAL RESEARCH

PAUL F. LAZARSFELD

Columbia University, New York, N.Y., U.S.A.

It has been said of German professors at the turn of the 17th century that they wrote all their professional papers in Latin; when they wanted to be very condescending, they used French. In the same way, I feel that modern philosophers of science are only concerned with the natural sciences; when occasionally they turn to the social sciences, they talk of Herbert Spencer or some other scholar who concerned himself with the development of all societies from beginning to end. Philosophers of science do not pay attention to the empirical work in social research which is actually going on today.

In a way, this is easily understood. In the correct sense of the term, as yet there is no systematic theory in the social sciences, only research procedures and a number of low-level generalizations. This would force the philosopher to become acquainted with technical details and results which are often rather boring, and would put him at a disadvantage vis-à-vis a colleague who can speculate on the meaning of such basic ideas as the uncertainty principle or the notion of relativity. The reading of empirical social research, which often lacks the big sweep of the more developed natural sciences is not only personally unrewarding but also does not confer much prestige. Understandably the general reader is more curious about the philosophical implications of the natural sciences which have so greatly affected our daily lives.

My central theme, then, is "philosophers of science unfair to empirical social research". But I am not out of sympathy with the members of this congress, and I am doing my picketing not in the mood of accusation, but in an effort to obtain more cooperation. I will make my point by analyzing briefly two papers, each written by men whose good intentions toward us are beyond any doubt. Both authors want to make a contribution to the working men among the social scientists, and if, as I think, they fail in the examples chosen, it is against their will and, in effect, they are the victims of the general intellectual climate which I shall try to characterize.

My first example comes from Carl Hempel and has an ironic implication which I want to point out first. Hempel, probably without knowing it, has had a considerable and highly salutary effect on empirical social research. Almost thirty years ago, he and Paul Oppenheim wrote a paper on the notion of types in the light of modern logic [7]. They showed that when we describe a person or a group in the course of an empirical investigation, we unavoidably use a fixed number of properties. In a formal sense these are all variates but they can be of considerable diversity: quantitative variables such as age, ranks such as position in a competitive examination, dichotomies such as sex, or even unordered classes such as country of birth.

These variates form a property space, and their combinations are what today we would call a Cartesian product. Typologies, Hempel and Oppenheim pointed out, are selected sectors of this property space which come about by a variety of procedures which they called "reduction". In their original paper, the authors were able to show how many research procedures can be described and clarified by looking at them as various kinds of reductions. Since then, many investigators have used this idea. A collection of pertinent examples has been published by my collaborator, Allen Barton [1].

I was therefore very anxious to see how Hempel's own thinking on this matter had developed, and the present meeting gave me an opportunity to look at a symposium organized by the American Philosophical Association under the promising title, "Problems of Concept and Theory Formation in the Social Sciences". There Hempel again chose the problem of typologies as his theme [6]. But in the period of twenty years between the two papers, he obviously had succumbed to the occupational hazards of the philosopher of science isolated from the empirical social scientist. Already, the introductory pages are ominous. The only author referred to in the beginning is Max Weber and his notion of "ideal type". And Hempel's statement of what he intends to do contains the following sentence: "Our explicatory efforts will repeatedly invite comparative examples of concept formation in the natural sciences". As a matter of fact, he hopes that he will perform his major service by "a comparative examination of certain aspects of the methodology of natural and social science".

I call this beginning ominous because it implies the two main dangers which I tried to signal in the opening paragraphs of my paper. For one, what we really need is an *intrinsic* analysis of social science procedures. Anyone whose main interest is to compare these procedures with the natural sciences will have one or both of two effects. Either he will tell us that our achievements lag behind those in the natural sciences, which we know only too well, or he will make a dogmatic assertion on the unity of science, which I think is as useful as my doctor's admonishing me to lose weight without his helping me to attain this highly desirable goal. My second uneasiness comes from the invocation of the name of Max Weber, because he is probably the greatest symbol of what I might call "the old methodology", which has proved so wasteful.

Max Weber did spectacular work in historical sociology, a field badly neglected in recent years. But he also wrote a few pages on what he thought he did, calling his procedure the construction of ideal types. These self-declaratory statements contradict each other at many points; they have no visible relation to the actual content of his studies, and they have led to endless and confused literature which is concerned mostly with terminology and, as far as I can see, has resulted in no new investigations. No one has explicated what he did in his actual studies, which has contributed to the difficulty of emulating his skill.

After these first two introductory pages (pp. 66 and 67), Hempel devotes three-and-a-half pages to distinguishing a number of ways in which the term "type" has been used (classificatory types, extreme types); then, on page 71, he comes to his main topic, "Ideal Types and Explanations in the Social Sciences". At this point, there is still hope, partly because here a new name appears, Howard Becker. Now Becker was indeed the exponent of what he called "constructive typology in the social sciences". This is a modern version of Max Weber's ideas, but more easily accessible to explication. Becker was more concerned with the relation of his work to modern quantitative procedures, and therefore what he writes about his own methodology is easier to analyze than Max Weber's methodological pages, which have as their frame of reference the whole history of German legal and cultural philosophy. In addition, in his descriptive work, Becker dealt with a rather restricted number of types, especially with the definition of sacred and secular societal forms [2]. Finally, Becker directed a number of studies undertaken by his students; the analysis of these would permit us to obtain a fairly good picture of what he really had in mind [12]. For a harassed philosopher who wants to find out how the beleaguered minority of "ideal typologists" thinks and works today, Becker would indeed be a very good topic of analysis. And those of us who do not belong to this tradition would have been very grateful for an explication of Becker's work: it is quite likely that he had something important to say, and he is neglected by the majority of his colleagues mainly because it is so hard to find out what he had in mind.

This is, however, not the way Hempel proceeds. After he has mentioned Becker's name, he returns to Max Weber and for two pages quotes what Max Weber said about ideal types—quotations, incidentally, which are only too well known to every social scientist who has tried to forget them when he wanted to know what Weber really did. We still can think that Hempel considered this brief inventory necessary for the instruction of philosophers. It is Hempel's contention that "ideal types represent not concepts properly speaking, but rather theories". No one can quarrel with this position, because no one can tell what a practitioner of ideal types does as long as he has not analyzed actual investigations. But this is by no means what Hempel now does. As a matter of fact, he states his program quite bluntly:

> The idea naturally suggests itself that if those theories are to serve their purpose, *they must have a character quite similar to that of the theory of ideal gases, say.* To elaborate and substantiate this conception, I will first try to show that the alleged differences between the explanatory use of ideal types and the method of explanation in a natural science are spurious; then (in section 5) I will attempt a brief comparative analysis of the status of idealized concepts, and the corresponding theories, in natural and social science. (P. 73; emphasis mine.)

For the next seven pages Hempel gives a brilliant analysis of what in the natural sciences might be called an ideal-type analysis. He points out that in explaining an eclipse of the sun, the scientist only explains major features and not irrelevant details (p. 74). He has very interesting things to say about experiments-in-imagination in the physical sciences. His examples range from levers and pendula to the theory of relativity (pp. 76 f). Having thus defined what in his opinion ideal types are in the natural sciences, he discusses their relation to general laws; his most telling example is a discussion of the theory of ideal gases (p. 80). Having been myself a natural scientist in my better days, I read Hempel's material with great interest. Not for a long time had I been so vividly reminded of Maxwell Boyle, and other heroes of my student days. But I certainly was startled when I found the following conclusion on page 80: "The preceding analysis suggests the following observations on the 'ideal' and the empirical aspects of ideal type concepts in the *social sciences*." (Emphasis mine.)

This of course can only mean that the concluding pages of Hempel's paper would advise social scientists what to do if they wanted to do the same things which, according to Hempel, natural scientists did. Now this might be very good advice, but I always thought that the philosopher of social science would make an intrinsic analysis of what we practitioners actually do, and Hempel's paper has not yet dwelt on this point. Actually, I was willing to waive this objection because any advice from Hempel might be useful; so let us look. Of his four concluding pages, two again summarize what the natural scientist does and only two (pp. 82 and 83) give a concrete example of what all this might have to do with the social sciences. But even this happy ending is slightly marred, because the example he chooses is one which "approximates most closely the status of idealizations in natural science: the concepts of perfectly free competition".

In my opinion, it would have been more enlightening to take examples which are *least* comparable to the natural sciences, such as those with which Weber, Becker, and other men in this tradition were concerned: bureaucracy, folk society, etc. All this talk about ideal types, which never dies and still does not lead anywhere, might be indicative of a genuine problem of social research. The only way to find out is for a philosopher of science to analyze empirical studies and not the manifestos of the representatives of the tradition. I understand that Einstein once summarized his view on the appropriate mathematics for the problems of theoretical physics by saying that in his opinion God does not play with dice. It would hardly occur to Hempel that the issue could be settled by discussing what kind of dice Einstein thought of or how many players he had in mind. But when it comes to the social sciences, that is what he does in the paper which I picked as an example — an unfair one, I confess, as far as Hempel is concerned, but, I think, quite characteristic of the general state of affairs.

It would now be tempting for me to say that space does not permit me to give my own explication of what actually goes on when writers try to discuss historical data or contemporary field observations under the heading of ideal or constructed typologies. However, this happens to be one of the topics I meant for a long time to investigate, but never got around to, certainly, in part, because I knew it would be difficult, time consuming, and perhaps not too rewarding. This might also explain why I was so disappointed when I thought that Hempel had done the work, while actually he followed the tradition of philosophers of science in telling social scientists what he knew about the natural sciences. I will be somewhat better off with my second example because it deals with a topic on which I have written extensively myself.

A large part of our work requires us to translate concepts into operational instruments which permit us to classify people or groups. Such instruments are often loosely called "measurements" but I do not want to enter into the justification of this terminology; what matters here is the practice. The notions we translate sometimes come from everyday language, as in instances when we classify people according to their intelligence or their happiness. Sometimes the concept is newly created by sensitive analysts: the extraverted person or the cohesive group. In recent years, many empirical social scientists have analyzed such procedures and I will describe them only very briefly, referring the interested reader to typical publications [4, 9, 18]. Take, for example, the notion of cohesiveness. The investigator starts with a kind of vague imagery. In the cohesive group, people feel friendly toward each other, they like to be with the group, they would make sacrifices to maintain the existence of the group against outside attack, their self-respect is enhanced by the approval of other group members, and so on. A long list of such properties can be culled from the literature, and anyone who joins in the spirit of the game can add additional "indicators": the members like to meet or at least want to keep in communication with each other; there is a similarity of tastes and goals, agreement as to what is right and wrong, not too much fighting for individual advantages, and so on.

Suppose now a social research project is established to develop an instrument by which a number of specific groups should be ordered according to their degree of cohesiveness. The investigator will proceed in three steps. He will first make a list of all the indicators which have been proposed, often dividing them into subsets; these are called dimensions because they seem to represent various major aspects of the original image. Then, he will select a smaller number of this "universe of items" and combine them into a manageable "test".

Having thus constructed his instrument, he will collect statistical data along the following lines: he will observe a large number of groups and describe each in terms of the various indicators. He knows that rarely will any group be positive or negative on all the test items. There are groups in which people like each other very much but have little opportunity for communication; there are other groups in which everyone is imbued with the group goal although they do not feel very friendly to many of the other members. Each group will thus be characterized by a profile or response pattern. Using an appropriate statistical technique, the investigator will then compute the covariations between all the indicators taken over all the groups he is studying. His basic numerical material will be one or more matrices, the entries of which indicate how well pairs and perhaps triplets and quadruplets of indicators agree with each other in concrete situations.

Finally, he will submit these matrices to mathematical analysis. This can follow a variety of models, but each is explicitly or implicitly guided by the following considerations. The investigator wants to end up with an ordering which does not exist in advance, but is an *intended* classification. It is to be derived from the statistical behavior of the indicators, but, at the same time, it permits us to establish the diagnostic value of each of them. It may turn out, for instance, that mutual friendliness discriminates very well between more or less cohesive groups, while the amount of communication is less decisive. Whatever the empirical outcome, we know that there is only a probabilistic relation between the intended classification and the indicators. Even in the groups which are most cohesive according to the final ordering, no indicator has a probability of $+1$ of being observed; and even in the most disorganized groups, each of our test items has a more or less small opportunity to be observed.

There are quite a number of conflicting models which can be used for this analysis. But they all have two features in common. They do not use an outside criterion. No one tells us in advance which groups should be considered more cohesive than others; we do not calibrate indicators against superior knowledge. The ordering is derived from a mathematical analysis of the empirical covariation of these indicators. And as I mentioned before, the whole procedure implies a probabilistic mathematics. We pull ourselves up, so to say, by our own bootstraps. We end up by finding two things simultaneously: given that a group belongs at a certain point on the underlying continuum of cohesiveness, we can tell the probability with which it will manifest each indicator; and, given the profile or response pattern of the group, we can say with what probability the group belongs at various points along the intended classification. (For the sake of brevity, I omit here the possibility that the intended classification has more than one dimension, because this does not create any new logical problems and only requires additional computations.)

While we have by now some clarity on these matters and know quite well how the various mathematical models used in the third step are related to each other, there still are quite a number of problems which require further investigation. The matter is of great urgency for us and so it seems very appropriate to choose as my second example a paper by Max Black called "Definition, Presupposition, and Assertion"[3]. A reading of the introductory paragraphs shows how pertinent if could be to our topic. He begins by saying that definition "per genus et differentiam" is by no means the only or even the most frequent way by which we introduce a term into actual discourse. This is undoubtedly true for the type of procedures I have just sketched; as a matter of fact, Black mentions that what he has to say would apply to the notion of happiness (p. 48), which is certainly the type of concept with which we would be concerned. But a more careful reading of the paper again leaves us, I am sorry to say, in the lurch. Black has purposely avoided the kind of difficulty created by Hempel's paper; he makes no references to the natural sciences. But he joins Hempel in the second difficulty. He does not refer to any of the hundreds of concrete studies provided by empirical social research. His main example is the definition of a dachshund. I realize that there are more dog lovers in the world than social researchers and I am willing to accept Black's editorial policy as long as I can apply his examples to my problems. But here exactly is the rub—we have come from Scylla to Charybdis. Somehow between the austerity of Hempel's ideal gasses and the folksiness of Black's dachshund, social research is again squeezed out. I will now try to show briefly why we are frustrated by Black's analysis.

The dachshund becomes a legitimate member of the logician's circle by an initiation which Black describes (p. 41) as follows:

> This dog and that one and that one are clear cases of a dachshund. This one is very nearly a clear case, but has such and such a deviation. This other one is still further removed from being a perfectly clear case. And this one is a borderline specimen and could be called a dachshund or a basset indifferently. The specimens by means of which the meaning of the label "dachshund" is explained are presented in an order, determined by the degree of deviation from one or more specimens that are introduced as typical or "clear cases".

The author stresses that one would use criteria which are "very numerous, admit of variation in the degree to which they are met and no simple conjunctive or disjunctive combination of them is both necessary and sufficient." This is indeed very reminiscent of, say, an intelligence test. And I agree with him that this is "demanded by the complexity and variability of the phemonema to be described." But now let us look more closely at his summary statement:

> According to the account I have been giving, "range definition" as I propose to call it, *requires the exhibition or delineation of one or more typical, or "clear" cases.* Such cases I propose to call "paradigms". The traits or features or properties that vary from instance to instance, and are described in what I have been calling the "criteria", for application of the term, I shall call "constitutive factors". I have already proposed that the things to which the term is applied be called a "range"; it will be convenient to say that a word whose *instances* constitute a range is a "range word". (P. 43; emphasis mine.)

The difficulty here lies in emphasis on the phrase "exhibition or delineation of one or more clear cases". In the social sciences, we can rarely trot out clear cases. This is partly due to the nature of our beasts. But more often, there is not even the implication that such clear cases exist in social research. The actual procedure *moves in a direction opposite to the one Black describes.* He starts out by showing true dachshunds and then exhibits all sorts of transitional specimens. He mentions that as he inspects the less clear cases, not all constitutive factors will be present, but implies that they will be statistically related as a consequence of his ordering (p. 46). The social scientist who develops an instrument of measurement *begins* with this co-variation and then uses mathematical models to derive ways by which his specimens can be ordered according to their purity. This also precludes the imagery of the "range". We agree with Black that the traditional notion of class usually disappears. But it is substituted by the idea of order in which it is not even possible to distinguish "central ranges" without further assumptions. And Black nowhere introduces the *probabilistic relation between the intended classification and the indicators* (constitutive factors). If I am not mistaken, the word probability does not appear anywhere in Black's essay. One cannot say two sentences about classificatory procedures in the social sciences without introducing probability notions.

I am aware that in drawing on Black's paper, I am open to one objection. Hempel claims that he talks about the social sciences and therefore I can legitimately complain when he concentrates on theoretical physics. But why is it not Black's privilege to write about dog shows? I am afraid the matter cannot be settled without a full reading of his original text. I am confident that what Black really wanted to do is to explicate what we social scientists do when we develop our measurement instruments; there are enough asides in his paper to justify my imputation. But he does not take as his main example one of the numerous and I confess usually tedious papers in which such instruments are developed. By choosing the more attractive dachshund example, he probably retains more readers, but he misses what I think is the crucial point. And at the same time he deprives us of the help the philosopher can give us. I have in a recent paper listed a large number of philosophical problems related to our "measurements", which in my opinion are still unresolved [10].

This brings me back to the main message of my paper. Philosophers of science are not interested in and do not know what the work-a-day empirical research man does. This has two consequences: either we have to become our own methodologists or we have to muddle along without benefit of the explicating clergy. In certain areas, I suppose the simpler ones, we have done our own explications. In my opinion, they are not without merit and I want to bring a few of them to the attention of this audience. There exists something called "projective tests"—the idea is that you show people unstructured material such as ink blots, for instance, and ask them to tell you what they see. Some individuals will see flowers or dancing children; to others, the same ink blot will remind them of witches and skeletons. It is plausible to conclude that the latter person is more anxious than the former. A careful analysis of the procedures involved and the results obtained by a large variety of tests has shown the great complexity of such inferences. The interpretation of the subject may depend upon his mood at the moment rather than upon a more enduring trait; or he may unconsciously repress certain associations just because they would increase his anxieties. A careful collection of these and other possibilities makes it possible to show which kinds of unstructured materials are likely to be more useful and gives leads to better interpretation. Gardner Lindzey, a clinical psychologist, has provided this type of analysis, which in a better division of labor we should expect from a philosopher [11].

My other example is somewhat more complex and still leaves work to be done by volunteers from the philosophical camp. About two or three decades ago a great change came about in social research. The development of sampling and interviewing techniques temporarily shifted the trend of research in the direction of attitude surveys. Some sociologists have viewed this development with alarm: it is atomistic and it endangers insight into the role of the larger collective — be it the small informal group or the larger formal organization. Such "holistic" objections appear in many fields and they always leave one rather uneasy. They probably make a good point, but it is usually not quite clear precisely what point they are making. Now, in empirical research, owing to the increasing availability of funds and of computing devices, a new kind of material is available. We can study people in a large variety of comparable organizations: 200 schools, 150 hospitals, 100 locals of the same union. This permits a statistical analysis of behavior and attitudes within as well as between larger units. These larger units are not vague totalities but are themselves characterized by specified variables. A number of sociologists have recently begun to clarify the nature of this "contextual analysis" and an interesting review can be found in a paper by James Davis [5]. While we then know pretty well what we are doing and where we are going, it is not yet clear which part of the long-drawn-out holistic discussion is caught up by these procedures and what problems are still unresolved or even unexplicated. Here the philosopher with his wider knowledge of the non-empirical literature can be of great help if he were willing to look at these recent empirical developments.

I do not want to claim that we have received no help at all from the philosophers of science. Ernest Nagel has analyzed a paper by Robert Merton on functional analysis which testifies to a close reading of the original text and as a result makes a fine contribution to Merton's effort [14]. And I myself am certainly grateful to the way he has integrated some of my own work on survey analysis into a more general treatise on the philosophy of the social sciences [15]. But there is still a large amount of work to be done. Let me give just a few examples.

Take, for instance, the notion of social process. Every textbook on social change will deal with it in a more or less vague way. For the strict empiricist, a process consists of repeated observations of the same people or groups. Mathematically it can be represented by a system of simultaneous difference equations. What is the relation between these three approaches? What if the data are not only behavioral but include attitudes, plans, and expectations? What is added if the recurrent observations are characteristics of people as well as global characteristics of the collective to which they belong? What meaningful problems are left in the verbal literature after all those more tangible topics are taken care of? Or take the problem of diagnosis. Is what the medical doctor does the same as what we do when we notice that university professors in France do not have their telephone numbers listed in the directory, and when we take this as a sign of their aloofness from students? What is the logical difference between the latter example and the tendency of the clinical psychologist to make inferences from a patient's tone of voice? Philosophers have written much about signs and signals. How much of it applies to our empirical studies, and what new problems in our field do these writings pose? One more example may be taken from the Oxford group of analytical philosophers and their emphasis on careful linguistic distinctions. We must do the same when we translate concepts into indices. Should we think of the integration of a society as a single notion, should we distinguish value integration and social integration, or should we make even finer distinctions before we develop classificatory devices? What is the relation between this type of preliminary linguistic analysis and the one which is usually the end product of the analytical philosopher's work?

Some additional problems can be suggested to colleagues who are also interested in the history of science, which, incidentally, has been equally negligent of the social sciences. Fifty years ago, the French psychologist, Gabriel Tarde, made the notion of imitation a central concept. For several decades, he was forgotten or, if not, ridiculed. In the last ten years, we have a rapidly growing literature on what is called reference group analysis: the fact that people are greatly influenced by the groups they either belong to or want to belong to [13]. Do we face here a cycle in fashions or has something really new been added? And if the latter, why is there this discontinuity between Tarde and modern reference group thinking? To take one more historical example: from time to time, systems of basic categories are proposed and they acquire wide acceptance. At the turn of the century, the French school of Le Playistes had a basic "nomenclature", according to which they wrote hundreds of descriptive monographs [8]. In the 1930's, the Chicago school of Park and Burgess had a set of basic categories which provided the guidelines for numerous studies of specific groups such as juvenile gangs, residents of the ghetto, and others [16]. Today we have Talcott Parsons' pattern variables [17]. What is the relation between these categorical systems, what functions do they serve, and what accounts for their appearance and disappearance?

I do not expect that one short speech will suddenly make the philosophers of science rush to the rescue of people in empirical social research. What is needed to improve the situation are joint seminars at various universities, symposia which do not deal with generalities but discuss concrete studies from both sides, and fellowships which enable humanists to work for a while in a research bureau. Let me, however, stress once more the need to focus on the specific procedures of the social scientist. I obviously want to deny the unity of science as little as I would speak out for sin. But just as I believe that basically scientific work has a unifying rationality, I am also convinced that each subject matter has its own problems which need special attention. We should be guided by the inversion of a French proverb: the more it is the same, the more it is different. In my opinion, at this moment, the detailed explication of the *differential* aspects of empirical social research badly needs the attention of the philosopher of science.

References

[1] Barton, Allen. "The Concept of Property-Space in Social Research", in *The Language of Social Research*, Paul Lazarsfeld and Morris Rosenberg (eds.). Glencoe, Ill., The Free Press, 1955.

[2] Becker, Howard. *Through Values to Social Interpretation*. Durham, N.C., Duke University Press, 1950.

[3] Black, Max. "Definition, Presupposition and Assertion", in *American Philosophers at Work*, Sidney Hook (ed.). New York, Criterion Books, 1956.

[4] Cattell, Raymond. "Personal Theory Flowing from Multivariate Quantitative Research". *Psychology*, Vol. 111, S. Koch (ed.), New York, McGraw-Hill, 1959.

[5] Davis, James, Joe L. Spaeth, and Carolyn Huson. "Analyzing Effects of Group Composition". *American Sociological Review*, Vol. 26 (1961).

[6] Hempel, Carl. *Science, Language, and Human Rights*. Philadelphia, University of Pennsylvania Press, 1952.

[7] Hempel, Carl, and Paul Oppenheim. *Der Typusbegriff im Lichte der neuen Logik*. Leiden, 1936.

[8] Lazarsfeld, Paul. "Notes on the History of Quantification in Sociology". *Isis*, Vol. 52, Part 2, No. 168 (1961).

[9] Lazarsfeld, Paul. "Latent Structure Analysis". *Psychology*, Vol. 111, S. Koch, (ed.). New York, McGraw-Hill, 1959.

[10] Lazarsfeld, Paul. "Methodological Problems in Empirical Social Research". International Congress of Sociology, Stresa, 1959.

[11] Lindzey, G. "Thematic Apperception Tests". *Psychological Bulletin*, Vol. 49, No. 1 (1952).

[12] McKinney, J. C. "Procedures and Techniqes in Sociology", in *Modern Sociological Theory*, Becker and Boskoff (eds.). New York, Dryden, 1957.

[13] Merton, Robert, K. *Social Theory and Social Structure*, revised edition. Glencoe, Ill., The Free Press, 1957.

[14] Nagel, Ernest. "A Formalization of Functionalism", in *Logic Without Metaphysics*. Glencoe, Ill., The Free Press, 1956.

[15] Nagel, Ernest. *The Structure of Science*. New York, Harcourt, Brace, and World, 1961.

[16] Park, R. E., and E. W. Burgess. *Introduction to the Science of Sociology*. Chicago, Univ. of Chicago Press, 1933.

[17] Parsons, T., and E. Shils. *Toward a General Theory of Action*. Cambridge, Mass., Harvard Univ. Press, 1951.

[18] Tyron, Robert. "Identification of Social Areas by Cluster Analysis". *Univ. of Calif. Publications in Psychology*, Vol. 8, No. 1 (1955).

Symposium on Macro- and Microeconomics

MICROECONOMICS AND MACROECONOMICS

ABBA P. LERNER

Michigan State University, East Lansing, Michigan, U.S.A.

The essential difference between microeconomics and macroeconomics is in the nature of the abstractions made in the two approaches to comprehending the complexities of reality. In microeconomics attention is focused on a *part* of the economic system. It is recognized that what happens in this part of the system will have effects on the rest of the economy outside the part studied, but microeconomics is not concerned with these. It is also recognized that as a result of these effects there may be reactions from the outside back onto the part of the economy on which study is concentrated. What is distinctive about microeconomics is that such *reactions from the outside* are abstracted from. They are assumed to be negligible.

In macroeconomics attention is focused on the economic system as a *whole*, and it is complexities *within the system* that are abstracted from or disregarded. Heterogeneous collections of many different kinds of things are considered as if they were homogenous quantities of a simple substance. Thus in macroeconomics we speak of income, investment, output, consumption and the like as if they were simple unidimensional entities, such that the quantity of any one of them could be completely indicated by a simple number. This permits models to be built which have very few variables but which nevertheless help us to understand something about certain aspects of the economic system as a whole, such as the determination of the level of economic activity.

It is tempting to relate this distinction to the distinction between a specialist and a generalist, but that would be misleading if it suggested that the generalist is any less of a specialist than the specialist. Just like any other specialist he is constrained by the context of his study to select what seems relevant and to ignore what seems irrelevant. He too has to abstract from aspects of reality that may be of central importance to others, and if the specialist is one who knows more and more about less and less, the generalist is one who knows less and less about more and more.

Nor can the economist consistently keep to microeconomics or consistently concentrate on macroeconomics. If in some respects he appears to do so it is his manner of speaking that gives that impression rather than the real content of his work. Marshall, for instance, would seem to be an almost perfect model of a microeconomist. He is generally concentrating on the equilibrium of the firm or of the industry. But the flesh that he forms around the bare bones of such analysis tells us much about the economy as a whole. Walras, on the other hand, works with sets of equations that refer to the system as a whole, but the substance of his economics is much more microeconomic than Marshall's in its concentration on the behaviour of individual consumers, producers or firms in markets over which they have no influence.

The reason for this is that the dichotomy of economics into micro- and macroeconomics is itself much too violent an oversimplification. Rather than to classify different parts of economics as belonging to the one kingdom or the other it is much more useful to arrange them according to the *degree* to which they abstract from repercussions from parts of the economic system that are not under direct study. Instead of a dichotomy we then have a spectrum along which the different economic studies may be placed — or rather there turn out to be a number of different spectra according to what is the *kind* of reaction from outside that is being abstracted from in the different degrees.

The present interest in macroeconomics, and in its relation to microeconomics, is primarily an indirect result of the recent Keynesian emphasis on the effect of expenditure by an entity on the income received by it. This study has usually taken the form of a simple dichotomy between the microeconomic and the macroeconomic approaches. In terms of this dichotomy it is reasonable to say that for an individual, a firm, an industry or other section of the economy studied in microeconomics, there is no significant effect of the expenditure undertaken by the individual or other section of the economy on the income that it in turn receives (which consists mostly of expenditures by the rest of the economy). But when the economy as a whole is considered, any variation in expenditure results in an *equal* change in income. With all the payers and all the receivers included within the area of study, expenditure and income are nothing but two different aspects of the same transactions — as seen from the points of view of those making the payments and those receiving them.

The violence of this transition between the two extremes of the spectrum has proved a serious obstacle to the spread of economic understanding. There is too big a jump for many, if not most, people between the view that sees every decrease in consumption as necessarily involving an equal increase in saving (income being considered a constant) and the view that sees every decision to save more by spending less as necessarily frustrated (because it reduces income instead of increasing saving). The psychological resistances to so severe a shift have given rise to extreme opposition to the whole Keynesian "New Economics", to the "paradox of thrift" and the understanding of "poverty in the midst of plenty" in the "upside-down economy" of involuntary unemployment. It is possible to avoid much of this trouble by examining the whole spectrum of degrees of repercussion of expenditure on income as one moves from considering a very small part of the economy through the whole range up to the whole or 100 per cent of the economy. The dichotomy will then emerge naturally as the two extreme ends of the spectrum.

If this is done it is easy to see that the effect on income received by a section of the economy of money paid out by that section is related, or even closely proportional, to the fraction of the whole that the section comprises. We may begin by considering, say, a tremendous firm that has a sales volume of $4 billion, or 1 per cent of the national income of $400 billion. If such a firm were to reduce its expenditures by 10 per cent, cutting down its activities in that proportion, this would mean a reduction of $400 million in the income received in the economy. Since the economy as a whole has been spending 1 per cent of its income on the products produced by this firm and it is not unreasonable to suppose that a reduction of the national income would result in a reduction in expenditure on the products of this firm in about the same proportion, we may expect the income of the firm to fall by about $4 million (1 per cent of the $400 million fall in the national income).

If this firm decided to increase its saving (or accumulate cash reserves) by reducing its expenditure by $400 million, it should count on this increasing its saving (or its case reserves) not by $400 million but only by $396 million. This difference is probably well within the probable errors and uncertainties, so that it is quite reasonable for the complication to be neglected and for the firm to disregard any effects of its spending on its own income.

If we take a much smaller but by no means microscopic firm, say one with a sales volume of $4,000,000 per annum, and such a firm reduced *its* expenditure by 10 per cent, this would reduce national income by $400,000. Again we assume that expenditure on the output of the firm remains the same proportion of national income as before, and therefore falls in the same proportion as the national income does. National income falls by $400 thousand out of $400 billion or by one millionth. The income of the firm could therefore be expected to fall by one millionth of its sales volume, i.e., by $4 (four dollars!).

As appears from these examples the repercussion of expenditure on income varies as the square of the size of the firm. (I am, of course, abstracting from *independent* trends in expenditure, either in the economy as a whole or on the products of the firm or industry in question, as well as from *indirect* effects of the firm's or industry's action, which might go in either direction.) A firm *one thousandth* the size of another has a repercussion on its own income that is *one millionth* of that of the larger firms from the same percentage reduction in its own expenditure. In the case of a sector that is a small fraction of the whole economy the repercussion is completely negligible, and the microeconomic assumption that income is completely independent of expenditure is fully justified.

But this ceases to be true when the sector under examination is a large fraction of the economy. If we consider a quarter of the population, with a quarter of the income of the economy, it would be reasonable to suppose that something like a quarter of their expenditure constitutes income for the same quarter of the economy. A decrease in their spending by a million dollars could therefore be expected to increase their saving not by a million dollars but by only three quarters of a million dollars. The other quarter of a million dollars would be lost because of the reduction in their income from the reduction in their spending. Saving would be increased by only 75 cents for every dollar of decline in spending.

In exactly the same way a decrease in spending by a half of the economy would increase their saving by only fifty cents out of each dollar of reduction in spending; and for three quarters of the economy a dollar reduction in spending would increase saving by only 25 cents. For the economy as a whole, or 100 per cent of the economy, there would be a reduction of income of 100 per cent of the reduction in spending and no increase at all in the amount saved.

This way of putting the matter as a gradual transition along a continuum might not administer the shock to old habits of thought that gives rise to the passionate incredulity of a Henry Hazlitt.

The spectrum of the different degrees in which expenditure by a section of the economy reacts on its own income is however only one of many such spectra, at the microeconomic end of which some reaction is completely negligible while at the macroeconomic end it becomes overwhelming. The most perfect microeconomics is to be found in the study of the firm or the individual confronted only with perfect markets in a perfectly competitive economy.

By definition such an individual has no power over prices. Either he pays the market price or he cannot buy, and either he accepts the market price or he does not sell. But the firm in a perfectly competitive economy does not even have any power over the quantities that it buys or sells. If perfect competition is to persist, the firms must be small in relation to the market. There must be a barrier of costs increasing with output that prevents firms from growing too large (the increasing costs being the result of firms being able to expand only by adding variable factors of production to their fixed factors of production and so having to depart from the optimum proportion that minimizes cost of production).

With complete freedom of entry any excess of the price of the product over average cost (which means the emergence of profit) will attract more firms into the industry until the profit has been eliminated by increased competition. Each firm will then be able to make ends meet only by producing that output which minimizes average cost of production. The firm therefore has no option but must produce this particular output, at which the price, or average revenue, is equal to average cost, and profits are zero. Any other output would raise average cost above average revenue and result in a smaller profit than zero, i.e., in a negative profit — a loss. (Profit is here considered in its pure form, excluding wages, interest, rent and similar payments for the use of scarce factors of production.)

In this perfectly competitive situation, the price of the product is at the same time the firm's average revenue and its marginal revenue. If the price is $2 and a hundred units are sold, the average revenue, obtained by dividing total revenue ($200) by the number of units (100), is $2 — the same as the price. When a unit more is sold, total revenue increases from $200 to $202 (since the price remains the same) so that the marginal revenue, which is the increase in total revenue from selling a unit more, is also $2.

Similarly, marginal cost and average cost must also be equal to each other. If marginal cost were less than price, a profit (equal to the difference) could be made by expanding production. If it were greater than price a profit (equal to the difference) could be made by reducing production. Neither of these possibilities can exist when the best possible output has already been reached. Marginal cost therefore cannot be either greater or less than price but equal to it. It must therefore also be equal to average cost which, as we have seen, is made equal to price by freedom of entry into the industry.

In this rather special situation the four items — marginal cost, marginal revenue, average cost and average revenue — are all equal for the firm. Of the six equalities between the six different pairs that can be chosen out of the four items, one equality — that between marginal cost and average revenue (or price of the product) — is necessary for the efficient use of resources in the economy as a whole. The concentration, or perhaps overconcentration of much of economics on the pure microeconomics of perfect competition is responsible for a persistent tendency among economists to confuse the condition for the optimum use of resources, namely the equality between price and marginal cost, with the five other equalities that also result from perfect competition. This would not matter if the optimum use of resources could be reached or approximated only through the establishment of perfect competition. All the six equalities would then be satisfied, including the one that really matters. But often it is possible to establish or approximate one or another of the equalities by other means, and then it does matter if the wrong one is chosen.

The most thoroughly worked-out departure from the purest example of microeconomics is the study of what happens when the price paid or received by a firm is not independent of the amount that it buys or sells. Progress was limited for a long time in this field as long as economists tried to fit the phenomena into the two categories: competition and monopoly. An important breakthrough was made when Joan Robinson and Edward Chamberlin gave up this dichotomy in favor of a spectrum of the degree of influence of sales (or of purchases) over price (although they rather one-sidedly called the spectrum the degree of (monopolistic) imperfection of competition rather than the degree of (competitive) imperfection of monopoly). As a result it was possible to integrate the degree of monopoly (or monopsony) with elasticity of demand (or supply) as the measure of the degree of interaction between the firm (or the individual or the industry) and the economy outside.

This was, however, a very limited departure from pure microeconomics in that it could be considered as a one-sided influence on the outside exercised by the part of the economy studied. The elasticity measured the *passive response* of the economic universe of customers or suppliers, in the abstract form of *the market* on which the price responded passively to the quantity bought or sold or the quantity bought or sold responded passively to the price. It did not involve any *active reaction* of other members of the economy to the acts of the firm or industry in question.

A larger step from micro- toward macroeconomics was involved in the study of *oligopoly* (and *oligopsony*). Here it is not the *market* that comes into the picture, but the positive reactions of competing sellers (or competing buyers) to the behaviour of the firm in question.

Where customers or suppliers organize themselves to react in the manner considered under oligopoly, we have the *countervailing power* that has recently received much recognition as a force limiting monopoly power enjoyed by firms that have moved an alarming distance from the perfect competition end of the competition-monopoly spectrum. And the community at large may set effective limits to the powers of economic concentrations by the development of *consensus* as to what is considered permissible, as has been emphasized in recent writings by Adolph Berle.

Where consensus is insufficiently effective in deterring unacceptable exercise of economic power, legal sanctions come into being, adjusting the rules. The study of how this occurs brings economics back through political economy into politics itself along another dimension in the micro-macro vector, as more and more of the general public are organized so as to be able to react more and more effectively to the behaviour of the firm or industry, reaching ultimately to the level of action through government.

Another dimension of the micro-macroeconomics field is the effect on price flexibility of expected reactions of prices in the rest of the economy to price changes in the area of special study, i.e., of price changes in the macro field in response to price changes in the micro field. These relationships have been much less carefully explored although they are central to the Keynesian analysis and even more to further development of analysis along Keynesian lines. In pure microeconomics "outside" prices are assumed to remain unchanged. In the simplest case, a cut in, say, wages reduces cost and this makes it possible for output to be increased even though this results in increasing cost (because of the departure from the optimum combination of factors when variable factors are increased relatively to the fixed factors). The expansion is carried to the point where marginal cost is again equal to price.

The adjustments that have to be made for the case of various degrees of monopoly are pretty well understood, and something is understood at least about the problems involved in oligopoly. Not enough is known about the relationship of oligopoly-type considerations to the pure macroeconomics of what has become known as the Keynesian special case. This is the case where a reduction in the wage (the price of labor) results in an equal reduction in all other prices so that there is no effect at all on employment.

The Keynesian special case so raises the blood pressure of those habituated to pure microeconomics that it tends to fill their field of vision completely and they identify it with the whole of the much more general Keynesian analysis. Here too the difficulties seem to stem from a bilateral over-concentration on the extreme cases instead of a consideration of the whole spectrum.

The microeconomic procedure in its most extreme form assumes the price of the product to be given from outside. A movement in the macro direction along the spectrum permits one to consider the case where the costs of the producers of competing goods (including the producers of the "same" product) have also gone down. The main reason for the expansion of output by the firm originally considered, namely the *substitution* of its product for that of these others, disappears from the picture as a result of the wage cut. This movement along the spectrum may also be taken in smaller steps, so that at first only *some* of the substitution effect is negated.

There remains the *income* effect. At lower prices the public can buy more with the same expenditure, and there is still an increase in (real) sales and in employment even if all (competing) goods have cut their prices in the same degree as the item first considered. But a further movement along the spectrum brings out the reduction of income that comes with the reduction of wages and prices. When this has worked itself out completely, incomes will have fallen in the same degree as prices (and costs and wages) and there is no increase in output or employment from the income effect. This again may be considered in smaller steps where only some of the fall in income takes place and only some of the income effect is negated.

There still remains the *cash balance* effect. With the reduction in all wages, costs, prices and incomes, an unchanged stock of cash is increased in real value or purchasing power, and that may give rise to an increase in sales, output, income and employment. This effect bears sufficient similarity to the original purely microeconomic proposition, i.e., that a wage cut (directly) increases employment, for it to be clutched at eagerly by more extreme addicts to pure microeconomics as a sophisticated rehabilitation of their fundamentally sound classical instincts. (This is of course not done by the economists who developed and elaborated the analysis of the cash balance effects — Professors Pigou and Patinkin.)

A movement still further along the spectrum in the macro direction uncovers the possibility of the cash balance effect being ineffective (because the economy is saturated with liquidity — it already has so much cash that increasing it has no further effect). The cash balance effect may, furthermore, be eliminated if the money supply is itself reduced as a result of the depression through which the price reductions are brought about. (In the reverse case of an increase in wages, costs, prices and incomes, the cash balance effect is eliminated if the supply of money is increased in response to political pressures generated by the price inflation.) This too may be considered as occurring in different degrees. In the most extreme case, where the cash balance effect is *completely* negated (together with the substitution and the income effects), we have the Keynesian special case.

At the microeconomic end of this spectrum, where a wage cut results in a reduction of cost in relation to the *price* of the product, it is perfectly reasonable to suppose that quite small wage and cost reductions can lead to quite large increases in the amount that it would pay to produce and the amount of employment that would be provided. The illegitimate application of this proposition to the macroeconomic end of the spectrum is strongly supported by businessmen who think only of how much more they would find it profitable to sell at current prices if only their costs (and their costs only) were (microeconomically) reduced by a wage cut.

Further along the spectrum, where we have not wages and costs reduced in relation to the price of the product but wages, costs and prices reduced in relation to the level of money *income*, much larger wage and cost and price reductions are needed to bring about the same increase in output and employment because with all prices moving together there is no substitution effect.

Further still along the spectrum, where we have not the reduction of wages and costs relative to prices of the product, and not even the reduction of wages, costs and prices in relation to income, but the reduction of wages, costs, prices and income in relation to the *cash balances*, it takes a still larger reduction of wages (and prices and incomes) to bring about the same increase in output and employment because there is now no income effect either. The *substitution effect* and the *income effect* have disappeared leaving only the *cash balance effect*.

This brings us to a higher or third level in the consideration of the complications abstracted from in microeconomics — the reaction of the firm to the reactions of the rest of the economy to the actions of the firm. The recognition by those in control of wages or prices, that it now takes a much larger reduction in wages or prices to bring about the same increase in employment or sales, makes them less willing to agree to wage or price reductions. This is the nature of the price rigidity which weakens the only remaining adjustment — the cash balance effect — and which permits the pure microeconomic addicts to blame the trade unions or the social security system or big business monopoly for the inflexibility of wages and prices that prevent the economy from working as it would appear to work when seen only through the microeconomic window.

Our micro-macro or spectrum analysis thus tells us that while wages and prices have to be much *more* flexible to cure any deficiencies in demand, as the portion of the economy involved becomes greater, the recognition of these more macroeconomic complications by those in position of power over wages or prices induces them to make prices and wages *less* flexible.

(Still further along the spectrum we have the Keynesian special case where a wage cut has no effect at all on employment because the cash balance effect is ineffective or is eliminated by the monetary authorities. This case is of course seized on with avidity by the macroeconomic addicts as well as by those who, for quite unrelated reasons, are especially eager for arguments against wage cuts.)

The resistances to wage and price cuts also have the effect of delaying even those cuts which cannot be avoided. The result is a climate of *expected* cost and price reduction which aggravates rather than cures a deficiency of demand and of employment as everybody postpones buying while waiting for the expected price reductions.

All this is quite apart from the consideration that even if a degree of price flexibility could somehow be brought about that was sufficient to give the desired results, the side effects of such a cure might kill the patient before curing the malady. The use of a money unit in an economy depends on its acceptability by the population, and this in turn depends on a minimum of stability in the value of the money unit. Where this stability is lost the money unit is rejected and another unit comes into use, as in the case of the postwar German Mark, which was displaced by cigarettes as a medium of exchange until a new and more stable Mark was established. The degree of price flexibility that is needed to deal with a variation in demand for a particular product is a natural and proper demand to make of the money and price mechanism. That is indeed nothing but its daily microeconomic work. But it is too much to ask for a degree of price flexibility that, without the substitution effect and without the income effect and working only with an attenuated cash balance effect and against perverse expectation effects, would nevertheless be able to maintain a satisfactory level of demand in the economy as a whole, making monetary and fiscal policy unnecessary. Such an extreme price flexibility would destroy the stability of the value of the money unit on which its acceptability as a money unit rests [1].

The wage and price policies that give rise to the rigidities cannot exist under perfect competition. There must be some significant imperfection of competition before the strategies can develop that produce the price rigidity. But once a large part of the economy has developed these strategies and the resultant rigidities are part of the economic climate, it becomes possible for the rigidity to invade the more competitive parts of the economy. Agreement to refrain from price cutting can become less formal and still remain effective and can operate where formal agreement is very difficult or even impossible to arrange. Firms can survive without reducing price to where it is equal to marginal cost, if their competitors also depart from the perfectly competitive norm in the same way. Unemployment can therefore live together with price stability in what looks like a very competitive situation with wages not falling because prices are not expected to fall and prices not falling because wages are not expected to fall.

The next step in the development of this kind of group consciousness in the economy is not merely for wages and prices to refrain from falling (in conditions where the microeconomics of perfect condition would dictate that they should) but for them to *rise* just because they are expected to rise. Of course, if the monetary authorities do not fill the need for additional cash balances as wages, prices and incomes rise, increasing unemployment would ultimately break up the syndrome. But the pressures on the government to provide the extra money seem pretty certain to prevail over any fiscal purism in politicians.

That, of course, means bringing in politics, but it is precisely the political element in the economy, the power of men over other men (by virtue of their power over prices and over outputs that does not exist in perfect competition) which is the source of the rigidity. It is this power that makes possible the emergence of severe unemployment and makes necessary the political measures for curing the unemployment. The rise of macroeconomics is part and parcel of the returning of economics to political economy [2]. This problem of integrating microeconomics with macroeconomics is a part of the integration of economic analysis with the development of useful prescriptions for economic policy.

This does not mean that the refinements of pure microeconomics or the different abstractions of pure macroeconomics are to be discouraged. On the contrary their improvement and further development may very well lead to their ultimate synthesis. The physicists seem to be moving toward a similar synthesis while going beyond the light-microscope to the electron-microscope in one direction and beyond the light-telescope to the radio-telescope in the other direction, in their search for a deeper understanding of the nature of the basic bricks of the universe. In economics we may also hope for fruits from refinements at the microscopic as well as at the macroscopic extremes. But it might occasionally also be useful to leave the microscope as well as the telescope for a while and use one's normal eyesight to observe such phenomena as rising prices together with substantial unemployment, which are no less important for normal economics just because they do not fit into the familiar models, micro or macro.

References

[1] Lerner, A. "The Essential Properties of Interest and Money," *Quarterly Journal of Economics*, May 1952, reprinted in *Essays in Economic Analysis*, Macmillan, London, and St. Martins Press, N.Y., 1953, pp. 354–385.

[2] Lerner, A. "Economics and the Control of Man," *The American Scholar*, Summer 1960.

RÉSULTATS ET DIRECTIONS DE RECHERCHE DANS LA THÉORIE DE L'AGRÉGATION

ANDRÉ NATAF

Ministère des Finances, Paris, France

Introduction

La vie économique d'une société résulte des actions et réactions reciproques de phénomènes économiques élémentaires. Le nombre très élevé de ces phénomènes, leur extrême diversité et, plus encore la rapidité avec laquelle ils se modifient dans le temps, rendent impossible l'appréhension immédiate de l'évolution finale de l'économie. D'une part en effet, au contraire des sciences de la nature, la méthode expérimentale est impraticable en économie, en raison de la sensibilité de tout ensemble économique aux influences extérieures, ce qui enleverait toute portée sérieuse à une expérience tentée dans un milieu économique maintenu artificiellement clos. D'autre part si l'emploi d'une méthode historique apporte de précieux et irremplaçables renseignements sur la nature et l'importance des grands phénomènes économiques et la façon dont ils impriment à une situation historique donnée sa physionomie propre, on ne peut songer à l'utiliser, par analogie avec des situations passées, pour prévoir un déroulement nouveau de l'économie: les phénomènes économiques sont en effet trop changeants et leurs combinaisons sont trop diverses pour nous laisser un tel espoir.

En revanche l'observation et l'esprit de déduction permettent d'étudier des comportements économiques élémentaires, ou, à tout le moins, d'avancer des hypothèses de travail raisonnables sur ces comportements. C'est ainsi que l'on a pu étudier par exemple le comportement de l'entrepreneur et celui du consommateur. C'est ainsi également, qu'à partir de l'analyse de situations historiques bien tranchées, se rapprochant beaucoup de circonstances théoriques simples, on peut dégager des caractéristiques de types possibles d'économie, comme l'économie concurrentielle ou l'économie monopolistique.

Mais pour intéressantes, et d'ailleurs indispensables à l'édification objective de la science économique que soient les analyses de comportements isolés ou de groupes restreints, elles sont insuffisantes. Pour être en mesure de décrire l'évolution économique d'une société quelconque il faut voir comment se combinent toutes ces lois élémentaires innombrables et être capable d'en déduire l'évolution résultante.

Les progrès réalisés dans cette direction, grâce à l'utilisation des méthodes mathématiques modernes, ont certes permis des résolutions rigoureuses de systèmes économiques complexes. On a pu dégager avec précision la nature et la forme des hypothèses permettant d'aboutir à des conclusions bien spécifiées et irréfutables dans ce corps d'hypothèses. On obtient ainsi des théorèmes d'existence non seulement souvent précieux par les résultats d'ordre général qu'ils apportent, mais aussi par la rigueur qu'ils assurent à des procédés pratiquement plus utilisables, mais dont la justification directe n'apparaîtrait pas aisément.

Cependant d'une part les résultats les plus détaillés ne sont pas explicités numériquement et d'autre part, quand bien même le seraient-ils qu'ils se présenteraient sous la forme d'une énorme quantité de chiffres relatifs à chaque agent ou entité économiques. Il y aurait lieu de classer, regrouper ces chiffres, et les analyser pour en déduire les valeurs globales qui caractérisent les aspects fondamentaux d'une économie.

C'est un des plus grands mérites de Keynes que d'avoir analysé l'économie sous son aspect global. Sans prendre en effet position sur le fonds même de ses idées, il faut souligner qu'il a été le premier, sinon à comprendre que des résultats à l'échelle microéconomique ne donnent pas de réponse significative aux problèmes cruciaux de l'économie, comme par exemple le problème de l'emploi, du moins à utiliser un procédé de pensée et d'analyse basé sur la considération de grandeurs macroéconomiques. Il est en effet plus important d'avoir une connaissance même approchée du volume global de l'emploi que de posséder une démonstration théorique de l'existence d'un état d'équilibre économique sur l'aspect social duquel il serait impossible de porter un jugement d'ensemble.

Déjà donc, d'un premier point de vue, ces considérations au fond purement économiques et d'économie proprement politique, nous incitent à rechercher si on ne peut agréger, selon des procédures à établir, les données économiques et relations existant entre ces données pour en déduire des résultats globaux. C'est ainsi que se pose, en gros, le problème qui, maintenant, est bien connu en économie sous le nom de problème de l'agrégation.

Mais une deuxième considération, aussi importante en théorie qu'en pratique, souligne en quelque sorte de façon absolue l'intérêt de ce problème. C'est qu'une recherche rigoureuse d'agrégation, la rigueur pouvant d'ailleurs sans aucune contradiction s'accompagner d'approximations reconnues et justifiées, pourra nous mettre sur la voie d'un procédé de résolution détaillée d'un modèle très complet. C'est ainsi, pour prendre une analogie mathématique, que bien souvent dans la résolution de systèmes d'équations, on peut circonscrire la difficulté à former et résoudre une équation résolvante, les valeurs des inconnues restantes se déterminant ensuite aisément.

Mais de plus, du point de vue pratique, le succès éventuel de telles recherches permettrait sans doute de grands progrès dans les problèmes de décentralisation coordonnée et cohérente de l'économie, à partir de la détermination de certains éléments essentiels du système économique.

À partir de ces prémisses nous nous proposons maintenant de voir dans une première partie comment le problème de l'agrégation a été considéré à l'origine et les premiers résultats obtenus, dans une 2e partie comment ces résultats assez négatifs ont infléchi la position du problème, et enfin dans la troisième partie nous indiquerons selon quelles directions, à notre avis, ces recherches devraient être poursuivies.

I. Premières Conceptions du Problème de l'Agrégation et Premiers Résultats Obtenus

Du point de vue historique le premier procédé d'agrégation, le plus simple, pour ne pas dire le plus simpliste du point de vue méthodologique, a consisté à admettre d'emblée une homothétie de comportement entre les comportements de chacun des secteurs microéconomiques et du secteur macroéconomique dans lequel on les agrège. C'est cette méthode, présentée néanmoins avec certaines précautions justificatrices, qu'a employée Keynes dans sa "Théorie générale de l'emploi, l'intérêt et la monnaie". Sans discuter les idées de base de Keynes, il suffit pour notre propos de fair remarquer que ces agrégations, comme on devait le démontrer plus tard, n'étaient pas théoriquement justifiées ni admissibles. Dès le débat donc, sous cet angle peut-être néanmoins mineur, l'oeuvre prêtait flanc à la critique. Et pour élucider ce point, Lawrence R. Klein [3] recherchait à quelles conditions on pouvait légitimement opérer des agrégations.

Klein posa le problème sous la forme précise suivante:

Etant donné un ensemble de relations

$$R_1 = 0, R_2 = 0, \cdots, R_i = 0, \cdots, R_n = 0,$$

chaque relation R_i ne portant que sur des éléments a_i, b_i, c_i, ne figurant pas dans les autres relations, à quelles conditions peut-on trouver des fonctions:

$$\begin{array}{ll} A \text{ des } a_i \text{ seuls} & A = A\,(a_i, a_2, \cdots, a_i, \cdots, a_n), \\ B \text{ des } b_i \text{ seuls} & B = B\,(b_1, b_2, \cdots, b_i, \cdots, b_n), \\ C \text{ des } c_i \text{ seuls} & C = C\,(c_1, c_2, \cdots, c_i, \cdots, c_n), \end{array}$$

qui soient liées, identiquement par rapport aux lettres $a_1, \cdots, a_n, b_1, \cdots, b_n, c_1, \cdots, c_n$ par une relation de la forme $R(A, B, C) = 0$.

Klein avait à peine posé le problème qu'une très intéressante discussion l'opposa dans *Econometrica* à Shou Shan Pu [9] et Kenneth O. May [5]. Il vaut la peine de s'y arrêter car cette discussion dévoile au fond deux aspects essentiels de l'agrégation, entre lesquels en définitive nous ne sommes pas libres de choisir mais qu'il convient tour à tour de considérer, selon que, dans la réalité on se trouve dans un cas plutôt que dans l'autre.

Le reproche adressé par Pu à la façon dont Klein posait le problème était le suivant: les possibilités d'agrégation que Klein pouvait mettre en évidence étaient à priori trop limitées, car le champ de variation dans lequel on considérait les variables a_i, b_i, c_i était à priori trop large. Dans un système reél en effet ces variables ne prennent en définitive qu'un ensemble unique de valeurs, défini non seulement par la liaison qu'impose la relation $R_i(a_i, b_i, c_i) = 0$ mais encore par le fait que l'on retrouve ces mêmes variables a_i, b_i, c_i dans d'autres équations du système que Klein ne prend pas en considération non pas évidemment dans l'absolu mais dans sa recherche d'une agrégation simplificatrice. Shou Shan Pu ne proposait évidemment pas de se limiter aux seules valeurs solutions définitives pour les variables

a_i, b_i, c_i, ce qui supposerait le problème résolu, mais d'essayer de limiter le champ de variation de ces quantités, eut égard à une partie au moins des autres relations où elles peuvent figurer. Il pourrait en résulter alors des possibilitiés d'agrégation que l'on ne trouverait pas si l'on faisait abstraction des autres relations. Et Shou Shan Pu illustra sa thèse d'un exemple expressif: il montra que dans un certain modèle économique, et dans une situation d'équilibre marginaliste, il existait un système microéconomique complet et où les agrégats avaient un sens économique simple, alors que les relations entre agrégats ne tenaient pourtant pas identiquement, mais seulement compte tenu des équations traduisant l'équilibre marginal.

Kenneth O. May [5] dans le numéro suivant de *Econometrica* arrive déjà à une conception très cohérente de l'agrégation, fortement liée, tant du point de vue économique profond, que du point de vue de l'utilisation de l'outil mathématique, à la théorie économique considérée dans son ensemble.

Il considère un systéme économique supposé complètement décrit en théorie et possédant p degrés de liberté. Mais les fonctions introduites dans le système complet ne sont souvent pas effectivement mesurables ni explicitables, et, même si p est petit, la forme du système est peut-être incompatible avec une résolution directe ou même une étude d'allure sans précision numérique. En revanche il peut exister des agrégats ayant un sens économique simple et important, susceptibles de vérifications ou déterminations statistiques, et définis à partir du système donné. Si l'on considère un nombre γ (supérieur à p) de ces agrégats il sont certainement liés par $\gamma - p$ relations independantes. On peut donc, par élimination des variables microéconomiques entre les γ agrégats et le système initial arriver à ce nouveau système de $\gamma - p$ relations indépendantes entre les agrégats. C'est ce système qui constitue le macromodèle.

En définitive Kenneth O. May établissait une correspondance biunivoque entre les deux systèmes micro- et macroéconomique en passant d'une façon rigoureuse et complète du premier au second. Du point de vue économique il liait de façon naturelle la détermination des agrégats à la considération tout à fait raisonnable et de bon sens de possibilités statistiques objectives, indispensables pour étayer solidement le système et, ultérieurement, pour en contrôler les résultats.

Il nous semble intéressant de schématiser les conceptions de Klein et May par deux tableaux (p. 488).

Par rapport aux idées de Klein les thesès de Shou Shan Pu et May avaient l'avantage de mieux insérer les recherches de l'agrégation dans le corps du système économique considéré et d'établir une correspondance précise (peut-être trop d'ailleurs comme on le verra plus tard) entre les modèles micro- et macroéconomiques. Cependant Klein avait posé de facon très correcte l'étude de conditions suffisantes sinon nécessaires d'agrégation. Son procédé avait l'avantage important de donner des résultats qui restaient valides à l'intérieur de la partie du système où il travaillait, alors que pour May tout changement même très partiel pouvait retentir partout dans le

Conception de Klein

Système microéconomique partiel	Système macroéconomique partiel
	Agrégats
$R_1(a_1, b_1, c_1) = 0$	$A(a_1, a_2, \cdots, a_n)$
$R_2(a_2, b_2, c_2) = 0$	$B(b_1, b_2, \cdots, b_n)$
.	$C(c_1, c_2, \cdots, c_n)$
.	$R(A, B, C) = 0$
.	
$R_i(a_i, b_i, c_i) = 0$	
.	
.	
.	
$R_n(a_n, b_n, c_n) = 0$	
complété	
$R_{n+1}(a_{n+1}, b_{n+1}, c_{n+1}) = 0$	
.	
.	
.	
$R_{n+k}(a_{n+k}, b_{n+k}, c_{n+k}) = 0$	

Conception de K. O. May

Système microéconomique complété	Système macroéconomique complété
	Equations agrégats
$R_1(x_1, x_2, \cdots, x_{q+\rho}) = 0$	$A_1(x_1, x_2, \cdots, x_{q+\rho}) = 0$
$R_2(x_1, x_2, \cdots, x_{q+\rho}) = 0$	.
.	.
.	.
.	$A\gamma(x_1, x_2, \cdots, x_{q+\rho}) = 0$
$R_i(x_1, x_2, \cdots, x_{q+\rho}) = 0$	$S_1(A_1, \cdots, A\gamma) = 0$
.	.
.	.
.	.
$R_q(x_1, x_2, \cdots, x_{q+\rho}) = 0$	$S_{\gamma-\rho}(A_1, \cdots, A_\gamma) = 0$

système agrégé. De toutes façons en raison de l'utilisation par Keynes d'agrégations sans justification serrée il valait la peine d'étudier le problème posé par Klein. En considérant les R_i comme des fonctions de production dont les a_i, b_i, c_i constituaient les arguments interprétables respectivement comme capital, fournitures, et main-d'oeuvre, nous avons pu établir [6] que l'existence des agrégats A, B, C n'était possible que si tous les R_i pouvaient se ramener à des egalités entre sommes de fonctions de a_i seul, de b_i seul et de c_i seul. La relation agrégée $R(A, B, C) = 0$ pouvait alors se ramener à la forme $A+B+C = 0$. Les conditions trouvées étaient donc bien irréelles.

Un problème relatif cette fois-ci à la consommation dans le cadre de la théorie des choix était ensuite attaqué indépendamment par Gorman [1] et nous-mêmes [7]. Il s'agissait de voir si la détermination de la consommation à partir de la théorie des choix pouvait se transposer du cas individuel au cas global par la simple considération d'un consommateur moyen unique, représentatif de la population tout entière, supposé nanti d'un revenu égal à la moyenne des revenus et muni d'une fonction d'indifférence à déterminer. Dans les deux études citées il était reconnu que la transposition n'était possible que dans le cas où, pour tous les individus, les variations de consommation correspondant, à prix constants, à d'égales variations de revenus, étaient identiques. Cette condition est invraisemblable dans la réalité.

Les résultats précis obtenus à ce stade étaient donc négatifs. Ils avaient cependant l'avantage de montrer les dangers d'utiliser sans précaution certaines hypothèses de travail trop agrégées, ce qui est important pour apprécier certaines conclusions de théories économiques. Ils suggéraient de chercher dans d'autres directions. D'ailleurs, comme nous le verrons un peu plus loin dans la 3e partie, des modifications relativement faibles à la façon par trop exigeante dont on posait le problème de l'agrégation permettent d'aboutir à des résultats qui semblent davantage susceptibles d'applications pratiques.

Mais ces résultats et les discussions sur la façon même de poser le problème avaient lancé beaucoup d'idées.

H. Theil [10] devant l'impossibilité de résultats positifs étudia alors la façon dont se modifiait le problème lorsqu'on abandonnait le domaine de relations de base macroéconomiques certaines pour un domaine où ces relations sont du type probabiliste. Nous n'entrerons pas dans la description des résultats obtenus puisque Theil lui-même en fait un exposé dans ce volume.[1]

En revanche nous allons exposer une conception synthétique très importante de l'agrégation dûe aux idées et travaux de L. Hurwicz [2] et E. Malinvaud [4].

II. Synthèse d'Ensemble d'Hurwicz et Malinvaud

Le courant d'idées que nous allons décrire trouve son origine dans une communication faite en décembre 1951 au Congrès de Boston de la Société d'Économétrie par L. Hurwicz. Peu après Malinvaud en avait connaissance grâce à un resumé publié dans *Econometrica* reprenait la question en l'enrichissant et en faisait l'objet de divers exposés. C'est essentiellement d'après son article paru dans "Les Cahiers du Séminaire d'Econométrie" de M. René Roy que nous exposons ses idées.

Les travaux de K. O. May avaient dégagé très utilement la nécessité de préciser les relations entre les systèmes macro- et microéconomique. Cepen-

---

[1]Cf. l'article de Theil, dans ce volume, page 507.

dant la liaison que May préconisait était trop étroite, trop stricte. Elle ne prenait pas suffisamment en considération les contingences rencontrées dans la pratique lorsqu'on veut appliquer les enseignements d'une théorie.

Au contraire dans les travaux d'Hurwicz et Malinvaud le problème de l'agrégation était posé en distingant nettement les données, les objectifs, et les moyens d'action intervenant dans une économie. Sans doute les difficultés et complications de calculs étaient-elles reconnues comme des raisons importantes pour substituer un système macroéconomique plus maniable à un système microéconomique plus complet. Mais la nécessité objective de prendre des décisions économiques dans un temps assez court et d'en assurer ensuite l'exécution et le contrôle, ou même simplement les questions posées par la seule diffusion de l'information économique dans un milieu réel très imparfait, toutes ces raisons contribuaient à mettre à sa juste place la recherche de la rigueur en face de celle de l'efficacité économique réelle. En conséquence pour augmenter cette dernière, il peut être parfaitement légitime d'admettre un certain flou dans la correspondance entre le système complet et le système agrégé. Il est évident cependant qu'il convient d'avoir quelque évaluation de la distance admissible entre les résultats de ces deux systèmes pour accepter ou rejeter des formes d'agrégation données. Utilisant les idées de Wald sur la théorie des décisions statistiques, Malinvaud a suggéré de mesurer la valeur d'un système macroéconomique en fonction inverse de la perte qui résulte de sa substitution à un système rigoureux. En particulier si les procédures d'agrégation à utiliser appartiennent, par exemple pour des raisons pratiques d'organisation sociale, à une classe donnée, la minimisation de la perte sur cette classe indiquera la meilleure agrégation à utiliser parmi celles dont on dispose.

Si l'on veut encore schématiser les conceptions d'Hurwicz et Malinvaud on peut dire que dans un système microéconomique les données et les objectifs sont des points bien précis auxquels on peut faire correspondre des moyens également bien précis qui assurent la réalisation des objectifs.

● données }
● objectifs } ⟶ moyens d'exécution → réalisation des objectifs
●   ●

Dans le système macroéconomique on se préoccupe surtout de déterminer des zônes pas trop erronées dans lesquelles se trouvent ces éléments de façon que le résultat final ne soit pas trop éloigné des objectifs ideaux, selon le schéma ci-dessous:

⊙ zône de flou des données }
⊙ zône admissible des objectifs } ⟶ zône où se trouvent les moyens d'action, ⊙ ⟶ de sorte que le résultat final soit dans une zône proche de l'objectif idéal ⊙

Ces travaux réalisent donc, du moins à notre avis, une décantation profonde entre l'objet, les méthodes et les résultats de l'agrégation. Ils constituent un système de référence pour mieux apprécier la place des résultats passés et à venir dans le domaine, et un guide du sens à donner aux recherches.

Il reste cependant un travail considérable à réaliser pour meubler concrètement ce cadre de travail de résultats concernant les possibilités d'agrégation dans les théories économiques les plus importantes ou les modèles qui en procèdent.

Nous nous proposons dans la troisième et dernière partie qui va suivre de dégager maintenant les voies d'études qui nous paraissent utiles et fécondes.

III. Directions Suggérées aux Recherches

Les réflexions sur le problème de l'agregation ont finalement dégagé l'idée qu'il y a nécessité de modeler l'agrégation sur la nature du système microéconomique considéré et en fonction des objectifs poursuivis. Il n'y a donc pas dichotomie entre l'étude d'un système microéconomique et celle d'un système macroéconomique qu'on en déduit. Ces deux systèmes doivent s'éclairer l'un l'autre. Il est tout à fait concevable par exemple que des formes de propriétés théoriques soient mises en évidence sur le microsystème mais que les conséquences pratiques que l'on puisse en tirer dépendent de la grandeur proprement numérique de certaines quantités. Bien souvent alors il faut s'attendre à ce que ces quantités soient des agrégats dont la définition découlera de l'étude microéconomique, mais dont la détermination numérique, même approximative, se déduira effectivement de la considération d'un système macroéonomique.

Un tel rapprochement entre les deux aspects micro et macro d'une économie doit permettre de baser plus solidement le choix des agrégats à considerer et mettre en évidence les plus importants. On peut espérer qu'il contribuera à faciliter le passage crucial et pourtant si délicat dans tous les systèmes sociaux, entre l'étude complète d'un système et les mesures les plus efficaces à prendre pour améliorer ou réaliser son fonctionnement, compte tenu des nécessités pratiques du temps d'information, d'étude et d'organisation pour préparer les décisions et en obtenir l'application.

Ce travail doit être entrepris sur des théories importantes et à l'occasion d'études effectives d'économies données, comme par exemple les économies des differentes nations, pour que l'agrégation sorte du domaine purement conceptuel et théorique et donne des résultats tangibles.

À cet égard les premières expériences malheureuses quand aux possibilités d'agrégation de la production ou de la consommation n'auront pas été si inutiles en définitive. Elles nous ont appris que nous étions trop exigeants en recherchant dans l'environnement économique le plus général des possibilités d'agrégation. Si l'on essaye d'être moins exigeant mais en faisant porter un effort de réflexion sur les circonstances où il peut être économiquement fondé de rechercher des possibilités d'agrégation, peut-être trouvera-t-on plus souvent des résultats utilisables.

Une première analyse dans ce sens nous avait amené à étudier les possibilités d'agrégation de la consommation dans le cadre de la théorie des choix, mais en se restreignant aux cas où les unités économiques ont même revenu.

Nous avons ainsi pu:

a) Tout d'abord trouver des cas assez étendus où la détermination de la consommation pouvait se ramener à celle d'un individu moyen virtuel, muni d'une fonction d'utilité bien déterminée à partir de celles de toutes les unités économiques [6].

b) En perfectionnant ensuite nos procédés de recherche [8] ramener non seulement dans le cas de revenus égaux, mais encore dans les cas ou ces revenus dépendent simplement d'un paramètre, la consommation moyenne de la population à la moyenne pondérée d'un nombre p d'individus virtuels, mais bien déterminés à partir de la population considérée. Le nombre p est inférieur non pas seulement au total N de la population, mais même au nombre beaucoup plus réduit n des biens de consommation existants.

Ces résultats, bien que dirigés vers les applications sont encore à ce stade d'ordre théorique. Leur véritable utilité se révèlera ou non si, en s'inspirant des idées et méthodes de recherche qui ont permis de les établir, des analyses concrètes de consommation à partir de données statistiques peuvent être menées à bien et si des interprétations raisonnables ou révélatrices se dégagent, du point de vue économique, à partir des structures pour l'instant formelles de cette théorie.

Il en va de même, pensons-nous, du côté de la production, sur laquelle la littérature économique est déjà assez riche, en particulier dans l'étude des possibilités d'agrégation des tableaux de Léontief.

Il nous semble qu'une intensification des recherches dans ces directions, explorant les cas qui semblent économiquement importants, est essentielle. C'est en effet à partir des résultats qui s'en dégageront et en les connectant, en toute rigueur si possible, ou bien en restant dans les limites d'une approximation admissible au sens d'Hurwicz et Malinvaud que l'on sera en mesure de dresser une étude rigoureuse, mais en même temps appréhensible par l'esprit humain, des systèmes économiques.

Références

[1] Gorman, "Community Preference Field", *Econometrica*, Vol. 21, No. 1, Janvier 1953.

[2] Hurwicz, L. "Aggregation in Macro-Economic Models", *Econometrica*, 1952, p. 489.

[3] Klein, L. R. "Macroeconomics and the theory of rational behavior", *Econometrica*, Vol. 14, No. 2, Avril 1946.

[4] Malinvaud, E. *Cahiers du Seminaire d'Econométrie*, pp. 69–146 (publiés avec le concours du CNRS), Paris, 1956.

[5] May, K. O. "Technological Change and Aggregation", *Econometrica*, Vol. 15, No. 1.

[6] NATAF, A. "Thèse", Paris, 1954 chez J et R Sennac ou Vol. II, fasc 4, 1953 des publications de l'ISUP ainsi que "Sur la possibilité de construction de certaines macromodèles", *Econometrica*, Vol. 16, No. 3, Juillet 1948.

[7] NATAF, A. "Possibilité d'Agrégation dans le Cadre de la Théorie des Choix", *Métroéconomica*, Vol. V, fasc 1, Avril 1953.

[8] NATAF, A. "Forme reduite d'Agrégats de Consommation dans le Cadre de la Theorie des Choix", *Publications de l'Institut de Statistique de Paris*, Vol. VIII, fasc 1, 1958.

[9] PU, SHOU SHAN, "A Note on Macroeconomics", *Econometrica*, Vol. 14, No. 4.

[10] THEIL, H. "*Linear Aggregation of Economic Relations*, Amsterdam, 1954.

THREE MODELS OF ECONOMIC GROWTH

RICHARD STONE

Cambridge University, Cambridge, England

1. Introduction

This paper is concerned with very simple models of economic growth. In micro-economics it is usual to deduce relationships by reference to some maximizing principle intended to reflect rational behaviour. A good example of this is the theory of consumers' behaviour. The formulation of such a theory is quite an achievement but one must recognise that its practical results are often disappointing. This is because it is static, it assumes important variables, like tastes, to be constant, and it is based on a rudimentary and amateurish psychology. In fact the main guidance this theory gives in applied work might almost equally well have been obtained from an empirical approach based on the observation that the consumer responds to changes in income and prices and on the assumption that other influences can be ignored. Market experience, in which individual behaviour is aggregated over the population of consumers, shows that this simple approach contains a good deal of truth and that when it fails, then the theory is of limited value in suggesting useful new avenues to explore. In fact its main value seems to be in suggesting manageable simplifications which will allow price interactions to be studied. But in practice we may have to concern ourselves with such things as the interaction of supply and demand, the phenomenon of saturation, and the time-form of responses to changes in income and prices. In setting up models which will enable us to study these aspects of the actual world, we leave the tidy consistency of static theory and become involved in piecemeal extensions of it which typically do not fit together into a new, more general, harmonious whole. An account of some of the problems encountered in this field is given in [5].

Thus the partial macro-economics of the market or the industry is based on micro-economic theory, which in its turn is based on a maximizing principle. In complete macro-economics, of which trade-cycle theory and growth theory are perhaps the most obvious examples, the position is different. In the first place, just because the models in this field aim at completeness it is more obviously important to put them in a dynamic form. In the second place, since the phenomena studied are so vast, it is usual to start off with aggregated variables such as total consumption or total investment, with the result that attention is fixed on variables which at the outset are distanced through aggregation from individual behaviour. As a consequence theories in this field tend to be relatively superficial and to ignore any optimizing principle which might be supposed to lie at the roots of human endeavour.

With this idea in mind I shall examine three models concerned with economic growth. The first is the familiar multiplier-accelerator model, or its variant, which involves a capital coefficient in place of the accelerator. This is a descriptive model which does not dig very deep. The second is Mahalanobis' two-sector model of economic growth. This traces out the consequence of a particular planning decision, namely, the proportion of investment to be devoted to expanding capacity in the investment goods industry. The consequences of varying this proportion are worked out, but no optimizing solution is considered. The third is Ramsey's model for determining at any time the optimum rate of saving. This can be regarded as a descriptive model based on an optimizing principle, and points the way to a rational solution of Mahalanobis' problem.

All three models are set out in a very simple form. It will be shown that the steady state to which the third model tends is identical with the outcome of the first model but that in addition it traces from the initial conditions to the steady state a transient path which connects some of the basic phenomena of economic development. It will also be shown that the second model tends to the first under certain simplifying assumptions.

2. The Multiplier-Accelerator Model

This model is so familiar and the version of it given here is so simple that it can be written down with very little comment. The first relationship states that saving S is a constant proportion σ of income or product Y. That is,

$$S = \sigma Y. \tag{1}$$

The second relationship states that investment V is a constant proportion α of the rate of change of income $\dot{Y} \equiv dY/dt$. That is,

$$V = \alpha\dot{Y}. \tag{2}$$

The third relationship is the accounting identity

$$S \equiv V. \tag{3}$$

The third equation enables us to equate the right-hand sides of (1) and (2), giving

$$\dot{Y}/Y = \sigma/\alpha, \tag{4}$$

a simple differential equation which, on integration, yields

$$Y = Y_0 e^{\sigma t/\alpha}, \tag{5}$$

where Y_0 is a constant of integration which is equal to the initial value of Y when $t = 0$.

So with this model we have exponential growth, the instantaneous rate of growth, λ say, being equal to σ/α. If $\sigma = 0.15$ and $\alpha = 5$, we should have $\lambda = 0.03$.

If the accelerator α is replaced by a capital coefficient k, then (2) is replaced by

$$\dot{Y} = kV, \tag{6}$$

whence, combining (1), (3), and (6), it follows that

$$Y = Y_0 e^{\sigma k t}, \tag{7}$$

in which case $\lambda = \sigma k$.

3. A Two-Sector Model for Investment Planning

In [3] Mahalanobis considers the following problem. In planning, one of the decisions that has to be taken is the allocation of investment resources between the investment-goods industries and the consumption-goods industries. If a large share of investment is allocated to the consumption-goods industries, they will be able to operate initially at a relatively high level. But if this is done, the investment-goods industries will receive only a small share, and so will grow slowly. With an allocation fixed over time, the result will be that the consumption-goods industries will receive a large share of a slowly growing total. In the short run this will lead to a relatively high output of consumption goods, but in the long run the output of consumption goods would be higher if they had had a smaller share in the output of an investment-goods industry which as a consequence of that smaller share would have been able to grow more rapidly. This model is designed to show how these alternative possibilities work out.

Suppose that total income (or product) Y is divided into two parts, the output of the investment-goods industry V, and the output of the consumption-goods industry C. Let the income-capital (product-asset) ratios in these two industries be k_v and k_c, respectively, and let the proportion of investment-goods output allocated in each period to the investment-goods industry be π.

At any moment the rate of investment in the investment-goods industry is πV, and so the rate of change of output of this industry is $k_v \pi V$. Thus

$$\dot{V} = k_v \pi V, \tag{8}$$

whence, on integration,

$$V = V_0 e^{k_v \pi t}, \tag{9}$$

where V_0 is the initial output in the investment-goods industry. By similar reasoning,

$$\begin{aligned} \dot{C} &= k_c(1-\pi)V \\ &= k_c(1-\pi)V_0 e^{\quad \pi t}, \end{aligned} \tag{10}$$

whence, on integration,

$$C = \left\{Y_0 - \left[1 + \frac{k_c(1-\pi)}{k_v \pi}\right] V_0\right\} + \frac{k_c(1-\pi)}{k_v \pi} V_0 e^{k_v \pi t}, \tag{11}$$

where the term in { } is the constant of integration consistent with the initial condition that the initial output of consumption goods C_0 is equal to the total initial output Y_0 minus the initial output of investment goods V_0.

Finally, if we add together (9) and (11), we have

$$Y = \left\{Y_0 - \left[1+\frac{k_c(1-\pi)}{k_v\pi}\right]V_0\right\} + \left[1+\frac{k_c(1-\pi)}{k_v\pi}\right]V_0 e^{k_v\pi t}. \tag{12}$$

We thus see that the output of investment goods grows exponentially, while the output of consumption goods has a constant and an exponential component. If $\pi = 1$, the output of investment goods grows as fast as possible, but from (11) it follows that the output of consumption goods never departs from its initial value C_0. Of course such a high rate of growth in the output of investment goods is useful only if it is intended eventually to lower the value of π when the output of the investment-goods industry has been built up as quickly as possible to what is considered a suitable level.

In this model k_v and k_c are constants and not necessarily equal. This being so, it is natural to inquire whether the planners, or the community, prefer the investment goods or the consumption goods which can be obtained from a marginal unit of investment, and to solve the allocation problem accordingly. Since these preferences are likely to change over time, it might be expected that π would be changed over time. But we will leave this question until we come to the next model.

If we assume that $k_v = k_c = k$, say, and also that the fixed allocation process has always been in operation, then the form of the model is greatly simplified. Thus in place of (9) and (12) we have

$$V = V_0 e^{k\pi}, \tag{13}$$

and

$$Y = Y_0 + \frac{1}{\pi}V_0(e^{k\pi t}-1), \tag{14}$$

so that in time $V \rightarrow \pi Y$ or, in other words, the proportion of income saved and invested tends to the proportion π of investment output allocated to the investment-goods industry.

4. An Optimizing Allocation Model

It is to the undying credit of Ramsey that over thirty years ago he propounded a solution to the kind of problem that has just been posed [4]. Both his model and the technique which it employs, the calculus of variations, have attracted remarkably little attention among economists despite an excellent introduction to both by Allen [1]. The technique in a form suitably modified for computing is only now coming into its own in the work of the dynamic programmers, well exemplified by Bellman [2].

In its simplest form Ramsey's model may be set out as follows. The productive system produces a single good which can be either consumed or invested. The amount produced Y depends on the amount of labour L and capital K employed. Let the production function take the form

$$Y = f(L, K). \tag{15}$$

Consumption C is the excess of production Y over investment $V \equiv \dot{K}$, where $\dot{K}$ is the rate of change of capital. Thus

$$C \equiv Y - \dot{K}. \tag{16}$$

The object of economic life is to maximise total utility, which is composed of the utility of consumption minus the disutility of labour. This utility is not just a thing of the moment but stretches out over an indefinitely prolonged future. We would like to know therefore how to allocate product between consumption and investment at every point of time so that the total utility of the system over time should be a maximum.

Let us denote the utility of consumption by M, the disutility of labour by N and total utility by U. Then, assuming that M depends only on C, we may write

$$M = \phi(C), \tag{17}$$

where ϕ is only restricted by the consideration that there is a finite upper limit to M, since economic considerations alone cannot yield an infinite utility. Further, assuming that N depends only on L, we may write

$$N = \psi(L). \tag{18}$$

Accordingly

$$U = \phi(C) - \psi(L), \tag{19}$$

and we wish to maximise an amount W, where

$$W = \int_{t_0}^{t_1} U dt. \tag{20}$$

In this formulation no account is taken of time discounting in calculating future utilities. This can be done without difficulty, but I shall not do it here.

If we consider the variables on which U ultimately depends, we see that they are L, K, and $\dot{K}$. So we may rewrite (20) in the form

$$W = \int_{t_0}^{t_1} F(L, K, \dot{K}) dt. \tag{21}$$

Labour and capital may be regarded as functions of time, and our problem is to choose these functions in such a way as to maximise W. The condition for this is that the time paths of labour and capital should be such as to satisfy Euler's equation; that is to say, if X stands for either L or K, then

$$\frac{\partial F}{\partial X} = \frac{d}{dt}\left(\frac{\partial F}{\partial \dot{X}}\right).$$

If we apply this condition to (21), we see that

$$\frac{\partial F}{\partial L} = \phi'(C)\frac{\partial Y}{\partial L} - \psi'(L) = 0, \tag{23}$$

where ϕ' and ψ' are the derivatives of ϕ and ψ with respect to C and L respectively. From (23) it follows that

$$\frac{\partial Y}{\partial L} = \frac{\psi'(L)}{\phi'(C)}, \tag{24}$$

or, in words, that at all times the marginal product of labour must equal the ratio of the marginal disutility of labour to the marginal utility of consumption.

In a similar way

$$\frac{\partial F}{\partial K} = \phi'(C)\frac{\partial Y}{\partial K} = \frac{d}{dt}[-\phi'(C)], \tag{25}$$

whence

$$\frac{\partial Y}{\partial K} = -\frac{1}{\phi'(C)} \cdot \frac{d}{dt}[\phi'(C)], \tag{26}$$

or, in words, at all times the marginal product of capital must be equal to the proportionate rate of decrease of the marginal utility of consumption over time.

The time paths of L, K, and C can now be found from the differential equations (16), (24), and (26), the boundary conditions, namely, the amounts of labour and capital, employed initially and aimed at in the final state, being used in determining the constants of integration. On this basis Ramsey shows that

$$\dot{K} = \frac{U^* - [\phi(C) - \psi(L)]}{\phi'(C)}, \tag{27}$$

where U^* is a measure of bliss, the maximum utility of which the economy is capable. Thus, saving should equal the excess of bliss over actual utility divided by the marginal utility of consumption. A remarkable feature of this result is that it is independent of the form of the production function except in so far as bliss is determined by limited production possibilities.

Having established this model at rather greater length than the preceding ones, let us now see what happens if we assume simple forms for the various functions, as we did in the earlier models. Let us suppose that the production function (15) is a linear homogeneous function of the first degree; that is,

$$Y = \omega L + \rho K. \tag{28}$$

With (28) the marginal product of capital is always equal to ρ. On substituting this value of $\partial Y/\partial K$ into the left-hand side of (26), we obtain

(29) $$\frac{1}{\phi'(C)} \cdot \frac{d}{dt}[\phi'(C)] = -\rho,$$

whence, on integration,

(30) $$\phi'(C) = Ae^{-\rho t},$$

where A is a constant of integration. Thus, over time, the marginal utility of consumption follows an exponential decay curve.

Now suppose that the utility function (17) takes the form

(31) $$M = \phi(C) = M^* - \beta(C - \bar{C})^{-\theta},$$

where M^* is the upper limit of M and $\bar{C}$ is the absolute subsistence level below which it is impossible to survive. If we differentiate this equation with respect of C, we obtain $\phi'(C)$, and if we equate the resulting expression to the right-hand side of (30), we obtain

(32) $$\beta\theta(C - \bar{C})^{-(\theta+1)} = Ae^{-\rho t},$$

whence

(33) $$C = \bar{C} + (C_0 - \bar{C})e^{\rho t/(\theta+1)},$$

where C_0 is the initial value of C at $t = 0$. Thus we find that the excess of actual consumption over the subsistence level shows simple exponential growth.

Finally, suppose that the disutility function (18) takes the form

(34) $$N = \psi(L) = \gamma L^{\eta}.$$

If we differentiate this expression with respect to L, we obtain $\psi'(L)$. Combining this result with (24) and (28), we obtain

(35) $$\gamma\eta L^{\eta-1} = \omega Ae^{-\rho t},$$

whence

(36) $$L = L_0 e^{-\rho t/(\eta-1)},$$

where L_0 is the initial value of L at $t = 0$. Thus, on the assumptions made here, the quantity of labour, like the marginal utility of consumption, follows an exponential decay curve. Eventually, no labour will be used, since some disutility attaches to it and, with a production function of the form of (15), it is possible to produce as much output as is wanted with capital alone. Accordingly, with this particular model we cannot have reached bliss until we are fully automated.

Before proceeding, let us observe that by combining (32) and (35), we can relate L to C. In fact

(37) $$L = \left(\frac{\beta\theta\omega}{\gamma\eta}\right)^{1/(\eta-1)}(C_0 - \bar{C})^{-(\theta+1)/(\eta-1)}\, e^{-\rho t/(\eta-1)}.$$

We will choose the initial period $t = 0$ as the last moment at which the economy is without capital. This is the last moment at which the whole product is produced with labour alone. Thus

$$Y_0 = \omega L_0, \tag{38}$$

and this relationship when combined with (37) gives, on dividing through by η,

$$\frac{Y_0}{\eta} = \left(\frac{\beta\theta}{\gamma}\right)^{1/(\eta-1)} \left(\frac{\omega}{\eta}\right)^{\eta/(\eta-1)} (C_0-\bar{C})^{-(\theta+1)/(\eta-1)}. \tag{39}$$

The purpose of this relationship will be apparent in a moment.

By combining (27), (31), and (34), we can now calculate the rate of saving on the specific assumptions made about the forms of the functions. Thus we obtain

$$\dot{K} = \frac{U^*-M^*+\beta(C-\bar{C})^{-\theta}+\gamma L^\eta}{\beta\theta(C-\bar{C})^{-(\theta+1)}} = \frac{(C-\bar{C})}{\theta} + \frac{Y_0}{\eta} e^{-\rho t/(\eta-1)} \tag{40}$$

from (37) and (39), since at bliss no labour is used and so, there being in those circumstances no disutility of labour, it follows that $M^* \equiv U^*$.

The time paths of Y, C, and $\dot{K}$ can now be written down explicitly. By combining (16) and (40), we find that, for $t = 0$,

$$Y_0 = \left[\frac{\theta+1}{\theta} \cdot \frac{\eta}{\eta-1}\right] C_0 - \frac{\eta}{\theta(\eta-1)} \bar{C}, \tag{41}$$

whence

$$\begin{aligned} Y = {} & C_0 \left\{\frac{\theta+1}{\theta} e^{\rho t/(\theta+1)} + \frac{\theta+1}{\theta(\eta-1)} e^{-\rho t/(\eta-1)}\right\} \\ & + \bar{C}\left\{1 - \frac{\theta+1}{\theta} e^{\rho t/(\theta+1)} - \frac{1}{\theta(\eta-1)} e^{-\rho t/(\eta-1)}\right\}, \end{aligned} \tag{42}$$

$$C = C_0\left\{e^{\rho t/(\theta+1)}\right\} + \bar{C}\left\{1 - e^{\rho t/(\theta+1)}\right\}, \tag{43}$$

and

$$\dot{K} = C_0\left\{\frac{1}{\theta} e^{\rho t/(\theta+1)} + \frac{\theta+1}{\theta(\eta-1)} e^{-\rho t/(\eta-1)}\right\} - \bar{C}\left\{\frac{1}{\theta} e^{\rho t/(\theta+1)} + \frac{1}{\theta(\eta-1)} e^{-\rho t/(\eta-1)}\right\}, \tag{44}$$

so that

$$\frac{\dot{K}}{Y} = \frac{C_0\left\{e^{\rho t/(\theta+1)} + \dfrac{\theta+1}{\eta-1} e^{-\rho t/(\eta-1)}\right\} - \bar{C}\left\{e^{\rho t/(\theta+1)} + \dfrac{1}{\eta-1} e^{-\rho t/(\eta-1)}\right\}}{C_0\left\{(\theta+1) e^{\rho t/(\theta+1)} + \dfrac{\theta+1}{\eta-1} e^{-\rho t/(\eta-1)}\right\} + \bar{C}\left\{\theta - (\theta+1) e^{\rho t/(\theta+1)} - \dfrac{1}{\eta-1} e^{-\rho t/(\eta-1)}\right\}}. \tag{45}$$

On integrating (44) with $K_0 = 0$, we see that

$$(46)\quad K = \frac{\theta+1}{\rho\theta}\left\{C_0[e^{\rho t/(\theta+1)} - e^{-\rho t/(\eta-1)}] + \bar{C}\left[\frac{\theta}{\theta+1} - e^{\rho t/(\theta+1)} + \frac{1}{\theta+1}e^{-\rho t/(\eta-1)}\right]\right\},$$

so that

$$(47)\quad \frac{Y}{K} =$$

$$\rho\left\{\frac{C_0\left[e^{\rho t/(\theta+1)} + \frac{1}{\eta-1}e^{-\rho t/(\eta-1)}\right] + \bar{C}\left[\frac{\theta}{\theta+1} - e^{\rho t/(\theta+1)} - \frac{1}{(\theta+1)(\eta-1)}e^{-\rho t/(\eta-1)}\right]}{C_0[e^{\rho t/(\theta+1)} - e^{-\rho t/(\eta-1)}] + \bar{C}\left[\frac{\theta}{\theta+1} - e^{\rho t/(\theta+1)} + \frac{1}{\theta+1}e^{-\rho t/(\eta-1)}\right]}\right\}.$$

The behaviour implied by this model can now be summarized. Before there is any capital, an amount L_0 of labour is used, but as capital is built up, this amount is gradually reduced, as shown in (36), and tends to zero as bliss is approached. By means of saving, as shown in (44), capital grows from zero and tends to infinity. The growth rates of capital, output, consumption, and investment all tend to $\rho/(\theta+1)$.

From (45) we can work out the initial and ultimate values of the saving ratio. The initial value, σ_0 say, is obtained by putting $t = 0$. Thus

$$(48)\qquad \sigma_0 = \frac{C_0(\eta+\theta) - \bar{C}\eta}{C_0\eta(\theta+1) - \bar{C}\eta},$$

which further reduces to

$$(49)\qquad \sigma_0 = 1/\eta$$

if $C_0 = \bar{C}$, that is, if initial consumption is equal to the subsistence level. Now the parameter η is simply the elasticity of the disutility of labour with respect to the amount of labour performed. Accordingly, the initial saving ratio is low if this elasticity is high and *vice versa*. At the other end of the time scale, the value of the ultimate saving ratio, σ_∞ say, is obtained by letting t in (45) tend to infinity. Thus

$$(50)\qquad \sigma_\infty = 1/(\theta+1).$$

Now the parameter θ is the negative of the elasticity of the short fall in actual utility $(M^* - M)$ with respect to the excess of actual consumption over the subsistence level $(C - \bar{C})$. So in the end the saving ratio depends on the attitude to consumption and not on the attitude to work.

In a similar way we can work out the initial and ultimate values of the income-capital ratio from (46). This ratio is initially infinite, since at $t = 0$ there is no capital, and tends ultimately to ρ.

Thus in the end this economy tends to a constant growth rate equal to the product of the saving ratio and the income-capital ratio as in the earlier models.

5. Some Comments on the Optimizing Model

We have just seen that in the optimizing model the saving ratio and the income-captial ratio tend to constant values as assumed in the first model. But in general these ratios are not constant in the optimizing model but take on values which change through time according to the values of the parameters and to the form given to the relationships of the model.

The time paths set out in (42) through (47) depend on ρ, θ, η, C_0, and $\bar{C}$. Let us consider these in turn, beginning with the marginal product of capital. In the specific version of the model given here this magnitude is treated as a constant, with the result that in (29) we obtain a very simple differential equation which we can integrate immediately. Such simplicity is not essential, but to reach definite conclusions we must know what we expect to be able to do with labour and capital over the time span we consider. To the extent that we are wrong about this we shall be mistaken in our calculation of the best course of action to pursue now.

At this point it is useful to introduce the complication of time-discounting which would probably make the model more realistic as a description of actual behaviour though it might be considered irrelevant from the point of view of investment planning. If people discount future enjoyments, they will be less inclined to save, since the future fruits of their saving will be less highly valued than the present equivalent. This consideration can be introduced into the present model by replacing the marginal product of capital with its excess over the rate of time-discounting; thus, if this rate is denoted by ρ^*, then the left-hand side of (26) becomes $(\partial Y/\partial K)-\rho^*$ and the analysis proceeds as before. In general, $\rho^* < \rho$. If $\rho^* = \rho$, there is no net advantage in saving and the economy will not add to its existing capital stock. If $\rho^* > \rho$, the economy will consume its existing capital stock and return to barbarism.

We come now to the utility function. What can we say about the value of the parameter θ? Suppose we were to ask the question: if at the toss of a coin you have an equal chance of a 5 per cent cut or an x per cent rise in consumption, what minimum value of x would induce you to accept this gamble? After repeating this question with different values of the proposed cut, we might come to the conclusion that θ was of the order of 2. In this case the community should ultimately save one-third of its income. If we look at statistics of national income and saving, we find that few countries save at anything like this rate and that it is certainly not the rich ones that tend to do so.

Probably the explanation is to be sought in the phenomenon of time-discounting which, whatever its relevance may be for planning purposes, is certainly a factor that tends to reduce individual rates of saving. It might also be supposed that as people get richer, their conception of what constitutes a subsistence level is revised upwards. This, however, would change the ultimate value of the saving ratio only on the unlikely assumption that there is no absolute subsistence level, that is, $\bar{C} = 0$. For in this case we have, writing $\bar{\bar{C}}$ for the conventional subsistence level,

$$\bar{\bar{C}} = \mu C, \tag{51}$$

so that the utility function takes the form

$$M = M^* - \beta[(1-\mu)C]^{-\theta}, \tag{52}$$

and the saving ratio tends to

$$\sigma = \frac{1}{1+\dfrac{\theta}{1-\mu}}. \tag{53}$$

If on the other hand $\bar{C} \neq 0$, then we must define $\bar{\bar{C}}$ as

$$\bar{\bar{C}} = \bar{C} + \mu(C-\bar{C}), \tag{54}$$

in which case

$$\begin{aligned} M &= M^* - \beta[(1-\mu)(C-\bar{C})]^{-\theta} \\ &= M^* - \beta^*(C-\bar{C})^{-\theta}, \end{aligned} \tag{55}$$

which is identical with (31) except that β is replaced by β^*.

This brings us to the disutility function. The measurement of η poses a similar problem to that of the measurement of θ and might be accomplished by a similar type of psychological experimentation. With the particular model adopted here one would expect η to be rather large, say between 10 and 100. From (48) we see the importance of an absolute subsistence level. We have seen that if $\bar{C} = C_0$, then $\sigma_0 = 1/\eta$. But if $\bar{C} = 0$, it follows from (48) that

$$\sigma_0 = \frac{\eta+\theta}{\eta(\theta+1)}, \tag{56}$$

so that even with $\theta = 5$ and $\eta = 100$ we should have $\sigma_0 = 1/6$, which seems impossibly high for the initial saving ratio.

6. Conclusions

From this short treatment of various growth models the following conclusions may be drawn.

1. We have contrasted the simple multiplier-accelerator model with a simple optimizing model and shown that, on very simple assumptions about the forms of the relationships, the optimizing model tends in its consequences to those which follow at all times from the multiplier-accelerator model.

2. The multiplier-accelerator model represents a form of steady-state dynamics which is of limited interest because it summarizes the complicated effects of human behaviour and of technology in terms of constant parameters. By contrast, the optimizing model gives an account of the transient behaviour between the initial and the ultimate states of the system.

3. The optimizing model provides another example of the importance of defining and measuring utility. The static theory of consumers' behaviour is organized around the concept of utility by means of the technique of undetermined multipliers. In the optimizing model we have the dynamic analogue which makes use of the technique of the calculus of variations.

4. In order to replace the *ad hoc* relationships which figure so largely in macro-economics, the optimizing model tries to penetrate more deeply into the springs of human action. For example, it provides a form of the saving function to replace the *ad hoc* assumption that saving is a constant proportion of income at all times. Thus the psychological motives of economic behaviour are brought into the picture. My version of Ramsey's model does this in a very crude way, but it should be enough to illustrate the unity of the social sciences. The limitations of pure economics as opposed to empirical economics are now becoming generally recognised, and it is high time economists took seriously the psychological and social postulates of their theory instead of squandering so much energy in preserving its purity, which beyond a certain age is just another word for sterility.

5. The optimizing model points the way to a rational solution of the problem posed by the planning model. This indeed is a central problem of political economy: the proper distribution of consumption between the present and the future. If the present is given too much, the economy will grow slowly, or even fail to grow at all, and people will become restive once they have abandoned a fatalistic outlook. If the future is given too much, the present generation, once its revolutionary fervour has abated, will come to question a regime which seems to treat them as peons. Either way the politician had better be on his guard.

6. Finally, it cannot be too strongly emphasized that the models in this paper are all three rather primitive and that the conclusions might be modified if one changed the forms of the relationships used. Such matters, however, can rarely be settled at the theoretical level. The model-builder must choose among acceptable alternatives those which not only are amenable to statistical analysis but also fit the facts. This, of course, is not to suggest that all we need are more and better observations. To suppose that the facts themselves will lead us to a clear and unequivocal system of relationships in a matter as complicated as an economic system is as absurd as to suppose that by purely theoretical processes we can discover a system which will turn out to square with all the facts. Only by going back and forth between theory and observations can we hope to progress in an empirical science like economics.

References

[1] Allen, R. G. D. *Mathematical Analysis for Economists*, Ch. XX. London, Macmillan and Co., 1938.

[2] Bellman, Richard. *Dynamic Programming*. Princeton, N.J., Princeton University Press, 1957.

[3] Mahalanobis, P. C. Some observations on the process of growth of national income. *Sankhya*, Vol. 12, pt. 4, 1953, pp. 307–12.

[4] Ramsey, F. P. A mathematical theory of saving. *The Economic Journal*, Vol. XXXVIII, No. 152, 1928, pp. 543–59.

[5] Stone, Richard and Giovanna Croft-Murray. *Social Accounting and Economic Models*. London, Bowes and Bowes, 1959.

ALTERNATIVE APPROACHES TO THE AGGREGATION PROBLEM

H. THEIL

Netherlands School of Economics, Rotterdam, The Netherlands

1. Introduction

The use of macroeconomic concepts is unavoidable in applied work, and their derivation and justification in terms of microeconomic concepts present difficult problems. These are the main reasons some economic theorists have suggested that it is preferable to approach macroeconomic problems directly without considering microeconomics first and then aggregating. This approach, which bears some resemblance to Cassel's desire for a demand theory that is not based on utility theory, has undoubtedly a considerable appeal because of its simplicity, but it is to be doubted whether it is generally applicable. For example, one might say that total consumption goes up because total income is increased, and that such a monotonic relationship is a macroeconomic theory. Whether or not this theory is tenable is an empirical matter; but there are at least some theoretical considerations which throw some doubt on its general validity. For if the increase in total income is the algebraic sum of a number of individual income increases and income decreases in such a way that the decreases refer to individuals with a large marginal propensity to consume, while the increases refer to individuals with low marginal propensities, then it is easily conceivable that the result of the aggregate income increase is a decrease in aggregate consumption. In such a case it must be considered appropriate to analyze the underlying microeconomic relationships as well as the aggregation procedure.

This article is an attempt to survey some of the work that has been done in the field of aggregation, in particular the aggregation of behavioural relations (Section 2), the aggregation of preferences (Section 3), and the aggregation of individual prices and quantities (Section 4). In each case, three alternative approaches will be considered. The first amounts to imposing certain requirements which the aggregation procedure should fulfill in order to be "acceptable," and to find the set of all acceptable aggregation procedures. Unfortunately, the result in all cases considered is that this set is empty, so that a second approach is worthwhile, viz., the one in which the consequences of well-known classical aggregation methods are analyzed. The third approach is of the optimization type: the aggregation procedure performs its task as well as possible according to some well-defined criterion. In all cases special attention is paid to the idea of autonomy of macrodescriptions, which amounts to the independence of a macroconcept of those quantities that do not correspond to this concept, like the independence of a macroeconomic consumption function of the parameters of microeconomic investment equations, the independence of a social preference function of the constraints which the individuals have to face, etc. Section 5 contains a number of conclusions.

2. On the Aggregation of Behavioural Relations

2.1. Nataf's Theorem. Suppose we are interested in replacing a number of microeconomic behavioural or technical relations by a single macroeconomic analogue. For example, we may consider — as Nataf [14] did — the aggregation of a number of production functions. Supposing that for each firm i, output (P_i) is functionally related to labour input (L_i) and capital input (K_i) according to

$$\phi_i(P_i, L_i, K_i) = 0, \quad i = 1, \cdots, I, \tag{2.1}$$

we may be interested in finding aggregates

$$P = \psi_P(P_1, \cdots, P_I); \quad L = \psi_L(L_1, \cdots, L_I); \quad K = \psi_K(K_1, \cdots, K_I), \tag{2.2}$$

which satisfy an exact relation of the type

$$\phi(P, L, K) = 0 \tag{2.3}$$

for whatever values of the microvariables. It will be noticed that two conditions are imposed: first, the macrovariables P, L, K should depend on corresponding microvariables only (i.e., ψ_P should not have L_2 or K_3 as arguments, etc.); second, the macrovariables should satisfy an exact relation — the aggregate production function — which holds identically for all microvalues. This is of course a very special case, but the result to be mentioned in the next paragraph suggests that it should be possible to generalize it rather easily.

Nataf showed that this problem admits of a solution only if the individual productions can all be written as the sum of three functions, one involving P_i only, the second L_i only, and the third involving K_i only. In that case the macrorelation can be found simply by adding the microrelations, and the macrovariables — which may be rather unusual aggregates — are then defined implicitly. If this condition is not satisfied, no aggregates exist which satisfy the requirements imposed.

2.2. Linear Aggregation of Single Sets of Linear Relations. The negative result just mentioned can be borne more easily when it is realized that behavioural relation at the microlevel are usually not exact. If we accept this, we may feel inclined to accept discrepancies at the macrolevel also. However, we should then specify certain properties of these discrepancies, for if this is not done, any macrorelation and its discrepancies are acceptable; and this, of course, does not carry us very far.

The presence of discrepancies suggests that a statistical approach is promising.[1] Suppose then that we deal with a set of I linear equations of the type

[1]See Theil [16, 19] and Boot and De Wit [5] for an empirical application.

(2.4) $$y_i(t) = \alpha_i + \sum_{h=1}^{H_1} \beta_{1h,i} x_{1h}(t) + \sum_{h=1}^{H_2} \beta_{2h,i} x_{2h}(t) + u_i(t)$$
$$(i = 1, \cdots, I;\ t = 1, \cdots, T),$$

where i refers to the ith individual, t to the tth time period, α_i, $\beta_{1h,i}$, $\beta_{2h,i}$ are microparameters, $u_i(t)$ a random microdisturbance, y_i a dependent microvariable, and x_{1h}, x_{2h} explanatory microvariables. For example, $y_i(t)$ is the demand for cheese of the ith family household in the tth period, $x_{1h}(t)$ is the cheese price charged by the hth retailer in the same period, and $x_{2h}(t)$ the price of a meat product in that period. For simplicity's sake, I consider the case of two explanatory variables only; the generalization is straightforward.

The microrelations (2.4) are linear, and I shall confine myself to linearity mainly because of its simplicity.[2] Accordingly, I will consider macrovariables which are linear functions of the corresponding microvariables. This is indeed the usual case in practice, most aggregates being either sums of microvariables or fixed-weight index numbers. Since the transition from sums to fixed-weight index numbers is trivial, I will confine myself to the former and hence use the following macrovariables:

(2.5) $$y(t) = \sum_i y_i(t); \quad x_1(t) = \sum_h x_{1h}(t); \quad x_2(t) = \sum_h x_{2h}(t).$$

To find which kind of relation among these aggregates exists, we add the microrelations (2.4):

(2.6) $$y(t) = \sum_i \alpha_i + \sum_h \beta_{1h} x_{1h}(t) + \sum_h \beta_{2h} x_{2h}(t) + \sum_i u_i(t),$$

where

(2.7) $$\beta_{1h} = \sum_i \beta_{1h,i}; \quad \beta_{2h} = \sum_i \beta_{2h,i}.$$

Now (2.6) contains only one macrovariable, viz., $y(t)$, and this is described in terms of explanatory microvariables. Only if all β_{1h} are equal and if all β_{2h} are equal, is it true that (2.6) can be regarded as a macroequation containing macrovariables only; otherwise, no linear relation in $y(t)$, $x_1(t)$, $x_2(t)$ exists. However, we may decide that this is a useless result for practical purposes and argue that since there are disturbances anyhow, we might just as well set up an equation in macrovariables only and include the resulting discrepancies in the macrodisturbance. Hence we consider

(2.8) $$y(t) = \alpha + \beta_1 x_1(t) + \beta_2 x_2(t) + u(t).$$

But as stated above, we should now formulate a criterion by which this macrorelation is completely specified. Suppose then that all microdisturbances $u_i(t)$ have zero expectation; also, that the explanatory microvariables take nonstochastic values. Then we define the parameters α, β_1, β_2 of (2.8) as the expectations of the least-squares coefficient estimators in the regression corresponding to (2.8), i.e., the regression of y on x_1 and x_2

[2]For a polynomial generalization, see Theil [16, pp. 126–132].

for the T periods considered. It can be shown that this leads to

$$\begin{aligned}
\alpha &= \sum_i \alpha_i + \sum_h A_{1h} B_{1h} + \sum_h A_{2h} \beta_{2h}, \\
\beta_1 &= \sum_h B_{1,1h} \beta_{1h} + \sum_h B_{1,2h} \beta_{2h}, \\
\beta_2 &= \sum_h B_{2,1h} \beta_{1h} + \sum_h B_{2,2h} \beta_{2h}, \\
u(t) &= \sum_i u_i(t) + \sum_h V_{1h}(t) \beta_{1h} + \sum_h V_{2h}(t) \beta_{2h},
\end{aligned} \tag{2.9}$$

where the A's, B's, and V's are the coefficients and residuals, respectively, of the *auxiliary regressions*, which are the least-squares regressions of the explanatory microvariables on the explanatory macrovariables:

$$\begin{aligned}
x_{1h}(t) &= A_{1h} + B_{1,1h} x_1(t) + B_{2,1h} x_2(t) + V_{1h}(t) \\
&\qquad (h = 1, \cdots, H_1; t = 1, \cdots, T); \\
x_{2h}(t) &= A_{2h} + B_{1,2h} x_1(t) + B_{2,2h} x_2(t) + V_{2h}(t) \\
&\qquad (h = 1, \cdots, H_2; t = 1, \cdots, T).
\end{aligned} \tag{2.10}$$

The result (2.9)–(2.10) shows that the macroparameters are not "autonomous" in the following sense: Take β_1; if it would be autonomous with respect to the behaviour pattern regarding changes in the noncorresponding microvariables x_{2h}, it would be independent of the $\beta_{2h,i}$, but in fact it is not as is seen from (2.9). This means that if the microbehaviour pattern with respect to x_{2h}-changes becomes different, this affects the prarameter β_1 which supposedly specifies the effect of x_{1h}-changes only. A similar lack of autonomy can be observed for the macroparameters α and β_2. On the other hand, there is an interesting asymmetry between the "weights" (the A's, B's, and V's) of corresponding parameters and those of noncorresponding parameters. It can be shown that the former weights add up to 1, the latter to 0:

$$\begin{aligned}
&\sum_h B_{1,1h} = \sum_h B_{2,2h} = 1; \\
&\sum_h A_{1h} = \sum_h A_{2h} = \sum_h B_{1,2h} = \sum_h B_{2,1h} = \sum_h V_{1h}(t) = \sum_h V_{2h}(t) = 0.
\end{aligned} \tag{2.11}$$

Hence the weights which are responsible for lack of autonomy are zero on the average, but they are in general not individually zero. There are special cases in which these weights are indeed all zero (e.g., when all corresponding microvariables move proportionally over time) or in which the weights are irrelevant (viz., when corresponding microparameters are all equal); reference is made to [5, 16].

2.3. Linear Aggregation of Several Sets of Linear Relations. The discussion of Section 2.2 was concerned with only one type of non-autonomy. As soon as we proceed to systems of simultaneous equations, another type comes into the picture. At the microlevel, we then have a set of consumption equations, a second set consisting of investment equations, a third set of import equations, etc., and such a microsystem is to be aggregated to a macrosystem consisting of one consumption equation, one investment equation, one import equation, etc. We should then expect to find — as in Section 2.2 — that the macroparameters of the consumption equation, say, depend on noncorresponding microparameters of the consumption equations of the microsystem; but in addition, we might expect that these macroparameters will in general depend on microparameters of noncorresponding equations of the microsystem such as investment and import equations. Indeed, this is what happens and it leads to an even greater lack of autonomy than in the case of Section 2.2.

A detailed account of the aggregation analysis of simultaneous equations is beyond the scope of this paper (reference is made to [19]), but the main ideas can be explained rather easily. First, we notice that sometimes the microvariable to be "explained" by some structural equation depends on a corresponding microvariable according to this equation. For example, i's consumption of a certain commodity may depend on j's consumption (and of course on other determining factors as well). Such interrelationships are elminated in such a way that all microvariables "explained" by structural microequations depend on noncorresponding microvariables only. After this, we add the microrelations by subset, so that one equation results which describes total consumption (say) in terms of noncorresponding microvariables, a second equation which describes total investment in terms of microvariables (other than investment), and so on. None of these equations is a macrorelation; they are all of the type (2.6) except that some of the right-hand microvariables are of the jointly dependent type. As in Section 2.2, we then proceed in a statistical manner. For example, we may apply two-stage least-squares and interpret the macroparameters as the asymptotic expectations of the two-stage least-squares estimators.[3]

A simple example can be given which illustrates this procedure. Suppose we have two commodities which are supplied by one firm and bought by one consumer. Let the supply equations be

$$\begin{aligned} x_1 &= \alpha_1 + \beta_{11}p_1 + \beta_{12}p_2 + \gamma_1 k + u_1, \\ x_2 &= \alpha_2 + \beta_{21}p_1 + \beta_{22}p_2 + \gamma_2 k + u_2, \end{aligned} \tag{2.12}$$

and the demand equations

$$\begin{aligned} x_1 &= \delta_1 + \varepsilon_{11}p_1 + \varepsilon_{12}p_2 + \zeta_1 y + u_3, \\ x_2 &= \delta_2 + \varepsilon_{21}p_1 + \varepsilon_{22}p_2 + \zeta_2 y + u_4, \end{aligned} \tag{2.13}$$

where x_1 and x_2 are the quantities bought and sold of the two commodities, p_1 and p_2 their prices, k the price of a factor of production, y the buyer's income, the u's disturbances, and the α's, β's, γ's δ's, ε's, and ζ's parameters. Now these microrelations form a system of 4 equations in 4 endogenous

[3]Asymptotic rather than finite-sample expectations are used here because simultaneous-equations estimators are only asymptotically unbiased.

variables (x_1, x_2, p_1, p_2) and 2 exogenous variables (k, y); and our objective is to aggregate this system to a macrosystem consisting of one supply equation and one demand equation:

$$\begin{aligned} x &= \alpha + \beta p + \gamma k + u \quad \text{(supply)}, \\ x &= \delta + \varepsilon p + \zeta y + u' \quad \text{(demand)}, \end{aligned} \tag{2.14}$$

where the following macrovariables are used:[4]

$$x = x_1 + x_2; \quad p = p_1 + p_2. \tag{2.15}$$

We can then apply the procedure outlined in the preceding paragraph. We note first that none of the variables "explained" in (2.12)–(2.13) is described there as dependent on corresponding microvariables; the reason being that there are no x_i on the right of the equality signs. This simplifies the procedure; as a matter of fact, the present example is even more simplified by the absence of any aggregation with respect to exogenous variables.[5] When pursuing the analysis, we find the following expression for ζ (the rate of change of total demand with respect to income) in terms of the microparameters:

$$\zeta = \zeta_1 + \zeta_2 + \frac{D_1}{D}\zeta_1 + \frac{D_2}{D}\zeta_2, \tag{2.16}$$

where

$$\begin{aligned} D_1 &= \gamma_2(\varepsilon_{11} + \varepsilon_{21} - \varepsilon_{12} - \varepsilon_{22}), \\ D_2 &= -\gamma_1(\varepsilon_{11} + \varepsilon_{21} - \varepsilon_{12} - \varepsilon_{22}), \\ D &= \gamma_1(\beta_{22} - \beta_{21} - \varepsilon_{22} + \varepsilon_{21}) + \gamma_2(\beta_{11} - \beta_{12} - \varepsilon_{11} + \varepsilon_{12}). \end{aligned} \tag{2.17}$$

The result (2.16) shows that the macroparameter ζ depends on *all* multiplicative microparameters, both of the supply and of the demand equations. Hence, if the supplier changes his behaviour pattern such that β_{22}, say, takes another value, while the buyer behaves as before, then the macrodescription of the buyer's behaviour pattern is affected. Of course, this lack of autonomy need not be very substantial. For example, if D_1 and D_2 are small in absolute value compared with D, then the effect on ζ is small as is seen from (2.16); and in the present case it is not unlikely that this is true, given some plausible sign guesses for the microparameters of (2.17). But the main point is that we cannot be sure in general.

2.4. Perfect Aggregation. If we raise the question whether it is possible to remedy the effects just mentioned, the answer is that this can be done in principle, but that the appropriate procedure is usually far from simple.

---

[4] For simplicity's sake, I use the total price ($p_1 + p_2$) instead of a fixed-weight price aggregate; the appropriate generalization is trivial.

[5] If there would be aggregation of this kind, then we would meet auxiliary regressions of the type (2.10); but here, of course, this is not the case.

Consider (2.6); and suppose that we do not use the aggregates x_1 and x_2 as defined in (2.5), but

$$(2.18)\qquad x_1'(t) = \frac{1}{c_1}\sum_h \beta_{1h}x_{1h}(t); \qquad x_2'(t) = \frac{1}{c_2}\sum_h \beta_{2h}x_{2h}(t),$$

where c_1 and c_2 are two non-vanishing constants. Then (2.6) can be written as

$$(2.19)\qquad y(t) = \sum_i \alpha_i + c_1x_1'(t) + c_2x_2'(t) + \sum_i u_i(t),$$

and this is an equation in macrovariables only, which has been derived by simply adding the microrelations (2.4). There can never be any contradiction, therefore, between any statement derived from the microtheory (2.4) and a corresponding statement of the macrotheory (2.19). Also, the macrodisturbance of (2.19) is simply the sum of the microdisturbances, whereas in the case of the sum aggregates, the macrodisturbance includes a linear combination of residuals of the auxiliary regressions; and under the assumption of nonstochastic values taken by the explanatory microvariables, the latter macrodisturbance has a larger second moment than the former.[6] In fact, perfect aggregation satisfies the optimum requirement (of the kind discussed in Section 1) of a minimal residual second moment in the class of all linear aggregates — at least, if the microrelations are linear too. On the other hand, it is seen that the macrovariables defined in (2.18) have two serious disadvantages: their construction requires knowledge of microparameters, at least of their ratios — which is frequently not available — and different macrorelations require in general different macrovariables corresponding to the same set of microvariables. Thus, if we have different marginal propensities to consume for different commodities, the micro-β's of these commodities will be different too and hence the same applies to the income aggregates in their demand equations. Furthermore, the situation becomes even more complicated when we deal with simultaneous equation systems. The prospect is therefore not completely promising; but I do believe that we can make some progress at the empirical level, in particular when this is done within the more general framework of specification analysis. This topic is, however, outside the scope of this article; reference is made to [17].

3. On the Aggregation of Preference Relations

3.1. Arrow's Theorem. Suppose now a certain number of alternatives $A_1, \cdots, A_n$ are available to a committee of persons $P_1, \cdots, P_N$, and that

[6] For any particular sample, of course, the estimated second moment of the macrodisturbances of the regression corresponding to (2.8) may be smaller than the estimated second moment of the sum of the microdisturbances. Moreover, when empirical applications are considered, it is always advisable to take account of the possibility that certain conditions (such as the nonstochastic character of explanatory microvariables) are not satisfied. Reference is made to Grünfeld and Griliches [10].

it is their task to choose one of these, to be called the "best" alternative. Since we want to take account of the possibility that this best alternative may turn out to be not available at the last moment, we need a second best alternative also, and so on; in other words, we need a ranking of all n alternatives. This will be done on the basis of the individual preferences. We will suppose that each of the N individuals is able to rank the n alternatives according to decreasing preference, and these individual rankings should provide the basis for the social ranking which is the object of the investigation.

Again, we start by imposing certain "reasonable" conditions and ask what is the set of social rankings which satisfy these. This is the subject of Arrow's well-known monograph [1], the results of which can be briefly and roughly described as follows. One requirement is that the social ranking is positively related to the individual rankings in the sense that if an individual changes his mind such that he interchanges A_1 and A_2 (say) in his ranking, the social ranking is either changed accordingly or not at all, but certainly not in an opposite direction. A second requirement is that there should be no "dictator" among the individuals whose preferences determine the social ranking (partly or wholly) no matter what the other individuals' preferences are. A third requirement is that the social ranking should not be "imposed" in the sense that it is determined in a way which is independent of the individual rankings. A fourth is that if we delete one or more alternatives, the position of the remaining ones in the social ranking should not be affected. The last requirement can be regarded as a condition of autonomy; for at the microlevel there are two groups of determining factors, viz., the individual rankings and the set of available alternatives, and if we wish to aggregate the former to a social ranking in a manner which is autonomous with respect to the set of alternatives, we should impose the fourth condition just mentioned.

Arrow's result, as is well known, is a negative one: there exists no social ranking which satisfies all four conditions simultaneously, except when the individual rankings satisfy certain restrictive conditions.[7]

3.2. Durbin's Theorem. A classical method of determining a social ranking on the basis of individual rankings consists of adding the individual ranks of all separate alternatives and ranking according to the resulting sums. I refer to the first four columns of Table 1, where a case of 3 persons and 4 alternatives is considered. The rank sums are 5, 9, 10, 6, so the social ranking according to this procedure is 1, 3, 4, 2. This procedure violates the fourth requirement of Section 2.2; this is illustrated in the last two columns which contain the same individual rankings after the alternatives A_2 and A_3 are deleted and which show a social preference of A_4 over A_1. It is easily verified that the procedure does satisfy the other three requirements. More

[7]Such as the condition of "single-peaked preferences"; see [1, pp. 75–80].

TABLE 1
ILLUSTRATION OF THE ADDING-RANKS METHOD

Persons	Alternatives					
	A_1	A_2	A_3	A_4	A_1	A_4
P_1	1	2	3	4	1	2
P_2	2	3	4	1	2	1
P_2	2	4	3	1	2	1
Total	5	9	10	6	5	4
Social ranking	1	3	4	2	2	1

important, however, is that this classical method has an optimal property, as was shown by Durbin [6]. Let us consider any two alternatives, say A_1 and A_2, and their ranks in an individual ranking (say, that of P_1) and the social ranking. In the present case these ranks are 1, 2 and 1, 3, respectively, so that there is agreement between P_1 and the social ranking as to the relative position of these two alternatives. This is not true, however, if we take A_3 and A_4: their ranks are 3, 4 for P_1, and 4, 2 for the social ranking. Now the optimal property of the adding-ranks method is that it minimizes a weighted sum of such inversions, where the weights are defined as follows. Let us rearrange the alternatives such that the social ranking is the natural order $1, 2, \cdots, n$; and let us write $r_1, r_2, \cdots, r_n$ for the preference ranking of any individual. Then an inversion occurs whenever $r_i > r_j$ for $i < j$, and the weight applied to this inversion is $r_i - r_j$. In this weighted-inversion sense, the method of ranking according to rank totals is optimal.

3.3. Social Decisions Based on the Loss Matrix (1). We now turn to an optimization procedure for a more specific set of conditions. Following Van den Bogaard and Versluis [4], we suppose that there are N individuals with preference functions $w_i(x)$ which are unique up to a linear transformation. A vector x is to be chosen by the group; and of course, each individual i prefers the vector x^i which maximizes his w_i to all others. The N maximizing vectors are supposed to be unique and to be pairwise different. Next, we introduce the individual loss functions

$$l_i(x) = w_i(x^i) - w_i(x), \tag{3.1}$$

which measure the difference between the attainable utility maximum, $w_i(x^i)$, and the utility level obtained by applying any vector x. These loss functions are unique up to a homogeneous linear transformation, i.e., they are well defined except for positive multiplicative scalars d_i which are to be chosen. This choice is based on the losses which any individual i suffers when any individual j imposes his own optimal decision x^j. This loss is $d_i l_i(x^j)$, where d_i is the scalar just mentioned; we shall write it simply $d_i l_{ij}$, and it is easily seen that there is an $N \times N$ matrix of such losses with zeros on the diagonal and positive off-diagonal elements. This matrix is called the loss matrix.

The procedure suggested amounts to minimizing the social loss function, which is defined as the sum of the individual loss functions,

$$l_S(x) = \sum_{i=1}^{N} d_i l_i(x), \tag{3.2}$$

where the d_i are chosen in such a way that the loss matrix is symmetric, or "as symmetric as possible." The idea behind this symmetry condition is that "fairness" requires that the individual preferences are compared with each other in a symmetric manner, and this is specified such that the loss which j inflicts upon i equals the loss which i inflicts upon j, $d_i l_{ij} = d_j l_{ji}$ for all pairs i, j. In some cases this condition can be met, but certainly not always; the reason being that symmetry of the loss matrix involves $\frac{1}{2}N(N-1)$ conditions, while the d's are less numerous as soon as $N > 2$. In the latter case, therefore, the condition is weakened such that the row sums of the loss matrix are equal to the columns sums:

$$\sum_j d_i l_{ij} = \sum_j d_j l_{ji}. \tag{3.3}$$

This condition leads to a unique set of d's whenever the loss matrix has zero diagonal and positive off-diagonal elements; and these d's are all positive, which is a sufficient condition in order that the x which maximizes (3.2) be a Pareto optimum. Further, it ensures a symmetric loss matrix when symmetry can be attained, and it seems to do so approximately when symmetry is not attainable; this will be illustrated numerically in Section 3.4 below.

A few specific examples may be useful to illustrate this procedure. Suppose first that the individual preference functions are quadratic, and let the homogeneous quadratic parts be the same for all individuals except for multiplicative scalars. By choosing appropriate scalars we can make these quadratic parts equal, so that i's preference function becomes

$$w_i(x) = k_{0i} + k_i' x + \tfrac{1}{2} x' K x, \tag{3.4}$$

where k_{0i} is a scalar, k_i a column vector (and k_i' its transpose), and K a symmetric and negative-definite matrix independent of i. We then have

$$x^i = -K^{-1} k_i, \quad l_i(x) = -\tfrac{1}{2}(x - x^i)' K (x - x^i) \tag{3.5}$$

for i's optimal decision and for his loss function, respectively. Hence $l_{ij} = l_{ji}$, as is easily verified, so that we can take $d_i = 1$ for $i = 1, \cdots, N$ in order to ensure a symmetric loss matrix. The social loss function is then

$$l_S(x) = -\tfrac{1}{2} \sum_{i=1}^{N} (x - x^i)' K (x - x^i), \tag{3.6}$$

and it is minimized when x equals

$$x^S = \frac{1}{N} \sum_{i=1}^{N} x^i, \tag{3.7}$$

which means that each element of the socially optimal decision vector equals the arithmetic mean of the corresponding elements of the individual optimal vectors.

Next, suppose that the individual preference functions are quadratic but such that the homogeneous quadratic parts are not the same. Then (3.4) and (3.5) remain valid for the individual preference functions, optimal vectors, and loss functions, except that we should replace K by K_i. This, however, implies that the loss matrix cannot in general be made symmetric. Hence condition (3.3) is applied, which leads to certain d's, and these enter into the social loss function:

$$l_S(x) = -\tfrac{1}{2}\sum_{i=1}^{N} d_i(x - x^i)'K_i(x - x^i), \tag{3.8}$$

which is minimized for

$$x^S = (\sum d_i K_i)^{-1} \sum d_i K_i x^i. \tag{3.9}$$

Here again, the socially optimal decision is an average of the individual optimal decisions; but it is a weighted average, the weights being such that all elements of the individual decision vectors enter into all elements of the social vector x^S.

3.4. Social Decisions Based on the Loss Matrix (2). Van den Bogaard and Versluis applied their theory to a macroeconomic policy case in the Netherlands, and since the application has some further interesting methodological features, it is worth while to pursue the analysis a little further. Their case refers to $N = 3$, individual 1 being an employee, 2 a Crown member of the Social and Economic Council, and 3 an employer. The three preference functions are all quadratic, but contrary to the case of Section 3.3, the arguments of these functions include variables which are government-controlled as well as variables which are not. Writing x for the vector of the first set of variables and y for the second set,[8] the preference function corresponding to i $(i = 1, 2, 3)$ is written as

$$w_i[x, y] = a_i'x + b_i'y + \tfrac{1}{2}(x'A_ix + y'B_iy + x'C_iy + y'C_i'x), \tag{3.10}$$

where a_i and b_i are given column vectors and A_i, B_i, C_i given matrices. Furthermore, it is assumed that y, although it is not controlled, is a stochastic linear function of x:

$$y = Rx + s, \tag{3.11}$$

R being a fixed and known matrix and s a vector of random elements. Sub-

[8]The controlled variables are the general wage rate, tax rates for indirect taxes, direct taxes on wage income, and direct taxes on non-wage income, and government expenditure on commodities. The non-controlled variables are employment, the price level of consumer goods, the share of wages in national income, and the surplus on the balance of payments.

stituting (3.11) into (3.10), we obtain a quadratic preference function in x only:

$$w_i(x) = k_{i0} + k_i'x + \tfrac{1}{2}x'K_ix, \tag{3.12}$$

where

$$\begin{aligned} k_{i0} &= b_i's + \tfrac{1}{2}s'B_is, \\ k_i &= a_i + R'b_i + (C_i + R'B_i)s, \\ K_i &= A_i + R'B_iR + C_iR + R'C_i'. \end{aligned} \tag{3.13}$$

Thus, the preference function (3.10) has been reduced to the simpler case (3.4) in which the square matrix K depends on i.

Van den Bogaard and Versluis used the econometric equation system of the Central Planning Bureau in order to specify the constraints (3.11) for 1957, and they used an earlier paper by Van den Bogaard and Barten [3] for the specification of the three preference functions. The uncertainty problem arising from the stochastic character of the vector s was solved by assuming that the three policy-makers aim at maximizing expected utility and by applying the theorem on certainty equivalence in quadratic decision-making; see [2, 15, 20]. Therefore, all losses to be discussed in the remainder of this paragraph are to be interpreted as expected losses. Table 2 gives a detailed account of the result. The leading 3×3 submatrix is the loss matrix; it is seen that the d-choice according to (3.3) brings this matrix close to symmetry. The social loss caused by the optimal decision x^1 of the employee (the sum of the first three elements of the first column) exceeds the social losses caused by the two other individual optimal decisions rather considerably. The Crown member's optimal decision x^2 is evidently better than the two others in this respect, but it is below the level of x^S for obvious reasons; the difference between the social loss caused by the "best" individual optimal

TABLE 2

LOSSES INFLICTED AND SUFFERED

(Van den Bogaard and Versluis, 1960)

Losses suffered by	Losses inflicted by x^1	x^2	x^3	x^S
1	0	141.9	197.2	60.7
2	141.1	0	12.8	19.0
3	197.4	12.4	0	20.3
Total	338.5	154.3	210.0	100*
Excess loss	238.5	54.3	110.0	0

*All losses are adjusted multiplicatively such that this loss equals 100.
Notes: 1 = employee, 2 = Crown member, 3 = employer.

decision (x^2 in this case) and that caused by x^S (the minimum) is to be regarded as the gain obtained by this procedure compared with that of selecting the "best" x^i. The row below that of the social losses measures these differences, which are called excess losses. The last column shows the losses inflicted by the socially optimal decision upon the three individuals.

Two additional remarks are in order. First, if we arrange the individuals according to increasing excess loss or according to increasing loss suffered by the socially optimal decision, then in both cases we obtain 2, 3, 1. It can be shown that if the individual quadratic preference functions have identical homogeneous quadratic parts, the loss suffered by each individual i due to the socially optimal decision is equal to his per capita excess loss (the excess loss divided by N). We might call this "justice." Second, it is not true that the procedure proposed is autonomous with respect to the alternatives available. This set is determined by the constraint (3.11); and if R changes, this affects the d's of (3.3) as well as the K_i and k_i of (3.12).

4. On the Aggregation of Prices and Quantities

4.1. Wald's Theorem. The construction of price index numbers is undoubtedly the oldest part of aggregation theory, and there can of course be no question of attempting to survey the large literature on that topic. Here, I shall confine myself to a few topics which are relevant in the present context, in the first place the autonomy problem. Let us consider the classical case of a base year and a current year, each of these being characterized by given prices and quantities of a number of commodities. An extreme way of imposing autonomy is that of requiring that the price index number be independent of the quantities, and the quantity index number be independent of the prices. This, of course, is possible when the individual prices and quantities move proportionally, but not in general. The further development leads to a number of "tests", which is an area in which Irving Fisher [7] especially was active. One of these is the identity test, which may be regarded as a very weak autonomy condition and requires that if the individual prices are the same in the two periods, the price index numbers should also be the same no matter what the quantities do. A second is the proportionality test; it can be considered as a stronger autonomy condition and requires that if the individual prices move proportionally, the behaviour of the price index number corresponds to this proportionality no matter what the quantities do. A third is the factor reversal test; this combines rather than separates prices and quantities and requires that the product of the price and quantity index numbers measures the total value correctly. A fourth is the time reversal test; it requires that interchanging the roles of the base and the current year leads to index numbers which are reciprocal to the original ones. A fifth is the circular test, which is similar to the time reversal test but stronger; it requires that if we have three years, t_1, t_2, and t_3, the price index number for t_3 with t_1 as base equals the product of the index for t_2 with t_1 as base and the index for t_3 with t_2 as base.

Essentially, all these tests amount to requiring that the price (and quantity) index numbers behave as individual prices and quantities do. There can no hope that all tests can be met at the same time. This is Wald's theorem; he showed [22] that the proportionality test, the factor reversal test, and the circular test are in general incompatible.[9]

4.2. Best Linear Index Numbers (1). If we want to formulate "good" or even "best" index numbers, the result will of course depend on the criterion chosen. One criterion is that of ensuring perfect aggregation (see Section 2.4) of a given set of microrelations; it implies a weighting procedure in terms of microparameters. A second criterion is that of the constant-utility price index. Here I want to confine myself to a simple criterion of the economic-statistical type which can be described as follows. Suppose we have T periods instead of two, and let us write the price and quantity information in the form of two matrices, the rows of which refer to time, the columns to the commodities:

$$(4.1) \qquad P = \begin{bmatrix} p_1(1) \cdots p_I(1) \\ \cdots\cdots\cdots\cdots \\ p_1(T) \cdots p_I(T) \end{bmatrix}; \qquad Q = \begin{bmatrix} q_1(1) \cdots q_I(1) \\ \cdots\cdots\cdots\cdots \\ q_1(T) \cdots q_I(T) \end{bmatrix}.$$

Our objective is to represent P and Q by two column vectors p and q of T price index numbers and T quantity index numbers, respectively. To specify the way in which we want to do this, we consider cross-values of the type

$$(4.2) \qquad \sum_i p_i(t) q_i(t'),$$

which is the aggregate value of all quantities of period t' valued at the prices of t. It is well known that the classical index numbers such as Laspeyres', Paasche's, and Fisher's are all expressed in terms of such cross-values. In the present case there are T^2 sums of the type (4.2), which can be arranged in the cross-value matrix

$$(4.3) \qquad C = PQ'.$$

Now for any given vectors p and q, there is also a cross-value matrix based on index numbers, viz., pq'. Given the importance of cross-values in index number theory, it seems natural to construct p and q such that pq' is as close to C as possible; and this will be specified by requiring that the sum of squares of all cross-value discrepancies (the elements of $C - pq'$) is a minimum. Hence we minimize

$$(4.4) \qquad \operatorname{tr}(C - pq')(C - pq')' = \operatorname{tr} CC' - 2p'Cq + p'p \cdot q'q.$$

Partial differentiation of (4.4) with respect to p and q gives

$$(4.5) \qquad Cq - q'q \cdot p = 0; \quad C'p - p'p \cdot q = 0.$$

---

[9] Frisch [8] deduced some results of the same type seven years earlier.

After premultiplication of the second equation of (4.5) by C and substitution of the first (and a similar operation applied to the first equation), we obtain

$$(4.6) \qquad (CC' - p'p \cdot q'q \cdot I)p = 0; \quad (C'C - p'p \cdot q'q \cdot I)q = 0,$$

which specify p and q as characteristic vectors of CC' and $C'C$, respectively, both corresponding to the same root $p'p \cdot q'q$. Substitution into the function to be minimized, (4.4), shows that we should take the largest root. Since the largest root of a matrix of positive elements, like CC' and $C'C$, is a single root, the price index vector p and the quantity index vector q are thus well defined except for a multiplicative scalar.[10]

To show how this method works in a particular case, we consider the classical situation of two periods — a base period and a current period. Dropping the matrix notation (4.1) for a moment, we write P for the Laspeyres price index in the current period (defined such that the base period value of the index is 1), Q for the Laspeyres quantity index, and $P(1+\eta)$ for the Paasche price index. Let us take money units such that the value of the base period basket at base period prices is 1, then the cross-value matrix is

$$(4.7) \qquad C = \begin{bmatrix} 1 & Q \\ P & PQ(1+\eta) \end{bmatrix},$$

where use is made of the fact that the Paasche price index multiplied by the Laspeyres quantity index equals the value ratio. Now η can be shown to have the same sign as the weighted correlation of the individual price changes and the individual quantity changes (the weights being equal to the shares of the commodities in the base period's basket value); and since this correlation is usually negative, owing to the tendency to substitute in favour of goods which have become relatively cheaper, it is worth while to consider in particular the case $\eta < 0$. Furthermore, I shall confine myself to terms which are linear in η, and hence neglect higher powers. Then it can be shown that the matrix of cross-value discrepancies corresponding with (4.6) for the present special case $T = 2$ is:

$$(4.8) \qquad E = \eta \frac{PQ}{D} \begin{bmatrix} PQ & -P \\ -Q & 1 \end{bmatrix},$$

where

$$(4.9) \qquad D = (1 + P^2)(1 + Q^2).$$

The sum of squares of the cross-value discrepancies is $\eta^2 P^2 Q^2 / D$. This is further pursued in Table 3, which contains in its first row the sum of squares

[10]The term "best *linear* index numbers" is used because it can be shown that they are linear (with constant weights) in the individual prices: $p = P\alpha$, where α is the vector of weights and equal to the characteristic vector of the matrix $Q'QP'P$ corresponding with the largest root (which is the same as the largest root of $C'C$). See [21]. Note, however, that linearity is not imposed as in the case of the best linear unbiased property of least-squares according to the Gauss-Markov theorem.

TABLE 3

SUMS OF SQUARES OF CROSS-VALUE DISCREPANCIES AND CROSS-VALUE EFFICIENCIES

	Best Linear	Laspeyres	Paasche	Fisher*
		Sum of squares		
No unbiasedness constraint imposed	$\eta^2 \frac{P^2Q^2}{D}$	$\eta^2 \frac{P^2Q^2(1+P^2+Q^2)}{D}$	$\eta^2 \frac{P^2+Q^2+P^2Q^2}{D}$	$\eta^2 \frac{(P^2+Q^2)(1+P^2Q^2)}{4D}$
Averagely unbiased	$\eta^2 \frac{2P^2Q^2}{D+(P-Q)^2}$	$\eta^2 \frac{P^2Q^2(2+P^2+Q^2)}{(1+PQ)^2}$	$\eta^2 \frac{P^2+Q^2+2P^2Q^2}{(1+PQ)^2}$	$\eta^2 \frac{P^2+Q^2}{4}$
Unbiased	$\eta^2 \frac{P^2Q^2}{P^2+Q^2}$	—	—	$\eta^2 \frac{P^2+Q^2}{4}$
		Cross-value efficiency for $P = Q = 1$		
No unbiasedness constraint imposed	1	0.33	0.33	1
Averagely unbiased	0.5	0.25	0.25	0.5
Unbiased	0.5	—	—	0.5

*Geometric mean of Laspeyres and Paasche.

of the cross-value discrepancies for the present index numbers as well as for Laspeyres, Paasche, and Fisher.[11] It is to be noted that the latter index numbers do not supply a unique cross-value matrix, since they imply value ratios rather than values proper. Thus, the cross-value matrix based on Laspeyres index numbers is of the general form

$$(4.10) \qquad (1+\varepsilon)\begin{bmatrix} 1 \\ P \end{bmatrix}[1 \quad Q] = \begin{bmatrix} 1+\varepsilon & Q(1+\varepsilon) \\ P(1+\varepsilon) & PQ(1+\varepsilon) \end{bmatrix},$$

where ε is an arbitrary number > -1. To give a fair comparison between Laspeyres and the index numbers defined by (4.6) we should select ε such that it minimizes the sum of squares of the cross-value discrepancies corresponding to (4.10). This leads to $\varepsilon = \eta P^2Q^2/D$ and to the second expression in the first row of Table 3. It is easily seen that Laspeyres' and Paasche's performances are rather poor when the present criterion is adopted. This is further illustrated in the first row of the second half of the table, which deals with the cross-value efficiency, i.e., with the ratio of the minimal sum of squares to the sum of squares for the index numbers considered. The efficiency depends of course on P and Q; in Table 3 the special case $P = Q = 1$ is considered. It turns out that Laspeyres and Paasche are quite inefficient but that Fisher is much better off. The other rows of Table 3 will be considered in Section 4.3.

4.3. Best Linear Index Numbers (2). Going back to the cross-value discrepancy matrix (4.8), we observe that its elements obey a very regular sign pattern: under the reasonable assumption $\eta < 0$, the diagonal elements are negative and the off-diagonal elements positive. This is the direct consequence of the substitution effect. For buying at current prices takes place such that relatively cheap commodities are favoured, and this leads to relatively small diagonal elements c_{tt} of the C-matrix and hence to negative diagonal elements of the cross-value discrepancy matrix. It seems therefore that this feature is unavoidable, although a statistically minded person would of course prefer randomness for such residuals. Some further evidence is supplied by Table 4, which deals with a 16-year application to Dutch imports. It shows that the 16 diagonal elements e_{tt} of the cross-value discrepancy matrix have a mean of -20 millions of guilders per year, that the 15 elements $e_{t,t+1}$ immediately above the main diagonal have an average of -14 millions of guilders per year, and that these diagonal averages become gradually less negative and then positive when we move away from the main diagonal. A similar situation exists for the elements below the diagonal. Evidently, this picture is similar to (4.8) but more subtle.

This result was used by Kloek and De Wit [13] as a starting point for a further analysis. They argued that it is preferable to control the sign pattern of the cross-value discrepancies if such a definite pattern is bound to exist.

[11]For a more extensive comparison, see [11].

TABLE 4

MEANS OF DIAGONAL ELEMENTS* OF THE CROSS-VALUE DISCREPANCY MATRIX OF THE BEST LINEAR INDEX NUMBERS OF DUTCH IMPORTS, 1921–1936

(Kloek and De Wit, 1960)

	$\|t-t'\|$								
	0	1	2	3	4	5–6	7–8	9–10	11–15
Above main diagonal	−20	−14	−10	−4	−3	3	5	9	7
Below main diagonal	−20	−10	−7	−4	0	7	9	12	16

*Defined as the sum of all e_{tt} for given $t-t'$, divided by their number; and expressed in millions of guilders per year. The index t refers to prices, t' to quantities; above the main diagonal are those discrepancies which correspond to prices that are dated earlier than the quantities, and vice versa for those below the main diagonal.

For suppose that we decide to enlarge the set of observations, so that the order of the cross-value discrepancy matrix is likewise enlarged. Then we should expect that the additional elements of this matrix, especially those in the Northeastern and the Southwestern parts, will be mostly positive and large. However, the procedure of minimizing the total sum of squares of all cross-value discrepancies will in general imply a tendency for the diagonal elements to become more negative than they were before the set of observations was enlarged, since this enables the additional elements to become less positive. But this implies that the price index vector and the quantity index vector are affected: if the diagonal cross-value discrepancies take larger negative values, the elements of the index vectors must take larger positive values. Hence one should expect that enlarging or reducing the set of observations affects the index vectors systematically, quite apart from the (obvious and trivial) effect of enlarging or reducing the number of elements of these vectors.

Kloek and De Wit decided to remedy this defect by applying zero constraints on the diagonal of the cross-value discrepancy matrix. This can be done in two alternative ways. First, one can impose the weak scalar constraint of a zero average of the diagonal elements. It can be shown that this leads to

$$\begin{aligned}[(C-\mu I)(C-\mu I)' - p'p\cdot q'q\cdot I]p &= 0,\\ [(C-\mu I)'(C-\mu I) - p'p\cdot q'q\cdot I]q &= 0,\end{aligned} \tag{4.11}$$

where μ is a scalar Lagrangean multiplier corresponding with the constraints. Second, one can impose the stronger vector constraint of a zero diagonal. This leads to

$$\begin{aligned}[(C-\bar{M})(C-\bar{M})' - p'p\cdot q'q\cdot I]p &= 0,\\ [(C-\bar{M})'(C-\bar{M}) - p'p\cdot q'q\cdot I]q &= 0,\end{aligned} \tag{4.12}$$

where $\bar{M}$ is a diagonal matrix of Lagrangean multipliers.[12]

[12]Cf. [12].

A survey of the results for the two-period case is presented in Table 3. The first expression of the second row is the sum of squares of the cross-value discrepancies corresponding to (4.11) — the "averagely unbiased" variant. It is seen that this sum tends to be much larger than the corresponding sum without constraint; its cross-value efficiency is $\frac{1}{2}$ when $P = Q$. For the other three methods, too, there are averagely unbiased variants; e.g., in Laspeyres' case we have a zero sum of diagonal elements if we take $\varepsilon = \eta PQ/(1 + PQ)$, as is easily verified from (4.7) and (4.10). Table 3 shows that this reduces the cross-values efficiency of Laspeyres and Paasche still further. The situation with respect to Fisher's index is more favourable; also, imposing a zero average of diagonal elements leads to a diagonal which consists of zeros only, so that this variant is completely unbiased as far as the diagonal is concerned.[13] For Laspeyres and Paasche no such variant exists.

5. Conclusions

The main conclusions can be arranged under the following three headings:

1. In all three fields of aggregation considered here, the procedure of imposing "reasonable" conditions on the aggregation procedure has not been very successful in the sense that the results turned out to be negative. Thus, Nataf found that his production functions cannot be aggregated according to his requirements except when they satisfy certain restrictive linearity conditions; Arrow showed that individual rankings cannot be aggregated to a social ranking which satisfies his conditions, except when the individual rankings are sufficiently restricted; and Wald showed that in general no index numbers can be constructed which satisfy a number of tests simultaneously. Of course, these results are interesting only insofar as the conditions imposed are indeed "reasonable." I certainly do not want to claim that these conditions are all "wrong", but given the fact that they cannot be satisfied all at the same time, it is apparently unreasonable to ask this. One of the most difficult conditions to be met is that of autonomy. We saw this when aggregating linear relations linearly; also when we required social rankings to be independent of the set of alternatives.[14]

2. Granted the difficulties just mentioned, an alternative approach is to delete one or more requirements such that one or more aggregation procedures exist which satisfy the remaining requirements; and if more than one aggregation turns out to be admissible in this way, one can then optimize according to some appropriate criterion. This was the index number procedure of Section 4.2: no *a priori* condition was imposed, and the sum of squares of the cross-value discrepancies was minimized unconditionally. We then found that the result was subject to a certain defect, so that we decided to minimize under the constraint that this defect should be eliminated. The

---

[13] Note that all cross-value discrepancy matrices used here for the case $T = 2$ are correct to the order η only.

[14] For an alternative approach in which this condition is deleted, see [9].

social choice mechanism based on the loss matrix is essentially similar: we imposed the condition of a symmetric loss matrix (or of a loss matrix whose row and column sums are pairwise equal) and minimized the sum of the individual losses. Perfect aggregation of linear microrelations can be regarded in the same light, since it minimizes the second moment of the macrodisturbances.

3. If we accept such an optimizing procedure, we can measure the merits of commonly used aggregation procedures by comparing their levels of the optimality function with the attainable extremum. For example, one might measure the second moment of the macrodisturbances of linear macrorelations and compare them with the attainable minimum. This analysis was pursued in more detail for the index number problem on the basis of the sum of squares of the cross-value discrepancies. It turned out that the cross-value efficiency of Laspeyres and Paasche index numbers is poor — at least for the two-period case — and that of their geometric mean (Fisher) much better. Obviously, such an evaluation depends largely on the optimality criterion chosen. In the social ranking case, for example, it appears that the classical procedure of adding the individual ranks is optimal if the criterion is that of a minimum of the sum total of the weighted inversions of the social ranking on the one hand and the individual rankings on the other.

References

[1] Arrow, K. J. *Social Choice and Individual Values*. Cowles Commission Monograph No. 12. John Wiley and Sons, New York, 1951.

[2] Van den Bogaard, P. J. M. "On the Static Theory of Certainty Equivalence." Report 6010 of the Econometric Institute of the Netherlands School of Economics (1960).

[3] Van den Bogaard, P. J. M., and A. P. Barten. "Optimal Macroeconomic Decision Rules for the Netherlands, 1957–1959." Report 5915 of the Econometric Institute of the Netherlands School of Economics (1959).

[4] Van den Bogaard, P. J. M., and J. Versluis. "The Design of Socially Optimal Decisions." Report 6004 of the Econometric Institute of the Netherlands School of Economics (1960).

[5] Boot, J. C. G., and G. M. de Wit. "Investment Demand: An Empirical Contribution to the Aggregation Problem," *International Economic Review*, Vol. 1 (1960), pp. 1–30.

[6] Durbin, J. "Incomplete Blocks in Ranking Experiments," *The British Journal of Sociology* (Statistical Section), Vol. 4 (1951), pp. 85–90.

[7] Fisher, I. *The Making of Index Numbers*. Cambridge (Mass.), 1922.

[8] Frisch, R. "Necessary and Sufficient Conditions Regarding the Form of an Index Number Which Shall Meet Certain of Fisher's Tests," *Journal of the American Statistical Association*, Vol. 25 (1930), pp. 397–406.

[9] Goodman, L. A., and H. Markowitz. "Social Welfare Functions Based on Individual Rankings," *American Journal of Sociology*, Vol. 58 (1952), pp. 257–262.

[10] Grünfeld, Y., and Z. Griliches. "Is Aggregation Necessarily Bad?", *The Review of Economics and Statistics*, Vol. 42 (1960), pp. 1–13.

[11] Kloek, T. "A Comparison of Index Numbers of the B.L. Type with Classical Index Numbers." Forthcoming Report of the Econometric Institute of the Netherlands School of Economics.

[12] KLOEK, T. "On Best Linear and Best Linear Unbiased Index Numbers (Con tinued)." Forthcoming Report of the Econometric Institute of the Netherlands School of Economics.

[13] KLOEK, T., and G. M. DE WIT. "On Best Linear and Best Linear Unbiased Index Numbers." Report 6006 of the Econometric Institute of the Netherlands School of Economics (1960).

[14] NATAF, A. "Sur la possibilité de construction de certains macromodèles," *Econometrica*, Vol. 16 (1948), pp. 232–244.

[15] SIMON, H. A. "Dynamic Programming Under Uncertainty With a Quadratic Criterion Function," *Econometrica*, Vol. 24 (1956), pp. 74–81.

[16] THEIL, H. *Linear Aggregation of Economic Relations*. North-Holland Publishing Company, Amsterdam, 1954.

[17] THEIL, H. "Specification Errors and the Estimation of Economic Relationships," *Review of the International Statistical Institute*, Vol. 25 (1957), pp. 41–51.

[18] THEIL, H. "Linear Aggregation in Input-Output Analysis," *Econometrica*, Vol. 25 (1957), pp. 111–122.

[19] THEIL, H. "The Aggregation Implications of Identifiable Structural Macro-relations," *Econometrica*, Vol. 27 (1959), pp. 14–29.

[20] THEIL, H. *Economic Forecasts and Policy*. North-Holland Publishing Company, Amsterdam, 1958.

[21] THEIL, H. "Best Linear Index Numbers of Prices and Quantities," *Econometrica*, Vol. 28 (1960), pp. 464–480.

[22] WALD, A. "Zur Theorie des Preisindexziffern," *Zeitschrift für Nationalökonomie*, Vol. 8 (1937), pp. 179–219.

SECTION

IX

METHODOLOGY AND PHILOSOPHY OF LINGUISTICS

EXPLANATORY MODELS IN LINGUISTICS

NOAM CHOMSKY

Massachusetts Institute of Technology, Cambridge, Massachusetts, U.S.A.

The goal of a traditional descriptive grammar is to enable the reader to understand and freely produce arbitrary sentences of the language it treats; to enable him, in other words, to match the judgment and behavior of the native speaker. Paired with an intelligent and comprehending reader, a good traditional grammar often achieves a high degree of success in this attempt. I think it is fair to say that we have very little understanding of how this success is attained, and that a sharp reversal in the direction of current linguistic studies will be necessary if any substantial insight into such questions is to be achieved.

A traditional grammar has serious limitations so far as linguistic science is concerned. Its basic inadequacy lies in an essential appeal to what we can only call the 'linguistic intuition' of the intelligent reader. It is important to realize that a taxonomic grammar of the traditional kind is not merely a partial grammar that omits certain facts about the language. The understanding reader contributes not new facts but a technique for organizing and arranging facts. What he accomplishes can fairly be described as theory construction of quite a nontrivial kind. The abilities that he develops constitute an implicit theory of the language that he has mastered, a theory that predicts the grammatical structure of each of an infinite class of potential physical events, and the conditions for the appropriate use of each of these items. The reader is, of course, not at all aware of what he has done or

---

This work was supported in part by the U.S. Army (Signal Corps), the U.S. Air Force (Office of Scientific Research, Air Research and Development Command), and the U.S. Navy (Office of Naval Research); and in part by the National Science Foundation.

how he has done it. For the student of human psychology, this fact merely adds to the interest and importance of the process of mastering a language.

Reliance on the reader's intelligence is so commonplace that its significance may easily be overlooked.[1] The best grammars contain a full treatment of exceptions, but only representative examples of regular constructions. This is quite appropriate in a grammar addressed to an intelligent reader who can be counted on to use his intuitive grasp of the general features of language structure to construct a correct theory of the language on the basis of these fragments. However, since the grammar itself does not express the fundamental underlying regularities of the language, it gives not only a very incomplete, but also a rather false picture of the language that it treats, attributing to it far too large an element of irregularity and caprice.

With diligence and application, an intelligent adult can use a traditional grammar to develop some degree of mastery of a new language. A young child is able to gain perfect mastery of a language with incomparably greater ease and without any explicit instruction. Mere exposure to the language, for a remarkably short period, seems to be all that the normal child requires to develop the competence of the native speaker. There is actually very little support for the view that careful instruction and guidance, or careful arrangement of 'reinforcing contingencies' (in any interesting sense of this phrase), are necessary for developing language skills in the young child; nor can this view claim any serious analogical support from the study of lower organisms.[2] It goes without saying that the problem of explaining how an untutored child can attain full mastery of a language is of much greater

[1]Furthermore, we tend to take for granted the successes of the language learner and to mark only his (much more noticeable) errors, thus receiving an entirely false picture of the nature of his accomplishment.

[2]One of the two main modern schools of behavioral study has concentrated on behavior (e.g., maze-running, patterns of pecking or bar-pressing) that can be established and maintained only with carefully scheduled and continuing reinforcement. The second (comparative ethology) has devoted its primary attention to the acquisition and function of intricate behavior patterns (involving, for example, care of young, topographical orientation, mating, etc.) that the animal develops as a result of simple exposure to appropriate stimuli. (We can, of course, call these 'reinforcing' if we wish to trivialize reinforcement theory by making its basic concepts utterly vacuous.) One can argue plausibly that acquisition of language is as natural to man as courtship and mating patterns to a bird (both apparently require early exposure to appropriate stimulation that partially determines the character of mature behavior) and that, therefore, the study of so-called 'instinctive behavior' is likely to supply analogic hints more useful to the study of language learning than the findings of the reinforcement theorist that are often 'extrapolated' to complex behavior (in a highly misleading use of the term 'extrapolate' that is often justified by vague and even more misleading analogies to the physical sciences).

For discussion of speculative attempts to apply reinforcement theory to language learning, see Chomsky, 'Review of Skinner, *Verbal Behavior*,' *Language*, **35** (1959). See also, in this connection, Lenneberg, 'Language, Evolution and Purposive Behavior' (to be published), and 'Review of Penfield and Roberts' *Speech and Brain Mechanisms*, *Language*, **36** (1960), for very illuminating comments.

dimensions and importance than that of accounting for the ability of an intelligent adult to learn something of a second language from a well-constructed grammar.[3]

The child who has not yet learned a language is a physical system with characteristics that are at present unknown. Clearly, he is not adapted to learning some particular language. Placed in an English-speaking community, he will learn English; in a Chinese-speaking community, he will, with equal facility, come to speak and understand Chinese. A reasonable, though still remote, goal for linguistics and psychology would be to construct a device capable of duplicating this performance, or certain aspects of it. The linguistic abilities of the mature speaker can in part be characterized by what we might call a 'formalized grammar' of his language.[4] I will, for the remainder of this discussion, consider only these aspects of linguistic competence. Accepting this limitation, we might attempt to construct a device of the kind

(1) utterances of L → ☐ → formalized grammar of L

This represents a function that maps a set of observed utterances into the formalized grammar of the language of which they are a sample. Given as input a sufficiently large and representative set of utterances of any language (English, Chinese, or whatever), the device (1) would provide as output a formalized grammar of this language. A description of this device would therefore represent a hypothesis about the innate intellectual equipment that a child brings to bear in language learning.

That it is possible to construct a device with these characteristics may well be doubted. Other data that the child has available to him may play an essential part in language learning. Thus he may have available a set of nonsentences (that is, corrections by the speech community). He may need information about repetition of utterance tokens. The sequence in which elements are presented may have some importance. Assuming all of this, we might try to construct a device such as (2),

(2) A →, B →, C → ☐ → formalized grammar of L

---

[3]Here too, the child's occasional errors are so striking, and his correct generalizations so 'natural' (from the viewpoint of one who knows the language), that the magnitude of his accomplishment may be obscured.

[4]I do not know what the bounds of grammatical study are, but will attempt below to indicate something of its scope, as I see it. I do not, by any means, intend to imply that these are the only aspects of linguistic competence that deserve serious study, though it does seem to me not unlikely that it is in this area that systematic investigation will, for the present, be most rewarding.

where A is a sequence of utterance tokens of L, B a sequence (perhaps interpenetrating A) of nonsentences, and C a set of conforming pairs of items of A and B, i.e., tokens that are, in the appropriate sense, repetitions of one another. There are still other possibilities concerning the inputs to this hypothetical language-learning device that merit consideration.[5] The question is an important one, and should be amenable to experimental study.

Whatever such study might reveal, however, the problem of constructing a universal language-learning device cannot be stated clearly until we determine the properties of the formalized grammar that is to be its output. It is first of all clear that the formalized grammar, regarded as a predictive theory, is an idealization in at least two respects: first, in that it considers formal structure independently of use; and second, in that the items that it generates will not be the utterances of which actual discourse is composed, but rather they will be what the untutored native speaker knows to be well-formed sentences. Actual discourse consists of interrupted fragments, false starts, lapses, slurring, and other phenomena that can only be understood as distortions of an underlying idealized pattern. It would be absurd to try to incorporate these phenomena directly into a formalized grammar. Actual speech is clearly a complex process in which many interacting factors play a part, not all of which fall within the domain of grammatical study.

The formalized grammar is intended to be a characterization of certain of the abilities of the mature speaker. It should, first of all, concern itself with his ability to determine what is a properly formed sentence.[6] Thus, for example, given the sequences

(3)
(a) the dog looks terrifying
(b) the dog looks barking
(c) the dog looks lamb

any speaker of English knows that (a) is well-formed, and that (b) and (c) are formally deficient (although, if they were sentences, their meaning would be clear and fairly unambiguous). He also knows that (b) is somehow closer to well-formedness than (c). In this and innumerable other perfectly clear cases, we should require that the formalized grammar make the same discrimination, assigning to each sequence of words or morphemes what we

---

[5]For example, it might be maintained, not without plausibility, that semantic information of some sort is essential even if the formalized grammar that is the output of the device does not contain statements of direct semantic nature. Here, care is necessary. It may well be that a child given only the inputs of (2) as nonsense elements would not come to learn the principles of sentence formation. This is not necessarily a relevant observation, however, even if true. It may only indicate that meaningfulness and semantic function provide the motivation for language learning, while playing no necessary part in its mechanism, which is what concerns us here.

[6]I do not mean to imply that speakers can always decide consistently and unequivocally on the relative well-formedness of sequences of words or morphemes. Rather, we want the formalized grammar to match such judgments approximately, wherever we have clear cases, as in (3).

can call a 'degree of grammaticalness.' For convenience of exposition, I will, in this discussion, simplify this requirement, insisting only that the grammar provide a list of fully grammatical sentences, a recursive definition of 'grammatical sentence.'[7]

There is other information about sentences that clearly belongs to the domain of grammar; in particular, information about the units of which sentences are constructed, the grouping and arrangement of these units, the formal relations between sentences and their elements, and so on. A mass of information of this sort I will call a *structural description* of a sentence. The formalized grammar, then, is to provide an explicit enumeration of grammatical sentences, each with its structural description. We would like the structural description to provide the basis for explaining a great deal of what the speaker knows to be true of speech events, beyond their degree of well-formedness. Thus every speaker of English knows that the sentences

(4) (a) I dislike visiting relatives
(b) I do not approve of John's driving (the fact or the manner)

are structurally ambiguous in a way in which (3a) or

(5) the dog is barking

is not. He knows that

(6) (a) John is easy to please
(b) John is eager to please

are sentences of different types, while

(7) (a) who(m) did you see
(b) who saw John

despite differences in word order, are sentences of the same type. The structural description must be rich enough to provide the basis for explaining such facts as these, of which an indefinite number can be amassed.

A successful and interesting formalized grammar is one that assigns appropriate structural descriptions to each member of an infinite class of sentences and that does this in a formally motivated way. The latter requirement is of course essential. A collection of ad hoc rules may succeed in enumerating a great mass of facts without thereby giving any insight into the formal properties that distinguish the correct set of structural descriptions from alternative sets that would be given by totally different grammars;

[7]For a discussion of how a grammar that generates well-formed sentences can automatically assign to each sequence of elements a degree of grammaticalness, see the chapter on 'Grammaticalness' (chapter 4 in some versions, chapter 5 in others) in my 'Logical structure of linguistic theory', 1955 (mimeographed; microfilm available at M.I.T. libraries, reference department). See also Paul Ziff, 'On understanding 'understanding' ' (1959, unpublished), for interesting observations on this question.

without, in short, contributing seriously to the study of general features of linguistic structure or the study of the nature of a universal language-learning device that exhibits the intellectual abilities of the child. Thus, for example, on the basis of categorial theories such as the Theory of Immediate Constituents, one should predict a triple ambiguity in (5), since *barking* is both adjective ('barking dogs never bite') and noun phrase ('barking is annoying'), as well as verb, and all three constructions appear in the context 'the dog is—' ('dangerous,' 'a danger'). In this case, the correct structural description can be provided within the framework of Immediate Constituent Theory, but only by rules that are completely ad hoc and unmotivated. There would be no basis, within this theory, for selecting the grammar that provides the correct structural description over the grammar that falsely predicts a triple ambiguity. The latter, in fact, would be the simpler.

What we seek, then, is a formalized grammar that specifies the correct structural descriptions with a fairly small number of general principles of sentence formation and that is embedded within a theory of linguistic structure that provides a justification for the choice of this grammar over alternatives. Such a grammar could properly be called an explanatory model, a theory of the linguistic intuition of the native speaker.

There is a certain irreducible vagueness in describing a formalized grammar as a theory of the linguistic intuition of the native speaker. It is sometimes claimed that operational tests for degree of grammaticalness and the like can guarantee both objectivity and significance for the theory of grammar, but this is a misconception. If an operational measure for grammaticalness were devised, we would have to test it by determining how well it accords with the linguistic intuition of native speakers. In exactly the same way, we judge the adequacy of a proposed theory of English structure (an English grammar). The situation is perfectly symmetrical. There is no sense in which the operational test is 'prior' to the theory, or conversely. Optimally, we would like to have both, and we would like them to converge, but they must, for significance, converge on the linguistic intuition of the native speaker. Nothing is more simple than to construct a definition of 'grammaticalness' and an associated behavioral test that specify the same set of events.[8] Clearly, these will not be of the slightest interest unless the events specified are, to a good approximation, what the native speaker knows to be well-formed sentences. As to the twin projects of developing grammatical theories and constructing behavioral tests, the former is clearly the much more interesting, since the theory provides us with a variety of insights and hypotheses concerning the manner of organization and the underlying structure of the system of sentences that it specifies, while the operational test does no more than specify this set.

---

[8]To pick one of innumerable, equally absurd proposals that might be invented, we can train subjects to identify a pitch pattern of some arbitrarily selected sort and define a 'sentence' as any sequence of morphemes with that pitch pattern.

In fact, we do not have a satisfactory formalized grammar for any language. As I mentioned above, a traditional grammar is more similar to the set of inputs for a language learning device such as (2) than to the formalized grammar that this device is to provide. Modern structural linguistics has concentrated almost exclusively on the inventory of elements of which utterances are composed and, less typically, on methods for categorizing such elements. It has provided no grammars that go beyond or even attempt to approach traditional grammars in explicit coverage of grammatical sentences. A recent revival of interest in descriptive syntax has provided, for the first time, grammatical descriptions that are recursive and explicit, but none that succeed in characterizing closely the set of grammatical sentences and correct structural descriptions. Furthermore, much of this work is not really relevant here (whatever its other interest may be) because it provides or suggests no conceivable basis for justifying the rules that assign structural descriptions. As I mentioned above, mere coverage of a mass of facts is not in itself of any particular interest in the context of the present discussion.

In short, I think that the development of the theory of grammar, and intensive application of this theory, is a necessary prerequisite to any serious study of the problem of language acquisition and many other problems of immediate psychological significance. This theory must contain a precise specification of the class of formalized grammars;[9] it must provide a precise definition of this notion, that is, an explicit schema and notation for grammars and a specification of the conditions that a set of rules, stated in these terms, must meet in order to qualify as a grammar of some natural language. Secondly, it must show how a grammar meeting these conditions gives an explicit enumeration of sentences with structural descriptions, where each sentence is given in a fixed, universal system of phonetic transcription. These specifications must involve no appeal to the intelligence or linguistic intuition of the reader because it is just this that we are attempting to characterize.

The theory of grammar must, therefore, precisely specify:

(8)
(a) a class $G_1, G_2, \ldots$ of potential grammars
(b) a class $s_1, s_2, \ldots$ of potential sentences (in phonetic transcription)
(c) the notion 'structural description' and a function f that assigns the structural description $f(i, j)$ to the item s_i of (b) with respect to the grammar G_j of (a).

We may suppose, in addition, that the ordering of grammars in (8a) is significant and indicates increasing complexity. That is, we assume that the general theory of linguistic structure provides an evaluation procedure that will justify the selection of a grammar over presented alternatives.[10]

---

[9] I will henceforth drop the word 'formalized.'

[10] Note that many of the grammars of (8a) may enumerate the same language (i.e., the same infinite subset of (8b)) and even the same set of structural descriptions.

A particular grammar G_i of (8a) can now be regarded as being, in effect, a theory of the language that it enumerates by means of the function f of (8c); a theory that accounts for certain aspects of the linguistic intuition of the native speaker.

With a general theory of the form (8), we could return to the problem of constructing a language-learning device, making the assumption that this device essentially incorporates the theory of linguistic structure. That is, corresponding to the specifications in (8), the device (2) has available to it an advance specification of

(a) the form that a grammar may assume and an evaluation procedure;
(b) a phonetic alphabet;
(c) a method for determining the structural description of an arbitrary sentence, given one of the permitted grammars.

This information is part of the internal structure of the device (2). Suppose that this device is now presented with examples of sentences and nonsentences partitioned into conformity classes (classes of repetitions).[11] The task for the language-learning device is to select the highest-valued grammar that is compatible with these data, in the sense that all sentences and no nonsentences are enumerated and nonrepetitions differ at the appropriate points in the structural descriptions assigned to them. Having selected this grammar, the language-learning device is capable, in principle, of assigning a structural description to each sentence, by virtue of its incorporation of the function f of (8c).

A general theory of linguistic structure of the sort just outlined would, in this way, provide an account of a hypothetical language-learning device and could thus be regarded as a theoretical model for the intellectual abilities that the child brings to language learning. We can evaluate this general theory by determining how well the structural descriptions provided for sentences in the highest-valued grammar we can discover do, in fact, match the linguistic intuition of the native speaker and provide a basis for explaining it. As I have tried to indicate above, there is an enormous variety of perfectly clear cases that provide a very strong, though indirect, empirical condition of adequacy for this general theory. Failure to meet this empirical condition may mean that the theory must be revised or that we have failed to find the highest-valued grammar.

To make this model realistic (that is, to make the language-learning device practical), we must supply it with some sort of heuristic or inductive principles that enable it, given input data, to make a rapid selection of several potential grammars to be submitted to the procedure of evaluation.[12]

---

[11]We assume, in other words, a partitioning of utterance-tokens (the items of (8b)) under an equivalence relation of 'conformity' that is (within rather strict limits) specific to each language. One might argue that 'conformity,' in the desired sense, can be defined in terms of a simple nontransitive matching relation. For some discussion of this point, see my review of Hockett's *Manual of Phonology, International Journal of American Linguistics*, **23** (1957).

[12]Similarly, though an explicit formulation of f of (8c) would show how, in prin-

One might include in (8) a specification of such heuristic procedures, or one might argue that they are not a reasonable concern of linguistic theory. In any event, it seems to me that the scope and effectiveness of heuristic, inductive procedures has been greatly exaggerated. To select a recursive, formalized grammar, given fragmentary data, a learning device must obviously contain both heuristic procedures and a specification of the form of grammars, as part of its internal structure. But the task remaining to heuristic procedures is obviously lightened as we make the specification of the form of grammars increasingly narrow and restrictive. It seems to me that the relative suddenness, uniformity, and universality of language learning, the bewildering complexity of the resulting skills, and the subtlety and finesse with which they are exercised, all point to the conclusion that a primary and essential factor is the contribution of an organism with highly intricate and specific initial structure.

I have been discussing some aspects of general linguistic theory from the point of view of what it can contribute to the understanding of human intellectual capacity. When we consider, instead, the more immediate problems that face the descriptive linguist, we arrive at much the same conclusions. The linguist tries to discover the grammatical structure of some language, bringing to bear, in this attempt, a selected array of concepts that give an implicit picture of what a natural language, in his view, must be like. He brings to bear, in other words, a more or less detailed general theory of linguistic structure, which must, furthermore, have the features of the language-learning device described above. The linguist will accumulate data as to which phonetically transcribed items are well-formed and which pairs conform (are repetitions); he tries to find the optimal grammar consistent with these data. He thus performs a genuine act of discovery. No doubt something can be said about the heuristic and inductive principles that can be used as an aid to discovery. However, this is, at most, a marginal concern of linguistic theory. What must concern the linguist primarily is the precise specification of (a) the form of grammars (with a measure of evaluation and a system of phonetic transcription), (b) the notion 'structural description,' and (c) a way of determining the structural description of an arbitrary sentence, given a grammar. His goal, in other words, must be to construct a theory of language having the features outlined in (8), above.

The theory thus constructed is a theory of linguistic universals. Specification of the form of grammars excludes certain infinite sets of sentences from consideration as possible natural languages. A system of phonetic transcription limits the possible physical realization of the sentences of a language. Procedures for evaluating grammars and determining structural descriptions impose strict conditions on the kinds of units that can be at-

---

ciple, one who has mastered the grammar G_i can understand a sentence s_j (to the extent of recovering its structural description), a realistic perceptual model would have to incorporate some sort of heuristic principles to guarantee rapid selection of the structural description. We return to this question briefly below.

tributed to a natural language and the manner of their arrangement and interconnection. This general theory can therefore be regarded as a definition of the notion 'natural language' (insofar as we are concerned with its formal properties). Its goal should be to exhibit the built-in data-organizing capacities of the child that lead him to develop the specific linguistic competence characterized in a fully explicit grammar. In this sense, it should aim to express just what is 'essential' to natural language.

The general theory of linguistic structure will, ideally,[13] take the form of a system of definitions in which such notions as 'grammar,' 'phoneme,' and so forth, are analyzed in terms of certain primitive notions. Pursuing further the connection between linguistic theory and a universal language-learning device, we might take as primitive the predicates 'observed sentence,' 'observed nonsentence,' and 'conforms'; that is, the inputs to (2). In addition, the primitive basis must include certain physical features that provide a system of phonetic transcription and further notions that we can regard as purely mathematical, belonging to an abstract theory of representation and generation of infinite sets of strings.[14] The fundamental notions to be defined are 'grammar' and 'structural description,' and the relation between these (that is, the function f of (8c)). We can then define 'phoneme of L, ' 'morpheme of L,' and so forth as the elements that appear at a specified point in the structural descriptions generated by the highest-valued grammar of L. Thus over-all systematic considerations of complexity play a part in the choice of elements at every level.

In contrast, the dominant view in recent years has been that linguistic theory should consist of a set of analytic procedures for the discovery of

---

[13]Linguistics is, of course, far from being able to realize such an ambitious goal as this at present, and can only approach it in various aspects of the general theory.

[14]Perhaps other notions must be taken as primitive. Thus the view that linguistic analysis must be 'based on meaning' might be interpreted as a claim that such notions as 'synonymy' and 'significance' can usefully (or, perhaps, must necessarily) be added to the primitive basis for grammatical theory. Unfortunately, despite the almost universal support for this view, there has been no attempt to formulate it in such a way as to meet the most obvious difficulties, so that there is little point in discussing it further. See in this connection my 'Semantic considerations in grammar,' Monograph no. 8 of the Institute of Languages and Linguistics, Georgetown University (1955); *Syntactic Structures* (The Hague, 1957, pp. 92–105); review of Greenberg, *Essays in Linguistics*, *Word*, 15 (1959); and Lees, 'Review of *Syntactic Structures*', *Language*, 33 (1957).

The issue has been much obscured by a peculiar failure to realize that the claim that linguistic analysis can (or must) be based on meaning requires the same kind of support (namely, a careful definition of fundamental notions in these terms) as the claim that it can be based on some other specific notion. The question is generally begged, as when linguists describe themselves, or criticize others, as attempting to 'avoid the use of meaning,' though in fact it has not yet been shown that there is anything of substance to avoid. Similarly, there are numerous articles and comments claiming to show that reliance on meaning is, after all, essential, since one or another explicitly formulated approach has proven to be deficient, something which clearly has not the slightest bearing on the question of whether there are semantically based alternatives.

linguistic elements such as phonemes and morphemes, to be applied systematically in sequence (either from sound to sentence, as in most American approaches; from sentence to sound, as in glossematics;[15] or in some sort of cycle, as in the theories of Harris and Pike). The grammar is, then, the inventory of these elements. The procedures involve successive segmentation and classification, and choice of elements at a later level of analysis either is specifically excluded from consideration at earlier levels or is allowed to play a marginal role, in cyclic approaches. Although there is near unanimity on the fundamental place of procedures of analysis in linguistic theory, the appearance of agreement is misleading because the word 'procedure' is understood in so many different senses. Thus for Harris, procedures are rigorously defined techniques of data-organization aimed at giving a 'compact one-one representation of the stock of utterances in the corpus'[16] and serving the purpose of making explicit the linguist's arrangement of his data. They do not, in this interpretation, lead to a generative grammar of the kind discussed above,[17] and it is a matter of relative unimportance which procedures a linguist uses, so long as he makes his choice explicit. For Fries and Pike, at the other extreme, the term 'procedure' is interpreted so loosely that they suggest as one possible procedure, quite objective though ultimately inadequate, 'to study the data carefully and attempt to make the simplest description which includes all the facts.'[18] On the basis of the work of the last quarter-century, I see no reason to believe that we are at all close to having rigorous procedures that lead in a mechanical way to the kind of grammatical description that a trained linguist (in a nonmethodological frame of mind) would consider important and illuminating, although this work has provided suggestions that many linguists appear to find useful as a guide in their analytic work. As I mentioned above, I do not see how we

[15]Thus 'our only possible procedure if we wish to order a system to the process of that text [i.e., to construct a grammar for the given corpus, N.C.], will be an analysis in which the text is regarded as a class divided into segments, then the segments as classes divided into segments, and so on until the analysis is exhausted' (Hjelmslev, *Prolegomena to a Theory of Language* (Baltimore, 1953), p. 7.

[16]Harris, *Methods in Structural Linguistics* (Chicago, 1951), p. 366.

[17]Though some of Harris' procedures, e.g., those of chapter 16, *ibid.*, are intended to lead to statements of a recursive character, and thus do not serve to provide a one-one representation of the corpus. There is a serious point at issue here. Procedures that merely lead to a one-one representation of the corpus have no empirical import and can be neither criticized nor supported by any evidence. They are merely a convenience for the analyst, and he can select those he likes at will. Procedures that take an 'inductive step,' however, as the morpheme-to-utterance procedures of chapter 16 of Harris' *Methods*, make an important empirical claim (i.e., that such-and-such items not in the corpus are grammatical sentences — and are, furthermore, sentences of a particular structural type), and thus can be judged in terms of truth and falsity. This distinction has not been clearly drawn in procedural linguistics, with the result that it is next to impossible to determine what, in fact, is its aim and what constitutes support for its methods.

[18]'Coexistent phonemic systems,' *Language*, 25 (1949), p. 32.

can hope to perfect interesting procedures of analysis before we have succeeded in specifying the goal to which they are expected to lead; that is, before we have a clear conception of the form of grammars and the nature of structural descriptions. It is this problem that is central to linguistic theory, and it has scarcely been raised in procedural approaches.

Turning now to this central question, what can we say at present about the form of grammars, the nature of structural description, and the relation between the two? Clearly, a grammar must contain two basic elements: a 'syntactic component' that generates an infinite number of strings representing grammatical sentences and a 'morphophonemic component' that specifies the physical shape of each of these sentences. This is the classical model for grammar. A string of symbols generated by the syntactic component I shall call a *terminal string*; the symbols appearing in terminal strings, *terminal symbols*.

I think there is, by now, fairly strong empirical support for the view that each of these components consists of two fundamentally different parts, a set of what I shall call 'rewriting rules' and a set of 'transformational rules.' A rewriting rule is a special case of a production in the sense of Post; a rule of the form $ZXW \rightarrow ZYW$, where Z or W (or both) may be null. In the syntactic component we must impose several other conditions — in particular, that X be a single symbol in the rule $ZXW \rightarrow ZYW$. A syntactic rule of this kind can be interpreted as asserting that a phrase of the type X can be analyzed into a sequence of phrases of type Y in the phrase-context Z--W. Thinking of morphemes as minimal phrases, we can include the lexicon among these rewriting rules, introducing lexical morphemes by such rules as $N \rightarrow$ *boy*, etc., where each lexical morpheme is regarded as a single terminal symbol.

We assume that among the symbols employed in the syntactic component there is a designated nonterminal symbol S (standing for *sentence*) and a boundary symbol #. We define a *derivation* as a sequence of strings $X_1, \ldots X_m$, where X_1 is #S# and each string follows from its predecessor by application of one of the rewriting rules; that is, if $ZXW \rightarrow ZYW$ is a rule and $X_i = \ldots ZXW \ldots$, then X_{i+1} can be $\ldots ZYW \ldots$. A derivation is *terminated* if its last string contains no subpart that is the left-hand member of one of the rewriting rules. The last line of a terminated derivation is a terminal string.

Each derivation imposes a labeled bracketing on its final line. The formal representation of this bracketing is part of the structural description of the generated sentence and is assigned by the function f of (8c).

The rewriting rules are ordered and apply in sequence to generate a finite number of terminal strings, each with a labeled bracketing as its structural description. The recursive property of the syntactic component is then provided by the transformational rules. Each of these applies to terminal strings with a labeled bracketing meeting some fixed condition, and carries out some formal operation on these terminal strings, assigning to the resulting terminal string a new labeled bracketing. Each grammatical transformation is, therefore, a mapping of strings with labeled bracketing into strings with labeled bracketing. Furthermore, a transformational rule can apply to two or more terminal strings of a specified structure to form a new, more complex string with a labeled bracketing determined by those of the underlying strings and the nature of the formal operation. Thus, for example, the terminal string representing 'I was annoyed by his refusal to participate' would be formed by a nominalization transformation applying to the strings that represent 'I was annoyed by it' and 'he refuses to participate,' each of which, in turn, is the result of further transformations. In fact, associated with each of the major syntactic categories (i.e., Noun, Verb, Adjective, and Adverb), there is, at least in English, a set of transformations that makes this category infinite in extension by permitting transforms of sentences of arbitrary complexity to be embedded within it. In this way, a few transformational rules, each quite simple in itself, can lead to sentences of great complexity by repeated application.

The syntactic component operates in the following manner: Construct a set of terminated derivations by means of the rewriting rules; apply a sufficient number of transformations to these, including in particular all obligatory transformations and observing ordering requirements, so that the result is a single terminal string with a labeled bracketing as part of its structural description. The terminal strings generated in this way constitute the output of the syntactic component. These are the strings that represent grammatical sentences.

When the form of the syntactic component is precisely stated, it is possible to undertake certain interesting studies of a completely abstract nature. In particular, we can study the kinds of languages and systems of structural descriptions that can, in principle, be generated; the relative richness and power of different conceptions of the form of grammars; decision problems of various kinds; the exact respects in which grammars are more powerful than strictly finite automata (a study that has immediate empirical consequences because it leads to hypotheses about understanding and production of sentences by a speaker with bounded memory); and so on. There has been some work of an introductory nature in each of these areas — enough, I think, to show the potential importance of such studies. If a genuine mathematical theory of language ever develops, questions of this sort will surely be central to it.[19]

The morphophonemic component, too, consists of transformational and rewriting rules. The role of these is to assign a phonetic representation to

---

[19]For a more precise characterization of systems of this sort and bibliographic references to descriptive and formal studies involving such systems, see my 'On the notion "rule of grammar"', *Proceedings of the Symposia in Applied Mathematics*, Volume XII, American Mathematical Society, 1961. For further material and references, see the paper by Y. Bar-Hillel in the *Proceedings* of this Congress.

each terminal string generated by the syntactic component.[20] The phonetic representation of an utterance can best be regarded as a matrix in which the rows represent the physical properties taken as primitive in the linguistic theory in question, and the columns stand for successive segments of the utterance. The entry (i, j) indicates whether or not the j'th segment has the i'th property (or, the degree to which it possesses this property, in the case of such features as stress, aspiration, etc.). The symbols of a phonetic alphabet are merely abbreviations for sets of properties, that is, for columns of such matrices; they have no independent status in themselves. Matrices of this sort constitute the output of the morphophonemic component of the grammar.

Now let us consider the input to the morphophonemic component. Each lexical morpheme will be represented as a string of symbols called 'morphophonemes.'[21] The terminal string, therefore, will consist of morphophonemes, special symbols for certain 'grammatical morphemes,' and certain 'junctural' symbols introduced by syntactic rules[22] to indicate positions where morphological and syntactic structures have phonetic effects.[23] Each morphopho-

---

[20]More exactly, to each string with labeled bracketing generated by the syntactic component. The phonetic output is uniquely determined (up to free variation) by the structural description, but not necessarily by the terminal string itself. That is, the constituent structure of the terminal string may partially determine the phonetic output by transformational rules of the type described below.

[21]Though it seems to me that 'phoneme' would be a preferable, and a historically justified term for these units (if we consider modern phonology from its origins to the mid-thirties), I use 'morphophoneme' to avoid pointless terminological confusion and dispute.

[22]Including, in particular, lexical rules.

[23]There has been an attempt, in modern procedural studies, to define junctures in purely phonetic terms, e.g., by considering features internal to an utterance that are similar to those at utterance boundary. It does not seem likely that any such attempt can succeed. Consider, for example, the common American English contrast *adept* [ɨdept]–*attend* [ɨtend]–*at Ed's* [ɨDedz] ([D] indicating alveolar flap). The context determining the presence of [D] as a variant of /t/ in such dialects is /V̌–BV́/ (where B is word boundary) — it is, in fact, more general. But the variant of /t/ preceding this boundary never occurs finally. Thus the juncture cannot be placed in what is obviously the correct position (from the point of view of the grammar as a whole — the grammar that concerns itself with both syntactic and phonetic structure) on purely phonetic grounds. The phonologist who, for some reason, refuses to use information provided by syntactic considerations in statements of allophonic variation is forced to place a juncture before the onset of stress, giving /ɨ+dept/, /ɨ+tend/, /ɨtedz/ (that is, to place juncture exactly where we do not want it, and not where we do – similarly, /pɨ+teytow/ *potato*, /fɨ+naenšɨl/ *financial*, etc.; this is the course taken by Hill in his *Introduction to Linguistic Structures*, New York, 1958); or, alternatively, to accept a phonemic contrast /t/–/d/–/D/. Either of these consequences seems to me sufficient to show that the concepts on which they are based are unfortunately chosen. For further objections to a nonsyntactic approach to juncture, see Chomsky, Halle, Lukoff: 'On accent and juncture in English,' *For Roman Jakobson* (The Hague, 1956); particularly, pp. 68–69.

Discussion of such questions seems sometimes to bring forth a hidden assumption

neme belongs to several overlapping categories in terms of which the morphophonemic rules are stated; that is, we shall attempt to discover rules that apply to large classes of elements such as consonants, stops, voiced segments, and so forth, rather than to individual elements. In fact, we can represent each morphophoneme simply by the set of categories to which it belongs; or, in other words, we can represent each lexical item by a matrix[24] in which columns stand for morphophonemes and rows for categories, and the entry (i, j) indicates whether or not the j'th morphophoneme belongs to the i'th category. The morphophonemes are abbreviations for sets of categories that we can call 'distinctive features'; like the phonetic symbols, the morphophonemes have no independent status in themselves. It is an extremely important and by no means obvious fact that the distinctive features of the classificatory, morphophonemic matrix define categories that correspond closely to those determined by the rows of the phonetic matrices.[25]

The morphophonemic component thus receives as input a string of classificatory matrices, morpheme symbols, and junctures, with constituent structure marked. It gives as output a phonetic matrix. Obviously, we want the rules of the morphophonemic component to be as few and general as possible. In particular, we prefer rules that apply to large classes of elements and that have a simple and brief specification of relevant context; and we prefer a set of rules in which the same classes of elements figure many times. These and other requirements are met if we define the complexity

---

that any set of procedures or concepts is perfectly all right, as good as any other, as long as they are consistently followed and applied. Surely this view cannot survive outright formulation.

[24]Which, from the point of view of the syntactic component, is regarded as a single symbol. The classificatory matrices are thus a notation chosen to facilitate the statement of morphophonemic rules.

[25]This point, which is as ancient as Panini, has been emphasized and elaborated particularly in recent years by Jakobson and Halle. Jakobson, however, insists on a virtual identity of phonetic and classificatory matrices. That is, he requires that for each phoneme there must be a set of phonetic properties that uniquely identify all of its variants. A similar requirement is made by Bloch. This requirement is perhaps motivated by a certain theory of perception which holds that an object is identified by its possession of some distinctive physical property that distinguishes it, in whatever context, from all others. Thus recognition of sounds would proceed as follows: first segment the utterance into successive parts, each of which is marked by a set of properties; then identify each segment as an X, just in case it possesses the properties that uniquely characterize X. I do not see any reason for accepting this view, and on linguistic grounds the requirement that all variants of the segment X possess a set of features distinct from those possessed by all other segments seems to me to have quite undesirable consequences. For discussion of this question, see the forthcoming *Sound Pattern of English* by Halle and Chomsky. The form of the morphophonemic component sketched here is discussed in considerable detail in this publication, both in general and with reference to English, and contrasted with alternative conceptions. This discussion, in turn, leans heavily on Halle's important *Sound Pattern of Russian* (The Hague, 1960) and 'Questions of linguistics,' *Nuovo cimento*, 13 (1959).

of the morphophonemic component in terms of the number of features mentioned in the rules, where the form of rules is specified in such a way as to facilitate real rather than spurious generalizations. We then choose simpler (that is, more general) grammars over more complex ones with more feature specifications (that is, more special cases).[26] This consideration, precisely spelled out, provides one aspect of the general evaluation procedure for grammars that is required for general linguistic theory (see (8) above).[27]

The morphophonemic component will consist of a sequence of rewriting rules called 'morpheme structure rules,' a sequence of transformational rules, and a sequence of rewriting rules that we can call 'phonetic rules,' applied to a terminal string in this order. The morpheme structure rules enable us to simplify the matrices that specify the individual lexical morphemes by taking advantage of general properties of the whole set of matrices. Thus, in English, if the three initial segments of a lexical item are not vowels, the first must be /s/, the second a stop, and the third a liquid or glide. This information need not therefore be specified in the matrices that represent such morphemes as *string*, *square*, and so forth. Similarly, the glide ending an initial cluster need not be further specified, since it is determined by the following vowel; it is /y/ if followed by /u/, and it is /w/ otherwise. Thus we have *cure* and *queer*, but not /kwūr/ or /kyīr/. There are many other rules of this sort. They permit us to reduce the number of features mentioned in the grammar, since one morpheme structure rule may apply to many matrices, and they thus contribute to simplicity, as defined above. Thus the columns of the classificatory matrices are, in general, 'archiphonemes,' in the terminology of the early Prague circle.[28]

---

[26]For further discussion of this definition of 'complexity,' and an indication of the consequences to which it leads, see Halle, 'On the role of simplicity in linguistic descriptions,' *Proceedings of the Symposia in Applied Mathematics*, Vol. XII (1961), and Halle and Chomsky, *op. cit.* Notice that to specify a single morphophoneme, we must mention all of its features, and to specify such an unnatural class as, e.g., that consisting of just /a/, /b/, /c/, /d/, we would have to mention nearly all of the features of each member. On the other hand, to specify what would be recognized by any linguist as a 'natural class' such as, e.g., voiced consonants, we need specify only the features common to all.

[27]For an indication of how this simplicity measure can be extended to the whole of grammar, see the chapter on 'Simplicity and the form of grammars' in *The Logical Structure of Linguistic Theory*.

[28]The morpheme structure rules are no more exceptionless than the morphological, syntactic, or phonetic rules. Where there are sporadic exceptions (e.g., 'svelte' /svelt/, etc.), it is generally simpler (in terms of minimization of features) to specify these individually and preserve the general rule. This point of view, universally accepted in morphology (where no one, for example, would seriously propose eliminating from the grammar the rule for forming regular plurals because of *children* and *sheep*), is, for some reason, considered heretical in phonology, where sporadic exceptions are regarded as overthrowing the system. Thus, given the unique exception 'today' ([tɨDey], with alveolar flap) in many American dialects (where elsewhere we find [d] or [t], phonetically, unless word boundary follows — cf. footnote 23,

Incorporation of morpheme structure rules overcomes an inadequacy in this theory of the form of grammars that was pointed out by Lees,[29] namely, that it does not make a distinction between permissible and nonpermissible nonsense syllables. The lexicon lists, of course, only morphemes that actually belong to the language. Operating on terminal strings, the morphophonemic component will produce, therefore, only sentences with actual morphemes. The morphophonemic component does, however, specify precisely the set of 'permissible' nonsense syllables, namely, just those that the morphophonemic component gives as output when an arbitrary matrix (not necessarily one listed in the lexicon) is given to it as input.[30] It is important to see that this inadequacy is overcome not by altering the general point of view but by pursuing it more consistently.

The transformational rules of the morphophonemic component determine the phonetic effects of constituent structure. In English, for example, there is a complex interplay of rules of stress assignment and vowel reduction that leads to a phonetic output with many degrees of stress and an intricate distribution of reduced and unreduced vowels. These rules involve constituent structure in an essential manner, both on the morphological and the syntactic level. Consequently, they must be transformational rather than rewriting rules. They are ordered, and apply in a cycle, first to smallest constituents (that is, lexical morphemes), then to next larger ones, and so on, until we reach the largest domain of phonetic processes.[31] It is a striking fact, in English at least, that essentially the same rules apply both inside and outside of the word. Thus we have only a single cycle of transformational rules which, by repeated application, determine the phonetic form of isolated words as well as of complex phrases. The cyclic ordering of these rules, in effect, determines the phonetic structure of a complex form, whether morphological or syntactic, in terms of the phonetic structure of its underlying elements.

---

above), phonemic theories as currently accepted would be forced to accept /D/ as a new phoneme, to be marked as such wherever heard, even when its occurrence is predictable. Or, given the Russian {boγ}, the unique morpheme with intervocalic [γ], such theories would insist on marking the [γ]—[x] distinction even where it is predicted by general phonetic rules (cf., e.g., Ferguson, 'The emphatic *l* in Arabic,' *Language*, **32** (1956). If such conclusions really follow from accepting the procedural approach, as is claimed, they simply provide a further reason for rejecting this approach in general.

[29] *Op. cit.*, p. 403. The matter was taken up again by Householder ('On linguistic primes,' *Word*, **15** (1959)) and Contreras and Saporta ('The validation of a phonological grammar,' *Lingua*, **9** (1960)), who argue that an independent generative grammar should be constructed to make the distinction between 'grammatical' and 'ungrammatical' phoneme sequences. We see, however, that this distinction is directly provided by the sentence-generating grammar itself. The role of morpheme structure rules was pointed out by Halle, *Sound Pattern of Russian* and 'Questions of linguistics.'

[30] That this statement is true may not seem obvious. It depends, in fact, on a more exact specification of the way in which rules apply to matrices. Cf. Halle, *op. cit.*, Halle and Chomsky, *op. cit.*, for a full account.

[31] What Trager and Smith have called the 'phonemic clause.'

The rules of stress assignment and vowel reduction are the basic elements of the transformational cycle. Placement of main stress is determined by constituent type and final affix. As main stress is placed in a certain position, all other stresses in the construction are automatically weakened. Continued reapplication of this rule to successively larger constituents of a string with no original stress indications can thus lead to an output with a many-leveled stress contour. A vowel is reduced to [ɨ] in certain morphophonemic positions if it has never received main stress at an earlier stage of the derivation, or if successive cycles have weakened its original main stress to tertiary (or, in certain positions, to secondary). The rule of vowel reduction applies only once in the transformational cycle; namely, when we reach the level of the word.

A detailed discussion of these rules is not possible within the limits of this paper, but a few comments may indicate how they operate. Consider in particular, the following four rules:

(a) a *substantive* rule that assigns initial stress to nouns (also adjectives) under very general circumstances;
(b) a *nuclear stress* rule[32] that makes the second of two main stresses dominant, thus weakening all other stresses in the construction;
(c) the *vowel reduction* rule, described above;
(d) a rule of *stress adjustment* that weakens all nonmain stresses in a word by one.

The rules apply in the order given.

From the verbs *permít, tormént,* etc., we derive the nouns *pérmit, tórment* in the next transformational cycle by the substantive rule, the stress on the second syllable being automatically weakened to secondary. The rule of stress adjustment gives primary-tertiary as the stress sequence in these cases. The second syllable does not reduce to [ɨ], since it is protected by secondary stress at the stage at which the rule of vowel-reduction applies.

In the word *tórrent,* on the other hand, the morphophonemic /e/ (cf. 'torrential') does reduce, since, in contrast to *tórment,* it has not received main stress in an earlier cycle; it is not derived from a verb *torrént.* Thus we have reduced and unreduced vowels contrasting in *tórment-tórrent.* The same rule that forms *tórment* from *tormént* changes the secondary stress of the final syllable of the verb *advocate* to tertiary,[33] so that it is reduced to [ɨ] by the rule of vowel reduction. Thus we have reduced and unreduced vowels

---

[32]Cf. Newman, 'On the stress system of English,' *Word,* **2** (1946).

[33]That is, this rule assigns main stress to the initial syllable in the nominalized forms *torment, advocate.* Primary stress of *ment* is thereby weakened to secondary; the secondary stress of *ate* is correspondingly weakened to tertiary, so that the vowel is reduced to [ɨ]. For a detailed account of everything covered here, see Halle and Chomsky, *op. cit.*

Notice that the rule of stress adjustment would have weakened the stress of *-ate* in the verb *advocate* to tertiary, if this word were not nominalized, but only *after* the rule of vowel reduction applies, so that the final vowel remains in the verb, giving the contrast [ǽdvɨkèt] (V)—(ǽdvɨkɨt] (N)

contrasting in the noun *advocate* and the verb *advocate,* and generally, with suffix *-ate*. Exactly the same rules give the contrast between reduced and unreduced vowels in the noun *compliment* ([. . . mɨnt]) and the verb *compliment* ([. . . mènt]), and similar forms.

Now consider the word *condensation*. In an early cycle, we assign main stress to the second syllable of *condense*[34] and to the first syllable of *ation.*[35] In the next cycle, the rules apply to the form *condensation* as a whole, this being the next larger constituent. The nuclear stress rule weakens the syllable *dens* to secondary. The rule of vowel reduction does not apply to this vowel, since it is protected by secondary stress, and the rule of stress adjustment weakens it to tertiary. A final rule of some generality[36] replaces an initial stress sequence 43 by 34, so that the resulting form has a nonreduced vowel in the second syllable with stress four. Consider, in contrast, the word *compensation*. The second vowel of this word, also morphophonemically /e/ (cf. 'compensatory'), has not received stress in any cycle prior to the word level at which the rule of vowel reduction applies (i.e., it is not derived from *compense* as *condensation* is derived from *condense*). It is therefore reduced to [ɨ]. We thus have a contrast of reduced and unreduced vowels with weak stress in *compensation-condensation,* as an automatic, though indirect effect of difference in constituent structure.

Exactly the same cycle of transformational rules produces such contrasting forms as [télɨgræ̀f] — [tɨlégrɨf] — [tèligrǽf] in *telegraph-telegraphy-telegraphic,* all from the underlying representation /tele + græf/, and handles many other cases of considerable complexity. The same rules apply beyond the word level as well. Thus the nuclear stress rule gives the stress sequence secondary-primary in adjective-noun and verb-object constructions (e.g., *ôld mán, rêad the létter,* etc.), and many others, and the substantive rule gives the sequence primary-secondary in nominal compounds such as *élevator ôperator, brídge constrûction,* etc. As has been shown elsewhere,[37] the same rules generate the correct stress sequences in the more complex constructions that have been used to demonstrate the multileveled character of stress; e.g., *lîght hóusekeèper — lìght hóusekeèper* (person who does light housekeeping) — *líghthoùse keêper*; *smâll bóys schòol* (small school for boys) — *smàll bóys schòol* (school for small boys), *John's blackboard eraser* (which has the sequence 213545), and many others.[38] These forms result from application of the same rules in various orders, the order being determined by the con-

[34]This is a general rule for verbs with final double consonant or tense vowel.

[35]Since the suffix *-ion* assigns main stress to the immediately preceding vowel.

[36]This also applies in such words as *àrchipélago, vìrtuóso,* etc. It also may be the rule that converts *fìftêen mén* to *fîfteèn mén,* etc., though we have not worked out the details of this.

[37]Chomsky, Halle, Lukoff, *op. cit.* The rules given there can actually be simplified and generalized. See Halle and Chomsky, *op. cit.*

[38]These specific examples are among those analyzed in my 'Transformational basis of syntax,' University of Texas Symposium on Syntax, 1959 (*Proceedings* to appear), where an earlier version of these morphophonemic rules is presented.

stituent structure and the general principle that the transformational cycle operates on successively larger constituents.

In short, a phonetic output that has an appearance of great complexity and disorder can be generated by a very small number of simple transformational rules in systematic cyclic application, where the order of application is determined by what we know, on independent grounds, to be the syntactic structure of the utterance. It therefore seems reasonable to assume that rules of this kind underlie actual speech production and perception. On this assumption, we have a plausible explanation for the fact that native speakers uniformly and consistently produce and identify new sentences having these intricate physical characteristics (without, of course, any awareness of the underlying processes or their phonetic effects). This suggests that identifying an observed physical event as such-and-such a particular phonetic sequence is, in part, a matter of determining its syntactic structure (to this extent, understanding it). A more usual view[39] is that we determine the phonemic constitution of an utterance by observing in the sound wave a sequence of physical properties, each of which is the defining property of some particular phoneme. In contrast, we might try to develop a sentence-recognizing device (that is, a perceptual model) that incorporates both the generative rules of the grammar and a 'heuristic' component that samples an input to extract from it certain cues as to which rules were used to generate it, selecting among alternative possibilities by a process of successive approximation.[40] With this approach, which, I think, has much to recommend it,[41] there is no reason to assume that each segmental unit has a particular defining property, or, for that matter, that morphophonemic segments literally occur in sequence at all.

Such an approach to perceptual processes has occasionally been suggested.[42] Recognition and understanding of speech is the obvious topic to study

---

[39]Cf. footnote 25.

[40]Though the problem of constructing a perceptual model is quite independent of that of constructing a model for learning, there is an obvious resemblance between the point of view regarding perception expressed here, and the approach to language learning suggested above. Similarly, the traditional view that linguistic analysis is essentially a matter of successive procedures of segmentation and classification usually goes hand in hand with the perceptual theory that regards identification of the structure of an utterance as a process of segmenting and classifying by defining properties, though in principle the two are independent.

[41]For example, it offers a natural way of accounting for the fact that speech recognition is relatively unimpaired by rather gross distortion of the physical input — a fact which is difficult to explain if we do not assume that underlying generative rules operate in normal recognition. This point of view also has the advantage of giving a uniform treatment to recognition of so-called 'segmental elements' (e.g., phonemes), stress and pitch contours, and syntactic structures. It also avoids the quite implausible assumption that there is a 'grammar for the hearer' quite distinct from the 'grammar for the speaker.' The same generative grammar is regarded now as a basic component in both production and recognition of speech.

[42]E.g., MacKay, 'Mind-like behavior in artefacts,' *British Journal of Philosophy*

in developing this idea. It is extremely complex and 'natural' to normal human beings; and it is unique in that we have, in this case, at least the beginnings of a plausible and precise generative theory that gives a picture of the organizing principles underlying the input stimuli.

Morphophonemic processes of the kind just described are not easily accommodated within the framework of purely taxonomic grammars. Nor can we expect to discover them by applying procedures of segmentation and classification. In fact, modern classificatory linguistics has rarely tried to state the rules that determine the phonetic content of utterances. It has rather been concerned with providing a notation for transcribing whatever utterance may be heard. Thus, in all of the intensive and fruitful investigation of English phonology that has been a major occupation of American linguists, there has been no attempt to study the relations between constituent structure and phonetic form, as in the case of such items as *condensation-compensation*, *tórment-tórrent*, *small boys school*, and so forth, or to explain why a lexical item such as *telegraph* has just the allomorphs [télɨgræ̀f], [tilégrɨf], [tèlɨgræ̀f], rather than three quite different ones, or a single form in all contexts. A generative theory containing a cyclic transformational component can propose an explanation for such facts; just these allomorphs result from the operation of rules that are demanded, independently, by many other examples. A classificatory grammar that does not go beyond a statement of allomorphs would be no more complex if the actual variants were replaced, in each case, by arbitrary different ones. It would, in fact, be simpler if there were a single form in all contexts. It thus offers no explanation at all for facts which it is content merely to list.[43]

Such examples as those discussed above can serve as a kind of crucial experiment to adjudicate between alternative conceptions of the form of grammars. Clearly a grammar that predicts phonetic form in a large class of cases by general rules is to be preferred over a list of variants and their distribution.[44] And the success of a grammar in providing a simple and unified treatment for such cases is strong evidence in support of the correctness of the general theory of linguistic structure that underlies it.

Any serious investigation of syntax, too, will quickly bring to light peculiarities of distribution that appear to require numerous special and isolated

---

of Science, **2** (1951); Bruner, 'Neural mechanisms in perception,' *The Brain and Human Behavior*, Solomon, Cobb, and Penfield, Editors, p. 122f; Halle and Stevens, 'Analysis by synthesis,' *Proceedings of the Seminar on Speech Compression and Production*, AFCRC-TR-59-198 (September 1959).

[43] This narrowing of interest in modern linguistics has not gone unnoticed, and has, in fact, been considered by some to be a great merit (and a defining feature) of modern linguistic work. Cf. Joos' Introductory comments to *Readings in Linguistics* (Washington, 1957).

[44] Although in principle it is possible to limit the morphophonemic component to a set of classificatory statements of allomorphic and allophonic variation and distribution, because of the bound on size of the phonemic clause, the domain of morphophonemic processes.

rules. The so-called 'anomalous finite verbs' of English provide a simple illustration. A constituent structure grammar containing only rewriting rules can cover all the facts only by a variety of special rules. On the other hand, it can be shown that the whole range of their behavior, superficially quite irregular and specific, is the result of the systematic functioning of a few simple transformational rules which are, furthermore, in part required for the 'regular' constructions.[45] Or, as a second example, consider the behavior of such words as *eager* and *easy*, both of which can appear in the context 'he is — to please' (cf. (6), above). We have such phrases as 'his eagerness to please, 'he is eager to please us,' 'for us to please him is easy,' 'it is easy for us to please him,' 'he is an easy fellow to please,' etc., but not the corresponding forms 'his easiness to please,' 'he is easy to please us,' 'for us to please him is eager,' 'it is eager for us to please him,' 'he is an eager fellow to please,' and so on.[46] A grammar that consists only of rewriting rules would have to state these facts as totally distinct and unrelated cases. In a transformational grammar, it is not difficult to show a deeper relation among them.

Again, it is to examples such as these that we must turn in attempting to evaluate alternative theories of linguistic structure. A characterization of the form of grammars will be of limited interest if, when we observe its requirements strictly, we must formulate completely ad hoc and disconnected rules for choice of allomorphs; for statement of complex distributional patterns; for prediction of structural ambiguity in such cases as 'the dog is barking' or 'I don't approve of his drinking'; for prediction of sameness and difference of sentence type; and so on, for a wide range of examples. Gross coverage of many facts can undoubtedly be obtained in many different ways. What we want in a grammar is not mere coverage of facts, but insightful coverage, something much more difficult to define or to attain. And what we demand of a linguistic theory is a general account of the formal features of those grammars that correctly predict the linguistic intuition

---

[45]For details of this and similar illustrations of the effectiveness of transformational rules, see my *Logical Structure of Linguistic Theory*, chapter 9 in some versions, 10 in others; *Syntactic Structures*, chapter 7; 'A transformational approach to syntax,' Proceedings of the Third University of Texas Conference on Problems in the Analysis of English (May 1958, in press). For further discussion of many aspects of English syntax from the point of view of a generative grammar utilizing transformations, see Lees, *Grammar of English Nominalizations, Supplement to International Journal of American Linguistics*, July 1960. Also forthcoming papers by Lees, Lees and Klima, and Klima, and an unpublished Master's Thesis by L. Gleitman, University of Pennsylvania, 1960. All of this derives from earlier studies by Harris, described briefly in 'Discourse analysis' and 'Discourse analysis; a sample text,' *Language*, **28** (1952), and elaborated in his 'Coocurrence and transformations in linguistic analysis,' *Language*, **33** (1957).

[46]Notice that one can hardly seriously maintain that these forms are merely semantically excluded as nonsense. Thus, 'he is an eager fellow to please' or 'his easiness (difficulty) to please us' would be unambiguously interpreted, no doubt, if they met the formal conditions of well-formedness.

of the native speaker, and that give what the skilled linguist knows to be significant generalizations. What we must demand, in other words, is that the general theory of linguistic form lead to the selection of grammatical descriptions that are true and insightful. As I emphasized earlier, the central problem in developing such a theory is to specify precisely the form of grammars — the schema for grammatical description that constitutes, in effect, a theory of linguistic universals and a hypothesis concerning the specific nature of the innate intellectual equipment of the child.

Symposium on Models in Linguistics

SOME RECENT RESULTS IN THEORETICAL LINGUISTICS

Y. BAR-HILLEL

Hebrew University, Jerusalem, Israel

Linguistics, as every other empirical science, is a complex mixture of theory and observation. The precise nature of this mixture is still not too well understood, and in this respect the difference between linguistics and, say, physics is probably at most one of degree. This lack of methodological insight has often led to futile disputes between linguists and other scientists dealing with language, such as psychologists, logicians, or communication theoreticians, as well as among linguists themselves.

Recently, however, considerable progress has been made in the understanding of the function of theory in linguistics, as a result of which *theoretical linguistics* has come into full-fledged existence. Interestingly enough, the present customary name for this new subdiscipline is rather *mathematical linguistics*. This is slightly unfortunate: though the adjective 'mathematical' is quite all right if 'mathematics' is understood in the sense of 'theory of formal systems', which is indeed one of its many legitimate senses, it is misleading inasmuch as it is still associated, at least among the non-specialists including the bulk of the linguists themselves, with numbers and quantitative treatment. That subdiscipline of linguistics, however, which deals with numbers and statistics should better be called *statistical linguistics* and rather carefully be kept apart from mathematical linguistics qua theoretical linguistics. Should one prefer to regard 'mathematical linguistics' as a term for a genus of which statistical linguistics is a species, then the other species should perhaps be named *combinatorial linguistics*.

After this terminological aside which, I think, was not superfluous, let us

This work was supported by the United States Office of Naval Research, Information Systems Branch, under Contract N 62558–2214.

briefly sketch the background and development of combinatorial linguistics. In the hands of such authors as Harris [1] and Hockett [2] in the United States, Hjelmslev [3] and Uldall [4] in Europe, structural linguistics became more and more conscious of the chasm between theory and observation, and linguistic theory deliberately got an *algebraic* look. At the same time, Carnap [5] and the Polish logicians, especially Ajdukiewicz [6], developed the logical syntax of language which was, however, too much preoccupied with rules of deduction, and too little with rules of formation to exert a great influence on current linguistics. Finally, Post [7] succeeded in formally assimilating rules of formation to rules of deduction, thereby paving the way for the application of the recently developed powerful theory of recursive functions, a branch of mathematical logic, to all ordinary languages viewed as combinatorial systems [8], while Curry [9] became more and more aware of the implications of combinatorial logic to theoretical linguistics. It is, though, perhaps not too surprising that the ideas of Post and Curry should be no better known to professional linguists than those of Carnap or Ajdukiewicz.

It seems that a major change in the peaceful but uninspiring co-existence of structural linguists and syntax-oriented logicians came along when the idea of *mechanizing the determination of syntactic structure* began to take hold of the imagination of various authors. Though this idea was originally but a natural outcome of the professional preoccupation of a handful of linguists and logicians, it made an almost sensational break-through in the early fifties when it became connected with, and a cornerstone of, automatic translation between natural languages. At one stroke, *structural linguistics had become useful*. Just as mathematical logic, regarded for years as the most abstract and abstruse scientific discipline, became overnight an essential tool for the designer and programmer of electronic digital computers, so structural linguistics, regarded for years as the most abstract and speculative branch of linguistics, is now considered by many to be a must for the designer of automatic translation routines. The impact of this development was at times revolutionary and dramatic. In Soviet Russia, for instance, structural linguistics had, before 1954, unfailingly been condemned as idealistic, bourgeois and formalistic. However, when the Russian government awakened from its dogmatic slumber to the tune of the Georgetown University demonstration of machine translation in January 1954, structural linguistics became within a few weeks a discipline of high prestige and priority. And just as mathematical logic has its special offspring to deal with digital computers, i.e., the *theory of automata*, so structural linguistics has its special offspring to deal with mechanical structure determination, i.e., *combinatorial linguistics*. As a final surprise, it has recently turned out that these two disciplines, automata theory and combinatorial linguistics, exhibit extremely close relationships which at times amount to practical identity.

To complete this historical sketch: around 1954, Chomsky, influenced by, and in constant exchange of ideas with Harris, started his investigations into a new typology of linguistic structures. In a series of publications, of which the booklet *Syntactic Structures* [10] is the best known, but also the least technical, he defined and constantly refined a complex hierarchy of such structures. Acquaintance with this book will be presupposed. Since Chomsky's own later work is presented by himself elsewhere in this volume [11], we can now turn to the presentation of some results in combinatorial linguistics recently obtained by my group in Jerusalem.

In 1938, I came across Ajdukiewicz's work [6] while working on my master's thesis on the logical antinomies. Thirteen years later, having become acquainted in the meantime with structural linguistics, and especially with the work of Harris [1], and instigated by my work at that time on machine translation, I realized the importance of Ajdukiewicz's approach for the mechanization of the determination of syntactic structure, and published an adaptation of Ajdukiewicz's ideas [12].

The basic concept behind the type of grammar proposed in this paper and later further developed by Lambek [13, 14], myself [15], and others, is the following: the grammar was meant to be a *recognition* (*identification* or *operational*) *grammar*, i.e., a device by which the syntactic structure of a given string of elements of a given language could be determined. This determination had to be formal, i.e., dependent exclusively on the shape and order of the elements, and preferably effective, i.e., leading after a finite number of steps to the decision as to the structure, or structures, of the given string, in some appropriate sense of this word. This aim was to be achieved by assuming that each of the finitely many elements of the given material language has finitely many syntactic functions, by developing a suitable notation for these syntactical functions (or categories, as we became used to calling them, in the tradition of Aristotle, Husserl, and Leśniewski), and by designing an algorithm operating on this notation.

More specifically, the assumption was investigated that natural languages have what is known to linguists as a *contiguous immediate-constituent structure*, i.e., that every sentence can be parsed, according to finitely many rules, into two or more contiguous constituents, either of which is already a final constituent or else itself parsible into two or more immediate constituents, etc. This parsing was not supposed to be necessarily unique. Syntactically ambiguous sentences allowed for two or more different parsings. Examples should not be necessary here.

The decisive variation introduced by Ajdukiewicz into this conception of language function, known and practiced in a crude form already by high school students, was to regard the combination of constituents into *constitutes* not as a concatenation *inter pares* but rather as the result of the operation of one of the constituents upon the others. The result of this view was to assign to each word (or other appropriate element) of a given material language a finite number of *fundamental* and/or *operator categories* and to employ corresponding 'cancellation' rules.

Just for the sake of illustration, let me give here the definition of *bidirectional categorial grammar*, in slight variation of the one presented in a recent publication of our group [16]. We define it as an ordered quintuple $< V, C, \Sigma, R, \mathfrak{A} >$, where V is a finite set of elements (the *vocabulary*), C is the closure of a finite set of *fundamental categories*, say $\Gamma_1, \ldots, \Gamma_n$, under the operations of right and left diagonalization (i.e., whenever α and β are categories, $[\alpha/\beta]$ and $[\alpha\backslash\beta]$ are categories), Σ is a distinguished category of C (the category of *sentences*), R is the set of the two *cancellation rules* $[\Phi_i/\Phi_j], \Phi_j \rightarrow \Phi_i$ and $\Phi_i, [\Phi_i\backslash\Phi_j] \rightarrow \Phi_j$, and $\mathfrak{A}$ is a function from V to finite sets of C (the *assignment* function).

We say that a category sequence α *directly cancels* to β, if β results from α by one application of one of the cancellation rules, and that α *cancels* to β, if β results from α by finitely many applications of these rules (more exactly, if there exist category sequences $\gamma_1, \gamma_2, \ldots, \gamma_n$ such that $\alpha = \gamma_1$, $\beta = \gamma_n$, and γ_i directly cancels to γ_{i+1}, for $i = 1, \ldots, n-1$).

A string $x = A_1 \ldots A_k$ over V is defined to be a *sentence* if, and only if, at least one of the category sequences assigned to x by $\mathfrak{a}$ cancels to Σ. The set of all sentences is then the *language determined* (*or represented*) *by the given categorial grammar*. A language representable by such a grammar is a *categorial language*.

In addition to bidirectional categorial grammars, we have also dealt with *unidirectional categorial grammars*, employing either right or left diagonalization only for the formation of categories, and more specifically with what we call *restricted categorial grammars*, whose set of categories consists only of the (finitely many) fundamental categories Γ_i, and the operator categories $[\Gamma_i\backslash\Gamma_j]$ and $[\Gamma_i\backslash[\Gamma_j\backslash\Gamma_k]]$(or, alternatively, $[\Gamma_i/\Gamma_j]$ and $[\Gamma_i/[\Gamma_j/\Gamma_k]]$).

One of the results obtained by Gaifman in 1959 was that *every language determinable by a bidirectional categorial grammar can also be determined by a unidirectional grammar and even by a restricted categorial grammar.* I shall return to this result below.

Before that, however, and before we lose ourselves in other mathematical technicalities, something should be said about the adequacy of categorial grammars for the description of natural languages. As a matter of fact, and as forcefully stressed by Chomsky, we have here two problems, the one of *adequacy-in-principle*, the other of *adequacy-in-practice*. Whereas the logician will probably be mostly interested in the first problem, the linguist is more interested in the second one. The situation is even more complicated than might appear on first sight. Not only is adequacy-in-principle not sufficient for adequacy-in-practice, since the number of steps required for testing, in accordance with some categorial grammar, sentencehood and other structural properties and relations of given strings, though finite, could still be so large as to defy even the most powerful electronic computer, it is not even always necessary. Adequacy-in-practice is better regarded as a matter of degree, and it is therefore possible that a language which could demonstrably not be *completely* described by any categorial grammar could be described by some categorial grammar with a degree of approximation that would be satisfactory for many practical purposes.

It is clear that a higher degree of theoretical adequacy can in general be obtained only by increasing the number of categories assigned to the words. This very same procedure, however, tends to reduce the practicality of the grammar. Whether a workable compromise can be obtained remains to be seen.

A different approach to the formalization of immediate constituent grammars was taken by Chomsky, within the framework of his general typology. He looked upon a grammar as a device, or a system of rules, for *generating* (or recursively enumerating) the class of all sentences. In particular, a *simple phrase structure grammar* — also called by Chomsky [17] a *type 2 grammar* or *context-free phrase structure grammar* — may be defined, again in slight variation from Chomsky's original definitions, as an ordered quadruple $< V, T, S, P >$, where V is the (total) *vocabulary*, T (the *terminal* vocabulary) is a subset of V, S (the *initial* symbol) is a distinguished element of $V-T$ (the *auxiliary* vocabulary), and P is a finite set of *production rules* of the form $X \rightarrow x$, where $X = V-T$ and x is a string over V.

We say that a string x *directly generates* y, if y results from x by one application of one of the production rules, and that x *generates* y, if y results from x by finitely many applications of these rules (more exactly, if there exist sequences of strings $z_1, z_2, \ldots, z_n$ such that $x = z_1$, $y = z_n$ and z_i directly generates z_{i+1}, for $i = 1, \ldots, n-1$).

A string over T is defined to be a *sentence* if generated by S. The set of all sentences is the *language determined* (or represented) *by the given simple phrase structure grammar*. A language representable by such a grammar is a *simple phrase structure language*.

My conjecture that the classes of simple phrase structure languages and bidirectional categorial languages are identical — in other words, that for each simple phrase structure language there existed an equivalent bidirectional categorial language and vice versa — was proved in 1959 by Gaifman [16], by a method that is too complex to be described here. He proved, as a matter of fact, slightly more, namely, that the same equivalence holds also while replacing bidirectional categorial language by unidirectional categorial language and restricted categorial language, and thereby obtained as a corollary the above-mentioned result of the equivalence of the bidirectional categorial grammars, unidirectional categorial grammars, and restricted categorial grammars among themselves. The equivalent representations can in all cases be effectively obtained from the original representations.

The equivalence proof was preceded by another one in which it was shown that the notion of a *finite state grammar*, occupying the lowest position in Chomsky's hierarchy of generation grammars, was equivalent to that of a *finite automaton* as dealt with by Rabin and Scott [18], for instance, and which can be viewed as another kind of recognition grammar. The proof itself was rather straightforward and almost trivial, relying mainly on the equivalence of deterministic and non-deterministic finite automata, shown by Rabin and Scott. For lack of time, I shall not go into this part of our work, especially since it has already been adequately described in a recently published paper [19].

Chomsky had already shown that the finite state languages formed a proper subclass of the simple phrase structure languages. We have recently been able to prove [20] that the problem whether a simple phrase structure language is also representable by a finite state grammar — a problem which has considerable linguistic importance — is recursively unsolvable. The method used was reduction to Post's correspondence problem.

Among other results recently obtained, let me only mention the following: whereas finite state languages are, in view of the equivalence of finite state grammars to finite automata and by well-known results of Kleene [21] and others, closed under various Boolean and other operations, *simple phrase structure languages whose vocabulary contains at least two symbols are not closed under complementation and intersection*, though closed under various other operations. *The union of two simple phrase structure languages is again a simple phrase structure language*, and a representation can be effectively constructed from the given representations. *The intersection of a simple phrase structure language and a finite state language is a simple phrase structure language.*

Undecidable are such problems as the equivalence problem between two simple phrase structure grammars, the inclusion problem of languages represented by simple phrase structure grammars, the problem of the disjointedness of such languages, etc. In this connection, *interesting relationships have been shown to exist between simple phrase structure grammars and two-tape finite automata* as defined and treated by Rabin and Scott, for which the disjointedness problem of the sets of acceptable tapes is similarly unsolvable.

For theoretical purposes, such as a better understanding of the processes of the speaker's producing and the hearer's grasping of utterances, as well as for practical purposes, such as machine translation and other types of mechanical processing of linguistic data, the problem to what degree simple phrase structure languages and languages of still more complex structure can be approximated by finite state grammars is of greatest interest. Human beings are surely finite in some pregnant sense, and it is well known that we have troubles in grasping the structure of certain strings generated by simple phrase structure grammar-like devices, as every student of the propositional calculus, for instance, realizes pretty soon. What is evidently needed here is some measure of complexity of the sentences generated. Useful beginnings have been made by Chomsky [22], Yngve [23], and others, but much more could and should be done in this direction, and my group has already started investigations towards this goal.

References

[1] Harris, Z. S. *Methods in structural linguistics*. Chicago, University of Chicago Press, 1951, xv+384 pp.

[2] Hockett, C. F. Two models of grammatical description. *Word*, Vol. 10 (1954), 210–231 (reprinted as ch. 39 in *Readings in Linguistics*, M. Joos, ed., Washington, D.C., American Council of Learned Societies, 1957, viii+421 pp).

[3] Hjelmslev, L. *Prolegomena to a theory of language* (tr. by F. J. Whitfield), Baltimore, Waverly Press, 1953, 92 pp.

[4] Uldall, H. *Outline of glossematics*. Copenhagen, Nordisk Sprog- og Kulturforlag, 1957.

[5] Carnap, R. *The logical syntax of language*. New York, Harcourt, Brace & Co., 1937, xvi+352 pp.

[6] Ajdukiewicz, K. Die syntaktische Konnexität. *Studia Philosophica*, Vol. 1 (1935), pp. 1–27.

[7] Post, E. L. Formal reductions of the general decision problem. *American Journal of Mathematics*, Vol. 65 (1943), pp. 197–215.

[8] Davis, M. *Computability and unsolvability*. New York, McGraw-Hill, 1958, xxv+210 pp.

[9] Curry, H. B. and R. Feys. *Combinatory logic*. Amsterdam, North-Holland Publishing Co., 1958, xvi+417 pp.

[10] Chomsky, N. *Syntactic structures*. 's-Gravenhage, Mouton & Co., 1957, 116 pp.

[11] Chomsky, N. Explanatory models in linguistics. These *Proceedings*, pp. 528–550.

[12] Bar-Hillel, Y. A quasi-arithmetical notation for syntactic description. *Language*, Vol. 29 (1953), pp. 47–58.

[13] Lambek, J. The mathematics of sentence structure. *American Mathematical Monthly*, Vol. 65 (1958), pp. 154–170.

[14] Lambek, J. Contributions to a mathematical analysis of the English verb-phrase. *Journal of the Canadian Linguistic Association*, Vol. 5 (1959), pp. 83–89.

[15] Bar-Hillel, Y. The present status of automatic translation of languages. Appendix II, in *Advances in Computers*, Vol. I, F. L. Alt, ed., New York, Academic Press, 1960, x+316 pp.

[16] Bar-Hillel, Y., C. Gaifman, and E. Shamir. On categorial and phrase-structure grammars. *Bulletin of the Research Council of Israel*, Vol. 9F (1960), pp. 1–16.

[17] Chomsky, N. On certain formal properties of grammars. *Information and Control*, Vol. 2 (1959), pp. 137–167.

[18] Rabin, M. O., and D. Scott. Finite automata and their decision problems. *IBM Journal of Research and Development*, Vol. 3 (1959), pp. 115–125.

[19] Bar-Hillel, Y., and E. Shamir. Finite-state languages: Formal representations and adequacy problems. *Bulletin of the Research Council of Israel*, Vol. 8F (1960), pp. 155–166.

[20] Bar-Hillel, Y., M. Perles, and E. Shamir. On formal properties of simple phrase-structure languages. Applied Logic Branch Technical Report No. 4 (prepared for the Office of Naval Research, Information Systems Branch), Jerusalem, Israel, Hebrew University, July, 1960.

[21] Kleene, S. C. Representation of events in nerve nets and finite automata. In *Automata Studies*, C. E. Shannon and J. McCarthy, eds., Princeton, Princeton University Press, 1956, viii+285 pp.

[22] Chomsky, N. On the notion rule of grammar. *Proceedings of the Symposium on the Structure of Language and Its Mathematical Aspects* (American Mathematical Society, Providence, Rhode Island, 1960), 1961, pp. 6–24.

[23] Yngve, V. H. A model and a hypothesis for language structure. *Proceedings of the American Philosophical Society*, Vol. 104 (1960).

MODELS IN LINGUISTICS AND MODELS IN GENERAL

YUEN REN CHAO

University of California, Berkeley, California, U.S.A.

The term 'model' is relatively new in linguistics, but the use of what may reasonably be regarded as models is as old as the study of language. As in the case of many concepts of science, progress consists not so much in the addition of new concepts and new terms as in the gradual sharpening and differentiation of hitherto blurred notions. Examples of this kind will readily come to mind: force, momentum, action, and energy; or, to come closer home, phone, allophone, phoneme, and morphophoneme; or, again, morph, allomorph, morpheme, and word.

The term 'model' in linguistics is mainly modeled after models in mathematics. According to Professors V. F. Lenzen and Henry Hiz, in discussions at this 1960 Congress for Logic, Methodology and Philosophy of Science, the first users of models, at least the concept, if not the term, were Eugenio Beltrami and Felix Klein, in connection with the non-Euclidean geometries of the 1870's, followed by Frege and Russell for mathematical logic. A geometry, whether Euclidean or non-Euclidean, is a set of uninterpreted sets of marks. But the set of rules of behavior of what Einstein calls "practically rigid bodies" constitutes a model of Euclidean geometry. In fact one important use of models in mathematics is to prove the internal consistency of a theory by finding for it an interpretation in the form of an actually existing model, since what exists cannot be self-contradictory. In this respect, as Professor Hiz notes, the usage among mathematicians seems to be almost the exact opposite of that of the social sciences, if linguistics is called a social science. In mathematics a model is more concrete than what it is a model of, while in the social sciences a model is more of an abstraction.

While linguists have consciously borrowed the concept of models from mathematics, they have not been uninfluenced by the use of models in the other sciences, and indeed by the various uses in everyday life, to which I will now turn for a few moments. In everyday usage a model is usually something similar to, but not quite the same as, the thing of which it is a model. A clay model of the human body or even of one particular person is a good imitation, in many respects, of the actual body. But it is without life and the internal parts are not in the model. So, at the very moment we are admiring a statue for its being life-like, we are saying that it is only life-*like* and not alive. From an examination of the model we gain information about, or aesthetic appreciation of, the thing, as if we were dealing with the original, or in ways we could not with the original.

Everyday usage usually limits itself to models in the form of 3-dimensional spatial shapes, with or without additional features, such as the power supply used in driving toy models. Two-dimensional diagrams are not commonly called models. Nor is a piano arrangement of a symphony ordinarily considered a model of the symphony, since it is not in 3-dimensional space, even in the form of printed music; nor, for that matter, is a score usually called a model of the symphony, either as performed or as composed.

Another aspect of ordinary usage is the idea of a norm to which actual things conform more or less imperfectly. Thus, the clay figure is a model, in the first sense, of the human body, but the human body is also a model which the artist takes as a norm to reproduce or from which he brings out certain features and leaves out others. One also speaks of a model husband or the model of a modern major general. Here the model begins to acquire the status of a set of qualities or specifications to which actual cases conform instead of a model approximating imperfectly some concrete thing of which the model can do only partial justice.

Does all this not remind one of the classical problem of things and ideas? Things are imperfect samples of pure ideas; ideas are partial abstractions of real things. One is a model, in one sense, of the other; the other is a model, in the other sense, of the one. Which of these two is nearer to the kind of models that linguists have been concerned with? As we shall see from a review of models used in linguistics, it is sometimes one, sometimes the other, and sometimes something in between.

As far as I am aware, the earliest mention of models in linguistics was by Z. S. Harris. In comparing the methodology of Stanley Newman and that of Sapir, Harris says: "Each worker will use whatever models and habits of thinking come most naturally to him" [6.1, p. 205]. That was in 1944. Then in 1951, Harris characterized a certain kind of model by saying that Sapir "also used this model of an 'entity as a result of process' within descriptive linguistics proper" [6.2, pp. 289—290]. He also contrasted Sapir's process model and the patterning of data [6.2, p. 292].

The first extensive, explicit use of models in linguistics was that by C. F. Hockett in his two Models of Grammatical Description [7] in 1954, of which multigraphed copies had been circulated around 1950. Hockett said that it was from mathematics that he had borrowed the idea. As is now well known, Hockett's two models are item and process, or IP for short, and item and arrangement, or IA. The model IA, which consists of taking language as items in a certain arrangement, without moving parts, as he puts it, has recently been in vogue because of its apparent simplicity, while process, if not properly defined, seems to have anthropomorphic, if not metaphysical, connotations. But Hockett shows by concrete cases the primacy of certain elements, such as hierarchical structure (that is, the grouping of immediate constituents, or IC, as in *old men and woman*), and choice of constructions for otherwise homophonous sequences of items in the same order (as in Chinese *ch'ao*^{3} *fan*^{4} 'to fry rice' or 'fried rice'), show that many things in languages can be handled in terms of processes better than by pure arrangement. Besides IA and IP Hockett also cites, without discussing it in detail, the model of word and paradigm, or WP, which is "older and more respectable" than either IA or IP and naturally most useful for the description of highly inflected languages, already so thoroughly studied in Indo-European linguistics.

Discussing models as a methodological concept, Hockett says, "By a 'model of grammatical description' is meant a frame of reference within which an analyst approaches the grammatical phase of a language and states the results of his investigations. In one sense, there are as many models as there are different descriptions. . . . But in another, and very important sense, most grammatical descriptions seem to cluster about a relatively small number of distinct models; it is with these archetypical frames of reference that we are concerned here" [7, p. 210].

Close upon the publication of Hockett's Two Models was the publication, in 1956, of Noam Chomsky's Three Models for the Description of Language [3]. Since Professor Chomsky will present a paper on Explanatory Models in Linguistics at this Congress, I shall mention only briefly his Three Models: (1) Finite-state grammar or the word-by-word model, which fails to allow for sentences like "colorless green ideas sleep furiously," a form which one would obviously like to regard as being grammatical; (2) phrase-structure grammar, based on "immediate constituent analysis," which takes care of constructional homonymity in cases like "they are flying-planes" and "they are flying planes", but leaves other problems of analysis unsolved, such as "the shooting of the hunters," thus leading to the setting up of model (3) a transformational grammar, which will refer grammatical forms to a relatively small, perhaps finite, number of kernel sentences, so that "the growling of lions" goes back to the kernel sentence "lions growl," while the "raising of flowers" goes back to "they raise flowers." The importance of the transformational model is that it not only is powerful for analysis but also functions as an explanatory theory of grammar.

The work of Morris Halle and K. N. Stevens applies mainly to a different part of linguistics from that of grammar. Their paper on Analysis by Synthesis [5] and Stevens' paper Toward a Model for Speech Recognition [12] are concerned with the physical signals and thus have more to do with the phonological level than the morphological or syntactical level of linguistic structure. In these papers, especially in the second paper, models are used as (1) a set of rules stored physically, (2) an analog of the vocal tract, and (3) a complete input-output setup for speech analysis-synthesis.

A. G. Oettinger's paper on Linguistics and Mathematics [10], 1957, contains a rather full discussion of the notion of models. Oettinger says, "when applied to the study of phenomena of nature, rather than developed for its own sake, a mathematical system serves as a *model*. . . . The key idea is that of 'representation', of 'abstraction', but a good model may also play more active roles." Then he goes on to illustrate the use of the architect's model of a house which represents some but not all of its properties. He cites E. V. Condon's and G. K. Zipf's use of the well-known frequency-rank equation $f = c/r$ (where f is the logarithm of the frequency of occurrence and r the frequency rank) as a model for the occurrence of linguistic units in extended texts. Models sometimes only describe, as given in the above empirical formula, but are more useful if they can explain, and here Oettinger cites the work of V. Belevitch, *Langage des Machines et langage humain*, and of B. Mendelbrot, who formalized Zipf's principle of least effort and deduced the formula as being more than mere empirical description.

V. H. Yngve, in his paper on A Model and An Hypothesis for Language Structure, gives no explicit definition of a model, but comes nearest to one when he says, "The model consists of a grammar and a mechanism. The grammar contains the rules of the particular language that is being produced. The mechanism, on the other hand, is quite general and will work with the grammar of any language [14, p. 3 of dittoed copy].

Of the five papers in the 1958 Symposium on Operational Models in Synchronic Linguistics, published in 1959 as Vol. 1, No. 1 of *Anthropological Linguistics*, three deal explicitly with models, namely, those by C. F. Voegelin [13], Z. S. Harris [6.3], and J. B. Carroll [2]. Because there will not be space here to summarize the development of the concept of model in those papers, I shall include them in the lists of synonyms and non-synonyms of 'model', as given toward the end of this paper.

Since there are at this Congress several other Symposia and lectures on models in various fields, it may be of interest to compare notes with the treatment of models in some of them. Those who were at the Symposium on Models in the Empirical Sciences will recall Professor R. Braithwaite's characterization of model as being a formalized theory or a semi-formalized theory, but a model, being more modest than a theory, and only partially valid for the theory, he would rather regard as a 'theoruncula' or a 'theorita.' Professor Braithwaite considered and rejected the view that an elaborate deductive theory cannot be properly understood without constructing a model for the theory. Models have also been regarded as being useful for leading to predictions which would not be possible without the model. Professor Braithwaite said that for this purpose a model may be psychologically suggestive but no more, or to use Professor H. Putnam's phrase, the model is used here only as a "psychological crutch." On this point I might cite again Oettinger, who says: "The discovery that the replacement of concrete objects by diagrams, and of operations on these objects by corresponding operations on the corresponding diagrams can lead to useful results provides the very justification of models. Unfortunately, this discovery must be made anew, at least in part, each time a new model is applied to a new type of situation" [10, p. 181].

Then, at the same Symposium, Professor Suppes says, in his paper on Models of Data: "a model of a theory may be defined as a possible realization in which all valid sentences of the theory are satisfied, and a possible realization of the theory is an entity of the appropriate set-theoretical structure. For instance, we may characterize a possible realization of the mathematical theory of groups as an ordered couple whose first member is a non-empty set and whose second member is a binary operation on this set. A possible realization of the theory of groups is a model of the theory if the axioms of the theory are satisfied in the realization."[1] This, as you see, is model in the usual mathematical sense, in which the model is something more concrete than that of which it is a model.

There are two other uses of the notion of model I wish to mention before I close. One is the use of the term model by Professor S. P. Diliberto, at a recent lecture before the Kosmos Club, University of California, on Notions About Motions, in which he set up the following tripartite division: (1) First, there is the system of concrete objects, e.g., the sun, the moon, and the planets. (2) Then there is the model, which is an abstraction, e.g., the Ptolemaic, the Copernican, Newtonian, Einsteinian, or what have you (although these are commonly called 'systems'). This is the sense in which R. O. Kapp uses the term when he says: "I constructed in thought the cosmological model that is implicit in the principle [of Minimum Assumption] and then compared the model with actuality. Occasionally there seemed to be a contradiction between the inferred model and actuality, but further research always removed it" [8, p. 15]. (3) Finally there is in Diliberto's schema the representation, in printed words, in diagrams, or in solid — 'solid models', I was going to say, but to avoid confusion, I shall just have to say 'solids'. It is also along the lines of (2) and (3) above that Gordon Pask speaks, in connection with self-organizing systems, of the physical model, whose fabric may have extraneous properties irrelevant to the model, as distinguished from the abstract model, as a set of constraints defining a universe in which the transfer of energy (or currency) may cause a self-organizing system to develop [11, p. 156].

The other use of models I want to mention is that of programmed production processes in industry. To produce a 1961 model of a TV set or a 1962 model of an automobile, there will of course have to be a complicated system of specifications, and, as more and more of the design gets into automation and recorded on punch-hole or magnetic tapes, the program gets to be more and more like models of theories both in structure and in physical makeup. This is particularly significant in that models in industry are already looking beyond their technological aspects toward their behavioral and institutional aspects, as reported by H. R. Karp on Corporate Models [9].

Summarizing the usages by linguists and non-linguists, we have the following lists of synonyms or characterizations of 'model' and of non-synonyms or notions contrasted with 'model'. We see here that things synonymous with the same thing are not always synonymous with each other, and that sometimes the same thing is not even synonymous with itself (e.g., items 27 and 105).

Now what is my view of models, models in general and models in linguistics? Well, my job here is to introduce the subject and the speakers on the subject and not to have a theory of my own. However, I would like to offer a little theoruncula or a theorita, or a model of models.

[1]This volume. p. 252.

I. Synonyms and Characterizations of 'Model'

		Author	*Ref.*	*Page*
1.	A frame of reference	Hockett	7	210
2.	Archetypical frames of reference	Hockett	7	210
3.	A description	Hockett	7	210
4.	A way of handling language	Hockett	7	229
5.	A conception of linguistic structure [to provide a grammar that generates all and only the sentences of English]	Chomsky	3	113
6.	A grammar	Chomsky	3	120, 123
7.	A theory	Chomsky	3	120, 123
8.	An impersonal plan (or model)	Voegelin	13	10
9.	A Standpunkt (transl. from Kleinschmidt as 'model')	Voegelin	13	12
10.	(Model or) style	Voegelin	13	9
11.	Analog (or model)	Stevens	12	52
12.	A proposed method of research (rather than No. 102, q.v.)	Stevens	12	54
13.	(Quoting Webster) a miniature representation of a thing	Oettinger	10	180
14.	A representation (but cf. 109)	Oettinger	10	180
15.	An abstraction (cf. 27)	Oettinger	10	180
16.	A grammar and a mechanism	Yngve	14	
17.	(Four) programs for separate aspects of behavior	Carroll	2	39, 40
18.	A framework in respect to which language is described	Harris	6.3	27
19.	A picture of how the linguistic system works	Harris	6.3	27
20.	A particular style of grammar	Harris	6.3	27
21.	A particular uninterpreted or partially interpreted system of marks, which becomes:	Harris	6.3	27
22.	A theory of the structure of something (when interpreted)	Harris	6.3	27
23.	A formalized or semi-formalized theory	Braithwaite	0	
24.	Theoruncula, theorita	Braithwaite	0	
25.	A psychological crutch	Putnam	0	
26.	A possible realization (of a theory) in which all valid sentences of the theory are satisfied	Suppes	0	
27.	An abstraction of a system (but cf. 105)	Diliberto	4	
28.	An abstraction	Kapp	8 15	
29.	A set of constraints	Pask	11	156

	Author	Ref.	Page
30. (The corporate model will be) a formulation of the company's strategy in optimizing its profit	Karp	9	136

II. Non-synonyms of 'Model'

	Author	Ref.	Page
101. Framework of representation (half a dozen of which can be reduced to two or more models)	Voegelin	13	15, 20, 23
102. A design for a complete machine	Stevens	12	54
103. The language system (of which the model is a model)	Harris	6.3	27
104. A structure, since several apparently different structures may have the same model and vice versa	Harris	6.3	27
105. An abstract system, since the same abstract system can have different styles of description (models)	Harris	5	27
106. Concrete system	Oettinger	10	181
107. Reality	Oettinger	10	182
108. A system, or the set of physical objects	Diliberto	4	
109. A representation, or physical realization of the model (in the form of symbols, etc., but cf. 14)	Diliberto	4	

In my model of models there are things and models of things, the latter being also things, but used in a special way. A model M and a thing T are related in various degrees of fitness or modelity from zero to 1. If we take any two things, say cabbages and kings, and make, say, a cabbage the model of a king, there is not likely to be much that is true of one that is also true of the other, though usually not zero, e.g. both are living things or can be, etc., but the modelity of cabbages with respect to kings is fairly low. At the other extreme is the trivial case of a thing being a model of itself, with a modelity of 1, or Model T, as everything that is true of one is true of the other. I am taking a thing as being bounded by both time and other dimensions, so that if the child is father of the man, the man may still be a model of the child, or vice versa, in a non-trivial sense. A set of genes will probably have a very high modelity with respect to the organism it will grow into.

My next step is to allow my notion of thing to range from dated sense-data, to physical events, to material objects, and arbitrary classes of things and organized classes of things, so that my thing can be *any thing*. Envisaging thing in this way will make room for models being concrete or abstract to various degrees and in various manners. In linguistics, as distinguished from philology, one does not deal with tokens of speech or writing occurring in dated history, but primarily with types, and so there is that much abstraction to start with already. A model for any phase of linguistics is at least of that degree of abstraction.

But how does one tell, given two entities, which is the thing and which its model? The answer will have to be a pragmatic one. In general, that which can more conveniently be handled — that is, seen, heard, remembered, recorded, communicated, manipulated, experimented upon, inherited, etc. is the model and that about which corresponding information or results are hoped to be obtained through such handling (in the broad sense) is the thing. Here, as several users of models quoted above have warned, one should always be on guard in discriminating between relevant and irrelevant features of model and thing.

We may also consider an alternative definition of modelity, not as above, in terms of isomorphism, but as an increasing function in which various factors affecting convenience, efficiency, fruitfulness, etc. enter as arguments. In this way we may be able to tell which of two things is the thing and which its model by looking at the value of the modelity, say the modelity of M with respect to T being always positive, while the reverse will be always negative (in which case the modelity of Model T will presumably be zero). Another advantage of such a definition is that it will differentiate 'model' from 'analog' by making the relation 'is a model of' non-reflexive and leaving that of 'is an analog of' reflexive. Or, finally, we can combine the measures of isomorphism with that of efficiency, etc. into some function so defined as will result in assigning values to actual cases in a way which will seem most reasonable and useful.

In setting up this modelita, it is not claimed that much is being said. But it may be of some help in easing the apparent paradox that a model is sometime more concrete and sometimes more abstract than the thing. Moreover, with all its as yet unclarified diverse ramifications, I think there is more to the notion of model than mere fortuitous usages of the same word in different senses. It is hoped that these far from being developed ideas will stimulate further discussion among modellists as well as anti-modellists. As for anti-modellists, I should be just as happy using models in linguistics as doing without. To those who attend congresses such as that for Logic, Methodology and Philosophy of Science, it is of course a truism that no term is absolutely indispensable and any term can be defined out — by the use of a suitable model.

References

[1] Belevitch, V. *Langage des Machines et Langage Humain.* Office de Publicité, S.A. Bruxelles, 1956.

[2] Carroll, J. B. An operational model for language behavior. *Anthropological Linguistics,* Vol. 1, No. 1 (1959), pp. 37–54.

[3] CHOMSKY, NOAM. Three models for the description of language. *IRE Transactions on Information Theory*, Vol. IT–2, No. 3 (1956), pp. 113–124.

[4] DILIBERTO, S. P. Notions About Motions, a lecture given at the Kosmos Club, University of California, June 6, 1960.

[5] HALLE, MORRIS, and K. N. STEVENS. Analysis by synthesis. *Proceedings of the Seminar of Speech Transmission and Processing*, Dec., 1959, AFCRC–TR 59–198, Vol. II, Paper D–7.

[6.1] HARRIS, Z. S. Yokuts Structure and Newman's Grammar. *International Journal of American Linguistics*, Vol. 10 (1944), pp. 196–211.

[6.2] HARRIS, Z. S. Review of *Selected Writings of Edward Sapir in Language, Culture, and Personality*, ed. by D. G. Mandelbaum. *Language*, Vol. 27 (1951), pp. 288–333.

[6.3] HARRIS, Z. S. The transformational model of language structure. *Anthropological Linguistics*, Vol. 1, No. 1 (1959), pp. 27–29.

[7] HOCKETT, C. F. Two models of grammatical description. *Word*, Vol. 10, No. 2–3 (1954), pp. 210–234.

[8] KAPP, R. O. *Towards a Unified Cosmology*. New York (1960), 303 pp.

[9] KARP, H. R. Using corporate models for business control. *Control Engineering* (September, 1960), pp. 135–137.

[10] OETTINGER, A. G. Linguistics and mathematics. *Studies Presented to Joshua Whatmough on His Sixtieth Birthday* (1957), pp. 179–186.

[11] PASK, GORDON. Artificial organisms. *General Systems. Yearbook of the Society for General Systems Research*, Vol. iv (1959), pp. 151–170.

[12] STEVENS, K. N. Toward a model for speech recognition. *Journal of the Acoustical Society of America*, Vol. 32, No. 1 (1960), pp. 47–55.

[13] VOEGELIN, C. F. Model-directed structuralization. *Anthropological Linguistics*, Vol. 1, No. 1 (1959), pp. 9–25.

[14] YNGVE, V. H. A model and an hypothesis for language structure. *Proceedings of the Amer. Philos. Soc.*, Vol. 104, No. 5 (1960).

[15] ZIPF, G. K. *Human Behavior and the Principle of Least Effort*. Cambridge, Mass., Addison-Wesley, 1949.

LISTS IN GRAMMARS

F. W. HOUSEHOLDER

Indiana University, Bloomington, Indiana, U.S.A.

It is a commonplace nowadays that the most neutral technical terms of a science may acquire emotional coloring for their users. Among many linguists the word 'list' has acquired a definitely negative tone. Here is a quotation taken from a recent article by John Lotz: 'we have to resort to lists of morphemes'[2]. The context does not matter; all I want to show is that here, for Lotz, lists are something that one *has to resort to*, i.e., something bad, uneconomical, implying sloppy workmanship, to be avoided at all costs. In its original context such an attitude may be perfectly reasonable and proper; in this context (the context of most American post-Bloomfieldian grammar-writing) a list is 'resorted to', i.e., the members of a class are listed in full, only if they share just one property (and one which you cannot reasonably omit from your discussion), and that usually a negative property. For if they share two or more properties, one is used to make what is called in this tradition a 'definition' of the class, and the reader is left to determine the class-membership for himself, if he cares to and has the means. In fact, of course, he seldom has the means, which would be in some cases what is called a corpus (that is, a very large sample of utterances in the language) and in others a hypothetical dictionary constructed according to some (usually unspecified) plan.

So it may be interesting to examine the ways in which lists of some sort or other are in fact used in grammars of three different vintages.

The reason for this interest, of course, is that lists play a very large and important role in the most recently discussed of these three types — what are known as generative grammars. And the presence of these lists in generative grammars is one of the facts which elicit violent reactions from linguists who have been concerned only with other kinds of grammar.

A generative grammar of a language is a sequence of rules or instructions (customarily of the form 'rewrite X as YZ), written $X \rightarrow YZ$ such that by proceeding through them in order the last rewriting will yield a grammatical sentence of the language (accompanied by an indication of its structure and derivation). In an ideal complete grammar of this sort, every grammatical sentence of the language may be so arrived at, and nothing that is not a grammatical sentence of the language. Although many partial or restricted grammars of this type have now been written, I know of very few which aim at anything like completeness (one is a generative grammar of Ilocano by a former student of my own, Ernesto Constantino); however, the general characteristics of such grammars are clear, and one of them is the presence of many instructions of the form $X \rightarrow X_1, X_2, X_3 \ldots X_n$, which are called lists; furthermore,

Research for this paper was supported in part by the United States Air Force (Air Research and Development Command).

every item in the language which is not generated by some other sort of rule must appear on some list—in short, a complete dictionary is scattered through the grammar. It would, of course, be possible to apply a differential marking to every member of each list and then throw all the lists together into a kind of dictionary placed, say, near the end of the grammar. Let me say again, as clearly as I can, that it is meaningless to ask why these lists cannot be replaced by definitions. Let us take an example. Every descriptive linguist starts off with a list (or 'inventory') of phonemes; in fact he may break this list into separate lists of 'vowels', 'stops', 'labials', 'continuants', and the like. Does anyone ask him to replace these lists by definitions? Should we say, not that language X has vowel phonemes /a/, /i/, /u/ with such-and-such allophones in such-and-such positions, but merely that it has vowels, defined as 'syllabic vocoids' or something of the sort? We realize that such a demand would be foolish, because the actual phonemic inventory simply cannot be defined. Even if a distinctive-feature analysis of the familiar type is adopted, we could not 'define' the phonemic inventory, though we might conceivably write a set of rules to 'generate' it; but we would then have to *list* the distinctive features. The reason why this is so, obviously, is that phonemes are primitive elements, or primes, whose precise number and character are arbitrary and unpredictable. But exactly the same thing is true of the stock of morphemes or lexemes or idioms, or whatever name you choose to give to the primes of sentence-grammar, and true on a much larger scale. How can one give a definition of, say, the masculine given names of American English? One can specify their privileges of occurrence, but that is precisely what the rules of a generative grammar do, and does not answer our question, which is: 'What particular items may occur in the masculine proper-name slot in these rules?' Obviously, no linguistic definition can answer such a question, and this whole misunderstanding could not have arisen if the question had been properly asked and understood in the first place. If, in answer to the question 'what fits slot 2 in rule 7?' one answers 'anything that fits slot 3 in rule 49', and then, when asked 'what fits slot 3 in rule 49?' answers 'whatever goes in slot 2 in rule 7', we have a clear case of circularity, and circularity of the kind which does not help in grammar. The only non-circular answer is a list, either explicit or indirect (cross-reference to a dictionary, which is in fact merely all the lists of the grammar combined in a less accessible way). If someone complains that his request for a definition means 'How do you tell to which list or lists a given *new* item of vocabulary belongs?', then the answer is 'By testing it in all the formulas where the various class-symbols from which the lists are generated occur.' But this procedure is not itself part of a generative grammar. I do not belong to those linguists (if there are such linguists) who say that this testing is part of discovery procedure and that discovery procedure is incompetent, irrelevant and immaterial. Of course it is relevant, but it is not a proper part of a generative grammar; make it a footnote, an appendix, or a preface, if you like, and I will agree that it can be interesting and important.

There is, in some cases, another sort of non-linguistic answer which may be given to a request for definition. In the instance cited above, for example, where masculine given names are involved, one can give instructions to look at a certain spot on all United States birth certificates for male infants and copy what is there. Such sociological procedures will work quite well for many lists, though they may often seem to be dangerously 'semantic.' They are, in fact, procedures for eliciting, rather than definitions, and are available or convenient to use only for a few special lists of this sort. Others of this variety are, for instance, color-terms, city-names, words for materials, etc., but *not* such as (say) 'prepositions', 'emphatic particles', 'abstract nouns', 'verbs of motion', and the like.

For the other two types of grammar of which I spoke earlier I have chosen to spend some time examining one more or less typical specimen of each, in order (a) to offer some sort of useful general description of the purposes and arrangement of these grammars and (b) in particular to determine the ways in which they use lists or arrangements which are superficially similar to lists. The specimens I have selected are, for the older traditional type, George M. Lane's *A Latin Grammar* [1], originally published in 1898 by the American Book Company, and, for the more recent type, Leonard Newmark's "Structural Grammar of Albanian" [3], which was submitted as a doctoral thesis in 1956 and published in 1957 by the Indiana University Research Center in Anthropology, Folklore, and Linguistics. The latter is not wholly typical, partly (I am afraid) because Newmark had been somewhat influenced by me — for instance, on page 123 he remarks that it would be desirable if his grammar would 'enable one to generate all legitimate utterances and *only* legitimate utterances in the language' — but it is not so greatly aberrant that it cannot fairly well represent the class of partial grammars and structural sketches that were produced by American linguists between 1940 and the present.

Now if we carefully study these two grammars to determine the purposes which their authors hoped they would serve, we can get a fair idea in the case of Lane, though less so in Newmark's case.

Numerous allusions throughout the book make it clear that Lane conceives his primary purpose as facilitating the translation by his users of Latin into English *and* of English into Latin. This might suggest something like Harris's Transfer Grammar or more recent studies in Contrastive Grammar, except that Lane is rarely explicit about English structure, assuming that his readers understand that well enough already. Now, as far as the production of Latin sentences is concerned, this goal is a little stronger than that which I have assigned to simple generative grammars. *They* guarantee that you will produce, *eventually*, any grammatical sentence of the language, but leave the determination of *which* particular sentence you produce on any given run through the grammar largely to chance; grammars like Lane's, however, assume that you have a clear idea *what* sentence you want to say in English, and give you instructions for producing some equivalent sentences in

Latin, or, conversely, assume that you have before you a sentence in some Latin text and give instructions to arrive at a corresponding English sentence. This would naturally affect the shape of lists: in the unmodified generative grammar all members of a given list are equal, and no special procedure for choosing is needed; in a Lane-type grammar, if lists were used, they would have to be bilingual, allowing choice of the proper English or Latin equivalent of a given Latin or English item.

A very minor part in Lane's grammar is played by two other purposes (which often bulked larger in other nineteenth-century grammars): (1) interesting facts about the history of Latin, most of which, in Lane, can be justified by the assumption that the user might want to read some specimens of old Latin, and (2) structural details about Latin which contribute nothing to the goal of translation or understanding. Such an item occurs, for instance, in § 52 (which may well be due to Hans Oertel, not to Lane himself, by the way): 'Contact of the semivowels I and U with their corresponding vowels I and U is avoided in classical times.' The most one could say is that some of these distributional statements might help readers occasionally in detecting misprints in a text; there is no suggestion of systematizing such statements so as to generate all and only the grammatical sequences of phonemes (or letters), thus indicating restrictions on possible additions to lists in later parts of the grammar.

The purposes of Newmark's grammar and others like it are more difficult to determine. The remark I quoted from Newmark about generation of all and only the legitimate utterances of the language appears in a context which implies that he considers his grammar a first step toward some such goal (his grammar is restricted to what he calls '*constructions*' as opposed to *combinations* and *additive elements*). Furthermore he speaks of 'this grammar and the proper dictionary it must be used with,' implying some deliberate relegation of the necessary lists in some such manner as that which I mentioned earlier. But in most parts of the grammar, and throughout most other American grammars of this kind and date, several other purposes seem to bulk much larger. (1) To classify the linguistic data appearing in some finite corpus in as many 'interesting' or 'revealing' ways as possible. This includes at least some items which might be of use to the reader of Albanian texts in arriving at a clearer understanding and hence a better translation; in Newmark's case (again owing in part to my influence and that of Harry Velten) this also included a Prague-school diagrammatic presentation of the semantic contrasts present in the case-system and in the verb-system, though such frivolities would not be common in other American work of this period. (2) To demonstrate improvements in the 'definition' of grammatical terms and categories. Newmark says [3, p. 8], 'this discussion has attempted to show how some of the traditional grammatical categories, so often mentalistically conceived and subjectively developed, can be treated with some rigor in order to give them their useful and rightful place in the description of Albanian.' What precedes is a kind of operational definition of the categories called by Newmark 'nominative', 'marginal', and 'accusative' — collectively 'case'.

It is perhaps worth while to digress briefly on the question of form-classes (morphological and syntactical). Many linguists seem to feel that the most significant and useful grammatical statements they can make are definitions of a few large form-classes. This appears to be a direct inheritance from the tradition of Dionysius Thrax and nineteenth-century grammar, where a list of 'parts of speech' is given very early. American linguists of the recent period attempt to do the same thing in a more scientific way, often implying that old-fashioned definitions were exclusively 'semantic' and worthless. (This, by the way, is not always true: the ancient grammarians offered definitions of 'noun' — subdivided into 'substantive' and 'adjective' — and 'verb' which were primarily morphological, and quite sound by 'modern' standards.) So we often read statements of the following type: "stem-morphemes (or 'words' or 'lexemes' or 'bases') of the language L may be classified into three classes, nouns, defined by such-and-such properties, verbs, defined in such another way, and particles." They may also add special 'overlap' classes, e.g., 'noun-verb', having the defining characteristics of both nouns and verbs. An attempt is then occasionally made to begin constructing a syntax from these few simple classes, but it never gets very far. Nor could it: the number of necessary lists for a reasonable syntax cannot well be less than fifty in any natural language, and certainly runs over two hundred in most. Nor are 'overlap classes' of any use, except as a convenient device to avoid repeating the same partial list within two or more complete lists. The reasons for all this are simple: There are many different grammatical environments, and it must generally be due either (a) to pure chance or (b) to the existence of a transformational relation when exactly the same set of items will fit into two of them. Complete mutual exclusion is often the case (where ultimate membership in different so-called 'major' form-classes is likely), but partial overlap, in varying degrees, is common. Moreover, many primes occur in environments where they are unique (commutable with nothing else, or occasionally with their own absence), or are members of very small classes. In such cases it is quite meaningless to say that they are (or are not) members of some large class. The grammar must handle them explicitly. (3) A purpose not mentioned by Newmark, but often present in other descriptions of this vintage is typological: to give a taxonomic description of a language which will enable it to be more readily compared and contrasted with all the other languages of the world.

Now for the last twenty years or more, American linguists (with occasional honorable exceptions) have spent a good deal of time criticizing nineteenth-century grammars such as Lane's mainly for their use of vague and subjective definitions and for failure to state the procedures used in arriving at their classes and rules. They failed to note that in fact these classes and rules were often very well chosen and that the vague definitions were frequently superfluous frosting since the class-membership was fully listed anyway.

Then when a few years ago Chomsky's *Syntactic Structures* appeared, and a few students started producing sketches of generative grammars, these same linguists began reacting very emotionally. Three things, in my experience, seem to irritate them particularly.

1. Since they have long prided themselves on rigorous methods of extracting structure from a corpus (procedures such as those called immediate constituent analysis and commutation or frame substitution, which they look upon as the really great achievements of modern linguistics), they are quite annoyed to find these things omitted entirely from the new grammars and dismissed with what they consider the contemptuous label of 'discovery procedures.' They say, 'you have set up a class called N; how did you get it? How do you tell when a new item appears whether or not it belongs to this class?' And if you answer, 'try adding the new item to the expansion of N and see if all the resulting generations are grammatical sentences,' they dismiss this as a quibble. If you say, 'O.K., I'll add an appendix to my grammar discussing some of my preliminary attempts to determine the class N,' they complain that you are inverting the order of nature, that such definitions should be the main part of your grammar, not a footnote or appendix. In fact, of course, any test 'frame' that could be used as a definition of this sort is included as a rule of the grammar. The only possibility of a 'definition' which is not so included would be a non-syntactic one; if in a language X, all transitive verb stems and no other morphs contain front vowels (say), then a definition of transitive verb might be given which differs from any rules of the grammar. But it would still not replace a list; a list is the *only* way to tell what primes of this form are in fact used in the language. You might invent several hundred morph-shapes containing front vowels and find that only three or four of them were in fact transitive verb stems of X. The less rare situation (as in Latin) where a morphological class (inflected for case, say) nearly coincides with a syntactic one (possible government by prepositions, say) is of no use either, since both of these conditions must be rules of the grammar. Such convergences, of course, increase the utility of a class, but that is all.

2. Since they regard grammar as a science of classification, in which there is an accepted conventional order (first phonology, then morphology, then — for those who believe such a thing exists, and many do not—syntax), and that within each portion only a conventional arrangement of topics is reasonable, they look upon the generative sequence of rules as eccentric, machine-oriented, 'synthetic' when it should be 'analytic', and in general fail to grasp the purpose. As far as I can tell, it is hopeless to argue in a situation like this. The obvious point that *only* such a grammar can be tested for accuracy and completeness usually draws some such answer as, 'Oh, well, it's hopeless under practical conditions to expect completeness. The important thing is to classify as much data as you can and move on to the next language.'

3. There are several other features of generative grammar that draw

agonized or contemptuous cries from the traditionalists, but the one that I have undertaken to discuss today is the presence of rules which ideally give complete lists of all idioms or elements of a given class. Just why this distresses them so I have already suggested in my first paragraph; in their sort of grammar any list of elements is a kind of admission of failure, a desperate expedient which should only be resorted to under the pinch of dire necessity. And very often they will adopt strange expedients to avoid using lists.

First let us consider an example of a typical list from a generative grammar:

$$V_{T_e} \text{ — see, surprise, find, catch, hear, } \ldots$$

This is not, of course, a complete list (as the dots signify), but it should not be impossible to make it complete for any given speaker's idiolect at a given time. It represents a class of verbs which occur in certain constructions such as 'I saw John stealing an apple.' Now it would be possible (though uneconomical) to lump all lists together into one big dictionary by the simple device of adding an arbitrary label; in this case our dictionary would include, say, a number of words with initial W, namely Wsee, Wsurprise, Wfind, Wcatch, Whear, etc., and our rule would read, 'rewrite V_{T_e} as any idiom with initial W.' But then, (a) the dictionary would still be an integral part of the grammar, and (b) the grammar would have to include a rule deleting the initial W's. Many dictionaries do in fact include such markers, though rather clumsily and often sketchily and inconsistently, so that it would be very difficult if not quite impossible to extract the complete list from the dictionary. But the tediousness of doing so is the worst fault of this method: it may be necessary to inspect 45,000 entries in order to find four items. Making the class-marker the initial letter, by which the item is alphabetized, as I suggested for 'see, surprise, find, etc.', would expedite this search, but be an inconvenient arrangement for most other dictionary purposes.

Now let us do what I originally promised: glance quickly at various list-like passages in Lane's grammar and in Newmark's. The striking thing here is the similarity between the two. The most frequent occurrence in both is the group of illustrative examples, intended in general to be a small sample from a large (or perhaps infinite) population.

Lane § **191**. 'Verbs in -ēre, and those in -āre and -īre in which the ā or ī is confined to the present system, usually have parallel nouns formed directly from a root: as, doc-tor, *teacher*, doc-umentum, *lesson*, doc-ilis, *teachable* (doc-, docēre); sec-tor, *cutter* (sec-, secāre); dom-itor, *tamer*, dom-inus, *master*, dom-itus, *tamed* (dom-, domāre); sarc-ina, *package* (sarc-, sarcīre).'

This is from the 'word-formation' section, where no grammar even attempts to be complete. The information given, even with the list, is inadequate for successful generation of other derivative nouns, even if we added the information from the dictionary implied by the words 'verbs in ēre' and from the cross-reference paragraphs. These references are sufficient, however, to generate a list of 'roots' from which *some* such nouns might be formed.

Lane §1062. 'A verb agrees with its subject in number and person: as, praedia mea tū possidēs, ego aliēnā misericordiā vivō, R.A. 145, *you, sir, hold my estates, it is by the compassion of other people that I am supported.* Rhodanus fluit, 1, 6, 2, *the Rhone flows.* nōs, nōs, dīcō apertē, cōnsulēs dēsums, C. I, 3, *it is ourselves, yes, ourselves, I will speak without reserve, the consuls, who fail in our duty.* vōs vōbīs cōnsulite, 7, 50, 4, *do you look out for yourselves.* diffūgēre nivēs, H. 4, 7, I, *scattered and gone are snows.*'

Here the examples constitute a partial definition of the term 'agrees with' used in the rule.

Lane §1220. 'There are many of these datives, mostly abstracts and all singular; some of the commonest are cūrae, ūsuī, praesidiō, cordī, odiō, auxiliō, impedīmentō, salūtī, voluptātī. The adjectives magnus, maior, maximus, or tantus and quantus, are sometimes used in agreement with them; and the dative frūgī sometimes has bonae.'

The implication here is that either a complete list could be given, or perhaps rules of generation, but Lane is too busy to do the job.

Lane §1851. 'quod, *that, because,* is used to denote cause with verbs of emotion. . . . Such verbs are: gaudeō, laetor; mīror; doleō, maereō, angor, indignor, suscēnseō, īrāscor, &c. . . .'

Here the suggestion is that the combination of the partial list with the description 'verbs of emotion' should enable the reader to complete the list by going through the dictionary. Such 'semantic' definitions are common in the syntactical portions of most nineteenth-century grammars, but the modern traditionalist would scarcely be happier if we replaced the list 'see, surprise, find, catch, hear, etc.' by a definition such as 'verbs of observation and detection.' Yet that is the *only* alternative to a list.

Notice that in two of the above cases (and many more like them) there is an implicit reference to the dictionary. This, as we have remarked, is equivalent to a complete list if the words are adequately marked in the dictionary, which is not always the case. At other times this implicit listing is clearer, as in §451, 'Stems in -o- with nominative in -r are declined as follows,' which is a perfectly adequate instruction to construct a list from the dictionary of all nouns ending in -(e)r, with a genitive (given by all standard dictionaries) ending in -rī. Lane does not constructs such a list, because the particular noun will be chosen on other grounds, and only if it happens to satisfy these conditions will the rule be relevant. A generative grammar would do much the same thing as Lane, in this case.

Illustrations like this are frequent in Newmark also, who makes some explicit references to a dictionary, e.g., p. 39: 'Their classification as Nu, Nna, Na, and mN, fN, or pN is to be given in a dictionary of stems.'

One important class of complete lists consists of those which are really definitions, e.g. Lane §419. 'Nouns have five case, the *Nominative, Genitive, Dative, Accusative, and Ablative.*' This constitutes a definition of the word 'case'.

Newmark has an almost identical one (p. 4): 'Finally, the preceding statement can be put in a more general form if we use a single term, say case, to refer without distinction to any of the categories nominative, marginal, or accusative.' And this kind of list (always relatively short) is frequent in both grammars.

But the only other lists which are generally complete are such as these:

Lane §1379. 'The instrumental ablative is used with the five deponents fruor, fungor, potior, ūtor, vēscor, and several of their compounds, and with ūsus est and opus est.'

Newmark (p. 69). "Deictics (Qd) are each composed of two parts. A morpheme k(ë)- 'near' or a- 'far *or* unspecified' is followed by one of a special set of declensional category markers: -'y (after k-) ~ 'i (freely after a-) 'masculine singular nominative' -j'o 'feminine singular nominative' -t'ë ~ -t (freely when lacking phrase stress) 'singular accusative' -t'ij ~ -t'ijt (optionally when deictic is preceded by a preposition) 'masculine singular marginal' -s'aj ~ -s'ajt (as -t'ijt above) 'feminine singular marginal' -t'a 'masculine plural non-marginal' -t'o 'feminine plural non marginal' -t'yre ~ -tyreve (in free alternation) 'plural marginal'." In these we have small, peculiar classes which must be listed.

And similarly Lane §993. 'The following verbs in -āre have the perfect stem in -u (§874), and the perfect participle, when used, in -tus: crepō, cubō, domō, ē-necō, fricō, micō, - plicō, secō, sonō, tonō, vetō'. (This is part of a complete list of exceptions to an earlier rule about the perfect stem and perfect participle of verbs in -āre.)

Newmark (p. 50). "ll-i ~ -u (after /k/,/g/,/h/ and after vowels, except after the morphemes bab'a 'father', jaj'a 'uncle: father's brother' and vëLa 'brother') 'masculine non-plain'."

These are the typical truly complete lists in both Lane and Newmark: short lists of peculiar and irregular items. So all classes which are assumed to be permanently closed (e.g., personal pronouns, short prepositions, articles, subordinating conjunctions, etc.) are regularly listed, and it is only these which the traditional view regards as proper parts of the grammar; all large and presumably open classes are supposed to be 'defined' somehow, or recoverable from the dictionary.

Let us now sum up briefly. Nineteenth-century grammars such as Lane's use two devices to avoid lists: (1) reference to a standard dictionary, available to all readers, for morphological classes; (2) partial lists combined with 'semantic' definitions for syntactic classes, except where a syntactic class coincides with a morphological class, in which case the dictionary again serves. Recent twentieth-century grammars like Newmark's use a deceitful form of the first device, referring the reader to a non-existent dictionary with class-marks attached, but avoid the second device in one of two ways. Either (a) they postpone treatment of syntax to an indefinite future, thus solving the problem for the time being, or (b) they use one rule as a 'definition' for a given class which occurs in one or more other rules, and avoid all rules involving unique classes. This course cannot remain open as soon as linguists begin to attempt complete grammars. It should be obvious by now that there are only two available procedures: either (1) all classes must be completely listed at the proper point in the grammar, or (2) a companion dictionary must be prepared along with the grammar, and every necessary class membership be fully marked in that dictionary. This may well become cumbersome (as well as inconvenient on other grounds), since many morphs are likely to belong to twenty or more distinct syntactical classes. Still, it is possible, and lexicographers might be well advised to prepare a complete syntactical grammar of their language as a necessary preliminary to writing their dictionary. Then such class-membership marks provide a convenient reference to the proper rules of the grammar, avoiding the necessity of repeating detailed syntactic information under fifty different entries in the dictionary. So, though the companion dictionary as a repository of class-membership lists for the grammar may be somewhat unwieldy, the companion grammar or grammatical sketch as a collection of all class-behavior information for the dictionary seems not only practical, but eminently desirable.

References

[1] Lane, George M. *A Latin Grammar.* New York, American Book Company, 1903, xvii+584 pp.

[2] Lotz, John. The Imperative in Hungarian, pp. 83–92 in *American Studies in Uralic Linguistics.* I of the Uralic and Altaic Series. Thomas A. Sebeok *et al.*, (eds.), Bloomington, Ind., Indiana University Publications, 1960, vi+356 pp.

[3] Newmark, Leonard. Structural Grammar of Albanian. *International Journal of American Linguistics*, Part II, Vol. 23, No. 4 (1957), pp. 1–130.

CRITERIA FOR A MODEL OF LANGUAGE

FRANCIS J. WHITFIELD

University of California, Berkeley, California, U.S.A.

Nicht der Sieg der Wissenschaft *ist Das, was unser 19. Jahrhundert auszeichnet, sondern der Sieg der wissenschaftlichen* Methode *über die Wissenschaft. – Der Wille zur Macht,* 466.

Nietzsche's double-edged dictum, which may appropriately be recalled at this Congress, is well illustrated by the victory of a particular methodology that is the outstanding characteristic of nineteenth-century linguistic science. As Antoine Meillet most clearly pointed out, at the very foundation of the magnificent edifice of nineteenth-century linguistics lies the essentially arbitrary relationship between the two immediate constituents of the linguistic sign, the content and the expression; 'Les moyens d'expression n'ont avec les idées qu'une relation de *fait,* non une relation de *nature* et de nécessité; rien ne saurait les rappeler à l'existence lorsqu'ils ne sont plus . . . Si donc deux langues présentent dans leurs formes grammaticales, leur syntaxe et leur vocabulaire un ensemble de concordances de détail, c'est que ces deux langues n'en font en réalité qu'une . . .' [5, p. 15].

At a time when the structure of the linguistic sign is very much in dispute, it is not irrelevant to keep in mind this basis of the greatest triumphs that linguistic science has so far known. It is quite another question, however, whether comparative linguists drew the full consequences from this fundamental feature of the linguistic sign, or whether all the consequences that were drawn can now be accepted. Even over the last sentence quoted from Meillet there lies the shadow of a dangerous reductionism. To illustrate it, he offers the examples of Italian, French, Spanish, and Latin — which are not, of course, 'in reality', one language. Or, perhaps better to say, if our methods produce identical models for them, then our investigations have sacrificed vast areas of applicability, and it becomes worth while to consider whether the cost has been justified.

Hans Arens, in his historical anthology of linguistic science, has schematized the progress of nineteenth-century linguistics in a series of pseudo-equations: Linguistics = Historical Linguistics = Historical Indo-Germanic Linguistics = (we might add, following his own elaboration) Historical Phonology and Morphology of the Indo-Germanic Languages = Historical Phonology and Morphology of the Indo-Germanic Languages with almost exclusive reference to the expression-substance — that is to say, in its phonetic aspects [1, p. 338]. Each successive narrowing of the field of productive interest — each step away from the central concept of the linguistic sign — can be amply documented and demonstrated to be an impoverishment of linguistics, both internally and in its relations to other scientific and humane studies. As the universal attitudes and programs of a Wilhelm von Humboldt rapidly lose their influence, there develops — in the words of one of the participants in this Congress, Louis Hjelmslev — a comparative grammar that has the peculiar distinction of not being a grammar [**3**, p. 59]. Concentration on a restricted type of language and on certain favored features of expression within that type lead to a damaging parochialism with long-lasting consequences — as, for example, in the unfruitful cleavage of morphology and syntax, reflecting the relative autonomy of the 'word' in Greek and Latin. Concentration on the expression side of the linguistic sign leads to the neglect of the more specifically human elements in language and widens the chasm between linguistics and the humanities. Finally, concentration on the *substance* of the expression tends to disintegrate language into a mere collection of acts of speech, taken in their physical aspect alone, to be described as directly and economically as possible, without regard for their content.

If we are able to see more clearly today this impoverishment of linguistics and reduction of its aims, it by no means follows that we have succeeded in eliminating all the causes. Deep-seated peculiarities of traditional linguistics not only persist but also are reenforced — as, for example, the concentration of attention on the expression-substance (and, indeed, on only one of the possible expression-substances) of language. Meanwhile, problems not amenable to treatment under the presuppositions of such a linguistics are swept under the rug or prematurely consigned to some no-man's land outside linguistics for unsystematic investigation. I do not mean such obviously complex problems as are invariably mentioned when the broadest possible applications of linguistics are being considered — questions of poetics and literary stylistics, for example, or artistic translation, or any of the many equally complex problems that do *not* involve the aesthetics of language. It is healthy for linguistics that increasing attention is being directed to such avenues of inquiry, even though linguistics in its present state may be ill prepared to do much about them. At least one may hope that these distant perspectives will serve to keep open lines of inquiry that a narrowly conceived linguistics might be led to block. But I am thinking rather of more homely problems, where it seems undoubtedly legitimate to look for the application of linguistics, more or less broadly conceived and more or less aided by other disciplines. The few examples that follow have been chosen, not as having anything novel about them, but, on the contrary, as being representative of questions constantly recurring in speculation about language and therefore likely to be of importance to the linguist when he is testing the appropriateness and adequacy of his theoretical constructs.

A linguistic treatise by one of the world's greatest poets is more likely than not to be ignored even in a fairly detailed review of the history of linguistics; it seems to have been completely ignored even by his contemporaries. Yet, one of the principal questions to which Dante addresses himself in the *De Vulgari Eloquentia* — the possible relationships between a standard language and its dialects — can hardly be said to have received satisfactory treatment in the six and a half centuries since he proposed it. The inadequacy of linguistics to deal with the problem in conventional terms has recently received striking illustration in the debate concerning the rise of Modern Standard Polish — a debate already half a century old, which, in the last few years, has led some of its participants to radical reviews of basic linguistic concepts [2]. Yet the general importance of the question and the wealth of disposable data are obvious to anyone who considers the rise and standardization of all the vernaculars in modern Europe. The relevance to linguistics — as opposed, for example, to sociology or history — if it needed demonstration, has certainly received it in the Polish discussions, most particularly in the beautiful and important monograph by Zenon Klemensiewicz on the varieties of contemporary Polish [2, pp. 178–241], which arose from those discussions and places them against a broad background of general linguistic theory. The specifically linguistic problem that is principally involved — the possibility of manifestation of a single pattern in a variety of regional and social, spoken and written, usages — turns out to require for its treatment a refined and universally applicable distinction of linguistic form and substance, such as conventional linguistics has not yet absorbed. Saussure's other distinction — between content and expression — comes into full play when the development of a standard language takes place under the strong influence of another language, as exemplified by some of the relationships of Latin to the modern European vernaculars, or, as most recently pointed out by Vladimir Nabokov in a discussion of translations from Pushkin [6], by a comparable relationship of French to Russian.

A more exotic example of an essentially similar range of problems was encountered a few years ago by Paul Garvin in his work on Ascension Island towards the establishment of a standard Ponapean. Here, as in many other such instances, the matter of writing introduced further complications. To return once again to the Polish example, which has required the most careful reexamination of a large amount of written material, it is worth observing that investigators who started with what would appear to be simple, straightforward, practical aims have been led to theoretical considerations of the broadest general interest. In particular, their experience confirms the suspicion that a linguistic theory will be inadequate for many of our purposes if it assumes that the phonetic substance is the only 'real' expression-substance of language and that all other candidates must, in some sense, be derived from it and remain dependent on it.

This view, which may fairly be described as still the predominant one among linguists and which is hotly defended whenever questioned, has most far-reaching consequences when it is incorporated in the foundations of a linguistic theory and thereby affects the form of a linguistic model. It has a venerable tradition. Aristotle, as is well known, identified the relationship of content to expression-in-speech with the relationship of the latter to expression-in-writing, and the *De Interpretatione* contains the locus classicus of that hypothesis. Given the restricted aims of comparative Indo-Germanic linguistics, the notion rendered positive service in clearing away irrelevancies from investigations which, by their very nature, had to be focused on the phonetic expression. The Romantic environment in which comparative linguistics developed no doubt had its effect as well. But clearly of more lasting importance has been the hope of maintaining for linguistics an anchor in a single, universal, and apparently immediately given material reality — a hope that continues to be reenforced as new attempts are made at establishing universally valid linguistic categories on the bases of physical science.

It will not be my purpose here to argue against this venerable tradition, despite the difficulties which, as I have indicated, seem to follow from it. I would merely suggest that the assignment of any special primacy to the phonetic substance of language is at best a superfluous axiom for linguistics and that, if we include it among our assumptions, we run the grave risk of blocking important lines of inquiry. A linguistic model that allows for the possibility of more than one linguistic substance (in this case, expression-substance) therefore has the enormous advantage of not prejudging a question that we can afford to leave open. Such an allowance both presupposes an anterior distinction between linguistic form and linguistic substance and helps us to establish natural and universally applicable boundaries between the two — that is, to isolate those relationships which will be admitted in the theory as constituents of purely formal definitions. This approach leaves open the possibility that the two commonly encountered expression-substances — those of speech and writing — may in particular instances turn out to be isomorphic. It also foresees the possibility that they may not and that more than one *form* of the expression may be in semantic relationship to a single content. As Louis Hjelmslev has pointed out, such a view finds correspondence in, and gives precision to, the intuitive identification of, say, written English and spoken English, where unity can be maintained in the content although the conventional written form is not a mere mapping of the spoken form on a graphic substance.

The history of individual languages will always be an important concern of the humanities, which must evaluate the linguistic documents of human expression and which must therefore have under control both philological tools for the understanding of texts and criteria for interesting comparison and judgment of the means of expression available at different times — the frames of possibility within which given texts make their appearance. If this sounds like a truism, one has only to consider the relationship — or, better to say, absence thereof — between the linguistic and literary parts of typical programs of graduate study in our universities. Where historical linguistics, continuing the main tradition of the last century, is reduced to a review of the evidence for genetic relationships between languages, the situation is understandable enough. The predominantly anecdotal and material character of such studies is enough to eliminate any possible contact with the rest of the program. Generations of English students sweat their way uncomprehendingly through the prescribed course of Gothic until a merciful Department eliminates the requirement — often salving its conscience by substituting a Latin reading examination. The fact that study of a language as a tool has thus replaced what was no doubt originally intended as an immanent study of language usually escapes attention and further testifies to the divorce between linguistics and literary research.

Structural linguistics — especially in recent years — has been developing in a much more propitious atmosphere so far as concerns its application to historical humanistic studies. It has become increasingly clear that "synchronic" and "descriptive" are not to be identified with "static" and that the once imagined cleft between descriptive and historical linguistics can be successfully bridged to the enrichment of both. From this point of view, variation within a single linguistic state — *état de langue* — can be given adequate recognition, and linguistic history becomes something quite different from anecdotal comparison of essentially unrelated systems. Place can also be found for the phenomena of linguistic convergence and those other non-genetic relationships between languages with which the older comparativism and a narrowly conceived descriptivism were helpless to deal. New vistas are being opened on a truly explicative historical and comparative linguistics — one that can relate the observed phenomena to a general scheme of possibilities and thereby even develop predictive powers.

Here again, a necessary condition seems to be a linguistic model so articulated as to reveal universally present and therefore comparable strata in language. Thus, these strata are indeed produced, in a sense, by our method of inquiry — "on dirait que c'est le point de vue qui crée l'objet", says Saussure [7, p. 23] — but by a method independent of contingent, arbitrary relationships found in any single language or language type. With the superior explicative power of such a model, it becomes possible to distinguish between shifts of formal pattern and shifts of substance and to base a rational history of linguistic change on the interactions of the two. Kuryłowicz's work on the Germanic consonant shifts [4] provides an especially interesting example of the fruitfulness of this approach, casting, as it does, new light on a classic problem of comparative linguistics, in the favored domain of traditional comparativism — the expression-substance. But on both sides of the linguistic sign — in the content as well as in the expression — the distinction between a formal, systematic pattern and a variety of usages in which the pattern is manifested proves its worth in explicating both the conservative and dynamic elements of language and describing their interplay. Linguistic history so conceived — especially as it addresses itself to the content side of language — has the brightest prospects of regaining a meaningful position within the humanities while strengthening its scientific foundations.

I have been concerned in these remarks with some questions of adequacy of linguistic theory — adequacy as tested by a small sample set of possible applications of linguistics. I have assumed that it is legitimate to look to linguistics for the solution — or, at least, for the main contribution to the solution — of the problems I have touched upon, problems of continuing and weighty import in the humanities. I hope I have made clear my view that the divorce of linguistics from the humanities — although a matter of mounting concern to linguists as well as non-linguists — is far from being the result of recent trends in linguistics. On the contrary, as I tried to suggest in my beginning remarks, it is in large measure traceable to a certain restricted methodology whose triumph was the outstanding characteristic of linguistic science in the last century. To the extent that modern linguistics has sought to regain lost ground by broadening its fundamental concepts, to study language in more than its material expression, and to study even its material expression under more than its genetic aspect, it has moved toward renewed contact with other branches of the humanities.[1] In so far as that renewed contact of which I speak has brought again to the attention of linguists long neglected aspects of the linguistic sign, their own immediate study of language, viewed in and for itself, has been demonstrably enriched.

This last point has, I hope, received some little illustration in the examples I have offered. In each instance, what I have tried to bring to the fore is the confrontation of variety and unity at certain points within linguistic phenomena — variety of usages, extending over both space and time, as opposed to a single, unifying pattern; variety of substances in the linguistic expression as contrasted with unity of distributionally defined form; variety of expression form in the face of a single content (for which examples are to be sought not merely in the differing written and spoken forms of individual languages, but also in the several language members of a single linguistic league). In my analyses of these examples, it will have been obvious how completely indebted I have been to Saussure's distinctions between content and expression, and linguistic form and linguistic substance, and to the development that those distinctions have received in glossematic theory. My purpose has not been, however, to argue in support of a particular linguistic theory but to urge that any adequate theory must find place for the type of interplay of linguistic strata that I have been discussing.

---

[1]And here we may profitably recall that it was a linguist — and one of the greatest — who said, in effect, that linguistics is too important to be left to the linguists alone; again I quote Saussure: "Plus évidente encore est l'importance de la linguistique pour la culture générale: . . . Il serait inadmissible que son étude restât l'affaire de quelques spécialistes . . ." [7, p. 21].

Taking "model" in the very simple sense of a schematic representation designed to set in relief important structural relationships within the represented object, I conclude that an adequate model of a language will be prominently articulated at such points of interplay between variety and unity and that the articulation we seek must be a universally applicable one, which alone can provide a rational basis of comparison between languages and thereby reveal the variety within unity that is human language itself.

References

[1] Arens, H. *Sprachwissenschaft.* Orbis Academicus I/6. München, 1955.

[2] Budzyk, K., ed. *Pochodzenie polskiego języka literackiego.* Studia staropolskie III. Wrocław, 1956.

[3] Hjelmslev, L. La Catégorie des cas, I. *Acta Jutlandica, Aarsskrift for Aarhus Universitet,* Vol. 7 (1935).

[4] Kuryłowicz, J. Le Sens des mutations consonantiques. *Lingua,* Vol. 1, pp. 77–85.

[5] Meillet, A. *Introduction à l'étude des langues indo-européennes.* Paris, 1937.

[6] Nabokov, V. The Servile Path. *On Translation,* R. A. Brower, ed., Cambridge, Massachusetts, 1959, pp. 97–110.

[7] Saussure, F. de. *Cours de linguistique générale*³, Paris, 1949.

SECTION

X

METHODOLOGY AND PHILOSOPHY OF HISTORICAL SCIENCES

SCIENTIFIC METHOD AND THE WORK OF THE HISTORIAN

G. BARRACLOUGH

University of London, London, England

Historians as a body have done little to clarify the position of their work in relation to science and to scientific method. Their attitude for the most part is that of craftsmen who are suspicious of theory and are perfectly satisfied with the product of their trade. [1] As a profession, they stand consciously on the borderline between the sciences and the humanities, veering in the direction of the latter and very conscious of the alleged dichotomy between natural science and humane studies. They are also intensely critical of the concept of social science and of the attempt to 'reduce' history (as historians would say) to the status of a social science. If a poll were to be taken, an overwhelming majority of professional historians today would be found to reject the notion that history can or should be classified with the sciences or that the methods of science and, still more, the purposes or objects of science are applicable to their work. On the other hand, it is evident that history does not fall into the same category as imaginative literature — or that, if it does, it will be bad history. In other words, if history is delimited against the sciences on the one side, it must be delimited against the arts on the other side; and for this reason the majority of historians assert that history is a discipline *sui juris* and *sui generis*, a discipline

[1]An attitude expressed to perfection in a remark in *History*, Vol. XLV (1960), p. 304: 'That philosophies of history have nothing to do with the historians' history is well known. It is however interesting to discover that modern philosophers have only trivialities to contribute to the understanding of the historian's activity'.

in its own right, distinct from other disciplines and possessing a methodology of its own. Historical method, they argue, is not simply a particular application of scientific method, but is a method devised by historians themselves from their own experience to cope with problems arising from the particular body of materials, or the particular evidences, with which history deals.

The purpose of this paper is to examine these attitudes, to see how far, if at all, they are justified, and to establish the points where they are in need of modification. The position I shall adopt is that of an intermediary seeking a reconciliation which can (I believe) only be beneficial to all parties. As a historian, I share the horror felt by the historical profession as a whole at what seems to us to be the attitude of social scientists to history. It seems to us that, for them, history is only material to be processed, and that they regard historians as purveyors of material for them to process; which, if true, reveals in our view a total misunderstanding of the abstruse and complex nature of historical 'fact'. Social scientists, we believe, are prepared to manipulate historical data in ways which historians regard as illegitimate; they seek results which we do not consider the material, of its nature, is capable of giving. On the other hand, if I dissociate myself from my profession, I feel the same sense of horror at the negative attitude most historians adopt towards the achievements of scientific thinking and at their failure to explore the possibilities which a scientific approach has to offer. It is certainly not true that the assimilation of history to science is a simple process which could be accomplished without difficulty but for the stubborn resistance of historians. On the contrary, it will need a great deal of patient analysis of historical data before we can decide what is, and what is not, susceptible of scientific analysis, and it is quite certain that a too hasty attempt to subject historical data to scientific manipulation will only result in the sort of gross simplification which, because of its pseudo-scientific character, is perhaps even more dangerous than plain falsification. Indeed, the resistance of historians is largely based on their belief that such attempts at scientific formulation as have been made so far, do not conform to observable historical fact. Furthermore, it would be absurd to push generalization or theoretization to extremes, as though it were the only object of historical study. History subserves a number of legitimate purposes; its human or educative value is not exhausted by the degree to which it can be brought within the scope of scientific or conceptional analysis, and there is no doubt that, unless the historian is left free to examine or re-examine particular situations for their own sake, without concerning himself with the further results which may, or may not, follow from their scientific analysis, this analysis itself will quickly be stultified. The immediate difficulty arises from the fact that the historian regards his work as consisting exclusively of the examination of particular situations, while the social scientist is concerned exclusively with the theoretical analysis of those situations. Hence the dichotomy to which I have referred, the belief that the historian and the scientist are following two different roads which never meet and which may even, some think, lead in different directions. The question is whether this dichotomy is real.

If we examine the arguments used by historians to prove to their own satisfaction that history is not a science and is not susceptible of scientific treatment, it needs little analysis to discover that they are a singular combination of subjective prejudices, ignorance, misunderstanding, and legitimate limitative considerations. Before we can assess them, it is necessary to analyse them into their constitutive elements and see what is and what is not valid. The most important single factor, without doubt, is a fundamental misconception of the nature of science, coupled with an outmoded view of nature and the universe due to the persistence of mechanistic and positivistic assumptions which scientists have long discarded. But anyone who has studied the relations of history and science as a historical problem will also be aware that, apart from avoidable misconceptions, there are deep psychological factors involved; and it is important to emphasize these psychological factors since, precisely because they are unconscious and irrational, they are perhaps the most stubborn obstacle of all. Much of the historical argument seems to be a rationalization of emotional prejudice, dating from the origins of the controversy in the middle of the nineteenth century, and owing something to the fact that it was closely associated with the even more virulent controversy then raging between science and religion. The depth of feeling aroused is revealed by the emotional terms in which the German historian Droysen attacked the attempts of Comte and Buckle to establish patterns of uniformity in human behaviour. He was, he proclaimed, defending human history against 'the polytechnical misery which since 1789 has fouled and dried up France', against a 'Babylonian mixture of dissoluteness and calculation'.[2] These are certainly not the terms of rational argument. What is significant, however, is that, whereas in the century that has followed, theology has successfully come to terms with science, historians are for the most part still defending the old positions.

The emotional content of the attack on Comte and Buckle is too obvious to need further elaboration.[3] Droysen believed that it was necessary to defend free will, as expressed in human history, against materialistic determinism. He believed that it was necessary to defend the dignity and individuality of man against any attempt to reduce his conduct to the terms of

---

[2]Cf. W. Kluback, *Wilhelm Dilthey's Philosophy of History* (New York, Columbia Univ. Press, 1956), p. 31.

[3]Nor should we think that this emotional reaction is merely a thing of the past. On the contrary, it seems to me to be discernible in such books as K. R. Popper, *The Poverty of Historicism* (London, Routledge & Kegan Paul, 1957), or Isaiah Berlin, *Historical Inevitability* (London, Oxford Univ. Press, 1954)—that is to say, their arguments seem to reflect the belief that scientific history is a bad thing, with bad consequences politically, and that it should be resisted as such, and not to spring from a simple desire to examine the possibility dispassionately. Whether they are right or wrong is, of course, irrelevant from this point of view.

scientific 'laws'. He believed also that it was necessary to defend German idealism against western, i.e., French and English, positivism and naturalism. And finally he believed that it was essential to insist on the moral factor which, in his view, was the distinguishing feature of the human species, on the power of the individual to make decisions which might change the course of events, and on the element of human responsibility; all of which, because they introduced an unpredictable voluntary element which was more than fortuitous or incidental, seemed to preclude scientific generalization. This rejection of scientific history sprang from the very heart of German idealism, and led through the teaching of Wilhelm Dilthey and Heinrich Rickert to the doctrine of historicism; indeed, the Swiss philosopher, Karl Heussi, refused to concede that 'historicism' was more than a convenient label to describe the particular attitudes of German historians at the turn of the nineteenth and twentieth centuries.[4] This fact of the German origins of historicism is not without importance. It explains why, as the influence of the German historical school penetrated to England and America,[5] the tenets of the German idealists — long since outmoded in philosophical thought — became and still remain the stock-in-trade of historians everywhere.

For Dilthey, as for others of the idealist school, the foundation of their rejection of scientific history was the contrast between *Natur* and *Geist,* between nature and spirit, and particularly between what they called *die Welt als Natur* and *die Welt als Geschichte* — that is to say, between the world with which natural science deals and the world with which history deals. The particular element that distinguished history from natural science, they held, was that history dealt with a moral world, a world of free judgements, which could not possibly be studied by means of statistics or causal 'laws', for such methods obliterated the creative role of the individual. History was concerned with the realm of the unique, of the spirit, and of change; natural science was concerned with the consistent, with the repeatable, and with the discovery of general principles. While science was interested in particular facts only for the sake of discovering or testing general laws, the historian was concerned with the evaluation of particular facts whose nature cannot be fully explained, if it can be explained at all, by general laws; his task, in short, was to appreciate individuality and value.[6]

The immediate consequences of this approach to history may be summarized as follows. First, it implies the denial of a systematic approach to history. Secondly, it rests upon the belief that the basic concepts of history are change and particularity. Thirdly, it leads to the conclusion that the primary aim of the historian is to make particular statements rather than to

---

[4]Cf. K. Heussi, *Die Krisis des Historismus* (Tübingen, 1932).

[5]Cf. G. P. Gooch, *History and Historians in the Nineteenth Century* (Longmans, London, 1913).

[6]For a recent restatement of these views, cf. H. G. Wood, *Freedom and Necessity in History* (London, Oxford Univ. Press, 1957), pp. 13 sqq.

assert general laws. The assertion of the ineffable particularity of historical events — with the corollary, emphasized by Dilthey, that they are therefore fundamentally different from natural events — has in practice four implications: (i) that the historian's business is to catch every shade and tone of individuality; (ii) that his concern must therefore be with minute detail (for how else can the inexhaustible meaning of events be elaborated?); (iii) that his instrument must be 'trained intuitive insight', since the mere 'facts' of history (including not merely documentary records but also all artefacts and relics, such as sculpture or architecture) are only an incomplete, fragmentary, external 'shell', which without 'intuitive insight' can give us no real understanding of 'the truly existing inner reality';[7] and finally (iv) that his essential task is to discover (in Ranke's well-worn phrase) *wie es eigentlich gewesen* — that is to say, to narrate and relate events rather than to generalize or draw 'lessons'.

It is impossible to criticize these arguments and assumptions in detail on this occasion. Nevertheless it may be questioned whether the underlying dichotomy between *Natur* and *Geist* and between history and natural science, on which they rest, is as compelling as its proponents appear to believe. Many branches of the natural sciences — botany, zoology, astronomy, geology, palaeontology, for example — deal with data which are essentially historical in character, and it would be necessary, in the first place, to determine where, if anywhere, they differ from the materials of the historian. It would seem that the view of science which historians resist reflects a mechanistic conception in which scientists no longer believe, and pays scant attention to the revolutionary changes in the conceptions of nature and of the universe which have so profoundly affected scientific thinking since the beginning of the present century. It can no longer be maintained, for example, that scientific theory is incompatible (if it ever was) with the concept of free will. More generally, it would be well if historians gave less attention to the 'exact' sciences and more to 'inexact' sciences, such as clinical medicine, which gets along without 'controlled experiment' and is yet quite clearly 'scientific'.[8] Nor is it clear that historical 'facts' — which, in reality, are not 'facts' at all, but verifiable statements about phenomena — are intrinsically different from the 'facts' with which science deals, or that the methods of arriving at them are intrinsically different either. Finally the argument of uniqueness — which is one of the main planks in the historicist argument — requires re-examination. It is certainly true that historical events are unique in the sense that they never repeat themselves and, since they take place in time, are irreversible and cannot be checked by experiment. The question is whether, as Dilthey appears to have believed, this is a special feature of historical events, distinguishing them from natural events. In fact, we all know that

---

[7]Cf. Kluback, *op. cit.*, pp. 60–62.

[8]As Crane Brinton has pointed out, *The Anatomy of Revolution* (New York, Vintage Books, 1959), pp. 12–13.

every drop of water and every grain of sand differs from every other drop of water and every other grain of sand, and that every penny struck from a mint turns out under microscopic examination to be an individual. It is probably equally true (though some of us may recoil from admitting it) that every tree of a species is as different from every other tree of the same species as one human being is from another, but this uniqueness does not prevent the botanist from making significant scientific generalizations.

There are thus good reasons for thinking that the barricade erected by historians between history and science is not so formidable as they have supposed. In fact, it is directed less against science than against pseudo-science — for example, against facile biological analogies which attempt to assimilate the history of a state or people or civilisation to the stages of the human life-cycle (childhood, youth, manhood, old age). It is directed against alleged 'laws' which are not based on empirical observation of historical data, but are introduced by analogy from outside — the argument, for example, that restoration cannot succeed because 'the life of peoples is not like the movement of a clock, which can be put back or forward at will, but proceeds according to a necessary inner natural law'.[9] No one is likely to quarrel with the rejection of analogies such as these; there has been too great a tendency to suppose that a metaphor is an adequate substitute for a conceptual scheme. But it is unfortunate that most historians seem to have believed that, in warding off the attacks of pseudo-science, they have disposed of the challenge of real science.

The historian's position is based on the distinction between the so-called 'nomothetic' and the so-called 'idiographic' principles[10] — that is to say, between methods designed to produce adequate theoretical generalization and methods designed to provide a full narrative description — and it is his case that his work can of its nature only be idiographic in character and that he has fully performed his function when he has given an accurate and comprehensive account of events. To go further, he would argue, would be to overstep the boundaries of his discipline. Whether, in the nature of historical knowledge, this ideal is capable of attainment, is a question which cannot be discussed here and now, though I believe that it is based on a number of dubious hypotheses. On the other hand, it is hard to see the validity of the arguments historians use to exclude nomothetic methods from their field of study. If, in Einstein's words, science is an 'attempt to make the chaotic diversity of our sense-experience correspond to a logically uniform system of thought' by correlating 'single experiences' with 'the theoretic structure',[11] we may legitimately ask what are the obstacles

[9]The example is taken from Lasaulx; cf. H. J. Schoeps, *Vorläufer Spenglers* (Leiden, E. J. Brill, 1955), p. 49.

[10]Cf. H. Meyerhoff, *The Philosophy of History in Our Time* (New York, Anchor Books, 1959), p. 203.

[11]Cited by O. F. Anderle, 'Theoretische Geschichte'. *Historische Zeitschrift,* Vol. 185 (1958), p. 28.

which prevent historians from proceeding in this way. The answer usually given is the immense complexity of human history, and still more the fact that, if we abstract from this complexity by isolating certain elements for study and examination — much as a scientist does in a model or in a controlled experiment — we cannot avoid falsifying the whole and thus robbing history of whatever value it possesses as a record of human experience. But this argument is more plausible than true. No more than the scientist is the historian capable of apprehending the whole of reality. He has no direct experience of the past and deals not directly with reality but with theoretical constructions. Inevitably he selects his evidence, whether he wants to or not; that is to say, he abstracts from the available body of material what seems to him relevant. There are thus good grounds for doubting whether the data or methods of the historian are intrinsically different from those of the scientist; and if that is the case, the whole theoretical argument for stopping short at an idiographical approach and refusing to proceed in the direction of nomothetic study becomes suspect. The result, in any case, seems to be that history has deliberately chosen to stop dead at a prescientific stage, or at the first and most rudimentary stage of science. The astronomer or the botanist collects the basic data, without which the progress of knowledge would be impossible, by observation or field-work; but then he goes on to use the data for the construction of theory. The same is true, in the realm of social science, of the archaeologist or the economist. Historians, on the other hand, because of their strict adherence to the idiographical principle, have so far not advanced from the first stage to the second; they have still to make the transition which comparable sciences, such as botany or zoology, had already made more than a century ago.[12] The explanation, beyond all reasonable doubt, is psychological: namely, the emotional revulsion against subjecting the human species to the same sort of theoretical analysis to which it seems legitimate to subject other living things.

The choice which the historian makes between the idiographic and the nomothetic approach — in particular, his refusal to proceed from descriptive narrative to theoretical construction — is not, as Dilthey and others sought to demonstrate, imposed upon him by the nature of his materials. It is a purely voluntary choice.[13] It is not difficult to show that there is no essential difference, in this respect, between the material the historian uses and the material the natural scientist uses. The difference lies in the emphasis placed by the observer on the elements of individuality. In the one case, individuality is usually reduced to a minimum, discounted, controlled and so far as possible excluded; in the other, it is picked out and emphasized. Nor can we say that the historian, in choosing to emphasize the unique and

---

[12]*Ibid.*, pp. 30–31.

[13]*Ibid.*, p. 28; cf. also P. Gardiner, *The Nature of Historical Explanation* (Oxford Univ. Press, 1952), pp. 44, 64.

the individual, is not within his rights. In fact, the emphasis on individuality, which became characteristic of the development of historical scholarship in the nineteenth century, reflected a justified reaction against the vague and platitudinous generalizations which historians of the Enlightenment had served up as the sum of historical knowledge, and no sensible person would question the gains which it brought with it. It provided, beyond doubt, a new awareness of the richness of man's experience, a fuller appreciation of the variety of human endeavour and achievement; and it is far from likely that such an enrichment would have been secured by a generalizing and theoretical approach. In other words, it would be a mistake to think that the model of hypothetico-deductive explanation characteristic of the natural sciences exhausts the potentialities of history and that no other approach is worthy of consideration.[14] On the contrary, it seems to me that it is for the historian to decide on purely pragmatical grounds what approach and methodology will give the best results in any particular case. The case against the current preoccupation of historians with narrative and description is that it unnecessarily narrows and restricts the scope of historical work by excluding certain well-defined historical phenomena which are not susceptible of treatment by ordinary descriptive processes. Among these one may instance such recurrent themes as dictatorship or revolution, such questions as whether, in the different civilisations of the world, the peak of political power is or is not simultaneous with the fruitful moments of artistic creation, such problems as the consequences of the supersession of an aristocratic by a middle-class society or the effects on the latter of the rise of the fourth estate. Questions such as these are not, as some historians appear to think, merely the fanciful speculations of dilettantes.[15] On the contrary, they are serious questions, the answers to which (if there are answers) lie embedded in history. But any attempt to answer them necessitates a shift in the focus of historical thinking away from the idiographic to the nomothetic; it necessitates the development of historical methodology in directions which can only be described as scientific. That is to say, it requires a search for uniformities within the chaotic diversity of recorded history; it requires emphasis on 'constants' as opposed to 'variables'; and it requires at least something in the nature of a model, though it will not, at any rate for the foreseeable future, be the precise mathematical model of the sociologist.

Nevertheless it would be a serious mistake to overlook the limitations within which such a process of adaptation is possible. As I indicated at the beginning, history stands at the frontier of science, perhaps in a nebulous frontier zone where scientific and non-scientific approaches to knowledge mix and mingle. It is by no means self-evident that human behaviour can be

---

[14]As was pointed out in the paper contributed to the Congress by L. O. Mink (*Abstracts of Contributed Papers*, p. 152).

[15]Cf. Joseph Vogt, *Geschichte des Altertums und Universalgeschichte* (Wiesbaden, Steiner, 1957), pp. 30–31.

explained in the same way as other phenomena can;[16] at this stage we shall do well to treat this as an open question which needs far more critical analysis than it has hitherto received. No one with practical experience of handling historical data would deny that the varying and conflicting relationships between the habits and desires of individuals and groups of individuals are so complex that mathematical treatment would not seem to offer much hope of significant results;[17] it would need, to be successful, a more accurate grasp of more numerous variables than we can at present command, and — many historians would add — than in the nature of historical knowledge we can hope to command. It might, for example, be possible to set up a model expressing the notion 'revolution'; but it seems clear that such a model, if it were to be an adequate representation of the observable phenomena, would need to be so general and so indeterminate that it is not easy to see what useful purpose it would serve. Certainly it is impossible to believe that it would extend to the possibility of prediction — in other words, that any conceivable amount of knowledge of past revolutions would enable us to predict the course of the next revolution, still less its incidence, except perhaps in so general a way that it would be quite useless for practical purposes (for example, in indicating to the State Department at the close of 1958 what course the Cuban revolution would take and therefore what course to adopt towards Castro). That does not mean, however, that it is fanciful and useless to attempt to discover uniformities in history, but simply that we must be aware of their limitations. It is quite certain that they will never amount to cast-iron (or even to malleable iron) laws; but there is no inherent reason why they should not perform the same sort of function for the social sciences as Keynes' General Theory of Money performs for the economist. No amount of historical analysis could have foretold that Castro *would* nationalize the Cuban sugar plantations, though it could easily have foretold that he *might*; but there is no reason why it should not have resulted in a useful clarification of possible situations.

In practice no historian, whatever his dogmatic position may be, can avoid the sort of theoretisation which is the foundation of a scientific approach. Even the Dutch historian, Geyl, the most outspoken contemporary critic of scientific history,[18] had no hesitation in writing a history of the Netherlands, although the term 'the Netherlands' is a distinctly ambiguous theoretical construction.[19] Similarly Dilthey himself wrote of Frederick the Great's relationship to the German Enlightenment, although the very conception of a German Enlightenment is a generalization, or theory, not a concrete historical fact. Without conceptualization, in fact, there could be

---

[16]Cf. Donald Davidson's conclusion, *Abstracts of Contributed Papers*, p. 74.

[17]Cf. D. E. Butler, *The Study of Political Behaviour* (London, Hutchinson, 1958), p. 35; Brinton, *op. cit.*, p. 38.

[18]Cf. P. Geyl, *Debates with Historians* (Groningen, Wolters, 1955).

[19]Cf. Anderle, *op. cit.*, p. 38.

no useful ordering of historical data.[20] As a consequence of the historian's suspicions of scientific method, however, the concepts he necessarily uses are all too often both unscientific and unconvincing. This is illustrated, for example, by his loose, untechnical and therefore unsatisfactory use of the word 'revolution' — the Roman revolution, the English revolution, the French revolution, the American revolution, the industrial revolution, the scientific revolution, etc. — which is too imprecise to be helpful as a principle of classification. And it may be said of Arnold Toynbee that, although he is commonly attacked by historians for 'scientism'[21] — that is, for allegedly inappropriate attempts to apply scientific principles to history — the really effective criticism is that his methods are unscientific: in other words, that, instead of applying a rigorous methodology to his study of the past, he has simply dressed up intuitions and analogies in pseudo-scientific terms. When we are told that we have not advanced far enough in knowledge for an attempt to construct a general theory of human history to be feasible, it might be more correct to reply that what makes such general theories dangerous and unsatisfactory at present is, on the contrary, that historians have not advanced far enough in scientific method. The idealist tradition of history, in spite of its incomparable enrichment of our view of the past, has resulted in a decidedly one-sided development. History is there to explain as well as to narrate; it is there to cast light on man's destiny against the background of what we can discover of his previous activities. It would be absurd to suggest that this task can be achieved as simply or as swiftly as Comte or Buckle appears to have thought. No educated person today would echo Buckle's belief that 'the progress of every people is regulated by principles — or, as they are called, laws — as regular and certain as those which govern the physical world'.[22] But when he went on to state that, whereas 'in all the other great fields of enquiry, the necessity of generalization is universally admitted', among historians 'a strange idea prevails that their business is merely to relate events', he was saying something true and important. And he was not entirely unjustified when he added that, in consequence, 'for all the higher purposes of human thought, history is still miserably deficient'.[23]

Generalization, as Buckle termed it, is not, of course, synonymous with scientific method; but it is surely the foundation of scientific method, and it is from this foundation that we must build. In other words, the first step is to secure from historians the admission that generalizing history is as valid as individualizing history, and to persuade them of the legitimacy and the value

[20]Even a purely chronological ordering requires periodization, with all its attendant problems, before it can be useful.

[21]Cf. *Toynbee and History,* ed. M. F. Ashley Montagu (Boston, 1956), p. 201.

[22]Cf. G. St. Aubyn, *A Victorian Eminence. The Life and Works of Henry Thomas Buckle* (London, Barrie, 1958), p. 6.

[23]*Ibid.*, p. 113.

of proceeding on this basis. Once they do this, we shall be able to test how far in this direction we can go. As Mr. Mink has pertinently observed,[24] it is little use setting up Hempelian models if historians are going to ignore them entirely, as in fact they have done. On the other hand, Mr. Wittenberg is surely right in insisting that questions such as the one we are here concerned with — namely, whether history is or is not susceptible of scientific treatment — will not be decided aprioristically but 'only by a slow and gradual appraisal' of the question 'on its merits'.[25] For myself, I believe that, within limits, generalizing and theoretical and scientific history is possible, and I also believe that it is a necessary step forward. But I have no doubt that there are limits. In the first place, as I have already indicated, it is only one of many types of history, not higher than others, but different and offering different results, and there seems no reason why historians should not pursue other paths if they believe that they have something to offer. If, for example, we take the view that the purpose of history is to reconstruct or recreate or relive a whole phase or period of past reality — to convey (as is sometimes said) the flavour of an epoch — then there would seem to be little scope for science. Instead, we shall rely on the historian's sensitivity, on his feeling for the past, on his trained intuition, on his familiarity with all facets of an age. But that is not the task historians normally set themselves. Usually they set out to investigate a particular concrete set of circumstances, which for this purpose they abstract (like the scientist) from reality, isolating for purposes of study a series of phenomena which are not isolated in nature. Here, quite clearly, the methods of the historian and the methods of the scientist are not basically dissimilar. As Herbert Butterfield once suggested,[26] the historian who seeks to discover what was the effect of the influx of American silver in Elizabethan England is in much the same position as the physicist who asks what is the pressure of steam that a given task will require in a given engine. If we were to start with limited practical questions such as this, instead of with the wider controversial issues, many unnecessary disagreements might be avoided, and I believe that, on this empirical basis, gradually widening our ground as we proceed, it should not be impossible to arrive in time at the maximum approximation between history and science which is possible. But the ultimate criterion must always be the increase of historical understanding. In so far as it increases historical understanding, the application of scientific method is to be welcomed; where it does not, or where it impedes it, it must be rejected. For the present, however, I believe that history has lost more than it has gained from the reluctance of historians to adopt a scientific approach, and that there are new dimensions of history waiting to be discovered by those who have the courage to seek new ways.

---

[24]In the paper referred to above, note 14.

[25]*Abstracts of Contributed Papers*, p. 70.

[26]H. Butterfield, *Man on His Past* (Cambridge Univ. Press, 1955), p. 14.

THE HISTORIAN'S PROBLEM OF SELECTION

WILLIAM DRAY

University of Toronto, Toronto, Ontario, Canada

I

When the problem of the possibility of "objectivity" in historical enquiry is raised, there is a well-known argument which any tyro can be depended upon to produce for the "nays". This argument, in spite of its venerability, has in recent writings by critical philosophers of history, fallen on evil days. It is the aim of this paper to present considerations in support of its rehabilitation.

The substance of the argument is the claim that the historian "always selects". No historian, we are reminded, can pack into his narrative all that he knows about the object of his enquiry; he can tell us only what he thinks important; and what he tells us thus has implicit in it a certain standard of value. As Beard puts it: "Every written history . . . is a selection and arrangement of facts, . . . an act of choice, conviction, and interpretation respecting values".[1] If true, it should be noted, this would appear to be more than just a *fact* about the way history happens to be written; it seems rather to be a necessary *predicament* of historical enquiry as such. To put it somewhat pretentiously, what we are being told is that the very "idea" of history is such that evaluation of what is known is required for the construction of the finished narrative. And since what is generally meant by an "objective" enquiry is incompatible with the notion of an "evaluative" one, the very suggestion that historians should strive towards objectivity, even as an ideal, must be utterly misconceived.

There is a simple reply to this kind of argument which is sometimes thought to put it immediately out of court. For it might be pointed out that history is not unique in being selective. Indeed, in some sense or other, *all* enquiries are surely selective, including physical science; and it is by *contrast* with the latter that history is usually described as evaluative, and hence non-objective. Yet although it is certainly useful to insist on this — as Christopher Blake and Professor John Passmore have recently done[2] — I do not think that by doing so we dispose of the present argument. For I think it can be shown that the historian's problem of selection is significantly different from that of the generalizing sciences. In considering this claim, let me ask you to take note of two distinctions.

The first is a distinction between the selection of a *problem* for study and the selection of what is offered as its *solution*. Philosophers who deny the

---

[1] "Written History as an Act of Faith", reprinted in H. Meyerhoff, *The Philosophy of History in Our Time* (New York, 1959), p. 141.

[2] "Can History be Objective?", *Mind*, January 1955; "The Objectivity of History", *Philosophy*, April, 1958.

objectivity of history often talk as if it were selection of the first kind which renders the resulting narrative non-objective. We are told by Dewey, for example, that all history is "relative to a problem", and that problems vary with historians.[3] And it is doubtless true that for different people it is different aspects of what happened which raise questions — the asking of different questions indicating a difference of evaluation on their part, if only with respect to what Professor Lovejoy has called the "extremely important and rather neglected" value of "interestingness".[4] When we ask whether historical *enquiry* is value-free however, our concern is surely not with this kind of variability. For if different histories are written in answer to different questions, the different evaluations of the historian will be ingredient, not in the enquiry itself, but in the *choice* of the enquiry. It is when historians give different answers to the *same* questions that the problem of objectivity *within* the enquiry arises. And it is only with respects to this that we should seek a contrast with allegedly "objective" types of enquiry — since they also require us to choose our questions.

Now I think it is clear that historians *do* give different answers to the same questions; and, unlike physical scientists, who also, of course, from time to time disagree, they do this in circumstances where the difference between them is attributable to a difference of value-judgment. In arguing for this contention, I think it will be helpful to draw a second distinction, this time between two kinds of historical writing. The first I shall call *explanatory*, the second *descriptive*. Perhaps the distinction will not be found unambiguously exemplified in any actual histories. But Cecil Woodham-Smith's *The Reason Why* (which explores the background to the charge of the Light Brigade) and Gibbon's *Decline and Fall of the Roman Empire* may serve as examples of predominantly explanatory histories, while G. M. Young's *Victorian England: Portrait of an Age* or Carlton Hayes' *Generation of Materialism* (which offers a general survey of European history during the last three decades of the nineteenth century) may serve as examples of predominantly descriptive ones. I draw this distinction because the problem of selecting answers or solutions seems to me to arise in a somewhat different way in each. I draw it also because if there is any case at all for saying that historians ought not to allow their value-judgments to affect the answering, by contrast with the asking, of their questions, that case seems to me to be limited to histories of the explanatory sort.

What I have just said about explanatory histories will appear most acceptable to anyone who accepts a certain widely held theory of what it is to give an explanation. On this theory, to explain something is to indicate those antecedent conditions from which what happened could have been predicted, with the help of known general laws or theories. The explanation, then, is given, ideally, by the specification of a set of conditions which are

---

[3] "Historical Judgments", reprinted in Meyerhoff, *op. cit.*, p. 165.

[4] "Present Standpoints and Past History", reprinted in Meyerhoff, *op. cit.*, pp. 175–6.

jointly sufficient for what occurred. On such a view, if disagreements about what is to be included in an explanatory account occur, they cannot legitimately have anything to do with the different interests or values of the historians concerned. For the issue will simply be whether what each historian includes was really among those conditions which together constituted the sufficient set. And this, it will be said, is a question to be settled by reference to appropriate general knowledge about the subject matter. If such knowledge is in a bad way — as is frequently the case in social studies — then disagreements may certainly be traceable to differences of judgment on the part of historians. But the judgment concerned will not be a *value*-judgment.

Now, for a number of reasons, I am far from satisfied with the theory of explanation just referred to — at any rate as an explication of a concept supposed to be employed in histories like those cited above as "explanatory". And I suspect, too, that a careful examination of the structure, presuppositions, and implications of explanations as they are actually offered in historical enquiry would make it difficult to claim that explanatory history is free from the value-judgment of the enquirer.[5] Let me admit, however, that if the above-mentioned account of what it is to explain something *were* accepted by historians, then there would be a non-evaluative criterion of selection for explanatory histories. For the point I want to emphasize in this paper is that, even for a person who held such a view, no similar solution of the problem is possible in the case of *descriptive* histories. It may, of course, be unrealistic in practice to expect historians, in offering explanations, to outline sets of jointly sufficient conditions; but the notion of such a set does at least offer an ideal of objective selection which could *conceivably* be realized. There is no corresponding ideal of selection for descriptive histories which could conceivably be realized. For the only candidate would appear to be the notion of a "complete description". And this is something which it is, in principle, impossible to give. That is not to say, of course, that the historian is not provided by his question with certain non-evaluative criteria of what can be *ruled out*. If he is writing a history of England, for example, there is no problem about whether to select an event which occurred in China during the fourth century B.C.; and if he is writing an economic history, he need not consider the claims of, say, a regligious revival, except insofar as he considers it a condition of an economic event already selected. But a history is not composed of everything that is left over when such negative criteria have been applied. It is an essential part of the historian's task to determine what shall be *ruled in*.

II

There is an objection to what I have just said about the "open-endedness" of historical description which has seemed to many philosophers to destroy

[5]See, e.g., my *Laws and Explanation in History* (Oxford, 1957), p. 100.

any implications for the problem of objectivity. Professors Lovejoy and Nagel, for example, contend that if two historians — in the absence of any obligatory criterion — make two different selections out of what is known in producing their accounts of the same subject, we do not need to conclude that either of them necessarily writes a false account.[6] Nor, for that matter, do we need to regard them as contradicting each other. On the contrary, so long as their different accounts are constructed entirely out of true statements, these accounts will supplement each other. If they do this, there seems to be something inappropriate about our considering them as offering competing answers to the same question. Their answers are better regarded as providing "contributions" to the history of the subject under investigation. And it may plausibly be claimed that this is all any self-respecting historian really hopes to do.

What makes such a rebuttal unsatisfactory, I think — in spite of its grain of truth — is the assumption it seems to make about the general nature of the problem of a descriptive history. Let us admit, with Dewey, that in some sense all historical enquiry is "relative to a problem". But the problem of a descriptive historian writing, say, a history of England, is not correctly formulated by such questions as "What are some of the things that happened in England?", or "What are some of the things that happened to Englishmen?" His problem is to relate the *significant* or *important* things which happened in England or to Englishmen — having regard, of course, to the limits of *scale* imposed by a dozen paragraphs, three hundred pages, or ten volumes, as the case may be, and perhaps some other limits as well. That historians really do accept such a tougher obligation is shown by their recognition of the legitimacy of a comparison between two differing accounts of the same subject, in terms of the "adequacy" of each. One can certainly be judged "better" than the other, and one can be so bad, without containing any false statements, that it becomes distorted; it no longer gives a "true picture". What, for example, should we think of a one-volume "portrait" of Victorian England that ignored the working-class movement? Or a history of Nazi Germany which failed to mention the mass murder of the Jews? On the view which I am rejecting, however, it should be sufficient excuse for the author simply to say, if challenged: "One can't include everything". And it is clear that this would not, in itself, be sufficient excuse. It would be necessary to show that what was included was *more* important. Thus descriptive history is a type of enquiry which cannot escape the obligation to distinguish between what is important and what is not. This obligation, furthermore, arises *in the course of*, not just *in the choice of*, the enquiry; it is concerned with the answering, not the asking, of questions.

To this it will doubtless be objected that one might agree with the dictum without conceding the point at issue — namely, that the enquiry must be

---

[6]*Op. cit.*, p. 182; "The Logic of Historical Analysis", reprinted in Meyerhoff, *op. cit.*, p. 210.

evaluative. For it might be argued (on the assumption — which we shall not question here — that causal judgment is value-free) that "importance" is a causal notion. And it might be claimed that the descriptive historian, like the explanatory, will therefore find the importance of each item of his narrative in its causal connection with other things.

Now it is obvious that the term "important", as applied within historical studies, is often open to such a causal interpretation. Even in descriptive histories, we may expect to find events judged important enough to be mentioned, whose status depends, not upon any *intrinsic* importance, but upon their importance *for* other events. But to say that this *must* be the principle of selection in a history that sets out to describe squares neither with the notion of description, nor with our expectations of historians, nor with their own normal practice. In a history of Victorian England, for example, the working-class movement may indeed be referred to because of its influence, say, on the political transition from liberalism to socialism; but it may equally well warrant a place in the story because it shows what human beings, challenged by the social chaos of industrialism, can do; and as such it may be judged *intrinsically* interesting. Similarly, reference to the mass murder of Jews may be helpful in explaining the functioning of the upper echelons of the Nazi Party and government; but even if it were not, it would have a claim to be mentioned because of its intrinsic importance as a monument of human depravity. Selection in history may indeed be "relative to a problem"; but the problem in descriptive history is, at least in part, to find out what is *worth* noticing. And what makes an event worth noticing does not *have* to be its tendency to produce something else.

Let me remark in this connection that even where an event or action described can hardly claim *in itself* to be intrinsically important, the criterion of relevance applied to it will not necessarily be a *causal* one — at any rate, not in the straightforward way considered so far. "More immediately significant than the growth of population," writes G. M. Young of early Victorian England, "was its aggregation in great towns."[7] What kind of significance is this? Not causal, surely; for Young's point is not that this aggregation *led* to something else. The significance lies, in this case, in the fact that the concentration of population was *part* of a new pattern of life which Young is trying to depict and characterize; it is significant, no doubt, in relation to something else — but that something is the whole social complex which is being contrasted here with what is referred to as an earlier "rural and patrician" way of life.

Against this, it may perhaps be objected that even if the criterion in such a case is not a causal one, it is clearly not evaluative either. The reason Young brings in the part — the population concentration — is because he is talking about the whole, the industrialization of England, or something of the kind. It may further be argued that what I say is mentioned because of

[7] *Op. cit.*, p. 21.

intrinsic importance — the industrialization — is itself non-evaluatively determined by the subject of the enquiry — Victorian England (or perhaps certain selected aspects of it). The force of the objection is thus to transfer the historian's evaluation from his selection of an answer to the question "What was Victorian England like?", to his selection of questions to ask about his object of enquiry, Victorian England. And the latter would involve only a kind of ingredient value-judgment which we have already ruled out of consideration as common to all enquiry.

In considering this objection, let me draw a further distinction between kinds of histories — this time within the descriptive class. The distinction is between what I shall call *theme* histories and *period* histories. Typical of the former is G. M. Trevelyan's *The English Revolution*. Typical of the latter are the descriptive histories by Young and Hayes which I have already mentioned. The basis of the distinction is that a theme history has a subject determined by the sort of unity which makes us call it a single event, movement, state of affairs, etc., whereas the subject of a period history is determined chiefly by spatio-temporal criteria. The limiting case of period history is universal history. It is sometimes objected that it is impossible to enquire about history-as-a-whole, on the ground that history is not a whole.[8] But this is to assume that only theme histories are legitimate. To assert the possibility of a study of history-as-a-whole does not imply that history is a whole of some kind apart from being history-as-a-whole. The assertion that history is a whole — which amounts to the assertion that all historical events of a certain scale of intrinsic importance form a single pattern, whether causal, purposive, or dramatic — is either an unlikely empirical hypothesis of historians, or a dubious *a priori* thesis of certain speculative philosophers of history. The attempt to write universal history of the period type, on the other hand, seems to face no problem except that of finding out enough to make it worth attempting.

Whatever we say about universal history, I think it is clear that Young's history is of the period type; its subject is defined by reference to the reign of Queen Victoria. It is quite possible, of course, that Young decided to write his history because he saw some kind of unity in the period. But having selected this subject, he is bound to convey to us only as much of this unity as a balanced "portrait" of the period warrants. The point is even clearer in the case of Hayes. For in his case, the very title of his book, *A Generation of Materialism*, may arouse the expectation that his history will have a thematic unity, as the exploration of the manifestations of a certain frame of mind or outlook. To think, however, that Hayes begins with the *topic*, "The Materialistic Generation of the Nineteenth Century", is to get the logical force of what he is telling us all wrong. "A Generation of Materialism" is not the specification of the subject of his enquiry; it is his considered description-

[8]E.g., J. H. Randall Jr., *Nature and Historical Experience* (New York, 1958), p. 39.

cum-assessment of it in a nutshell. He does not begin by setting himself the problem of describing something which stands out as a social unity. He begins, rather, by *looking for* unity in his period. If he had not found it, or had found many such themes, he would not in any sense have lost his grip upon his subject — although he might then have had to call his book simply "Europe in the Late Nineteenth Century". This interpretation, incidentally, finds an echo in the following instruction from his editor. Within the prescribed decades, he is told, the task of the work is to make clear "the main movements in European History".[9]

Now if it is allowed that the selection of "main movements", the criteria for which are not supplied by the specification of the subject of enquiry, involves the historian's use of value-judgments, and if it is allowed that it is legitimate to attempt the construction of histories of the period type at all, then the thesis of the present paper is established. I do not see how anyone could want to deny the first of these contentions. The second is, admittedly, sometimes brought into question. It seems to be on the ground, for example, that a projected "History of England" would have no unity of theme, and thus would be what we have called a period history in disguise, that Professor John Passmore declares: "there is no such subject of enquiry as the history of England". This is, he adds, a "preposterous" title for a book.[10] It seems to me, however, that any theory of history which results in the ruling out of such constructions is a preposterous theory of history. Furthermore, if it owes any of its attractiveness to the belief that theme histories, at least, can be constructed without *any* judgments of intrinsic importance, it seems to rest upon an illusion; for a historian of the French Revolution, for example, cannot determine what to include, non-evaluatively, from the fact that the event is a revolution and French and began in 1789. But this additional claim is not necessary for present purposes, and I shall not press it further here.

III

I have argued that historical enquiry is, in principle, at least covertly evaluative; and that since this is due to the kind of question the historian asks, this ingredient evaluation can be said to be derived from the "idea" of history itself. In the remaining space at my disposal, let me try to anticipate a misunderstanding that may arise in some quarters: a misunderstanding due to a feeling that what I have been talking about is history, not as science, but as literature.

The distinction between history as science and history as literature is one which is often drawn. The implication seems to be that verified statements that certain events occurred, and that their causes were such-and-so, can all be encompassed in the notion of "scientific history", while whatever

---

[9]Hayes, *op. cit.*, p. x.
[10]*Op. cit.*, p. 103.

is found in history books which goes in any way beyond this must be attributed to the fact that historians are also literary artists. At worst, this may simply mean that since there is at least a limited market for the sort of thing they find out, and since historians can seldom resist the temptation to "write up" their discoveries for sale, we must expect to find their conclusions generously garnished with purple passages and sprinkled with striking value-judgments, which are really extraneous to historical *enquiry* properly so-called. At best, it may mean that after historians have found out whatever it is their business to find out, *qua* historians, they generally accept it as a professional obligation to pay some attention to the problem of how best to express it; and this, of course, is a *literary* problem. It is this latter way of putting it that one finds, for example, in Trevelyan's many defences of the thesis that Clio is a Muse. History, says he, is the accumulation, interpretation, and *exposition* of facts about the past "in their full emotional and intellectual value to a wide public by the difficult art of literature".[11]

Now *of course* historians, when they come to present their conclusions, have some purely literary problems. It might be noted, furthermore, in view of our present interest in the argument from selection, that such problems are not confined, either, to questions of what *words* or *style* to employ; they can involve the question of *what* to mention as well as *how* to mention it. Note, for example, G. M. Young's selection of the following incident in the course of a discussion of the unhappy relations between England and Ireland in the mid-nineteenth century: the adventures of a certain Smith O'Brien, who, as a strong supporter of Corn Law Repeal, "was caught levying war on the Queen's Majesty in the widow McCormack's cabbage garden. The campaign," we are told, "was brief, as O'Brien had forgotten to provide his army with anything to eat. He was sentenced to the usual penalty, which was at once commuted to transportation. With the maddening logic which Irishmen have at command," Young adds, "he argued that as he had not been convicted of anything deserving transportation, he must be pardoned or he must be hanged. The Law Officers admitted his contention, and a short Act had to be passed providing that . . . O'Brien and others in like case might lawfully be required to remain alive."[12] Now how did O'Brien get into a "portrait" of Victorian England that runs to less than two hundred pages? His intrinsic importance was obviously small; and his effect — say, on the course of English legislation — was not much larger. It is what Young calls the "Irish tragedy" that confers significance upon him; a tragedy of which he was neither cause, nor significant part. His adventures belong to the "story" of Victorian England because of what they *represent* — because of what, in the literary judgment of the historian, his case will convey to the reader.

It is important, however, to keep firmly in mind the difference between

---

[11] "Clio Rediscovered", in F. Stern, *The Varieties of History* (New York, 1956), p. 230.

[12] *Op. cit.*, pp. 46–7.

such *literary problems of history* and *problems of "literary" history* — if we are going to retain that rather unhappy expression for the kind of enquiry represented by the books to which this paper has appealed. The historian's evaluative *assessment* of his subject matter seems to fall *between* what is generally meant by those who distinguish between history as science and history as literature. And it is something which, in spite of Trevelyan's definition, falls within historical *enquiry*, in a sense in which literary problems do not; it is something properly represented as the historian's *conclusion*, something found out, something the reader wants to know. This claim, of course, and indeed this whole paper, depends upon a big assumption, which many will perhaps think me very naïve to have made. This assumption is that just as it is the purpose of engineering to design devices, and the purpose of science to discover laws and to elaborate theories, so it is the purpose of historical enquiry to construct histories.

SECTION

XI

HISTORY OF LOGIC, METHODOLOGY, AND PHILOSOPHY OF SCIENCE

REMARKS ON THE ROLE OF QUANTITY, QUALITY, AND RELATIONS IN THE HISTORY OF LOGIC, METHODOLOGY AND PHILOSOPHY OF SCIENCE

JOSEPH T. CLARK, S.J.

Canisius College, Buffalo, New York, U.S.A.

I

The analytic historian first observes that one of the two major foundation crises in Greek mathematics arose from the collapse of an older theory of proportion. This theory had erred not only in treating different magnitude types separately and so not rising to an abstract theory of proportionality at all, but also in a second way more fundamental still. Thus the magnitude pair (A, B) was formerly held to be proportional to the magnitude pair (C, D) if and only if at least one pair of natural numbers, x, y, existed such that simultaneously $xA = yB$ and $xC = yD$. If A and C are the sides and B and D the diagonals of two squares, this definition was discovered by the Pythagoreans to break down. For no such x and y exist. Two remedies for the debacle were discovered. The earlier and soon superseded revision made (A, B) and (C, D) lie in the same ratio if they had the same *antaneiresis*, or if their continued fractions had the same partial quotient sequence. This revision worked with rectilinear figures but less well with curvilinear figures and other types of magnitude. The later remedy was the theory of proportion created by Eudoxos (410—356 B.C.), enshrined in Book V of Euclid (325), and expounded indeed by all the historians of Greek mathematics. But it is at least questionable whether these standard expositions disclose clearly and decisively the precise elements therein which illuminate crucial problem areas for the philosopher of mathematics.

The class C to which Eudoxos applies what is in effect an isoid or equivalence process consists of all pairs of magnitudes (A, B), such as meet the following two conditions: (i) A and B are of the same type, e.g., both are lengths or both are durations, (ii) at least one natural number n exists such that $nA > B$. The further change introduced by Eudoxos in the Pythagorean test for proportionality was profound but not spectacular. He too compared xA with yB and xC with yD. But instead of requiring that some single pair of natural numbers, x, y, render once and for all and simultaneously $xA = yB$ and $xC = yD$, he stipulated that for any arbitrary x and y *either* simultaneously $xA > yB$ and $xC > yD$, *or* simultaneously $xA = yB$ and $xC = yD$, *or* simultaneously $xA < yB$ and $xC < yD$.

The first criterion for the success of this Eudoxian revision is that what was proportional in fact before remains proportional still. But more significant for our analytical purposes is the *isoid* character of the relation that Eudoxos establishes between one magnitude pair and another. The above corresponding simultaneities provide automatically for the relational characters of reflexivity and symmetry. But transitivity is still to be established. And this is in no sense a trivial requirement. For it demands nothing less than that '$xA >, = , < yB$ according as $xC >, =, < yD$ for any arbitrary x and y,' and '$sC >, =, < tD$ according as $sE >, =, < tF$ for any arbitrary s and t,' jointly entail '$pA >, =, < qB$ according as $pE >, =, < qF$ for any arbitrary p and q.' But this complex requirement Eudoxos correctly establishes in Proposition 11 of Book V of Euclid's *Elements*.

If in the context of its literate use by Eudoxos one translates *logos* as 'ratio class,' this proposition asserts and proves with finitist avoidance of transfinitist difficulties that if (A, B) and (C, D) are in the same ratio class and if (C, D) and (E, F) are in the same ratio class, then will (A, B) and (E, F) be in the same ratio class. Moreover it appears that the Eudoxian theory of ratio classes may have admitted pairs of integers to the classificanda so that the *classes* containing the pairs (2,1) and (3,1) and generally $(n, 1)$ were known, if not to be fully isomorph to the natural numbers 2, 3, and generally n, then at least in some ways to correspond to them.

Eudoxos proceeds further and establishes a relation of linear order among his ratio *classes*. Thus $(A, B) > (C, D)$ in a consciously new and different sense of '$>$' when once at least $xA > yB$ but $xC < yD$ instead of $xC > yD$. The transitivity of this relation of linear order is proved however only in part. Nor does Eudoxos show that a strict disjunction holds between the classmateship of (A, B) and (C, D) and $(A, B) > (C, D)$ and $(C, D) > (A, B)$. But Eudoxos does in fact significantly show in Proposition 13 that in the definition of '$(A, B) > (C, D)$' a magnitude pair may be replaced by any of its classmates so that the proposed relation of linear order holds between *whole classes* and *whole classes* as new logical units, distinct from the magnitude pairs which each such class contains. Finally, although Eudoxos proves that $(A+P, P)$ and $(B+Q, Q)$ are classmates whenever (A, P) and (B, Q)

are so, he never proves that $(A+A', P)$ and $(B+B', Q)$ are classmates whenever both (A, P) and (B, Q) are classmates and (A', P) and (B', Q) are classmates. In other words Eudoxos never establishes and proves there to be such any S-function or P-function relation between whole class and whole class. The ratio classes of Eudoxos stand forth as eligible candidates for the role of ring elements. But there are absent any generalized sum-addend and product-factor functions which could suitably serve as ring relations.

Another rich field for constructed interclass relations in Greek mathematics lies in one of two different treatments of oddness and evenness in integers. Euclid, for example, states side by side two definitions of an odd number: (i) an odd number is one not divisible by 2, (ii) an odd number is one which exceeds by 1 some even number.

Plato's own definition of *even* numbers is the usual and undisputed one of divisibility-by-2. But his definition of *odd* numbers is arresting to the sensitive and alert algebrist. For example, criticising in the *Phaedo* what were later and contemptuously called 'occult qualities,' Plato states that just as the true cause of a body's warm state is not some elusive warmness but detectable fire, and just as the true cause of a man's sick condition is not some recondite sickness but palpable fever, so too is the true cause of a number being odd not some mysterious oddness but the identifiable added one. He further calls the odd numbers one *stichos* or row and the even numbers another *stichos* or row in a technically sophisticated and systematic tabular distribution, as:

Class 0: $\cdots -2,\ 0,\ 2,\ 4,\ 6,\ \cdots\ 2n+0;$

Class 1: $\cdots -1,\ 1,\ 3,\ 5,\ 7,\ \cdots\ 2n+1.$

In the *Hippias Major* two parts of the class algorithm are mentioned in so far as both two evens and two odds are identified with some even sum. Finally, one sure indication to the historian that a process disclosed in fact was clearly recognized as such by its manipulators is evidence for its conscious repetition. Now the classes *modulo* 2 split *modulo* 4 as follows: Class 0 *modulo* 2 splits into both Class 0 and Class 2 *modulo* 4, and Class 1 *modulo* 2 splits into both Class 1 and Class 3 *modulo* 4:

Class 0: $\cdots\ -8,\ -4,\ \ 0,\ 4,\ 8,\ 12,\ 16,\ \cdots\ 4n+0;$

Class 3: $\cdots\ -9,\ -5,\ -1,\ 3,\ 7,\ 11,\ 15,\ \cdots\ 4n+3;$

Class 2: $\cdots\ -10,\ -6,\ -2,\ 2,\ 6,\ 10,\ 14,\ \cdots\ 4n+2;$

Class 1: $\cdots\ -11,\ -7,\ -3,\ 1,\ 5,\ 9,\ 13,\ \cdots\ 4n+1.$

The members of the Class 0 *modulo* 4 are called in Euclid *artiakis artioi,* those of Class 2 *modulo* 4 *perissakis artioi,* and those of Class 1 and Class 3 *modulo* 4 *perissakis perissoi.* And these three technically sophisticated class algorithm designations actually occur in Plato's *Parmenides.*

A further dense and therefore dull and therefore comparatively neglected problem in the history of mathematical thought is the set of later Platonic theories of Ideal Number. These numbers are said to be generated by the 'one' and the 'indeterminate dyad,' and to have puzzling properties, such as 'inaddibility.' It is now possible, I think, to identify the 'one' with the logical unity of the Eudoxian ratio class and the 'indeterminate dyad' either with a generic magnitude pair or with the set of magnitude pairs which are the members of such a unit class. In particular the number 1 is said to arise from 'the equalisation of the great and the small.' Evidence is at hand to suggest that by 'the great and the small' is meant the constituents of a magnitude pair construed as a member of some ratio class. It is therefore illuminating to conjecture at least that the class whose typical member is (a, a) and which in modern algebra does yield the isomorphism correlate of the integer 1 was similarly regarded in Platonic ideal number theory.

Again in the same theory it is contended that there is a gradation of 'ideas, mathematicals, and sensibles.' The ideas are said to be one but the mathematicals many. Moreover, whereas the mathematicals are immutable, the sensibles are described as mutable. These challenging characteristics seem to make acceptably intelligible sense if the 'ideas' are construed as individual ratio classes in the role of new logical units, the 'mathematicals' as individual member pairs of a ratio class, and the 'sensibles' as concrete magnitudes and multitudes. Furthermore, the strange alleged 'inaddibility' of the ideal numbers would be in fact a dated confession that the construction of a suitable *interclass* relation, or generalized sum-addend relation in the role of an S-function over the ratio classes, had not yet been achieved in contemporary mathematical researches. Hence the correspondence between the number n and the class $(n, 1)$ had not yet risen to the level of a functionally operative isomorphism.

Finally, the Platonic theories of ideal number assert not only that the dyad functions as the second principle of number generation but also that there is — in the conventional translation — "an issuing forth of all except the first as it were impressions from a seal." Obscure words indeed and a vexing puzzle to generations of interpreters. But the words make technically intelligible sense if one construes them as applicable to that ratio class, let us say, which contains (4,6) and (6,9) and (8,12) and generally $(2n, 3n)$ on the pattern of (2,3). That pattern is the normal representative of its class, unique in the fact that its two constituents, 2 and 3, are coprime to one another. If this insight be valid, then *protos*, which may be employed to mean either 'first' or 'prime' and even 'coprime,' is idiomatically reconstrued so that the former phrase 'except the first' now reads 'except the coprime couple' unique in its appropriate ratio class. And in this algebraically sophisticated perspective it is easy to comprehend the mathematical point of Plato's jibe in the *Republic* at the bunglers who attempt to cut the abstract number 1 into fractionated parts and his simultaneous praise of the experts who prefer to locate the number pairs (a, A) and (b, B) in the same ratio class if and only if $aB = bA$.

It is furthermore simply a report on recorded history and not a symptom of psychotic aggression to mention that this line of mathematical thought was abruptly broken by Aristotle (384 – 322 B.C.). This is indeed not the place to mount a comprehensive survey of the mathematical content of the

Corpus Aristotelicum. It is enough for our present philosophical purposes to examine afresh certain selected items therein contained which are especially pertinent to the preceding disclosures.

In Aristotle, for example, the older and defective theory of proportion survives intact. For we are told that $4 : 2$ and $2 : 1$ are equal in ratio because 2 is the same part of 4 that 1 is of 2. In Aristotle again there also endures the newer indeed but equally defective *antaneiresis* method of defining proportionality. Moreover, whereas Euclid after Eudoxos infers from both $A : B \equiv C : D$ and $A > C$ that $B > D$, Aristotle misconstrues the theorem and from both $A : B \equiv C : D$ and $A > B$ deduces $C > D$. Furthermore, where Eudoxos and after him Plato declare in terms of identity that some two given magnitude pairs lie in the *same* ratio class as comembers of it, Aristotle reports that the same two magnitude pairs have an *equal* ratio in the sense of the older theory of proportion. A further and insuperable obstacle to the prolongation of Eudoxian insights in and through the works of Aristotle is his *dictum* that 1 is *not* a number. Hence for Aristotle the first number is 2. But even here Aristotle's mathematical acumen remains suspect. For on the grounds of a multitude of valid instances of its computational success, such as $13-3 = 10$ and $13-1 = 12$, Aristotle endorses the common-sense rule that number *or* the monad subtracted from number leaves *number*. But if so, then the crucial case of $2-1 = 1$ arises to plague such a system of arithmetic with the stigma of inconsistency.

But the deeper, more significant, and more strategic reason for such failures to comprehend the construction of the ratio classes of Eudoxos by means of an isoid relation appears to lie in Aristotle's native preference in logic for the construction of dichotomized classes exclusively through a technique of strictly alternative predicates. In each case the central problem is the same: To partition the members of a main logical class into non-overlapping subclasses. Aristotle's chosen method of solution is to *pre*select a set of at least two strictly alternative predicates, such as P and non-P, and then test each member of the main logical class for inclusion in the appropriate subclass. It is an inescapable involvement of this method that the number of subclasses is predetermined by the number of predicates preselected. Omniscience therefore over a certain domain of entities is a helpful preliminary for one who hopes for solid success through the use of this partition technique. It is a necessary consequence of this method at work that the process of subclassification requires as many membership tests as there are relevant predicates. On the contrary, the technique of partition of main logical class members by means of an isoid relation establishes a single test criterion. Moreover such a single criterion does not function to determine whether a single main class member does or does not belong to a given proposed subclass. Rather the isoid relational test operates to decide only whether some two given main-class members do or do not belong to the same subclass. In place therefore of prior omniscience over a certain domain of entities such an isoid relational method requires only a high degree of perceptivity to whatever instances of identity may occur in the exploratory partitioning process.

Aristotle's personal preference for the system of partitioning the members of a main logical class uniquely by the method of strictly alternative predicates constrains him to propose the following classification of certain familiar sciences: Physics is concerned with separables (*chorista*) that are not immobile (*ouk akineta*), the non-astronomical parts of mathematics with immobiles (*akineta*) that are not separable (*ou chorista*) otherwise than from matter, and first philosophy with immobiles (*akineta*) that are separable (*chorista*). The strictly alternative interplay of *P* and non-*P* is conspicuous in this classification of sciences by their alleged objects. It is a further consequence of this same predilection that for Aristotle the mathematician is distinguished from the physicist solely by the fact that the mathematician abstracts surfaces and volumes, lines and points from the world of motion and change. Thus the *quantum*, as separated by thought and in thought from the welter of phenomenal change, is constituted as the specifying object of mathematics. The same technique of dichotomous division leads to a description of this *quantum* as that which is divisible — as distinct from that which is non-divisible — into two or more constituent parts.

At this stage of his systematic analysis Aristotle has no other alternative but to confront what he knows about the Platonic developments of the Eudoxian theory of ratio classes through an isoid relation and to condemn it as erroneous. He first inveighs against the Platonic definition of oddness by means of the added one. In order to correct this alleged mistake Aristotle proposes as a logical rule that all definitions are to be regarded as defective which, if they lead to two classes, proceed in any other way than by formal dichotomy through strictly alternative predicates, such as 'divisible-by-2' and 'non-divisible-by-2.' It is therefore Aristotle's studied opinion that those who treat the 'unequal' as 'one' thing and the 'dyad' as an indefinite compound of 'the great and the small' state what is very far from being probable or possible. For in his view these are rather modifications and accidents than substrata of numbers and magnitudes — 'many' and 'few' of number, 'great' and 'small' of magnitude, like 'even' and 'odd', 'smooth' and 'rough', 'straight' and 'curved'. Again, and apart from this mistake in classification, Aristotle argues that the great and the small and so forth must be relative to something. But what is relative is least of all the categories of a kind of entity or substance, and is posterior to quantity or quality. Moreover, asserts Aristotle, the relative is an accident of quantity, not its matter. The reason given is that something with a nature of its own must serve as matter, both to the relative in general and to its parts and kinds.

It is finally this same basic preference which forces Aristotle to prohibit any attempt to prove anything in one branch of mathematics, arithmetic, or geometry, by recourse to the resources of another branch, geometry or arithmetic. And here precisely Aristotle reverses the impact of the insight of an earlier Archytas (435–365 B.C.) to the effect that arithmetic is superior to geometry first because it can treat its chosen elements more clearly, and secondly because wherever geometry falls short of its tasks arithmetic steps in to complete the proofs. Where Plato after Eudoxos made mathematics a study of relations and inquiline to a generalized logic, Aristotle in opposition to Plato made mathematics a study of abstracted quantity and thus inquiline to physics.

This line of interdisciplinary enrichment, endorsed first by Archytas, proscribed abruptly by Aristotle, revived in part by Apollonius, reaches integrity again only in Descartes' *Géométrie* (1637). This epochal volume is often praised but seldom restudied and thus remains in fact a further comparatively neglected item in the history of mathematical thought. For it is at least questionable whether those who mention it most often report precisely on the character of its central contributions. In order to assay the *Géométrie* with historical and analytical accuracy, let us list six essential lines of development of algebraic geometry as a frame of reference: (1) One selects first a curve of type A and then suitable coordinates for its study, then one selects a curve of type B and then only suitable coordinates for its study; (2) One first spreads a network over the plane and then afterward invites various curves to appear for individual examination; (3) One finds that some individual problem in geometry is more readily solved in an algebraic paraphrase; (4) One finds conversely that an individual problem in algebra is more readily solved in a geometrical paraphrase; (5) An entire structure is transferred from an algebraic theory to a geometric theory; and (6) An entire structure is transferred from a geometric theory to an algebraic theory. In each of the two latter cases old and persistent problems are readily solved, new and exciting problems are spontaneously suggested, and whole ranges of standard materials are instructively realigned and redistributed. The first piecemeal line of development is already at a high level in Apollonius. The second line — despite superficial accounts to the contrary — is altogether absent from Descartes' *Géométrie*. His real contribution was rather to open up for fruitful exploration the fifth and the sixth lines by the introduction of five basic insights.

The first was to transcend the paralyzing inhibitions of a too geometrical imagination and to let the number x measure a length as well as an area and the number x to measure an area as well as a length. The second was to see that the genus of a curve, here a modification of its degree, is permanent amid changes in the temporary coordinates. This is in fact the seedbed of the notion of invariance under a group of transformations. The third — and to my mind the most important — was the indispensable effort to reduce, on the one hand, a given amount of algebra to further irreducible atomic computations and, on the other, to reduce a given amount of geometry to further irreducible geometric constructions. For Descartes' hope was high and correct that a larger incidence of parallelisms in the foundations of each would lead to a greater degree of parallelism in the superstructure of both. The fourth was to exploit the reduction of equations to pattern equations by means of a similar reduction of problems in geometry to pattern problems. For Descartes, like Archytas, saw that algebra must intervene in geometry as a principle of order, as a source of classifications, and as a criterion between the possible and the impossible. The fifth and last contribution was to realize that one must envision a hierarchy of mathematical methods and in every case of successful solution to test whether that problem could or could not have been solved at a lower level on the scale of methodological resources. In short, the colossal impact of the *Géométrie* on the course of mathematical thought was its fresh and courageous attempt to explore possible links of logical structure between two massive mathematical disciplines, to start in fact to test them for the existence of extensive isomorphisms, to hope to find therein identities of relational structure amid irreducibly different relations and relata.

II

And it is precisely that *kind* of fundamental task — of reciprocal reduction to irreducible elements, of confrontation for correspondences, of correlation for structural identities — which faces every conscientious collaborator in the scientific enterprise of mankind who ambitions to construct some schema for a comprehension and control over the repeatable patterns of interplay of empirical phenomena in *any* domain by linking them with the relations and relata of some one or other mathematical system, already *pre*constructed, *pre*comprehended, and *pre*controlled. And such, I think, is the core of the only consistent sense that critical intelligence can discern in basically confused and balefully confusing talk about 'the quantification of qualitative concepts' in areas of natural or social science.

The aim of mathematical physics is the exploitation of abstract mathematical objects for the description of the results of physical measurements. The success of this scheme depends upon the correct interpretation of the physical results and their proper identification with the appropriate mathematical objects. If these identifications are correct, observable relationships among the physical objects are predictable by the algebraic properties of the corresponding mathematical objects.

For these reasons the only really valuable — and as yet unwritten — history of physics is one that periodizes its subject, not according to an alien and irrelevant system of chronology for general history, but precisely according to the changing choices of a primary mathematical instrument for the ordering of phenomena. In the beginning of modern physics that instrument was naturally the elements of geometry. After sundry other phases the physics of the nineteenth century worked its way through the theory of derivates, the theory of integrals, the theory of differential equations and the theory of integral equations. If we further choose as specimens of later revolutions in physics relativity and quantum mechanics, the same analysis holds good. For relativity chose as its primary mathematical tool the theory of differential invariants — and so in effect, except for the word-bound, supplanted relativity with invariance. And quantum physics, as it grows, chooses now matrix algebra, now group representation theory, and even abstract algebra. And if current research efforts to unify in a single theory electromagnetism and gravitation are to succeed, the synthesis can never be established from mathematics alone, but only *from* physics *through* mathematics. The history of physics is thus a progressive search for more suitable isomorphisms for the better comprehension and control of other and more complex physical relational situations. For his own professional reasons and prompted by his own artistic motivations and aesthetic ideals the mathematician creates and preserves an expanding stock of isomorphism classes of systems of abstract relations. Now and again, at moments of crisis, the physicist borrows and makes use of a new one from that store.

But mathematics as such offers no obstacle to such use of its wares by other scientists than the physicist. In particular and by way of a suggestion it may be said that the social sciences will come of age and become really 'scientific' when and only when they also *consciously* undertake to discover and exploit similar instances of isomorphism. And it is to their very great advantage that the informed members of their profession can begin with a clear conception of this methodology and thus avoid, unlike physics, a long era of hit-and-miss efforts toward an unattainable because unintelligible 'quantification of qualitative concepts.' The prescription for success is straightforward and simple: (1) Inventory and reduce the items in your scientific problem area to further irreducible elements of objects and relations; (2) Forget the otherwhence, otherwise, and otherwhere relevant distinction between quantity and quality, and seek singlemindedly to discover a correspondence with some currently available mathematical system of relations and relata, and then exploit that isomorphism as long as it endures; and (3) If no such mathematical system is now available for a start or for a replacement after a challenging impasse, consciously stimulate mathematical genius to increase its stock in trade. For it is axiomatic to the analytical historian of science that the quantity — so to speak — and the quality of scientific advances in any given area are each a function — and by implication also a relation — of the reserve supply of available or forthcoming isomorphism classes of mathematical systems of abstract relations.

THE MAIN TRENDS IN THE FOUNDATIONS OF GEOMETRY IN THE 19th CENTURY

HANS FREUDENTHAL

Yale University, New Haven, Connecticut, U.S.A.
State University, Utrecht, The Netherlands

The best-known chapter in the history of mathematics is the history of non-Euclidean geometry. It has been seriously studied by competent scholars, and I do not pretend to add anything to their work. The *reception*, however, of non-Euclidean geometry is a less familiar chapter. It is worthwhile to say a few words about it.

Gauss, who had very early grasped the idea of non-Euclidean geometry (maybe as early as the last years of the 18th century) never published a single word about his discovery, fearing, he said, the clamour of the Bœotians. His fear, however, was unfounded. Nobody troubled about Lobačevski's and Bolyai's discoveries in the early thirties, so there was no one to warn the Bœotians. After Gauss' death there was some gossip that he had pursued non-Euclidean geometry. The rumor was confirmed by his correspondence with Schumacher, published in 1860 to 1863. But even Gauss' name was not strong enough an incentive to invite interest in non-Euclidean geometry.

The reception of non-Euclidean geometry started with three nearly contemporary events: Helmholtz's "Über die Thatsachen, die der Geometrie zum Grunde liegen" (1868), Beltrami's interpretation of non-Euclidean geometry in differential geometry (1868), and J. Houël's translations and re-editions of texts on non-Euclidean geometry (from 1866 onward). Riemann's "Über die Hypothesen, welche der Geometrie zugrunde liegen" (1954; first published 1867) unfortunately does not fit into this historical context, because in the first place, strangely enough, he never mentions non-Euclidean geometry, but mainly because for more than thirty years Riemann's contribution to the foundations of geometry was overshadowed by Helmholtz's. The Bœotians do not show up before the middle of the seventies — conceited people who claimed to prove that Gauss, Riemann, and Helmholtz were blockheads. If you witnessed the struggle against Einstein in the twenties, you may have some idea of this amusing kind of literature. The name of the new science seems to be metamathematics or metageometry, and mostly this is meant as an invective against something that is to respectable mathematics as metaphysics is to physics. Most of these people know nothing about this metascience except that it believes parallel lines intersect and space has more than three dimensions. Yet Helmholtz's popular expositions (especially his brilliant address of 1870)

For references, cf. H. Freudenthal, Die Grundlagen der Geometrie um die Wende des 19. Jahrhunderts. Semesterberichte Münster. The present paper was prepared as part of an N.S.F. project at the University of California, Berkeley, July 1-25, 1960.

do seem to have impressed the public. They are echoed by a philosopher such as Benno Erdmann who translated Helmholtz's brevity and flavor into philosophical prolixity and insipidity.

After 1868, mathematicians became aware of non-Euclidean geometry. One of them was F. Klein, who (in 1870) discovered in Cayley's famous "Sixth Memoir upon Quantics" (1859) a model of non-Euclidean geometry. Yet this discovery did not contribute to clarifying the foundations of geometry. Of course, such a sturdy model of non-Euclidean geometry was a pleasant tool to work with. But in those days people did not understand the logical function of a model, Klein no more than many others. He claimed that it is not a vicious circle to found non-Euclidean geometry on projective geometry that previously has been derived from Euclidean geometry. But he himself never succeeds in really understanding his claim. The logic of geometry was obscured rather than clarified by the discovery of a model for non-Euclidean geometry.

In Klein's work projective and non-Euclidean geometry meet. The digression at the beginning of the 19th century from the Euclidean to the projective approach was one of the historical presuppositions of the axiomatization of geometry that was to be achieved at the end of the century. Euclidean geometry is a logically involved structure. As long as axiomatic thinking had not grown into a habit, it could not be easy to draw up a complete system of axioms of geometry. In projective geometry, however, the diversity of geometrical relations was reduced to one only, that of incidence, though on closer inspection a second relation, that of order, was seen to be indispensable.

At a certain moment G. K. Ch. von Staudt in his "Geometrie der Lage" (1847) seems to have reached the goal of a purely deductive (projective) geometry. He never appeals to metric relations. Harmonicity is defined by incidence relations only (the theorem of the complete quadrangle). Invariance of harmonicity is chosen as the defining property of projective mappings between straight lines. Through this modern-looking artifice he at once gets the fundamental theorem of projective geometry that really proves to be the key theorem of this field.

F. Klein (1873) was the first to notice the disguised continuity assumptions in von Staudt's proof, by which properties of the everywhere dense harmonic net are conferred upon the whole line. Klein was not able to fill this gap or even to understand the true nature of the problem. Several times he comes back to this point. All he writes about it is utterly confused. He does not properly distinguish between continuity and monotony. He confuses continuity as a property of functions with continuity as a property of the real number system (called connectedness at present).

To Klein the line, the plane, the space were still "number manifolds" such as they were to Helmholtz and Riemann. He was unable to formulate the topological properties of these structures in any other way. This is one of the reasons that many of his contemporaries consider his autonomous foundation of projective and hyperbolic geometry as a vicious circle: you start, they say, with a number manifold, but through this number manifold you have already accepted Euclidean space. Of course Klein was right, but even after Pasch and Hilbert he never truly understood that one can dispense with the number manifold in the *Foundations of Geometry*. Klein was not alone in being troubled by this. The conviction that analytical continuity was indispensable was so strong that people still suspect Hilbert of having committed a paralogism in his *Foundations of Geometry*.

This is a strange fact. For as early as 1871 and 1872 Dedekind and Cantor had independently achieved the analysis of the number continuum. Of course the geometrical continuum was a less easy problem, since the density of the rational net, which is self-evident in analysis, has to be enforced by axiomatic means in geometry. This is the essence of the so-called Archimedean axiom. In the early eighties Pasch and O. Stolz, independently I presume, grasped its full significance.

In the nineties the part of continuity in geometry was illuminated by the appearance of its counterpart. From G. Veronese's chaotic work the first non-Archimedean geometries emerged, more precisely worked out by T. Levi-Civita. What this meant to people can be judged from the reaction of Klein, who in 1898 still stuck to the number manifold as a substratum of geometry.

In its origin neither non-Euclidean nor projective geometry belonged to the "Foundation family" in the sense of a conscious quest into the essence of space. This problem is characteristic of a third current, heavily loaded with philosophy. Reviewing it, I should properly start with Kant or even with Newton and Leibniz. The struggle for and against non-Euclidean geometry in the 19th century was fought upon the playground of Kant's doctrine of space, or rather of some superficial abstract that even today is taught in textbooks to be Kant's doctrine.

The aprioristic truth of geometry is a pretension of such a nature that it does not improve the understanding of the logic of geometry. Whether Kant's authority has hampered foundational research, I cannot decide. In any case it is evident that Riemann rejected Kant. He had carefully studied Herbart, who had been the first to remark that psychologically Euclidean space is preceded by topological space. According to Riemann, the topological substratum of geometry is the n-dimensional manifold. If there is any formal *a priori* in space, it is topology. Since topology is too poor, something from experience must be added. This additional element is the "Hypothesen welche der Geometrie zugrunde liegen", mathematically speaking, the Riemannian metric.

As a physiologist of perception, Helmholtz acknowledged Kant, but as a mathematician, he rejected him. He had a mathematical theory of space independent of Riemann's. Against Riemann he argued: Any spatial metric depends on the observation of congruence, and congruence supposes the existence of freely movable solid bodies. This existence is the "fact" (versus Riemann's hypothesis) that he alludes to in the title of his "Über die Thatsachen, die der Geometrie zum Grunde liegen". Starting from the number manifold and adding this fact as a postulate, he succeeds in proving that space must be Euclidean or non-Euclidean. As a by-product of his theory, Riemann had shown the same thing, but under stronger suppositions, in Riemannian spaces only, whereas Helmholtz did not suppose the infinitesimal Pythagorean character of the metric.

Of course Helmholtz' assertion that solid bodies are indispensable if distances are to be compared is not correct. We can content ourselves with rods, one-dimensional solid bodies, as it were. Nevertheless Helmholtz's objection is continuously repeated, not only by philosophers such as Erdmann, but also by Poincaré, who as late as 1902, in his review of Hilbert's *Grundlagen,* criticised Helmholtz's inference, which for thirty years had diverted the attention of geometricians from Riemann's work.

In the 19th century there was no free exchange of mathematical ideas among the European countries. The linguistic barriers were still strong. The lively discussion of the foundations of geometry, carried on in Germany since the late sixties, did not affect France until the nineties. A philosophical essay of Poincaré's appearing in 1891 in the *Revue générale des sciences pures et appliquées* caused, it seems, a tremendous sensation, though in this paper Poincaré did not essentially go beyond Helmholtz. The essay was immediately reprinted by *Nature.*

Poincaré's publication was well timed. It dropped into a current of critical interest in critical philosophy — in these very years the *Revue de Métaphysique et de Morale* was founded. This is the arena where in the nineties the foundations of mathematics were discussed by Poincaré, Russell, Couturat, Frege, and many others. One can still trace the introduction of Cantor's and Dedekind's ideas to this company, and in the late nineties even Peano's name was mentioned in a report of Couturat. Geometry, the main subject of the discussion, however, was still dealt with on the level of 1870. Nothing of what had since happened in Germany and Italy had crossed the linguistic frontiers. A rather amusing contribution to that discussion is Russell's book *An Essay on the Foundations of Geometry* (1897). It has recently been reissued after sixty years.

Somebody — I do not know who — has defined a philosopher as a man who at midnight in a dark room looks for a black cat that isn't there. With an eye on those philosophers of the nineties I would like to add: Meanwhile the black cat is sitting in the broad light of the adjoining room.

Then the door opens — I mean the door of the Paris Philosophical Congress of 1900. In the field of the philosophy of sciences the Italian phalanx was supreme: Peano, Burali-Forti, Padoa, Pieri absolutely dominated the discussion. For Russell, who read a paper that was philosophical in the worst sense, Paris was the road to Damascus.

What had happened in the meantime? People usually think that Hilbert was the first to develop a logically closed system of Euclidean geometry that avoids any illegal appeal to intuition. This common belief is contradicted by M. Pasch's *Vorlesungen über neuere Geometrie* (1882). After a few pages the reader of this book knows that Pasch was scrupulously endeavoring to fulfill his program: "Whenever geometry has to be really deductive, the process of inferring must be independent of the *meaning* of the geometrical notions as well as of the figures. The only things that matter are the *relations* between the geometrical notions, as they are established in the theorems and definitions used."

Such a program could have been formulated before Pasch, and sometimes it was, but nobody had ever thought of carrying it out. As a deductive geometrician, Pasch had contemporaries and competitors, such as O. Stolz and F. Schur, but he had no precursors. The Italians, such as Veronese, Enriques, Pieri, and Padoa were influenced by him, and I am sure that Peano, when working on logistics, was greatly indebted to Pasch, who first showed how to formulate axioms.

Since ancient times an axiom has been an evident truth that neither can nor ought to be proved. Mostly this meant that axioms need not even be formulated. Most people (especially Klein) speak continually of geometrical axioms and never state a single one explicitly. If someone points out a gap in a geometrical proof, he is likely to meet the answer: "Oh, that is just an axiom." This is one of the usual contexts of the word "axiom".

Pasch's book is an axiomatic system of projective geometry, the very field in which von Staudt had failed. But meanwhile Cantor and Dedekind had shown how to attack the continuum.

Up to the end of the century Pasch's work was continued mainly by the Italians. I mentioned the discovery of non-Archimedian geometries. Finite geometries date from the same time (G. Fano, 1892; E. H. Moore, 1896). Much earlier the idea of non-Desarguian geometry had occurred to Klein, who lacked only the exact expression.

Nevertheless it was still a long step from Pasch to Hilbert, whose *Grundlagen der Geometrie* was first published in 1899. Progress would probably have been less striking had not Pasch published in our century numerous vast philosophical papers, explaining views that form a painful contrast to Hilbert's. Whereas Pasch was anxious to derive his fundamental notions from experience and to postulate no more than experience seems to grant, Hilbert started: "Wir denken uns . . ." we imagine three kinds of things . . . called points . . . called lines . . . called planes . . . we imagine points, lines, and planes in some relations . . . called lying on, between, parallel, congruent . . .".

As stated, an axiom has long been considered an evident truth that neither can nor ought to be proved. Those who did not like evidence called the axiom a postulate, or spoke of hypotheses (Riemann) or of facts (Helmholtz). It has been controversial whether axioms derive from pure intuition (Kant) or whether they are idealised experience (Helmholtz) or hypothetical judgments about reality (Riemann) or statements transcending reality (Klein).

In any case, geometry deals with real space — Pasch, Enriques, Veronese, Pieri, Klein stressed this, and at the eleventh hour (1897) Russell wrote his philosophy *Foundations of Geometry,* which reveals the faint footstep of Kant rather than the paw of the lion.

"Wir denken uns . . ." — the bond with reality is cut. Geometry has become pure mathematics. The question of whether and how to apply it to reality is the same in geometry as it is in other branches of mathematics. Axioms are not evident truths. They are not truths at all in the usual sense.

Of course, after Pasch's serious attempt at deductiveness, after the discovery of non-Desarguian, non-Archimedean, and finite geometries, this idea was overdue. One forerunner of Hilbert, G. Fano, starts one of his papers with a sentence (*Giornale di Mat.*, Vol. 30, pp. 106–132) foreshadowing Hilbert's words quoted above. Two more Italians, Padoa and Pieri, should be noted as competing with Hilbert on this point. Pieri's address at the Paris Philosophical Congress of 1900 had the highly significant title, "Sur la géometrie envisagée comme un système purement logique", and Padoa, at the International Congress of Mathematicians (Paris, 1900), read two papers in which the logical status of geometry and the outlines of axiomatics are drawn more sharply and more distinctly than Hilbert ever drew them.

What was expressly formulated by Padoa, was tied up in Hilbert's work with the mathematically important facts, i.e., the idea of implicit definition, a logical monster and nuisance to many people at that time. Hilbert never uses the term "implicit definition". But he introduces the axioms of order by a sentence like "the axioms of this group define the notion of betweenness". And again with the congruence axioms: "the axioms of this group define the notion of congruence or motion". One can trace this idea back to the setting of 1894, but at that early date nobody paid attention to it.

The meaning of undefined notions such as point, line, plane, lying on, between, congruent, is implicitly defined by the axioms, by rules as it were which tell us how to play the game. Nonsense, people objected, if I map Euclidean space by an inversion, straight lines and planes are replaced by circles and spheres, which fulfill all the axioms though they are very different from straight lines and planes, and this proves that the axioms do not define the notions they deal with.

Frege, rebuking Hilbert like a schoolboy, also joins the Bœotians. (I have never understood why he is so highly esteemed today.) Your system of axioms, he says to Hilbert, is like a system of equations you cannot solve. "If we are to answer the question whether some object, say my watch, is a point, we are already frustated by the first axiom where two points are in question . . .". Frege parodies Hilbert's system:

"Erklärung. Wir denken uns Gegenstände, die wir Götter nennen. Axiom 1. Jeder Gott ist almächtig. Axiom 2. Es gibt wenigstens einen Gott."

Frege could hardly have contrived a more effective demonstration. Before Hilbert, mathematicians behaved as though they could decide mathematically whether Frege's watch was a point. Axiom systems such as Frege's caricature existed (Spinoza's and many others) as long as geometry was believed to assert something about reality.

But Hilbert's view finally prevailed. The younger generation was thankful to be delivered from Euclidean definitions like "a point is that which has no parts", and "a unit is that according to which anything is called one". Hilbert's clean cut between mathematics and realistic science became the paradigm of a new methodology. Through Einstein's booklet of 1916 "Über die spezielle und allgemeine Relativitätstheorie" this doctrine made its way into the lobbies of science and philosophy. A few sentences coined by him in his 1921 lecture "Geometrie und Erfahrung" have become classic: "In so far as the mathematical theorems refer to reality, they are not certain, and insofar as they are certain, they do not refer to reality .... The progress entailed by axiomatics consists in the sharp separation of the logical form and the realistic and intuitive contents .... The axioms are voluntary creations of the human mind .... To this interpretation of geometry I attach great importance because if I had not been acquainted with it, I would never have been able to develop the theory of relativity."

In a lengthy review of the 8th edition of Hilbert's *Grundlagen,* I analysed this work in detail.[1] I identified its forerunners and competitors. The more I discovered, the more clearly I could distinguish what has been historically decisive in Hilbert's work. The father of rigor in geometry is Pasch. The idea of the logical status of geometry occurred at the same time to some Italians. Implicit definition was analysed much earlier by Gergonne. The proof of independence by counter-example was practised by the inventors of non-Euclidean geometry, and more consciously by Peano and Padoa. The segment calculus was prefigured in von Staudt's "throw calculus". The purport of the "Schliessungssätze" had been grasped by H. Wiener (1893). Even the title *Grundlagen der Geometrie* is far from original. Before Hilbert, a name like this indicated research like Riemann's and Helmholtz's. Lie's papers of 1890 appeared under this title, and so did Killing's book in 1893, 1897. In my review I explained why, in spite of all these historical facts, we are accustomed to identify the turn of mathematics to axiomatics with Hilbert's *Grundlagen*: This thoroughly and profoundly elaborated piece of axiomatic workmanship was infinitely more persuasive than programmatic and philosophical speculations on space and axioms ever could be.

There is one name in the *Foundations of Geometry* I have nearly neglected, that of Poincaré. Reading the chapter on geometry in Poincaré's *La Science et l'Hypothèse* (1903?), one is in no doubt that one is breathing the air of Hilbert's *Grundlagen* (1899), the modern spirit of axiomatics, though one may perhaps wonder why Hilbert's name is not mentioned. So I was greatly surprised when I hit upon the first edition of this chapter, published as early as 1891, a good many years before Hilbert's *Grundlagen.* (The greater part

[1]Nieuw Archief voor Wiskunde (4) 5 (1957), 105—142.

of *La Science et l'Hypothèse* is an almost textual reprint of essays published in periodicals in the nineties.) Is it true that Poincaré had anticipated Hilbert on some important points?

My surprise increased further when I read all the other papers by Poincaré and the controversies they had caused. It appeared that Poincaré's reflections had almost nothing to do with the quest into the logical status of geometry, though after Hilbert's *Grundlagen* they are readily interpreted in this sense. I must confess this has been a bewildering experience for me. Historians who believe they might understand a philosopher by reading his work isolated from its environment in a more recent edition or perhaps even translated into another language should be warned. In another context a whole book may take on quite another meaning — as was the case with *La Science et l'Hypothèse.*

I cannot adduce here the lengthy quotations and references by which I have elsewhere established the proof of this thesis. I can only give a resumé of the results.

In the *Foundations of Geometry,* Poincaré leaned heavily on Helmholtz. Like Helmholtz, he originally rejected Riemann. Clearly he knew nothing about Pasch and the Italians. His mathematical contribution to the *Foundations of Geometry* is insignificant. More copious is his philosophical production, which started in 1891.

Never once in all these papers did Poincaré deal with the problem that occupied mathematicians after Pasch: that of finding a place for geometry in pure mathematics. Though Poincaré clearly distinguishes between the mathematical and physical continuum, he never uses these adjectives in speaking of geometry. One never knows whether in any given connection he is using the words space, point, line, and so on, in a mathematical or in a physical sense. Poincaré looked to geometry as to a natural science, using mathematical methods like mechanics, thermodynamics, electricity. In his book all these sciences are forced into the same pattern, different from arithmetic, which, according to Poincaré, knows judgments *a priori.* He speaks mostly of axioms, without quoting anyone. Sometimes in his terminology axiom means everything the geometrician uses without proof. In other cases he presumably had in his mind axioms from some textbook, and sometimes he thought of what Helmholtz called the "facts". Pasch's idea of axiomatic systematisation and rigorous deductivity had not yet touched Poincaré.

You know perhaps that, according to Poincaré, the geometrical axioms (but which?) are conventions. Originally this is meant as a metaphor. But gradually he becomes fond of this word and finally he calls every theoretical proposition of science convention, even a linguistic convention. To avoid inconsistencies he flees from one convention to another. According to the method finally applied in *La Science et l'Hypothèse,* it would be a linguistic convention to assert that Napoleon was born in 1769 at Ajaccio, because it is an arbitrary procedure to count years from Jesus Christ, to call Napoleon Napoleon and not Wellington, and to call Ajaccio Ajaccio and not Rome.

When in the *Foundations of Geometry* the word "convention" appears, we are at once reminded of Hilbert's *Grundlagen*. Since Hilbert, an axiomatic system has often been compared with a game played according to conventional rules. But when using this image, we aim at a geometry detached from real space. As long as geometry is still a physical science, however, the assertion that its axioms are conventional does not make more sense than the broader assertion that all propositions from physics are conventions, hence, as far as I can see, make no sense at all.

When originally used, the word convention did not imply any more than that there are several kinds of geometry and that any one of them is no more true than the others. This is actually what Poincaré learned from Helmholtz; and the statement does not aim at much more than Helmholtz pretended. Poincaré's conception of what geometry is, is extremely restricted. He does not admit any other choice than that between Euclidean and non-Euclidean geometry. Again and again he stresses: "Si donc il n'y avait pas de corps solides dans la nature, il n'y aurait pas de géométrie." This is the very purport of Helmholtz's objections against Riemann, and it shows how far Poincaré still was from Hilbert's view on the logical status of geometry. For Poincaré the homogeneity of space was necessary, and in one of his papers he even tried to prove it. Actually for Poincaré the only conventional thing is the value of the curvature of space. Before reading Hilbert it had never occurred to him that there were more axioms that could be dropped. Every line of his review on Hilbert's *Grundlagen* (*Bull. Sci, math.* (2) 26 (1902), 249—272) reveals his surprise. He was surprised because he did not know what had happened in the last thirty years. At once he became aware of a much greater variety of geometries than he had known before. He admitted Riemannian spaces, and he discovered the paralogism in Helmholtz's argument against Riemann. He seized upon the idea of rigorous deductivity in geometry so eagerly as to exclaim: "On pourrait confier les axiomes a une machine à raisonner, . . . et l'on verrait sortir toute la Géométrie." And finally he noticed the relation with the ideas of the Italians, as expounded in Paris.

There is no clearer evidence for the persuasiveness of Hilbert's *Grundlagen*, for the convincing power of a philosophy that is not preached as a program, but that is only the silent background of a masterpiece of workmanship. "Exempla trahunt." This great success was bestowed upon Hilbert in geometry only. He starts the *Foundations of Mathematics* at the other extremity, with a program — a chimerical program, Padoa says in 1900.

The saying "Exempla trahunt" also characterizes Russell and Whitehead's *Principia Mathematica*, again an overpowering work, though less profound than Hilbert's.

The triumph of the Italian foundationalists recalls that of Pyrrhus. After the *Grundlagen der Geometrie* they ceased pursuing the foundations of geometry, and after the *Principia Mathematica* they bade farewell to logistics.

MODALITY DE DICTO AND DE RE

W. KNEALE
Oxford University, Oxford, England

1

There was a saying of mediaeval logicians, *De modalibus non gustabit asinus*, which means, I suppose, that modal logic is difficult and unappetizing. In this paper I propose to consider the origin and the value of a technical distinction that was much used by mediaeval logicians in their discussion of the subject, and I fear that what I have to say will not be very entertaining. I believe, however, that it has some importance for logic as well as for the history of logic. My reason for thinking so is not that I wish to re-introduce the distinction, as Professor von Wright has proposed in his *Essay in Modal Logic*. On the contrary, I shall argue that it is badly drawn and misleading. But one of the questions at issue in debates about the value of the distinction is essentially the same as that raised by Professor Quine in a number of recent papers on modal logic,[1] namely whether quantifiers can be allowed to operate across modal signs, and it may be useful to consider the problem in the setting in which it was first posed.

2

In his *De Interpretatione* Aristotle tries to determine the rules of opposition between statements of various kinds, and in particular to say what shall count as the contradictory of what. Modal statements give him some trouble because of his attachment to the mistaken view that "possible" (δυνατόν) and "contingent" (ἐνδεχόμενον) mean the same, but he leaves us in no doubt of the fact that modal predicates take for their proper subjects the states of affairs indicated by phrases like "that there is a man".[2] In this connexion he expressly compares modal predicates with truth, and it is probable that what he says here is the source of the mediaeval tradition whereby *verum* and *falsum* may be reckoned as modal words. In his *Prior Analytics* he makes the same point again when he says that a statement of the form "It is possible that no *S* should be *P*" or of the form "It is possible that some *S* should not be *P*" is to be regarded as affirmative.[3] These passages amount in effect to a declaration that modal sentences express second-order propositions, i.e., propositions about propositions. It is true that Aristotle had no single word like our modern "proposition" to cover premisses, conclusions, theorems, suggestions, hypotheses, theories, beliefs, tenets, and dogmas; but he says clearly that what is necessary or possible is the existence

[1] See especially his collection of essays, *From a Logical Point of View.*

[2] *De Interpretatione,* 12 (21^b 26–32 and 22^a 8–13).

[3] *Analytica Priora,* i. 3 (25^b 19–25).

or holding (εἶναι, ὑπάρχειν) of something. Unfortunately in his theory of modal syllogisms this comparatively simple doctrine is complicated by a development which has worried many succeeding logicians.

The puzzling passage occurs in *Prior Analytics*, i. 9, where Aristotle writes "It happens sometimes also that the conclusion is necessary when only one premiss is necessary, not, however, either premiss taken at random, but the major premiss."[4] From what he goes on to say it is clear that he intends to allow the validity of the form "If every *M* is necessarily *P* and every *S* is *M*, then every *S* is necessarily *P*" while rejecting the form "If every *M* is *P* and every *S* is necessarily M, then every *S* is necessarily *P*". In his commentary on the *Prior Analytics* Alexander of Aphrodisias tells us that this part of Aristotle's modal logic was rejected even by his pupils Eudemus and Theophrastus.[5] Many later writers have been inclined to agree with their judgement, and we too may wish to follow them, but we must first try to understand why Aristotle said what he did. Obviously he had considered the matter carefully, and we must suppose that he thought he had found some good reason for the guarded assertion which I have quoted. Now the only suggestion which makes his remark seem plausible is that an expression of modality may sometimes be taken to form part of the predicate phrase of a statement in which it occurs. It must be admitted that there is nothing to support this interpretation in Aristotle's Greek (εἰ τὸ *A* τῷ *B* ἐξ ἀνάγκης εἴληπται ὑπάρχειν), but if we write "necessarily-*P*" and "necessarily-*M*" in our two English formulae, we see immediately that the first looks like a simple variant of *Barbara* while the second seems to involve the fallacy of four (or rather five) terms. If this was indeed Aristotle's thought, he had already committed himself to the technical distinction I wish to discuss, though many centuries were to pass before it was set out explicitly.

Apart from the passage just noticed, there is one little bit of evidence to show that Aristotle had thought of the distinction. It does not come from a discussion of modality, but from a section on fallacies of composition and division in his *De Sophisticis Elenchis*.[6] There he says that a statement such as "It is possible for a man who is sitting to walk" or "It is possible for a man who is not writing to write" may be understood in either of two ways. Thus if the speaker of the second example says what he does, putting things together (συνθείς), his sentence means that it is possible to write while not writing, which is obviously false. But if he says what he does, separating things (διελών), his sentence means only that a man who is not writing has the power to write, which may very well be true. Aristotle does not himself make the point, but it is worth remarking that here, as in his disputed modal syllogisms, he seems to recognize that sentences which contain modal expressions need not always be understood as formulations of second-order

[4] *Analytica Priora*, i. 9 (30^a 15).

[5] *In Aristot. An. Pri. Lib. I Com., C.I.A.G.*, ii(i), ed. Wallies, p. 124.

[6] *De Sophisticis Elenchis*, 4 (166^a 23–31).

propositions, since they may sometimes be taken as statements about persons or things, even though their grammatical form is appropriate to the other interpretation.

3

Latin translations of the *Prior Analytics* and the *De Sophisticis Elenchis* were not generally available until the middle of the twelfth century, but when Abelard composed his commentary on the chapters of the *De Interpretatione* which have to do with modality, he knew already of the passage in the *De Sophisticis Elenchis* to which I have just drawn attention, and he thought it worth detailed discussion.[7] According to him there are two different ways in which sentences with modal words may be analysed (*exponi*). One is *expositio per compositionem*, the other *expositio per divisionem*, and the first is *de sensu*, while the second is *de re*, or *de rebus*. In his *Dialectica*, which was probably written later, he has a similar discussion in which he tells us that one of this teachers (perhaps it was William of Champeaux) had maintained that every modal statement was about the sense of another statement, so that to say *Possibile est Socratem currere* was to predicate possibility of *id quod dicit ista propositio "Socrates currit"*.[8] He himself does not deny that expressions containing *possibile* and similar words may be interpreted in this way. On the contrary, he points out that this interpretation agrees well with what he has said about truth as a property of propositional contents.[9] And he seems to have this interpretation in mind when he says *"Verum" . . . antecedit quidem ad "possibile", sequitur vero ad "necessarium"; "falsum" autem ad "impossibile" tantum sequitur.*[10] But in both his discussions he says that a statement which bears this interpretation is not strictly speaking modal, since it involves no modification or qualification of the propositional link between things but is merely the application of a special kind of adjective to a propositional content. A genuinely modal statement, he thinks, is one which involves modality *secundum expositionem de rebus.*[11] This may be constructed by means of an adverb such as *possibiliter*, but it may on the other hand be constructed by means of a modal adjective with an accusative and infinitive clause. For although *Nullum hominem possibile est esse album* can be taken to be a true singular affirmative statement with the meaning "It is possible that no man should be white", it can also be taken to be a false universal negative statement with the meaning "No man can be white"; and according to Abelard it is not really a modal statement unless taken in the second sense, when the modal word belongs in effect to the predicate and may therefore be said to express a mode or manner in which the subject is characterized.

---

[7]*Abaelardiana Inedita*, ed. L. Minio Paluello, pp. 13ff.
[8]*Dialectica*, ed. De Rijk, p. 195.
[9]*Ibid.*, p. 205.
[10]*Ibid.*, p. 204.
[11]*Ibid.*, p. 206.

It is not possible to say for certain when the distinction was first established in mediaeval Latin philosophy. But Abelard seems to imply that it is not his own invention, when he writes *Solet quaeri qualiter expositae de rebus ad expositas de sensu secundum inferentiam sese habeant.*[12] His own answer to the question which he calls customary is that, when a statement of possibility can bear both interpretations, the interpretation *de sensu* entails the interpretation *de rebus*, but not *vice versa*. Thus if the statement *Omnem stantem possibile est sedere* is taken to mean that it is possible for everyone to be seated while standing, it cannot be true, but no one could concede what is conveyed in this interpretation without conceding also what is conveyed in the other interpretation, namely that everyone who is in fact standing might be seated.[13] On the other hand, Abelard says that assertions of necessity *de rebus* and necessity *de sensu* seem to entail each other, that is to say, if the two kinds can be expressed by the same form of words.[14] This doctrine, if true, would preclude the use of the distinction of the two *expositiones* for justification of Aristotle's theory of modal syllogisms with only one apodeictic premiss. But Abelard did not discuss that problem. His pronouncement here seems to be a hasty generalization from a rather unusual example, *Necesse est Deum esse immortalem.*

In his *Logica Ingredientibus* Abelard had used the phrase *dictum propositionis* as short for *id quod dicit propositio*,$_{ii}$ and his distinction of two interpretations passed into currency as one between modality *de dicto* and modality *de re*. Thus William of Shyreswood says that it is necessary to distinguish between statements which ascribe *modi* to *dicta* and statements which ascribe characters modally, i.e., in a qualified way, to subjects other than *dicta*.[16] The distinction is to be found also with this terminology in the work of Peter of Spain[17] and in the little tract *De Modalibus* which has sometimes been attributed to St. Thomas Aquinas. According to the author of this last-named work a modal statement taken *de dicto* is inevitably singular, whereas a modal statement *de re* may be universal or particular according to the sign of quantity occurring in it.

When Aristotle's *Prior Analytics* were studied intensively, it was natural that the distinction should be used in defence of the disputed thesis of Aristotle's modal logic. Such an application of it can be found in the remarkable work *In Universam Logicam Quaestiones* which was formerly attributed to Duns Scotus and printed as his work in the first volume of Luke Wadding's

---

[12] *Abaelardiana Inedita*, p. 29.

[13] This example suggests that Abelard knew Aristotle's *De Caelo*, i. 12 (281^b16)

[14] *Abaelardiana Inedita*, p. 33.

[15] *Peter Abaelards Philosophische Schriften*, ed. B. Geyer, *Beiträge zur Geschichte der Philosophie und Theologie des Mittelalters*, xxi (1919–33), p. 275.

[16] *Die Introductiones in logicam des Wilhelm von Shyreswood*, ed. M. Grabman, *Sitzungsberichte der Bayerischen Akademie der Wissenschaften, Phil.-hist. Klasse*, 1937, Heft 10, pp. 42–3.

[17] *Petri Hispani Summulae Logicales*, ed. Bochenski, §7.26.

seventeenth-century edition. There, however, the distinction is expressed as one between *sensus compositus* and *sensus divisus*.[18] Interesting passages which combine the two ways of phrasing the distinction are to be found in St. Thomas's *De Veritate* (*qu.* 2, *art.* 12., *ad* 4) and his *Summa Contra Gentiles*, i. 67, which both deal with the problem of future contingents. The question as posed in the second of these passages is whether, if Socrates is seated, God's foreknowledge, which has been traditionally described as the seeing of all things in a timeless present, makes it necessary that Socrates should be seated; and St. Thomas answers that a statement which might be cited as a premiss in the dispute, namely *Quod videtur sedere necesse est sedere,* is true in one sense but not in another: *Patet eam de dicto intellectam et compositam esse veram, de re vero et divisam esse falsam.*

4

What shall we say now of the value of the distinction? If it is no more than a recognition that some sentences containing modal words are not intended to be taken as statements asserting the absolute possibility, impossibility, necessity, or contingency of a *dictum,* it is a gain to philosophy. For if I say "It is possible that every U.S. senator is over forty years of age", I do not just mean that the *dictum* of the sentence "Every U.S. senator is over forty years of age" is self-consistent, though no doubt it is, but rather that I know nothing about any senator which excludes the truth of the *dictum.* And again if I say "Every Scotsman must have heard of Burns", I do not mean that the dictum of the sentence "Every Scotsman has heard of Burns" is intrinsically necessary, which it is certainly not, but rather that there is a fact about present Scotsmen, namely that they have been subject to Scottish national propaganda, which makes it inevitable that they have heard of Burns. My examples are in fact elliptical statements of relative modality, and just for that reason unsuitable as illustrations for a formal theory of absolute modality in which modal statements are assumed to be fully explicit. But defenders of the theory of modality *de re* have not made that point about it. On the contrary they have sometimes talked as though it were an independent use of modal words and even perhaps the basic use.

Now whatever we may in the end come to think of the value of the distinction, we can scarcely deny that there is something unfortunate in Abelard's doctrine that genuine modal statements never involve application of modal adjectives to *dicta.* For it seems obvious to us that the use of modal words *de dicto* is fundamental even for the explanation of cases where they are said to occur *de re,* and that if modal words are sometimes used in such a way as to convey a qualification that is inextricably internal, this should not be taken as a simple and basic usage but rather as evidence of the complexity of the discourse in which it occurs. In some respects modal words are like negative particles. As Abelard rightly remarked, in order to obtain

[18] *Quaestio,* 28 on the first book of the *Prior Analytics.*

the negative of a given statement, we must introduce a negative particle in such a position that it can operate upon the whole of the original.[19] But a negative particle may nevertheless occur within a complicated statement at some place in which it does not operate upon all the rest and from which it cannot be extracted by any ingenuity of paraphrase. It would obviously be foolish in this case to say that only complicated sentences of the second kind are truly negative. On the contrary, it is more reasonable to say, as Abelard does in effect, that a statement of the second kind need not be negative as a whole. So, too, if there are statements which involve modality internally, these need not be modal as wholes; and on the other hand denial of the name to statements like "It is possible that no man should be white" seems to be no more than pedantic adherence to misleading suggestions of the word *modus*. Some of later schoolmen came near to realizing the point, but in general the influence of tradition was too strong for them.

In order to get this point clear and at the same time to test the theory of modality *de re* when this modality is supposed to be not merely elliptical and relative but explicit and absolute, let us try to express the distinction in modern symbolism, starting once more with the disputed theses in Aristotle's modal logic. If his mediaeval defenders are right, Aristotle wished to maintain that an ordinary-language statement of the form "Every F thing is necessarily G" might be understood either *de dicto*, in which case it meant (existential import apart) $\Box(x)\ [Fx \supset Gx]$, or *de re*, in which case it meant $(x)[Fx \supset \Box\, Gx]$, and that with the second interpretation, but not the first, a conclusion containing "necessarily" might be derived syllogistically from a pair of premisses of which only the major contained the word "necessarily". This is a reasonable doctrine provided we can find some true statements which are genuine examples of the form $(x)\ [Fx \supset \Box\, Gx]$, i.e., examples which retain that form even when expressed in completely explicit fashion. And it agrees with what I have just said about the primacy of modality *de dicto*. For obviously nothing of the form $(x)[Fx \supset \Box\, Gx]$ can make sense unless something of the form $\Box\, Gx$ makes sense, i.e., unless there can be a functional expression whose values are propositions ascribing necessity to singular *dicta*. Conversely, if we can produce true statements of the necessity of singular *dicta*, there should be no difficulty in constructing statements of the form $(x)\ [Fx \supset \Box\, Gx]$ which are also true, and so the admissibility of modal assertions *de re* may be established. It seems therefore that everything depends on what we can discover about the propriety of describing some singular *dicta* as necessary.

5

On first reflection it seems easy to find true statements in which necessity is ascribed to singular *dicta*; for we often make remarks which look like specimens of the kind required. But on further examination many of these turn

[19] *Dialectica*, p. 178.

out to be elliptical. Consider, for example, the statements "My wife must have missed her train", "Caesar inevitably made enemies", and "It is necessary that the earth should travel round the sun in a closed orbit". In the first the word "must" indicates that there is something known to the speaker, and possibly also to the hearer, which allows the speaker to infer that his wife has missed the train. In the second the fact that Caesar made enemies is presented as something necessitated by other facts about him. If the sentence occurs in a work of history, it is to be presumed that the other facts which are relevant have been stated earlier. In the third the motion of the earth is considered as something determined by laws of nature and initial conditions which the speaker will specify on demand. Frege indeed was so much impressed by examples of this kind that he thought the subject of modality belonged to epistemology rather than to logic and should have no recognition in his *Begriffsschrift*. This seems to me shortsighted, since elucidation of examples such as I have produced always requires the introduction at some stage of a non-elliptical notion of necessity, or rather necessitation, and logic without such a notion is like *Hamlet* without the Prince of Denmark. But it is true that any attempt to elucidate one of these examples by expressing it in more explicit fashion with the help of the terminology of modal logic must open with some phrase such as "There is a piece of information which . . ." And it is clear that a statement whose analysis begins in that way cannot be an ascription of absolute necessity to a singular *dictum*.

There are, however, some statements containing modal words which seem much better qualified for the title. Let us take for example "The Queen is necessarily a woman". Here the use of the word "necessarily" does not depend on the assumption of any evidence not explicitly given, and it seems reasonable to render the whole thing in the symbolism of modal logic by the formula $\Box W\ [(\imath x)\ Qx]$. But here we come on a new difficulty. The grammatical subject of our original statement was a definite description, "the Queen"; and if its use is to be explained in accordance with Russell's theory of descriptions, our transcription into logical symbolism is unsatisfactory. For it apparently commits us to the false assertion that it is absolutely necessary that there should be a queen now reigning. If, on the other hand, we say that the existential presupposition of our original statement is not part of what we want to declare necessary, it is no longer plausible to say that we are ascribing necessity to a singular *dictum*. For now it seems that what we want to declare necessary is the proposition that the Queen, if there is one, is a woman; and this must be rendered in the symbolism of logic by a formula such as $\Box(x)[Q'x \supset Wx]$, where $Q'x$ is short for "x is the sole Q thing." It is true that we may perhaps escape these troubles by choosing for consideration a statement in which the existential presupposition of our grammatical subject term is itself necessarily true, e.g., "The least prime number greater than two must be odd". But our new example is not much better. For if it is superior in any way to that which we had before, the difference is merely that it allows us to retain Russell's theory of descriptions and so to talk of the necessity of our whole *dictum*. Yet the essence of Russell's theory of descriptions is precisely the thesis that a formula which has a definite description for subject is not to be regarded as the expression of a simple singular proposition but rather as the expression of somewhat complicated existential proposition.

At this stage in the argument someone may object that we are wasting time by considering statements which have definite descriptions for their grammatical subjects. "Why", he may ask, "should we not go straight to the point and look for things, in a large sense of that word, which have their attributes necessarily? If the theory of modality *de re*, or of that understanding of modal statements which Abelard called *expositio de rebus*, is to be taken seriously, the important thing is to indicate the *res* concerned". This seems to have been the thought of Prof. G. H. von Wright when he suggested in a section on modality *de re* the following Principle of Predication: "If a property can be significantly predicated of the individuals of a certain Universe of Discourse, then either the property is necessarily present in some or all of the individuals and necessarily absent in the rest, or else the property is possibly but not necessarily (i.e., contingently) present in some or all individuals and possibly but not necessarily (i.e., contingently) absent in the rest."[20] In the first, or formal group, he tells us, there fall the arithmetical properties of numbers, since any given natural number is either necessarily or impossibly a prime number, and in the second, or material, group fall the colours of material objects, since any given piece of solid matter is either contingently red or contingently not red. Unfortunately this declaration is much too simple, for it is based on the mistaken assumption that properties may be said to belong to individuals necessarily or contingently, as the case may be, without regard to the ways in which the individuals are selected for attention. It is no doubt true to say that the number twelve is necessarily composite, but it is certainly not correct to say that the number of the apostles is necessarily composite, unless the remark is to be understood as an elliptical statement of relative necessity. And again it is no doubt correct to say that this at which I am pointing is contingently white, but it is certainly not correct to say that the white paper at which I am looking is contingently white, unless again the remark is to be understood as elliptical. We may say, if we like, that in certain usages the numeral "twelve" is the arithmetical proper name of the number twelve, but we should not think that in the sentence "Twelve is necessarily composite" it refers to that abstract entity without expressing any sense relevant to the truth of our remark. On the contrary, it expresses the same sense as "the number exemplified by all sets that can be put into one-one correspondence with the set of numerals {"1", "2", "3", . . ., "12"}", and this is why the sentence expresses a true proposition. Why indeed should we suppose that the sense of the name is irrelevant here, since even ordinary proper names of people

[20]*An Essay in Modal Logic*, p. 27.

are not, as John Stuart Mill supposed, signs without sense? While it may be informative to tell a man that the most famous Greek philosopher was called Socrates, it is obviously trifling to tell him that Socrates was called Socrates; and the reason is simply that he cannot understand your use of the word "Socrates" at the beginning of your statement unless he already knows that it means "the individual called Socrates".

If what I have just said is right, it is clear that there can be no ordinary properties of which it is proper to say that they belong to any individuals with absolute necessity regardless of the way in which those individuals are selected for attention. But there may be, and indeed obviously are, some extraordinary properties of which we can say just this, namely categorial properties such as being a natural number and truistic properties such as being-prime-or-not-prime. For each such property belongs necessarily to all individuals of the appropriate category, however they may be selected for attention. If what we want is a statement of the form $G(Y)$, in which the truth of the whole is independent of the sense of the designation represented by the letter Y, the only way of achieving the desired result is to choose such a truistic property for predication of the individual we designate. In a modal context, where the sense of a designation is irrelevant to the truth of the whole, the reference of the designation must *a fortiori* be irrelevant also; and that is as much as to say that the sign could be replaced *salva veritate* by any other of appropriate type.

6

Returning now to our original problem, we find that in any context in which it is correct to make a statement of the form $(x)[Fx \supset \Box\, Gx]$ it is equally correct to make a statement of the form $\Box(x)[Fx \supset Gx]$, since if Gx expresses a truistic property, so too must $Fx \supset Gx$. That is to say, any ordinary-language statement of the pattern "Every F thing is necessarily G", if true when understood *de re* in this sense, must also be true when understood *de dicto*. But we may go further. According to our analysis, absolute modality *de re* is no more than a special case of modality *de dicto*, and a rather uninteresting special case for which the title of modality *de re* is inappropriate. When Abelard first introduced the phrase *expositio de rebus*, he had in mind, it seems, the idea that certain things in their own right as individuals were capable or incapable of having certain characters. And this notion was obviously in the minds of some mediaeval philosphers who tried to defend the dubious theses of Aristotle's modal logic by means of a distinction between modality *de dicto* and modality *de re*; for no one could wish to defend the disputed syllogisms of Aristotle without making such an assumption. But when it is closely examined, the assumption proves to be either a mistake or a triviality. Probably those philosophers who have thought it more important have been misled by the elliptical usages of modal words to which I have already drawn attention more than once. No one would think that there was anything to be gained in argument by use of a syllogism such as "Every writer of Latin is necessarily either dead or not dead; and every mediaeval European philosopher is a writer of Latin; therefore every mediaeval European philosopher is necessarily dead or not dead." On the other hand, someone familiar with Scottish customs might conceivably think it worth while to argue as follows: "Every Scot must have heard of Burns; and every inhabitant of Inverness is a Scot; therefore every inhabitant of Inverness must have heard of Burns". If he did, his reasoning would be quite respectable, but it would not justify him or anyone else in speaking of modality *de re* as though this were a separate kind of absolute modality. At the best, then, the distinction of modality *de dicto* and modality *de re* is a distinction between different ways in which modal words may occur in ordinary language, and not, as some philosophers appear to think, a metaphysical distinction important for formal logic where all is supposed to be made explicit.

In justice to Abelard, from whom we have our first account of the distinction, it should be pointed out that he wrote of two *expositiones*, i.e., two ways of understanding some sentences which contain modal words, and that his chief example in his *Dialectica* is a sentence for which both *expositiones* yield propositions of the same fundamental kind. For when *Nullum hominem possibile est esse album* is understood *secundum expositionem de rebus*, it is taken to mean "No man can be white", or "It is impossible that any man should be white", where impossibility is asserted of a *dictum*, though not, of course, of that *dictum* of which possibility is asserted in the *expositio de sensu* of the original. But he goes on to consider other cases for which the *expositio de rebus* does not work out in that way, and what he says of them suggests that he is influenced by elliptical usages. For *Omnem hominem possibile est esse album* understood *de rebus* he offers the equivalent *Natura omnis hominis patitur albedinem*, and for *Quemdam hominem necesse est esse album* the equivalent *Cuiusdam hominis natura albedinem exigit.*[21] What he calls here the *natura* of an individual is not further explained. Perhaps his use of the phrase is mere periphrasis for talk of individuals as such. On the other hand, it may signify some unspecified attribute or set of attributes, in which case it implies recognition of the truth that possibility and necessity can be defined by reference to the relational notions of compatibility and necessitation.

The two examples of Abelard which I have just noted are especially interesting because they involve the operation of quantifiers across modal signs in a fashion that has been much debated in recent years. It is generally agreed that the patterns $(x)\Box Gx$ and $(\exists x)\Diamond Gx$ can be safely admitted, since they may be treated as equivalent, respectively, to $\Box(x)\ Gx$ and $\Diamond(\exists x)\ Gx$. But $(\exists x)\ \Box\ Gx$ and $(x)\ \Diamond\ Gx$ are found puzzling, because they cannot, it seems, be equated with any expressions in which modal signs come first, i.e., with any expressions of modality *de dicto*. Those who wish to retain

[21]*Dialectica*, p. 200.

them rely on analogies from modal logic without quantifiers, and suggest that $(\exists x) \Box Gx$ should be regarded as stronger than $\Box (\exists x) Gx$ and $(x) \Diamond Gx$ as weaker than $\Diamond (x) Gx$. This seems plausible so long as we do not try to interpret the resulting system; but when we look for examples of the two new patterns, we find ourselves thrown into perplexities of just the same sort as those we met in our investigation of the mediaeval doctrine of modality *de re*.

Construction of a formula such as $(\exists x) \Box Gx$ or $(x) \Diamond Gx$ presupposes that we know already what is meant by formulas like $\Box G(Y)$ and $\Diamond G(Y)$. Let us consider the first case in some detail. From the argument set out above it follows that a designation occurring within a modal context can always be eliminated. If the designation is not a definite description but a proper name (e.g., "Socrates"), we first of all replace it by a definite description with the same sense (e.g., "the person called Socrates"). Next we extract from our description, say $(\iota x) Fx$, the predicate $F'x$, which means "x is the sole F thing". And finally for $\Box G[(\iota x) Fx]$ we write $\Box (x) [F'x \supset Gx]$. Now when we meet the formula $(\exists x) \Box Gx$, we do not know what is the relevant description of the thing or things which are said to be necessarily instances of the character expressed by Gx, but there are only two possibilities to be considered. $(\exists x) \Box Gx$ may mean "There is something which under any description is necessarily G", and it may mean "There is something which under some description is necessarily G". If the first interpretation is that intended, $(\exists x) \Box Gx$ cannot express a true proposition unless Gx is a truistic predicate and therefore entailed by any conceivable description. But this is as much as to say that the disputed formula is equivalent to $\Box (x) Gx$. If, on the other hand, the second interpretation is that intended, $(\exists x) \Box Gx$ cannot express a true proposition unless there is something which among its permissible descriptions has one entailing the predicate Gx. But this is as much as to say that the disputed formula is equivalent to $(\exists x) Gx$. Therefore $(\exists x) \Box Gx$ cannot on either interpretation represent a new kind of proposition. By a similar argument it can be shown that, if $(x) \Diamond Gx$ has any meaning at all, it must be equivalent either to $(x) Gx$ or to $\Diamond (\exists x) Gx$; and so here too it appears that there is no need to admit the operation of quantifiers across modal signs.

The moral of the whole debate is that modal assertions can only be made significantly about those abstract entities which some modern logicians call intensions. When Abelard distinguished an *expositio de sensu* from an *expositio de rebus*, he did not have in mind any general theory of sense and reference such as Frege was to formulate more than seven hundred years later; but because his *sensus*, or *dictum propositionis*, was in fact what Frege later called the sense of an indicative sentence, his contrast tended to develop in the Fregean way. The fault of the doctrine of modality *de re* is indeed just this, that it tries to allow for modal assertions which are not about the senses of signs but about their references. And the temptation to adopt it seems to be due primarily to the fact that our modal talk is very often elliptical. When logicians undertake to set up a theory of necessity and possibility which shall be fully explicit and well articulated, they sometimes unfortunately fail to realize that fragments of discourse which appear simple because they are familiar may not be really basic for the purpose they have in mind.

CONTRAPOSITION IN INDIAN LOGIC

J. F. STAAL
University of London, London, England

I

An inference in Indian logic can generally be written in the following form:

$$(x)(A(h, x) \rightarrow A(s, x)). \qquad (1)$$

Here $A(y, x)$ denotes the relation of occurrence of a term y in its locus x; h denotes the reason (*hetu*) and s denotes the thing-to-be-inferred (*sādhya*). In the stock example h denotes smoke and s denotes fire. The relationship of inference is often called *vyāpti*, "pervasion", which may be written $V(h, s)$. It is said that the *hetu* is "pervaded" (*vyāpya*) by the *sādhya*, its "pervader" (*vyāpaka*).

In any given inference the place of the variable x is taken by a preferential locus, which is called *pakṣa* and which will be denoted by p. The question is then asked whether s occurs in p if h occurs in p. In the stock example p is the mountain where fire is to be inferred from smoke. The conclusion that s actually occurs in p when $A(h, p)$ is given is proved by means of a quantified inference of the form (1).

In the VIIth century A.D. the Buddhist logician Dharmakīrti mentions three conditions which are required for establishing the validity of such an inference. This doctrine originated, in an unquantified form, before Dignāga, who lived in the Vth or VIth century.[1] In the formulation of Dharmakīrti, quantification is expressed by the position of the particle *eva*, "only, just", in the following manner:

(a) "occurrence in the inferred (*anumeya*) of h *only*"[2] which can be expressed by: (*anumeya*) A (h, *anumeya*). The words "of h", mentioned only here, belong to all three conditions;

(b) "occurrence of h in similar instances (*sapakṣa*) *only*",[3] which can be expressed by: $(x)(A(h, x) \rightarrow (x = sapakṣa))$; and:

(c) "non-occurrence in dissimilar instances (*asapakṣa*) of h *only*",[4] which can be expressed by: (*asapakṣa*) $\sim A$ (h, *asapakṣa*).

The meaning of these conditions depends on the meanings of the terms *anumeya*, *sapakṣa* and *asapakṣa* which are subsequently defined as follows:

---

[1] A *Tarka-śāstra*, ed. by G. Tucci (*Pre-Diṅnāga Buddhist text on logic from Chinese sources*, Baroda, 1930) mentions the doctrine of the three conditions (G. Tucci, Buddhist logic before Diṅnāga, *Journal of the Royal Asiatic Society*, 1929, p. 483).

[2] *liṅgasyānumeye sattvam eva:* Dharmakīrti's *Nyāyabindu* with Dharmottara's *ṭīkā* (*NB*), ed. by Candraśekhara Śāstrī, Banaras, 1954, p. 22. Cf. Th. Stcherbatsky, *Buddhist Logic II*, 's-Gravenhage 1958 (reprint of: *Bibliotheca Buddhica XXVI 2*, Leningrad, 1930), pp. 51–9.

[3] *sapakṣa eva sattvam:* *NB*, p. 23.

[4] *asapakṣe cāsattvam eva:* loc. cit.

"*anumeya* is here the substratum (*dharmin*), the characteristic (*viśeṣa*) of which it is desired to know".[5] The commentator Dharmottara (VIIIth or IXth century) explains *viśeṣa* by *dharma*, "property".

"*sapakṣa* is what is similar through similarity with the property *s*";[6] and:

"*asapakṣa* is what is not *sapakṣa*".[7]

In later texts the place of *anumeya* is taken by *pakṣa* and the place of *asapakṣa* by *vipakṣa*; in both cases these latter terms will be adopted here. As in a given inference there is only one p, the first condition amounts to: $A(h, p)$. Dharmottara explains similarity (*sāmānya*) as similarity of the *sapakṣa* with p. This similarity consists in the fact that s actually occurs in the *sapakṣa* cases and does not occur in the *vipakṣa* cases.

In order to formalize these conditions in a manner which preserves as far as possible the structure of the Sanskrit expressions, use will be made of the expression $\alpha x F(x)$ for a *restricted-variable* denoting any of the values of x such that $F(x)$. The use of this expression may be illustrated by the formalizations of :"h is what is pervaded by s" as: $h = \alpha x V(x, s)$ and of: "s is what pervades h" as: $s = \alpha x V(h, x)$. The use of the expression $\alpha x F(x)$, which may occur either free or bound, is governed by various laws, the following three of which will be utilized:

$$(\alpha x F(x)) G(\alpha x F(x)) \leftrightarrow (x)(F(x) \rightarrow G(x)), \tag{2}$$

$$(Ey)(y = \alpha x F(x)) \leftrightarrow (Ex) F(x), \tag{3}$$

$$(y)(y = \alpha x F(x)) \leftrightarrow (x) F(x). \tag{4}$$

The terms *sapakṣa* and *vipakṣa* can now be defined as follows:
sapakṣa:

$$\alpha x((x \neq p) \wedge A(s, x)); \tag{5}$$

vipakṣa:

$$\alpha x \sim A(s, x). \tag{6}$$

If these two expressions are substituted, respectively, in the second and third conditions of Dharmakīrti mentioned above, the result is:

$$(y)(A(h, y) \rightarrow (y = \alpha x((x \neq p) \wedge A(s, x)))), \tag{7}$$

$$(\alpha x \sim A(s, x)) \sim A(h, \alpha x \sim A(s, x)). \tag{8}$$

The question now arises whether (7) and (8) yield (1), as is the contention of Dharmakīrti. Starting from (7) we derive:

$$(y) A(h, y) \rightarrow (y)(y = \alpha x((x \neq p) \wedge A(s, x))),$$

---

[5] *anumeyo'tra jijñāsitaviśeṣo dharmī*: *NB*, p. 24.

[6] *sādhya-dharma-sāmānyena samāno'rthaḥ sapakṣaḥ: loc. cit.*

[7] *na sapakṣo'sapakṣaḥ: loc. cit.*

and hence with the help of (4):

$$(y)A(h, y) \to (y)((y \neq p) \wedge A(s, y)),$$
$$(y)(A(h, y) \to ((y \neq p) \wedge A(s, y))),$$
$$(y)(A(h, y) \to A(s, y)),$$

or (1), which has been thus derived from (7) only.

The expression (8), on the other hand, yields with the help of (2):

$$(9) \qquad (x)(\sim A(s, x) \to \sim A(h, x)).$$

This is the contrapositive of (1), which has been thus derived from (8) only. Summarizing these results it may be said that the second condition implies (1) directly, whereas the third condition implies either (1) or the second condition through contraposition.

The original Buddhist theory of the three conditions in their unquantified form may mainly have been a kind of argument by reference to analogous cases. Its indeterminate status prevents a judgment on the interdependence of the three conditions. Dharmakīrti quantifies the conditions by means of *eva*. Thus it was recognized that the second and third conditions are equivalent and that this equivalence constitutes a logical relationship, namely, contraposition.

Although Stcherbatsky and, following him, Bocheński, have studied the three conditions of Dharmakīrti and have explicitly mentioned the special use of *eva* in his formulation, they have neither stated what was in their opinion the exact significance of these conditions, nor have they investigated whether an inference can be proved from any of these three conditions separately, or only from all the three together. Bocheński, after having mentioned Dharmakīrti's use of *eva*, again expresses the opinion that Buddhist logic was "noch ganz durch die Beispiele bestimmt".[8] Frauwallner does not seem to have paid much attention to the problems of quantification and independence of the three conditions, but apparently attributes the discovery of contraposition to Dignāga on account of the latter's *hetucakra*.[9] We do not know, however, how the various clauses of the *hetucakra* were thought to be related to each other and this seems to prevent a very definite conclusion. The mere occurrence of contrapositive clauses does not prove much, since the classification is exhaustive. Randle states rightly, referring to the second and third conditions, that "both clauses say exactly the same

---

[8]I. M. Bocheński, *Formale Logik*, Feiburg/München, 1956, p. 506.

[9]Frauwallner's formulations seem to attribute quantified expressions to logicians prior to Diṅnāga, while suggesting at the same time that the three conditions are jointly necessary: E. Frauwallner, Dignāga, sein Werk und seine Entwicklung. *Wiener Zeitschrift für die Kunde Süd- und Ostasiens und Archiv für indische Philosophie*, Vol. 3 (1959) p. 85. Later he refers to contraposition when speaking about the same period (*op. cit.* pp. 93–4). For Plato's "struggling" with this (or a very similar) false principle, cf. I. M. Bocheński, *Ancient formal logic*, Amsterdam, 1951, p. 17.

thing",[10] but he does not pay much attention to the law of contraposition which underlies this statement.

That *either* the second *or* the third condition yields the required inference is due to the fact that the third condition is the contrapositive of the second condition. If in either condition the constant p is substituted for the variable x, the first condition $A(h, p)$ immediately yields the required result $A(s, p)$. This result has been derived by first formalizing the second and third conditions in (7) and (8), respectively, and by subsequently deriving conclusions from these formulas. Such a purely logical interpretation can be assumed to be justified, since it seems reasonable to treat the Sanskrit text itself as a product of logical activity. That Indian and Western arguments are not different in this respect follows from the commentary on Dharmakīrti's text, which confirms the above conclusion. After having commented upon all the three conditions, Dharmottara asks: "But does the expression 'occurrence in the *sapakṣa* only' not entail 'only non-occurrence in the *vipakṣa*'?"[11] Asking this question can only be explained by assuming that the author knew the law of contraposition and its relevance to the present context. He then continues: "Why then are two clauses (*upādāna*) mentioned? The answer is as follows. *Either* the *anvaya*, *or* the *vyatireka* should be used, each with necessity, and not otherwise".[12] Here *anvaya* refers to the second condition, and *vyatireka* to the third; in other words, *vyatireka* denotes the contraposition or *anvaya*. The required necessity (*niyama*) refers to the use of *eva* or to the quantification of the expressions, as is evident from the subsequent lines, where it is said that without this necessity, even when both conditions are assumed to be valid, an invalid inference can be derived. The example which is given to show this is the following: "it is black because it is that person's child".[13] Here blackness occurs in *some* of the children (*sapakṣa*) but it is also absent from *some* other children (*vipakṣa*). This inference is invalid. Hence the conditions should be properly quantified and "of both only one should be used and not two" [14] Lastly Dharmottara summarizes his interpretation as follows: "With necessity, either the *anvaya* or the *vyatireka* should be used".[15]

Many of these sentences were translated in similar terms by Stcherbatsky,[16] but he failed to appreciate their significance adequately, mainly on account of his special interest in "universal and necessary propositions",

---

[10]H. N. Randle, *Indian logic in the early schools*, London, etc., 1930, p. 183.

[11]*nanu ca sapakṣa eva sattvam ity ukte vipakṣe'sattvam eveti gamyata eva*: *NB*, p. 24.

[12]*anvayo vyatireko vā niyamavān eva prayoktavyo nānyatheti: loc. cit.*

[13]*śyāmas tatputratvāt* (Stcherbatsky translates this differently, with reference to the *upādhi*). This type of (invalid) inference may be a forerunner of the type of (valid) inference in the latter schools: *kapisaṃyogy etadvṛkṣatvāt*, "it has contact with a monkey because it is this tree".

[14]*dvayor eka eva prayoktavyo na dvāv iti*: *loc. cit.*

[15]*niyamavān evānvayo vyatireko vā prayoktavya iti: loc. cit.*

[16]*Op. cit.* pp. 57–8.

i.e., mainly because of his Kantian bias. In the chapter on contraposition in the first volume of his monumental "Buddhist Logic"[17] Stcherbatsky states that the second and third conditions "are two manners of expressing the same idea", but he then adds the apparently meaningless sentence: "But in order to express the *necessary* dependence of the reason upon the predicate both must be stated, either expressedly or by implication".[17] The same insistence on necessary propositions causes a term like *samāna* in the same passage to be variously translated by "similar", "common", or "universal".

In the above translation no attention has been paid to the occurrence of the term *niścitam*, "ascertained, necessary" at the end of the third condition, which Stcherbatsky accordingly translates as: "its absolute absence in dissimilar cases is necessary". With this translation the problem arises why only the third condition would have to be ascertained as necessary. This problem is solved by Dharmottara, according to whom the term should be applied to all the three conditions. In the commentary upon the first condition he says: "Even though the word *niścita* is not mentioned here, it is mentioned at the end and should be considered with reference to the two preceding expressions".[18]

II

After a millenium, the requirement of necessity forms part of the definitions of *sapakṣa* and *vipakṣa* in the texts of the modern school of Indian logic (*navya-nyāya*). The *pakṣa* is again defined with reference to the occurrence of *s*, which is not ascertained but merely desired. In a well-known manual of Indian logic, the *Tarka-saṃgraha* (*TS*) of Annaṃbhaṭṭa, written in the XVIIth century A.D., the same concepts are utilized but form part of a newly elaborated system of formal logic.[19] The definitions are given as follows:

"*p* is the locus of *s* which is doubted",[20] e.g., the mountain;
"*sapakṣa* is a locus of *s* which is ascertained",[21] e.g., the kitchen; and:
"*vipakṣa* is a locus of absence of *s* which is ascertained",[22] e.g., the lake.

With the help of these terms three types of inference can be distinguished, which are called: (I) *kevalānvayī*, "universally positive, unnegatable"; (II) *kevalavyatirekī*, "universally negative, unexampled"; and: (III)

[17] *Buddhist logic I*, 's-Gravenhage, 1958 (reprint of: *Bibliotheca Buddhica XXVI 1*, Leningrad, 1932), pp. 301–3. The Kantian predisposition is so strong as to obliterate the problem in: Th. Stcherbatsky, *Erkenntnistheorie und Logik nach der Lehre der späteren Buddhisten*, München/Neubiberg, 1924, p. 206.

[18] *yady api cātra niścita-grahaṇaṃ na kṛtaṃ tathāpyante kṛtaṃ prakrāntayor dvayor api rūpayor apekṣaṇīyam: NB*, p. 22.

[19] Cf. the present author's Formal structures in Indian logic, *Synthese*, Vol. 22 (1960), pp. 279–86.

[20] *saṃdigdha-sādhyavān pakṣaḥ: TS*, ed. by Y. V. Athalye, Bombay, 1930, pp. 43, 290–3.

[21] *niścita-sādhyavān sapakṣaḥ: loc. sit.*

[22] *niścita-sādhyābhāvavān vipakṣaḥ: TS*, p. 44.

anvaya-vyatirekī, "positive-negative". This classification was already given by logicians of the old Hindu school, such as Uddyotakara (early VIIth century),[23] and is dealt with in the *TS*.[24] The three types are defined by means of the above terminology in the *Siddhānta-muktāvalī* (*SM*) of Viśvanātha Pañcānana (XVIIth century) as follows:

(I) "Universally positive is what has no dissimilar instances",[25] which can be written with the help of (6) as:

$$\sim(Ey)(y = \alpha x \sim A(s, x)),$$

and hence with the help of (3) as:
kevalānvayī:

$$(10) \qquad \sim(Ex) \sim A(s, x) \quad \text{or:} \quad (x)A(s, x).$$

EXAMPLE: the inference $A(\textit{namability}, x) \rightarrow A(\textit{knowability}, x)$.[26]

(II) "Universally negative is what has no similar instances",[27] which can be written with the help of (5) as:

$$\sim(Ey)(y = \alpha x((x \neq p) \wedge A(s, x))),$$

and hence with the help of (3) as:
kevalavyatirekī:

$$\sim(Ex)((x \neq p) \wedge A(s, x)).$$

This may be written as:

$$(11) \qquad (x)(A(s, x) \rightarrow (x = p)).$$

EXAMPLE: the inference

$$A(\textit{smell, earth}) \rightarrow A\ (\textit{being different from other things, earth}).$$

This may be explained along the following lines. In the traditional physics adopted by the logicians, earth (the *pakṣa*) is the only substance which smells or has smell (*gandha*) or *g*:

---

[23]See: S. C. Vidyabhusana, *A history of Indian logic*, Calcutta, 1921, p. 130.

[24]*TS*, pp. 40, 281–90. Cf. A. Foucher, *Le compendium des topiques*, Paris, 1949, p. 132–5.

[25]*asadvipakṣaḥ kevalānvayī: SM*, ed. by Hari Rāma Śukla, Banaras, 1951, p. 501.

[26]The relation of *kevalānvayī* cases to the definitions of *vyāpti* is further discussed in the present author's Correlations between language and logic in Indian thought, *Bulletin of the School of Oriental and African Studies*, Vol. 23 (1960), pp. 116–7.

[27]*asatsapakṣaḥ kevalavyatirekī: loc. cit.* It is generally the inference which is called *kevalavyatirekī*, but it is the *hetu* according to the *Nyāyakośa* (Poona, 1928, p. 241) in a quotation from the *TS* or the *Nyāya-siddhānta-mañjarī*. As in some other cases, this reading differs considerably from the reading of the printed edition by Jīvanātha Miśra (Banaras, 1916, p. 97; a critical edition with translation is being prepared by T. Gelblum).

$$p = (E!x)A(g, x),$$

or:

(12) $$A(g, p) \wedge (x)(A(g, x) \rightarrow (x = p)).$$

The right member of this conjunction and (11) show that the inference is universally negative.

While (I) and (II) are relatively exceptional cases, the general situation is dealt with in the remaining possibility:

(III) "Positive-negative is what has both similar and dissimilar instances",[28] which can be written as:
anvayavyatirekī:

(13) $$(Ex) \sim A(s, x) \wedge (Ex)((x \neq p) \wedge A(s, x)).$$

EXAMPLE: the inference $A(smoke, hill) \rightarrow A(fire, hill)$.

PROOF: $\alpha x \sim A(s, x)$ is *lake*; $\alpha x((x \neq p) \wedge A(s, x))$ is *kitchen*.

The term *anvayavyatirekī* can at the same time denote the law of contraposition, which transforms a "positive pervasion" (*anvaya-vyāpti*) into a "negative pervasion" (*vyatireka-vyāpti*). We have seen that Dharmottara used *anvaya* and *vyatireka* already in this sense. The Mīmāṃsaka Kumārila Bhaṭṭa (VIIIth century), a famous and well-informed opponent of Buddhist doctrines, describes contraposition in the following verse of the *Śloka-vārttika*:

> If the relation of pervader and pervaded holds between two entities, it follows that the converse *(viparīta)* relation holds between their negations.[29]

The commentator Bhaṭṭomveka (late VIIIth century?) explains these two lines as referring to *anvaya* and *vyatireka*, respectively.[30] Similar formulations are given by the later logicians. Keśava Miśra (between 1200 and1400) quotes the same lines in his *Tarka-bhāṣā* and adds the following verse:

> In positive inference the reason is pervaded and the thing-to-be-inferred is the pervader; in the other case the negation of the thing-to-be-inferred is pervaded and the negation of the reason is the pervader. First the pervaded is stated and next the pervader. Thus examined the true nature of pervasion becomes manifest.[31]

The *TS* uses the terms as follows: "'Where there is smoke, there is fire, as in the kitchen' is a positive pervasion. 'Where there is no fire, there is no smoke either, as in the lake' is a negative pervasion".[32]

---

[28] *satsapakṣavipakṣo'nvayavyatirekī: SM, loc. cit.*

[29] *vyāpya-vyāpaka-bhāvo hi bhāvayor yādṛg iṣyate/tayor abhāvayos tasmād viparītaḥ pratīyate//Śloka-vārttika anumāna:* 121b–122a.

[30] *Śloka-vārttika-vyākhyā* (ed. by S. K. Rāmanātha Śāstrī, Madras, 1940, p. 335).

[31] *anvaye sādhanaṃ vyāpyaṃ sādhyaṃ vyāpakam iṣyate/sādhyābhāvo'nyathā vyāpyo vyāpakaḥ sādhanātyayaḥ//vyāpyasya vacanaṃ pūrvaṃ vyāpakasya tataḥ param/ evaṃ parīkṣitā vyāptiḥ sphuṭī bhavati tattvataḥ//Tarka-bhāṣā*, ed. by S. N. Dvivedi, Banaras, 1952, p. 22. Cf. transl. by P. Tuxen, Copenhagen, 1914, p. 22.

[32] *TS*, p. 40.

In these various texts contraposition is postulated with reference to pervasion and inference in the following terms:

$$V(h, s) \leftrightarrow V\ (\textit{negation of } s, \textit{ negation of } h),$$

or:

$$(14) \qquad (x)(A(h, x) \rightarrow A(s, x)) \leftrightarrow (x)(\sim A(s, x) \rightarrow \sim A(h, x)).$$

The expressions (13) and (14) are related to each other in the following manner: (14) is only meaningfully applicable if (13) holds. This can be shown with reference to the left member L of (13) and the right member R of (14) as follows:

A. If: $\sim(Ex) \sim A(s, x)$, i.e., in a case of *kevalānvaya*, R is not defined.

B. If: $(x)(\sim A(s, x) \rightarrow \sim A(x = p))$, i.e., in a case of *kevalavyatireka*, L implies $x = p$; but this would be useless, for it is impossible to establish an inference if only the *pakṣa*, where s is doubted, is available, while the similar instances, where s would have been ascertained previously, are absent.

III

Next some refinements of (14), which may illustrate the subtleties and complexities of the *navya-nyāya* style and formalisms, will be considered.

The occurrence relation $A(x, y)$ is always an occurrence through a relation (*saṃbandhena*[33] *vṛttitva*), which relation should be specified if certain ambiguities are to be avoided. The various relations, such as *saṃyoga*, "contact" (c), *samavāya*, "inherence" (i), etc., will be written as subscripts attached to A: A_c, A_i, etc.[34] For instance we have $A_c(\textit{smoke, hill})$, but on the other hand: A_i (*smoke, particles of smoke*). In general the occurrences in an inference may be specified, for instance as follows:

$$(x)(A_p(h, x) \rightarrow A_q(s, x)).$$

In a contraposition of the form (14) the negated occurrence is required to occur through the same relation as the origninally affirmative occurrence. In other words, two conditions should be fulfilled for a contrapositive to be valid:

$$(15) \qquad \alpha y \sim A_y(h, x) = \alpha y A_y(h, x),$$

$$(16) \qquad \alpha y \sim A_y(s, x) = \alpha y A_y(s, x).$$

In Sanskrit (15) could be expressed by the formula: *yatsaṃbandhena hetor vṛttitvaṃ tatsaṃbandhāvacchinna-pratiyogitāka-hetvabhāva*, "the absential

[33]For this use of the instrumental case ending cf. H. Jacobi, Über den nominalen Stil des wissenschaftlichen Sanskrits, *Indogermanische Forschungen*, Vol. 14 (1903), pp. 239–40; L. Renou, *Histoire de la langue sanskrite*, Paris, 1956, p. 141.

[34]In the article quoted above, note 26, these subscripts are within parentheses, as unbracketed subscripts are used to denote case-endings.

correlate[35] of the negation of h is limited by the relation through which h occurs". Analogously (16) could be expressed by: *yatsaṃbandhena sādhya-vṛttitvaṃ tatsaṃbandhāvacchinna-pratiyogitāka-sādhyābhāva*, "the absential correlate of the negation of s is limited by the relation through which s occurs".

By introducing the conditions (15) and (16) into the contraposition formula (14), we arrive at:

$$(17) \quad (x)(A_p(h, x) \rightarrow A_q(s, x)) \leftrightarrow (x)(\sim A_{\alpha y A_y(s,x)}(s, x) \rightarrow \sim A_{\alpha y A_y(s,x)}(h, x)).$$

In this formula: $\sim A_{\alpha y A_y(s,x)}(s, x)$ could be expressed in Sanskrit by: *sādhya-vṛttitvāvacchedaka-saṃbandhāvacchinna-pratiyogitāka-sādhyābhāva*, "negation of s, the absential correlate of which is limited by the limiting relation through which s occurs". Analogously: $\sim A_{\alpha y A_y(h,x)}(h, x)$ could be expressed in Sanskrit by: *hetu-vṛttitvāvacchedaka-saṃbandhāvacchinna-pratiyogitāka-hetvabhāva*, "negation of h, the absential correlate of which is limited by the limiting relation through which h occurs".

If the suggested substitutions are made, (17) may be further simplified to:

$$(18) \quad (x)(A_p(h, x) \rightarrow A_q(s, x)) \leftrightarrow (x)(\sim A_q(s, x) \rightarrow \sim A_p(h, x)).$$

The four Sanskrit expressions in the foregoing lines may illustrate how certain logical relationships can be expressed in the formalized and technical Sanskrit of *navya-nyāya*. They do not acutally occur in the *SM*, but are constructed along similar lines as the more complicated expressions given there. This additional complication is due to the fact that certain other conditions are required at the same time to hold as well. This requirement corresponds to universal quantification in Western logic, which is expressed by means of abstractions in Indian logic.[36] The abstraction of a term x, which will be written as $\hat{x}$, can be expressed in Sanskrit by adding the suffixes *-tva* or *-tā* to the stem, or by the use of such terms as *jāti*, "class" or *dharma*", "property".

If an expression $F(x)$, in which a term x occurs, is universally quantified with respect to x, this is expressed in Sanskrit by saying that the expression $F(x)$ is limited by $\hat{x}$, the abstraction of x. In the formalism which represents the Sanskrit expressions this could be expressed by adding an additional subscript to the functions and relations which are generalised with respect

[35]The "thing-negated" or *abhāvīya-pratiyogī*. See: D. H. H. Ingalls, *Materials for the study of Navya-nyāya logic*, Cambridge, Mass., 1951, p. 55. A formalisation is suggested by the present writer in: *Indo-Iranian Journal*, Vol. 4 (1960), pp. 68–73. While Ingalls translated this *pratiyogī* by "counterpositive", J. Brough suggested in his review (*Journal of the Royal Asiatic Society*, 1954, p. 88) "absential correlate" in order to avoid confusion with "contrapositive". In the present context this translation has naturally been adopted, allthough *abhāva* is here translated by "negation" and not by "absence".

[36]See the present writer's Means of formalisation in Indian and Western logic, *Proceedings of the XIIth International Congress of Philosophy* (Venice, 1958). Firenze, 1960, pp. 221–227.

to their variables. This cannot give rise to confusion with a relational subscript, for the subscript which denotes universal quantification is always marked with the circumflex accent, while there are few relations which are abstractions.[37] Hence universal quantification can be expressed as follows:

$$(19) \qquad F_{\hat{x}}(x) =_{d} (x)F(x)$$

where the left member corresponds to the Sanskrit expression.

The *SM* expresses the various conditions referred to earlier in the following sentence,[38] parts of which have been numbered 1–8: *yatsaṃbandhena*[1] *yadavacchinaṃ prati*[2] *yena saṃbandhena*[3] *yena rūpeṇa*[4] *vyāpakatā gṛhyate tatsaṃbandha*[5]*-avacchinna-pratiyogitāka taddharma*[6]*-avacchinnābhāvavattā-jñānāt tatsaṃbandha*[7]*-avacchinna-pratiyogitāka taddharma*[8]*-avacchinnābhāvasya siddhiḥ.* A literal translation would run as follows:[39] "by which form[4] through which relation[3] with respect to what (i.e., *s*) is limited by which[2] through which relation[1] the pervasion (i.e., of *h*) is understood, the negation (of *h*) is inferred which is limited by that property[8] the absential correlate of which is limited by that relation[7] on account of the knowledge of the negation (of *s*) which is limited by that property[6] the absential correlate of which is limited by that relation[5]". As *h* and *s* are not mentioned explicitly, this is a formulation of generalized contraposition without special reference to the inferential process. An English translation is bound to be hardly intelligible, but a translation into a formula expresses the meaning more directly and can also give a picture of the structure of the Sanskrit original. Restricted-variables represent the four pairs of correlative pronouns (relative *yad* — demonstrative *tad*) which express identity.[40] As in the text the abstractions (expressed twice by *dharma*, once by *rūpa* and once merely by *-yad*) are given with reference to the negation, negation will now be expressed by means of a negating function, as in Łukasiewicz' terminology, by defining:

$$(20) \qquad Nx =_{d} \sim x.$$

Then: $\sim A_{\hat{m}p}(x, y)$ (where: $x = x(m)$ and/or $y = y(m)$) may be written as: $NA_{\hat{m}p}(x, y)$ and as the occurrence A is negated with respect to the relation p, this may be written as: $N_p A_{\hat{m}}(x, y)$.

The Sanskrit expression may now be represented by the following formula,

---

[37]One such exception is the relation *viśeṣaṇatā: Nyāyakośa* ss. vv. *viśeṣaṇam, svarūpasaṃbandhaḥ*. This relation does not occur in the present context.

[38]*SM*, pp. 501–2.

[39]Without the excellent translation and notes of Svāmī Mādhavānanda (Calcutta, 1954, p. 235) it would have been difficult to understand the original. There is one confusing error. The last three lines of page 235 should be read as: ". . . that non-existence which is determined by that attribute, and the counterpositiveness of which is determined by that relation". In his notes the Svāmī gives the following instances for the parts of the expression which have been numbered 1–8 in the above: 1, 3, 5, 7: *conjunction;* 2, 8: *smokehood;* 4: *as fire* (i.e., *firehood*); 6: *firehood.*

[40]Cf. P. Hartmann, *Nominale Ausdrucksformen im wissenschaftlichen Sanskrit*, Heidelberg, 1955, pp. 66, 140–4.

corresponding parts of which are numbered with the same numbers 1–8, respectively, as the above:

$$(21)\qquad (x)\big(A_{\underset{4\quad 3}{\hat{m}p}}(h, x) \rightarrow A_{\underset{2\quad 1}{\hat{n}q}}(s, x)\big)$$

$$\leftrightarrow (x)\big(N_{\underset{6}{\alpha y A_{yq}(s,x)}} A_{\underset{5}{\alpha y A_{\hat{n}y}(s,x)}}(s, x) \rightarrow N_{\underset{8}{\alpha y A_{yp}(h,x)}} A_{\underset{7}{\alpha y A_{\hat{m}y}(h,x)}}(h, x)\big).$$

This expression can be further simplified as follows:

$$(x)\,(A_{\hat{m}p}(h, x) \rightarrow A_{\hat{n}q}(s, x)) \leftrightarrow (x)\,(N_{\hat{n}} A_q(s, x) \rightarrow N_{\hat{m}} A_p(h, x)).$$

Hence, because in the case of inference: $m = h$ and $n = s$:

$$(22)\quad (h)(s)((x)\,(A_p(h, x) \rightarrow A_q(s, x)) \leftrightarrow (x)\;(\sim A_q(s, x) \rightarrow \sim A_p(h, x))),$$

which is a generalization of (18).

Whoever has mastered this terminology may well ask what purpose it serves. The answer is that it excludes certain invalid inferences. For instance, if again c denotes *saṃyoga*, "contact", and i denotes *samavāya*, "inherence", we have:

$$A_c(\mathit{smoke, hill}) \rightarrow A_c(\mathit{fire, hill}),$$

and hence with (22):

$$\sim A_c(\mathit{fire, lake}) \rightarrow \sim A_c(\mathit{smoke, lake}),$$

but we are not entitled to infer:

$$\sim A_i(\mathit{fire, particles\ of\ smoke}) \rightarrow \sim A_i(\mathit{smoke, particles\ of\ smoke}),$$

for in the traditional physics which the Naiyāyikas adopt, fire does not occur in particles of smoke through inherence, while smoke does occur in particles of smoke through inherence.

IV

The Indian logicians had a special reason for being interested in contraposition and in inferences with negative premisses. It enabled them to do without an additional category, which some other schools of Indian thought held to be indispensable. The high evaluation of such economy of thought may have been taken from the Sanskrit grammarians.[41] But while the grammarians often preferred the shortest possible expression (*sūtra*), the logicians, not shrinking, as we have seen, from long and complicated expressions, attempted to manipulate a relatively small number of elementary concepts.

---

[41] Both grammarians and logicians prefer a "light" (*laghu*) expression to a "heavy" (*guru*) expression "for the sake of lightness" (*lāghavārtham*). See: L. Renou, *La Durghaṭavṛtti de Śaraṇadeva*, Paris, 1940, Vol. I (*Introduction*), pp. 1, 81–2 note. For *navya-nyāya* see Ingalls, *op. cit.*, p. 47. Cf. also the discussions concerning *anyathāsiddhi*, litt. "establishment by other means", i.e., "superfluity": *SM* pp. 86–91.

Accordingly the logical style can be characterized not only by its extreme nominalisation and paucity of verbal forms, but also by its limited vocabulary.

The additional category which can be avoided by considering it a special kind of inference is the category of *arthāpatti*, "presumption", adopted by the Mīmāṃsakas.[42] The latter argued that there are cases where neither the category of direct perception, nor that of inference, is a valid means of knowledge. The following is an example. Suppose it were known from astrology that Devadatta shall live a full hundred years, and suppose that it were known from direct perception that he is not at home.[43] It may then be presumed that Devadatta is outside his house. On account of this presumption the Mīmāṃsakas postulate a special means of knowledge, namely, *arthāpatti*. The Naiyāyikas on the other hand class it under inference, because the reasoning involved can be represented by the following metatheorem:

$$A \rightarrow (B \vee C), A, \sim B \vdash C. \tag{23}$$

This metatheorem involves the use of an inference with a negative premiss ($\sim B \rightarrow C$). While this metatheorem is not explicitly stated, it is utilized and it is recognized that it necessitates an inference with a negative premiss. Such inferences were rejected by the Mīmāṃsakas, but the Naiyāyikas proved their validity by referring to the principle of contraposition. Hence the latter principle helped them to explain *arthāpatti* as a special kind of inference.[44]

The same metatheorem is applied in another example, the treatment of which is formulated in the *SM* in the following terms: "In cases such as 'Fat Devadatta does not eat by day', it is known that fatness is pervaded by eating, and hence eating is proved. And as eating by day is contradicted, eating at night is proved".[45]

Not only the Mīmāṃsakas but also the Advaitins adopted *arthāpatti*. Both

---

[42]See G. N. Jhā, *Pūrva-Mīmāṃsā in its sources*, Banaras, 1942, pp. 157–60, and the manuals of Indian philosophy. The two schools of the Mīmāṃsā disagreed on the nature and function of *arthāpatti*. The followers of Kumārila Bhaṭṭa expressed their dislike of the views of the rival school thus: "Well, alas, who are they who, kissing the backs of the followers of Prabhākara, babble thus?" (*Mānameyodaya*, ed. and transl. by C. Kunhan Raja and S. S. Suryanarayana Sastri, Madras, 1933, p. 124). For views of the Advaitins, cf. D. M. Datta, *The six ways of knowing*, London, 1932, p. 216 sq.; A. B. Shastri, *Studies in Post-Śaṁkara dialectics*, Calcutta, 1936, pp. 67–7.

[43]In order to account for such negative knowledge the Mīmāṃsakas postulate another special means of knowledge, *anupalabdhi*, "non-apprehension", which the Naiyāyikas again reject as a distinct category and class under *pratyakṣa*, "perception".

[44]*Presumption* was rejected already in the *Nyāyasūtra* (2.2.3) and in the *Tarkaśāstra* (see above note 1), p. 25. Cf. JRAS (1929), pp. 485–6.

[45]*pīno devadatto divā na bhuṅkta ity ādau pīnatvasya bhojana-vyāpyatvāvagamād bhojanaṃ siddhyati/divā-bhojana-bādhe ca rātri-bhojanaṃ siddhyati: SM*, pp. 503–4; transl. pp. 238–9.

agreed, accordingly, in rejecting the *kevalānvayī* and *kevalavyatirekī* cases of inference recognized by the Naiyāyikas, but for different reasons. The Advaita position directly implies that *kevalānvayī* cases are impossible. For according to the Advaitins there is an absolute entity, *brahman*, and no other entity can reside where *brahman* resides. In the *Vedāntaparibhāṣā* (XVIIth century) this is expressed as follows: "In our view every property is an absential correlate of relational negation located in the Absolute".[46] If *brahman* be denoted by b, this may be expressed by:

$$(24) \qquad (x) \sim A\,(x, \alpha y A\,(b, y)).$$

Hence for any *sādhya* s we have:

$$\sim A\,(s, \alpha y A\,(b, y),$$

hence: $(Ex) \sim A\,(s, x)$ or: $\sim (x) A\,(s, x)$, which contradicts (10); i.e., *kevalānvayī* inferences are impossible. The *kevalavyatirekī* inferences are rejected as well, this time not by means of a definite proof, but in an apparently circular argument. The *Vedāntaparibhāṣā* says that there is no use for *kevalavyatireka*, since in cases where no positive inference is available, another category, namely, *arthāpatti*, will be shown to provide the required knowledge.[47] In a later chapter, when dealing with *arthāpatti*, the text establishes its use as an independent means of knowledge by saying that it was previously shown that no inference can be *kevalavyatirekī*.[48]

The Mīmāṃsakas of the Bhaṭṭa school rejected *kevalavyatireka* cases as they would constitute an exception to a general law. The argument of the *Mānameyodaya* (early XVIIth century) runs as follows: "(for) by inference, what has been established somewhere is established elsewhere",[49] i.e., it is always presupposed that:

$$(25) \qquad (Ex)\,((x \neq p) \wedge A\,(s, x)).$$

In *kevalavyatirekī* cases, on the other hand, the *sādhya* "is not established anywhere else",[50] i.e.:

$$(26) \qquad \sim (Ex)\,((x \neq p) \wedge A\,(s, x)).$$

Since (26) contradicts (25), *kevalavyatireka* is excluded.

A Mādhva author of the XIVth or XVth century rejected the entire classification of inference in three types,[51] but the famous dualist Jayatīrtha

---

[46] *sarvasyāpi dharmasyāsmin mate brahma-niṣṭhātyantābhāva-pratiyogitvena* .... *Vedāntaparibhāṣā*, ed. and transl. by S. S. Suryanarayana Sastri, Madras, 1942, pp. 55–6.

[47] *Loc. cit.* (*vakṣyāmaḥ*).

[48] *Op. cit.*, p. 93 (*prāg eva nirastam*).

[49] *kvacit prasiddham anyatra sādhyate hy anumānataḥ*: *Mānameyodaya*, p. 56.

[50] *siddho nānyatra kutracit*: *loc. cit.*

[51] *Pramāṇa-candrikā*, ed. and transl. by S. K. Maitra under the title *Mādhva logic*, Calcutta, 1936, pp. 77, 149.

(XIIth century) agreed in his *Pramāṇa-paddhati* with the logicians in considering *arthāpatti* as a kind of inference.[52]

V

It is hardly possible to sketch in a few lines the context and background of Indian thought, in which Indian logic plays its part. Such a survey could show how Indian logic constitutes an autochthonous development within Indian culture and cannot be convincingly derived from hypothetical contacts with the West.[53] Presently it may only be attempted to give in conclusion an idea of the context and background of the main terms which have been discussed.

The word *pakṣa* means primarily "wing" and has come to denote "alternative" and hence in general "view", "hypothesis". Frequent uses are *pakṣe*, "on the other hand" ("on the other wing"), *pakṣāntara*, "in the other case".[54] In Sanskrit scholarly literature it has become the commentator's custom to interpret any given text in three successive stages: the first interpretation is the *pūrva-pakṣa*, "*prima facie* view"; the second is the reply to this: *uttara-pakṣa*; and the third and final interpretation is the *siddhānta*, "final and established view". This practice is found since Śabara (Vth century A.D.) but may be older.

The terms *pūrva-pakṣa* and *uttara-pakṣa* can also mean Eastern and Northern wing, respectively, or first and second half of the lunar month. It seems probable that the earliest technical or semi-technical use of the term *pakṣa* originated in the Vedic ritual. The *Taittirīya-saṃhitā* had identified the sacrificial fire with a bird, *vayas* or *pakṣin* (i.e., "winged").[55] In some sacrifices the fire altar is accordingly built in the shape of a bird with two wings.[56] The right wing (*dakṣiṇa pakṣa*) points to the South (*dakṣiṇa*) and the left wing (*uttara pakṣa*) points to the North (*uttara*). Moreover, each wing is further enlarged into the direction it points to,[57] for the longer the wings, the stronger the bird and the wider its flight.[58] The idea is, that the bird

---

[52]See S. N. Dasgupta, *A history of Indian philosophy IV*, Cambridge, 1955, p. 202.

[53]As actual contacts between European Antiquity and India have been frequent from Alexander onwards, it is impossible to prove that no Indian had ever heard of Aristotelian logic. Actual influence on Indian logic is a different matter: it is *a priori* unlikely because of the intimate relationship between logic and language, and moreover seems to become the more improbable, the more our knowledge of Indian systematic and scientific thought (i.e., primarily of ritual, grammar, and logic) increases.

[54]Monier-Williams' Sanskrit-English dictionary, s.v.

[55]5.7.6.1.

[56]See A. Weber in: *Indische Studien*, Vol. 13 (1873), pp. 233 sq.; cf. A. Hillebrandt, *Rituallitteratur*, Strassburg, 1897, p. 164; L. Renou-J. Filliozat, *L'Inde classique*, Vol. I, Paris, 1947, p. 351: L. Renou, *Vocabulaire du rituel védique*, Paris, 1954, p. 88.

[57]*Āpastamba Śrautasūtra* 16.17.10,12,13. Transl. by W. Caland, Amsterdam, 1928, p. 35.

[58]Cf. *Taittirīya-saṃhitā* 5.2.5.1.

thus carries the sacrificer to heaven.[59] Similarly do the strong wings of *pūrva* and *uttara pakṣa* carry the philosopher to his final view, while *sapakṣa* and *vipakṣa* cases lead the logician to his final proof.

The Sanskrit grammarians use *pakṣa* for "alternative, view, hypothesis". The terms *vyakti-pakṣa* and *jāti-pakṣa* are utilised for referring to the use of a word as denoting, respectively, the individual (*vyakti*) and the class (*jāti*) to which it belongs.[60]

The compound *anvaya-vyatireka* seems to have originated among the grammarians and occurs probably for the first time in a *vyārtikka* of Kātyāyana (ca. 200 B.C.) mentioned by Patañjali (ca. 50 B.C.) in his discussion of a *sūtra* of Pāṇini.[61] In this *sūtra* Pāṇini defines a nominal stem as what is meaningful but is neither a verbal root, nor a suffix,[62] nor what ends in a suffix.[63] One of the sections of the commentary deals with the problem of whether a nominal stem in itself can be meaningful. The question arises how to distinguish between meanings of stems and of suffixes. The *vārttika* is then quoted: "it is established by means of *anvaya* and *vyatireka*".[64] Patañjali elucidates this further in the following terms: "If in this case *vṛkṣaḥ* ("tree") is pronounced, a certain sound is heard which consists of the sound *vṛkṣa* ending in *a* and of a termination *s*.[65] A certain meaning is also conveyed, which consists of what has roots, branches, fruits, and leaves, and of singularity. If then *vṛkṣau* ("two trees") is pronounced, some sound disappears (*hīyate*), something comes into being (*upajāyate*) and something remains (*anvayī*): *s* disappears, *au* comes into being, and *vṛkṣa* ending in *a* remains.[66] Also with regard to meaning, something disappears, something comes into being, and something remains: singularity disappears, duality comes into being, and what has roots, branches, fruits, and leaves remains".[67]

It is clear that here *anvayī* denotes "what remains", while it is but natural to infer that *vyatirekī*, which is not mentioned by Patañjali, denotes what changes (either comes into being or disappears). The terms *anvayī* and

---

[59]Cf. *Śatapatha-brāhmaṇa* 6.1.2.35, also: H. Hubert-M. Mauss, Essai sur la nature et la fonction du sacrifice, in: *Mélanges d'histoire des religions*, Paris, 1909, p. 38 note 4.

[60]L. Renou, *Terminologie grammaticale du Sanskrit*, Paris, 1957, p. 148, 193.

[61]*Mahābhāṣya* 1.2.2 (Kielhorn I 219). Cf. Renou, *Terminologie*, p. 43, and P. S. Subrahmanya Sastri, *Lectures on Patañjali's Mahābhāṣya*, Tiruchirapalli, 1956, p. 90.

[62]*pratyaya:* Renou specifies (*La Grammaire de Pāṇini*, Paris, 1948, p. 21) "un affix en général ou un mot terminé par ces affixes particuliers que sont les désinences casuelles".

[63]*arthavad adhātur apratyayaḥ prātipadikam:* Pāṇini 1.2.45.

[64]*siddhaṃ tv anvayavyatirekābhyām.*

[65]This *-s* becomes *-ḥ*.

[66]The *a* disappears in the process: *vṛkṣa-au* > *vṛkṣau*.

[67]*iha vṛkṣa ity ukte kaścic chabdaḥ śrūyate vṛkṣaśabdo'kārāntaḥ, sakāraś ca pratyayaḥ/ artho'pi kaścid gamyate mūla-skandha-phala-palāśavān ekatvaṃ ca/vṛkṣāv ity ukte kaścic chabdo hīyate kaścid upajāyate kaścid anvayī/sakāro hīyate aukāra upajāyate vṛkṣaśabdo'kārānto'nvayī/artho'pi kaścid dhīyate kaścid upajāyate kaścid anvayī/ ekatvaṃ hīyate dvitvam upajāyate mūla-skandha-phala-palāśavān anvayī//*

vyatirekī refer to what in modern linguistics R. S. Wells called "environment" and "focus", respectively.[68] Applications of the method of "replacement" go back to Pāṇini.

The term *vyatireka* is used in a similar sense in later philosophical literature. The *Nyāyasūtra* (IIIrd century A.D.) discusses transformation (*vikāra*) of gold in earrings and necklaces, and states that under such transformations "there is no *vyatireka* of the essence of gold".[69] The commentator Vātsyāyana (*ca.* IVth century) explains this further in a similar terminology as that used earlier by Patañjali: "gold is the continuing (*avasthita*) substratum (*dharmin*) with properties (*dharma*) which are disappearing (*hīyamāna*) and coming into being (*upajāyamāna*)".[70]

Here *vyatireka* denotes change or difference. This seems to be widespread by the VIIIth century, when it is characteristically interpreted by Śaṅkara in a reference to "the theory of the non-difference (*avyatireka*) of the material cause and its transformations".[71] In the present paper we have seen how in logic, from the VIIth century onwards, *anvaya* denotes the occurrence of the *sādhya* in similar instances and *vyatireka* the absence of the *sādhya* from dissimilar instances. Accordingly, the term *anvaya-vyatireka* can refer both to an inference which possesses similar (positive) and dissimilar (negative) instances and to the contraposition of an inference.[72]

---

[68]Immediate constituents, *Language*, Vol. 23 (1947), p. 86. Cf. E. Haugen, Directions in modern linguistics, *Language*, Vol. 27 (1951), p. 214.

[69]*suvarṇabhāvāvyatireka*: *Nyāyasūtra* 2.2.49.

[70]*avasthitaṃ suvarṇaṃ hīyamānena dharmaṇopajāyamānena ca dharmeṇa dharmi bhavati.*

[71]*prakṛti-vikārāvyatireka-nyāya*: *Brahma-sūtra-bhāṣya* ad. 2.3.6.

[72]I should like to express here my gratitude to Dr. D. L. Friedman (London) and to Professor Benson Mates (Berkeley) for their valuable suggestions in connection with the present article. The use of the term *anvayavyatireka* by both grammarians and logicians was noted by Ruegg, who supposed that also the reasoning process was the same in both cases: D. S. Ruegg, *Contributions à l'histoire de la philosophie linguistique indienne*, Paris, 1951, pp. 32, 37. Cf. the present author in: *Philosophy East and West*, Vol. 10 (1960), pp. 53–57. While it is of course possible that the later grammarians made use of the logical method concerned, it is certain that they knew Kātyāyana's use of the term (e.g., *Paramalaghu-mañjūsā*, ed. by S. S. Shastri, Banaras, 1935, p. 2).

APPENDIX

PROGRAM

1960 INTERNATIONAL CONGRESS FOR LOGIC, METHODOLOGY AND PHILOSOPHY OF SCIENCE

Stanford University, August 24–September 2, 1960

WEDNESDAY MORNING, AUGUST 24

Opening Ceremonies

Alfred Tarski, Chairman of the Organizing Committee, Presiding

J. E. Wallace Sterling, President, Stanford University

S. C. Kleene, President, Division of Logic, Methodology and Philosophy of Science, International Union of History and Philosophy of Science

Alan T. Waterman, Director, National Science Foundation, U.S.A.

Patrick Suppes, Secretary of the Organizing Committee, Announcements

WEDNESDAY AFTERNOON, AUGUST 24

A. Fraenkel (Israel), Chairman

Invited Hour Address—Section II. A. Robinson (Israel), "Recent Developments in Model Theory"

Invited Symposium on Current Views of Subjective Probability—Section V

H. Chernoff (U.S.A.), Chairman
I. J. Good (England)
L. J. Savage (U.S.A.)
G. H. von Wright (Finland)

Contributed Papers—Section I. Mathematical Logic

A. Church (U.S.A.), Chairman

S. Feferman (U.S.A.) and C. Spector (U.S.A.), "Incompleteness Along Paths in Recursive Progressions of Theories"

M. Davis (U.S.A.), "Extensions and Corollaries of Recent Work on Hilbert's Tenth Problem"

H. Putnam (U.S.A.) and R. M. Smullyan (U.S.A.), "Exact Separation of Recursively Enumerable Sets within Theories"

D. Kaplan (U.S.A.), "Separability in the Arithmetical Hierarchy"

W. W. Tait (U.S.A.), "Continuity Properties of Partial Recursive Functionals of Finite Type"

J. C. Shepherdson (England) and H. E. Sturgis (U.S.A.), "The Computability of Partial Recursive Functions"

A. Nerode (U.S.A.), "Positive Sentences About Isolic Integers"

G. F. Rose (U.S.A.), "An Extended Notion of Computability"

THURSDAY MORNING, AUGUST 25

Invited Symposium on Macro- and Microeconomics—Section VIII

K. Arrow (U.S.A.), Chairman
A.P. Lerner (U.S.A.)
A. Nataf (France)
R. Stone (England)
H. Theil (The Netherlands)

Contributed Papers—Section VII. Methodology and Philosophy of Biological and Psychological Sciences

A. Toda (Japan), Chairman

S. S. Stevens (U.S.A.), "The Pinning of Numbers on Subjective Events"
J. Pfanzagl (Austria), "A General Theory of Measurement-Applications to Utility"
A. Norris (U.S.A.), "On the Theory of Value Judgments"
H. R. Shuford, Jr. (U.S.A.), "Logical Behaviorism and Intentionality"
M. Maruyama (U.S.A.), "Communicational Epistemology"
G. S. Woodson (U.S.A.), "Inductive Inference in Clinical Medicine and the Inverse H. Theorem"
L. G. Rather (U.S.A.), "The Status of the Disease Entity"

THURSDAY AFTERNOON, AUGUST 25

G. H. von Wright (Finland), Chairman

Invited Hour Address—Section V. R. Carnap (U.S.A.), "The Aim of Inductive Logic"

Invited Symposium on Metamathematics of Algebra and Geometry—Section II

W. Szmielew (Poland), chairman
J. Łoś (Poland)
R. Lyndon (U.S.A.)
M. Rabin (Israel)
W. Schwabhäuser (Germany)

Contributed Papers—Section V. Foundations of Probability and Induction

G. Polya (U.S.A.), Chairman

A. H. Copeland, Sr. (U.S.A.), "Statistical Induction and the Foundations of Probability"
J. Dreze (Belgium), "The Logical Foundations of Cardinal Utility and Subjective Probability"
D. Davidson (U.S.A.), "Some Methodological Aspects of Formal Decision Theory"
H. Gaifman (Israel), "Probability Models and the Completeness Theorem"
H. E. Kyburg (U.S.A.), "A Generalization of the System of 'Probability and Randomness, II', and a Problem"
P. Caws (U.S.A.), "A Paradox of Induction and the Inductive Wager"

FRIDAY MORNING, AUGUST 26

Invited Symposium on Alternative Approaches to the Theory of Choice—Section VII

W. K. Estes (U.S.A.), Chairman
R. J. Audley (England)
G. Bower (U.S.A.)
A. Deutsch (England)
M. Toda (Japan)

Contributed Papers—Section I. Mathematical Logic

M. Krasner (France), Chairman

H. F. Schott (U.S.A.), "The Solution of Antinomies in Many-Valued Logic"
K. J. J. Hintikka (Finland), "Modality and Quantification"
S. Kanger (Sweden), "A Simplified Effective Proof Method"
G. Matthews (U.S.A.) "Computing Symbolic Transformations via a Gödel-Type Numbering"
G. Stahl (Chile), "The Problematic of the Incompleteness Proof"

FRIDAY AFTERNOON, AUGUST 26

D. Davidson (U.S.A.), Chairman

Invited Hour Address—Section VIII. J. Harsanyi (Australia), "Models for the Analysis of the Balance of Power in Society"

Invited Symposium on the Role of Mathematics in the Formulation of Physical Theories—Section VI

H. Margenau (U.S.A.), Chairman
A. Froda (Roumania)
G. Mackey (U.S.A.)
J. Schwarz (U.S.A.)
I. Segal (U.S.A.)
J. Wheeler (U.S.A.)

Contributed Papers—Section VIII. Methodology and Philosophy of Social Sciences

E. Walter (Switzerland), Chairman

P. L. Shiman (U.S.A.), "Myth-Making and Public Prediction in the Behavioral Sciences"
H. Tennessen (U.S.A.), "Empirical Semantics and the Soft Sciences"
B. K. Rome (U.S.A.) and S. C. Rome (U.S.A.), "The Leviathan Technique for Large-Group Analysis"
K. W. Back (U.S.A.), "The Game and the Myth as Two Languages of Social Science"
J. L. Magrish (U.S.A.), "Knowledge and the Justification of Judicial Decisions"
T. A. Goudge (Canada), "The Genetic Fallacy"

SATURDAY MORNING, AUGUST 27

Invited Symposium on Theoretical and Empirical Aspects of Science—Section IV

H. Mehlberg (U.S.A.), Chairman
G. Bergmann (U.S.A.)
J. Kotarbińska (Poland)
K. Popper (England)
J. H. Woodger (England)

Contributed Papers—Section I

L. Henkin (U.S.A.), Chairman

W. P. Hanf (U.S.A.), "Models of Languages with Infinitely Long Expressions"
C. R. Karp (U.S.A.), "Independence Proofs in Predicate Logic with Infinitely Long Expressions"
S. Kochen (U.S.A.), "On Beth's Theorem and Extensions"
Gr. C. Moisil (Roumania), "Sur le calcul des prédicats dans la logique à trois valeurs"

SATURDAY AFTERNOON, AUGUST 27, AND SUNDAY, AUGUST 28

Tours of the Area

MONDAY MORNING, AUGUST 29

Invited Symposium on the Notion of Recursiveness—Section I

S. C. Kleene (U.S.A.), Chairman
J. Addison (U.S.A.)
D. Lacombe (France)
J. Myhill (U.S.A.)
J. Shoenfield (U.S.A.)

Contributed Papers—Section XI. History of Logic, Methodology and Philosophy of Science

J. Bochenski (Switzerland), Chairman

A. Joja (Roumania), "Implications logiques de l'hèn diapherómenon d'Héraclite"

A. Kawczak (Poland), "Aristotle's Classification of Fallacies"
C. Goekoop (Netherlands), "Formal Logic in Gangeça's Tattvacintamāni"
R. H. Popkin (U.S.A.), "Scepticism and Empirical Method in the Seventeenth Century"
R. E. Butts (U.S.A.), "Hypothesis and Explanation in Kant's Philosophy of Science"
R. S. Cohen (U.S.A.), "The Relevance of the History of Science to the Philosophy of Science: Emile Meyerson"
F. Seaman (U.S.A.), "Research and Analysis in the History of Science"
F. Caldiero (U.S.A.), "Contemporary Man and Modern Physical Science"
H. Rogosin (U.S.A.), "Extra-Sensory Perception—Science Fiction of the 20th Century"
C. Eisele (U.S.A.), "Charles S. Peirce, Father of the Logic and Philosophy of Science in America"

MONDAY AFTERNOON, AUGUST 29

M. Schiffer (U.S.A.), Chairman

Invited Hour Address—Section VI. S. Ulam (U.S.A.), "Future Role of Computing Machines in Mathematical Sciences"

Invited Symposium on Models in the Empirical Sciences—Section IV

R. Braithwaite (England), Chairman
L. Hurwicz (U.S.A.)
H. Putnam (U.S.A.)
P. Suppes (U.S.A.)
J. P. Vigier (France)

Contributed Papers—Section VI. Methodology and Philosophy of Physical Sciences
M. Bunge (Argentina), Chairman

J. Rothstein (U.S.A.), "Thermodynamics and Some Undecidable Physical Questions"
A. Bressan (Italy), "An Axiomatic Way of Founding Classical Particle Mechanics"
E. Farber (U.S.A.), "The Concept of Limit States in Physics and Chemistry"
Y. Ueno (Japan), "On the Nature of Physical Space"
G. L. Farre (U.S.A.), "The Structure of Physics Viewed as a Language"
G. Maxwell (U.S.A.), "Theories, Frameworks, and Ontology"
S. Ohe (Japan), "The Multiple Structure of Our External Knowledge and Mr. Edwin Land's New Experiment in Color Vision"
D. Gruender (U.S.A.), 'Uses of Reality"
M. Omelyanovski (U.S.S.R.), "Dialectical Contradiction in Modern Physics"

General Assembly. Division of Logic, Methodology and Philosophy of Science, International Union of History and Philosophy of Science

TUESDAY MORNING, AUGUST 30

Invited Symposium on Decision Problems—Section I

J. Robinson (U.S.A.), Chairman
R. Buchi (U.S.A.)
R. L. Vaught (U.S.A.)

Contributed Papers—Section X. Methodology and Philosophy of Historical Sciences
J. Goheen (U.S.A.), Chairman

M. Brodbeck (U.S.A.), "Explanation, Prediction, and the Notion of Imperfect Knowledge"
R. H. Weingartner (U.S.A.), "The Quarrel About Historical Explanation"
G. Tagliacozzo (U.S.A.), "Branches, Tree and Taxonomy of Knowledge"
J. Stannard (U.S.A.), "Is History Continuous?"
L. O. Mink (U.S.A.), "Detachable and Ingredient Conclusions in Historiography"

Contributed Papers—Section VII

J. Woodger (England), Chairman

V. M. Dolphin (U.S.A.), "Wholistic Method and the Functioning Systems of Macromolecular Biology"

A. Lindenmayer (U.S.A.), "An Axiom System for 'Mitosis,' 'Meiosis,' and 'Gametic Fusion' "

S. G. Vandenberg (U.S.A.), "Methodology in Human Genetics of Behavior"

A. L. Fisher (U.S.A.), "Explanation in Psychology"

TUESDAY AFTERNOON, AUGUST 30

K. R. Popper (England), Chairman

Invited Hour Address—Section VII. E. R. Hilgard (U.S.A.),"Scientific Status of Psychoanalysis"

Invited Symposium on Foundations of Set Theory—Section II

A. Tarski (U.S.A.), Chairman
H. J. Keisler (U.S.A.)
A. Levy (Israel)
R. Montague (U.S.A.)
D. Scott (U.S.A.)
E. Specker (Switzerland)

Contributed Papers—Section IV. General Problems of Methodology and Philosophy of Science

G. Bergmann (U.S.A.), Chairman

H. W. von Guerard (U.S.A.), "The Role of Functional Equations in Mathematical Models on Transportation Systems"

K. H. Schaeffer (U.S.A.), and A. Shapero (U.S.A.) "A. Methodology for Modeling in General System Studies"

W. J. Strauss (U.S.A.), "Model and Testability in Certain Types of Operations Research"

M. A. Geisler (U.S.A.), "Man-Machine Simulation Progress"

M. R. Kenner (U.S.A.), and G. T. McClure (U.S.A.) "The Development of a Logical Model for a Hospital System"

J. Wilkinson (U.S.A.), "The Philosophic Significance of Information Theories"

T. Pawlowski (Poland), "On Conditions for the Scientific Usefulness of Concepts in the Natural Sciences"

C. J. Clark (U.S.A.), "On the Function Concept"

C. J. Maloney (U.S.A.), "Contribution to the Foundations of Logic and Information Retrieval"

WEDNESDAY MORNING, AUGUST 31

Y. Bar-Hillel (Israel), Chairman

Invited Hour Address—Section X. G. Barraclough (England), "Scientific Method and the Work of the Historian"

Invited Symposium on Models in Linguistics—Section IX

Y. Chao (U.S.A.), Chairman
Y. Bar-Hillel (Israel)
F. W. Householder (U.S.A.)
F. J. Whitfield (U.S.A.)

Contributed Papers—Section IV. General Problems of Methodology and Philosophy of Science

Z. Suetuna (Japan), Chairman

R. E. Robinson (U.S.A.), "A Set-Theoretical Approach to Empirical Meaningfulness"

R. Rudner (U.S.A.), "The Reducibility of Types of Weights in the Acceptance of Scientific Theories: Evidence, Cost and Formal Simplicity"
D. Harrah (U.S.A.), "A Model for Applying Utility and Information Functions"
W. Yourgrau (U.S.A.), "Verification of Proof—An Undecided Issue?"
M. Scriven (U.S.A.), "The Concept of Cause"
W. H. Kane (U.S.A.), "The Potency of Matter According to Heisenberg and Aristotle"
A. M. Bork (U.S.A.), "Pictures of Science"
A. Wittenberg (Canada), "May Philosophy of Science Preach Empiricism and Practice Apriorism?"
B. Kedrov (U.S.S.R.), "The Relation between Historical and Logical Aspects in the Development of Scientific Knowledge"

WEDNESDAY AFTERNOON, AUGUST 31

Tour of San Francisco

THURSDAY MORNING, SEPTEMBER 1

B. Mates (U.S.A.), Chairman

Invited Half-Hour Addresses to Sections X and XI

W. Dray (Canada), "The Perspective Theory of History"
J. F. Staal (England), "Contraposition in Indian Logic"
W. Kneale (England), "Modality *de dicto* and *de re*"
H. Freudenthal (Netherlands), "The Main Trends in the Foundations of Geometry in the 19th Century"
J. Clark (U.S.A.), "Remarks on the Role of Quantity, Quality and Relations in the History of Logic, Methodology and Philosophy of Science"

Contributed Papers—Section II. Foundations of Mathematical Theories

R. M. Robinson (U.S.A.), Chairman

E. Wette (Germany), "Intuitionistisch-rekursiver Konsistenzbeweis für die axiomatische Mengenlehre"
B. van Rootselaar (Netherlands), "Tale of the Fan"
R. Fraissé (Algeria), "Une tentative pour simplifier et généraliser les notions d'ensemble et de classe constructible"
J. H. Monk (U.S.A.), "Relation Algebras and Cylindric Algebras"
S. Kuroda (Japan), "Foundations of Mathematics"

THURSDAY AFTERNOON, SEPTEMBER 1

H. Solomon (U.S.A.), Chairman

Invited Hour Address—Section VIII. P. Lazarsfeld (U.S.A.), "Philosophy of Science and Modern Social Research"

Invited Symposium on Contemporary Trends in the Philosophy of Mathematics—Section III

A. Heyting (Netherlands), Chairman
A. Church (U.S.A.)
L. Henkin (U.S.A.)
M. Krasner (France)
G. Kreisel (England)

Contributed Papers—Section IV

A. Joja (Roumania), Chairman

H. G. Alexander (U.S.A.), "A Suggestion Concerning Empirical Foundations of Imagination"
M. Bunge (Argentina), "The Complexity of Simplicity"
H. Elliott (U.S.A.), "Science is Metaphysics"
S. Dockx (Belgium), "Philosophy and Science"
E. R. Stabler (U.S.A.), "On Scientific Method and the 'Central Problem of our Time'"
P. Pinxter (U.S.A.) "Heisenberg's Microscope"
FF. Gonseth (Switzerland), "Philosophie de sciences exactes"

Banquet

FRIDAY MORNING, SEPTEMBER 2

F. J. Whitfield (U.S.A.), Chairman

Invited Hour Address—Section IX. L. Hjelmslev (Denmark), "Methodological Prerequisites of Structural Linguistics"

A. Tarski (U.S.A.), Chairman

Invited Hour Address—Section IV. T. Kotarbiński (Poland), "Meaning and Foundation of Praxeological Statements" (read by D. Rynin)

Contributed Papers—Section IX

F. J. Whitfield (U.S.A.), Chairman

H. Hiz (U.S.A.), "Grammatical Category as a Relation"
T. M. Williams (U.S.A.), "On a Restricted Logistic Grammar for Topics"

Contributed Papers—Section V

A. H. Copeland, Sr. (U.S.A.), Chairman

R. C. Jeffrey (U.S.A.), "Betting, Learning, and Confirming Generalizations"
R. W. Workman (U.S.A.), "The Logical Status of The Principle of Induction"
H. Finch (U.S.A.), "Confirming Power of Observations Metricized by Bayes' Theorem and a Measure of Choice Uncertainty"

FRIDAY AFTERNOON, SEPTEMBER 2

H. Freudenthal (Netherlands), Chairman

Invited Hour Address—Section IX. N. Chomsky (U.S.A.), "Explanatory Models in Linguistics"

W. Kneale (England), Chairman

Invited Hour Address—Section XI. J. M. Bochenski (Switzerland), "Aristotle the Methodologist"

Contributed Papers—Section III. Philosophy of Logic and Mathematics

E. McMullin (U.S.A.), Chairman

M. Dummett (England), "The Epistemological Significance of Gödel's Theorem"
H. C. Kennedy (U.S.A.), "The Mathematical Philosophy of Guiseppe Peano"
K. Lambert (Canada), "The Definition of E(xistence)! in Free Logic"
Z. Suetuna (Japan), "On the Variable in Symbolic Logic"

CONTRIBUTED PAPERS PRESENTED BY TITLE

Section I

P. C. Gilmore (U.S.A.), "The Simple Theory of Types and the Skolem Paradox"
S. Jaskowski (Poland), "On Some Non-Classical Implications"
J. Porte (France), "Congruences over Connective Calculi"
D. Schroer (U.S.A.), "Unified Formulation and Interpretation of Logical Systems"
K. Suprunowicz (U.S.A.), "Diagram Normal Forms and Applications"

Section II

R. O. Gandy (England) and M. Löb (England), "Countable Standard Models for Ordinals"
J. J. de Jongh (Netherlands), "The Inconsistency of the Strong Intuitionistic Interpretation of Classical Analysis"
A. Monteiro (Argentina), "Linéarisation des algèbres de Heyting"
H. Ribeiro (U.S.A.), and R. Schwabauer (U.S.A.) "Remarks on Equational Completeness and on Equational Classes of Algebras"

Section III

N. Barraclough (Spain), "The Problem of Plurality"
M. Kokoszynska-Lutman (Poland), "On Logical Systems"

Section IV

K. Ajdukiewicz (Poland), "The Limits of Arbitrariness of the Measurement Definitions"
A. Malewski (Poland), "Some Problems of Systematization of Theory in Behavioral Sciences"

Section V

M. Kobayashi (Japan), "Foundation of Probability and Induction—Current Views of Subjective Probability"
H. Leblanc (U.S.A.), "On a Recent Allotment of Probabilities to Open and Closed Sentences"
N. Rescher (U.S.A.), "A Problem in the Theory of Numerical Estimation"
S. Watanabe (U.S.A.), "A Mathematical Model of Inductive Inference"

Section VI

E. W. Bastin (England), "A Model in Theoretical Physics which Affects our View of the Process of Measurement"
C. Bory (France), "De l'Ambiguité des Notions de Base de la Thermodynamique Classique"
B. Mandelbrot (U.S.A.), "The Role of Statistics in the Formulation of the Structure of Thermodynamics"

Section VII

E. Egana (Chile) and A. Valenzuela (Chile), "Notes on the Teaching Methodology of Experimental Medicine (Pathological Physiology)"
D. Ueda (Japan), "Does the Body of Living Organism Consist of Atoms and Obey the Laws of Physics?"

Section VIII

F. G. Asenjo (U.S.A.), "The Application of Some Mathematical Concepts to Social Sciences"

P. Crosser (U.S.A.), "Macroeconomics and Microeconomics–A Re-evaluation of Keynes' Position"
L. Guttman (Israel), "A Facet Framework for Measurement in the Social Sciences"
C. C. McFarling (U.S.A.) and E. A. Robinson (U.S.A.), "The Impact of Computing Machines on the Social Sciences Through Simulation and Theory Construction"
M. Ralea (Roumania), "Le Problème de la Méthode dans une Psychologie et Sociologie du Succès"
G. Tintner (U.S.A.), "The Application of Carnap's Theory of Probability to Operations Research"
J. Wroblewski (Poland), "Semantics as Applied to Legal Interpretation"

Section IX

E. Albrecht (Germany), "The Relation between Language and Logic in Perception"
J. Jorgensen (Denmark), "On Some Differences between Languages, Calculuses, and Logic"
M. Masterman (England), "The Thesaurus-Model of Translation in Language"

Section X

H. T. Bernstein (England), "Methodological Problems of Selection in Narrating History of Science"

Section XI

S. Uyeda (Japan), "A Reflection on the Trend of Logic in Japan"
A. Virieux-Reymond (Switzerland), "L'importance du rôle joué par Gaston Milhaud (10 août 1858–1er octobre 1918) en Histoire et en Philosophie des sciences"